42nd European Photovoltaic Solar Energy Conference and Exhibition (EU PVSEC 2025)

Bilbao, Spain
22-26 September 2025

Volume 4 of 6

ISBN: 979-8-3313-2987-7

Printed from e-media with permission by:

Curran Associates, Inc.
57 Morehouse Lane
Red Hook, NY 12571

Some format issues inherent in the e-media version may also appear in this print version.

WIP – Renewable Energies
Sylvensteinstr. 2
81369 Munchen
Germany

Phone: +49 89 72012735
Fax: +49 89 72012791

wip@wip-munich.de

Additional copies of this publication are available from:

Curran Associates, Inc.
57 Morehouse Lane
Red Hook, NY 12571 USA
Phone: 845-758-0400
Fax: 845-758-2633
Email: curran@proceedings.com
Web: www.proceedings.com

42nd European Photovoltaic Solar Energy Conference and Exhibition

Proceedings of the International Conference

22 September – 26 September 2025

Edited by:

C. DEL CAÑIZO
Solar Energy Institute
UPM
Spain

R. KENNY
European Commission
Joint Research Centre
Italy

J. BERGMILLER
WIP Renewable Energies
Germany

J. DE GREGORIO
WIP Renewable Energies
Germany

Edition Team:

B. Yildiz
L. Großhans
A. Michaelsen
U.E. Birgi
WIP Renewable Energies
Germany

Photos at:

Coordination of the Technical Programme:

European Commission Joint Research Centre
Via E. Fermi 1
21020 Ispra (VA)
Italy

Institutional Support:

European Commission

Institutional PV Industry Cooperation:

SolarPower Europe

ESMC – European Solar Manufacturing Council

Supporting Organisations:

AUSTRALIAN PV INSTITUTE

ASOM – Alliance for Solar Mobility

BASQUE ENERGY CLUSTER

BILBAO CONVENTION BUREAU

EASE – European Association for Storage of Energy

ETIP PV – European Technology & Innovation Platform PV

GÜNDER – Turkish Solar Energy Society

IEA PVPS - IEA Photovoltaic Power Systems Programme

INSTITUTO SOLAR DE ENERGÍA SOLAR

LDES – Long Duration Energy Storage Council

NSEFI – National Solar Energy federation of India

NUS /SERIS – National University of Singapore / Solar Energy Research Institute of Singapore

UPM - Polytechnic University of Madrid

Supporting Associations:

EERA – European Energy Research Aliance

EREF – European Renewable Energies Federation

EUREC – The Association of European Renewable Energy Research Centres

VDMA Photovoltaic Equipment

Local Support:
ENTE VASCO DE LA ENERGÍA
EUH – University of the Basque Country

EU PVSEC 2025 realised by:

WIP Renewable Energies
Sylvensteinstr. 2, 81369 Munich, Germany
Tel: +49 89 720 12 735, Fax: +49 89 720 12 791
Email: pv.conference@wip-munich.de
www.eupvsec.org
www.wip-munich.de

Proceedings produced and published by:

WIP Renewable Energies
Sylvensteinstr. 2, 81369 Munich, Germany
Tel: +49 89 720 12 735, Fax: +49 89 720 12 791
Email: pv.conference@wip-munich.de
www.eupvsec.org
www.wip-munich.de

42nd EUROPEAN PHOTOVOLTAIC SOLAR ENERGY CONFERENCE AND EXHIBITION
22 SEPTEMBER – 26 SEPTEMBER 2025

EU PVSEC 2025 COMMITTEES

INTERNATIONAL SCIENTIFIC ADVISORY COMMITTEE (ISAC)

Chair
P. Szymanski, European Commission Joint Research Centre, Director of Energy, Transport and Climate, Petten, The Netherlands

Committee Members
V. Bermúdez Benito, Founder & Principal Consultant, Berbetin, Antibes, France
G.C. Eder, OFI, Vienna, Austria
P. Frankl, Head of the Renewable Energy Division, International Energy Agency, France
M. Getsiou, European Commission, DG RTD, Brussels, Belgium
S.W. Glunz, Head of Division Photovoltaics - Research, Fraunhofer ISE, Freiburg, Germany
N.M. Haegel, Director of the National Center for Photovoltaics, NREL, Golden, USA
R. Kenny, European Commission Joint Research Centre, Directorate for Energy and Transport and Climate, Ispra, Italy
S. Nowak, Managing Director of NET Nowak Energy & Technology, St. Ursen, Switzerland
R. Schlatmann, Chairman of ETIP PV, Head of the Solar Energy Division at Helmholtz-Zentrum Berlin, Germany
W.C. Sinke, TNO Energy Transition, The Netherlands
M. Topič, Head of Laboratory of Photovoltaics and Optoelectronics of the University of Ljubljana, Slovenia
P. Verlinden, Director at Amrock, Visiting Professor at Sun Yat-Sen University, Guangzhou, China
E. Voroshazi, Head of PV module process laboratory, CEA, Le Bourget-du-Lac, France
J. Bergmiller, Managing Director Events & Knowledge Transfer, WIP Renewable Energies, Munich, Germany
J. de Gregorio, Head of Unit, Scientific Services and Cooperation, WIP Renewable Energies, Munich, Germany

CONFERENCE EXECUTIVE COMMITTEE

Conference General Chair
C. del Cañizo, UPM, Madrid, Spain

Technical Programme Chair
R. Kenny, European Commission Joint Research Centre, Directorate for Energy and Transport and Climate, Ispra, Italy

Committee Members
W.C. Sinke, Program Development Manager, TNO Energy Transition, The Netherlands
S. Nowak, Managing Director of NET Nowak Energy & Technology, St. Ursen, Switzerland
M. Topič, Head of Laboratory of Photovoltaics and Optoelectronics of the University of Ljubljana, Slovenia
V. Bermúdez Benito, BERBETIN, France
E. Voroshazi, Head of PV Module Process Laboratory, CEA, Le Bourget-Du-Lac France
H. Ossenbrink, Former European Commission Joint Research Centre, Germany
J. Bergmiller, Managing Director Events & Knowledge Transfer, WIP Renewable Energies, Munich, Germany
J. de Gregorio, Head of Unit, Scientific Services and Cooperation, WIP Renewable Energies, Munich, Germany

2025 SCIENTIFIC COMMITTEE

Programme Technical Chair
R. Kenny, European Commission, Joint Research Centre, Italy

Topic Chairs

Topic 1: Silicon Materials and Cells
F. Schindler, Fraunhofer ISE, Germany

Topic 2: Thin Films and New Concepts
I. Gordon, imec, Belgium

Topic 3: Photovoltaic Modules and BoS Components
T. Barnes, NREL, USA

Topic 4: PV Systems Engineering, Integrated/Applied PV
A.M. Gracia Amillo, FUNDACION CENER, Spain

Topic 5: PV in the Energy Transition
C. Agraffeil, CEA / INES, France

Topic Organisers and Paper Review Experts

Topic 1: Silicon Materials and Cells
F. Schindler, Fraunhofer ISE, Germany
C. Fischer, Wacker Chemie, Germany
G. Hahn, University of Konstanz, Germany
K. Ding, Forschungszentrum Jülich, Germany
P. Roca i Cabarrocas, CNRS-LPICM, France
A. W. Weeber, TNO Energy Transition, The Netherlands
D. Muñoz, CEA / INES, France
S. W. Glunz, Fraunhofer ISE, Germany
K. Bothe, ISFH, Germany
M. Topic, University of Ljubljana, Slovenia
P. Fath, RCT-Solutions, Germany
S. Peters, Hanwha Q CELLS, Germany

M.P. Bellmann, SINTEF, Norway
A. Ciesla, UNSW, Australia
C. Hagendorf, Freiberg Instruments, Germany
X. Yu, Zhejiang University, China
J.S. Lee, KIER, South Korea
R. Brendel, ISFH, Germany
T. Dullweber, ISFH, Germany
J. Horzel, Fraunhofer ISE, Germany
W. Nemeth, NREL, United States of America
R. Turan, METU, Türkiye
F. Menchini, ENEA, Italy
W. Favre, CEA, France

J. Meier, Meier Technologies, Switzerland
J. Schmidt, ISFH, Germany
M. Wright, University of Oxford, United Kingdom
J. Zhao, CSEM, Switzerland
A. Morisset, CSEM, Switzerland
A. Richter, Fraunhofer ISE, Germany
J. Linke, ISC Konstanz, Germany
B. Geerligs, TNO Energy Transition, The Netherlands
S. Dubois, CEA, France
M. Hermle, Fraunhofer ISE, Germany
B. Terheiden, University of Konstanz, Germany
P. Delli Veneri, ENEA, Italy
T. Matsui, AIST, Japan
Y. Ohshita, Toyota Technological Institute, Japan
E. Bruhat, HOLOSOLIS, France
A. Augusto, Dalarna University, Sweden
F. Ferrazza, ENI S.p.A., Italy
A. Otaegi, UPV/EHU, Spain
M.C. Schubert, Fraunhofer ISE, Germany
H. Duman, KalyonPV, Türkiye
N. Usami, Nagoya University, Japan
Y. Zhu, UNSW, Australia
D. Brunner, RENA Technologies, Germany
A. Danel, CEA, France
C. Gerardi, 3Sun, Italy
H.J. Nonnenmacher, Meyer Burger, Germany
P. Verlinden, AMROCK, Australia
Q. Wang, Wang, Qi, China
W. Zhang, Zhang, Weiming, China
Y. Chen, Trina Solar Energy, China
E. Krassowski, CE Cell Engineering, Germany
M. Foti, 3Sun, Italy
D.L. Bätzner, Meyer Burger Research, Switzerland

Topic 2: Thin Films and New Concepts
I. Gordon, imec, Belgium
J.C. Goldschmidt, Marburg University, Germany
F. Schoofs, Oxford PV, United Kingdom
N. Kyranaki, Hasselt University, Belgium
S. Veenstra, TNO Energy Transition, The Netherlands
T. Aernouts, imec, Belgium
A.N. Tiwari, SOLTIWA, Switzerland
G. Siefer, Fraunhofer ISE, Germany
M. Edoff, Uppsala University, Sweden
A. Martí Vega, UPM, Spain
J. Poortmans, imec, Belgium
I. Ramiro, UPM, Spain
T. Magorian Friedlmeier, ZSW, Germany

S. Albrecht, HZB, Germany
S. Berson, CEA, France
P. Carroy, CEA, France
C. Case, Oxford PV, United Kingdom
G. Coletti, FuturaSun, Italy
S. De Wolf, KAUST, Saudi Arabia
U.W. Paetzold, KIT, Germany
H. Sivaramakrishnan Radhakrisnan, imec, Belgium
P. Schulze, Fraunhofer ISE, Germany
L. Wang, Technology Innovation Institute, United Arab Emirates
Y. Smirnov, Applied Materials, United States of America
B. Stannowski, HZB, Germany
F. Fertig, Hanwha Q CELLS, Germany
L. Lancellotti, ENEA, Italy
S. Cros, CEA, France
S. Hayase, The University of Electro-Communications, Japan
S. Huang, Macquarie University, Australia
M. Khenkin, HZB, Germany
C. Lin, National Taiwan University, Taiwan
M.S.H. Norton, University of Cyprus, Cyprus
P. Pistor, Pablo de Olavide University, Spain
W. Tress, Zurich University of Applied Sciences, Switzerland
A. Aguirre, imec, Belgium
D. Lan, UNSW Sydney, China
M. Saliba, University of Stuttgart, Germany
P. Manshanden, TNO Energy Transition, The Netherlands
L. Vesce, University of Rome II, Italy
I. Dogan, TNO Solliance, The Netherlands
Y. Kuang, imec, Belgium
M. Al Katrib, IPVF, France
M.I. Hossain, QEERI, Qatar
W.H. Chiu, Chang Gung University, Taiwan
C. Chen, Ming Chi University of Technology, Taiwan
C. Fell, CSIRO Energy Technology, Australia
G. Brammertz, imec, Belgium
T. Dalibor, Avancis, Germany
S. Ishizuka, AIST, Japan
A. Redinger, University of Luxembourg, Luxembourg
A. Romeo, University of Verona, Italy
V. Sittinger, Fraunhofer IST, Germany
M. Theelen, TNO/Solliance, The Netherlands
G. Timò, RSE, Italy
A. Kanevce, ZSW, Germany
A. Pérez-Rodríguez, IREC, Spain
R. Gutzler, ZSW, Germany
W. Witte, ZSW, Germany
T. Nishimura, Tokyo Institute of Technology, Japan
C. Qian, University of New South Wales, Australia
J.P. Connolly, CentraleSupelec, France
J.P. Kleider, CNRS/GeePs, France
I. Konovalov, University of Applied Sciences Jena, Germany
Y. Okada, University of Tokyo, Japan
M. Rusu, HZB, Germany
H. Meddeb, DLR, Germany
E. Saucedo, Universitat Politècnica de Catalunya (UPC), Spain
P. Vidal-Fuentes, FUNDACIÓ INSTITUT DE RECERCA EN ENERGIA DE CATALUNYA, Spain
C. Malerba, ENEA, Italy
C. Becker, HZB, Germany
D. Kuciauskas, NREL, United States of America
M. Ochoa, University of Cantabria, Spain
T. Tayagaki, AIST, Japan
S. Wasmer, WAVELABS Solar Metrology Systems, Germany
S. Zandi, UNSW, Australia
C. Messmer, University of Freiburg, Germany
J.B. Puel, Institut Photovoltaïque d'Ile de France (IPVF), France
S. Ternes, University of Rome II, Italy

Topic 3: Photovoltaic Modules and BoS Components
V. Bermúdez Benito, BERBETIN, France
R. Preu, Fraunhofer ISE, Germany
R. Gottschalg, Fraunhofer CSP, Germany
T. Barnes, NREL, United States of America
G. Friesen, SUPSI, Switzerland
G. Bardizza, TÜV Rheinland Solar, Italy

V. Barth, CEA, France
A. Faes, CSEM, Switzerland
A. Lennon, Sundrive Solar, Australia
M. Mittag, Fraunhofer ISE, Germany
M.A. Muñoz-Garcia, UPM, Spain
H. Nagel, Fraunhofer ISE, Germany
S. Pietralunga, CNR, Italy
T. Timofte, ISC Konstanz, Germany

S. Feldbacher, PCCL, Austria
A. Halm, ISC Konstanz, Germany
H. Hanifi, AESOLAR, Germany
E. Warren, NREL, United States of America
S. Zhang, Trina Solar Energy, China
X. Zhen, Canadian Solar, China
G. Beaucarne, Dow Silicones Belgium, Belgium
T. Bejat, CEA, France
C. Camus, LayTec, Germany
U. Jahn, Fraunhofer CSP, Germany
G. Oreski, PCCL, Austria
M. Pander, Fraunhofer CSP, Germany
T. Sample, European Commission JRC, Italy
A. Morlier, imo-imomec, Belgium
C. Barretta, PCCL, Austria
P. Gebhardt, Fraunhofer ISE, Germany
C. Sen, UNSW, Australia
O. Arriaga Arruti, CSEM, Switzerland
X. Gu, NIST, United States of America
C. Xiao, Chinese Academy of Sciences, United States of America
R. Aninat, TNO/Solliance, The Netherlands
S. Mitterhofer, NIST, United States of America
B. Hoex, UNSW, Australia
E. Özkalay, SUPSI, Switzerland
M. Bokalič, University of Ljubljana, Slovenia
S. Bordihn, ISFH, Germany
M. Despeisse, CSEM, Switzerland
J. Govaerts, imec, Belgium
J. Lopez-Garcia, STS-Certified, Spain
M. Pravettoni, Technology Innovation Institute, United Arab Emirates
T. Stoyanova Lyubenova, Joint Research Centre, Italy
C. Ulbrich, HZB, Germany
J. Moereke, Avancis, Germany
Y.S. Long, ITRI, Taiwan
D. Pavanello, European Commission JRC, Italy
A.K. Vidal de Oliveira, UFSC, Brazil
J. Bengoechea, CENER, Spain
M. Ernst, ANU, Australia
H. Ellis, European Commission JRC, Italy
B. Mihaylov, European Commission JRC, Italy
G. Chowdhury, 3E, Belgium
B. Aissa, QEERI - Qatar Environment and Energy Research Institute, Qatar

Topic 4: PV Systems Engineering, Integrated/Applied PV
A. Gracia Amillo, CENER, Spain
W.G.J.H.M. van Sark, Utrecht University, The Netherlands
K. Lappalainen, Tampere University, Finland
J.M. Almeida Serra, University of Lisbon, Portugal
I. Tsanakas, CEA, France
C. Buerhop-Lutz, HI ERN, Germany
D. Moser, Becquerel Institute Italia, Italy
F. Frontini, SUPSI, Switzerland
G.C. Eder, OFI, Austria
A. Scognamiglio, ENEA, Italy
A. Chatzipanagi, European Commission JRC, Italy
I. Antón Hernández, UPM, Spain
R.M.E. Valckenborg, TNO, The Netherlands
T. Reindl, SERIS, Singapore
J.R. Gonzalez, European Space Agency, The Netherlands
G. Mütter, Gerhard Mütter e.U., Austria
T. Merdzhanova, Forschungszentrum Jülich, Germany

V. Lara-Fanego, Solargis, Spain
A. Louwen, Eurac Research, Italy
A. Martinez Fernandez, European Commission JRC, Italy
T. Oozeki, AIST, Japan
J. Remund, Meteotest, Switzerland
M. Sengupta, NREL, United States of America
M. Zehner, Rosenheim Technical University of Applied Sciences, Germany
B. Nouri, German Aerospace Center, Spain
S. Poddar, UNSW, Australia
D. Bachour, HBKU/ Qatar Foundation, Qatar
J. Yang, NREL, United States of America
S. Bouguerra, imo-imomec, Belgium
C. Alonso-Tristán, UBU, Spain
M. Carbone, ENEL Green Power, Italy
M. Dennenmoser, BayWa r.e. Solar Projects GmbH, Germany
C.W. Hansen, Sandia National Laboratories, United States of America
A. Neubert, DNV Maritime Software GmbH, Germany
D. Berrian, Belectric, Germany
M. Oliosi, PVsyst, Switzerland
J. Moschner, KU Leuven / EnergyVille, Belgium
C. Bucher, BUAS, Switzerland
B. Wittmer, PVsyst SA, Switzerland
M. Bolen, SB Energy, United States of America
D. Daßler, Fraunhofer CSP, Germany
R. Einhaus, ZSW, Germany
P. Hacke, NREL, United States of America
A. Heimsath, Fraunhofer ISE, Germany
J. Lin, PV Guider, Taiwan
A. Migan-Dubois, GeePs, France
M. Rinio, University of Karlstad, Sweden
J.S. Stein, Sandia National Laboratories, United States of America
D. Stellbogen, ZSW, Germany
M. Theristis, Sandia National Laboratories, United States of America
A. Virtuani, CSEM, Switzerland
A. Driesse, PV Performance Labs, Germany
M. Øgaard, IFE, Norway
A. Nobre, SERIS, Singapore
T. Trupke, UNSW, Australia
C. Cornaro, University of Rome II, Italy
G. A. dos Reis Benatto, DTU, Denmark
S. Malik, Fraunhofer CSP, Germany
S. Lindig, Univers SAS, France
M.M. Nygård, Institute for Energy Technology, Norway
P. Alonso Gomez, BayWa r.e., Germany
Y. Assoa, CEA, France
P. Bonomo, SUPSI, Switzerland
V. D'Ambrosio, University of Naples Federico II, Italy
E. Román Medina, Tecnalia, Spain
L.H. Slooff, TNO Energy Transition, The Netherlands
S. Villa, TNO, The Netherlands
M. La Rosa, Glass to Power, Italy
T. Del Caño, Onyx Solar Energy, Spain
X. Zhihao, AIST, Japan
P. Sharif, ODTU-GUNAM, Türkiye
K. Umeda, TAISEI CORPORATION, Japan
S. Boddaert, CSTB, France
N. Lysgaard Andersen, DTU, Denmark
K. Meyer, ISFH, Germany
T. Biel, NET Nowak Energy & Technology, Switzerland
F. Colucci, ENEA, Italy
A. Pascaris, NREL, United States of America
C. Dupraz, INRAE, France
C. Alonso-García, CIEMAT, Spain
A. Lefort, BayWa, Germany
H.N. Riise, IFE, Norway
M.A. Schüler, Next2Sun Technology GmbH, Germany
P.J. Pérez-Higueras, University of Jaén, Spain
K. Oda, Agritree,

M. Berwind, Fraunhofer ISE, Germany
M. Dörenkämper, TNO, The Netherlands
M. Heinrich, Fraunhofer ISE, Germany
B. Newman, Lightyear, The Netherlands
A. Reinders, Eindhoven University of Technology, The Netherlands
T. Tanahashi, AIST, Japan
J. Leloux, LuciSun, Belgium
E. Shirazi, University of Twente, The Netherlands
K. Araki, University of Miyazaki, Japan
K. Nishioka, University of Miyazaki, Japan
R. Campesato, CESI, Italy
V. Khorenko, Azur Space, Germany
G. Kakoulaki, European Commission Joint Research Centre, Italy
H. Toyota, JAXA, Japan
P. Garcia-Linares, UPM, Spain
I. Weiss, Weiss, Ingrid, Germany
A. Hensel, Fraunhofer ISE, Germany
J.S. da Fernandes, Hochschule Offenburg, Germany
Y. Ueda, Tokyo University of Science, Japan
J. Braid, Sandia National Laboratories, United States of America

Topic 5: PV in the Energy Transition
J. Stierstorfer, WIP Renewable Energies, Germany
R. Pestana, R&D Nester, Portugal
P.J. Alet, CSEM, Switzerland
C. Agraffeil, CEA, France
K. WAMBACH, Wambach-Consulting, Germany
C. del Cañizo, UPM, Spain
L. Großhans, WIP Renewable Energies, Germany
M. Getsiou, European Commission DG RTD, Belgium
S. Nowak, NET Nowak Energy & Technology, Switzerland
C. Breyer, LUT University, Finland
I. Kaizuka, RTS Corporation, Japan
G. Masson, Becquerel Institute, Belgium
P. Baliozian, VDMA, Germany
L. Großhans, WIP Renewable Energies, Germany
C. Candelise, Bocconi University, Italy
S. Caneva, WIP Renewable Energies, Germany

G. Barchi, Eurac Research, Italy
R. Bründlinger, AIT, Austria
V. Efthymiou, University of Cyprus, Cyprus
M. Centeno Brito, University of Lisbon, Portugal
F. Carigiet, ZHAW, Switzerland
B. Gaiddon, HESPUL, France
F.Z. Ouchani, Green Energy Park, Morocco
M. Rennhofer, AIT, Austria
G. Adinolfi, ENEA, Italy
W. Schaffer, Salzburg Netz, Austria
A. Haber, e-control, Austria
G. Heilscher, Technische Hochschule Ulm, Germany
A. Anctil, Michigan State University, United States of America
S. Arancón, Plug and Play, Spain
S. Capaccioli, ETA - Florence Renewable Energies, Italy
V. Fthenakis, Columbia University, United States of America
G. Heath, NREL, United States of America
K. Komoto, Mizuho Research & Technologies, Ltd., Japan
W. Palitzsch, LuxChemtech, Germany
S. Ovaitt, NREL, United States of America
M. de Wild-Scholten, SmartGreenScans, The Netherlands
S. Herceg, Fraunhofer ISE, Germany
C. Polacchi, Eurac Research, Italy
N. Espinosa, Universidad de Murcia, Spain
E. Drahi, TotalEnergies OneTech, France
S. Guastella, RSE, Italy
H. Ossenbrink, Band Gap, Germany
D. Polverini, European Commission DG GROW, Belgium
N. Taylor, European Commission JRC, Italy
K.A. Weiß, Fraunhofer ISE, Germany
I. Kafedjiska, Helmholtz Zentrum Berlin, Germany
P. Malbranche, Solar Action, France
S. De Iuliis, ENEA, Italy
T. Haarberg, BNW-Energy, Norway
A. Nayfeh, Khalifa University, United Arab Emirates
E. Vartiainen, Fortum Renewables Oy, Finland
E. Veronese, Eurac Research, Italy
P. Sanchez-Friera, Solkeys, Spain
N. Cherradi, Desert Technologies, Saudi Arabia
S. Nold, Fraunhofer ISE, Germany
H.J.J. Yu, CEA, France
M. Beck, U.S. Department of Energy, United States of America
M. Woodhouse, NREL, United States of America
A.B. Cristóbal, UPM, Spain
G. Ruggieri, Insubria University, Italy
S. Tay, NUS, Singapore

Awards Coordinators

Student Awards Coordinator
A.H.M. Smets, Delft University of Technology, The Netherlands

Student Awards Committee
R. Kenny, EU PVSEC Technical Programme Chair, Italy
C. del Canizo, Conference Chair, UPM, Spain
E. Voroshazi, CEA, France
J. Poortmans, imec, Belgium
P.J. Alet, CSEM, Switzerland
S. Caneva, WIP Renewable Energies, Germany
A. Romeo, University of Verona, Italy
G. Friesen, SUPSI, Switzerland
F. Schindler, Fraunhofer ISE, Germany
J.C. Goldchmidt, Marburg University, Germany
D. Moser, Becquerel Institute, Italy
K. Ding, FZJ, Germany
W.C. Sinke, TNO Energy Transition, The Netherlands
M. Topic, University of Ljubljana, Slovenia
R. Schlatman, HZB, Germany
S. Glunz, Fraunhofer ISE, Germany
A.M. Vega, UPM, Spain
I. Kaizuka, RTS, Japan
P.D. Veneri, ENEA, Italy
J. Bengoechea, CENER, Spain

Poster Awards Coordinator
P. Malbranche, Solar Action, France

Poster Awards Committee
R. Kenny, European Commission JRC, Italy
C. del Canizo, UPM, Spain
W. van Sark, Utrecht University, The Netherlands
I. Tsanakas, CEA INES, France
L. Miranda, Oxford PV, United Kingdom
D. Munoz, CEA INES, France
I. Gordon, imec, Belgium
E. Roman, Tecnalia, Spain
G. Eder, OFI, Austria
I. Antón, UPM, Spain
S. Veenstra, TNO, The Netherlands
J.M. Almeida Serra, University of Lisbon, Portugal
T. Magorian Friedlmeier, ZSW, Germany
J. Stierstorfer, WIP Renewable Energies, Germany

G. Kakoulaki, European Commission JRC, Italy
T. Barnes, NREL, USA
T. Merdzhanova, Forschungszentrum Jülich, Germany

Highlights Committee
C. del Cañizo, UPM, Madrid, Spain
R. Kenny, European Commission Joint Research Centre, Directorate for Energy and Transport and Climate, Ispra, Italy
W.C. Sinke, TNO Energy Transition, The Netherlands
S. Nowak, Managing Director of NET Nowak Energy & Technology, St. Ursen, Switzerland
M. Topič, Head of Laboratory of Photovoltaics and Optoelectronics of the University of Ljubljana, Slovenia
V. Bermúdez Benito, BERBETIN, France
E. Voroshazi, Head of PV Module Process Laboratory, CEA, Le Bourget-Du-Lac France
H. Ossenbrink, Band Gap, Germany
J. Bergmiller, Managing Director Events & Knowledge Transfer, WIP Renewable Energies, Munich, Germany
J. de Gregorio, Head of Unit, Scientific Services and Cooperation, WIP Renewable Energies, Munich, Germany
S. Leanza, Marketing and PR Manager, WIP Renewable Energies, Munich, Germany
B. Yildiz, Project Manager Events & Knowledge Transfer, WIP Renewable Energies, Munich, Germany
F. Schindler, Fraunhofer ISE, Freiburg, Germany
I. Gordon, imec, Leuven, Belgium
T. Barnes, NREL, Evergreen, USA
A.M. Gracia Amillo, FUNDACION CENER, Sarriguren, Spain
C. Agraffeil, CEA / INES, Le Bourget-du-Lac, France

SUBJECT INDEX

Silicon Materials and Cells

Sessions 1CP.1, 1EP.3, 1AO.4, 1AO.5, 1AO.6, 1BO.1, 1BO.2, 1BO.3, 1BO.4, 1DO.9, 1BV.5, 1CV.2

Thin Films and New Concepts

Sessions 2CP.2, 2BO.1, 2CO.1, 2CO.2, 2DO.9, 2DO.6, 2DO.7, 2DO.8, 2AO.2, 2AO.3, 2AO.1, 2BO.8, 2BO.9, 2BO.10, 2BV.1, 2BV.2, 2CV.3

Photovoltaic Modules and BoS Components

Sessions 3CP.1, 3CP.3, 3CO.10, 3CO.11, 3DO.12, 3DO.16, 3DO.19, 3DO.20, 3BO.11, 3BO.12, 3BO.14, 3BO.15, 3AV.1, 3AV.2, 3AV.3

PV Systems Engineering, Integrated/Applied PV

Sessions 4AP.1, 4AO.7, 4AO.8, 4AO.9, 4DO.1, 4DO.3, 4BO.6, 4BO.7, 4CO.8, 4CO.9, 4DO.10, 4DO.17, 4BO.5, 4BO.16, 4BO.17, 4DO.2, 4DO.4, 4DO.5, 4CO.3, 4EO.2, 4BV.3, 4BV.4, 4CV.1, 4DV.1, 4DV.4,

PV in the Energy Transition

Sessions 5CP.1, 5CP.2, 5DO.14, 5DO.15, 5CO.4, 5CO.5, 5CO.6, 5DO.18, 5CO.4, 5CO.5, 5CO.6, 5DO.18, 5EO.3, 5EO.1, 5DV.2, 5DV.3,

Topic Code	**Session Type**	**Day Codes**
1 Silicon Materials and Cells	P = Plenary Session	A = Monday, 22 September 2025
2 Thin-Films and New Concepts	O = Oral Session	B = Tuesday, 23 September 2025
3 Photovoltaic Modules	V = Visual Session	C = Wednesday, 24 September 2025
4 Photovoltaic Systems		D = Thursday, 25 September 2025
5 Photovoltaics in the Energy Transition		E = Friday, 26 September 2025

e.g. 1AO.4 ⇒ 1= Silicon Materials and Cells, A=Monday, O=Oral session, 4=Session 4

FOREWORD

The European Photovoltaic Solar Energy Conference and Exhibition (EU PVSEC) stands as the World's leading and most renowned forum for PV research and development and the biggest conference on PV solar energy. In 2025, celebrating its 42nd edition, the EU PVSEC was the essential meeting and exchanging point for global PV experts from research, development, and industry.

Held from 22–26 September 2025 in Bilbao, Spain, the EU PVSEC 2025 was a resounding success, showcasing a wide range of cutting-edge research results. Bringing together both the Conference and the Exhibition, this edition attracted more than 1600 participants from 61 countries who contributed over 1000 presentations across various fields of science and technology. The event provided an essential platform for the exchange of knowledge and ideas on photovoltaic research, innovations, and applications. In the exhibition area 51 companies from all parts of the world welcomed visitors and presented their products and services.

Conference Highlights

The EU PVSEC covered a broad range of topics with an extensive programme that offers an opportunity for workers from across the entire field of photovoltaics to share their findings, as well as an opportunity for multidisciplinary learning. Rapid advances in materials, designs, and manufacturing processes reflect the accelerating expansion of the global PV market. The programme was arranged into 5 topics as follows:

- Silicon Materials and Cells;
- Thin Films and New Concepts;
- Photovoltaic Modules and Balance of System Components;
- PV Systems Engineering, Integrated/Applied PV;
- PV in the Energy Transition.

Communicating the key messages from the conference, not only to participants, but also to other researchers, key stakeholders, policy makers and the general public was an important added value. We thank the Highlights Committee, composed of selected members of the Scientific Committee, as well as the Session Chairs, for providing a comprehensive summary of the findings and state of the art research that were delivered during this year´s event. Some key highlights are listed below, while further details may be found in the dedicated highlights presentation in the annex of these proceedings.

Cross-cutting themes:

- Demonstrated the versatility of solar technologies, spanning traditional and emerging application areas.
- Sustainability and circularity remain central, with research focused on reducing material use, such as replacing silver with copper, and advancing end-of-life management of modules.
- Ensuring long-term stability and predictable energy yield is equally essential, with many examples of studies on degradation mechanisms and efforts to elucidate their root-causes, such as in the case of UVID.
- The role of artificial intelligence across the PV value chain is rapidly expanding, from design to operations and maintenance, including among many others drone applications.

Latest Solar Innovations in Materials, Cells, Modules and PV Systems:

While silicon solar cells remain the cornerstone of PV technology, perovskite solar cells continue to stand out as the leading complementary technology to silicon, both as standalone devices and in tandem configurations. Research efforts are increasingly focused on enhancing stability, understanding degradation mechanisms, improving durability and scalability, and ensuring full industrial compatibility.

Many companies presented impressive results on industrial-size single-junction perovskite modules as well as perovskite-based tandem modules, and several new efficiency records were announced during the event. The rapid pace of innovation in cell and module architecture underscores the need for accelerated and more robust testing and qualification methodologies. Both the industry and the research community are moving swiftly to assess and improve reliability in this fast-evolving PV landscape.

A major focus in module research remains the optimisation of materials and packaging to ensure long lifetimes and predictable energy yields from high-efficiency cells. In parallel, many innovative advances in the operation and maintenance (O&M) of PV systems were presented and discussed.

Applications, Grid Integration and Storage

"PV can be deployed everywhere": from space applications to agrivoltaics, PV noise barriers, building-integrated photovoltaics (BIPV), floating PV systems, and even vehicles. Among these, agrivoltaics is gaining momentum as a promising dual land use approach, offering economic benefits for farmers while increasing resilience to climate change.

Flexibility solutions, particularly through battery storage, were recognised in many technical presentations as essential to accommodate higher PV penetration levels and to reduce energy curtailment. At the same time, strengthening grid infrastructure and enhancing grid management capabilities remain critical to enable the next phase of large-scale PV integration.

Photovoltaics in the Energy Transition

Options for re-establishing competitive module manufacturing in Europe were extensively analysed, including detailed policy recommendations for industrial support and market growth. Currently, a mismatch persists between global PV module installation rates and production rates, resulting in growing inventories and sharply reduced prices.

Finally, inclusiveness, diversity, citizen participation, awareness, education, and social engagement were underlined as vital dimensions of the sector's long-term sustainability and innovation capacity.

EU PVSEC 2025 Proceedings

Selection for inclusion in the conference was made by the Scientific Committee's paper review experts and topic organisers (see the listing on pages 010002-001-005), to whom we express our sincere gratitude for their comprehensive review work and overall contribution to the success of the conference.

The EU PVSEC 2025 Proceedings contain the full papers covering most of the highlights described above and more. The Proceedings provide a comprehensive overview of the PV solar sector, its current status and future prospects in science, research, innovation, development and deployment extending to 3,750 pages. In addition to the 299 submitted papers, the proceedings include 101 presentations (slides) shown during the plenary and oral presentations as well as 176 poster files of the visual presentations. In total this amounts to 576 publications.

The Conference Proceedings are published as downloadable files and are also fully accessible online. A DOI code (Digital Object Identifier) has been assigned to each paper. This ensures unequivocal and permanent identification and full citability. The EU PVSEC 2025 papers can be viewed and downloaded in a full free open access from the EU PVSEC's Proceedings website https://userarea.eupvsec.org/proceedings.

The proceedings of the EU PVSEC 2025 strengthen the commitment to providing quick and open access to high quality scientific results. This is a powerful source for targeted and quick information search and retrieval, enabling you to search by topic, keywords, paper title, DOI, author, or organization.

We are confident that these Proceedings will play an important role in providing a comprehensive overview of the current actors and activities in the global PV sector and that they will disseminate information on the state-of-the-art of technologies and applications. This can generate further research, add momentum to innovation and promote interest in PV worldwide.

We would like to cordially thank all authors and participants of the EU PVSEC 2025 for their contributions and look forward to welcoming you in Rotterdam, The Netherlands from 14 – 18 September 2026 at the EU PVSEC 2026, the 43rd European Photovoltaic Solar Energy Conference and Exhibition

The Editors

TABLE OF CONTENTS OF EU PVSEC 2025 PROCEEDINGS PAPERS

Oral SESSION 1BO.4 Novel Metallisation Techniques

Visual SESSION 1BV.5 Crystalline Silicon Material: Defects and Recycling | Processes and Concepts for the Manufacturing of Silicon Solar Cells

Visual SESSION 1CV.2 Si Solar Cells | Characterisation & Modelling of Silicon Cells and Their Building Blocks

[1] Anhalt University of Applied Sciences, Köthen, Germany; [2] Fraunhofer CSP, Halle, Germany

Oral SESSION 2AO.2 Advances in Chalcogenide Devices

2AO.2.3 A New Method for Sb-doped CdSeTe/CdTe Devices with Superior Stability 020057
Elisa Artegiani[1], Mariyam Mukhtar[1], Alessandro Romeo[1]
[1] University of Verona, Verona, Italy

Oral SESSION 2AO.3 III-V Based Devices | Tandem and Perovskite Solar Cells

2AO.3.3 Micro-Crystal GaAs Array Sub-Cells for Si Tandem Solar Cells 020058
James Patrick Connolly[1], Ahmed Nejim[2], Alexandre Jaffré[1], José Alvarez[1], Jean-Paul Kleider[1], Denis Mencaraglia[1], Laurie Dentz[3], Géraldine Hallais[3], Frederic Hamouda[3], Laetitia Vincent[3], Daniel Bouchier[3], Charles Renard[3]
[1] CNRS, Gif-sur-Yvette, France; [2] SILVACO, St. Ives, United Kingdom; [3] CNRS, Palaiseau, France

2AO.3.5 Multiscale Models for Perovskite Optimisation 020060
Philippe Baranek[1], James Patrick Connolly[2], Antoine Gissler[1], Philip Schulz[3], Michel Rerat[4], Roberto Dovesi[5]
[1] EDF R&D, Palaiseau, France; [2] CNRS, Gif-sur-Yvette, France; [3] IPVF, Palaiseau, France; [4] IPREM, Pau, France; [5] Academy of Sciences of Turin, Torino, Italy

2AO.3.6 Modelling Recovery in Perovskite Solar Cells under Light and Dark to Address Stability Challenges 020062
Guillem Álvarez-Pérez[1], Jean Baptiste Puel[1], Jean François Guillemoles [1]
[1] IPVF, Palaiseau, France

Oral SESSION 2BO.10 Advanced Modelling and Characterisation of Perovskite Solar Cells

2BO.10.2 On Perimeter Losses in Perovskite Top- and Poly-Si-Passivated Silicon Bottom Cells – Do Small Area Tandems Reveal the Full Efficiency Potential? 020063
Felix Haase[1], Lukas Brockmann[1], Annika Raugewitz[1], Verena Steckenreiter[1], Verena Barnscheidt[1], Roland Clausing[1], Sara Baumann[1], Joachim Vollbrecht[1], Welmoed Veurman[1], Johannes Löhr[1], Dongyang Liu[1], Mircea Turcu[1], Lasse Nasebandt[1], Udo Römer[1], David Sylla[1], Jessica Strey[1], Martha Löhning[1], Larissa Mettner[1], Renate Winter[1], Anja Christ[1], Heike Kohlenberg[1], Cornelia Marquardt[1], Emanuel Brueckner[1], Hossein Rabiei[1], Michael Rienäcker[1], Sarah Kajari-Schröder[1], Tobias Wietler[1], Robby Peibst[1]
[1] ISFH, Emmerthal, Germany

2BO.10.5 In-depth Characterization and Simulation Approach for the Understanding of In- and Outdoor Degradation of Perovskite Solar Cells 020064
Jonathan Parion[1], Amit Kumar Harit[1], Elias Peraticos[2], Vasiliki Paraskeva[2], Maria Hadjipanayi[2], Aranzazu Aguirre[1], Filip Duerinckx[1], Hariharsudan

Visual SESSION 2CV.3 Perovskite-based Tandems and Multijunctions

Visual SESSION 3AV.1 PV Module Design and Manufacturing

Visual SESSION 3AV.2 PV Module Durability and Reliability

Visual SESSION 3AV.3 PV Modules Characterisation and Performances Assessment

Oral SESSION 3BO.11 Imaging Techniques for PV Modules

Cristian Terrados[1], Eva de la Viuda[1], Kabir Paul Sulca[1], Julian Anaya[1], Miguel Ángel González[1], Oscar Martínez[1]
[1] *University of Valladolid, Valladolid, Spain*

Oral SESSION 3BO.12 Characterisation and Energy Rating of PV Modules

Oral SESSION 3BO.14 Characterisation and Outdoor Monitoring of Perovskite-based PV Modules

Oral SESSION 3BO.15 Outdoor Performances and Degradation Analysis of PV Modules

3CO.11.5 Indoor Characterization and Analysis of Reverse Breakdown Behavior of Solar Cells with Different Cell Architectures — 020223

Bengt Jaeckel[1], Jens Froebel[1], Matthias Pander[1], Andreas Maixner[2], Hamed Hanifi[2]

[1] Fraunhofer CSP, Halle, Germany; [2] AESOLAR, Koenigsbrunn, Germany

Plenary SESSION 3CP.1 Si PV Manufacturing: Pushing the Limits of Performance

3CP.1.2 IBC4EU: European Back Contact Technology — 020225

Florian Buchholz[1], Daniel Tune[1], Tobias Meßmer[1], Jonathan Linke[1], Manjunath Prasad[1], Valentin D. Mihailetchi[1], Juras Ulbikas[2], Arne Dahle[3], Martijn Meereboer[4], Francesca Fabris[5], Erik Eikelboom[5], Tom Borgers[6], Rik Van Dyck[6], Filip Duerinckx[7], Hariharsudan Sivaramakrishnan Radhakrishnan[7], Timea Bejat[8], Samuel Harrison[8], Ashish Binani[9], Nicolas Guillevin[9], Jan Kroon[9], Yevgeniya Larionova[10], Thorsten Dullweber[10], Ofer Shochet[11], Isaac Rosen [11], Ingo Röver [12], Wolfram Palitzsch[12], Yasmin Zaror[13], Johannes Stierstorfer[14], Aurimas Radzevicius[15], Julius Denafas[16], Tuomas Vanhanen [17], Tuukka Savisalo[17], Maximilian Pospischil [18], Marian Breitenbücher [18], Özlem Coşkun[19], Melodie de l`Epine [20], Philippe Macé[20], Ian Kenchington[20]

[1] ISC Konstanz, Konstanz, Germany; [2] Protechnology, Vilnius, Lithuania; [3] Norsun, Oslo, Norway; [4] Energyra, Westknollendam, The Netherlands; [5] Futurasun, Citadella, Italy; [6] IMEC, Genk, Belgium; [7] Hasselt Unversity, Genk, Belgium; [8] CEA, Le Bourget-du-Lac, France; [9] TNO, Petten, The Netherlands; [10] ISFH, Emmerthal, Germany; [11] Copprint, Jerusalem, Israel; [12] LuxChemTech, Freiberg, Germany; [13] WIP Renewable Energies, Munich, Germany; [14] WIP - Renewable Energies, Munich, Germany; [15] Valoe Cells, Vilnius, Lithuania; [16] Solitek, Vilnius, Lithuania; [17] Valoe, Mikkeli, Finland; [18] Highline Technologies, Freiburg, Germany; [19] Kalyon PV, Ankara, Türkiye; [20] Becquerel Institute, Brussels, Belgium

Plenary SESSION 3CP.3 Perovskite – Silicon Tandems: Towards Commercialisation | PV Stability in the Field

3CP.3.4 Outdoor Performance and Reliability of Perovskite (Pk)-Silicon (Si) Tandems: >1 year of Monitoring in the NEXUS Project — 020226

Atse Louwen[1], Jordi Veirman[1], Alexander Astigarraga[1], Juan José Stivanello[1], David Moser[2], Perrine Carroy[3], Vincent Barth[3], Delfina Muñoz[3], Markus Lenz[4], Anika Sidler[4], Jorge Ferrando[5], Maximiliano Alejandro Senno[5], Henk J. Bolink[5], Talat Özden[6], Hisham Nasser[6], Shuaifeng Hu[7], Xinyi Shen[7], Henry Snaith[7]

[1] Eurac Research, Bolzano, Italy; [2] Becquerel Institute Italy, Trento, Italy; [3] CEA / INES, Le Bourget-du-Lac, France; [4] School of Life Sciences FHNW, Muttenz, Switzerland; [5] University of Valencia, Paterna, Spain; [6] ODTÜ-GÜNAM, Ankara, Türkiye; [7] University of Oxford, Oxford, United Kingdom

Oral SESSION 3DO.12 Innovative Encapsulation Materials

Oral SESSION 4BO.6 Assessing the Reliability of PV Systems

Oral SESSION 4BO.7 Field Insights, Performance and Modelling of PV Systems

Visual SESSION 4BV.3 Solar Resource and Forecasting

Visual SESSION 4BV.4 BIPV

Oral SESSION 4CO.8 Soiling and Snow Effects in PV Systems

Oral SESSION 4CO.9 Data-driven and AI-based O&M of PV Systems

Visual SESSION 4CV.1 Advances in Operation, Performance and Maintenance of PV Systems

Oral SESSION 4DO.1 PV Tracking and Simulation

4DO.17.2 Model Optimization for Multi-Class Real Time UAV Thermal Anomaly Detection in Solar PV Systems 020374

Ghaem Taghipour Kani[1], Seyyed Majid Esmailifar[1], Amirreza Ghahremani[1], Mohammadreza Aghaei[2]

[1] Amirkabir University of Technology, Tehran, Iran; [2] NTNU, Ålesund, Norway

4DO.17.3 Optimizing Autonomous Aerial Monitoring of Photovoltaic Power Plants via an Integrated Software Package and a Digital Twin Based Simulation Environment 020375

Mohammad Kolahi[1], Seyyed Majid Esmailifar[2], Amirmohammad Moradi Sizkouhi[3], Mohammadreza Aghaei[4]

[1] University of Isfahan, Isfahan, Iran; [2] Amirkabir University of Technology, Tehran, Iran; [3] Concordia University, Montreal, Canada; [4] NTNU, Ålesund, Norway

4DO.17.4 Influence of Irradiance and Drone Altitude in Infrared Thermography Inspections of Photovoltaic Plants 020376

Rodrigo del Prado Santamaría[1], Gisele A. dos Reis Benatto[1], Mahmoud Dhimish[1], Timurhan Koc[1], Rizal Friansyah[1], Thøger Kari[1], Aysha Mahmood[1], Peter B. Poulsen[1], Sergiu V. Spataru[1]

[1] DTU, Roskilde, Denmark

4DO.17.6 Strategy for Simple, On-Site Failure Analysis: Investigating Bubbles and Burn Marks in Backsheets of PV Modules 020377

Claudia Buerhop[1], Aline Vidal de Oliveira[2], Oleksandr Mashkov[1], Lucas Nascimento[2], Ricardo Rüther[2], Ian Marius Peters[1]

[1] Forschungszentrum Jülich, Erlangen, Germany; [2] UFSC, Florianopolis, Brazil

Oral SESSION 4DO.2 Agrivoltaic Technologies

4DO.2.1 Design and Testing of an Innovative Closed Agrivoltaic System: "Algaevoltaics" 020378

Alessandra Scognamiglio[1], Aniello Borriello[1], Carmine Cancro[1], Mariam De Blasi[2], Maria Genovese[2], Marcello Diano[3], Stefano Mazzoleni[4], Fabrizio Carteni[4], Paola Delli Veneri[1]

[1] ENEA, Portici, Italy; [2] Enel Green Power, Pisa, Italy; [3] M2M Engineering, Naples, Italy; [4] University of Naples Federico II, Naples, Italy

4DO.2.2 Experimental Investigation of an Agrivoltaic Collector with Planar Spectral Beam Splitting 020379

Inga Krasilnikov[1], Abraham Kribus[1], Gur Mittelman[2], Liad Reshef[3], Shay Ozer[3], Lavi Rosenfeld[3], Helena Vitoshkin[3]

[1] Tel Aviv University, Tel Aviv, Israel; [2] Afeka Tel-Aviv Academic College of Engineering, Tel Aviv, Israel; [3] Agricultural Research Organization, Rishon LeZion, Israel

4DO.2.3 Agri-PV Potential in Northern Climates An Experimental Study on Panel Transparency, and Leafy Vegetable Productivity 020380

Matas Rudzikas[1], Giedrė Samuolienė[2], Justinas Raginskis[3], Piotr Dubravskij[4], Algirdas Baležentis[1], Skirmantė Baležentienė[1]

[1] The Applied Research Institute for Prospective Technologies, Vilnius, Lithuania; [2] The Lithuanian Research Centre for Agriculture and Forestry, Kaunas, Lithuania; [3] Kaunas University of Technology, Kaunas, Lithuania; [4] Modern E-Technologies, Vilnius, Lithuania

4DO.5.4 Development and Evaluation of Agrivoltaic System in Olive Groves based on a Novel Smart Tracking Algorithm 020392

Ildefonso Muñoz[1], Irati Amatriain[1], Gregorio Olivares[1], Gillen Abrego[2], Eusebio Gainza[2], Iñaki Cornago[1]

[1] CENER, Sarriguren, Spain; [2] ALLOTARRA, Allo, Spain

4DO.5.5 Adoption and Optimisation Analysis of Agrivoltaic Systems for Horticultural Production and Energy Autonomy in Lubumbashi/DR Congo 020393

Eddie Bilitu[1], Shu-Ngwa Asaa[2], Sara Bouguerra[3], Nikoleta Kyranaki[3], Ismail Kaaya[3], Yannick Useni[4], Michael Daenen[3]

[1] Hasselt University, Hasselt, Belgium; [2] imo-imomec, Genk, Belgium; [3] imec, Genk, Belgium; [4] University of Lubumbashi, Lubumbashi, Congo (DRC)

Visual SESSION 4DV.1 Agrivoltaics Approaches, Experiences, Results | Integrated and Innovative PV Applications

4DV.1.5 Maximizing Economic Performance of Agrivoltaic Systems through Module Array Design 020394

Habeel Alam[1], Jenny Nelson[2], Alona Armstrong[1], Duncan Whyatt[1], Nauman Butt[3]

[1] Lancaster University, Lancaster, United Kingdom; [2] Imperial College London, London, United Kingdom; [3] Lahore University of Management Sciences, Lahore, Pakistan

4DV.1.7 Bifacial and Mismatch Factors of Agri-Photovoltaics Systems 020396

Keith R. McIntosh[1], Solomon Freer[1], Bastien J. J. Ardissone[1], S. Ramirez[1], Ben A. Sudbury[1], Malcolm D. Abbott[1]

[1] PV Lighthouse, Coledale, Australia

4DV.1.10 Performance Analysis of Agrivoltaic System Configurations in Nordic Conditions 020398

Magda Szarek[1], Sami Jouttijärvi[1], Lauri Karttunen[1], Samuli Ranta[2], Kati Miettunen[1]

[1] University of Turku, Turku, Finland; [2] TUAS, Turku, Finland

4DV.1.11 Irradiance Management in Agrivoltaic Systems with Varying Designs Across Latitudes: Toward Finland's First Significant Demonstration 020400

Shuo Wang[1], Soroush Moradi Zavie Kord[2], Hugo E. Huerta[1], Antti Lajunen[2], Samuli Ranta[1]

[1] TUAS, Turku, Finland; [2] University of Helsinki, Helsinki, Finland

4DV.1.12 An Innovative Agrivoltaic System for Desert Climates with Anti-Soiling, Irradiance Control, and Water Management 020402

Sagarika Kumar[1], Min Hsian Saw[1], Ahmed Shaaban[1], Kamil Jaworczak[1], Nursulu Kuzhagaliyeva[1], Carlos G. Parrilla[2], Francois M. Tsombou[2], Fouad Lamghari[2], Mauro Pravettoni[1]

[1] Technology Innovation Institute, Abu Dhabi, United Arab Emirates; [2] Fujairah Research Centre, Fujairah, United Arab Emirates

4DV.1.15 Review of Sensor Technologies for Monitoring Agrivoltaic Systems 020403

Sara Pereira[1], José A. Silva[1], Luís Fialho[2], Pedro Horta[1]

[1] University of Évora, Évora, Portugal; [2] Eurac Research, Bolzano, Italy

Visual SESSION 4DV.4 PV System Engineering

Oral SESSION 5CO.4 Life Cycle Assessment of Silicon and Perovskite-based Cells and Modules

Oral SESSION 5CO.5 Life Cycle Assessment of New PV Applications and Recycling

Oral SESSION 5DO.18 PV Recycling and Material Demand

Visual SESSION 5DV.2 Life Cycle Analysis and PV Recycling | Citizens Participation and Awareness

Visual SESSION 5DV.3 Grid Integration and Flexibility Enablers | Global, Country- and Application-Specific Analysis of PV Deployment Aspects | Costs, Economics, Finance and Markets

Oral SESSION 5EO.1 Citizens Participation and Awareness

ECONOMIC VALUE OF BUILDING-INTEGRATED PV PRODUCTION AT HIGH-LATITUDE LOCATIONS

Sami Jouttijärvi[1*], Lauri Karttunen[1], Magda Szarek[1], Bergpob Viriyaroj[2], Samuli Ranta[3], Kati Miettunen[1]
[1]Department of Mechanical and Materials Engineering, University of Turku, Vesilinnantie 5, 20500 Turku, Finland
[2]Department of Architecture, Aalto University, Otakaari 24, 02150 Espoo, Finland
[3]New Energy Research Group, Turku University of Applied Sciences, Joukahaisenkatu 7, 20520 Turku, Finland
*sami.jouttijarvi@utu.fi

ABSTRACT:
This work evaluates the status and prospects of building-integrated solar photovoltaic (BIPV) production in Finland, focusing on maintaining the value of the produced PV electricity during the lifetime of the system. The rapid increase of PV capacity in Finland causes major effects to the power system and the electricity market price, especially by lowering the price during the best PV production hours. This phenomenon can demotivate individual citizens and companies to invest in their own PV systems. To tackle the challenges related to the future uncertainties in the electricity price, maximizing the self-consumption of the planned BIPV system is important. Self-consuming the produced PV electricity allows avoiding transfer fee and taxes, which form, on average, most of the electricity purchase costs for the Finnish individuals. This work presents the recent research in the fields of BIPV and electricity price at high-latitude locations. Based on the existing scientific knowledge, we develop solutions for residential and commercial building-owners for designing PV systems that are resilient and profitable. The economic feasibility of these solutions with the 2019-2023 electricity price data is analyzed. The results show that high self-consumption rates result in high economic value: net present values were 665–883 EUR/kW for the studied systems during the years 2019-2023, covering more than half of reasonable investment costs.
Keywords: building-integrated PV, electricity price, self-consumption

1 INTRODUCTION

Building-integrated and building-applied solar photovoltaic (BIPV and BAPV) solutions allow the utilization of PV in urban areas, where dedicating large land areas solely for PV is often practically impossible. Moreover, BIPV enables using the produced electricity at the spot (self-consumption), thus avoiding the additional costs due to electricity transfer and taxes. The importance of PV self-consumption for economic profitability is highlighted when the revenue from PV electricity sold to the power grid is low.

In Finland, the electricity grid price is usually low and often only available option for small-scale producers is to sell their surplus production to the grid with the price defined by the day-ahead auction in the Nordpool market. Thus, even with the current PV production levels, the revenue for selling the electricity is low. As PV production is growing rapidly in Finland [1], the spot price is expected to decrease during PV peak production hours. Therefore, maximizing the self-consumed kilowatt-hours (kWhs) compared with PV system cost should be the key target for the BIPV systems in Finland.

One approach to improve self-consumption is investing in energy storage. Batteries can store PV electricity generated during the day for later use. In the central Europe batteries are common, but the low electricity price reduces the possibility to earn money with a battery in Finland, thus compromising their economic feasibility [2]. Due to a high heat demand, also thermal energy storages (TESs) can act as a flexible load for PV production. Our previous work showed the potential of TES in a Finnish residential house [3], and in Norway, larger TES was applied to improve the self-consumption of PV system in a high school [4].

However, as energy storage requires additional investments, the option to improve self-consumption by matching PV production and residential load becomes attractive. Even with historical electricity prices, where the impact of PV to the electricity price is negligible, east-and-west-oriented rooftop panels suffered only 13% economic loss compared with their south-facing counterparts, although the annual production loss was 23% [3]. As the national PV capacity grows and starts to impact to the spot price, which can occur with reasonable capacity additions [5], the mean price close to noon drops. Thus, the surplus production in the middle of the day is practically worthless, and even for the self-consumed production the value is higher in the morning and evening at least for the consumers with spot price or time-of-use electricity purchase contracts.

In densely built urban areas with multi-story buildings, the low roof-area-to-volume ratio of the buildings limits the rooftop PV generation potential, creating the need to utilize building facades. Compared with locations further south, high annual variation in the solar resource and low solar elevation angles characterize PV production in Finland. Considering BIPV, the low solar elevation opens possibilities to use building facades for PV production, since the relative loss in PV production is lower compared with regions where the solar elevation is high. Using facades for PV generation is thus relevant for the Finnish multi-story buildings, where the roof-area-to-volume ratio is small.

Moreover, the mismatch between the residential electricity load and PV production with conventional, south-facing systems reduces the economic value of PV generation. These factors encourage to build PV systems that produce better during the morning and evening. Our previous findings show that applying vertical bifacial PV (VBPV) installed in perpendicular to the south-facing façade of a multi-story building reaches slightly higher annual production compared with their monofacial PV (MPV) counterparts [6], with improved load-matching.

For detached houses, the ownership structure of the installed PV system is simple: the owner-resident of the building owns the system and either uses its production or sells it to the grid. For multi-story buildings, the ownership structures can be more complicated, which raises questions about sharing the benefits of the building's BIPV system. Conflicts between the stakeholders may even prevent the building of the system, thus halting PV growth in Finland.

Our work presents existing research on the economic

profitability of BIPV in Finland. As a novel contribution, we complement the existing literature by including diverse electricity pricing scenarios when calculating the economic indicators for BIPV systems. The aim is to find the systems that are resilient towards the future price uncertainties, i.e., that achieve feasible economic performance and outperform their counterparts under studied scenarios.

2 METHODS

A flowchart showing the simulation workflow is presented in Figure 1. The chart is categorized into data, simulation, and results. A more detailed description of each step will follow.

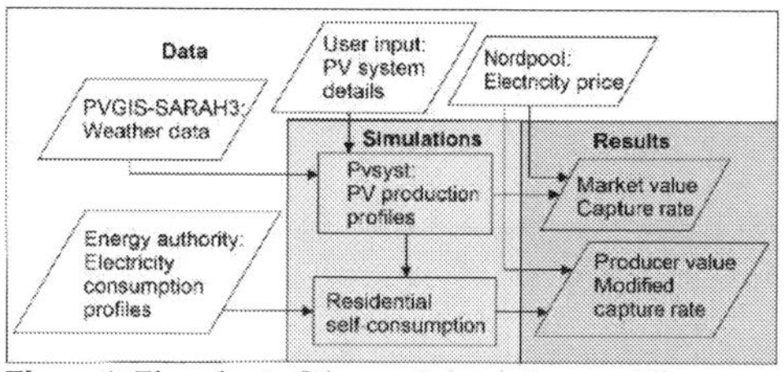

Figure 1. Flowchart of the used simulation workflow.

3.1 Data sources

The weather data used for our simulations was acquired from PVGIS-SARAH3 database [7] for the years 2019-2023. The period was chosen to cover the last 'old normal' energy year in Finland with limited variable renewable energy capacity (2019), the recent major crises, COVID-19 (2020-2021) and Russia's attack on Ukraine (2022), and the first 'new normal' energy year (2023). The electricity prices were acquired from Nordpool [8], FI market zone, covering the whole Finland. We used day-ahead spot price for the price of electricity and real electricity transfer costs from Turku, Finland in the economic calculations. We used type consumer profiles from [9] as the electricity consumption data.

To focus on the year-on-year variation of the weather and electricity price, we used the transfer fees and electricity tax for a typical residential apartment in 2023, while value-added tax was kept as 24%. Thus, the impact of the annual variation of the transfer fees and taxes, and the differences of the transfer cost of the residential building and a commercial building are excluded from this study.

3.2 Case studies and PV modelling

We studied two different buildings in this work: First, a residential multi-story building (Figure 2a-b) was adapted from our previous work [6]. The consumption profile of a residential building was created from two different types of consumer profiles, representing a small and a large apartment. The total electricity consumption of the building was scaled to 50 MWh, which is credible amount for a medium-sized multi-story building in Finland.

Second, a commercial building (Figure 2c) was simulated by using type consumer profile of an enterprise which is open daily. The total consumption of this building was 600 MWh, which is typical for a large grocery store in Finland. The rooftop power plant of the commercial building was expected to have a shading-free location.

PV production was modelled in a commercial software, PVsyst [10]. For the residential building, we used the 3D-scenarios from [6], with year-specific weather data. For the commercial building, we expect that the rooftop provides a shading-free location for PV production. The modelled panel was 'Generic 440 W 144 twin half-cell bifacial' from PVsyst-library.

Altogether, we modelled three different scenarios over five years. For the residential building, a small rooftop MPV system (5.3 kW, 22° tilt, facing south) was combined with MPV and VBPV façade systems (9.2 kW), noted as ResM and ResV, respectively. A commercial building was equipped with a bifacial system (south-facing, 30° tilt, 5 m row spacing, albedo 0.3), noted as ComB. Schematics of the buildings and systems are shown in Figure 2, and the key parameters of the simulated PV systems are given in Table I.

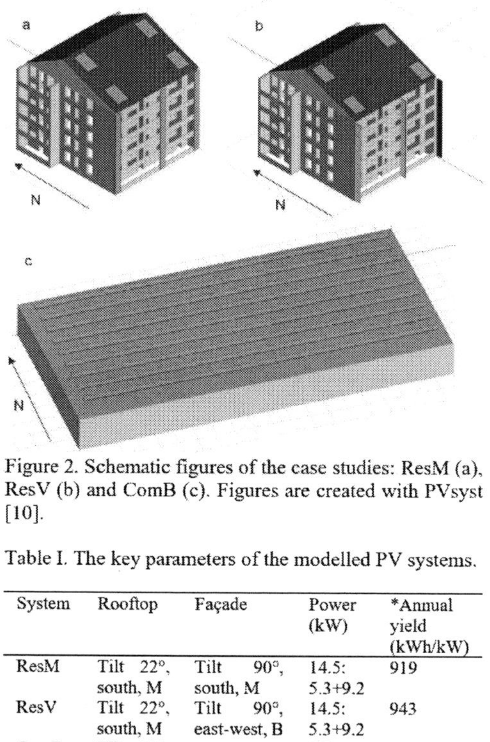

Figure 2. Schematic figures of the case studies: ResM (a), ResV (b) and ComB (c). Figures are created with PVsyst [10].

Table I. The key parameters of the modelled PV systems.

System	Rooftop	Façade	Power (kW)	*Annual yield (kWh/kW)
ResM	Tilt 22°, south, M	Tilt 90°, south, M	14.5: 5.3+9.2	919
ResV	Tilt 22°, south, M	Tilt 90°, east-west, B	14.5: 5.3+9.2	943
ComB	Tilt 30°, south, B	-	174	1230

M = monofacial; B = bifacial
* Mean value for the years 2019-2023

3.3 Economic analysis

The market value (MV) of PV electricity is defined as a weighted average of the electricity spot price, normalized with the hourly PV production:

$$MV = \frac{\sum_{t=1}^{8760}(E_t \cdot C_t)}{\sum_{t=1}^{8760}(E_t)}, \quad (1)$$

where E_t is PV production and C_t the electricity price during hour t. Capture rate (CR), sometimes referred as value factor in the literature, is the fraction of MV and the mean electricity price ($\bar{C}$). CR higher than one means that PV production is focused on the high-price hours, whereas

CR lower than one means that the priced during the best PV production hours is low. The equation for *CR* is:

$$CR = \frac{MV}{\bar{C}}. \quad (2)$$

While *MV* and *CR* can be calculated based on PV production and electricity price, the actual value of PV electricity for a small-scale producer depends on the self-consumption: for self-consumed PV, the producer saves the electricity transfer fee and taxes besides the electric energy itself. Self-consumption is defined on hourly basis: if PV production is lower than demand, all production is self-consumed, whereas when the production is higher than demand, the excess is sold to the grid. PV production value is defined as:

$$VAL_{PV} = \sum_{t=1}^{8760}(E_{SC,t} \cdot C_{purchase,t} + E_{sur,t} \cdot C_{sell,t}), \quad (3)$$

where $E_{SC,t}$ is the self-consumed and $E_{sur,t}$ the surplus PV generation, $C_{purchase,t}$ the electricity purchase cost and $C_{sell,t}$ the electricity sell revenue. Here, we assume that the customer has a spot price contract, when $C_{purchase}$ includes the spot price, value-added tax, a margin charged by the electricity company (0.4 c/kWh), and a lumped sum including the electricity transfer cost and electricity tax (8.73 c/kWh). C_{sell} is the spot price deducted by the margin (0.4 c/kWh).

The electricity transfer fee varies depending on the year and geographical location within Finland. Here, the value 8.73 c/kWh for the transfer fee and electricity tax was chosen to represent a typical apartment in southwestern Finland in the year 2023. The year-to-year variation of the transfer fee was neglected to highlight the impact of the electricity price and weather on PV value.

Modified capture rate (*MCR*) was defined to compare the actual value of the PV production to the mean electricity price. It is defined as:

$$MCR = \frac{VAL_{PV}}{\bar{C}}. \quad (4)$$

3 RESULTS

3.1 PV production and its value factor

During our study period, the annual mean electricity price in the Nordpool day-ahead market varied from 28.0 (2020) to 154 (2022) EUR/MWh. The primary causes for the variation were COVID-19 (year 2020) and the Russia's attack on Ukraine (resulting from stopping the electricity import to Finland from Russia in year 2022). Figure 3 shows the annual trends in *MVs* and *CRs* of the studied systems, and $\bar{C}$ in 2019-2023. *MV* of different PV systems varies with the electricity price on yearly basis, whereas the variation between the different PV systems during the same year is low. *CRs* vary from 0.91 to 1.22, with the lowest *CRs* from the year 2023, the last year in this work. This trend shows that until 2022, the impact of PV on the electricity price in Finland has been negligible, and the exclusion of the low nighttime prices allow PV to reach high *CR*. However, starting from 2023, the increase of national PV capacity in Finland reduces the price during PV peak production hours, making planned and existing PV systems vulnerable to the electricity price cannibalization, i.e., the dampening of PV electricity value due to over-generation of PV.

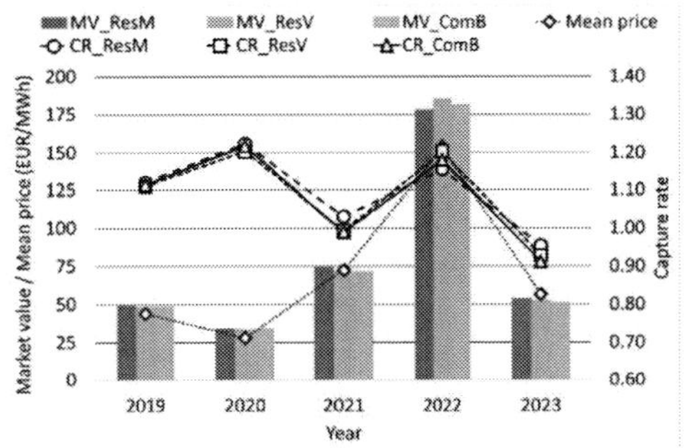

Figure 3. The development of market value and capture rate of the studied systems during 2019-2023.

3.2 Self-consumption and modified value factor

The annual productions of the studied systems were 880–943 kWh/kW, 907–969 kWh/kW, and 1190–1260 kWh/kW for ResM, ResV, and ComB, respectively (Figure 4a). The high production of ComB compared with the residential systems results from using bifacial panels elevated 1 m above the roof. The self-consumption rates of the systems were high: 80.1-80.7% for ResM, 85.8-86.5% for ResV, and 81.2-81.9% for ComB, respectively. For the generated electricity value, the shares of self-consumption were even higher: excluding the energy crisis year 2022, 91.8-94.1% and 94.3-96.1%, and 93.2-95.4% of the generated annual value resulted from self-consumption with ResM, ResV, and ComB, respectively (Figure 4b). Only during the year 2022, high revenues were available for the surplus PV production. The annual value of the residential PV production reached values up to 292 EUR/kW in 2022, but during the rest of the study period, the variation range was 105-155 EUR/kW. For ComB, the value peaked in 2022 at 367 EUR/kW, and varied from 143 to 197 EUR/kW during other years. These values are high compared with the investment costs in 2023, 81.5 EUR/kW [5].

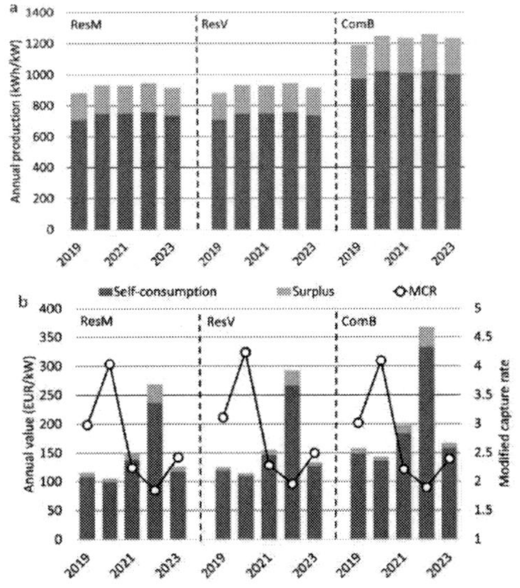

Figure 4. The annual production (a) and the value and *MCR* (b) of PV generation for ResM and ResV systems during 2019-2023.

10.4229/EUPVSEC2025/4BV.4.9

As MV of PV-generated electricity is expected to decrease in Finland as PV production increases [5], the profitability of PV becomes more dependent on the added value due to self-consumption. Therefore, we analyzed MCRs of all studied PV systems. MCR shows the fraction of PV production value and the mean electricity price (Eq. 4). Therefore, high MCR indicates either valuable PV generation or low electricity price.

MCRs peaked during the cheapest electricity year, 2020, when the value of PV electricity was over four times higher than the mean spot price of electricity. Respectively, during 2022, MCRs remained below two. This trend shows that self-consumption effectively balances the risk of PV unprofitability due to low electricity market price. MCR showed very similar trends for all studied systems: the importance of self-consumption is highlighted with the low energy prices.

4.3 Net present value considerations

Our previous work found that an annual value of 81.5 EUR/kW covers the initial investment costs of PV system by assuming 1250 EUR/kW investment cost, 30 years lifetime and an interest rate of 5% [5]. All reported annual values are above this threshold limit. The net present values (NPV) of the production during the first five years were 655, 700, and 883 EUR/kW for ResM, ResV, and ComB, respectively, covering more than half of the initial investment with only five years of operation. However, the energy crisis year 2022 boosted NPV significantly.

5 DISCUSSION

Historically, the major factor defining MV of PV electricity generated in Finland has been the mean electricity price. Until 2022, PV generation in Finland has been negligible, and CR of PV has been high since PV generation avoids the conventionally cheap nighttime hours. However, starting from 2023, PV generation in Finland has reached levels where it impacts the electricity price. Since PV capacity in Finland is expected to multiply within a few years, CR of PV will decrease [11]. This change drives us to focus on self-consumption, since it creates added value due to avoided transfer fees and taxes.

The analysis done for two buildings and three different PV systems showed that a high self-consumption rate effectively protects PV production against low prices. Especially, in the year 2020 with exceptionally low electricity price level due to COVID-19, the value of the generated PV electricity exceeded the mean electricity price by over four times. The annual value of the generated PV electricity was the lowest among the studied years in 2020, but the differences in the generated values were lower than the differences in MV.

When comparing the two different residential building façade systems, MPV and VBPV, the slightly higher value with VBPV system resulted from higher production and self-consumption rate. Considering MV, where only the electricity spot price was accounted, VBPV system showed similar performance to MPV system. However, as PV production will increase and result as lower electricity price around noon [5], VBPV provides more resilience towards the price cannibalization in the future.

6 CONCLUSIONS

This work analyzed the development in the value of PV generation in Finland during 2019-2023. The key findings are that the economic profitability of PV depends on the self-consumption of PV electricity. With historical electricity price data, the annual value of PV generation correlates with the mean electricity spot price, but the role of self-consumption significantly balances this variation. During the cheapest electricity year, 2020, MCR, defining the ratio of PV generation value and the mean electricity price, was over four, whereas during the most expensive electricity price year, 2022, MCR was below two.

Analysis of NPVs of PV production during 2019-2023 showed that with historical electricity prices, only five years of production allows to reach NPVs corresponding roughly half of the initial investment costs. However, when projecting the value creation to the future, the impact of increasing PV production on the electricity price will lower the profits. Therefore, the balancing role of self-consumption, shown by the negative correlation between MCR and electricity price, becomes more important in the future.

ACKNOWLEDGEMENTS

The work was funded by Strategic Research Council (FI), grants 358542 & 359141, and by University of Turku and City of Salo (LK) and UTUGS (LK).

REFERENCES

[1] Renewables Finland. Suunnittelussa olevat aurinkovoimalahankkeet 2025. https://suomenuusiutuvat.fi/aurinkovoima/aurinkovoimahankkeet-ja-voimalat-suomessa/suunnittelussa-olevat-aurinkovoimahankkeet/ (accessed June 16, 2025).

[2] Karttunen L, Jouttijärvi S, Niskanen J, Jasielec JJ, Huerta H, Ranta S, et al. Techno-economic analysis of residential PV-battery energy systems in Nordics. Conf. Proc. EU PVSEC 2024, Vienna: WIP Renewables; 2024, p. 020507. https://doi.org/10.4229/EUPVSEC2024/5DV.2.1.

[3] Jouttijärvi S, Karttunen L, Ranta S, Miettunen K. Techno-economic analysis on optimizing the value of photovoltaic electricity in a high-latitude location. Appl Energy 2024;361:122924. https://doi.org/10.1016/J.APENERGY.2024.122924.

[4] Kahsay MB, Völler S. Thermal energy storage for increasing self-consumption of grid connected photovoltaic systems: A case for Skjetlein High School, Norway. Energy Build 2025;335:115563. https://doi.org/10.1016/J.ENBUILD.2025.115563.

[5] Jouttijärvi S, Karttunen L, Tervo S, Huerta H, Ranta S, Syri S, et al. Sensitivity of electricity price in the Finnish market conditions with increasing solar energy production. Conf. Proc. EU PVSEC 2024, Vienna: WIP Renewables; 2024, p. 020547. https://doi.org/10.4229/EUPVSEC2024/5DV.3.27.

[6] Viriyaroj B, Jouttijärvi S, Jänkälä M, Miettunen K. Performance of vertically mounted bifacial photovoltaics on high-rise buildings in the Nordic conditions. Conf. Proc. EU PVSEC 2024, Vienna: WIP Renewables; 2024.

https://doi.org/10.4229/EUPVSEC2024/4BV.4.1.
[7] European Commission. Photovoltaic Geographical Information System (PVGIS) 2025. https://re.jrc.ec.europa.eu/pvg_tools/en/ (accessed September 3, 2025).
[8] Nord Pool AS. Nordpool 2025. https://www.nordpoolgroup.com/en/ (accessed June 16, 2025).
[9] Mutanen A, Lummi K, Pertti J. Valtakunnallisten tyyppikäyttäjämäärittelyiden päivittäminen ja hyödyntämisen periaatteet verkkopalvelumaksuihin liittyvissä tarkasteluissa. 2019.
[10] PVsyst. PVsyst 2025. https://www.pvsyst.com/ (accessed September 17, 2025).
[11] Heenatigala Kankanamge D, Jääskeläinen J, Jouttijärvi S, Syri S. Economic viability of large-scale solar PV implementation in the Nordic power market: Case Finland. Renewable Energy Focus 2026;56:100750. https://doi.org/10.1016/J.REF.2025.100750.

ECONOMIC VALUE OF BUILDING-INTEGRATED PV PRODUCTION AT HIGH-LATITUDE LOCATIONS

Sami Jouttijärvi[1*], Lauri Karttunen[1], Magda Szarek[1], Bergpob Viriyaroj[2], Samuli Ranta[3], Kati Miettunen[1]

[1]Department of Mechanical and Materials Engineering, University of Turku, Vesilinnantie 5, 20500 Turku, Finland

[2]Department of Architecture, Aalto University, Otakaari 24, 02150 Espoo, Finland

[3]New Energy Research Group, Turku University of Applied Sciences, Joukahaisenkatu 7, 20520 Turku, Finland

*sami.jouttijarvi@utu.fi

Introduction

Aim: Profitable BIPV production in Finland

Previous findings in Finland:

- Residential self-consumption is critical [1,2]
- Energy storages are unprofitable (currently) [3]
- Façade potential due to low solar elevation [4]

Data: Years 2019-2023, transfer fee & taxes with 2023 values

Workflow

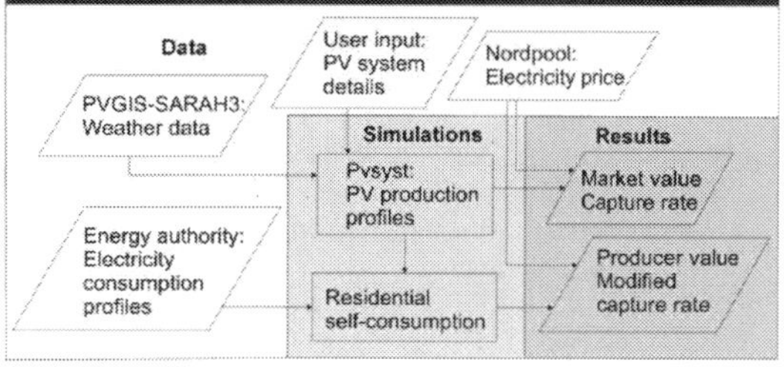

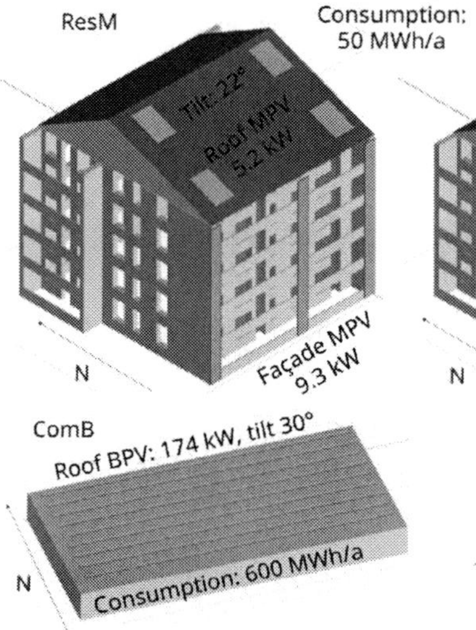

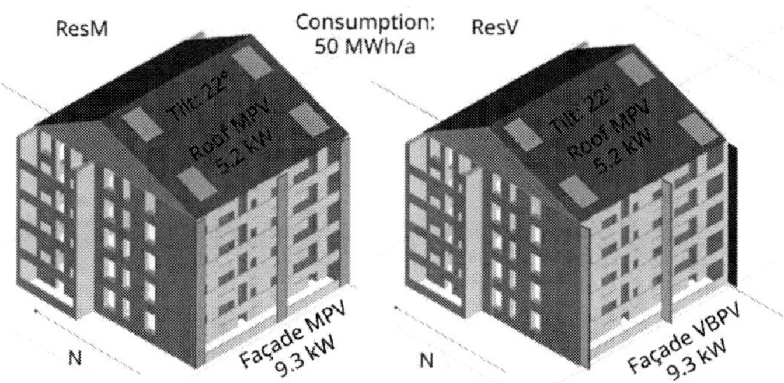

Figure 1. Schematic figures of the studied PV systems: ResM, ResV and ComB. Made with PVsyst [5], residential building based on [6].

Table 1. The average annual electricity production and self-consumption rate of the studied systems in 2019-2023.

System	Production (kWh/kW)	Self-consumption (%)
ResM	919	80.3
ResV	943	86.2
ComB	1230	81.6

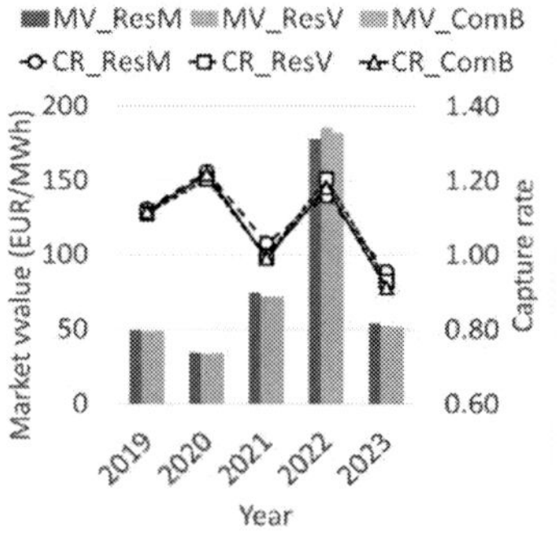

Figure 2. Market value and capture rate of the studied PV systems during 2019-2023. Until 2023, the PV production in Finland was very small.

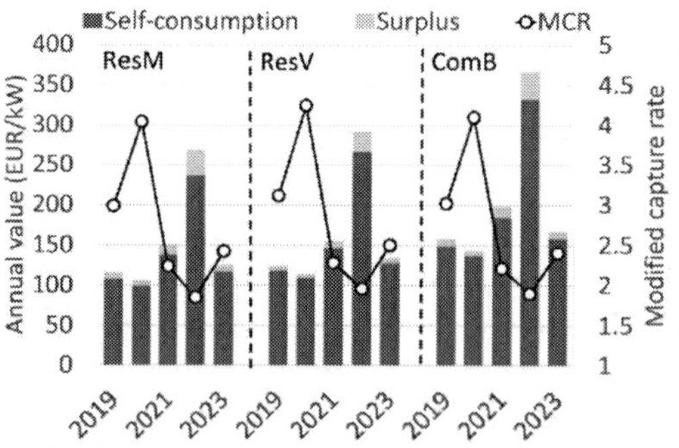

Figure 3. Annual production value and modified capture rate (inc. self-consumption) of the studied PV systems during 2019-2023. Self-consumption protects the value against market variation.

Discussion and Conclusions

PV market value dominated by electricity mean price with historical price data

Self-consumption protects against low prices (year 2020)

Energy crisis decreases the importance of self-consumption (high revenue from market)

References

[1] S. Jouttijärvi et al., Appl Energy 2024;361:122924
[2] S. Jouttijärvi et al., Conf. Proc. EU PVSEC 2024, 020547
[3] L. Karttunen et al., Conf. Proc. EU PVSEC 2024, 020507
[4] B. Viriyaroj et al., Conf. Proc. EU PVSEC 2024, 020362
[5] PVsyst-software, https://www.pvsyst.com/, read 12.9.2025
[6] City of Helsinki. Make 2.0 Puinen mallikerrostalo

Acknowledgements

The work was funded by Strategic Research Council (FI), grants 358542 & 359141, and by University of Turku and City of Salo (LK) and UTUGS (LK).

UNIVERSITY OF TURKU

strategic RESEARCH

TOWARDS SUSTAINABLE CITIES WITH INTEGRATED PHOTOVOLTAIC CERAMIC ROOF TILE

Alicia Buceta[a], Jaime Polo[a], Roberto Díaz[b], Marta Alvarez[a], Eugenia Zugasti[a] and Jaione Bengoechea[a]
[a] National Renewable Energy Center (CENER)
Avenida Ciudad de la Innovación, 7, 31621 Sarriguren (Navarra) SPAIN
Tel.: +34 948 25 28 00; info@cener.com
[b] Notio Association, Clay Technological Centre of Castilla-La Mancha (CTAC)
Calle Río Cabriel, 45007, Toledo (Castilla-La Mancha), SPAIN
Tel: +34 925 24 11 62; info@notio.es

ABSTRACT: Most of the existing PV roof tile solutions are either not based on clay substrates or consist of the adhesion of a PV module onto a ceramic tile. In this work we wanted to prove the possibility to integrate the PV module into the ceramic tile in a one-step lamination process. The first step was to assess the adhesion of the encapsulant to the clay substrate by peeling tests. Then, the encapsulant that demonstrated the best performance was selected to produce a range of samples in various configurations. These samples have first been subjected to the hail impact test and only the samples that passed this test were then tested in climatic chambers to assess their reliability. As a result, a one-step solution for flat roof tile using crystalline silicon solar cells was found, able to withstand humidity freeze based on the IEC 61215 standard for PV and its equivalent from the UNE-EN 539-2 standard for tile. Other tests, specific for photovoltaic devises, such as hail impact and damp heat were also successfully passed.
Keywords: c-Si, BIPV, clay, ceramic, roof tile

1 INTRODUCTION

The integration of photovoltaic (PV) modules into different architectural elements will play an important role towards increasing PV energy production using existing man-made surfaces and shaping sustainable cities towards energy independence. This is the main goal of Building Integrated Photovoltaics (BIPV), with rooftops offering the greatest potential, given their superior exposure to sunlight in building structures.[1–3] Furthermore, a recent study has indicated the advantages of installing photovoltaic systems on rooftops, even in circumstances where they are not optimally oriented.[4]

There are already in the market solutions to be used as PV rooftop tiles using different types of substrates and also with a wide range of colours. Nevertheless, our aim is to demonstrate the possibility to fabricate the PV tile in a single step lamination, compatible with existing fabrication technologies, without compromising neither the PV module integrity nor that of the ceramic tile.

Aesthetics are also an important point to be taken into account in BIPV. Not only the end buyer of the house, but also the architects are demanding a wider variety of colours and even conceal the solar cell to the extent that it does not look like a PV module.[5,6] These requirements could be mandatory when the building is in a historical area where aesthetic uniformity is to be maintained.

Whithin this context, this work presents the results obtained within the CECOM4PV project, a public-private collaboration project granted by the Ministry of Science and Innovation of Spain in the framework of the State Plan for Scientific and Technical Research and Innovation. The primary focus of this study is threefold: (i) obtaining a ceramic roof tile with PV integrated through a one-step lamination process, (ii) demonstrating that the resulting PV device meets both PV and roof tile standards and (iii) assessing the influence of different colour options on PV efficiency.

2 METHODOLOGY

Comercial roof tiles provided by San Javier Bricks were adapted to the size of 10 cm x 10 cm x 2 cm and 20 cm x 20 cm x 2 cm for the fabrication of the BIPV prototypes. Prior to the fabrication, peel-off tests were performed to select the best performing encapsulant when laminated on to a clay substrate.

Subsequently, the reliability of the produced prototypes has been assessed following the conditions laid down in PV module qualification standard IEC 61215-2,[7] with increased severity. More specifically, the Hail impact test, UV weathering, damp heat (DH), thermal cycling (TC) and humidity freeze (HF) tests have been performed on the modules. These Module Quality Tests (MQT) were conducted at CENER's laboratory, which is accredited to perform IEC standard tests for PV modules.

On the other hand, the reliability as roof tile has been assessed following the conditions laid down in the UNE-EN 539-2 standard.[8] Specifically, the frost resistance test standard was conducted at NOTIO's laboratory.

Additionally, given the importance of the aesthetic, different colour configurations were tested to determine the detriment caused in efficiency due to colour.

2.1 Hail impact test

The hail impact resistance test was performed with an ice ball launcher LBH-25 from ARIES. The experiment was implemented according to the IEC 61215-2 standard; 25 mm diameter ice balls were launched at a velocity of 23 m/s ± 2% (MQT 17).

2.2 Ultraviolet exposure

The UV irradiation was applied in a weathering chamber using light source lamps with a dedicated filter to match the spectral distribution stated in the qualification standard of PV modules. The temperature of the samples during UV irradiation was fixed at 60 °C and a total dose of 15 kWh/m^2 was applied as stated in IEC 61215-2 standard.

2.3 Climatic chamber

Their resistance to temperature and humidity was tested in a C-70/200 climate chamber from CTS. The damp heat test (MQT 13), 1,000 h at 85 °C and 85% relative humidity (RH); thermal cycling (MQT 11), 50 cycles from -40 °C to 85 °C and humidity freeze (MQT 12), 10 cycles from -40 °C to 85 °C with 85% RH were completed in accordance with the IEC 61215-2 standard.

2.4 Frost Resistance

The reliability of the prototype as a ceramic roof tile was tested in a Dycomental CHD-525 chamber with a thermostatic tank, air cooling unit and hydraulic circuit for circulating decalcified water. Based in the UNE-EN 539-2:2013 Clay roofing tiles for discontinuous laying - Determination of physical characteristics, the samples were exposed up to 100 cycles from -16 °C in air to 17 °C submerged in water.

3 RESULTS AND DISCUSSION

In order to achieve a suitable solution for PV ceramic roof tiles fabricated in a one-step lamination it is necessary to determine its reliability under degradation tests. Therefore, after selecting the best performing encapsulant compering their peel-off values, different configurations were tested under hail impact test. The configurations that were able to withstand it without showing any damage in the solar cell were subjected to further degradation testing. As a result, a solution was found that was able to withstand hail impact, damp heat, UV weathering, thermal cycling, humidity freeze and frost resistance tests.

3.1 Hail impact test

One of the main mechanical stresses that PV modules on rooftops need to withstand is hail impact. The test is performed in accordance with the stipulated IEC 61215-2 requirements and having the samples in a free-standing position (figure 1). The first hail impact tests were performed on 10 cm x 10 cm x 2 cm samples to facilitate the testing of a wider number of configurations.

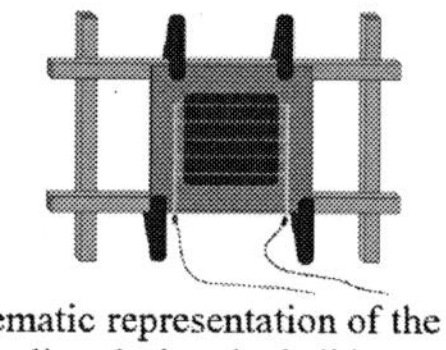

Figure 1: Schematic representation of the set up with the sample free-standing during the hail impact test.

Several configurations were subjected to hail testing and two of them, with and without glass as front sheet (FS), achieved a satisfactory result. In figure 2, the electroluminescence (EL) image of two different configurations that passed the test can be observed. After two impacts the solar cell remains intact, not even the propagation of preexisting crack was observed.

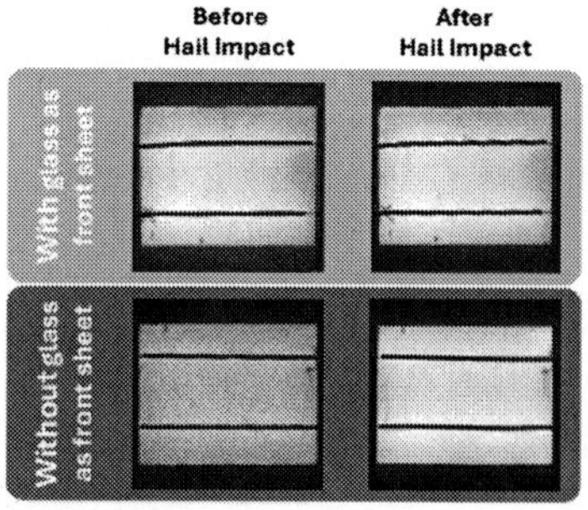

Figure 2: EL image of two different configurations: with and without glass as front sheet(FS) before hail impact (left) and after two hail impact (right).

The two configurations that withstand the hail impact will undergo the humidity freeze degradation test. As anticipated, no deterioration was detected in the clay substrate integrity.

3.2 Humidity freeze test

One of the concerns that may arise when combining materials with different coefficients of contraction and expansion is how they will behave in response to temperature changes. To this end, the humidity freeze test will allow us to evaluate this effect in the prototypes. In order to gain an initial understanding of the samples' behaviour, instead of following the sequence described in the IEC 61215 standard (UV + TC[50] + HF[10]) the prototypes were subjected directly to ten cycles of HF. As it can be observed in figure 3, while the sample with glass remains stable, the sample without glass as front sheet shows a significant loss in performance, decreasing its maximum power by 29.6%. This degradation can also be observed in the electroluminescence measurements, where the deterioration of the solar cell is evident when no glass is used as front sheet.

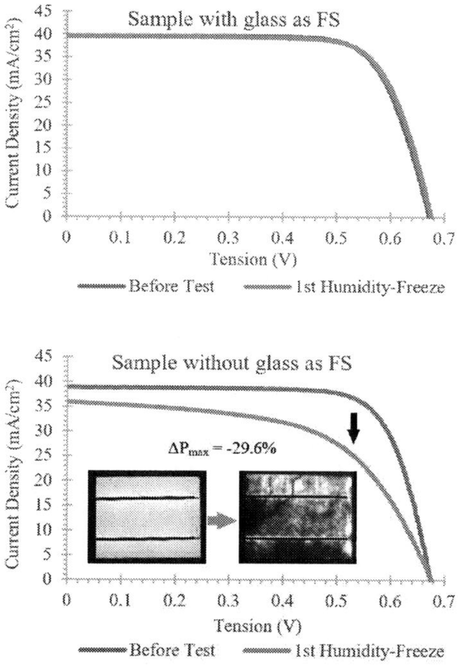

Figure 3: JV curve of the prototype with glass as front sheet (upper graph) and the one without glass as front sheet (lower graph) before and after 10 cycles of HF, including EL images for the sample without glass.

Therefore, in order to test further the sample with glass as front sheet, the sample was additionally subjected to the UV + TC(50) + HF(10) sequence. figure 4 presents the JV curve and EL of the sample after the sequence, and as it can be observed no significant degradation is observed.

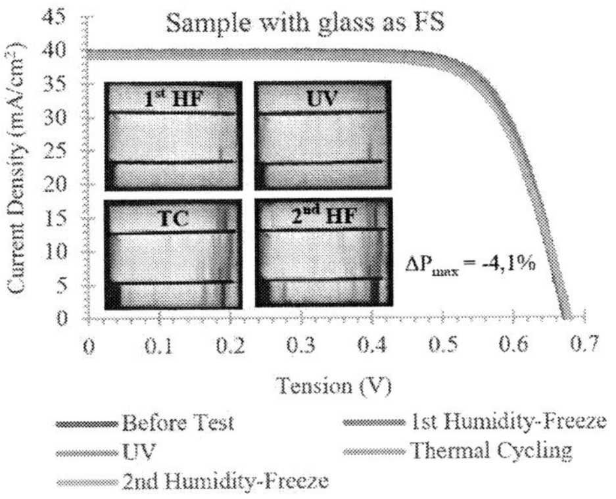

Figure 4: JV curve of the prototype with glass as front sheet before and after 10 cycles of HF, UV, 50 cycles of TC and 10 cycles of HF; including EL images.

The total loss in maximum power, after the whole sequence when glass is used as front sheet, is of 4.1%, therefore it would fall within the acceptable limits established by the standard. Furthermore, after all these tests, no deterioration was detected in the clay substrate integrity.

3.3 Frost resistance test

It is important that, as a prototype photovoltaic roof tile, it is also capable to withstands tests in accordance with the ceramic roof tile regulations. In this case, the frost resistance test from UNE-EN 539-2 standard was performed, which will also allow to compare its behaviour with the results obtained in the humidity freeze test. The winning configuration with glass as front sheet has been tested up to 100 cycles of frost resistance. In the course of the experiment, the substrates demonstrated no signs of physical deterioration after undergoing 50 cycles. However, one of the three samples subjected to testing exhibited minor damage to the clay substrate after 100 cycles. Consequently, it can be considered that the prototype meets the requirements of the standard to be installed in locations requiring frost resistance of 50 cycles or less. In figure 5, the photographs of the sample that showed some damage is presented, and as it can be observed, not only the clay substrate was affected, but also the glass front sheet exhibited a distinct crack.

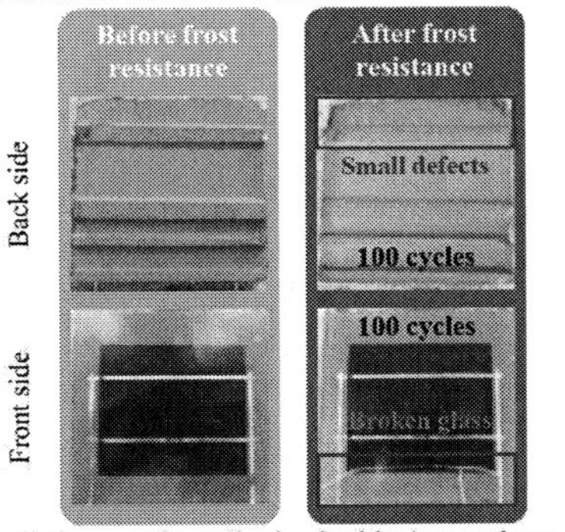

Figure 5: Images from the back side (upper images) and front side (lower images) of the prototype with glass as front sheet before and after the frost resistance test.

On the other hand, the photovoltaic performance remains practically unaltered in all the tested samples. In figure 6 the average JV curve before and after the test are presented, as for the EL images of one of the samples. No significant degradation occurs except for a small drop in the short-circuit current (I_{SC}) value which results in the loss of 2.4% of the maximum power.

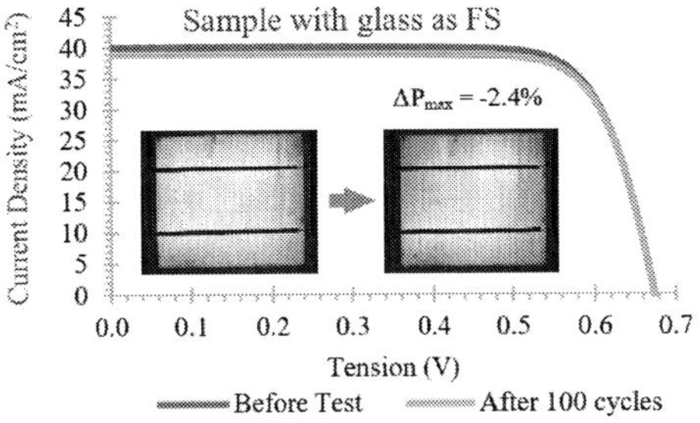

Figure 6: JV curve of the prototype with glass as front sheet before and after 100 cycles of frost resistance; including EL images.

Therefore, the prototype configuration with glass as front sheet demonstrates adequate resilience to this test up to 50 cycles, exhibiting no significant damage or defects from the photovoltaic and ceramic roof tile's perspective.

3.4 Damp heat test

In order to assess the effect of elevated temperatures and humidity on the integrity of the prototype with glass as front sheet, the damp heat test was performed. In figure 7, the JV curve and the EL images are presented before and after the test. As it can be observed, there is a slight drop in the I_{SC} value that result in the drop of the maximum power by 3.8%. Although, on the EL images no degradation is observed, but a clear crack in the glass appears after 1,000 h of DH, which can be related to the I_{SC} drop (figure 7).

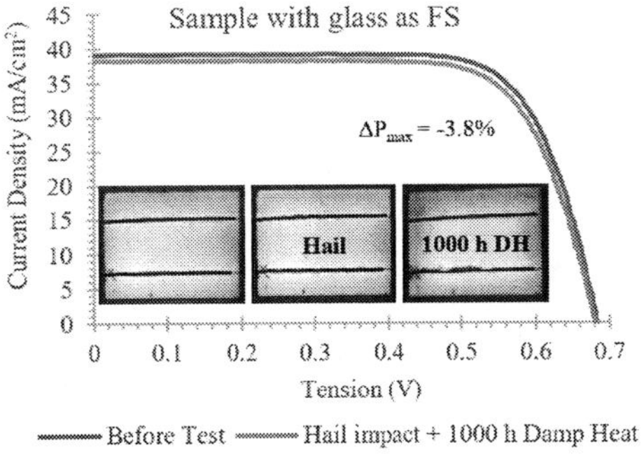

Figure 7: JV curve of the prototype with glass as front sheet before and after hail impact and 1000 h of DH; including EL images.

In order to avoid the glass cracking, several strategies were studied, focused on minimizing the internal glass tensions. Once a suitable solution was found, to ascertain the extent of the prototype's durability, the sample was sized up to 20 cm x 20 cm x 2 cm and subjected to an additional hail impact and damp heat test. Additionally, the edges of the sample were covered with silicone to minimize water penetration. The complete sequence of tests that was followed is illustrated in figure 8: the sample was exposed to a total of 2,000 h of damp heat and two hail impact tests.

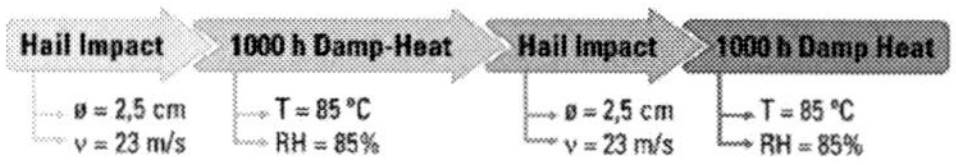

Figure 8: Schematic representation of the followed sequence of hail impact and damp heat testing.

As it can be observed in figure 9, the prototype withstands the whole sequence with insignificant change in its properties. Moreover, the final maximum power increases a 3.6%.

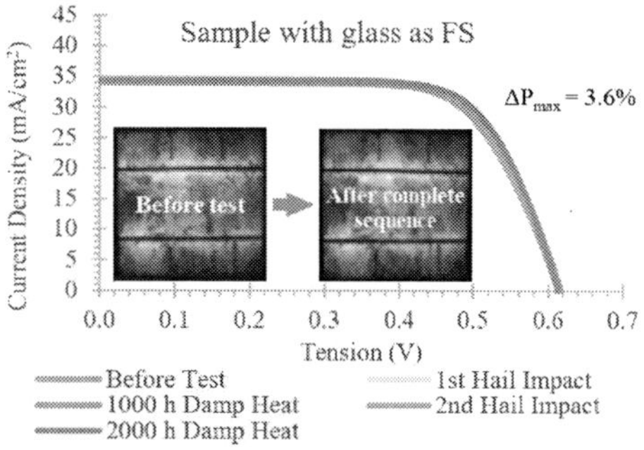

Figure 9: JV curves and EL images of the sample with glass as front sheet after each hail impact and damp heat.

Therefore, it can be concluded that the prototype with glass as front sheet safely meets the requirements established by the photovoltaic standard for damp heat.

3.5 Coloured configurations

As the aesthetics play an important role in the implementation of solar roof tiles, different colour options were fabricated to determine the effects in the photovoltaic performance. In this project, four colour options were studied: transparent, black appearance, terracotta and light grey (Figure 10).

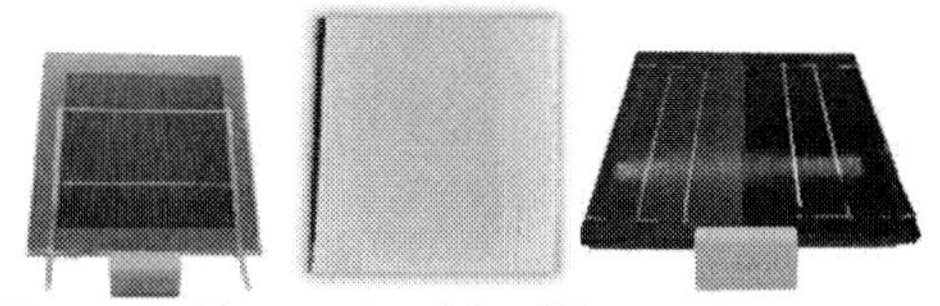

Figure 10: Photographs of the different colour samples: transparent (left), light grey (centre) and terracotta and black appearance (right).

In figure 11 it is clearly observed how an increase in colour coverage is associated with a subsequent decrease in I_{SC} as it would be expected. In the terracotta and light grey samples, the short-circuit current drops around a 30% compared to the transparent and black appearance options.

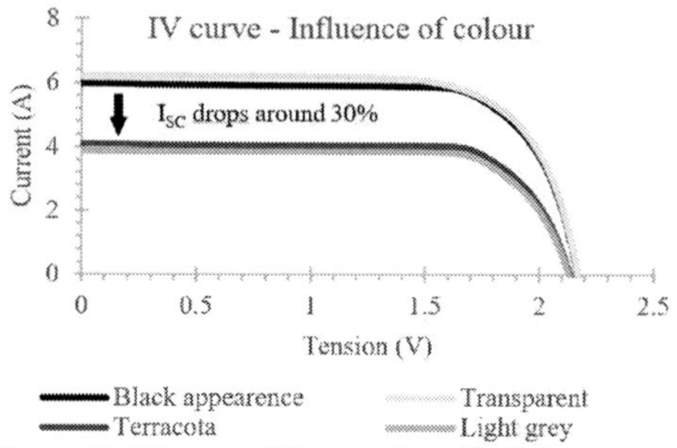

Figure 11: IV curve of the samples with different colour appearance.

It was demonstrated the compatibility of colouring the samples although a detriment in the short-circuit current is expected when the coverage of the solar cell increases.

4 CONCLUSIONS

The results showed that it was possible to produce a one-step lamination photovoltaic ceramic roof tile able to withstand hail impact test, damp heat, UV weathering, thermal cycling and humidity freeze tests based on the IEC 61215 photovoltaic standard. After the sequence HF(10) + UV + TC(50) + HF(10) the drop of the maximum power was of 4.1%. When the prototype was exposed to hail impact + DH(1,000 h) + hail impact + DH (1,000 h) the maximum power unexpectedly increased 3,6% after the whole sequence.

On the other hand, the prototype has demonstrated to be fitted for locations where less than 50 cycles of frost resistance are required as stated in the UNE-EN 539 clay roof tile standard. The prototypes resisted with no signs of damage up to 50 cycles, nevertheless, one of the three tested samples showed small imperfections when the test was carried out up to 100 cycles. Nevertheless, the photovoltaic performance of the samples after the 100 cycles test, a drop in the maximum power was observed of only 2.4% in average.

The application of different colour options to the samples was studied, showing its compatibility with the process and the expected drop in the short-circuit current when the colour coverage of the solar cell is higher. In our study, the terracotta and light grey options showed a drop in I_{SC} of around 30%.

5 ACKNOWLEDGEMENTS

These results are part of project CECOM4PV.[9] It is a public-private collaboration project granted by the Ministry of Science and Innovation of Spain in the framework of the State Plan for Scientific and Technical Research and Innovation. The primary focus of this study is to ascertain the following: obtaining a ceramic roof tile with PV integrated able to withstand both PV and roof tile standards and testing different colour options and their effect in PV efficiency.

6 BIBLIOGRAPHY

1. AER. *State of the Energy Market 2015*.; 2015.
2. Collins SP, Storrow A, Liu D, et al. EU Solar Energy

Strategy. Published online 2022:167-186.
3. Ürge-Vorsatz D, Chatterjee S, Cabeza LF, Molnár G. Global and regional estimation and evaluation of suitable roof area for solar and green roof applications. *Dev Built Environ.* 2025;21(December 2024). doi:10.1016/j.dibe.2025.100607
4. García-Suso F, Molina-García A, Fernández-Guillamón A, Bueso MC. Alternative non-optimal orientations in highly PV self-consumption integration: Exploring Spanish prosumers as a case study. *Renew Energy.* 2026;256(July 2025). doi:10.1016/j.renene.2025.123987
5. Kuhn TE, Erban C, Heinrich M, Eisenlohr J, Ensslen F, Neuhaus DH. Review of technological design options for building integrated photovoltaics (BIPV). *Energy Build.* 2021;231:110381. doi:10.1016/j.enbuild.2020.110381
6. Fraunhofer Instotute for Solar Energy Systems (ISE). Colored modules for building-integrated photovoltaics. *PV Mag.* Published online 2025. https://www.pv-magazine.com/2025/02/24/colored-modules-for-building-integrated-photovoltaics/
7. IEC. *IEC 61215-2 Terrestrial Photovoltaic (PV) Modules – Design Qualification and Type Approval – Part 2: Test Procedures.* 2nd ed.; 2021.
8. AENOR. *UNE-EN 539-2: Tejas de Arcilla Cocida Para Colocación Discontinua. Determinación de Las Caracteristicas Físicas. Parte 2: Ensayo de Resistencia a La Helada.*; 2013.
9. CENER. CECOM4PV. Published 2022. https://www.cener.com/en/areas/photovoltaic-solar-energy-department/outstanding-projects/cecom4pv-photovoltaic-devices-based-on-ceramic-materials-and-composites/

EVALUATING PVT MODULE PERFORMANCE ACROSS DIVERSE EUROPEAN CLIMATES: A SIMULATION STUDY

A.Saretti[1], G. Vero[1], A.Chouder[2], S. Vergura[1] and S. Silvestre[3]
1- Department of Electrotechnics, Politecnico di Bari, St. E. Orabona, 4, 70125 Bari, Italy.
2- Laboratory of Electrical Engineering (LGE), Electrical Engineering department, University of M'sila, PO Box 166 Ichebilia, 28000 M'sila, Algeria.
3- MNT-Solar - Grup de Micro i Nano Tecnologies per Energia SolarElectronic Engineering Department, Universitat Politècnica de Catalunya BarcelonaTech. Jordi Girona 1-3, 08034, Barcelona, Spain.

ABSTRACT: This study explores the potential for increased energy production by using four distinct cooling techniques applied to photovoltaic (PV) modules in photovoltaic-thermal (PVT) systems for buildings. The simulations, conducted using PVSOL and MATLAB, evaluated the performance of a 160Wp c-Si PV module integrated with four different cooling systems at each location. To assess performance under varying climate conditions, three European cities were selected for the analysis of one week per season: Barcelona, Berlin, and Paris, each representing distinct latitudes and climatic conditions. Simulation results include the energy generated by the PV module, yields, and energy surplus obtained at each location for the different cooling systems under study.

Keywords: PVT, PV and Buildings, simulation.

1 INTRODUCTION

This study explores the potential for increased energy production using four distinct cooling techniques applied to photovoltaic (PV) modules in photovoltaic-thermal (PVT) systems for buildings.

To assess performance under varying climate conditions, three European cities were selected for analysis. The simulations, conducted using PVSOL and MATLAB, evaluated the performance of a 160Wp c-Si PV module integrated with four different cooling systems at each location.

2 METHODS

The study examines four cooling systems for PV modules described below in Table I.

Table I: Cooling systems included in the study

Cooling System	Refrigerator
Water-cooled hybrid photovoltaic-thermal (PV/T) panels Standing waves ratio [1]	1
heat pipe photovoltaic-thermal (PV/T) hybrid system [2]	2
hybrid PV/T water collectors [3]	3
Passive cooling methodologies [4]	4

The simulation is based on the temperature reduction achieved by each cooling system, with temperature profiles derived from PVSOL simulations for each location and adjusted accordingly.

The simulations were performed in Matlab environment, with inputs including irradiance profiles from PVsol, the modified temperature profiles, and the parameters of the PV module model.

The PV module model was validated by comparing simulation results from Matlab with those from PVsol. The analysis spans one week per season in three European cities: Barcelona, Berlin, and Paris, each representing distinct latitudes and climatic conditions. Simulation results include the energy generated by the PV module, yields, and energy surplus at each location for the different cooling systems under study.

3 RESULTS

The top section of the following figures illustrates the strong alignment between the results generated by the two software applications for the output power of the PV module.

The middle section shows the energy output derived from MATLAB, comparing scenarios with and without the integration of the four cooling systems.

Finally, the bottom section highlights the energy surplus achieved by each cooling system.

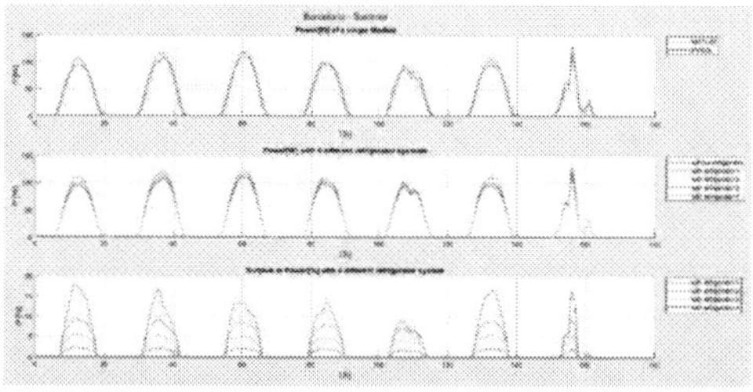

Figure 1: Results obtained in summer for Barcelona.

An analysis of weekly trends in Barcelona reveals that during peak temperature periods, cooling systems produce an energy surplus of 15% to 20%. In contrast, Berlin experiences a surplus ranging from 5% to 15%, depending on seasonal conditions. However, during the winter months, the use of cooling systems is deemed unnecessary in Berlin and Paris.

These systems demonstrate greater efficiency in warmer climates and at lower latitudes.

10.4229/EUPVSEC2025/4BV.4.14
020301-001

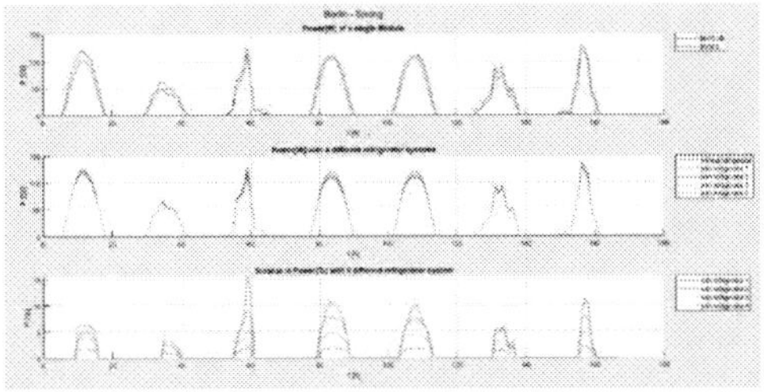

Figure 2: Results obtained in spring for Berlin.

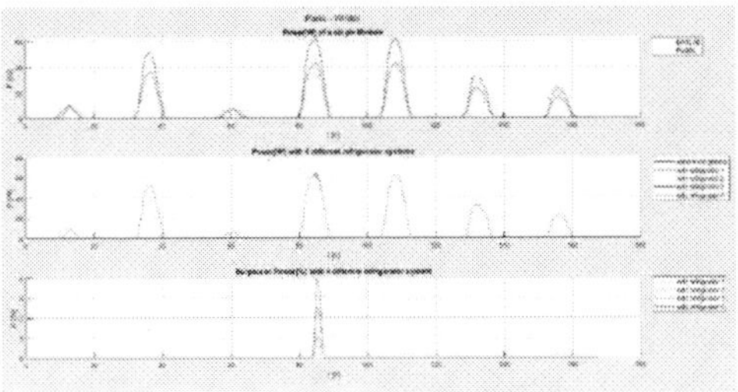

Figure 3: Results obtained in winter for Paris.

The following tables present key results obtained from the study over a one-week period in each yearly season for location analyzed: Total Irradiance, generated energy, Yield and energy surplus for the different systems under study.

Table II: Results obtained for Barcelona.

Season	City	Barcelona				
		Without refrigeration	cooling system 1	cooling system 2	cooling system 3	cooling system 4
Winter	Irradiance [kWh/m^2]	27,37				
	Total Energy [Wh]	3823,36	3985,48	4002,72	3932,40	3869,30
	Y [Wh/Wp]	23,90	24,91	25,02	24,58	24,18
	Energy Surplus[%]	-	4,24	4,69	2,85	1,20
Spring	Irradiance [kWh/m^2]	38,14				
	Total Energy [Wh]	4938,58	5273,64	5209,01	5102,62	5007,57
	Y [Wh/Wp]	30,87	32,96	32,56	31,89	31,30
	Energy Surplus[%]	-	6,78	5,48	3,32	1,40
Summer	Irradiance [kWh/m^2]	46,42				
	Total Energy [Wh]	5613,83	6176,75	5987,59	5839,81	5708,60
	Y [Wh/Wp]	35,09	38,60	37,42	36,50	35,68
	Energy Surplus[%]	-	10,03	6,66	4,03	1,69
Fall	Irradiance [kWh/m^2]	35,14				
	Total Energy [Wh]	4529,44	4867,51	4798,99	4692,93	4598,19
	Y [Wh/Wp]	28,31	30,42	29,99	29,33	28,74
	Energy Surplus[%]	-	7,46	5,95	3,61	1,52

Table III: Results obtained for Berlin.

Season	City	Berlin				
		Without refrigeration	cooling system 1	cooling system 2	cooling system 3	cooling system 4
Winter	Irradiance [kWh/m^2]	5,34				
	Total Energy [Wh]	681,72	681,72	681,72	681,72	681,72
	Y [Wh/Wp]	4,26	4,26	4,26	4,26	4,26
	Energy Surplus[%]	-	0,00	0,00	0,00	0,00
Spring	Irradiance [kWh/m^2]	36,24				
	Total Energy [Wh]	4810,13	5065,23	5040,99	4949,96	4868,86
	Y [Wh/Wp]	30,06	31,66	31,51	30,94	30,43
	Energy Surplus[%]	-	5,30	4,80	2,91	1,22
Summer	Irradiance [kWh/m^2]	40,66				
	Total Energy [Wh]	5267,24	5628,51	5553,70	5441,33	5340,57
	Y [Wh/Wp]	32,92	35,18	34,71	34,01	33,38
	Energy Surplus[%]	-	6,86	5,44	3,31	1,39
Fall	Irradiance [kWh/m^2]	18,59				
	Total Energy [Wh]	2612,56	2689,68	2698,07	2664,92	2634,75
	Y [Wh/Wp]	16,33	16,81	16,86	16,66	16,47
	Energy Surplus[%]	-	2,95	3,27	2,00	0,85

As anticipated, each cooling system contributed additional energy across all seasons and cities, except for Berlin during winter; in that specific season, the temperatures are so low that enhancing energy output with a cooling system is unnecessary.

Examining the energy output across seasons in the three cities, the best cooling systems are identified as the first and the second ones, as they result in a more significant reduction in temperature.

On the other hand, the optimal performance was achieved in the city characterized by the highest temperature and irradiance, namely Barcelona, while the least favorable performance was observed in the city exhibiting the lowest values, specifically Berlin.

Table IV: Results obtained for Paris.

Season	City	Paris				
		Without refrigeration	cooling system 1	cooling system 2	cooling system 3	cooling system 4
Winter	Irradiance [kWh/m^2]	9,25				
	Total Energy [Wh]	1265,44	1268,18	1268,83	1268,03	1266,54
	Y [Wh/Wp]	7,91	7,93	7,94	7,93	7,92
	Energy Surplus[%]	-	0,22	0,33	0,28	0,09
Spring	Irradiance [kWh/m^2]	36,43				
	Total Energy [Wh]	4665,42	4983,94	4903,32	4809,37	4725,89
	Y [Wh/Wp]	29,16	31,15	30,64	30,06	29,54
	Energy Surplus[%]	-	6,83	5,09	3,08	1,30
Summer	Irradiance [kWh/m^2]	36,04				
	Total Energy [Wh]	4691,69	5015,53	4934,08	4839,19	4753,88
	Y [Wh/Wp]	29,32	31,35	30,84	30,24	29,71
	Energy Surplus[%]	-	6,90	5,17	3,14	1,33
Fall	Irradiance [kWh/m^2]	18,13				
	Total Energy [Wh]	2255,29	2364,73	2361,24	2319,85	2282,55
	Y [Wh/Wp]	14,10	14,78	14,76	14,50	14,27
	Energy Surplus[%]	-	4,85	4,70	2,86	1,21

Upon analysis across different seasons, it appears that the second system demonstrates greater efficacy during periods of lower temperatures, whereas the first system performs more effectively under higher temperature conditions. This phenomenon can be elucidated by examining the temperature variation effects.

The first system experiences a percentage-based drop, resulting in a substantial decline in performance at elevated temperatures and a minimal decrease at lower temperatures. Conversely, the second system exhibits a delta-based decline, rendering the impact of temperature variation more significant at lower temperatures compared to higher ones.

4 CONCLUSIONS

In conclusion, cooling systems enhance the PV module's capability to generate additional electrical energy while concurrently producing heat. This thermal energy can be used in multiple applications as mentioned in preceding sections.

The implementation of these systems is particularly advantageous in climatic and irradiance scenarios where the system's costs are more effectively amortized, particularly in warm climates and conditions of high irradiance.

5 ACKNOWLEDGMENTS This work is supported by the Agencia Estatal De Investigacion of Spain.
Funding code: PID2022-140226OB-C32

References

[1] A. A. Naqvi, A. Ahmed, T. Bin Nadeem, L. A. Khan, and I. U. Ahad, Case Studies in Thermal Engineering, 47 (2023) 103114.
[2] C. Rossi, L. A. Tagliafico, F. Scarpa, and V. Bianco, Energy Convers Manag. 76 (2013) 634.
[3] K. P. Amber, W. Akram, M. A. Bashir, M. S. Khan, and A. Kousar, J Therm Anal Calorim. 143 (2021) 2355.
[4] S. Y. Wu, Q. L. Zhang, L. Xiao, and F. H. Guo, "A heat pipe photovoltaic/thermal (PV/T) hybrid system and its performance evaluation," Energy Build. 43 (2011) 3558.

EXTENDED KPIS FOR DECISIONS-MAKERS IN THE DEVELOPMENT OF BIPV SOLUTIONS

Simon BODDAERT[1,*], Olaia AURREKOETXEA[2], Julius JACOB[3], Simone GERMANI[4], Ignas CEUPPENS[5], Hervé LAMBLOT[6], Tatjana VAVILKIN[7], Maria JIMENEZ[8], Xavier GAUVIN[9], Tonis EELMA[10]

[1]CSTB, [2]TECNALIA, [3]METABUILD, [4]CEI, [5]BUILD'UP, [6]SUNSTYLE, [7]SOLTECH, [8]ONYX SOLAR, [9]BOUYGUES CONSTRUCTION, [10]IBS

* E-mail to: simon.boddaert@cstb.fr; phone: +33 (0)680 58 1001

ABSTRACT: Innovative components commonly use key performance indicators to assess their relevance. For BIPV solutions, it's the energy indicator that is commonly favored. In the European INCREASE project, we wanted to extend these indicators to provide strong decision-making keys for determining which BIPV solutions are the most appropriate for all stakeholders. Based on the work initially carried out as part of T15 of the IEA's PVPS program, we have identified additional parameters to take account of sustainability and reliability issues. To meet the expectations of the construction industry and the multifunctionality of BIPV components, we have also defined two new performance indicators to provide extended decision-making tools for all players in the value chain. These elements not linked with energy production focus on building capabilities and end-users' feelings.
Keywords: BIPV, KPI, Durability, Constructability, Comfort.

1 OBJECTIVES

The work carried out aims to define a set of KPIs that can be used as a reference decision-making tool to objectivize the use of BIPV solutions, under the best possible conditions of implementation and relevance use. The KPIs dealing with ENERGY, ECONOMY, ENVIRONMENT and AESTHETICS, initially defined in IEA T15 works REFERENCES

[1], have been revised and extended to meet the challenges of the project. Two new KPIs were created. The COMFORT criterion was introduced, to ensure that end-users benefit from a level of comfort at least equal to traditional solutions. The BUILDABILITY criterion has been emphasized to ensure the applicability of BIPV solutions and to meet quality and insurability requirements for operators and manufacturers. These KPIs will be validated and consolidated on the CSTB and TECNALIA pre-demo sites (under controlled conditions), before being deployed on the nine project demonstration sites that will host the final solutions. They will be used to define an overall assessment of each site and the impact of the chosen BIPV solution. The parameters will be fed by numerical calculations, but also by data measured on sites, to determine possible deviations before/after implementation of the BIPV solutions. Once the models have been calibrated, the relevance and accuracy of the KPIs will be fine-tuned, enabling them to be applied more effectively to the BIPV market.

KPIs will be used again during the operational phase to assess the impact of aging on KPI deviations and define acceptability thresholds. Graphical display provides easy and explicit reading for decision-makers with common allowing comparative solution/solution analyses to determine the optimal solution while considering all local constraints.

2 AIM AND APPROACH

The need to objectively evaluate technical solutions becomes preponderant to ensure relevant choices to meet the challenges of construction and energy. If solutions are identified, they are mainly dedicated to a single application and not duplicates. Faced with the proliferation of BIPV solutions, indicators must adapt and propose an objective method allowing to accommodate all innovations, as well as solutions for infrastructures. The four initial performance indicators are increased within the project framework allowing an evaluation of the technical performance of the solution. ENERGY, ECONOMY, ENVIRONMENT and AESTHETICS KPIs are derived from the work of IEA PVPS T15 [2] and implemented for the needs of the project. A similar graphic representation will be used.

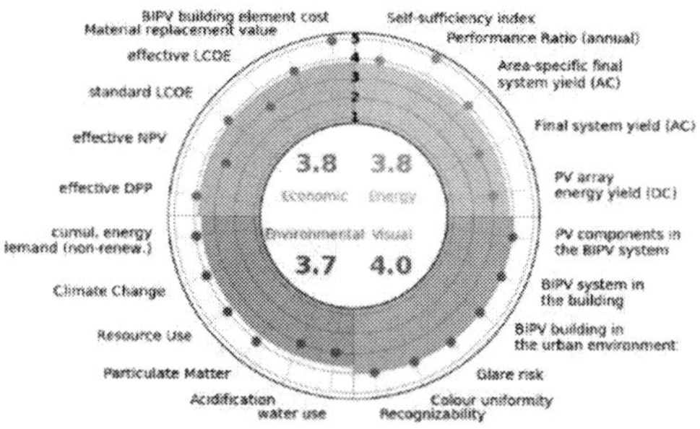

Figure 1: Example of KPIs results display taking into account BIPV solution and surrounding implementation conditions.

2.1 Base calculation approach

Definition of KPI's try to fit with project expectations to promote BIPV solutions through several indicators, addressing different markets or customers. To be objective enough, KPIs are calculated based on a representative set of parameters which are directly tied, somehow, to the considered indicator. So, each KPI value comes from the calculation of the arithmetic value of the parameters of its field of application. Each parameter is evaluated over a range of values defined by a rating scale (from 0 to 5). In this way, an isobarycentre value can be determined for each parameter independently, considering only the criteria to be evaluated. Calculating the average value of all the KPIs will enable us to determine an average value for the BIPV solution evaluated, which will then enable us to rank each solution according to all the indicators.

KPIs have been developed to be applied to new-builds as well as to renovation projects, so that we can determine which solutions will be the most relevant and help decision-makers.

2.2 Final calculation and assumption

The present work is an extension of the multi-dimensional evaluation tool developed under the framework of the IEA PVPS T15. This tool fits perfectly with the expectation of BIPV performance assessment solution to define the best solution to promote or that fits with building needs. An additional work has been done in BIPVBOOST EU project with the feedback of BIPV market and stakeholder analysis [3]. The approach of the tool is intended to be objective and therefore does not lead to favouring one KPI among all.

Indeed, every KPI is calculated with the same calculation methodology, a mean value of all parameters embedded in the KPI. Every KPI is calculated using the arithmetic average with its own parameters. The value weight of each parameter is currently the same for all parameters. although it may be possible to change the weight of each parameter later, and according to project of solution expectations.

Each assigned value's parameter is provided from a range of value described by calculation or provided by experts from corresponding domain. Each range is divided in 5 subranges where each corresponds to a parameter value. The smallest value of subrange corresponds to the smallest value of the parameter and is therefore the worst notation; 1. On the other hand, the highest subrange value corresponds to the best rating; 5, expressing that the parameter has reached its best score. The final KPI value is the arithmetic mean value calculated with all parameters' values. This calculated value is the corresponding score of the respective KPI, score value is between 1 and 5.

3 CREATION OF NEW KPIs

The new KPIs introduced in the INCREASE project [4], use a scale (Metric or unit) that must be defined and the associated score range validated. This Deliverable presents the quantitative rating basis, from former investigation and including the last two KPIs developed in the framework of the project with all partners involved in. Two new parameters raised from this work carried out in workshops with various stakeholders from different fields and using co-creation process to harvest suggestions and define needs. COMFORT and BUILDABILITY, are the fruit of this work, introducing two new indicators in addition of well-known indicators.

The Figure 2 presents complete indicators and parameters used to calculate the final score of every BIPV solution. Using the same display, it allows to have a quick review of contribution of each KPI.

4 KPIs DEFINITION AND RANGE

To handle correctly this tool, it's required to have the definition of every parameter and to know corresponding range to reach appropriate score. Hereafter explanation of the six indicators and parameters used. First four are well known and already validated, the two last will be validated during on site implementation during INCREASE project.

To figure out best use as possible of this tool, a parameter reduction has been conducted to reduce with only four parameter per indicator. This assumption will be validated during the validation phase on the field, with operating systems and with stakeholders.

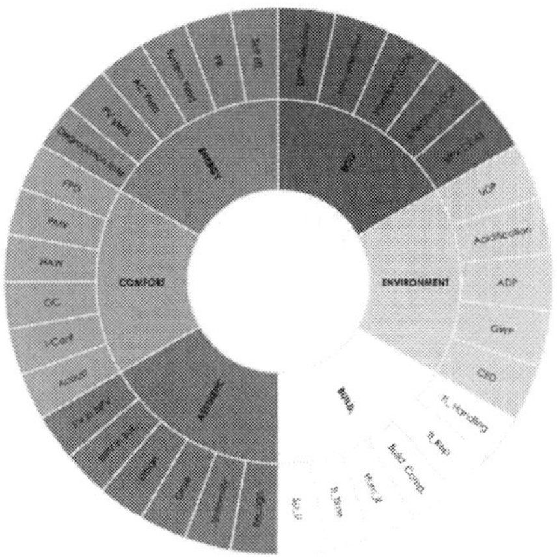

Figure 2: Final KPIs display with innovative BIPV indicators and parameters to fit with builders and end-users needs.

4.1 KPI ENERGY: Definition and parameters

Energy key performance indicator aims to manage parameters dealing mainly with energetic values or metrics allowing to monitor or express PI. This PI refers to the electrical performance of energy systems as described in IEC reference standard[5]. The considered parameters are:

- The final system AC yield (Yf)
- The area-specific AC final system yield
- The annual performance ratio (PR)
- The self-sufficiency index (SSI)

Yf is the net AC electricity output of the entire BIPV system (kWh) per unit of rated installed power (kWc) including the conversion efficiency. The area-specific AC final system yield implicitly includes the BIPV module efficiency, which is intrinsically dependent on the PV technology, BIPV design, and efficiency of all electrical parts. The performance ratio PR is defined as the ratio of the system's final yield Yf (kWh/kW) to its reference yield Yr (h) and represents the overall effect of losses on the BIPV. The self-sufficiency index (SSI) describes the percentage of electricity consumed by the building that is generated by the BIPV system. Corresponding ranges and notations are described hereafter

Table 1: Energy Performance indicator, references and parameter values.

Energy-relevant PIs	Ref.	Unit	min. value	max. value
PV array energy yield (DC)	Ya	kWh/kWp	0	1500
Area-specific AC final system yield	AC	kWh/m^2	0	300
Performance Ratio (annual)	PR	%	0	100
Self-sufficiency index	SSI	%	0	100

Table 2: Energy Performance indicator ratings

10.4229/EUPVSEC2025/4BV.4.15

rating 1	rating 2	rating 3	rating 4	rating 5
<550	550 - 825	825 - 1100	1100 - 1375	> 1375
<100	100 - 150	150 - 200	200 - 250	> 250
< 50	50-60	60-70	70-80	>80
<5	5-20.	20-50	50-80	>80

4.2 KPI ECONOMY: Definition and parameters

The performance indicators chosen for this evaluation are based on the approach described in [6]. The considered parameters for economy performance indicator are:

- The BIPV building element costs (BIPV_Cost)
- The material replacement value (MRV)
- The standard LCOE (LCOE)
- The net present value (NPV)

The BIPV_Cost is the BIPV building element costs including all stage from conception to installation, defined in terms of cost per square meter. The LCOE is defined as the ratio of the total lifecycle cost over the total lifetime output electricity, with the unit as €/kWh and will be compared to grid prices. The MRV is the cost of equivalent building materials that are replaced by the BIPV modules, and the net present value (NPV) is defined as the net value of life cycle costs and life cycle income.

All these four parameters are used to calculate the mean value of ECONOMY KPI according to the calculation methodology explained above.

Table 3: Economic Performance indicator, references and parameter values.

Economic Pis	Ref.	Unit	min. value	max. value
BIPV system costs	BIPV_Cos	€/m²	130	1550
Material replacement value	MRV	€/m²	0	460
Eff. LCOE	LCOE	€/kWh	(-0,5)	0,65
Eff. eNPV	NVP	€/m²	(-9700)	13700

Table 4: Economic Performance indicator ratings

rating 1	rating 2	rating 3	rating 4	rating 5
> 1400	1400 -1100	1100 - 700	700 - 300	< 300
< (-1000)	(-1000)- (-600)	(-600)- 0	0 - 200	> 200
> 0.4	0,4 - 0,24	0,24 - 0	0 - (-0,3)	< (-0.3)
< (-5000)	(-5000) - 0	0 - 5000	5000 - 10000	> 10000

4.3 KPI ENVIRONMENT: Definition and parameters

The environmental PIs include metrics for consumption of non-renewable primary energy (mineral and metal resources, as well as water consumption, greenhouse gas emissions), particulate matter emissions and emissions contribution to acidification. The four PIs are calculated with data partially given PV datasheets but must be filled with all surrounding components used in the BIPV final solution. The first data are provided with the environmental product declaration of modules (if available) and the standard date required to perform a complete LCA analysis, such as the bill of materials and country of manufacturing of the module and components, the size and number of the elements, the power and the PV technology applied. Once again, the work carried out by IEA PVPS is used as a working base. The Report IEA-PVPS T12-19:2020 "Life Cycle Inventories and Life Cycle Assessments of Photovoltaic Systems" [7], gives the description of the indicators the PIs name and the references data for the rating. The considered parameters for environment performance indicator are:

- The Global Warming Potential (GWP)
- The Abiotic resource depletion (ADP) use
- The impact on human health (PM/particulate matter)
- The water consumption, User Dep. Pot.(UDP)

Note that these variables are evaluated over the entire LCA of the BIPV system according to the calculation methodology described in [7].

The environmental impacts are quantified per kWh electricity generated by the BIPV system assessed. All the elements comply with the weather protection function (façade/roof/infrastructure) are assigned to the life cycle assessment (LCA) of the building and thus excluded when evaluating the environmental impacts of electricity generation.

Table 5: Environment Performance indicator, references and parameter values.

Environmental Pis	Ref.	Unit	min. value	max. value
CED non renewable	CED	MJ oil eq. / kWh	0,22	1,25
Climate Change GHG	GWP	g CO2 eq. / kWh	15	88
Resource Use, Minerals+Metals	ADP	mg Sb eq. / kWh	1,06	6,53
Particulate Matter	PM	10-9 disease incidence/kWh	0,55	4,29

Table 6: Environment Performance indicator ratings

rating 1	rating 2	rating 3	rating 4	rating 5
> 1,25	1,25 -0,91	0,91 - 0,56	0,56 - 0,22	< 0,22
> 88	88 - 63,7	63,7 - 39,3	39,9 - 15	< 15
> 6,53	6,53 - 4,71	4,71 - 2,88	2,88 - 1,06	< 1,06
> 4,29	4,29 - 3,04	3,04 - 1,80	1,80 - 0,55	< 0,55

4.4 KPI AESTHETICAL: Definition and parameters

KPI aesthetic try to handle all the visual parameters that could characterize a BIPV project. The aesthetic PIs include different aspects related to the visual rendering of the BIPV system, including the recognizability as a PV system and the colour uniformity in the surrounding building elements. These visual or aesthetical indicators will play a significant role for historical sites or landscape protection zones which must comply with restrictive visual appearance. Coloured or textured modules are a commonly used solution to meet the aesthetical requirements. The work carried out by Babin et Al.[8] focused on the glare risk (GLARE) in close proximity with a particular attention for dense urban districts or areas with specific regulation (Highways, airports, ...). The considered parameters for aesthetic performance indicator are:

- The recognizability of PV solutions (Reco.)
- The colour uniformity of the BIPV array (Unif.)
- The glare effect of BIPV solution (GLARE)
- The identification of a building using BIPV (Ident.)

The three last PIs are relative to the degree of visual integration into the environment on three different scales: At the module level (considering integration into the BIPV system), at the system level (considering integration into the building) and at the building level (considering integration into the urban environment), based on the hierarchical description developed by ENEA in [9] and described on three different scales the level of visual integration into the built environment. For a simplified use and exploitation, the initial last three identification parameters are grouped together into a single one, Ident.

For the colour measurement a specific protype colourimeter tool to measured colour behind transparent

10.4229/EUPVSEC2025/4BV.4.15
020302-003

front-sheet will be developed by EPFL in INCREASE project. The colour variation (Delta-E) can be calculated in the CIELab color space as the distance between points in a 3-dimensional space as described in [10].

Table 7: Aesthetical Performance indicator, references and parameter values.

Aesthetical PIs	Ref.	Main parameter
Recognizability	Reco.	Y/N
Colour	Unif.	Spatial ΔC(A) and angular ΔC(θ) colour uniformity (validation needed)
Glare	Glare	Glare risk
BIPV identification	Ident.	(example calculations and validation needed)

Table 8: Aesthetical Performance indicator ratings

rating 1	rating 2	rating 3	rating 4	rating 5
ΔC(A) > 10 / --*	ΔC(A) < 10 /--*	ΔC(A) < 7 / --*	ΔC(A) < 4 / --*	ΔC(A) < 1 / --*
ΔC(θ) > 10 / --*	ΔC(θ) < 10 / --*	ΔC(θ) < 7 / --*	ΔC(θ) < 4 / --*	ΔC(θ) < 1 / --*
*if desired	*if desired	*if desired	*if desired	*if desired
Risk for	Risk for	Risk for	Risk for	Risk for
flash blindness	flash blindness	discomfort glare	discomfort glare	discomfort glare
>10 hours annually	1-10 hours	>10 hours	1-10 hours	<1 hour annually

4.5 KPI COMFORT: Definition and parameters

Comfort KPI should not be viewed as fixed metrics tied solely to a BIPV technology. Instead, they are highly dependent on the specific building context—including geometry, orientation, occupancy, and HVAC strategy—and on the way BIPV is integrated (e.g., façade vs. roof, transparent vs. opaque modules). The impact of BIPV on comfort emerges from this unique interaction, not from the technology in isolation.

While BIPV can influence thermal and visual conditions (e.g., by providing shading or altering heat gains), its direct impact on thermal comfort is limited in most cases. This is because HVAC systems automatically regulate indoor temperatures to meet setpoints, adjusting heating or cooling output as needed. As a result, changes in thermal load caused by BIPV are typically compensated by the building's systems, and the perceived comfort remains stable, even if energy use changes.

Common comfort categories in building assessment include thermal comfort, visual comfort, acoustic comfort, and indoor air quality—each focusing on occupant well-being and performance. This assessment focuses on thermal and visual comfort, while acoustic comfort and indoor air quality are not included, as justified in the following sections.

Table 9: Comfort Performance indicator, references and parameter values.

Comfort PIs	Ref.	Unit	Minimum values	Mximum values
Overheting hours	OH	h/y	0	8760
Underheating hours	UH	h/Y	0	8760
Spatial Daylight Autonomy	sDA	% (floor area)	0%	100%
Useful Daylight Illuminance	UDI	%(floor area)	0%	100%

Table 10: Comfort Performance indicator ratings

rating 1	rating 2	rating 3	rating 4	rating 5
>500	301-500	151-300	51-150	0-50
>900	601-900	301-600	101-300	0-100
<30%	30-44%	45-59%	60-74%	≥ 75%
<35%	35-49%	50-64%	65-79%	> 80%

4.6 KPI BUILDABILITY: Definition and parameters

Buildability KPI, is the fruit of work carried out in workshops close to urban planners' and builders' requests. It considers manufacturers metrics to identify how long is the work duration.

The four indicators are:

- Installation rate (pace) of IPV solutions – InR
- Installation Human Resources - InHR
- Replacement rate (pace) of IPV solutions - RR
- Replacement Human resources – RepHR

References and parameter values and specific ranges are detailed hereafter.

Table 11: Buildability Performance indicator, references and parameter values.

Buildability PIs	Ref.	Unit	Minimum values	Mximum values
Installation rate of PV solutions	InR	h/m2	1 / 6	1
Installation Human Resources	InHR	n.worker/solution	1	5
Replacement rate of PV solutions	Rep.R	h/m2	0,5	4
Replacement Human resources	Rep.HR	n.worker/solution	1	5

Table 12: Buildability Performance indicator ratings

rating 1	rating 2	rating 3	rating 4	rating 5
> 1	0,7 - 1	0,4 - 0,7	0,2 - 0,4	<0,2
5	4	3	2	1
> 4	3-4	2-3	1-2	<1
5	4	3	2	1

5 ONGOING WORK AND VALIDATION

With finalization of selection parameters and performance key indicators, BIPV solutions could be assessed objectively with a fair approach including needs of all stakeholders including manufacturers or builders and especially the end-users. Next step will be to assess in real test conditions on pre-demo and then on demo sites from INCREASE project, and to evaluate implementation in the field of a such methodology.

Initial stage preformed on pre-demo locations will allow to validate and strengthen the use of such parameters and performance indicators. Next stage will be to apply a possible solution that may eventually be implemented to meet the needs of real operations on the nine demo sites of the project.

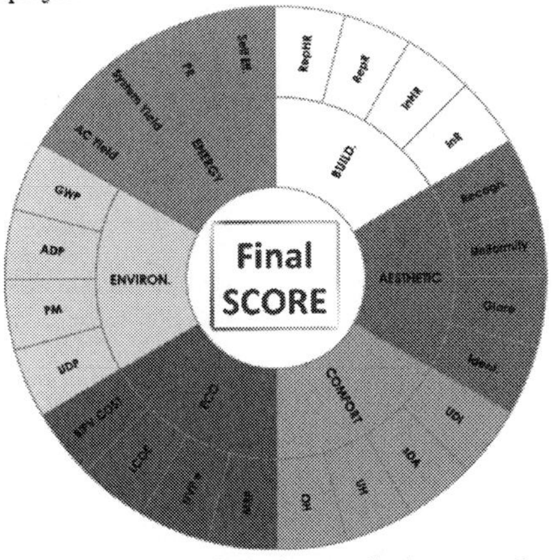

Figure 3: Exemple of Final score display according to BIPV solution, building specificities, location and needs.

10.4229/EUPVSEC2025/4BV.4.15

Final score will be displayed as presented in the Figure 3. The value is calculated as the average value of all calculated KPIs, values are calculated talking into account the rating tables and parameters values presented in the tables, related to each KPI.

The Figure 4 presents the display score of the BIPV solution studied. Even if the layout is not final, KPIs subscores and final average value will remain presented. That will allow to decision makers to have a quick overview of the solution and contribution of each KPI.

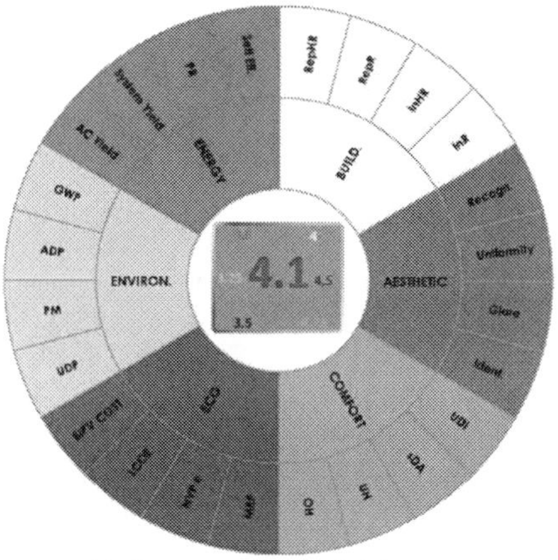

Figure 4: Final score value and dislplay of subscores of each KPI developed. Including value to the tenth.

6 CONCLUSION AND PERSPECTIVES

There are currently few objective indicators, and these do not allow all actors in the value chain to be included, preventing them from providing informed opinions to decision-makers.

Current tools, which are geared towards photovoltaic expectations, do not consider the expectations of the construction industry or end users. In this work, we have developed indicators that allow all stakeholders to be included, thus ensuring that all opinions are taken into account and enabling objective decision-making.

This approach, developed jointly with stakeholders, also enables a harmonized and unbiased approach to be implemented. This approach thus ensures that different solutions are analyzed and compared based solely on the intrinsic data of the identified solutions. Decision-makers can thus select the solutions with the best final score or determine which KPIs they wish to focus their efforts on. This should enable them to respond in a targeted manner to local, regulatory, or even national requirements.

Simple implementation makes it possible to provide data that is accessible to all decision-makers and stakeholders using the same interpretation grid, in a straightforward manner.

It is desirable to make the tool sufficiently versatile to be able to dynamically integrate data measured on site and to be able to integrate it into digital energy management tools in buildings.

Implementation at demonstration sites will enable us to see how these indicators will be implemented and to identify and resolve any difficulties encountered. Similarly, we will analyze the ability to implement dynamic monitoring of indicator trends and determine their usefulness, particularly in terms of their impact on recycling, maintenance, and, above all, the effects of aging and the management of sustainability and reliability for this type of BIPV solution.

REFERENCES

[1] G. Eder, H.R. Wilson, S. Boddaert and Al. : Multi-dimensional evaluation of BIPV installations: Development of a tool to assess the performance as building component and electricity generator. Energy and Building, Vol 31, 2024.

[2] Report IEA-PVPS T15-06:2019; Compilation and Analysis of User Needs for BIPV and its Functions; Wilson, H.R., Kapsis, K., Delisle, V., et al.: https://iea-pvps.or g/key-topics/compilation-and-analysis-of-user-needs-for-bipv-and-its-functions.

[3] Eu, H2020 BIPVBOOST project report: Update on BIPV market and stakeholder analysis, available at https://bipvboost.eu/public-reports/download/update-onbipv-market-and-stakeholder-analysis.

[4] Eu, H2020 INCREASE project report: KPIs and monitoring approaches (v1), available at https://www.increaseipv.eu/_files/ugd/2c16bd_c27d8c41d3124dc2b20820c49c7b614c.pdf

[5] IEC, 61724–1:2021 Photovoltaic system performance - Part 1: Monitoring, Int. Elec. Commission (2021).

[6] R.P.N.P. Weerasinghe, R.J. Yang, A review of 45 non-domestic buildings 12 western countries, Renewable Sustainable Energy Rev. 137 (2021) 110622. https://doi.org/10.1016/j.rser.2020.110622.

[7] Report IEA-PVPS T12-19:2020; Life Cycle Inventories and Life Cycle Assessments of Photovoltaic Systems, Frischknecht, R., et al. https://iea-pvps.org/key-topics/life-cycle-inventories-and-life-cycle-assessments-of-photovoltaic-systems/.

[8] Glare Potential Evaluation of Structured PV Glass Based on Gonioreflectometry; Babin, M., Thorsteinsson, S., Jakobsen, M.L., and Spataru, S.V., IEEE Journal of Photovoltaics, 2022, 12, 6, 1314-1318, 2022, DOI: 10.1109/JPHOTOV.2022.3189779.

[9] A Trans-Disciplinary Vocabulary for Assessing the Visual Performance of BIPV; Scognamiglio, A.; Sustainability 2021, 13(10), 5500; DOI: 10.3390/su13105500.

[10] Accurate color characterization of solar photovoltaic modules for building integration; Alejandro Borja Block, Jordi Escarre Palou, Antonin Faes, Alessandro Virtuani, Christophe Ballif; Solar Energy, 2024, 267; DOI: https://doi.org/10.1016/j.solener.2023.112227A

ACKNOWLEDGMENTS

Authors would like to thank IEA PVPS T15 members for feeding the base of this work as well as BIPVBOOST project partners with their valuable inputs and contributions.

This project has received funding from the European Union's HORIZON research and innovation program under grant agreement No 101136112.

THE USE OF LIFE CYCLE ASSESSMENT TO SUPPORT DEVELOPMENT OF AN INNOVATIVE BIPV SYSTEM WITH A STEEL FRAME

Roulleau Léa[1], Bailhache Simon[1], Boddaert Simon[1,*], Reyal Jean-Pierre[2], Biard Yves[2]

CSTB[1] / SEMPERSTYL[2]
84 avenue Jean Jaurès 77447 Marne-la-Vallée Cedex 2 / 31 RUE DES ETOURNEAUX 95610 ERAGNY

*simon.boddaert@cstb.fr

ABSTRACT: Building-integrated Photovoltaic solutions (BIPV) help optimizing the use of available areas for PV implementation. With growing concerns about the environmental impacts of the construction sector, BIPV system manufacturers are challenged to evaluate the impacts of their solutions and consider them as key criteria for decision-making in their design process. In this context, this study aims at correctly define the calculation protocol and assess the impact on climate change of an innovative BIPV solution named SOLARSTYL® in development.
To this end, a cradle-to-grave life cycle assessment (LCA) of the SOLARSTYL® system is performed, using a method inspired by the French accredited PEP Ecopassport program for Environmental Product Declarations (EPD). Environmental performance comparisons are made with a standard BIPV solution considered as a reference in order to guide design choices. More specifically, the study addresses the influence of the metal on the environmental impacts. A steel frame is considered for the SOLARSTYL® system, together with a plug-and-play connecting technology to facilitate assembly, maintenance and replacement. Cable routing solution and hazards management option will be included in this study. In addition, micro-inverters are expected to be integrated in the frame in a future design. In contrast, the reference system includes the most common current solution, i.e. an aluminium frame in a conventional PV module equipped with an external junction box.
Keywords: Building Integrated PV (BIPV), Comparative Life Cycle Assessment (LCA)

1 CONTEXT, GOAL AND SCOPE OF THE STUDY

Since its application in 2022, French Environmental regulation RE2020 [1] enforces thresholds on climate change footprint for each new building construction projects to meet climate change mitigation targets. Threshold values will decline every three years to reach carbon neutrality towards 2050. The French National decarbonation roadmap [2] also encourages the use of photovoltaic renewable energy to decrease fossil energy consumption in building, reduce electricity mix carbon footprint and increase network's resilience and reliability.

Thus, environmental performances of SolarStyl® Building Integrated PV (BIPV) [3] innovative solution are assessed in this study to optimise its potential environmental impacts reduction gains and make better environmental choices (*Figure 1*). This solution is a steel-frame and "plug-and-play" connecting technology designed for PV by SemperStyl company. It integrates electric connectivity, junction boxes, as well as modularity functions enabling its repair and the replacement of PV modules at their end-of-life. Moreover, this solution is conceived to be easy to install and maintain. Standard reference comparable solution is made from aluminium, does not integrate electric connections, neither modularity nor repairability functions.

The goal of this study is firstly to **evaluate environmental footprint of SolarStyl® solution with cradle-to-grave life cycle assessment** and analysing the process contribution to environmental impacts. Secondly the objective is to **compare the environmental impacts of SolarStyl® solution with BIPV aluminium standard reference system having external junction boxes and inverters to identify the best scenario and ways of improvement.**

Figure 1. Solarstyl® solution, PV with steel-frame and integrated connection

2 METHODOLOGY

2.1 Functional unit and system boundaries

The functional unit is "*to ensure electricity production and waterproofing of the facade using a PV module integration system*". The reference flow is 1 m² of framed module. The reference service life (RSL) of the system is 50 years, according to standard reference life of a building in the RE2020 regulation. The system is composed of a metallic frame, a PV module, a junction box, cable and electric connections, and an inverter. The different elements have their own RSL described in Table 1.

Composition	Reference system in aluminium	SolarStyl
Frame	Aluminium RSL : 30 years (= limited by PV module RSL) Repairable : NO	Steel RSL : 50 years (RSL from EN 15804) Repairable : YES
PV module	RSL : 30 years	
Junction box	Deported 1 box / module RSL : 30 years (= limited by PV module RSL) Repairable : NO	Integrated 1 box / module RSL : 30 years (= limited by PV module RSL) Repairable : YES
Cable + connections	Deported RSL : 30 years Repairable : YES	Integrated RSL : 50 years Repairable : YES
Inverter	Deported RSL : 10 years	Deported RSL : 10 years

Table 1. System description

10.4229/EUPVSEC2025/4BV.4.17

The lifespan of the frame is defined at 30 years for aluminium (limited by RSL of PV module) and 50 years for steel (SolarStyl® system is fully repairable, allowing to extend of the reference service life of the frame until 50 years).

The study is cradle-to-grave, from production of raw materials, until the end-of-life. Module D is not considered. Raw materials production takes place in Europe, except for the PV module which is produced in China. Two scenarios are considered for the aluminium frame of the reference system: production in Europe or mixed supply from China (90%) and Europe (10%). The rest of the life cycle takes place in France (from assembly of the system, installation until end-of-life).
Neither photovoltaic electricity production nor its substitution to electricity imports are calculated in the study.

Life cycle stages are presented in Figure 2 and follow EN15804+A2 standard [4]. The life cycle considers the maintenance stage with the replacement of inverters every 10 years and the replacement of the PV module and junction box at 30 years for the SolarStyl® system. For the aluminium system, the whole system is replaced at 30 years and inverters replaced every 10 years.

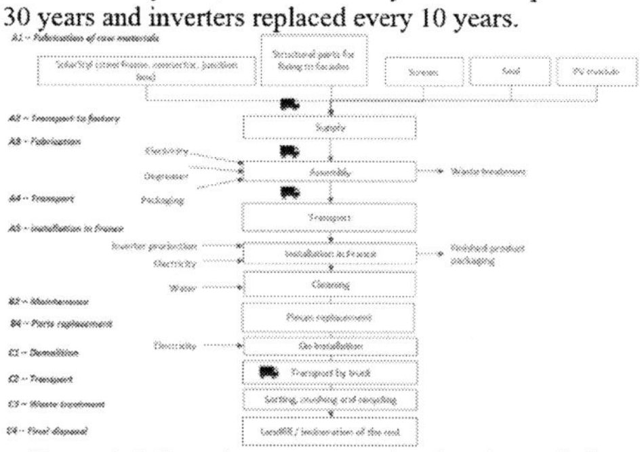

Figure 2. Life cycle stages considered in the study for Solarstyl® system and system boundaries

2.2 Life cycle inventory

All inputs and outputs are quantified for each life cycle stages. Data are collected for each life cycle stages, based on SolarStyl® 2024 data for a 1.8 m² module on its actual v0 development.
The aluminium reference system relies mostly on data from the SolarStyl® system for quantities and compositions of components. The main difference between the two systems is the **lifespan of the frame (30 years for aluminium vs. 50 years for steel), as the end-of-life of the PV module requires a complete replacement of the system, whereas in SolarStyl® system the replacement of the PV module is possible.**

No allocation is made. Materials have been weighted, electricity consumption for the production has been calculated based on machines power specifications.

For the aluminium solution, cable trays are not integrated. Circuit breaker boxes are not integrated, by lack of data, for both scenarios.

2.3 Life cycle assessment

LCA methodology is inspired by internationally recognized LCA standards ISO 14040 [5] / ISO 14044 [6], as well as standard NF C08-100-1 [7] and PEP ecopassport program (French EPD program for Electrical, Electronic and Heating Ventilation Air Conditioning-Refrigeration) [8]. The quantified inputs and outputs are modeled in the Simapro software [9] using ecoinvent v9.6 database [10] and Environmental Product Declaration of steel suppliers. EN15804+A2 environmental impact assessment method is used for impact categories assessment. The study is not peer-reviewed by LCA experts.

2.4 Scenarios

Several parameters were identified as influents for results: aluminium quantity, aluminium geographical area of production and to a lesser extent aluminium recycled content. Thus, different scenarios were assessed to cover the multiple possibilities.

3 LCA RESULTS AND INTERPRETATION

Figure 3 presents climate change comparison in kg CO_2eq per m² of installed solution over 50 years of reference service life of the SolarStyl® solution (left bar) and the aluminium reference solution (middle and right bars). Reference case SolarStyl® solution uses 9.5 kg of steel produced in Europe with 31% of recycled content. The standard aluminium solution uses 19 kg with 32% of recycled content produced in Europe or in China (90%)/Europe (10%).

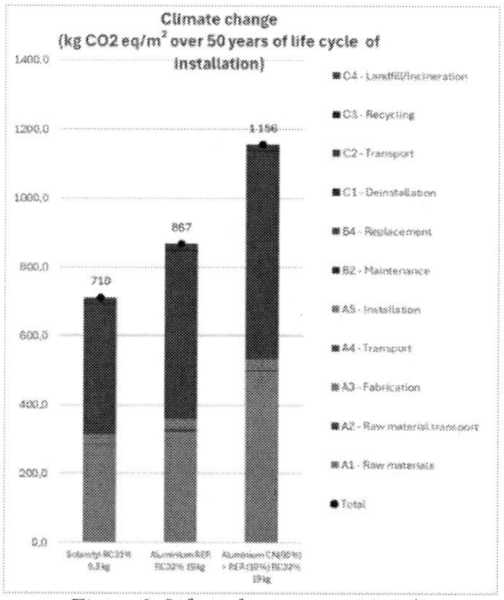

Figure 3. Life cycle assessment results

The lifecycle stages that contribute the most to global warming potential are ***A1 – Raw materials production*** (especially for PV module which requires lots of energy and materials and represents 92% of A1 impact) and ***B4 – Parts of maintenance*** (due to replacement of PV module and inverter which represent respectively 30% and 46% of B4 impact) over the 50 years of the system lifespan.

The difference between SolarStyl® and reference aluminium solution can be explained mainly by the following reasons:

- The shorter lifespan of the aluminium frame (30 years) implies a greater quantity needed to cover the 50 years study-period.
- Twice as much aluminium is needed to perform the same functions as steel according to SemperStyl.

- The carbon footprint between aluminium and steel differs:
  - Steel (with 5.5-55% of recycled content) produced in Europe = 2.5-5.3 kg CO_2 eq/kg
  - Aluminium (with 32% of recycled content) produced in Europe = 5.8 kg CO_2 eq/kg
  - Aluminium (with 32% of recycled content) produced in China (90%), Europe (10%) = 22.2 kg CO_2 eq/kg

If the quantity of steel and aluminium were the same, there would still be 14% of difference between the scenarios (due to the different frame RSL: 30 versus 50 years).

4 DISCUSSION

4.1 Aluminium scenario definition

Aluminium solution scenario is based on the same data collection as SolarStyl® system, as first approach as no production data were available. The study relies in particular on the hypothesis that aluminium quantity needed for the functional unit is twice as much as steel quantity (SemperStyl data). Sensitivity analysis has been conducted to measure the influence of aluminium quantity on the comparison of the life cycles. Results have shown that with same metal quantity, Solarstyl® system remains a better choice for the climate, thanks to its modularity functions which enable to extend the reference service life of the frame and cables and avoid production of new materials.

Other uncertainties have been identified in the aluminium scenario definition such as place of production and recycled content. The absolute value results depend on those parameters. Conclusions are however unchanged, as reference service life and weight of aluminium have more influence.

4.1 Uncertainties and limits of LCA

Results depend strongly on PV module technology, inverters technology, their reference service life and place of production.

Also, LCA focused on climate change results generated by the life cycle of the system with an attributional approach. No prospective analysis was carried out, neither steel or aluminium availability, criticality, nor supply risks were assessed.

Finally, to compare both solutions, other choice criteria should be observed such as fire safety features implemented in SolarStyl® solution, mechanical strength, watertightness, theft protection, ease of installation and repair, building thermal performance…

5 CONCLUSION

This study shows that SolarStyl® solution has less environmental impact than the aluminium solution, thanks to its repairability function that enables to change the PV module without having to change the whole system. Furthermore, steel quantities needed for the functional unit are smaller than in aluminium in the reference solution.

The parameters that differentiate SolarStyl® from aluminium standard solution in terms of environmental results are the lifespan of the system that avoids producing new materials, the metal country of production and its energetic carbon footprint, the metal quantity needed of 1 m² of solution and, to a lesser extent, the metal recycled content.

Future work will focus on reducing environmental impacts of SolarStyl® solution applying eco-design principles.

6 ACKNOWLEDGEMENTS

The authors wish to acknowledge ADEME for their fundings support.

7 REFERENCES

[1] RE2020, https://www.ecologie.gouv.fr/politiques-publiques/reglementation-environnementale-re2020

[2] Ministère de la Transition Ecologique et de la cohésion des territoires, Feuille de route décarbonation du cycle de vie du bâtiment Les propositions de la filière JANVIER 2023, https://www.ecologie.gouv.fr/sites/default/files/documents/Feuille_de_route_decarbonation_batiment.pdf

[3] SolarStyl® system, version 2025, SemperStyl, 2025, https://solarstyltechnologies.fr/ , consulted on 25th of August 2025

[4] NF EN 15804+A2 (octobre 2019), Contribution des ouvrages de construction au développement durable — Déclarations environnementales sur les produits — Règles régissant les catégories de produits de construction

[5] ISO 14040:2006 - Gestion environnementale — Analyse du cycle de vie — Principes et cadre (publiée en 2006)

[6] ISO 14044:2006 - Gestion environnementale — Analyse du cycle de vie — Exigences et lignes directrices (publiée en 2006)

[7] NF C08-100-1, Déclarations environnementales relatives aux équipements électriques, électroniques et de génie climatique - Partie 1 : règles d'élaboration communes - Usage dans les ouvrages de bâtiment

[8] PEP ecopassport rules, http://www.pep-ecopassport.org//fr/, consulted on: 25th of August 2025 Ecoinvent, www.Eco-invent.org

[9] Simapro v9.6, https://simapro.com/, consulted on: 25th of August 2025

[10] ecoinvent, https://ecoinvent.org/, consulted on: 25th of August 2025.

ACKNOWLEDGMENTS

Authors would like to thank SOLARSTYL project members for supporting this work with valuable inputs, disseminating information and contributions.

This project has received funding from ADEME, French National Agency for the Environment and Energy.

ECONOMIC ANALYSIS OF BUILDING INTEGRATION OF FLEXIBLE PV MODULES

Paulo Carmo[1], José A. Silva[1], Luís Fialho[2], Afonso Cavaco[1], Pedro Horta[1]
[1]Renewable Energies Chair, Polo da Mitra da Universidade de Évora, Edifício Ário Lobo de Azevedo, 7000-083 Nossa Senhora de Tourega, Portugal
[2]Eurac Research-Institute for Renewable Energy, 39100 Bolzano, Italy

ABSTRACT: This paper presents a study that makes a thorough evaluation of the economic competitiveness of building integration of flexible PV modules in the European Union (EU) by comparing the levelized cost of electricity (LCOE) of flexible modules with rigid modules considering different locations in several European countries. The countries and cities chosen were Stockholm (Sweden), Évora (Portugal), Munich (Germany), Bordeaux (France), Vienna (Austria), Amsterdam (Netherlands), Rome (Italy), Warsaw (Poland), Athens (Greece), Dublin (Ireland), for each country an economic analysis was made. The analysis was based on the evaluation of the average installation and maintenance costs for each country, and by using PVGIS, the annual energy production of the system (kWh) was estimated for each location. The LCOE was calculated for all locations, both residential and industrial installations, considering an installed power of 3 kWp for residential systems and 300 kWp for the industrial ones.
Keywords: Flexible Modules, BIPV, LCOE, Residential, Industrial.

1 INTRODUCTION

In the last years the need to decarbonize the energy sector to mitigate the impact of global warming caused by the usage of fossil fuels has become a priority, and as a response the deployment of renewable energies is increasing. The European Union (EU) has set a target that by 2030 there will be a reduction in greenhouse gas emissions by 55% relative to 1990 levels and ensure that at least 42.5% of the energy needs come from renewable sources, but aiming for 45%. The renewable energy sources represented 24.5% of EU final energy use in 2023. Although solar photovoltaics (PV) only accounted for 2% of the EU energy consumption, it can have a major role in achieving the 42.5% target. For this to be possible, it is necessary to use different approaches to the installation of PV modules, as the conventional PV power plants occupy significant amounts of space, and the land-use competition with other activities is becoming an issue, as much of the spaces without constructions are either used for agriculture or forestry, so it is necessary to look at different technologies and think of alternative ways to integrate PV into already existing constructions as well as new ones such as in facades, rooftops, or road barriers [1],[2].

Rigid silicon PV modules nowadays correspond to more than 90% of the global market, thanks to its efficiency and low price, but there are some limitations to its applications due to their weight and rigid nature. So, as the photovoltaic industry seeks innovative solutions to integrate solar into a broader range of applications, flexible PV modules appear as a lightweight and bendable solution that permits its installation into low load bearing structures, and a large variety of surfaces, namely curved ones, both in buildings and vehicles [3]. Figure 1 shows an example of one of these applications [4].

Figure 1: Building with flexible modules on rooftop

Some of the issues that limit a widespread adoption of this technology are the higher costs and shorter lifetime when compared to the conventional crystalline silicon modules [5]. On the other hand, their reduced weight and flexibility can make transport and installation less work intensive.

All the previously mentioned topics will affect the levelized cost of electricity (LCOE). This research aims to do a comprehensive analysis of the LCOE of the building integrated flexible PV modules and compare it with the traditional rigid crystalline silicon-based modules, accounting for differences in material costs, installation costs and long-term performance.

2 METHODOLOGY

First, it was defined that the residential system would have a power peak of 3 kWp. While for the industrial system a 300 kWp installation was considered, this choice was based on the International Energy Agency reports that describe an industrial system as a grid-connected roof-mounted with at least 250 kW [8].

Next, the CAPEX was determined. The value which can be divided into cost of equipment, labour, profit and other costs that an installation has in all countries.

For the industrial PV system, it was not possible to find a CAPEX for every location, so from the values taken from national reports and other sources it was estimated that the CAPEX for an industrial PV system that the price per Wp would be approximately half of the Residential PV.

Using PVGIS it was found the yearly PV energy production (YEP) for all the chosen locations: Stockholm, Évora, Munich, Bordeaux, Vienna, Amsterdam, Rome, Warsaw, Athens, Dublin [6].

Two cases were studied, the ideal mounting and the vertical mounting. The ideal case is when the PV is mounted with the optimal slope and azimuth for the location. And the vertical case where the slope is assumed as 90° and the azimuth is 0°, which simulates the PV being mounted on walls facing south.

For the two cases referred, the rigid modules will always need a mounting structure due to their weight, but for the vertical case, the flexible modules will be considered as mounted without the use of a mounting structure, being instead directly attached to the surface by gluing for example, which in conjunction with the reduced

10.4229/EUPVSEC2025/4BV.4.22

weight of the modules means it would be possible to install it 40% quicker and reduce labour costs by that amount [7]. While in the ideal case flexible modules would still need a structure to get the optimal slope, so in this case the reduction on labour cost assumed as only 20%. As it was not always possible to determine the labour costs, it was assumed that in those cases the installation cost would be 20% of the CAPEX value, as that was the average obtained from the values available.

Assuming the cost of operation and maintenance, OPEX, is equal to 1.5 % of the CAPEX, as it normally ranges between 1% and 2%, and a lifetime of 30 years for the rigid modules and 25 years for the flexible ones it is then possible to calculate the LCOE using the following equation:

$$LCOE = \frac{CAPEX + OPEX \cdot lifetime}{YEP \cdot lifetime}$$

It is important to highlight that this LCOE expression is a simplified version that does not include discount rates; consequently, the values obtained are lower than the LCOEs usually obtained for PV systems, and should not be compared with them. The main goal of this study is to compare the economic competitiveness of the flexible PV modules with the rigid ones, so the figure of merit is the relative difference between the LCOEs for these two technologies, which was obtained for each type of PV system and location.

3 RESULTS

The results obtained for each case and location have significant differences so in the following tables not only are presented the LCOE values for two PV technologies, but also the relative difference between LCOE values for the flexible (F) and rigid modules (R). This difference was calculated using the equation:

$$\frac{F}{R} = \left(\frac{LCOE_F}{LCOE_R} \times 100\right) - 100$$

Where $LCOE_F$ and $LCOE_R$ are the LCOE for flexible and rigid modules, respectively.

3.1 Residential LCOE ideal

Using the cost values found for residential installations and the expected yearly energy production of a 3 kWp PV system mounted with the optimal slope and azimuth it was possible to obtain the following LCOE values.

Table I: Residential LCOE ideal

	Rigid [€/kWh]	Flexible [€/kWh]	F/R [%]
Stockholm	0.070	0.093	+32.9
Évora	0.027	0.036	+33.3
Munich	0.059	0.077	+30.5
Bordeaux	0.098	0.145	+48.0
Vienna	0.085	0.124	+45.9
Amsterdam	0.056	0.076	+35.7
Rome	0.047	0.066	+40.4
Warsaw	0.160	0.211	+31.9
Athens	0.086	0.114	+32.6
Dublin	0.087	0.115	+32.2

3.2 Residential LCOE vertical

Here are presented the LCOE values obtained by calculating the expected yearly energy production for a PV installation with a slope of 90° and an azimuth of zero.

Table II: Residential LCOE vertical

	Rigid [€/kWh]	Flexible [€/kWh]	F/R [%]
Stockholm	0.093	0.113	+21.5
Évora	0.042	0.051	+21.4
Munich	0.082	0.100	+22.0
Bordeaux	0.140	0.190	+35.7
Vienna	0.121	0.160	+32.2
Amsterdam	0.079	0.105	+22.8
Rome	0.069	0.098	+33.3
Warsaw	0.225	0.297	+21.8
Athens	0.139	0.184	+22.3
Dublin	0.117	0.154	+21.4

3.3 Industrial LCOE ideal

Using the cost values found for industrial installations and the expected yearly energy production for a 300 kWp PV system mounted with the optimal slope and azimuth it was possible to get the following LCOE values.

Table III: Industrial LCOE ideal

	Rigid [€/kWh]	Flexible [€/kWh]	F/R [%]
Stockholm	0.041	0.054	+31.7
Évora	0.013	0.017	+30.8
Munich	0.026	0.035	+34.6
Bordeaux	0.038	0.056	+47.4
Vienna	0.039	0.056	+43.6
Amsterdam	0.024	0.032	+33.3
Rome	0.032	0.045	+40.6
Warsaw	0.078	0.103	+32.1
Athens	0.043	0.057	+32.6
Dublin	0.039	0.051	+30.8

3.4 Industrial LCOE vertical

By repeating the same process used for residential installations was possible to find the industrial LCOE values for the vertical installation.

Table IV: Industrial LCOE vertical

	Rigid [€/kWh]	Flexible [€/kWh]	F/R [%]
Stockholm	0.031	0.038	+22.6
Évora	0.021	0.025	+19.0
Munich	0.036	0.044	+22.2
Bordeaux	0.054	0.074	+37.0
Vienna	0.054	0.071	+31.5
Amsterdam	0.033	0.041	+24.2
Rome	0.048	0.064	+33.3
Warsaw	0.108	0.132	+22.2
Athens	0.070	0.085	+21.4
Dublin	0.051	0.063	+23.5

From the results it is possible to see that although the LCOE is dependent on both the installation costs and the solar energy available in the region, in all cases the LCOE for flexible modules is sig higher than for conventional rigid modules. As by looking at the values for Évora and Athens which are locations with the same latitude, so close values of solar irradiation, but the LCOE values for Athens is much higher than the one for Évora as the installation costs of a PV system in Greece are much higher than those of Portugal.

France is the country where the relative difference in LCOE is the highest for all cases, being its higher value verified as 48% for a residential installation mounted with the optimal slope, and this difference is a result of how expensive the materials are when compared with the labour costs so that the reduction in labour cost with the use of flexible modules will have the smallest impact on the LCOE of flexible modules in France.

It is possible to observe that Poland is the country with the highest LCOE for both rigid and flexible modules, this is mainly a result of Poland having the highest CAPEX for PV systems, this country also has one of the lowest shares of PV on the energy mix. In fact, our results suggest that there is a correlation between the country's PV installed capacity and the production installed and the respective LCOE.

Between the countries analysed, Portugal showed itself to be the country with the lowest LCOE, which is a result of the lower installation cost in Portugal, compared to the other countries, as well as having a very high solar energy potential.

The results also suggest that the building integration of flexible modules into building facades, where thanks to the lightweight nature of these modules, could avoid the use of a mounting structure, and reduce the difference between the values of LCOE for the two technologies much smaller. Although the LCOE for this case is still higher than for rigid modules, it can be seen as a viable option, especially because as they are lighter the forces imposed on the walls will be much smaller which is an important factor to consider when planning to install photovoltaic modules into a building facade.

Still, the most interesting applications for flexible modules are applications where the conventional rigid modules cannot be installed, either due to the curvature of the surface, due to limited weight supported by the structure, or surfaces that cannot be perforated to install a typical mounting structure. Another interesting application of flexible modules are mobile applications such as electric vehicles, where the reduced weight is an advantage, and to install modules onto the vehicle there can be no perforation, and the modules need to be as close to the car as possible to maintain the vehicle aerodynamics.

4 CONCLUSIONS

In conclusion, currently the flexible PV modules technology is only a good option for applications where the traditional rigid silicon modules cannot be installed, as the comparison of LCOE values of this PV modules with the conventional rigid ones showed that they are in all cases less competitive.

Whoever with the growth of the market for flexible modules, it is expected the costs of this technology will be reduced, making it more competitive and possibly a viable option for installations like rooftops.

It is important to note that this study took only into account the cost of production and energy production without looking at the cost of electricity and how its variations can influence the deployment of the different technologies, and as consequence their price evolutions.

5 ACKNOWLEDGEMENTS

The authors would like to thank the project SOCONEXGEN for the support.

6 REFERENCES

[1] European Environment Agency, "Share of energy consumption from renewable sources in Europe", [Online].Available: https://www.eea.europa.eu/en/analysis/indicators/share-of-energy-consumption-from

[2] EPJ Photovoltaics, "Communication on the potential of applied PV in the European Union: Rooftops, reservoirs, roads (R^3)", [Online]. Available: https://www.epj-pv.org/articles/epjpv/full_html/2024/01/pv230071/pv230071.html

[3] Solar Energy Materials and Solar Cells, "Development of lightweight and flexible crystalline silicon solar cell modules with PET film cover for high reliability in high temperature and humidity conditions", [Online]. Available: https://www.sciencedirect.com/science/article/pii/S0927024823003628

[4] Solar Constructions, "Flexible solar panels", [Online]. Available: https://solar-constructions.com/wordpress/flexible-solar-panel/

[5] Spreewati, "SMF430F-12X12UW", [Online]. Available: https://www.spreewatt.de/media/ac/21/4a/1686916029/SW-01-01-00008%20(12%20Jahre)%20Sunman%20eArc%20SMF430F.pdf?srsltid=AfmBOorbOI3imKOOWAukqGhxIA9peRCUH6o9kZu0CxFYrjfZ1laKcp5m

[6] Joint Research Centre European Commission, "Photovoltaic Geographical Information System (PVGIS)", [Online]. Available: https://joint-research-centre.ec.europa.eu/photovoltaic-geographical-information-system-pvgis_en

[7] Master instruments, "Sunman SMF430F-12X12UW", [Online].Available:https://www.master-instruments.com.au/products/67282/smf430f-12x12uw.html

[8] International Energy Agency, "National Survey Report of PV Power Applications in Sweden 2023", [Online]. Available:https://iea-pvps.org/wp-content/uploads/2024/09/National-Survey-Report-of-PV-Power-Applications-in-Sweden-2023.pdf

[9] Otovo, "Quanto custa instalar painéis solares?", [Online]. Available: https://www.otovo.pt/blog/sistemas-fotovoltaicos/precos-paineis-solares/

[10] International Energy Agency, "National Survey Report of PV Power Applications in France 2023", [Online].Available: https://iea-pvps.org/wp-content/uploads/2024/10/National-Survey-Report-of-PV-Power-Applications-in-FRANCE-2023v5-1.pdf

[11] Anker, "What Is the Cost of Solar System Roof in 2024 and Should You Get One?", [Online]. Available: https://www.anker.com/eu-en/blogs/balcony-power-plant-with-storage/cost-of-solar-panel-installation

[12] International Energy Agency, "National Survey Report of PV Power Applications in The Netherlands 2023",[Online].Available: https://iea-pvps.org/wp-content/uploads/2025/01/IEA-PVPS-Task-1-NSR-The-

Netherlands-2023.pdf
[13] International Energy Agency, "National Survey Report of PV Power Applications in Austria 2023", [Online].Available: https://iea-pvps.org/wp-content/uploads/2024/10/National-Survey-Report-of-PV-Power-Applications-in-Austria-2023.pdf
[14] International Energy Agency, "National Survey Report of PV Power Applications in Italy 2023", [Online].Available: https://iea-pvps.org/wp-content/uploads/2024/12/IEA-PVPS-2023-National-Survey-Report-Italy.pdf
[15] International Energy Agency, "Countries and regions",[Online].Available: https://www.iea.org/regions/europe

10.4229/EUPVSEC2025/4BV.4.22

UNIVERSITY OF ÉVORA

SOL4R

ECONOMIC ANALISYS OF BUILDING INTEGRATION OF FLEXIBLE PV MODULES

Paulo Carmo[1], José Silva[1], Luís Fialho[2], Afonso Cavaco[1], Pedro Horta[1]

[1]Renewable Energies Chair, University of Évora, Portugal

[2]Eurac Research-Institute for Renewable Energy, 39100 Bolzano, Italy

Introduction

According to European Environment Agency the minimum target for renewable energy consumption is 42.5% by 2030, in 2023 solar photovoltaics(PV) accounted for 2% of EU energy consumption a number that will increase as solar energy can have an important role in reaching this target. For that it is important to look at new PV technologies as the traditional rigid silicon PV modules that currently represent more than 90 % of the global market, thanks to their efficiency and low price, have their applications constrained by their weight and rigid nature. So other technologies such as flexible PV modules can increase the options for PV applications as their low weight and flexibility make them ideal to install low weight bearing structures as well as curved surfaces, such as buildings or vehicles [1].

Objectives

- Calculate the levelized cost of energy (LCOE) for residential and industrial building integration of rigid and flexible PV modules.
- Compare and analyse the **LCOE for the different applications and for the different countries.**

Methods

- 2 Systems: residential PV with 3 kWp and industrial PV with 300 kWp
- 2 Technologies: Rigid and flexible silicon modules.
- 10 different locations in Europe: Stockholm (Sweden), Évora (Portugal), Munich (Germany), Bordeaux (France), Vienna (Austria), Amsterdam (Netherlands), Rome (Italy), Warsaw(Poland), Athens (Greece), Dublin (Ireland).
- Determine CAPEX and OPEX for each country.
- Using PVGIS determine yearly energy production (YEP) for the 2 configurations: optimal slope and vertical (90°) mounting [2].
- Calculate LCOE and the difference between the rigid and flexible LCOE (F/R).
- $\text{LCOE} = \frac{\text{CAPEX+OPEX.lifetime}}{\text{YEP.liftime}}$ $\frac{F}{R} = \left(\frac{LCOE_F}{LCOE_R} \times 100\right) - 100$

Results

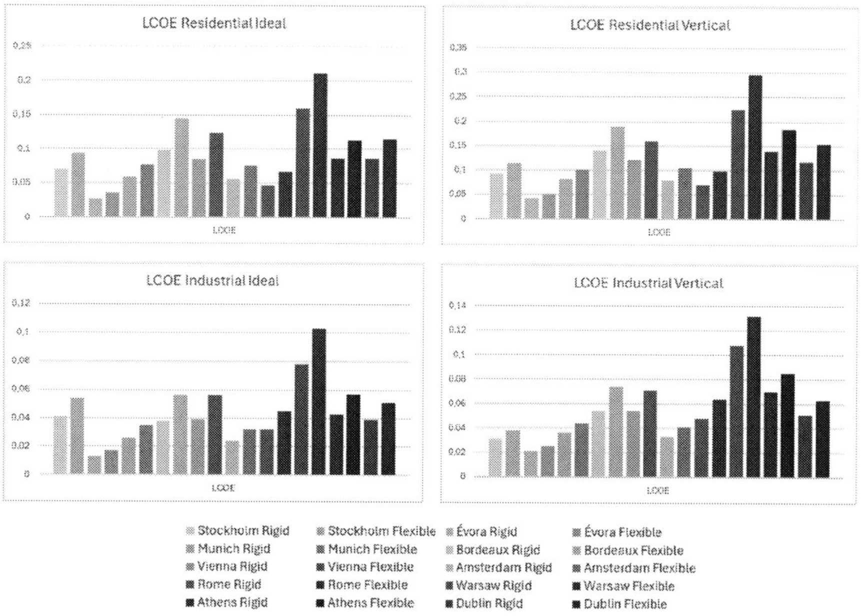

- Although having **similar solar potentials, Greece LCOE>> Portugal LCOE** due to **higher system costs.**
- **Poland** always has the **highest LCOE** which results from having the **highest CAPEX** for solar systems.
- **Portugal** as the **lowest LCOE** as a result of both **low system costs** and **high solar potential.**
- There seems to be a **strong correlation between** the **country's PV installed capacity** and the respective **LCOE**[4].
- The **most viable application** for **flexible modules** is **vertical mounting** for both residential and industrial as for most countries **F/R<25%.**
- Presently **flexible modules** are **only an attractive option** in applications **where rigid modules cannot** be used because of **weight limit or shape of the surface.**

Conclusion

In conclusion, currently this technology is only viable for use in applications where the traditional rigid silicon modules cannot be installed, as the LCOE values show how **they are not an economically viable technology to use instead of the traditional modules.**

Whoever by looking at how with the growth of the solar market for each of the countries analysed increased the cost for the rigid modules lowered over time it is possible to assume that the increase in the use of a technology will lower it cost, so it would be safe to assume that as the use of flexible modules for applications where rigid modules cannot be used increases, the price will drop making it more competitive and possibly even making it to be a viable option for installations like rooftops where the only thing keeping the rigid solar modules a better option is the significantly lower price of this technology compared to the flexible modules.

Acknowledgements

The authors would like to thank the project SOCONEXGEN for the support,

References

[1] European Environment Agency, "Share of energy consumption from renewable sources in Europe", [Online]. Available: https://www.eea.europa.eu/en/analysis/indicators/share-of-energy-consumption-from

[2] Joint Research Centre European Commission, "Photovoltaic Geographical Information System (PVGIS)", [Online]. Available: https://joint-research-centre.ec.europa.eu/photovoltaic-geographical-information-system-pvgis_en

[3] International Energy Agency, "National Survey Reports",[Online]. Available: https://iea-pvps.org/national-survey-reports/

[4] International Energy Agency, "Countries and regions",[Online]. Available: https://www.iea.org/regions/europe

CUSTOMIZABLE COLORFOIL FOR PHOTOVOLTAIC MODULES: A NEW APPROACH TO AESTHETIC AND EFFICIENT SOLAR ENERGY INTEGRATION

Ananta Paul[1,2], Jani Lamminaho[1,2], Catarina G. Ferreira[1,3], Markus Babin[4], Karlis Petersons[5], Nanna Lysgaard Andersen[4], Leif Yde[5], Jan F. Stensborg[5], Peter Behrensdorff Poulsen[4], Sune Thorsteinsson[4], Joel D. Cox[1,3,6], Morten Madsen[1,2]

[1] SDU Climate Cluster, University of Southern Denmark, Campusvej 55, 5230 Odense M, Denmark
[2] Mads Clausen Institute, Center for Advanced Photovoltaics and Thin Film Energy Devices (SDU CAPE), University of Southern Denmark, 6400 Sønderborg, Denmark
[3] POLIMA—Center for Polariton-driven Light-Matter Interactions, University of Southern Denmark, Campusvej 55, 5230 Odense M, Denmark
[4] Technical University of Denmark, Institute of Electrical and Photonics Engineering, 4000 Roskilde, Denmark
[5]Stensborg A/S, 4000 Roskilde, Denmark
[6] Danish Institute for Advanced Study, University of Southern Denmark, Campusvej 55, DK-5230 Odense M, Denmark

ABSTRACT: Integrating photovoltaic (PV) modules into building roofs and facades provides a practical route to maximize surface coverage for solar energy harvesting without expanding electrical power infrastructure. For architectural applications, PV modules must deliver high power conversion efficiency (PCE), durability, cost-effectiveness, and be visually appealing. The ability to control the color of PV modules thus emerges as a critical requirement for seamless design integration. Here we present a strategy to enhance the aesthetic integration of PV modules into building surfaces through the development of structural colored interlayers, fabricated by coating polymer foil substrates with colored thin multilayers of optimized thicknesses via Roll-to-Roll (R2R) magnetron sputtering. The proposed technology, which we designate *ColorFoil*, offers a key advantage of straightforward incorporation with commercial silicon (Si) solar cells to form colored PV modules. The results highlight a scalable and effective route for color-tunable, aesthetically integrated PV modules, offering new opportunities for widespread adoption of solar technology in architecture.
Keywords: ColorFoil, roll-to-roll sputtered system, aesthetic, diffuser, BIPV.

1 INTRODUCTION

Integrating photovoltaic (PV) modules into building surfaces such as rooftops and facades offers an effective way to expand renewable energy generation without requiring additional land use or new electrical infrastructure [1], [2]. Building-integrated photovoltaics (BIPV) not only contribute to renewable energy production but also provide opportunities to harmonize with architectural elements, which is essential for their widespread acceptance in urban environments [3], [4]. Despite their efficiency and durability, conventional PV modules are often considered visually monotonous, limiting their use in architectural applications where appearance is a critical design factor. To address this challenge, research has increasingly focused on the development of colored PV modules that achieve a balance between visual appeal and power conversion efficiency (PCE). Several strategies, including pigment-based coatings, photonic structures, and structural coloration, have been explored to enhance aesthetics with or without substantially compromising device performance [5], [6], [7]. Pigment-based coatings, while widely used, often suffer from significant performance limitations. Their color properties are highly dependent on the concentration and dispersion of pigments, which can lead to issues such as reduced optical efficiency, color fading, and limited spectral tunability. Additionally, high pigment loading can compromise the mechanical and electrical properties of the coating, making it less suitable for advanced optoelectronic applications.[8] These inherent drawbacks highlight the need for alternative approaches that can achieve vibrant, stable, and tunable colors without sacrificing performance.

To address the limitations of pigment-based coatings, structural colored elements can be introduced directly in front of the photovoltaic (PV) cell. By relying on nanoscale optical effects (such as scattering, diffraction, or interference) taking place in non-absorbing nanostructures and thin films, these elements are able to produce vivid colors while maintaining a high transmittance, which is critical for efficient light harvesting [9], [10]. Of particular interest is the use of nanometer-thin planar multilayers capable of leveraging optical interference to produce vivid colors with low optical losses, therefore outperforming the conventional absorptive pigments. By carefully controlling the configuration of the multilayer structure, this approach enables precise color tuning and the creation of customized visual appearances while preserving high transmittance within the PV cell's active spectral range, ensuring that optical performance is not compromised.

In this study, we propose a novel approach to improve the aesthetic integration of crystalline silicon (c-Si) solar cells using structural colored polymer-based interlayers, referred to as ColorFoil. These interlayers consist of color-customized thin multilayer stacks deposited on flexible polymer substrates (foils) via a scalable roll-to-roll (R2R) sputtering process, enabling cost-effective and durable fabrication. The foil design is supported by experimentally guided theoretical optimization of materials, refractive indices, and thicknesses to simultaneously ensure optical efficiency, environmental stability, and compatibility with module integration [11], [12]. We investigate two proof-of-concept foils, green and clay red, and evaluate their impact on both the optical properties and electrical performance of the resulting solar cells. Our results show that while coloration introduces some current loss (~10% for green foils and ~16% for red foils), the trade-off between aesthetics and efficiency is favorable for BIPV applications. Despite the expected current losses, we were able to keep the efficiency of the mini-modules high, clearly overperforming the use of traditional pigments.

Thus, the ColorFoil itself gives the advantages in terms of applicability over conventional color-coated glasses, where the coating process must be performed prior to the glass tempering process, limiting the flexibility to adapt to various PV module sizes and geometries often needed in BIPV applications. Along with that, this innovation lies in the ability of these foils to modify the appearance of standard Si solar cells while maintaining low current losses, thus enabling both functional and aesthetic integration of solar technologies into modern architectural environments.

2 METHODOLOGY

2.1 Interlayer requirements and design

To obtain a homogeneous, non-iridescent coloration in the PV modules, ColorFoil relies on the use of a polymer substrate containing an optical diffuser. This substrate is first coated with an acrylate-based UV-curable resin layer, which is subsequently textured using nanoimprint lithography to form an optical diffusive surface. Following this step, a multilayer stack of metal oxide thin films, specifically silicon dioxide (SiO_2 target from Polyteknik) and aluminum-doped zinc oxide (AZO: 2 wt% Al and 98 wt% ZnO from Polyteknik), is conformally deposited on the textured diffuser using large-scale Roll-to-Roll (R2R) sputter deposition.

2.2 Characterization

Optical properties of the colored multilayers are characterized through UV–visible transmittance and reflectance measurements in ambient atmosphere with a PVE300 photovoltaic quantum-efficiency system (Bentham). Current–voltage characteristics are measured for both raw contacted cells and laminated mini-modules using a Newport steady-state solar simulator as the illumination source, and a Keithley 2651A source measurement unit configured as a four-quadrant load. All I-V measurements are carried out under standard test conditions.

3 RESULTS

The schematic cross-section of the PV module structure incorporating our ColorFoil technology is shown in **Fig. 1.** The proposed design features structural colored interlayers, consisting of a thin multilayer element deposited on a flexible polymer diffuser foil (marked in red line), positioned between the front substrate and the Si PV cell.

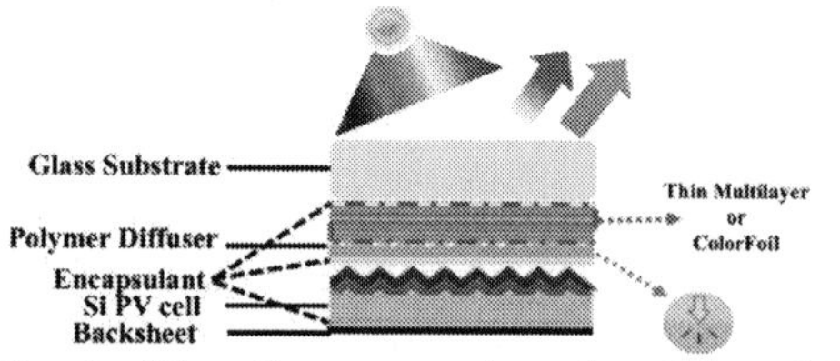

Fig. 1. Schematic representation of a PV module incorporating a ColorFoil interlayer.

ColorFoil design relies on the precise calculation of the optical properties of nanometer-thin multilayers made up of non-absorbing materials presenting high durability and compatibility with large-scale R2R deposition, which are embedded onto the PV laminate to form the colored PV module.[12] To determine the non-periodic individual layer thicknesses leading to the realization of specific hues, an optimization-based inverse design approach is employed, following its recently demonstrated success to identify thin multilayer structures providing user-defined colors [11], [12], [13], [14]. Here we fabricate two different ColorFoil configurations, with green and clay red coloration, which we later incorporate in front of commercial Si mini-module (see **Fig. 1**) to form colored PV mini-modules that serve as proof-of-concept for our proposed technology.

In **Fig. 2** we show a photo of the realized green and clay red ColorFoil, experimentally fabricated via Roll-to-Roll (R2R) sputtering. The dimensions of the deposited ColorFoil are 30 by 10 cm^2. A black background is placed beneath the foils to enhance contrast, clearly demonstrating their uniform coloration properties in addition to their high optical transparency.

Fig. 2 Photograph of the experimentally developed green and clay red ColorFoil.

The transmittance (T%) and reflectance (R%) spectra of the green and clay red ColorFoil are shown in **Fig. 3a**. The green ColorFoil exhibits a central reflectance maximum at ~570 nm, whereas the clay red ColorFoil shows its maximum at ~741 nm, in agreement with the design requirements for such colored elements. Outside their respective reflectance bands, both foils remain highly transparent, with the green ColorFoil transmitting >85% and the clay red ColorFoil transmitting >80% of incident light, demonstrating their suitability for integration in photovoltaic devices. Although both samples display absorption features in the 300–380 nm region, attributed to the band-edge absorption of the AZO layer,[15] we do not expect those to strongly influence the PV performance, as the photon flux from the sun is very low in this wavelength range. **Fig. 3b** shows the reflectance spectra of the green ColorFoil measured at different locations to evaluate the uniformity of the foil. The results indicate that the variation in the reflectance is minimal, with spectral

10.4229/EUPVSEC2025/4BV.4.23

peak position values ranging only from 560 nm to 584 nm, which confirms the high optical uniformity of the foil. Such uniformity highlights the quality and effectiveness of the Roll-to-Roll sputter deposition used, which is a reliable technique for producing large-area foils with consistent optical properties.

(a)

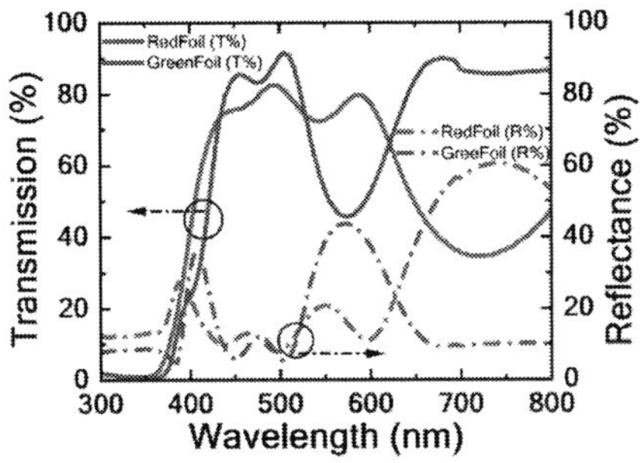

(b)

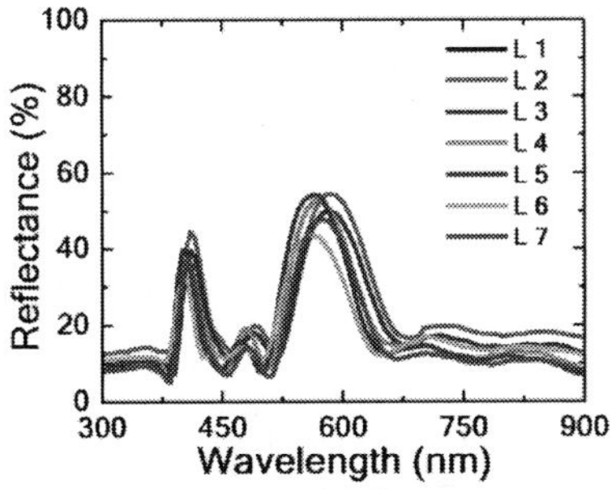

Fig. 3 (a) Transmittance and reflectance spectra of the experimentally fabricated green and clay red ColorFoil. (b) Reflectance spectra of the green ColorFoil at various locations (L1 to L7) are recorded to evaluate its high optical uniformity.

Fig. 4 presents the photograph of the experimentally fabricated reference Si mini-module alongside the mini-modules incorporating ColorFoil in green and clay red, clearly demonstrating the appealing optical characteristics of the modules with ColorFoil included.

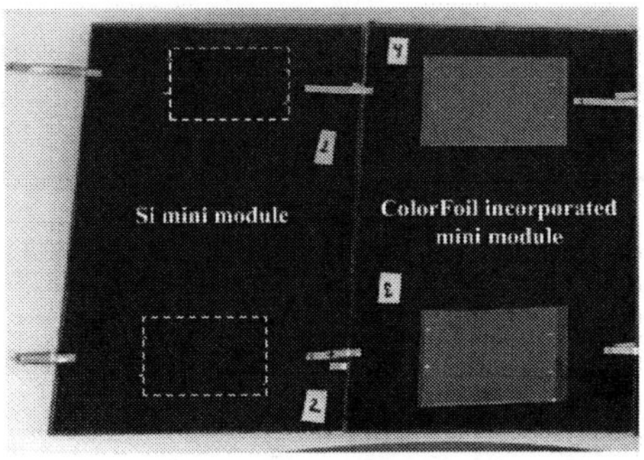

Fig 4. Photograph of the experimentally fabricated reference Si mini-module alongside the green and clay red ColorFoil-incorporated mini-modules.

In particular, the introduction of ColorFoil leads to a small reduction in light absorption in the active layer, which manifests as a loss in short-circuit current density. A direct comparison with the reference module confirms that, while ColorFoil enhances the visual appeal of the devices, they inevitably introduce a trade-off by compromising photocurrent generation and overall photovoltaic performance slightly. Despite the incorporation of coloration, the fabricated mini-modules exhibit remarkably good photovoltaic performance, as evidenced by the current–voltage ($I - V$) and external quantum efficiency (EQE) measurements shown in **Fig. 5** (a) and **Fig. 5** (b), respectively. The green and clay red mini-modules retain more than 86% and 82% of the photovoltaic performance relative to the reference c-Si mini-module of identical area without any coloring interlayer. Notably, the introduction of the colored interlayer does not affect the open-circuit voltage (V_{OC}) of the devices; however, it leads to a reduction in short-circuit current density (I_{SC}) of approximately 13% and 16%, for the green and clay red mini-modules, respectively. The $I - V$ parameters of reference Si, clay red and green mini-modules are summarized in **Table 1**. The observed I_{SC} reduction originates primarily from the expected optical coloration losses, reflected in the EQE dips around 550 nm and 695 nm (Fig. 5b). Additionally, parasitic absorption in the AZO layers of the colored stack further contributes to performance losses, as evidenced by a drop in EQE at wavelengths below 400 nm [15].

(a)

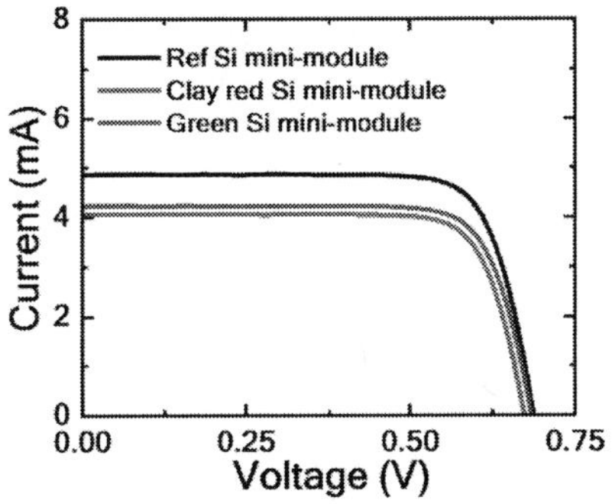

(b)

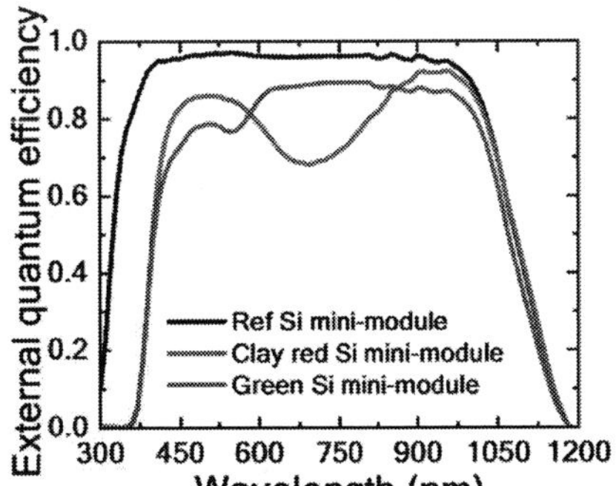

Fig. 5. (a) Current-voltage characteristics of the bare Si mini-module (black curves), green and clay red colored mini-module (olive green and red curve, respectively), including the corresponding photovoltaic parameters. (b) External quantum efficiency spectra of the green and clay red mini-module (olive green and red curve) in

comparison to the reference dark mini-module (black curve).

Table 1: $I - V$ parameters (i.e. short circuit current (I_{SC}), open circuit voltage (V_{OC}) and maximum power (P_{MPP})) of the ref Si, clay red and green mini-module.

$I - V$ Parameters	Ref Si mini-module	Clay red Si mini-module	Green Si mini-module
I_{SC} (mA)	4.87	4.07	4.23
V_{OC} (V)	0.70	0.70	0.70
P_{MPP} (mW)	2.61	2.15	2.26

Overall, the loss analysis of the reference Si, clay red and green mini-module are shown in **Fig. 6**. The loss analysis reveals that the green and clay red Si mini-module exhibited losses of ~10% and 16% compared to the reference Si mini-module (reference Si mini-module loss~ 5%).

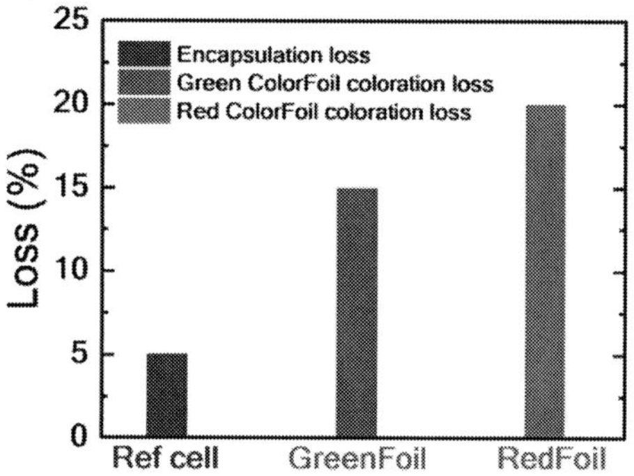

Fig. 6 presents the loss analysis of the Si solar cell before and after the introduction of ColorFoil (green and clay red).

The colored PV mini-modules incorporating ColorFoil interlayers exhibit excellent optical uniformity, stable reflectance properties, and strong compatibility with large-area Roll-to-Roll (R2R) processing. These attributes position them as a highly promising technology for photovoltaic and optoelectronic applications. Beyond solar cell integration, ColorFoil also hold potential in decorative energy-harvesting surfaces, building-integrated photovoltaics (BIPV), and consumer electronics where both aesthetics and functionality are essential. The potential applications of ColorFoil in building-integrated photovoltaics are highlighted in **Fig. 7**. For instance, the clay red ColorFoil matches well with the tiles characteristic of Danish architecture (left image), which can be replaced by colored PV modules incorporating ColorFoil technology to generate electricity while maintaining the aesthetic appearance of the building. In addition, we demonstrate the optical output and visual integration of the green ColorFoil into a model house (right image).

Fig. 7. Potential applications of ColorFoil in building-integrated photovoltaics.

4 CONCLUSIONS

This study presents a novel technology, which relies on polymer-based colored interlayers – ColorFoil – to achieve homogeneous structural coloration in PV modules with low optical losses. We demonstrate, as proof of concept, the fabrication of a green and a clay red ColorFoil, using a large-scale Roll-to-Roll (R2R) sputtering system. As we observed, the color of the resulting foils successfully matched the desired one, resulting from the excellent control of the spectral position of the reflectance peaks. This was achieved while maintaining the transparency outside the reflectance bands high: for the green ColorFoil transmittance reached 85% while for the clay-red ColorFoil, transmittance values as high as 80% were achieved. By applying our ColorFoil technology to commercial Si cells, we successfully assembled colored PV mini-modules, which shown relatively low performance penalty: modules made from the green ColorFoil showed ~10% relative I_{sc} loss, while the modules fabricated from the clay-red ColorFoil exhibited ~16% relative I_{sc} loss, when compared to a reference module where the Si cell was subjected to standard lamination procedure. These results demonstrate an effective balance between visual aesthetics and energy efficiency, and pave the way for the use of ColorFoil technology in colored PV devices. This approach enables seamless architectural integration of photovoltaic modules, promoting broader adoption of solar energy in modern building designs.

5 ACKNOWLEDGEMENTS

This work was funded by EUDP as part of the "ColorFoil" project under grant 64022-1027

7 REFERENCES

[1] M. Victoria *et al.*, "Solar photovoltaics is ready to power a sustainable future," May 19, 2021, *Cell Press*. doi: 10.1016/j.joule.2021.03.005.
[2] D. Gielen *et al.*, "The role of renewable energy in the global energy transformation," *Energy Strategy Reviews*, vol. 24, pp. 38–50, Apr. 2019, doi: 10.1016/j.esr.2019.01.006.
[3] J. M. Kiesecker *et al.*, "Land use and Europe's renewable energy transition: identifying low-conflict areas for wind and solar development," *Front Environ Sci*, vol. 12, 2024, doi: 10.3389/fenvs.2024.1355508.

[4] K. K. Shin Thant *et al.*, "Comprehensive Review on Slot-Die-Based Perovskite Photovoltaics: Mechanisms, Materials, Methods, and Marketability," Feb. 04, 2025, *John Wiley and Sons Inc.* doi: 10.1002/aenm.202403088.

[5] H. Lee *et al.*, "Current status and perspective of colored photovoltaic modules," Nov. 01, 2021, *John Wiley and Sons Ltd.* doi: 10.1002/wene.403.

[6] M. K. Basher *et al.*, "Design, Development, and Characterization of Highly Efficient Colored Photovoltaic Module for Sustainable Buildings Applications," *Sustainability (Switzerland)*, vol. 14, no. 7, Apr. 2022, doi: 10.3390/su14074278.

[7] M. Victoria *et al.*, "Solar photovoltaics is ready to power a sustainable future," May 19, 2021, *Cell Press.* doi: 10.1016/j.joule.2021.03.005.

[8] B. Sarkodie *et al.*, "Characteristics of pigments, modification, and their functionalities," Jun. 01, 2019, *John Wiley and Sons Inc.* doi: 10.1002/col.22359.

[9] S. Daqiqeh Rezaei *et al.*, "Nanophotonic Structural Colors," Jan. 20, 2021, *American Chemical Society.* doi: 10.1021/acsphotonics.0c00947.

[10] S. Kinoshita *et al.*, "Physics of structural colors," *Reports on Progress in Physics*, vol. 71, no. 7, Jul. 2008, doi: 10.1088/0034-4885/71/7/076401.

[11] C. G. Ferreira *et al.*, "Design and optimization of structural colored interlayers for building-integrated photovoltaic applications", doi: 10.4229/EUPVSEC2024/4BV.4.6.

[12] M. Babin *et al.*, "Reliability investigation of structural colour interlayers for coloured pv modules", doi: 10.4229/EUPVSEC2024/3AV.2.21.

[13] C. G. Ferreira *et al.*, "Optical Design of Structural Colored Photovoltaics for Building Integration: From Periodic Configurations to Optimization Algorithms," *Nano Energy*, 2025(preprint).

[14] C. G. Ferreira *et al.*, "Structural colored planar multilayers with minimal angular color dependence for building integrated photovoltaics," *Solar RRL*, 2025 (preprint).

[15] L. G. Daza *et al.*, "Understanding the Variations of Optical Bandgap in AZO Nanostructured Thin Films: Analysis of Possible Influences," *Physica Status Solidi (A) Applications and Materials Science*, vol. 222, no. 9, May 2025, doi: 10.1002/pssa.202400763.

PERFORMANCE, OPERATIONAL DATA AND STABILITY OF COMMERCIAL CIGS THIN-FILM PV MODULES IN BIPV SYSTEMS

Stefan Grünsteidl, Peter Borowski, Thomas Dalibor
AVANCIS GmbH, Otto-Hahn-Ring 6, 81739 München, Germany
Phone: +49(0) 89 219620 458, Email: stefan.gruensteidl@avancis.de

ABSTRACT: This work presents long-term operational data of CIGS-based PV systems across varying levels of integration and environmental exposure. Environmental data including module temperatures, air flow, surface moisture, and relative humidity of building integrated PV installations are shown. Different module orientations in the context of the usage of module optimizers were analysed. Performance evaluations of commercial and R&D systems confirm the long-term stability of CIGS PV modules with no or minimal degradation observed over more than a decade, including the latest generation of CIGS PV modules featuring gallium-rich absorbers, sodium post deposition treatment, and a dry ZnOS buffer.

Keywords: outdoor, performance, temperature, irradiance, yield, degradation, BIPV, CIGS, optimizers, orientations, environmental, wind flow, surface moisture, humidity

1 INTRODUCTION

Building-integrated photovoltaic (BIPV) installations are generally different to most common PV installations in terms of irradiance levels, shadowing conditions and operational temperatures. Realistic monitoring data sets are essential for yield assessments, predictive simulation, and degradation analyses.

Yet, extensive analyses on the operational data of running BIPV installations are still limited (see [1] for a notable exception). In this work, long-term operational data of CIGS BIPV systems with different building integration level are analysed, including systems featuring the latest generation of CIGS module development with gallium-rich absorbers, sodium post deposition treatment and a dry, sputtered ZnOS buffer.

The PV systems considered in the present article all consist of thin-film PV modules by the manufacturer AVANCIS and were produced in its factory in Torgau, Germany, under the product name PowerMax or SKALA (the latter one specifically for BIPV). The photovoltaic semi-conductive layer is based on a CIGS absorber, a material containing copper, indium, gallium, sulphur and selenium. Both the detailed composition of this absorber layer as well as the nature and properties of other layers in the stack can be varied leading to evolving generations of CIGS PV module technology, of which particularly the most recent one is considered in this work. The appearance of the PV module, particularly its colour, can differ from the standard black by varying the front glass [2].

The frameless module design (**Figure 1**) consists of two glasses in a laminate with a thickness of about 6 mm. Mounting of module is accomplished by two steel backrails glued to the backside of the glass-glass laminate. Laminate, backrail and glue beads between both lead to a total dimension of 38 mm perpendicular to the glass surface and a total weight of about 17 kg. Using specific metallic clamps, the backrails are mounted on four points to a conventional substructure, whose width together with the extension of the backrail typically define the minimum air gap between the rear glass of the PV module and the outer building wall in a BIPV facade system.

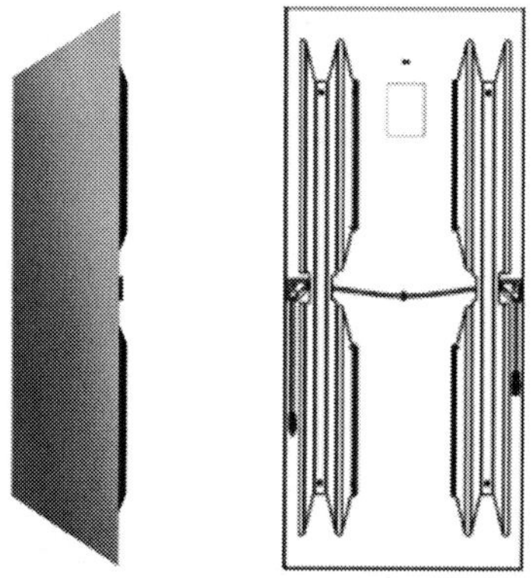

Figure 1: AVANCIS SKALA in standard size (dimensions 1587 × 664 × 38 mm^3) in its variety 7003 (blue) and a technical drawing of its rear side showing the two steel backrails for mounting.

Electrical yield and long-term performance of three vertically installed PV systems is presented in section 2 of the present paper. Two of these systems are typical BIPV systems. Section 3 presents monitoring data relevant for building physics for three systems, such as module temperature, air speed and relative humidity between vertically installed PV modules and the building wall. In section 4, we return to energy yield, focussing on long-term stability of yield and CIGS PV modules both from operational PV systems and a R&D test bench, with some data dating back 15 years.

10.4229/EUPVSEC2025/4BV.4.24

2 VERTICALLY INSTALLED PV SYSTEMS, PERFORMANCE DATA

The performance of three PV installations with vertically installed AVANCIS CIGS modules is shown in this section. An overview of the installations is given in **Figure 2**. Compared to yield-optimised inclined PV systems, vertically installed PV modules receive lower values of irradiance and therefore operate at low light conditions more often. Particularly for highly integrated BIPV systems, lower values for the performance ratio (PR) are to be expected in general. In the following, we show data for AC yield and PR, with the exception of the cube Torgau and the individual modules in section 4, for which DC values were evaluated.

PV installation: Cube Torgau (DE)	BIPV house: Mokropsy (CZ)	BIPV installation: Eichstätt (DE)

Vertical solar installation along all cardinal directions with module optimizers and irradiance sensors	Residential home with BIPV modules facing 3 different directions (SSE, SW, SE)	BIPV system on a south-facing facade with restricted ventilation behind the modules

Figure 2: Vertical PV systems with AVANCIS CIGS thin-film PV modules SKALA evaluated for performance data, operational in Germany and Czech Republic.

2.1 PV installation: Cube Torgau (DE)

The first vertical installation with AVANCIS CIGS modules shown in **Figure 2** was already introduced in [3] with solely irradiance data comparisons shown. Modules are installed in such a way on an open steel structure that the same number of modules is pointing into each of the four cardinal directions. Pairs of modules are connected to DC/DC power optimizers, which are connected in series to an inverter. Irradiance and module temperature are recorded with a data acquisition period of 15 minutes. In the following, performance data of the plant over several years are shown and compared to irradiance data over the seasons.

In this case, only DC yield of the optimizers can be analysed for the individual module planes as all optimizers form one electrical string. The results are shown in **Figure 3**. While the performance has been generally stable over the years, there are some general performance differences visible between the sides of the cubes, and some performance dips present for the western and northern directions towards the winter months.

The southern and eastern DC performance ratio lies at about 90%. The west-facing modules almost reach this level but show a lot less performance with low sun angles towards the winter months due to an adjacent building, which affects the modules stronger in comparison to the irradiance sensor. The performance dips of the north-facing modules have a different reason though, as these are quasi not influenced by shadowing. The overall lower performance level seems to originate firstly from low light losses of the PV modules, as the low light condition is the dominating condition for a north-facing PV installation in the northern hemisphere. Secondly, the DC/DC power optimizers, to which the modules facing North are connected, work mostly in the low power regime in comparison with the other facade sides. As 405 W optimizers were used for the nominal 260 Wp of a pair of modules, high conversion losses are expected for the north-facing system, specifically for the timeframes when a lot of current adaptation between optimizers must be done (sun on other module directions).

So even without the winter months, the performance ratio of the north-facing modules is more than 12 percentage points lower in comparison. For the whole timeframe evaluated, the PR for the north-facing part is at 72%, about 18 percentage points lower than for the other cardinal directions.

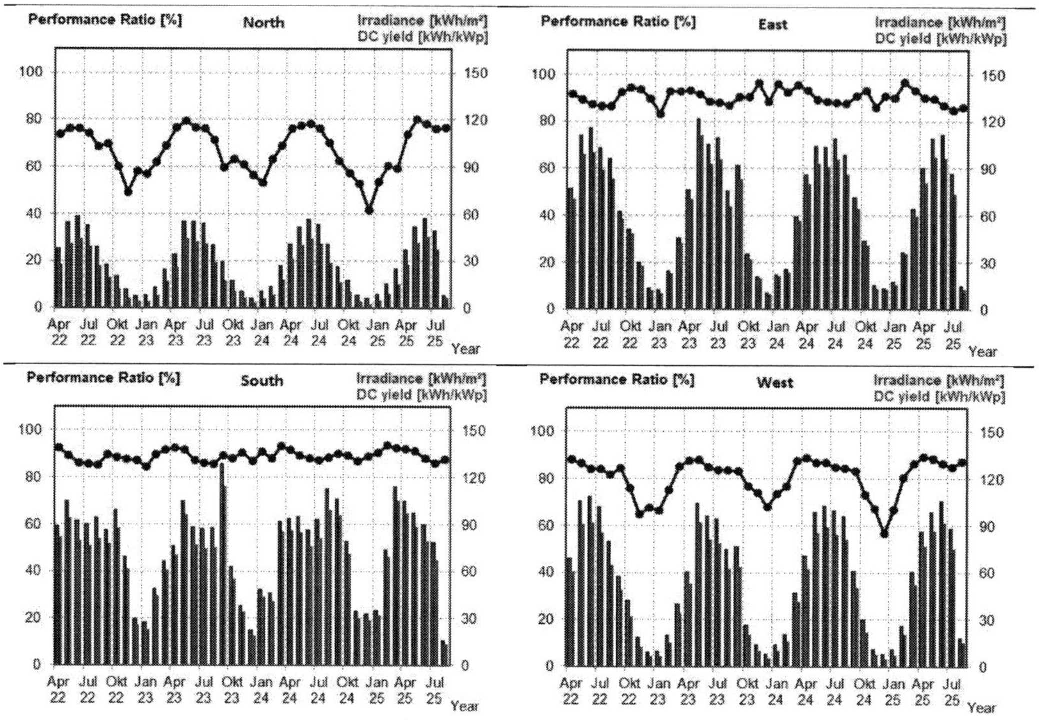

Figure 3: DC performance data of the vertical PV installation in Torgau (DE) for the individual cardinal directions. Since modules facing different directions are mixed within the strings, only the DC yield of the DC/DC power optimizers can be evaluated for the individual sides of the system. Shown is the monthly irradiance and DC yield (bars), as well as the monthly performance ratios (points and line).

2.2 BIPV house: Mokropsy (CZ)

Also the second vertical installation shown in **Figure 2** was introduced in [3]. The site consists of three BIPV facades, fully equipped with an optimizer system with two to five AVANCIS CIGS PV modules connected in parallel to a single DC/DC power optimizer. The electrical DC and AC data is monitored every 15 minutes with a commercial system. The sensor data is recorded every 5 minutes.

The site uses 4 miniature silicon pyranometers type ML 02 by EKO for the measurement of irradiance into the horizontal and three vertical modules' planes. The miniature sensors were chosen because only those were integrable into the residential building without any negative visual impact. When comparing data for the southern (SSE) façade, it was possible to quantify shading events, such as vegetation growth in summertime which diminishes the power by 10% to 15% for some optimizers, as shown in **Figure 4**. The other façade sides (SW/SE) were not influenced by plant growth to that extend and could not be analysed for AC performance ratio changes to that extend as SW/SE were both connected to the same inverter unit.

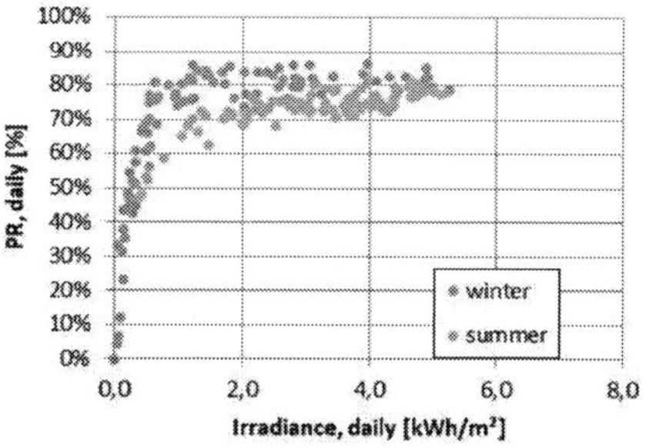

Figure 4: Seasonal performance data of the BIPV system Mokropsy (CZ), SSE facade, for the months July to September (summer), and October to December (winter) 2023/24.

Since the optimizers of the SE and SW facades are connected within one string to the same inverter, and the SSE inverter only reached full grid connectivity in summer 2023, the gathered data up to this point is still limited. Therefore, evaluations of the long- term performance have not been performed yet.

2.3 BIPV installation: Eichstätt (DE)

The BIPV system in Eichstätt (DE) is a commercial PV system on the southern facade of an indoor climbing gym that went into operation in late 2017. The plant shows good and reliable performance since then, as shown in **Figure 5**. The performance ratio is about 80%, despite partial shading by façade cover, inverter limitation, and high module temperatures due to limited ventilation. With more than 7 years in operation, this system is among the longest running monitored commercial BIPV systems with CIGS PV modules and its performance data has been reported earlier together with externally monitored data of a long-running free-field PV system, showing stable operation of AVANCIS CIGS PV modules for 10 years [4].

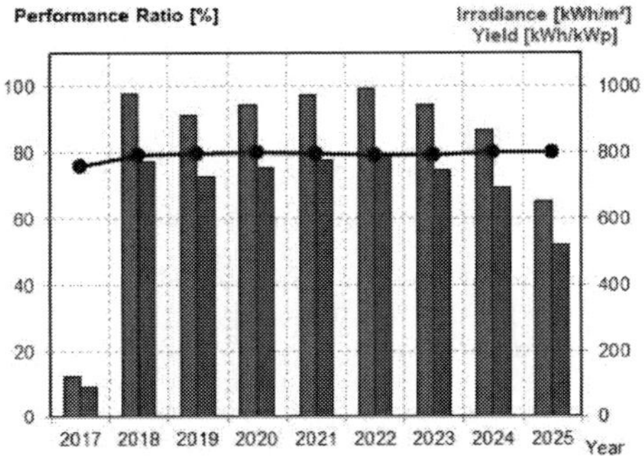

Figure 5: Performance data of the BIPV system in Eichstätt (DE): Yearly irradiance and yield (bars) and yearly PR (points and line). Lower values in 2017 and 2025 derive from the system not being operational during the whole year.

3 SENSOR DATA FROM BIPV SYSTEMS

Since a BIPV system by definition [5][6] fulfils an integral role for the building in which it is installed, other physical quantities than just electrical energy yield come into focus. Both the influence of the PV modules on the building as well as the operational conditions of the PV modules when installed in a non-conventional manner are of interest. To collect data for some of these quantities, we have equipped two commercial BIPV systems with additional sensors for building physics data and built a PV facade particularly for this purpose. In this section, data acquired for module temperature, air speed close to and behind a ventilated PV facade and data on moisture will be presented. Sensors are installed in the systems Mokropsy (CZ) and Eichstätt (DE) as introduced above, as well as a vertical PV installation in Torgau (DE) as shown in **Figure 6**. Following the definition of BIPV, the latter PV system constitutes a building-attached system, rather than being building-integrated.

Figure 6: Vertical PV installation on a south-west-facing building facade with advanced sensor system in Torgau (DE). Sensors for ambient air, wind speed and direction, rain and irradiance can be seen to the right of the PV modules.

3.1 Module temperatures

All module temperature sensors used in this study were PT1000 sensors, encapsulated with temperature conductive fluids into an aluminium housing and glued to the module glass backsides with durable double-sided adhesive tape. The data acquisition systems used were self-made (Mokropsy) and commercially available (Torgau, Eichstätt) systems using reference resistors for resistance measurements and a time resolution of 1 minute (Torgau) and 5 minutes (Mokropsy, Eichstätt).

As adhesive tapes can detach over time, monthly maximum values for each installation were checked over time for signs of detachment, which would show up as a drop in the highest temperature readings. This was only observed for the installation in Torgau, so the data set was reduced down to the initial year, and the final two years during which sensors were reattached. Also, for the system in Torgau, only one of the two sensors showed reliable results. For the installation in Mokropsy, PV modules face three different directions with three different sets of sensors installed. Irradiance was measured using silicon sensors, with the exception of the facade in Torgau having a pyranometer instead.

In summary, there were 2547291, 345501 and 172850 useable data sets for the sites Torgau, Mokropsy and Eichstätt, respectively. The data sets Torgau included the years 2018-2019 and 2022-2024, with two different sets of modules installed in these time frames (black and coloured). The site Mokropsy could only be evaluated between July 2023 and August 2025, while the site Eichstätt has fully useable data sets from October 2017 until August 2025.

All three installations shown in this section have a very different ventilation situation. While the façade in Torgau has a large air gap of about 25cm behind the modules, the gap behind the rear glass of the PV modules in Mokropsy and the building wall is only about 9cm. The modules in Eichstätt were directly mounted on covered wooden beams, which left only a small air gap of around 3cm and in addition stronger encapsulation towards the sides of the module field. For reasons of design, the module field is framed on all sides by cladding material, even slightly covering the modules in the West. Therefore, convection for the Eichstätt installation was reduced to a minimum, with gaps between the modules of 1.0-1.4cm (horizontally and vertically, respectively). The difference in ventilation can be seen in the results in **Figure 7**.

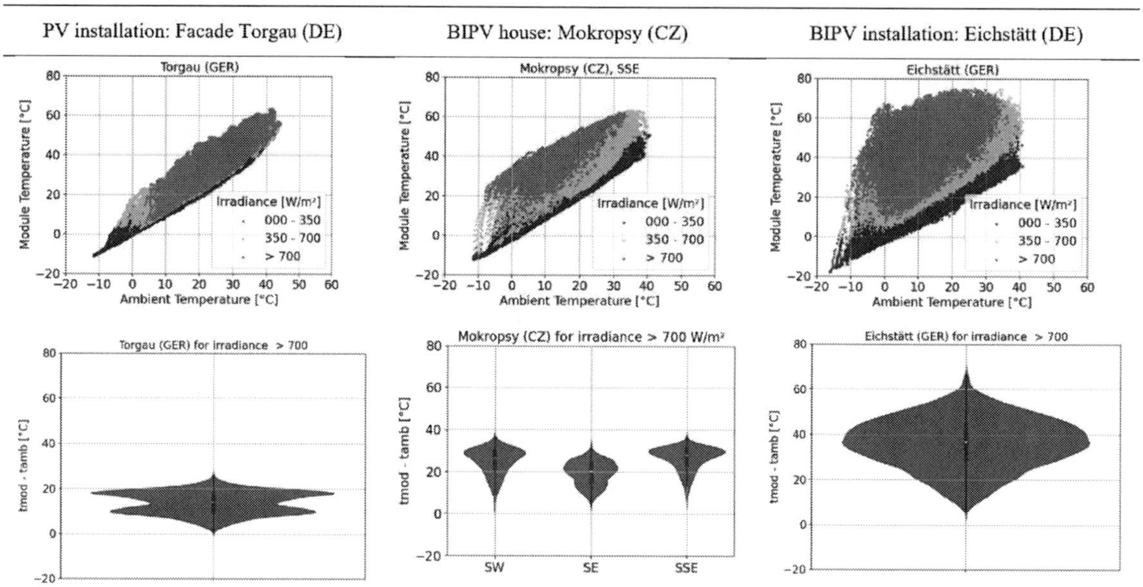

Figure 7: Module temperatures (as measured on the rear side of the PV modules) in comparison to ambient temperatures for the three vertical PV installations during operation. Top row: Module temperatures over ambient temperatures for three levels of irradiance. Bottom row: Frequency distribution of the difference between module temperature (tmod) and ambient temperature (tamb) for irradiance levels above 700 W/m².

Following the expectation [7], the PV modules installed with a large air gap and no restriction to the air flow below and above the PV installation showed the lowest temperature levels above ambient temperatures. In contrast, the PV modules in Eichstätt with the minimal air gap and air flow strongly restricted by the framing of the building envelope become much warmer. Module temperatures during operation in this non-ideal case can reach up to 70°C above ambient temperatures, but no module temperature above 80°C was observed. On average and for regular facade installations with CIGS PV modules, the module temperatures are between 20°C and 30°C above ambient temperature for high irradiance levels and during full operation of the PV façade installation. Compared to an optimally inclined free-field PV installation, ventilation and therefore cooling of the PV modules is often strongly reduced in a BIPV system and module temperatures are higher in the latter. However, since irradiance for vertical installations is strongly reduced compared to typical inclined rooftop systems, module temperatures in both cases can be comparable [1].

3.2 Air flow

Air flow sensors were installed for the facade installation in Torgau, with one being an environmental sensor including wind speed and wind direction, and two being sensors for monitoring wind speed and temperature behind the facade, each installed behind the portrait and landscape mounted modules (see **Figure 8**). The air flow sensor for the portrait mounted modules was located about 1m from the northern edge of the module field. The air flow sensor for the landscape mounted modules was located about 2m from the southern end of the module field, with both sensors being on a similar level above ground.

The data acquisition for all sensors was within the same system, which was well synchronized and with a time resolution of 1 minute. As one of the two sensors broke in July 2019, only 12 months of data were available, with a total of 697662 timestamps.

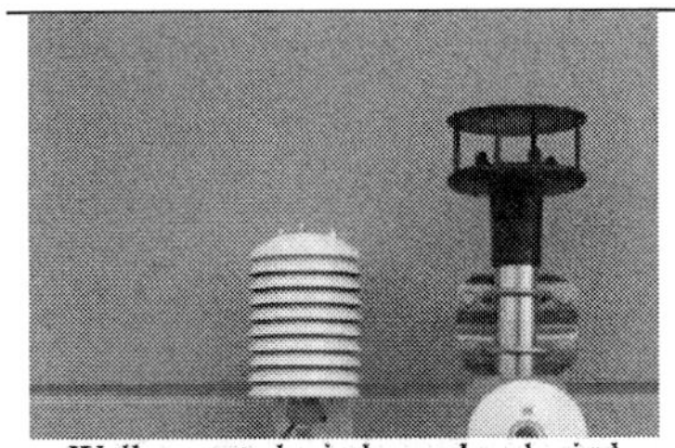

Wall mounted wind speed and wind direction sensor (Windsonic GILL), placed to the right of the PV modules. In the image the ambient temperature / relative humidity sensor (left – CS215 SDI-12) and pyranometer (bottom right – K&Z CMP3) are shown, as well.

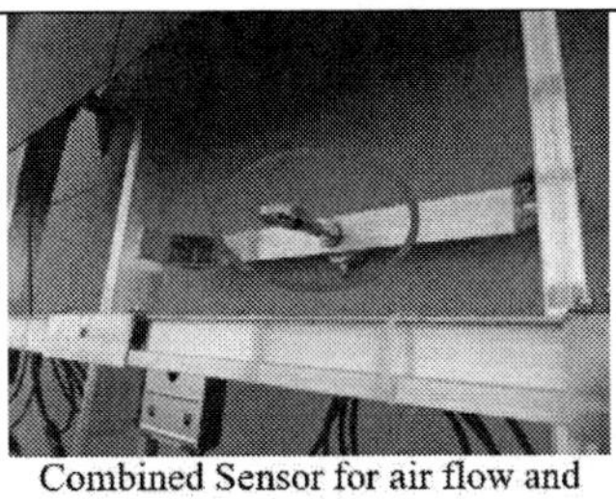

Combined Sensor for air flow and temperature (Schmidt SS 20.500 with guard bracket), behind portrait mounted modules (modules taken off the substructure for this image).

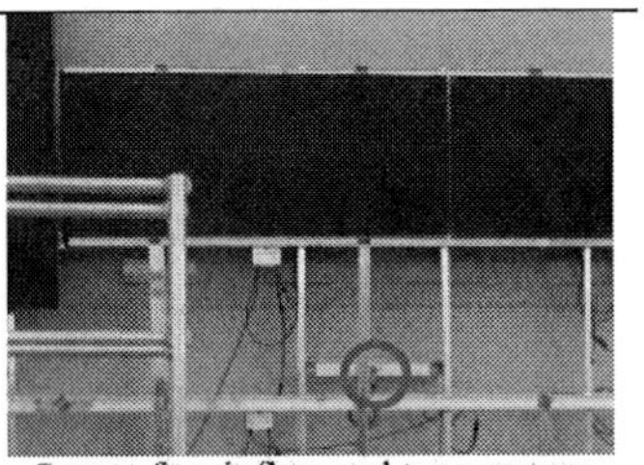

Sensor for air flow and temperature behind landscape mounted modules (modules taken off substructure for this image).

Figure 8: Wind and air flow sensors installed for the site Torgau.

The results of the air flow evaluations are shown in **Figure 9**. Generally, the wind directions for the façade installation follow the façade walls towards North-West and South-East, as this is a south-western facing façade. The dominant western winds of the northern hemisphere result in the largest wind portion of south-eastern directions.

Further, high wind speeds at the façade do not necessarily affect the air flow velocity behind the façade. The diagrams show that the highest air velocities behind the modules were reached for moderate wind speeds. Generally, the air velocity behind the modules is higher for the portrait mounted modules, as compared to the modules mounted in landscape orientation. The average difference between the two sensors (mounted between the modules in portrait and in landscape) for the complete time interval was 0.1 m/s. This could be attributed to the direction of the modules' backrails, as these are aligned along the long module side and thus could generate more air disturbances for the landscape mounted modules. It is also probable that the stronger enclosure of the landscape air flow sensor towards the sides leads to lower flow speeds behind the modules. The strength of air flow in the air gap behind the curtain wall made of PV modules depend in a complex manner on the details of the installation (obstruction), wind speed and direction outside, irradiance onto the PV modules and others. For the system considered, with a comparably large air gap of 25cm, the average air flow speed behind the facade modules is about 0.5 m/s.

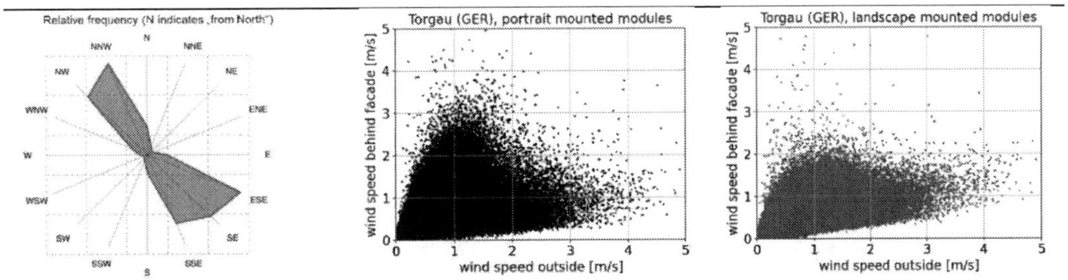

Figure 9: Measurement data of the wind and air flow sensors installed for the site Torgau. Left: Distribution of wind direction as measured by the wall-mounted wind sensor. Middle and Right: Air speed as measured by the sensors installed in the air gap behind the PV modules vs. wind speed outside the PV system.

10.4229/EUPVSEC2025/4BV.4.24

3.3 Surface moisture and dew

Due to the open construction of a curtain wall, rain, particularly wind-driven rain, can find its way to the rear side of the facade elements and accumulate, e.g., in hollows or recesses of the PV module or mounting structure. Also, since one advantage of a curtain wall is to keep moisture and particularly dew away from the building wall, the colder, inner surface of the facade PV modules are prone to dew and condensation during nighttime. Some of the components of a curtain wall or BIPV facade might be sensitive to prolonged exposure to water. To assess this effect quantitatively we measured the time during which water was present at certain positions of the rear side of the PV modules in the facade installation Torgau.

The backrails of the AVANCIS CIGS modules form a horizontally oriented pocket, when the module is mounted in landscape orientation. A total amount of eight self-made pairs of electrodes was glued onto the non-conductive part of the backrail glue bead of these pockets for resistance measurements over a time span of 11 months (Jul/28/18 – Jun/18/19). The sensors show low resistances if water is present in the pockets, and high resistances when it dries off. The placement, setup and sensor reactions after a rain event are shown in **Figure 10**.

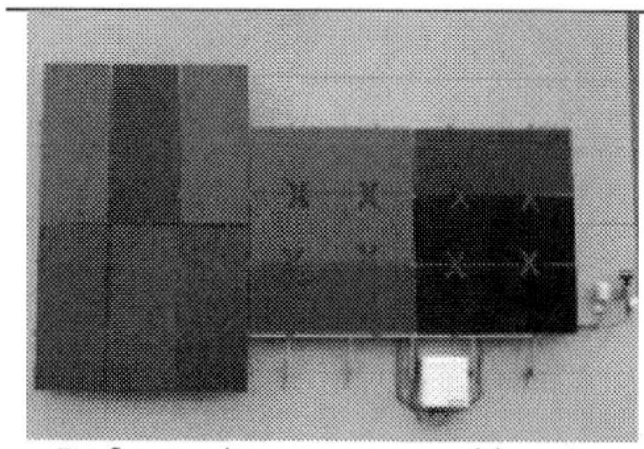

Surface moisture sensor positions (on the rear side of the PV modules) for the modules installed in landscape orientation for the system in Torgau.

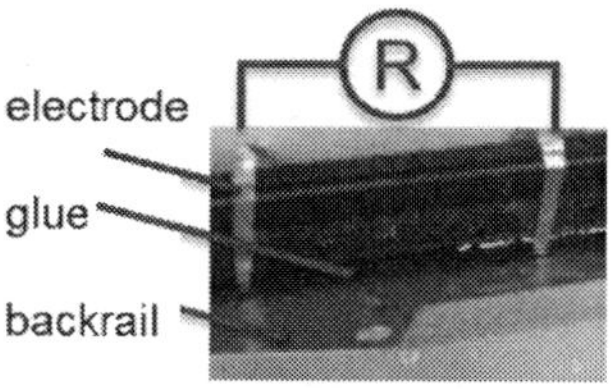

Outline of the setup, showing two metal electrodes attached to the rear glass and touching the glue bead that holds the backrail to the rear glass. Electrical resistance is measured between the two electrodes.

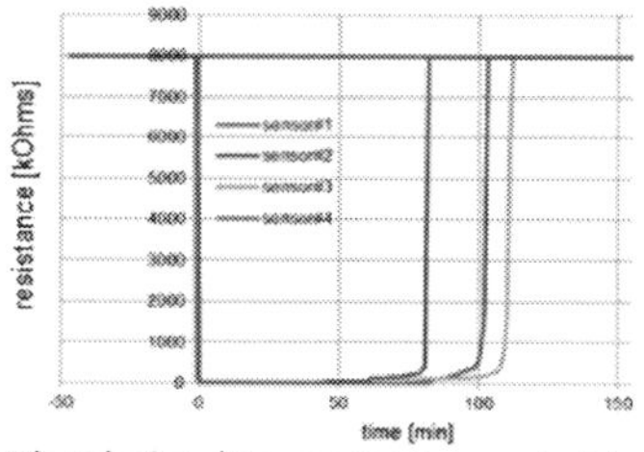

Electrical resistance measurement of 4 sensors after a rain event (at time 0). Resistance strongly decreases due to the presence of water in the "pocket" but returns to high values after the water has dried off within about 100 minutes.

Figure 10: Setup and exemplary data of surface moisture measurements on modules' backrails after a rain event.

On average, moisture was detected for less than 10% of the total time, with the longest duration of almost 4 days for one sensor. The maximum duration for each sensor measured is shown in Table I.

sensor#1	sensor#2	sensor#3	sensor#4	sensor#5	sensor#6	sensor#7	sensor#8
0d 18:36	2d 08:56	3d 19:04	2d 08:08	2d 02:17	1d 09:12	1d 19:11	2d 09:29

Table I: Longest duration of surface moisture being detected for the 8 installed sensors over a time period of 11 months.

3.4 Relative humidity

Curtain walls are meant to keep moisture away from the actual building wall [8] by providing an air gap (minimum 20mm [9]) for ventilation. BIPV facade installations can act as a curtain wall and by that influence the building envelope [10]. The drying potential and moisture transport are important parameter for architects and building constructors. Yet there is only limited data of humidity measurements behind BIPV modules.

For the facade installation in Mokropsy, complete data sets of temperature, humidity and irradiance have been recorded for all three module surfaces. Sensors for temperature and air humidity (type SHT-10) were incorporated into the gap behind the AVANCIS CIGS modules (centre of the top module row).

The results (**Figure 11**) for data sets between July 2023 to September 2025 show an influence of the irradiance on the façade humidity, in terms that it gets significantly lower than the ambient humidity with higher irradiance level.

10.4229/EUPVSEC2025/4BV.4.24

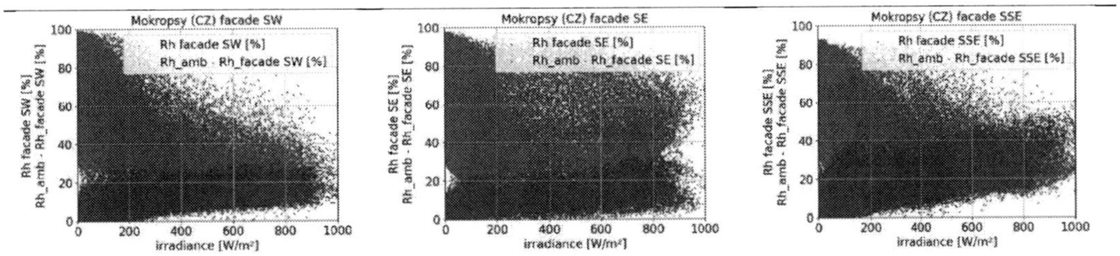

Figure 11: Relative air humidity (red) between PV modules and building wall for the site Mokropsy, with facade sides facing South-West, South-East and South-South-East plotted over irradiance. Also, the difference of the ambient relative humidity (Rh_amb) to the relative humidity behind the PV modules is shown (gray).

4 LONG-TERM PERFORMANCE DATA OF CIGS PV SYSTEMS

Stable electricity generation of a BIPV system built with AVANCIS CIGS thin-film PV modules over a duration of more than 7 years was shown earlier in **Figure 5**. In this section, we present monitoring data showing stable energy yield of AVANCIS CIGS PV modules for longer time durations both from operating PV systems and an R&D test bench. Since module technology has evolved over the years, we conclude the section with monitoring data obtained from AVANCIS CIGS PV modules of the latest generation.

4.1 Commercial systems

Within the framework of an outdoor monitoring project (see also [11]), several PV systems (mostly rooftop; typical size 5 kWp) were built using AVANCIS CIGS PV modules and equipped with sensors for monitoring. Monitoring of these systems (including environmental sensors for irradiance, ambient and module temperature) is facilitated by commercially available out-of-the-box solutions. As the maintenance of the systems and specifically the monitoring systems were not funded and not under control of AVANCIS, it proved to be difficult to keep these monitoring systems running reliably over longer periods of time. However, some of these systems delivering continuous data for more than six years are shown in **Figure 12**. The system in Switzerland is affected significantly by shadowing. The system in Kuwait by soiling by sand. Both effects are detrimental to the overall yearly performance.

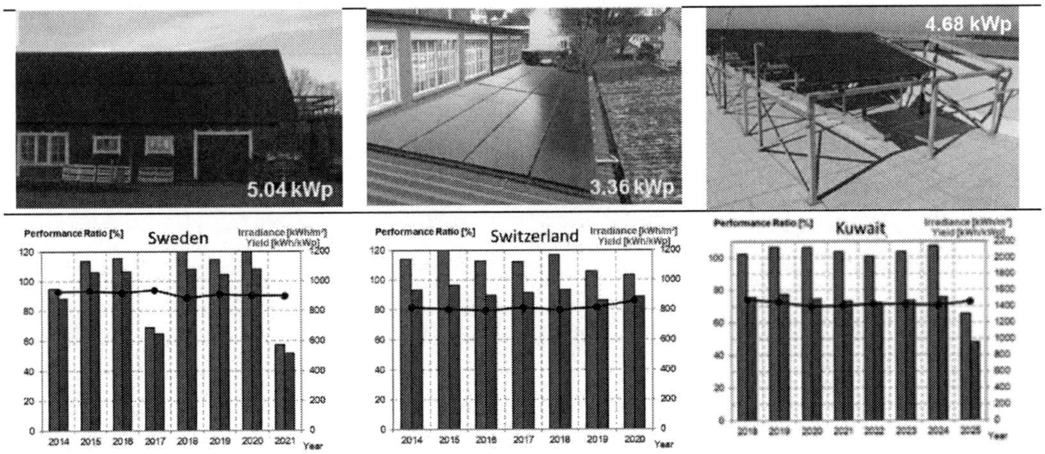

Figure 12: Commercial PV rooftop systems with AVANCIS CIGS PV modules showing stable performances over several years. Plotted is the yearly data for irradiance sum (red bar), electrical yield (gray bar) and performance ratio (points and line) for each year. Lower values in irradiance and yield are due to gaps in the data acquisition. The system in Switzerland is strongly affected by shadowing, the system in Kuwait by soiling, which is mitigated to some extent by regular cleaning of the PV modules.

4.2 Individual module monitoring

AVANCIS operates test rigs for R&D purposes at different locations for the outdoor monitoring of individual modules. The measurement setup on these test rigs traces the IV curve of each module every 10 seconds and records the environmental sensor data at the same time. Between IV sweeps, the modules are kept quasi steady state in their respective MPP. **Figure 13** shows filtered monitoring data of six modules, of which the oldest ones have been continuously monitored over the past 15 years since 2011. The high frequency of data acquisition combined with sensors for irradiance into the module plane, ambient and back-of-module temperature allows for a reliable analysis of stability and potential degradation of the PV modules. The data shown in **Figure 13** is filtered for data points near standard testing conditions (STC). PV module 6 has an initial stabilization phase, while this had a significant higher output power compared to the other modules (120 Wp). None of the six modules shows any clear sign of degrading of electrical power, with a very stable performance for the past 15 years. The continuous increase of power (as extracted from outdoor monitoring) for 4 of the 6 modules considered can in parts be due to stabilization effects known to exist in CIGS PV modules (lightsoaking) or an effect of the self-referencing ([12][13]) for irradiance monitoring. Using instead the data of the irradiance sensors installed, however, leads to a comparable evolution, with slightly decreased dynamics.

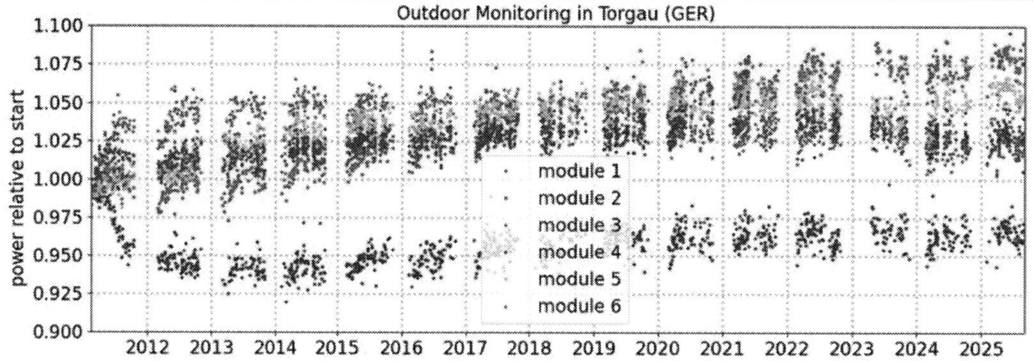

Figure 13: Electrical power relative to initial power (daily averages) for six long-running commercial AVANCIS CIGS modules over the past 15 years, filtered for temperature (23°C-27°C) and self-referenced irradiance close to STC conditions. The modules are operating and being monitored on a R&D test rig in Torgau, Germany.

As a result of continuous research and development, the composition and processing of commercially available AVANCIS thin-film PV modules underwent several generations, improving photon conversion efficiency and electrical energy generation. Accordingly, the long-running PV modules whose data is presented in **Figure 13** cannot contain the latest generation of AVANCIS PV modules. For the latter (comprising a gallium-rich absorber, sodium post deposition treatment and a dry, sputtered ZnOS buffer [14]). **Figure 14** shows the electrical power of the PV modules close to STC as derived from sensor data (self-referenced irradiance very close to 1000 W/m^2 and module temperature between 23 and 27°C). In Germany with the tilt angle as installed in the test rig, STC conditions are not met during wintertime and during summertime, typically only during sunrise or variable, partially cloudy weather conditions.

For all three modules, the monitoring data shown indicates stable electrical performance at STC during the course of a bit more than 4 years. From the data, a slight increase in electrical power could be concluded but further analysis (e.g., drift in sensor readings, soiling, ...) would be necessary to verify this.

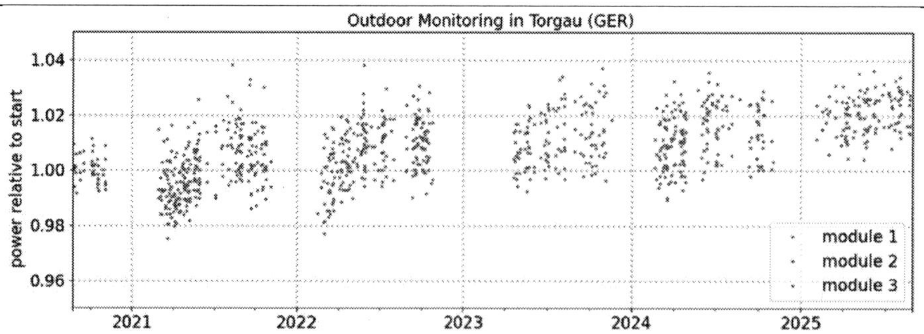

Figure 14: Electrical power relative to initial power (self-referenced close to STC conditions, daily averages) of three long-running AVANCIS CIGS modules of the latest generation of CIGS PV modules over the past 4 years.

5 CONCLUSIONS

10.4229/EUPVSEC2025/4BV.4.24
020307-009

This study presents long-term operational data from AVANCIS CIGS PV installations across different integration levels and environmental conditions. The results highlight significant differences in module temperature behaviour depending on ventilation and mounting configurations, with values typically ranging 20–30°C above ambient temperature and remaining below 80°C module temperature. Air flow behind modules was shown and found to be low even at high facade wind speeds, while surface moisture occurred only intermittently even for exposed module facades and for limited durations, being dried off after few days. Air humidity measurements behind the modules show a clear dependence on irradiance.

Performance monitoring of commercial and R&D systems showed excellent long-term stability of AVANCIS CIGS PV modules, with no or minimal degradation over more than a decade. Stability was also shown in the latest generation of CIGS module development with gallium-rich absorbers, sodium post deposition treatment and a dry, sputtered ZnOS buffer over a period of more than 4 years of outdoor operation. Losses of a system equipped with module DC/DC optimizers for a north-facing facade were shown when interconnected with modules facing other directions. Overall, the results demonstrate the robustness and reliability of advanced CIGS thin-film technologies for building-integrated and free-field PV applications, while also underlining the importance of ventilation, mounting, and system design for optimal performance.

6 REFERENCES

[1] N. Albinius et al., "A comprehensive case study of a full-size BIPV facade", Energies 18(5), 1293 (2025)

[2] T. Dalibor et al., "Cu(In, Ga)(Se, S)$_2$ thin-film technology: Aspects of historical development, current status, and future prospects", IJAGS 16(2) 16696 (2024)

[3] S. Grünsteidl et al., "Irradiance transposition and reflections in BIPV installations", Proc. of the 41st EUPVSEC, 020406 (2024)

[4] AVANCIS GmbH, "Long-term stability of PowerMax and SKALA CIGS modules: energy yield confirmed by Fraunhofer ISE", Press Release (2022) https://www.avancis.de/_Resources/Persistent/2/2/9/a/229a81486cf6c28669b78761f6416f8aea27ac6c/PR%20AVANCIS%20Long%20term%20stability%20PowerMax%20and%20SKALA%20090522%20engl.pdf

[5] EN 50583-1, "Photovoltaics in buildings" (2024)

[6] International Energy Agency, "International definitions of BIPV", Report IEA-PVPS T15-04 (2018)

[7] G. Girma et al., "Experimental investigation of cavity air gap depth for enhanced thermal performance of ventilated rain-screen walls", Building and Environment 194, 107710 (2021)

[8] W. Willems (Editor), "Lehrbuch der Bauphysik", 8th Edition, Springer Verlag

[9] DIN 18516-1, "Cladding for external walls, rear-ventilated" (2024)

[10] J. Brozovsky et al., "Modelling and validation of hygrothermal conditions in the air gap behind wood cladding and BIPV in the building envelope", Building and Environment 228, 109917 (2023)

[11] S. Grünsteidl et al., "Evaluation of Irradiance Sensor Technologies for Plant Monitoring of PV Systems with CIGS Thin Film Modules", Proc. of the 35th EUPVSEC, 2021 (2018)

[12] A. Jagomägi et al., "European Network of PV Outdoor Testing - Steps Towards Harmonized Procedures", Proc. of the 24th EUPVSEC, 3432 (2009)

[13] P. Borowski et al., "Energy rating of CIGS thin film modules and systems", Proc. of the 27th EUPVSEC, 2294 (2012)

[14] H. Elanzeery et al., "Beyond 20% World Record Efficiency for Thin-Film Solar Modules", IEEE Journal of Photovoltaics, 14(1), 107–115 (2023)

10.4229/EUPVSEC2025/4BV.4.24

4BV.4.24

PERFORMANCE, OPERATIONAL DATA AND STABILITY OF COMMERCIAL CIGS THIN-FILM PV MODULES IN BIPV SYSTEMS

Stefan Grünsteidl*, Peter Borowski, Thomas Dalibor

AVANCIS GmbH, Otto-Hahn-Ring 6, 81739 Munich, Germany
*stefan.gruensteidl@avancis.de

Abstract: This work presents long-term operational data of CIGS-based PV systems across varying levels of integration and environmental exposure. Environmental data including module temperatures, air flow, surface moisture, and relative humidity of building-integrated PV (BIPV) installations are shown. Different module orientation in the context of optimizer systems were analysed. Performance evaluations of commercial and R&D systems confirm the long-term stability of CIGS PV modules, with no or minimal degradation observed over more than a decade, including the latest generation of CIGS PV modules featuring gallium-rich absorbers, sodium post-deposition treatment, and a dry ZnOS buffer [1].

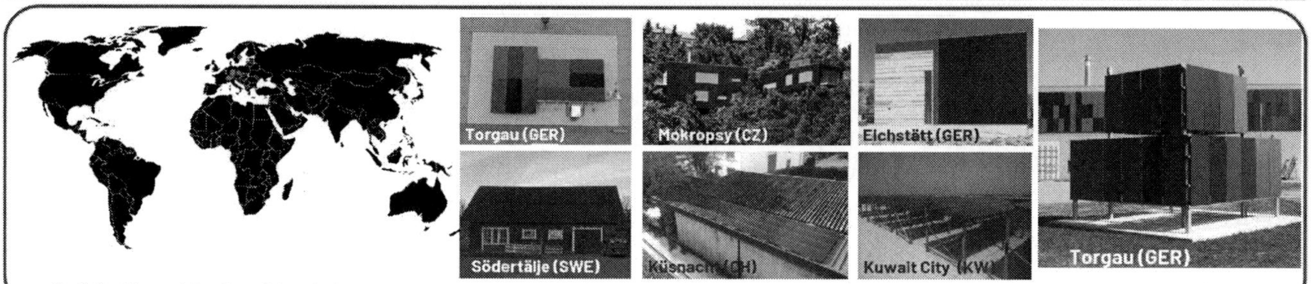

Fig. 1: Overview and locations of the solar installations covered in this study. All PV systems are built using commercial CIGS PV modules by AVANCIS (PowerMax or SKALA).

Module temperatures

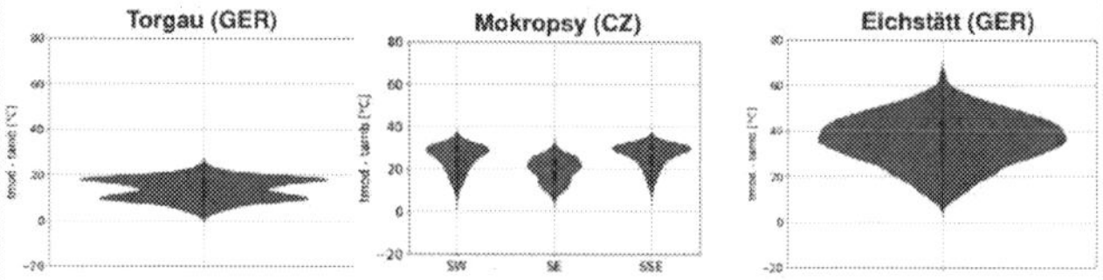

Fig. 2: Module temperature (as measured on the rear side of the PV modules) in comparison to ambient temperature for three sites [2] for irradiances above 700 W/m^2.

Façade air flows

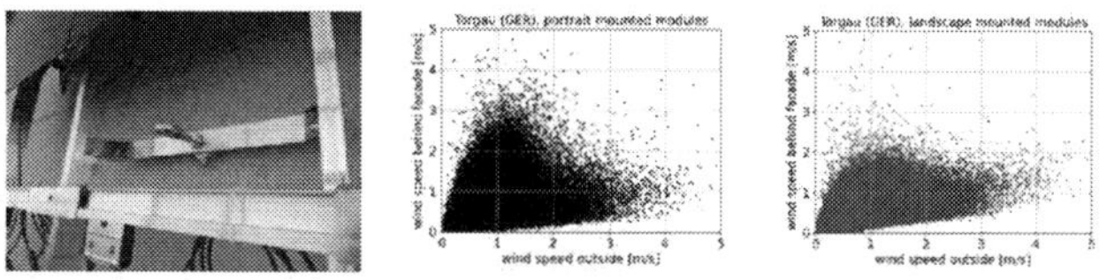

Fig. 3: Air flow speeds between PV modules and building wall over ambient wind speeds for vertically (black) and horizontally (red) installed modules in Torgau (GER).

Surface moisture and humidity behind façade

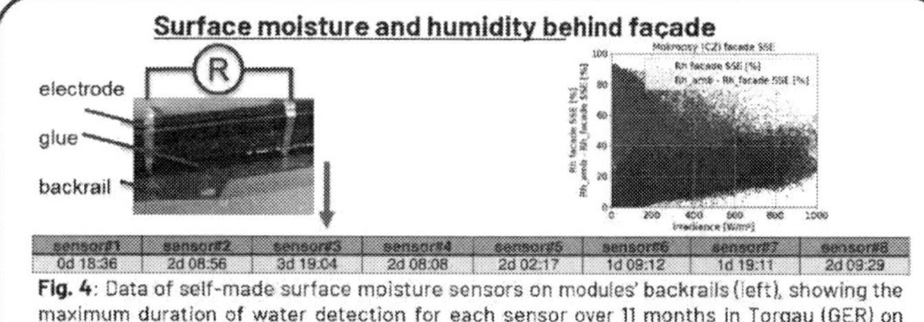

sensor#1	sensor#2	sensor#3	sensor#4	sensor#5	sensor#6	sensor#7	sensor#8
0d 18:36	2d 08:56	3d 19:04	2d 08:08	2d 02:17	1d 09:12	1d 19:11	2d 09:29

Fig. 4: Data of self-made surface moisture sensors on modules' backrails (left), showing the maximum duration of water detection for each sensor over 11 months in Torgau (GER) on modules installed in landscape orientation. – Also, relative air humidity between PV modules and building wall over irradiance (right) is shown for the site Mokropsy (CZ).

Outdoor monitoring newest CIGS generation

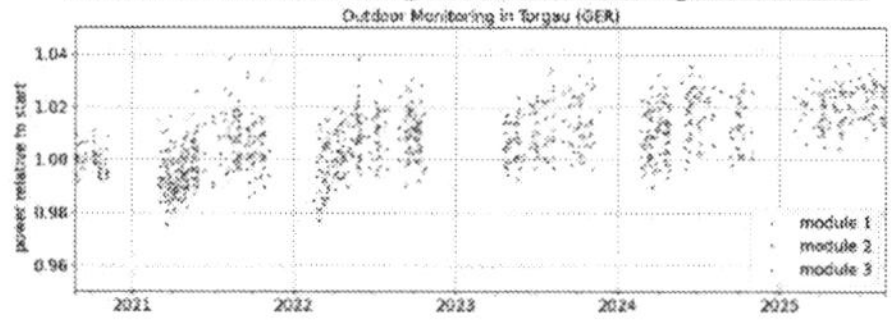

Fig. 5: Electrical power relative to initial power (self-referenced close to STC conditions, daily averages) of three long-running AVANCIS CIGS modules of the latest generation of CIGS PV modules over the past 4 years.

Long-term stability of commercial PV installations

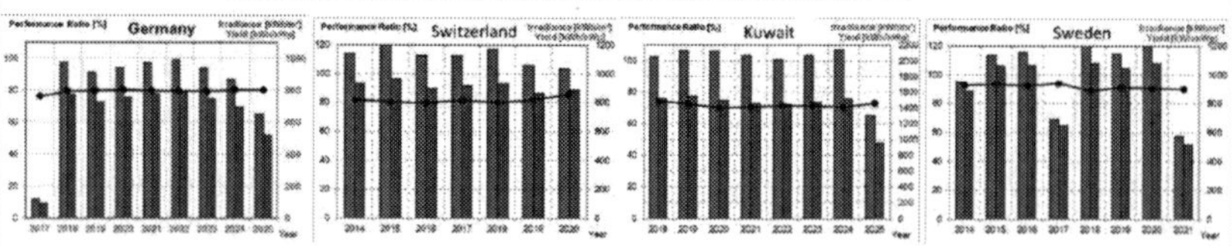

Fig. 6: Long-term performance data for PV systems in Eichstätt (GER), Küsnacht (CH), Kuwait City (KW) and Södertälje (SWE), showing performance ratio, yield and in-plane irradiance for each year.

Long-term stability of individual PV modules

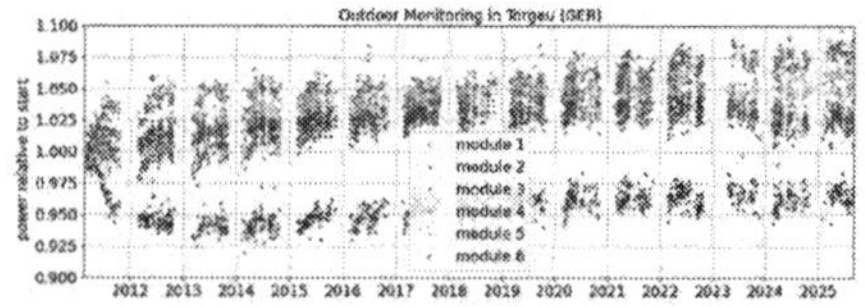

Fig. 7: Electrical power relative to initial power (self-referenced close to STC conditions, daily averages) for six randomly chosen long running commercial AVANCIS CIGS modules over the past 15 years

Conclusions

- Module temperatures typically ranging 20-30°C above ambient temperature, depending on ventilation situation, and remaining below 80°C
- Data sets of air flows behind PV modules, air humidity and surface moisture durations shown
- Performance monitoring of commercial and R&D systems show excellent long-term stability of AVANCIS CIGS modules, with no or minimal degradation over more than a decade.

References

[1] H. Elanzeery et al., "Beyond 20% World Record Efficiency for Thin-Film Solar Modules", IEEE Journal of Photovoltaics, vol. 14, no. 1, pp. 107-115 (2023)
[2] Irradiance and module temperature data sets for the 3 sites https://github.com/gruenst/PVsec2025

PHOTOVOLTAIC INTEGRATION IN FOOTBALL STADIUMS: GLOBAL TRENDS, REGIONAL DISPARITIES, FUTURE POTENTIAL

Johanna Buchmann†, Niels Feuerherdt†, Bert Stegemann*
University of Applied Sciences – HTW Berlin, Wilhelminenhofstr. 75a, D-12459 Berlin, Germany
*bert.stegemann@htw-berlin.de

ABSTRACT: Football stadiums are both major energy consumers and highly visible infrastructures, making them ideal showcase projects for renewable energies and, particularly, photovoltaics (PV). This study systematically evaluates the use of PV systems in professional football stadiums worldwide. A comprehensive overview is provided for Germany, Austria, and Switzerland, while highlights from other regions and countries illustrate global developments. The results show clear regional differences: Germany and Switzerland lead the way with widespread adoption, Brazil shows a tournament-driven catalyst effect, while major leagues such as Serie A, La Liga and the Premier League lag behind. Political measures, and to some extent major tournaments, proved to be the most important driving forces. Future developments are likely to combine PV with efficiency, storage and smart energy concepts, while falling costs and upcoming international tournaments (e.g. the 2030 FIFA World Cup) could promote further adoption.
Keywords: Photovoltaics, Football stadiums, Renewable energy, Policy impacts, Sustainability

1 INTRODUCTION, MOTIVATION, AND GOALS

Football stadiums represent both significant energy consumers and highly visible public infrastructures. Their transformation into sustainability showcases, particularly through the installation of photovoltaic (PV) systems, offers a unique opportunity to combine renewable energy production with global public outreach.

Recent publications on PV systems in stadiums show that there has been a development from early pilot roofs to building-integrated systems with a capacity of several MW, which can significantly cover the energy demands of the stadiums [1,2]. Case studies highlight architectural solutions such as thin-film or lightweight roofs, semi-transparent and façade PV, which adapt to complex geometries while preserving daylight and aesthetics [1,3]. Technical-economic studies show that PV, in combination with battery storage and smart operation, significantly improves profitability in addition to self-consumption [4]. More comprehensive reviews and case studies highlight the role of stadiums in supplying energy to communities and the importance of stable policy frameworks for sustainable deployment [5,6]. Major events can accelerate PV implementation, though in hot climates, solar-assisted cooling solutions may take precedence over rooftop PV systems [7].

So, current research exists, but there is a lack of comprehensive and up-to-date data across countries and leagues. Systematic evidence on the global distribution of PV systems in stadiums and their relationship to policy frameworks and major events is also limited. This study therefore aims to systematically document PV systems in football stadiums, assess their geographical and league-specific distribution, and evaluate the influence of regulatory frameworks and tournament-related dynamics. By combining detailed data collection with a comparative analysis of recent FIFA World Cups and UEFA European Championships, the study contributes to the understanding of how politics, market conditions and event-related incentives influence the adoption of PV systems. Particular attention is paid to regional differences and the role of tournament preparations as potential driver for the adoption of PV systems. In this way, the study provides an up-to-date data base that may enrich both academic research and public discussion about the future of PV in football stadiums.

2 APPROACH AND METHODOLOGY

This analysis is limited to football (soccer) stadiums and distinguishes between PV systems installed directly on the main stadium roof and those located on adjacent buildings or stadium grounds. Google Earth images were employed for verification where necessary. The league affiliation in the 2024/25 season served as the reference framework for the evaluation of the national leagues. Stadium projects under construction with scheduled completion in 2025 were also included. In cases of PV system expansions, cumulative installed capacities were reported. Where direct data were unavailable, capacities were estimated using yield numbers, module counts, or comparable indicators. This methodology ensures a systematic, reproducible, and up-to-date dataset.

3 STADIUM RANKINGS - BY GEOGRAPHY

This chapter contains a comparative ranking of football stadiums equipped with PV systems, sorted by geographical location: First, the 15 leading stadiums worldwide (outside Europe) are listed and ranked according to their installed PV capacity, followed by a ranking of the leading European and German stadiums. The year in which the PV system went into operation is also given for each case. The data was compiled through systematic research using the methodological approach described in chapter 2 to ensure consistency and comparability between regions.

3.1 Worldwide (except Europe)

The global ranking of PV systems integrated into stadiums outside Europe, see Table I, shows a striking pattern. Brazil dominates with several large-scale systems associated with the 2014 FIFA World Cup, including the Estádio Nacional Mané Garrincha in Brasília (2.5 MW_p) and other large PVsystems in Mineirão and Pernambuco. In Asia, the National Stadium in Kaohsiung, Taiwan (1 MW_p), and the Gelora Bung Karno Stadium in Indonesia are other notable examples.

A special case is the Stade du Sénégal in Dakar, where a 2.3 MW_p PV system is installed on carports rather than on the stadium roof. Though this does not strictly meet the criterion of a 'rooftop installation,' this project was included as the only representative from Africa and as a potential model for the future development of PV installations in stadiums on the continent.

In the US, numerous American football stadiums have been equipped with PV installations, but these were not included due to the different sporting context. Only venues that are regularly used for football (soccer), such as the stadium in Washington, D.C., were included.

Overall, the ranking shows that large PV stadium projects outside Brazil and Europe (see next section) remain exceptions, even in countries with a generally high level of PV deployment, such as China.

Table I: Top 15 football stadiums worldwide, but excluding Europe, ranked by installed PV capacity

Rank	Stadium	City	Country	Capacity kWp	Operation start
1	Estádio Nacional Mané Garrincha	Brasilia	Brazil	2500	2013
2	Stade du Senegal	Dakar	Senegal	2300 (carport)	2021
3	Mineirão Stadium	Belo Horizonte	Brazil	1420	2014
4	Al-Madina	Bagdad	Iraq	1050	2021
5	National Stadium	Kaohsiung	Taiwan	1000	2009
6	Gelora Bung Karno Main Stadium	Jakarta	Indonesia	1000	2019
7	Pernambuco Stadium	Recife	Brazil	1000	2013
8	Go Media Stadium	Auckland	New Zealand	780	2025
9	Audi Field	Washington, DC	USA	627.8	2020
10	Panasonic Stadium Suita	Osaka	Japan	504	2015
11	Itaipava Arena Fonte Nova	Salvador	Brazil	500	2014
12	Estádio Roberto Santos	Salvador	Brazil	400	2012
13	Estádio do Maracanã	Rio de Janeiro	Brazil	391	2014
14	Beijing Workers' Stadium	Peking, China	China	351	2023
15	Al-Bayt Stadium	Al Khor	Qatar	271	2021

3.2 Europe

In Europe (see Table II), four stadiums with PV systems of more than 2 MW_p stand out: Signal Iduna Park in Dortmund (4.2 MW_p, to be completed 2025), Rams Park in Istanbul (4.1 MW_p, 2023), Ernst Happel Stadium in Vienna (3.5 MW_p, 2023) and Europa Park Stadium in Freiburg (nearly 2.4 MW_p, 2022). All other stadiums in the ranking operate systems with capacities of above 1 MW_p, including notable examples in France, the Netherlands, the United Kingdom, Italy and Switzerland. Beyond the top 15, other European venues also exceed the 1 MW_p range, emphasizing the broad acceptance of stadium-integrated PV systems in Europe.

Table II: Top 15 European football stadiums ranked by installed PV capacity (* - estimated value)

Rank	Stadium	City	Country	Capacity kW_p	Operation start
1	Signal Iduna Park	Dortmund	Germany	4200	2025 (proj.)
2	Rams Park (Ali Sami Yen)	Istanbul	Türkiye	4100	2022
3	Ernst Happel Stadion	Vienna	Austria	3500	2025
4	Europa-Park Stadion	Freiburg	Germany	2387	2022
5	Merkur Spiel-Arena	Düsseldorf	Germany	1500	2025 (proj.)
6	Fritz-Walter-Stadion	Kaiserslautern	Germany	1350	2010
7	Allianz Riviera	Nice	France	1342.7	2013
8	Stadion Wankdorf	Bern	Switzerland	1300	2005
9	London Stadium	London	England	1256	2025 (proj.)
10	Kybunpark	St. Gallen	Switzerland	1205	2025
11	Stadion am Böllenfalltor	Darmstadt	Germany	1200	2024
12	RheinEnergie Stadion	FC Köln	Germany	1200	2025 (proj.)
13	Johan Cruijff ArenA	Amsterdam	Netherlands	1128	2014
14	Stadio Friuli	Udinese	Italy	1100	2024
15	Stadion Galgenwaard	Utrecht	Netherlands	1065*	2017

3.3 Germany

Germany is the country with the most advanced integration of PV systems in stadiums. The first PV system on the roof of a Bundesliga stadium was installed in 1995 at the Dreisam stadium in Freiburg. After expansions in 1999 and 2004, it reached a total output of 259 kW_p, making it a pioneer to set an important milestone for later projects. Since then, the use of PV systems has spread across both Bundesliga leagues as well as the lower leagues, with outputs ranging from small-scale to multi-MW systems. The top 15 are listed in Table III. The stadium in Dortmund (4.2 MW_p) will be the global leader, while existing stadiums e.g. in Freiburg, Mainz, Bremen and Frankfurt illustrate the continuity of PV integration in modern renovations.

A particularly innovative example is the Weser Stadium in Bremen, where three different PV components were implemented at an early stage. Lightweight thin-film modules were installed on the main roof to reduce wind load and structural stress. In addition, the inner roof ring features semi-transparent polycarbonate elements with integrated crystalline Si cells, while glass-glass PV modules were used for parts of the outer façade.

Table III: Top 15 German football stadiums ranked by installed PV capacity

Rank	Stadium	City	Capacity kW_p	Operation start
1	Signal Iduna Park	Dortmund	4200	2025 (proj.)
2	Europa-Park Stadion	Freiburg	2387	2022
3	Merkur Spiel-Arena	Düsseldorf	1500	2025 (proj.)
4	Fritz-Walter-Stadion	Kaiserslautern	1350	2010
5	Weserstadion	Bremen	1270	2009
6	Böllenfalltor	Darmstadt	1200	2024
7	RheinEnergieStadion	Köln	1200	2025 (proj.)
8	Mewa Arena	Mainz	846.3	2011
9	Erzgebirgsstadion	Aue	750	2021
10	Steigerwaldstadion	Erfurt	730	2016
11	Ostseestadion	Rostock	700	2010
12	Jahnstadion	Regensburg	632	2025
13	Olympiastadion Berlin	Berlin	605.25	2022
14	Deutsche Bank Park	Frankfurt	560	2024
15	Leuna-Chemie-Stadion	Halle	526	2011

4 STADIUM RANKINGS - BY NATIONAL LEAGUE

Beyond geographical distribution, the ranking by national leagues demonstrates how PV adoption differs structurally across football competitions. The German Bundesliga and 2nd Bundesliga show high acceptance rates compared to many other leagues, while Switzerland and Austria also have several notable projects. These rankings demonstrate that political framework conditions and club-level initiatives are decisive factors, rather than just solar potential or stadium size alone.

4.1 Germany - Bundesliga

In the Bundesliga, sustainability has clearly become an integral part of club strategies and stadium modernisation projects. Of the 18 clubs, seven currently operate PV systems directly on their stadium roofs, while another five have installed systems elsewhere on the stadium grounds, for example on ancillary buildings, car parks or other adjacent facilities. Several other clubs have projects in the planning or development phase. The analysis, see Table IV, therefore distinguishes between rooftop PV systems and systems located elsewhere on the stadium grounds.

10.4229/EUPVSEC2025/4BV.4.27
020309-002

Table IV: Ranking of 1. Bundesliga clubs (as of season 2024/25) by installed PV capacity (stadium roof vs. stadium grounds)

Rank	Stadium	Team	Capacity kWp Roof	Capacity kWp Grounds	Operation start
1	Signal Iduna Park	Borussia Dortmund	4200		2025 (proj.)
2	Europa-Park	SC Freiburg	2387		2022
3	Wesrerstadion	Werder Bremen	1270		2009
4	Mewa ARENA	1. FSV Mainz 05	846.3		2011
5	DB Park	Eintracht Frankfurt	560		2024
6	Millerntor	FC St. Pauli	316		2025
7	Voith-Arena	1. FC Heidenheim	303.56		2015
8	PreZero Arena	TSG 1899 Hoffenheim		1046.5	
9	Allianz Arena	FC Bayern München		834	2019
10	Borussia-Park	Borussia Mönchengladb.		127	2024
11	Ruhrstadion	VfL Bochum		97	2023
12	Red Bull Arena	RB Leipzig		71.5	2020

4.2 Germany -2nd Bundesliga

In the 2nd Bundesliga, the number of roof-mounted PV systems is particularly notable, with 12 out of 18 clubs operating installations on their stadium roofs and one additional club hosting a PV system elsewhere on the stadium premises, see Table V. Examples include Fortuna Düsseldorf (Merkur Spiel-Arena), SV Darmstadt 98 (Böllenfalltor), and Hamburger SV (Volksparkstadion). This indicates that PV integration is not limited to top-tier clubs but extends across professional football in Germany.

Table V: Ranking of 2nd Bundesliga clubs (as of season 2024/25) by installed PV capacity: stadium roof vs. stadium grounds (* - estimated value)

Rank	Stadium	Team	Capacity kW_p Roof	Capacity kW_p Grounds	Operation start
1	Merkur Spiel-Arena	Fortuna Düsseldorf	1500		2025 (proj.)
2	Fritz-Walter-Stadion	1. FC Kaiserslautern	1350		2010
3	RheinEnergieStadion	1. FC Köln	1200		2025 (proj.)
4	Böllenfalltor	SV Darmstadt 98	1200		2024
5	Jahnstadion	SSV Jahn Regensburg	632		2025
6	Olympiastadion Berlin	Hertha BSC	605.25		2022
7	Volksparkstadion	Hamburger SV	520		2011
8	Home Deluxe Arena	SC Paderborn 07	500*		2012
9	Sportpark Ronhof	SpVgg Greuther Fürth	319.8		2022
10	Max-Morlock-Stadion	1. FC Nürnberg	284		2010
11	Eintracht-Stadion	Eintracht Braunschweig	262.3		2023
12	Wildpark	Karlsruher SC	100		2022
13	Veltins-Arena	FC Schalke 04		600	2012

Table VI: Ranking of Swiss Superleague clubs (as of season 2024/25) by installed PV capacity (* - estimated value)

Rank	Stadium	Team	Capacity kW_p Roof	Operation start
1	Stadion Wankdorf/Stade de Suisse	BSC Young Boys	1350	2025 (proj.)
2	Kybunpark	FC St. Gallen	1205	2010
3	swissporarena	FC Luzern	1097	2025 (proj.)
4	Stade de Genève	Servette FC	942	2024
5	St. Jakob-Park	FC Basel	850	2025
6	Stade de la Tuilière	FC Lausanne-Sport	800*	2022
7	Stade Municipal	Yverdon Sport FC	500*	2011
8	Letzigrund Stadion	FC Zürich / GH Zürich	223	2012
9	Stadion Schützenwiese	FC Winterthur	63.44	2022

4.3 Switzerland - Super League

Switzerland features a strong presence of stadium-integrated PV systems. The Stade de Suisse in Bern pioneered this development with 1.35 MW_p in 2005. Other MW- or near-MW examples include Kybunpark in St. Gallen, Swissporarena in Lucerne, and Stade de Genève). These installations illustrate how early adoption, supported by national sustainability policies, established Switzerland as a regional leader.

4.4. Austria - Bundesliga

Austria presents fewer but still relevant cases, with the Generali Arena in Vienna and the Wörthersee Stadion in Klagenfurt. The most prominent example nationwide is the Ernst Happel Stadium in Vienna, with 3.5 MW_p (see Table II) and represents the largest single installation in the country. However, as this venue is not used for regular league matches, it does not appear in the Bundesliga-specific ranking presented here. Though Austria lags behind Switzerland and Germany in terms of numbers capacity, these projects indicate a growing awareness and commitment.

Table VII: Ranking of Austrian Bundesliga clubs (as of season 2024/25) by installed PV capacity.

Rank	Stadium	Team	Capacity kW_p Roof	Operation start
1	Generali Arena	FK Austria Wien	825	2018-2024
2	28 Black Arena / Wörthersee Stadion	SK Austria Klagenfurt	137.5	2013

4.5 Comparative PV Coverage in European Football Leagues

The diagram in Figure 1 illustrates the extent of PV coverage across different European football leagues, measured as the proportion of stadium roofs equipped with photovoltaic systems. The results reveal striking regional disparities: Swiss Super League leads with more than 70% coverage, followed by the German 2nd Bundesliga at around 65%. The German Bundesliga and 3rd Liga also show above-average adoption levels. In contrast, leading European leagues such as Serie A (Italy), La Liga (Spain), Premier League (UK), and Ligue 1 (France) remain far behind, with coverages below 20%. The findings highlight the central role of policy incentives and national sustainability agendas in driving adoption, while sporting or economic prominence of leagues alone does not guarantee PV integration.

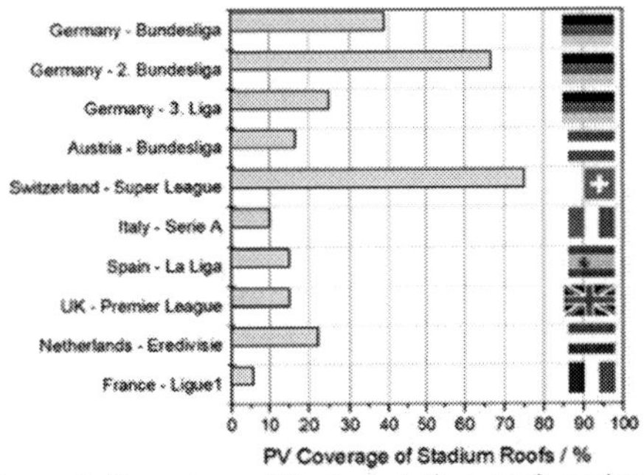

Figure 1: Percentage of football stadium roofs equipped with photovoltaic (PV) systems in selected European leagues (as of 2024/25 season).

5 POLICIES AND TOURNAMENT DRIVEN EFFECTS

This section examines how recent UEFA European Championships (EUROs) and FIFA World Cups (WCs) have influenced the installation of PV systems on football stadiums and places those impacts within broader regulatory and policy context. Covering briefly all EUROs and WCs since 2008, we compare and evaluate tournament-specific impulses with international and national policies, market conditions, and stadium renovation efforts. Subsequently, two countries are examined in detail, i.e. Germany and Brazil, as they represent typical but fundamentally different examples of PV adoption dynamics.

5.1. World Cups and European Championships

For EURO 2008 in Austria and Switzerland, the Green Goal 2006 sustainability principles [8] were integrated into planning, and some PV measures were implemented through the "Solar Stadia" initiative [2]. Though pioneering PV consideration, these efforts remained limited, and most substantial upgrades followed only later.

At the 2010 World Cup in South Africa, feasibility studies under the Green Goal 2010 framework [9] examined PV options for Cape Town Stadium, but the overall focus lay on efficiency and lighting. No large PV roof installations were realized, resulting in a weak impact.

During EURO 2012 in Poland and Ukraine, there is no evidence of PV roofs across host stadiums, and thus no tournament-driven rollout can be identified.

The 2014 World Cup in Brazil marked a breakthrough, with at least four stadiums equipped with PV systems with a total of around 5.4 MW_p. This demonstrates a strong and direct link between tournament preparation and PV adoption.

For EURO 2016 in France, individual strong cases existed, such as the energy-positive stadium in Nice and a large PV carport in Bordeaux. However, this tournament did not generate a broader wave of rooftop PV adoption, leading to a moderate overall impact.

At the 2018 World Cup in Russia, sustainability programs focused on certifications and efficiency upgrades (e.g., BREEAM, LED, HVAC) [10], but no significant PV roofs were documented. The PV-specific impact was weak.

EURO 2020, played in 2021 across multiple European host countries, lacked a tournament-wide PV program. Apart from the Amsterdam stadium, which already had a PV roof, there was little evidence of new event-driven deployments, resulting in a weak effect.

The 2022 World Cup in Qatar focussed on solar-supported cooling and broader renewable integration. However, only two stadiums were documented with roof-mounted PV, making the impact weak to moderate in terms of PV adoption.

At EURO 2024 in Germany, sustainability frameworks such as the UN Initiative for Climate Action [11] and UEFA's Climate Fund [12] were accompanied by several venue-driven PV projects and expansions. These illustrate a strong influence of the tournament on PV deployment.

5.2 Example: Germany

The timeline for the introduction of PV systems in German football stadiums (see Figure 2) reflects initially the general development of the German solar industry. The first growth phase (2009–2011) was driven by high feed-in tariffs under the Renewable Energy Sources Act (EEG) and falling module prices, which created extremely attractive investment conditions. The stagnation phase (2013–2022) was marked by the crisis in the solar industry and successive EEG reforms. The changes in 2012 and 2014 led to a significant reduction in feed-in tariffs, while low-cost imports from Asia intensified competition. As a result, many projects became unprofitable and expansion slowed down considerably.

Since 2022, there has been a renewed increase in installed capacity. Rising electricity prices due to the energy crisis made PV investments more profitable, while growing social awareness of sustainability raised expectations of football clubs. The German Football Association (DFB) joined the 'Sports for Climate Action' initiative of the Unite Nations in 2020 [13], and several clubs have set their own climate neutrality or emission reduction targets. As the electricity consumption of stadiums falls under Scope 2 emissions [14], on-site renewable energy generation directly improves their carbon footprint.

The EURO 2024 provided additional momentum. UEFA launched a climate fund under the motto 'United by Football. Together for Nature' [15]. 572 applications for PV projects were submitted by amateur clubs. While this study focuses on larger professional venues, the strong interest from amateur clubs underscores the broad relevance of PV. In preparation for the tournament, the Öko-Institut conducted a feasibility study for a 'climate-neutral' EURO 2024 [16], which identified mobility as the largest source of emissions but also highlighted PV systems as an important mitigation measure.

Overall, Germany is an example of a diffusion model for PV adoption: broad and gradual integration across all professional leagues, driven primarily by policy frameworks, falling costs and regular stadium renovations. International tournaments acted as supporting triggers but were not decisive factors.

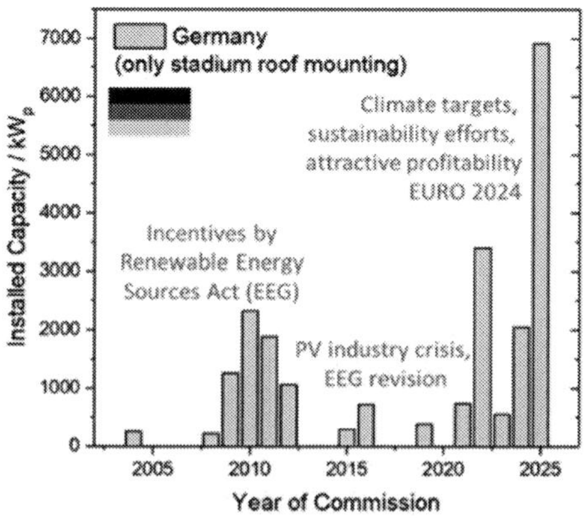

Figure 2: Temporal development of PV installations on German football stadiums

5.3 Example: Brazil

In Brazil, the 2014 FIFA World Cup was a clear catalyst for the installation of photovoltaic systems on football stadiums. Preparations for the tournament and the associated renovation of the venues triggered an extraordinary, event-driven increase in installations. Of the twelve stadiums used during the World Cup, four were equipped with PV modules. Furthermore, though not a World Cup venue, the Estádio de Pituaçu in Salvador is the actual pioneer as the first stadium in Latin America to host a PV system. Currently, the Brazilian national stadium in Brasília has the second-largest PV system on a football stadium worldwide, underscoring the extent of Brazilian commitment during this period.

The timing of these installations, reflects preparations for the 2014 World Cup, as shown in Figure 3, and supports the interpretation of Brazil as a catalyst model, where a single major event has concentrated and accelerated adoption rather than driving long-term diffusion.

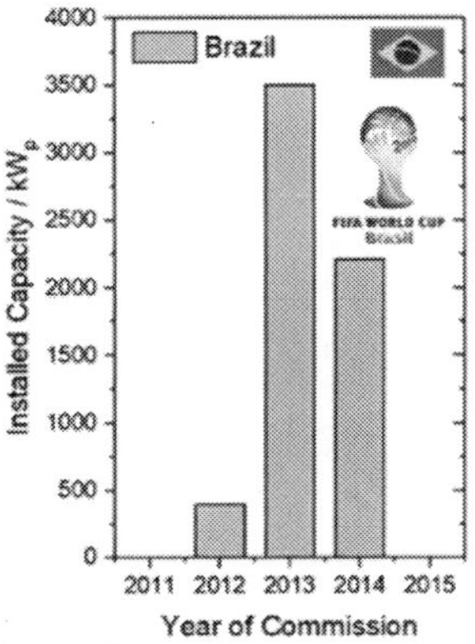

Figure 3: Temporal development of PV installations on Brazilian football stadiums

6 SUMMARY AND OUTLOOK

Since 2008, the integration of PV systems in football stadiums has increased significantly, although with considerable regional and temporal differences. A couple of European countries have emerged as pioneers, while adoption in other countries is progressing more slowly. International tournaments such as the FIFA World Cup and UEFA EURO have provided momentum, but have not led to a systematic push for the use of PV systems. Many current stadium projects focus more on energy efficiency and certification than on large-scale PV systems, and documented capacities ranging from small, rather symbolic installations to multi-MW systems.

Future growth is likely to be driven by climate policy and the visibility of football stadiums as showcase projects for sustainability. In future projects, PV systems are likely to be combined with energy efficiency solutions, storage systems and smart operating concepts. Regional differences are likely to remain, but falling PV prices and stronger climate commitments could accelerate global adoption. Major upcoming tournaments such as the 2030 FIFA World Cup could once again serve as promoter for new PV projects.

REFERENCES

[1] M. Manni, V. Coccia, A. Nicolini, G. Marseglia, A. Petrozzi, Energies 11 (2018) 2396.
[2] L.G. Monteiro, W.N. Macedo, P.F. Torres, M.M. Silva, G. Amaral, A.S. Piterman, B.M. Lopes, J.M. Fraga, W.C. Boaventura, Energies 10 (2017) 225.
[3] L. Barbaro, G. Battista, E. de Lieto Vollaro, R. de Lieto Vollaro, Appl. Sci. 14 (2024) 7344.
[4] K. Berg, M. Resch, T. Weniger, S. Simonsen, J. Energy Storage 34 (2021) 102190.
[5] M. Devetaković, D. Djordjević, M. Radojević, A. Krstić-Furundžić, B.-G. Burduhos, G. Martinopoulos, M. Neagoe, G. Lobaccaro, Appl. Sci. 10 (2020) 6696.
[6] A. Hadrović, Int. J. Multidiscip. Res. Growth Eval. 4 (2023).
[7] P. Sofotasiou, B.R. Hughes, J.K. Calautit, Sustain. Cities Soc. 14 (2015) 16–30.
[8] Green Goal 2006 (24 Sep 2025), https://www.oeko.de/oekodoc/292/2006-011-en.pdf
[9] Greening 2010 FIFA World Cup (24 Sep 2025), https://www.dffe.gov.za/greening-2010-fifa-world-cup
[10] Main stadium of Russia 2018 receives 'green' certification (24 Sep 2025), https://ipt.fifa.com/tournaments/mens/worldcup/2018russia/news/main-stadium-of-russia-2018-receives-green-certification-2927642
[11] Sports for Climate Action (24 Sep 2025), https://unfccc.int/climate-action/sectoral-engagement/sports-for-climate-action
[12] UEFA EURO 2024 climate fund for German amateur clubs (24 Sep 2025), https://www.uefa.com/news-media/news/0289-19ebcc000ecc-5d28436af2d0-1000--uefa-euro-2024-climate-fund-for-german-amateur-clubs
[13] Sports for Climate Action (24 Sep 2025), https://unfccc.int/climate-action/sectoral-engagement/sports-for-climate-action
[14] Scope 2 Guidance (24 Sep 2025), https://ghgprotocol.org/scope-2-guidance
[15] United by Football. Together for Nature' (24 Sep 2025), https://www.uefa.com/news-media/news/028c-1a98706e2386-d19fef44c053-1000--united-by-football-together-for-nature/
[16 Concept and Feasibility Study for a "Climate Neutral" UEFA EURO 2024 (24 Sep 2025), https://www.oeko.de/en/publications/concept-and-feasibility-study-for-a-climate-neutral-uefa-euro-2024]

Please note: The complete list of sources and references for all stadium data is available from the authors by request, as its length exceeds the scope of this publication.

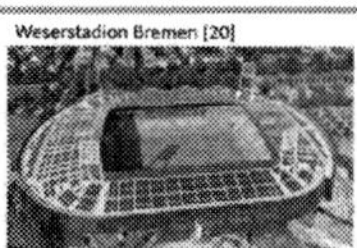

htw
Hochschule für Technik
und Wirtschaft Berlin
University of Applied Sciences

42nd European Photovoltaic Solar Energy Conference and Exhibition

PHOTOVOLTAIC INTEGRATION IN FOOTBALL STADIUMS: GLOBAL TRENDS, REGIONAL DISPARITIES, FUTURE POTENTIAL

EU PVSEC

Johanna Buchmann, Niels Feuerherdt, Bert Stegemann

HTW Berlin - University of Applied Sciences, Wilhelminenhofstr. 75A, D-12459 Berlin, Germany

Goals

- Establishing a systematic record of football stadiums equipped with photovoltaic systems
- Providing up-to-date data on the current status of PV implementation in professional football infrastructure
- Classification of developments in the D-A-CH region within an international context
- Quantitative assessment of deployment rates and qualitative investigation of underlying incentives in different regions and leagues
- Identification of global patterns and regional differences, including the role of major sporting events (European championships and World cups) as triggers for implementation

Approach + Methodology

- Analysis limited to football (soccer) stadiums
- PV systems differentiated between stadium roof and adjacent buildings
- Verification supported by Google Earth images
- League affiliation of the 2024/25 season used as reference
- Stadium projects completing in 2025 included
- Cumulative capacity reported for multi-stage installations
- Missing data estimated from generation numbers, module counts, or similar indicators

GBK Stadium, Jarkarta [1]

Kaohsiung, Taiwan[2]
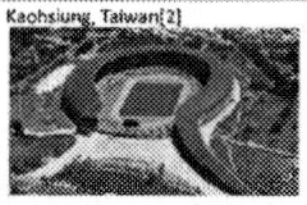
Mineirão, Belo Horizonte [3]

Al-Madina, Bagdad [4]

Audi Field, Washington [5]

Panasonic Stadium Osaka [6]

Stade du Senegal, Dakar [7]

Go Media, Auckland [8]

Pernambuco, Recife [9]

Stadium PV Rankings – by Geography

Worldwide (excl. Europe)

Rank	Stadium	City	Country	Capacity kWp	Operation start
1	Estádio Nacional Mané Garrincha	Brasilia	Brazil	2500	2013
2	Stade du Senegal	Dakar	Senegal	2300 (carport)	2021
3	Mineirão Stadium	Belo Horizonte	Brazil	1420	2014
4	Al-Madina International Stadium)	Bagdad	Iraq	1050	2021
5	National Stadium	Kaohsiung	Taiwan	1000	2009
6	Gelora Bung Karno Main Stadium	Jakarta	Indonesia	1000	2019
7	Pernambuco Stadium	Recife	Brazil	1000	2013
8	Go Media Stadium	Auckland	New Zealand	780	2025
9	Audi Field	Washington, DC	USA	627.8	2020
10	Panasonic Stadium Suita	Osaka	Japan	504	2015
11	Itaipava Arena Fonte Nova	Salvador	Brazil	500	2014
12	Estádio Roberto Santos	Salvador	Brazil	400	2012
13	Estádio do Maracanã	Rio de Janeiro	Brazil	391	2014
14	Beijing Workers' Stadium	Peking, China	China	351	2023
15	Al-Bayt Stadium	Al Khor	Qatar	271	2021

Europe

Rank	Stadium	City	Country	Capacity kWp	Operation start
1	Signal Iduna Park	Dortmund	Germany	4200	2025 (proj.)
2	Rams Park (Ali Sami Yen)	Istanbul	Türkiye	4100	2022
3	Ernst Happel Stadion	Vienna	Austria	3500	2025
4	Europa-Park Stadion	Freiburg	Germany	2387	2022
5	Merkur Spiel-Arena	Düsseldorf	Germany	1500	2025 (proj.)
6	Fritz-Walter-Stadion	Kaiserslautern	Germany	1350	2010
7	Allianz Riviera	Nice	France	1342.7	2013
8	Stadion Wankdorf	Bern	Switzerland	1300	2005
9	London Stadium	London	England (UK)	1256	2025 (proj.)
10	Kybunpark	St. Gallen	Switzerland	1205	2025
11	Stadion am Böllenfalltor	Darmstadt	Germany	1200	2024
12	RheinEnergieSTADION	FC Köln	Germany	1200	2025 (proj.)
13	Johan Cruijff ArenA	Amsterdam	Netherlands	1128	2014
14	Stadio Friuli	Udinese	Italy	1100	2024
15	Stadion Galgenwaard	Utrecht	Netherlands	1065*	2017

Germany

Rank	Stadium	City	Capacity kWp	Operation start
1	Signal Iduna Park	Dortmund	4200	2025 (proj.)
2	Europa-Park Stadion	Freiburg	2387	2022
3	Merkur Spiel-Arena	Düsseldorf	1500	2025 (proj.)
4	Fritz-Walter-Stadion	Kaiserslautern	1350	2010
5	Weserstadion	Bremen	1270	2009
6	Stadion am Böllenfalltor	Darmstadt	1200	2024
7	RheinEnergieStadion	Köln	1200	2025 (proj.)
8	Mewa Arena	Mainz	846.3	2011
9	Erzgebirgsstadion	Aue	750	2021
10	Steigerwaldstadion	Erfurt	730	2016
11	Ostseestadion	Rostock	700	2010
12	Jahnstadion	Regensburg	632	2025
13	Olympiastadion Berlin	Berlin	605.25	2022
14	Deutsche Bank Park	Frankfurt	560	2024
15	Leuna-Chemie-Stadion	Halle	526	2011

* Capacity estimated

Wankdorf, Bern [10]

Allianz Riviera , Nice [11]

Rams Park, Istanbul [12]

London Stadium [13]

Cruiff ArenA, Amsterdam [14]

Stadio Friuli, Udinese [15]

Kybonpark, St. Gallen [16]

Ernst Happel Stadium, Wien [17]

Stadium PV Rankings – by National League

German Bundesliga (1st Division)

Rank	Stadium	Team	Capacity kWp - Stadium Roof	Capacity kWp Stadium Grounds	Operation start
1	Signal Iduna Park	Borussia Dortmund	4200		2025 (proj.)
2	Europa-Park Stadion	SC Freiburg	2387		2022
3	WESERSTADION	Werder Bremen	1270		2009
4	MEWA ARENA	1. FSV Mainz 05	846.3		2011
5	DB Park	Eintracht Frankfurt	560		2024
6	Millerntor-Stadion	FC St. Pauli	316		2025
7	Voith-Arena	1. FC Heidenheim	303.56		2015
8	PreZero Arena	TSG 1899 Hoffenheim		1046.5	
9	Allianz Arena	FC Bayern München		834	2019
10	Borussia-Park	Borussia Mönchengladbach		127	2024
11	Ruhrstadion	VfL Bochum		97	2023
12	Red Bull Arena	RB Leipzig		71.5	2020

German 2. Bundesliga (2nd Division)

Rank	Stadium	Team	Capacity kWp Stadium Roof	Capacity kWp Stadium Grounds	Operation start
1	Merkur Spiel-Arena	Fortuna Düsseldorf	1500		2025 (proj.)
2	Fritz-Walter-Stadion	1. FC Kaiserslautern	1350		2010
3	RheinEnergieSTADION	1. FC Köln	1200		2025 (proj.)
4	Stadion am Böllenfalltor	SV Darmstadt 98	1.200		2024
5	Jahnstadion Regensburg	SSV Jahn Regensburg	632		2025
6	Olympiastadion Berlin	Hertha BSC	605.25		2022
7	Volksparkstadion	Hamburger SV	520		2011
8	Home Deluxe Arena	SC Paderborn 07	500*		2012
9	Sportpark Ronhof	SpVgg Greuther Fürth	319.8		2022
10	Max-Morlock-Stadion	1. FC Nürnberg	284		2010
11	Eintracht-Stadion	Eintracht Braunschweig	262.3		2023
12	Wildpark	Karlsruher SC	100		2022
13	VELTINS-Arena	FC Schalke 04		600	2012

Swiss Super League

Rank	Stadium	Team	Capacity kWp Stadium Roof	Operation start
1	Stadion Wankdorf/Stade de Suisse	BSC Young Boys	1350	2005
2	Kybunpark	FC St. Gallen	1205	2015
3	swissporarena	FC Luzern	1097	2016
4	Stade de Genève	Servette FC	942	2019
5	St. Jakob-Park	FC Basel	850	2013
6	Stade de la Tuilière	FC Lausanne-Sport	800*	2020
7	Stade Municipal	Yverdon Sport FC	500*	2024
8	Letzigrund Stadion	FC Zürich / GH Zürich	223	2007
9	Stadion Schützenwiese	FC Winterthur	63.44	2014

Austrian Bundesliga

Rank	Stadium	Team	Capacity kWp Stadium Roof	Operation start
1	Generali Arena	FK Austria Wien	825	2018-2024
2	28 Black Arena / Wörthersee Stadion	SK Austria Klagenfurt	137.5	2013

Dortmund [18]
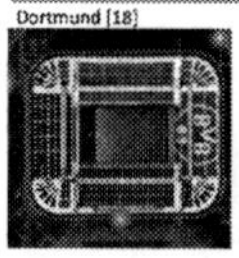
Millerntor, St. Pauli, Hamburg [19]

Weserstadion Bremen [20]

Fritz-Walter-Stadion, Kaiserslautern [21]

Europa-Park, Freiburg [22]

Böllenfalltor, Darmstadt [23]

Eintracht-Stadion Braunschweig [24]

Olympiastadion, Berlin [25]
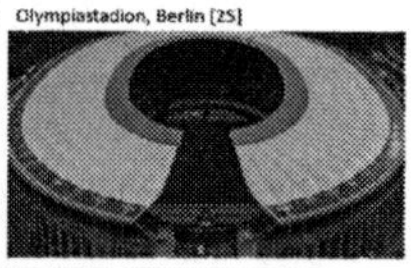

Regional Disparities

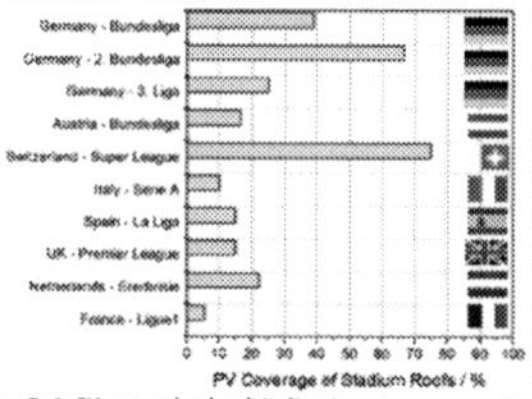

- **D-A-CH countries** lead, indicating strong support from policies as well as sustainability initiatives
- **Major leagues** lag: sunlight or budgets alone are not decisive factors for the introduction of PV

Tournament-Driven PV-Integration (2008-2024)

Tournament	Host(s)	Evidence of PV on (Host) Stadiums	Assessment
EURO 2008	Austria/ Switzerland	**Green Goal 2006** sustainability principles were integrated into planning, with some PV measures implemented. **Solar Stadia**: Initiative for PV on stadium roofs to raise awareness of sustainability	**Moderate** (pioneering initiatives, limited tournament-driven PV, upgrades came later)
WC 2010	South Africa	**Green Goal 2010** feasibility studies examined PV for Cape Town Stadium, overall focus on efficiency/lighting. No large PV roofs documented.	**Weak** (PV considered, but not widely implemented)
EURO 2012	Poland/Ukraine	No evidence of PV roofs across host stadiums	**Weak** (no clear EURO-driven rollout)
WC 2014	Brazil	at least four WC stadiums with ~5.4 MW_p PV combined	**Strong** (clear link between WC prep and PV roofs, visible PV boost)
EURO 2016	France	few strong cases (Nice: energy-positive on match days, Bordeaux: large PV carport), but not across all venues.	**Moderate** (no tournament-wide PV program or major new rooftop deployment)
WC 2018	Russia	focus on certifications/efficiency upgrades (BREEAM, LED, HVAC). No evidence of significant PV roofs at host stadiums	**Weak** (sustainability yes, PV roofs no)
EURO 2020 (played 2021)	Pan-European	no tournament-wide PV program, little evidence of new, event-driven PV rooftop deployments, Amsterdam stadium with existing PV roof	**Weak** (flagship example, but not generalized across venues)
WC 2022	Qatar	focus on solar-supported cooling/energy, only 2 documented stadium roof PV systems	**Weak to moderate** (solar present, but not mainly roof PV)
EURO 2024	Germany	UN: Initiative for Climate Action, UEFA: Climate Fund: United by football, together for nature, venue-driven PV installations or expansions	**Strong** (multiple PV stadium projects, partly accelerated by the tournament)

Policy and Tournament Effects

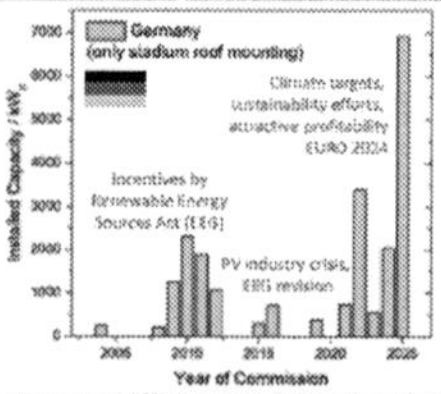

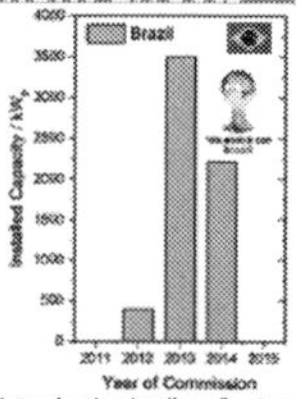

- **Germany** (*diffusion model*): Broad, gradual introduction in all professional leagues, mainly due to political framework conditions, falling costs and renovations; tournaments were supportive but not decisive
- **Brazil** (*catalyst model*): 2014 World Cup triggered event-related peak

Summary

- Strong rise in PV on stadiums since 2008, with clear regional and temporal disparities
- A few other European countries are pioneers; other regions show slower uptake
- International tournaments (WC, EURO) gave impulses but no systematic boost
- Many new projects focus on efficiency/certification more than PV
- Documented capacities range from symbolic to multi-MW installations

Outlook

- Growth driven by climate policies and the visibility of football stadiums as sustainability showcase
- Future installations might combine PV with energy efficiency, storage, and smart operation concepts
- Regional disparities may persist, but falling PV costs and climate commitments could globally accelerate
- Upcoming tournaments (e.g. WC 2030) may trigger further PV projects

References: [illegible] [25] https://www.polarstern-energie.de/mieterstrom/olympiastadion-berlin/

020310-001

42nd European Photovoltaic Solar Energy Conference and Exhibition

This presentation was selected by the Sc. Committee of the EU PVSEC 2025 for submission of a full paper to one of the EU PVSEC's collaborating peer-reviewed journals.

A TALE OF TWO DUSTS: MIMICKING SITE-SPECIFIC SOILING DYNAMICS AND CLEANING APPROACHES FOR PV PLANTS

J. Montoya[1], D. Olivares[1], E. Pilat[2], J. P Rakotoniaina[2], A. Marzo[3], V. Del Campo[4], E. Fuentealba[1], M. Gaete[1], J. Aimé[2], R. Couderc[2], D. Muñoz[2], J.A. Tsanakas[2]*

[1] Centro de Desarrollo Energético Antofagasta (CDEA), Universidad de Antofagasta, 02800, Antofagasta, Chile
[2] CEA, Liten, Univ. Grenoble Alpes, Campus INES, 73375 Le Bourget du Lac, France
[3] Departamento de Óptica, Universidad de Granada, Spain
[4] Departamento de Física, Universidad Técnica Federico Santa María, España 1680, Valparaíso, Chile

*corresponding author : ioannis.tsanakas@cea.fr

ABSTRACT: Replicating and understanding site-specific soiling dynamics is crucial for optimizing PV designs and modelling, in-field soiling monitoring and cleaning strategies. This study discusses a multi-parameter testing protocol for soiling and cleaning of PV modules, under controlled conditions using dust samples from two distinct environments: the Atacama Desert and Southern France. A novel experimental setup, incorporating a soiling and cleaning chamber, was employed to replicate real-world deposition and removal processes. The impact of soiling was assessed through I-V characterization, comparing different PV module configurations. Results indicate that anti-soiling and anti-reflective coatings mitigate optical losses more effectively than standard glass covers, whereas encapsulant choice has a negligible effect in soiling-induced optical losses. Cleaning tests revealed that high brush rotation speeds with soft bristles yielded the highest efficiency (68.2%). Additionally, the study successfully simulated desert cementation processes, validating the accelerated testing methodology. These findings provide valuable insights for optimizing PV maintenance strategies and enhancing module design, contributing to improved energy yield in soiling-prone regions.

Keywords: *PV systems; soiling; soiling losses; soiling mitigation.*

1 INTRODUCTION: CONTEXT and AIM

Photovoltaic (PV) systems, especially in soiling-prone sites such as in arid dusty regions, marine/coastal environments and sites near intense agricultural activities, suffer significant energy losses due to soiling. These losses can reach 20% to 30% per year, resulting in financial losses exceeding €10 billion in 2023 [1]. The behaviour and impact of soiling vary widely depending on environmental conditions, the dust composition, and the properties of PV materials. Regional factors such as dust origin, particle size, hydrophobicity, and mineral content all play critical roles in determining how soiling mechanisms develop and how effectively they can be mitigated [2]. Despite its importance, the influence of these diverse variables is not yet fully understood nor quantified, particularly when comparing starkly different climatic and environmental contexts. Therefore, next to advanced tools for in-field soiling monitoring and assessment, it is essential to develop indoor ("accelerated") soiling testing protocols, in order to mimic dust deposition (and eventual soiling losses) in controlled environment, under the combined influence of environmental and PV parameters. Understanding exactly such site- or climate- specific soiling dynamics, can, in turn, help PV industry in developing optimized soiling mitigation strategies at O&M level, as well as reinforce PV modules' resilience against soiling, at design level.

The Atacama Desert and Southern France represent two regions with vastly distinct environmental conditions and dust characteristics. The Atacama, one of the driest places on Earth, produces fine, hydrophobic dust particles that tend to adhere stubbornly to PV surfaces. In contrast, the dust in Southern France is generally coarser and more mineral-rich, with its soiling behaviour influenced by Mediterranean humidity and seasonal variability. These differences present an opportunity to study how dust properties and environmental conditions affect soiling losses, adhesion, and cleaning efficacy.

In this study, we employ a novel setup for accelerated soiling and cleaning tests of two distinct dust samples from the aforementioned regions. Through the designed testing protocol, overall aim of the study is to mimic soiling dynamics and evaluate cleaning strategies for PV modules, in controlled laboratory conditions, under the influence of: i) different bill of materials (BOMs) selection, ii) different environmental conditions and iii) different cleaning parameters. By systematically comparing and quantifying soiling dynamics and cleaning parameters, our end-goal is to draw valuable conclusions and insights into the interaction of PV site-specific factors with soiling and cleaning processes, to further guide towards streamlined O&M for soiling-prone PV plants.

2 METHODOLOGY – APPROACH

Two specific test benches developed and operating at CEA [3] were employed in this study (Fig. 1): a soiling chamber (Fig. 1, top) and a cleaning chamber (Fig. 1, bottom). For all the designed tests, the impact of soiling is evaluated through I-V characterization of the tested PV laminates under standard test conditions (STC), using a Class A+ PASAN solar simulator. The soiling chamber, equipped with a dust generator, enables the homogeneous and repeatable soiling of PV modules. A precise mass of pre-dehydrated dust is loaded into a piston, which forms part of the dust generator and ensures accurate control over the volume flow of injected dust. Carried by dry air at a controlled pressure, the dust is directed onto a deflector, creating a dust cloud within the chamber. This suspended dust gradually settles on the modules placed on the sample holder plate, which can be tilted between 0° and 90°. This process completes a fully controlled soiling operation, referred to as an "injection". The chamber also includes various devices for adjusting key parameters such as temperature and humidity during testing. The interior temperature can be regulated between 15°C and 50°C, the temperature of the sample holder plate can be set between 10°C and 50°C, and the relative humidity can be controlled up to 90%.

The studied samples, also fabricated at CEA-INES facilities, comprise of "mini PV modules" (i.e. single-cell PV laminates), with silicon heterojunction (SHJ) solar cells, in different bill of materials (BOM) combinations in terms of front cover coatings and encapsulants.

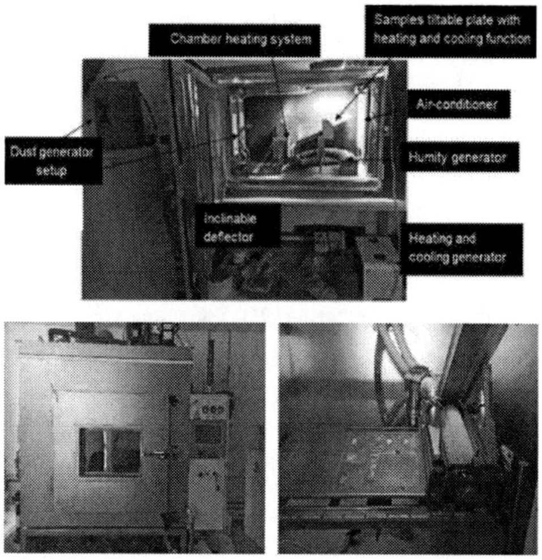

Figure 1: The lab setup at CEA-INES developed and employed for controlled replication of soiling, cleaning tests and dust characterization. Top: the soiling chamber and its different components. Bottom-left: External view of the cleaning chamber. Bottom-Right: Inside view of the cleaning chamber.

The entire experimental sequence applied, for the ***soiling study***, consists of four main steps: 1) Electrical characterization (I_{sc} and P_{max}) and transmittance measurements of PV laminate-sample and glass sample at clean state (reference measurements); 2) Soiling injection; 3) Post-soiling measurements; 4) Manual cleaning of PV laminate, return to clean state.

For the case of the ***cleaning study***, we have assessed 4 parameters with 3 configurations for each of them, as summarized in Table 1. It should be noted that, in the present study, we focus only on dry (waterless) cleaning. Follow-up work and results will also assess water-based cleaning sequences.

Parameters	Conf. 1	Conf. 2	Conf. 3
A : Robot moving speed	50 mm/s	250 mm/s	500 mm/s
B : Brush rotation speed	0 tour/min	100 tour/min	550 tour/min
C : Brush type	Rigid nylon	Soft nylon	horse hair (very soft)
D : front sheet	Solar	AR	Transparent

Two distinctively different types of dust (soiling) samples were applied and studied in this work. ***Dust 1*** originates from actual soiling collected in a utility-scale PV plant site located in southern France. This site has been identified by CNR (SERENDI-PV partner and PV plant owner) as susceptible to soiling due to its proximity to a quarry as well as to significant agricultural activity, both generating relatively important levels of soiling, in a region with generally little rainfall ("hot dry-summer" climate, classified as *Csa*, per the Köppen climate classification). A total 12 kg of dust/soiling was collected and sieved with a 1.6mm mesh, to be then used for the experiment. For each soiling injection experiment with Dust 1, we have adjusted the test chamber's environmental parameters taking into account typical site-specific conditions and the limits of the artificial soiling equipment:

1. 3g of dust injected (approximately 0.12 mg/cm^2), relative humidity (RH) > 80% and temperature of sample T_{sample} 17°C, (dew conditions).
2. 5g of dust injected (approximately 0.2 mg/cm^2), RH > 80% and T_{sample} 17°C (dew conditions).
3. 5g of dust injected (approximately 0.2 mg/cm^2), RH < 30% and T_{sample} 30°C (dry conditions).

Dust 2 originates from the Plataforma Solar del Desierto de Atacama (PSDA, for its acronym in Spanish). The PSDA is located in the Atacama Desert (24.09°S, 69.93°W) at an altitude of 963 meters above sea level, in a region classified as a cold and arid desert (BWk). The samples were exposed in the soiling chamber, specifically programmed to replicate the atmospheric conditions of the PSDA. To achieve this, meteorological data collected over a year was used, considering solar resource, temperature (°C), and relative humidity (RH) to generate a representative typical day. Based on this typical day, cycles were established to simulate nighttime conditions—characterized by high relative humidity (>70%) and low temperatures (~7°C)—while daytime conditions were recreated with high temperatures (>30°C) and low relative humidity (~40%). This indoor process was carried out in three sequential stages: (1) dust deposition, (2) simulated humidity condensation, and (3) final cementation. These conditions were applied sequentially to the samples, enabling the analysis of accelerated soiling effects under controlled laboratory conditions.

3 RESULTS and DISCUSSION

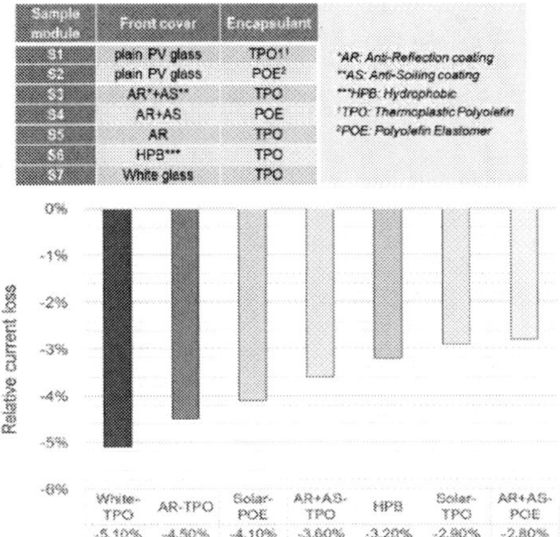

The ***soiling study*** of ***Dust 1*** was carried out for seven different BOM scenarios of tested PV laminates, in order to first quantify (and understand) the individual impact of soiling buildup on optical (and therefore power output) PV losses, for: i) different front cover (glass) coatings and ii) for different encapsulant types. So far, after a single soiling injection with *Dust 1* sample, results indicate soiling losses in the range of 3% to 5%, highly dependent on the type of front cover coating of the tested PV laminates. In particular, samples with white glass as front cover present the higher soiling losses, whereas PV laminates with anti-soiling (AS) and anti-reflective (AR) coatings on their front cover, as well as with hydrophobic (HPB) ones, seem to better "resist" against optical/current losses from soiling buildup (Fig. 2). On the other hand, the choice of the encapsulant plays minimal role to the light management and, eventually, the resulting optical/current losses from soiling, for the tested PV laminates, for the case of Dust 1. The slight absolute difference (0.5%) observed between the soiling losses for the two encapsulant types in comparison (Fig. 2) can be considered negligible, particularly with regard to the intrinsic uncertainty related to the experimental protocol. These observations are suggestive of the need to dissociate the PV laminates solely according to the nature and coating of their front cover.

Sample module	Front cover	Encapsulant
S1	plain PV glass	TPO*1
S2	plain PV glass	POE²
S3	AR*+AS**	TPO
S4	AR+AS	POE
S5	AR	TPO
S6	HPB***	TPO
S7	White glass	TPO

*AR: Anti-Reflection coating
**AS: Anti-Soiling coating
***HPB: Hydrophobic
¹TPO: Thermoplastic Polyolefin
²POE: Polyolefin Elastomer

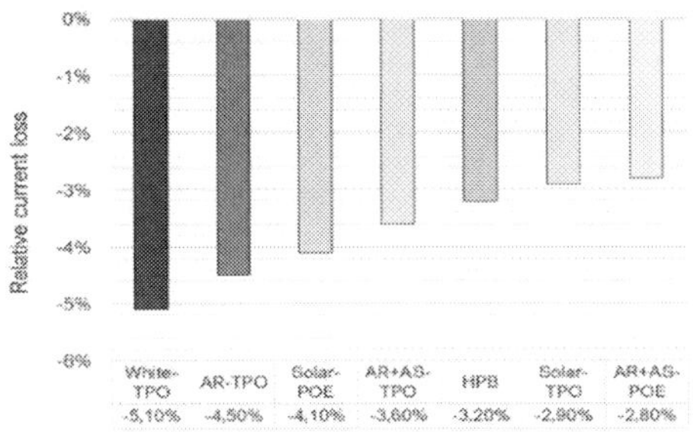

Figure 2: Relative soiling (current losses) for all PV laminates subjected to the indoor soiling testing protocol with Dust 1. Comparative results (bottom) for different bill of materials used for seven different samples (top).

For the ***cleaning study*** of ***Dust 1***, we have employed three of the tested PV laminates and performed three identical cleaning tests for each configuration. Prior to each cleaning sequence, each PV laminate was soiled with the same conditions and scale of dust particles (<35 μm) that were already used in the soiling study. The amount of dust deposited on each module is around 0.25 mg/cm², which corresponds to an I_{sc} loss of around 4.5%. The impact after each operation soiling and cleaning is assessed by measuring the I_{sc}, under STC, with the employed solar simulator. Preliminary results (Fig. 3), for the case of Dust 1 and the cleaning configurations described in Table 1, are suggestive of the higher average cleaning efficiency (68.2%) of Configuration 3, in comparison with that of Configurations 1 and 2 (25.1% and 41.9% respectively). From the results, we may also conclude that the process in Configuration 3 is significantly more repeatable, whereas it is preferable to use a high brush rotation speed, with brush made of soft bristles (e.g. horsehair), the latter being better suited to protect the PV modules' front cover coatings that are often sensitive to abrasion. Besides, such configuration allows also the cleaning cart to be driven at high speeds, which, in practice, can contribute to significant reduction in cleaning time and costs.

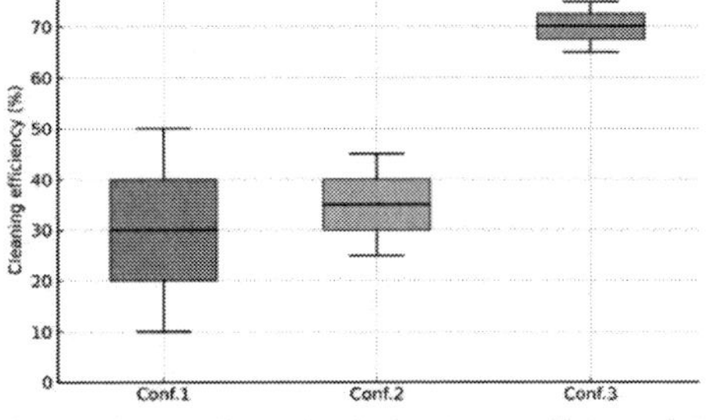

Figure 3: Comparative results for the cleaning efficiency of the three applied test configurations: Indicative results for the case of *Dust 1*, for the configurations described in section 2.

This section presents the preliminary results obtained in the study using ***Dust 2,*** a more detailed analysis and comparative discussion will be included in a future study. The deposition results, simulating the PSDA conditions, were analyzed using a FE-SEM Zeiss Sigma 360 scanning electron microscope. The analysis revealed well-defined prismatic particles, as shown in Fig. 4. The absence of erosion signs in these particles indicates the occurrence of a recrystallization process of soluble material. The high-humidity cycles during the night and high temperatures in the morning, replicated by the soiling chamber, facilitated crystal formation, recreating phenomena observed in real outdoor conditions, such as the formation of the well-known "desert rose."

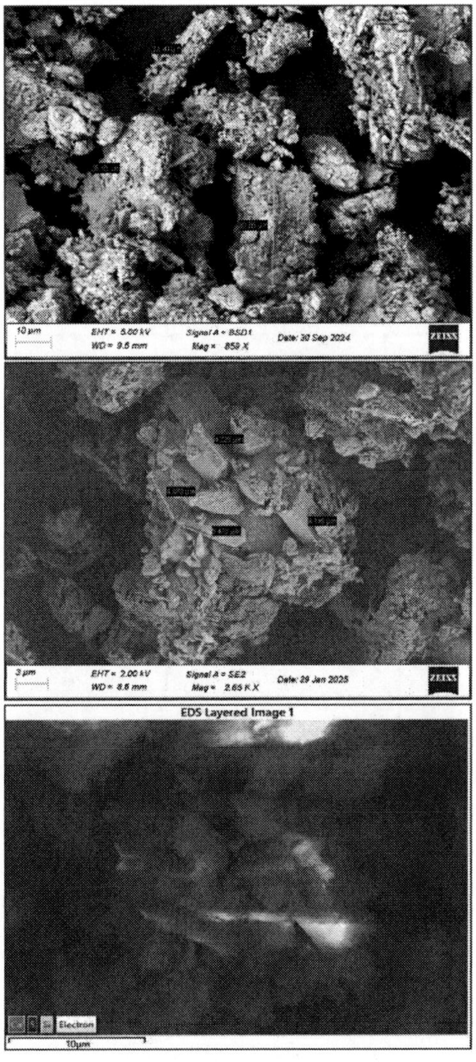

Figure 4: Top: Soiling sample obtained by sieving PSDA dust ("*Dust 2*"). Middle: Cemented soiling sample deposited on a module using the soiling chamber. Bottom: EDS image of the soiling sample deposited on a module using the soiling chamber.2.

Elemental analysis (Fig. 4, bottom) confirms these results, showing that the crystals are primarily composed of sulfur and calcium, indicating the presence of gypsum, a compound previously documented at the PSDA by Olivares et al [4]. Additionally, silicon was detected, associated with quartz, one of the most abundant materials in the desert. This quartz becomes trapped within the gypsum, clearly evidencing the cementation process. The soiling chamber demonstrated its ability to replicate the cementation process observed at the PSDA, achieving the effects of nighttime high humidity cycles and daytime high temperatures in a shorter period. This controlled environment allowed the formation of consolidated deposits like those found in real conditions, validating its effectiveness in accelerating and reproducing the deposition and recrystallization mechanisms characteristic of the region.

The ***soiling study*** for ***Dust 2*** was conducted on four samples to evaluate the impact of dust accumulation on optical and electrical losses. Results (Fig. 5) indicate an average decrease of the I_{sc} by 5%, for each increase in deposition density, which ranged between 0.45 mg/cm² and 1.15 mg/cm². Regarding optical losses, transmittance reductions were observed across the spectral range of 350 to 1100 nm, reaching 50% in samples with the highest dust density. Comparison with previous studies conducted at the PSDA indicates strong agreement with data obtained under real outdoor exposure conditions, particularly in material deposition patterns, accumulated dust density, and optical transmittance reduction [4].

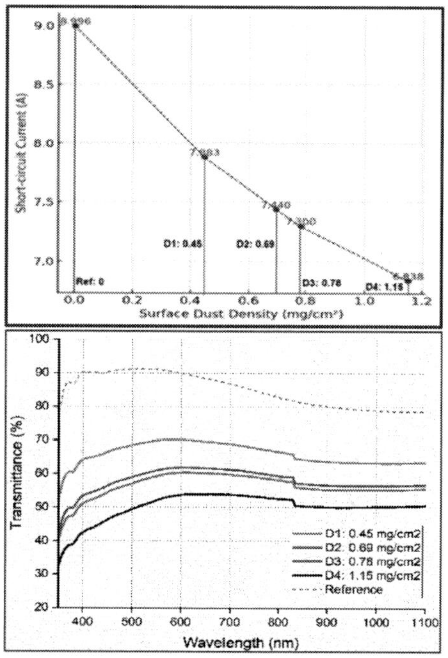

Figure 5: Top: Short-circuit current losses as a function of surface dust density. Bottom: Transmittance losses correspond to increasing dust density in each deposition: Indicative results for the case of *Dust 2*.

4 CONCLUSIONS - OUTLOOK

This work demonstrates the feasibility and relevance of employing accelerated soiling and cleaning protocols to systematically investigate the impact of site-specific dust characteristics and environmental conditions on PV module performance. By comparing dust samples from Southern France and the Atacama Desert, we highlighted the strong influence of dust morphology, mineral composition, and associated climatic conditions on soiling losses and cleaning efficiency. Results with Dust 1 (Southern France) indicate that front cover coatings play a much more critical role in mitigating soiling-induced losses than encapsulant choice, while dry cleaning efficiency is significantly improved when employing high brush rotation speeds with soft bristles. For Dust 2 (Atacama Desert), controlled indoor testing successfully replicated the cementation phenomena observed in outdoor conditions, reproducing gypsum recrystallization and dust consolidation under alternating humidity and temperature cycles. The agreement with outdoor data validates the effectiveness of the accelerated soiling protocol as a reliable surrogate for field exposure.

The study emphasizes that no universal soiling mitigation strategy can be applied across sites, as dust origin and environmental context fundamentally govern soiling dynamics and cleaning requirements. Instead, site-specific knowledge should drive both O&M strategies and PV material design. Future work will expand the testing framework by:

- extending cleaning studies to include water-based methods and hybrid approaches,
- assessing long-term durability of front cover coatings under repeated soiling/cleaning cycles, and
- refining the soiling protocols by integrating real-time outdoor data for more accurate climate-to-lab translation.

Ultimately, advancing such accelerated testing approaches can bridge the gap between laboratory investigations and real-world PV performance, thereby supporting the development of optimized, climate-tailored solutions to minimize soiling-induced energy and financial losses.

ACKNOWLEDGEMENTS

Part of this work has been carried out in the framework of the H2020 SERENDI-PV and Horizon Europe CACTUS projects. SERENDI-PV project has received funding from the European Union's Horizon 2020 research and innovation programme under grant agreement No. 953016. CACTUS project has received funding from the European Union's Horizon Europe research and innovation programme under grant agreement No. 101132182. For CEA team, part of this work was also supported by the French National Program "Programme d'Investissements d'Avenir - INES.2S" under Grant Agreement ANR ANR-10-IEED-0014 0014-01.

REFERENCES

[1] L. Micheli et al. (2024). In: *Proc. 41th EUPVSEC*, Vienna, Austria.
[2] Report IEA-PVPS T13-21:2022
[3] J.A. Tsanakas et al. (2024). In: *Proc. 41th EUPVSEC*, Vienna, Austria.

[4] D. Olivares et al. (2021). *Solar Energy Materials and Solar Cells,* 227, 111109.

10.4229/EUPVSEC2025/4CO.8.4

Zentrum für Sonnenenergie- und Wasserstoff-
Forschung Baden-Württemberg

Energie Baden-Württemberg AG

AI methods for the operation and maintenance of PV parks with bifacial photovoltaic modules

Dirk Stellbogen, Jonas Petzschmann, Elena Pabst, Roland Einhaus,
Zentrum für Sonnenenergie- und Wasserstoff-Forschung Baden-Württemberg (ZSW)

Timo Freund, Jan Wannenwetsch, Ajka Ockert, *EnBW Energie Baden-Württemberg AG*

EU PVSEC 2025, Bilbao, 24.09.2025

Motivation

- PV plants are getting larger and more complex:
  - Use of bifacially sensitive PV modules
  - Uneven possibly hilly sites
  - Various orientations
- Field measurements are often limited to aggregated currents
- Algorithmic and physical models face limits for dealing with complexity
- Delivery of reliable performance projections for monitoring and supervision is challenged

⇨ Development of AI based data models for bifacial PV parks for fault detection and power forecasts

- Installation plan details not necessary
- Generic structure for easy transfer and adaptation to other PV parks

Scope of Research Project „KIMBIF“

Joint work of research institute and owner and operator of PV plants

- ZSW: Development of data models, data processing and implementation
- EnBW: Field experimentation, provision of operational data and integration in O&M system

Bifacial PV parks by EnBW as test sites

- in Germany:
  - Alttrebbin, 151 MWp (North-East)
  - Brandscheid, 7.7 MWp (West)
  - Külsheim-Gickelfeld, 28 MWp (South-West)
- in France (VALECO):
  - Ayguetinte, 5 MWp (South-West)

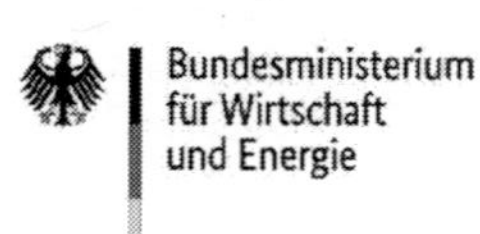

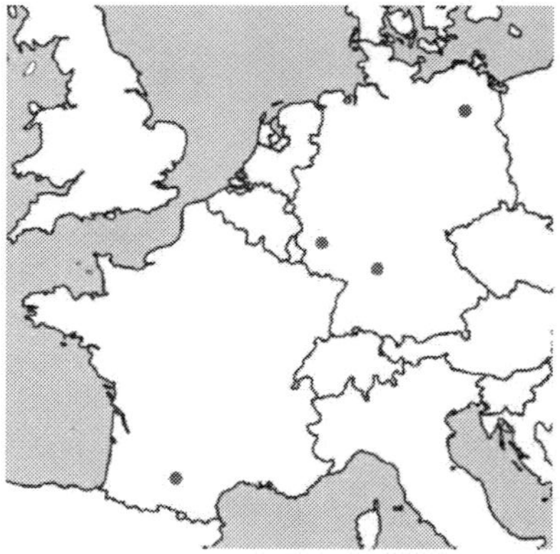

Funded by:

Bundesministerium für Wirtschaft und Energie

EnBW ZSW

Enhancement of PV Plant Monitoring System

- Addition of fault detection procedure based on data modelling
- Extension of input database with additional sensors and measurements
- Integration with existing supervision system by automized data exchange on dedicated interfaces

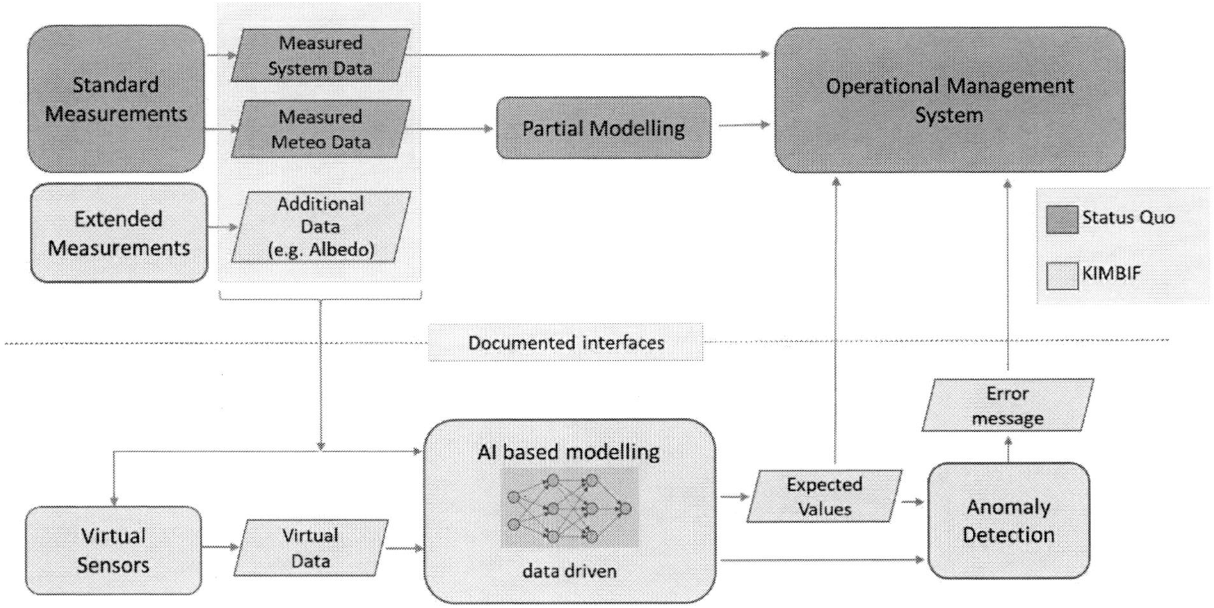

Extension of measurements

- Amplification of input data set with not commonly applied measurements
- Irradiance measurements:
  - Albedo (ground reflected irradiance)
  - Irradiance on module back plane

- Monofacial reference subsystem:
  - PV modules of selected strings covered on the backside with opaque foil
  - operating under identical conditions
  - allows direct determination of bifacial contribution

Pictures source: EnBW

Test site: Large-scale PV power plant Alttrebbin

Source: EnBW

- Location: approx. 50 km north-east of Berlin (D)
- Commissioning: 2022
- 345.072 bifacial glass-glass PV modules with 435 Wp - 440Wp
- Nominal installed power: 151 MWp
- Electrical concept: 553 DC combiner boxes connected to 30 central power stations

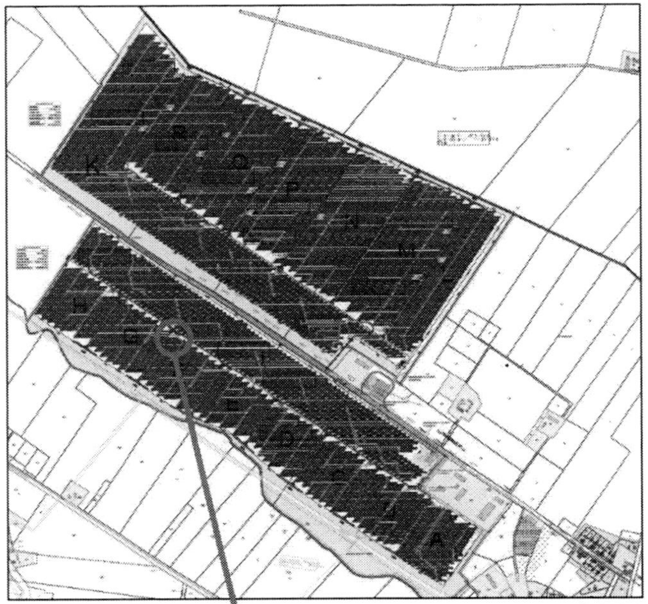

Source: EnBW

Primary testing unit

Model of PV Plant Subunit with Power Station

- Combiner box summed currents are measured at the DC inputs to the power units ("APUs")

⇨ Signals monitored for the detection of string level faults

⇨ Target figures for the data based modelling

- Pairs of power units operating independently
- Data can be used for mutual prediction with ANN

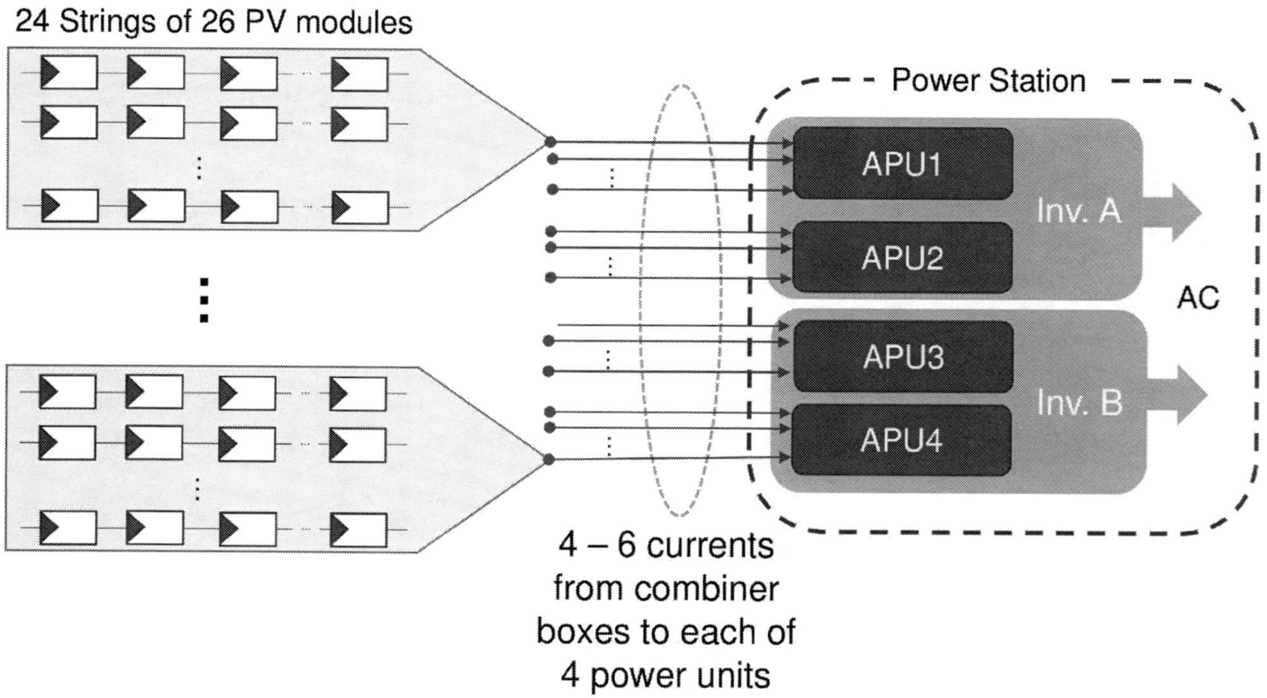

String fault experiments

- Faults were artificially implemented for development and testing of models and fault detection procedures
- 1-4 strings disconnected in combiner boxes on a daily basis
- First phase applied for training and tuning of models and algorithms, second phase used for evaluation

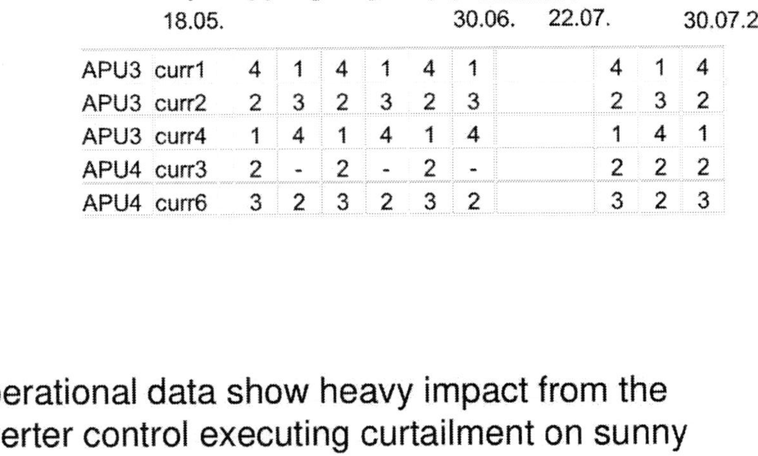

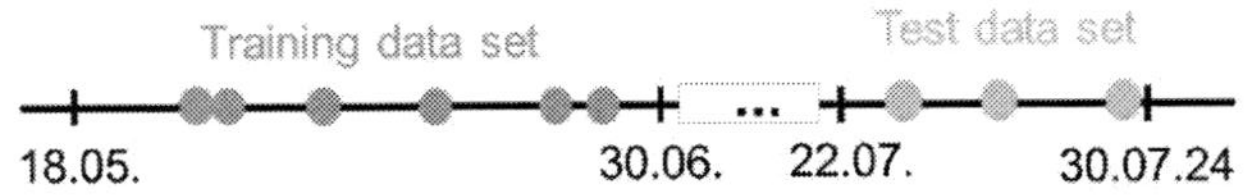

APU3	curr1	4	1	4	1	4	1		4	1	4
APU3	curr2	2	3	2	3	2	3		2	3	2
APU3	curr4	1	4	1	4	1	4		1	4	1
APU4	curr3	2	-	2	-	2	-		2	2	2
APU4	curr6	3	2	3	2	3	2		3	2	3

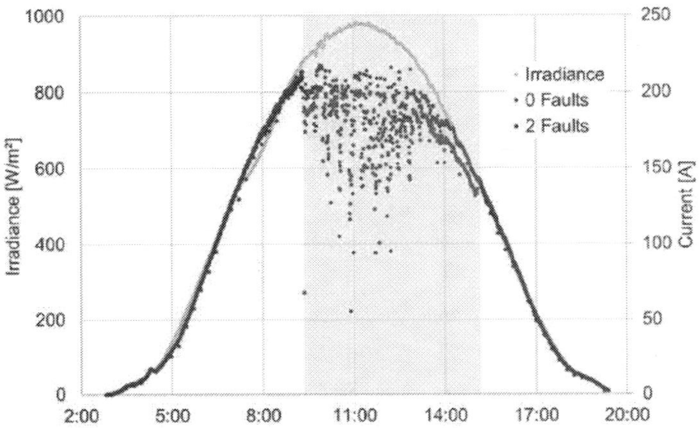

- Operational data show heavy impact from the inverter control executing curtailment on sunny conditions
- Complicates detection of string faults

EnBW ZSW

ANN structure applied for data model

- **Feed forward net**

Inputs: conditions + independent time correlated data

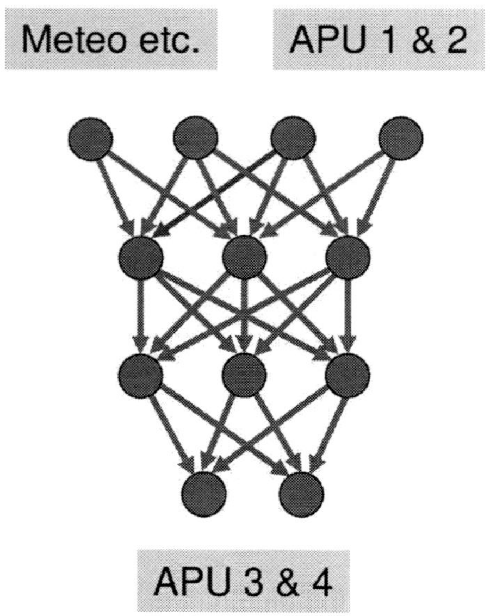

Target values

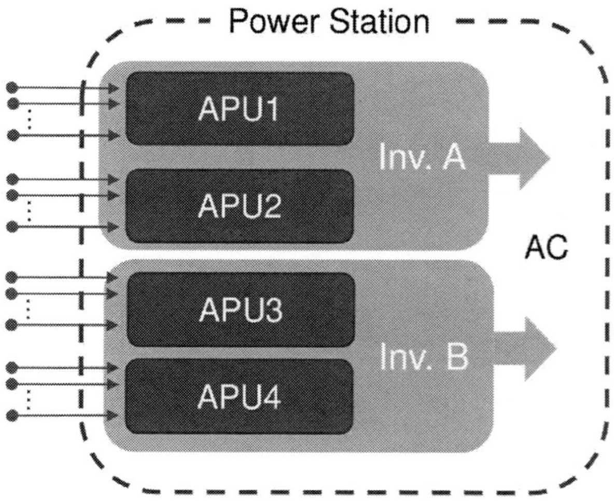

Evaluation of Fault Detection Procedures

Comparison of variant procedures:

A: ANN data model for reference values
+ algorithmic fault status analysis

B: ANN data model for reference values
+ ANN data model for error rating

C: ANN model for direct estimation of error rating

- Post-processing for combining individual error observations to string fault indications.

Variant A

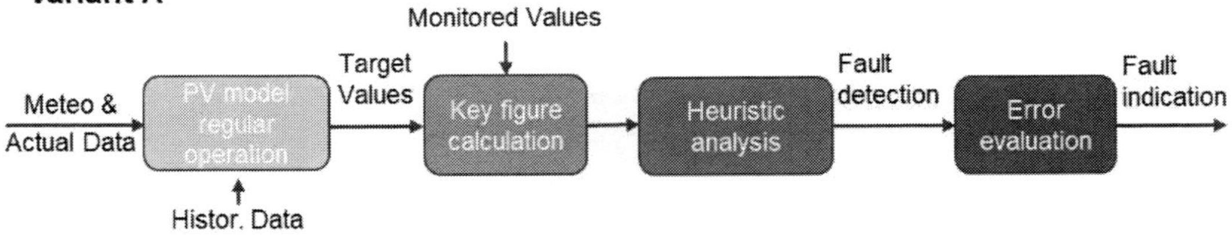

Variant B

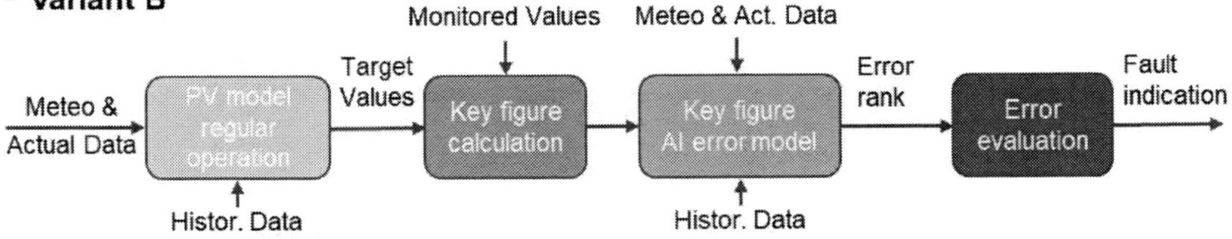

Variant C

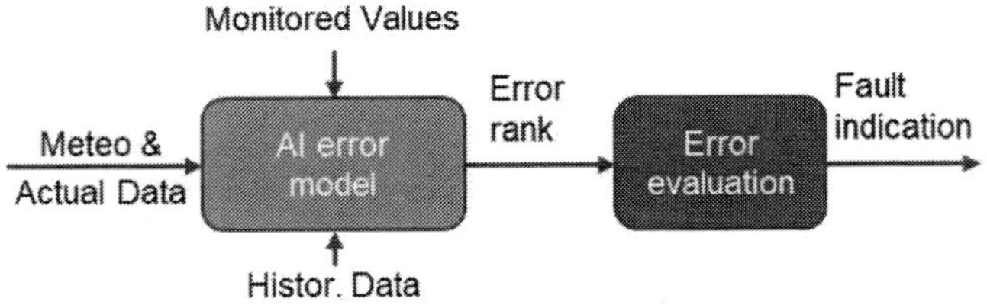

Test Results

- Data filtered for proper power unit operation states

- Generally good detection of ≥2 module string failures, single failures usually not clearly detected

- Evaluation of correct or wrong error and non-error classification with statistical metrices:
  - Accuracy: share of correct classifications
  - F1-Score: indicates how many of the error classifications are correct and how many error states are detected

⇨ Variant B with AI model for target values and AI error model performs best in all analysis

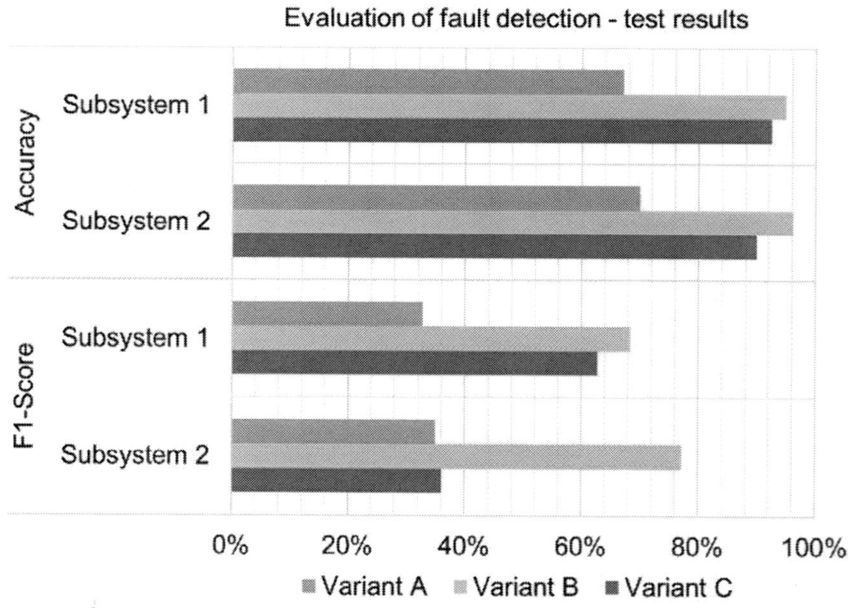

Alternative AI model type: Autoencoder

Feed forward net

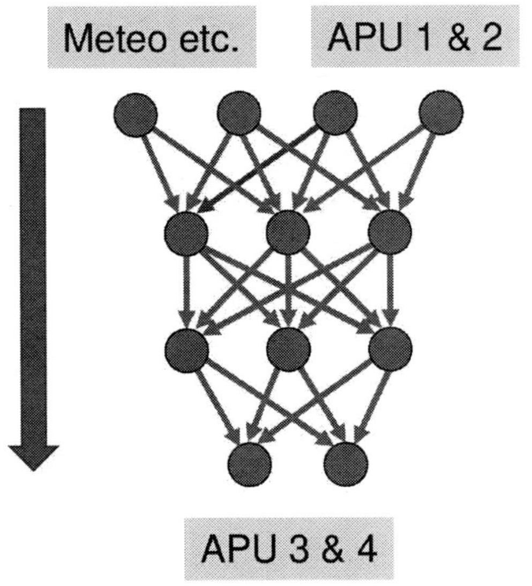

projected from independent inputs

Autoencoder

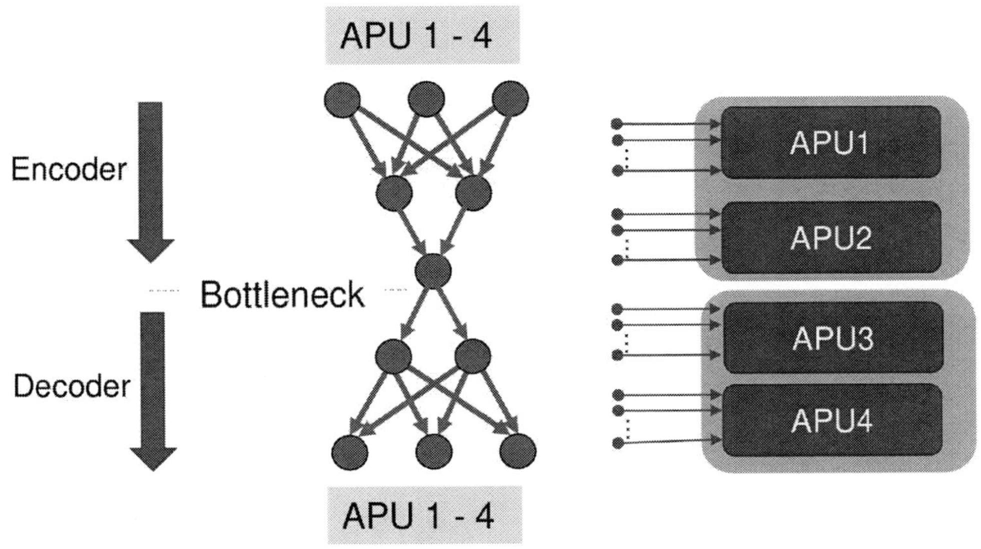

projected from internal correlations

Evaluation of Autoencoder

- Autoencoder approach reduces number of models to be trained for PV plant with multiple subunits
- Structure more easily transferable to other PV parks
- Performance allows for detection of ≥2 simultaneous string faults
- Further work is carried out bring sensitivity to 1 string fault level

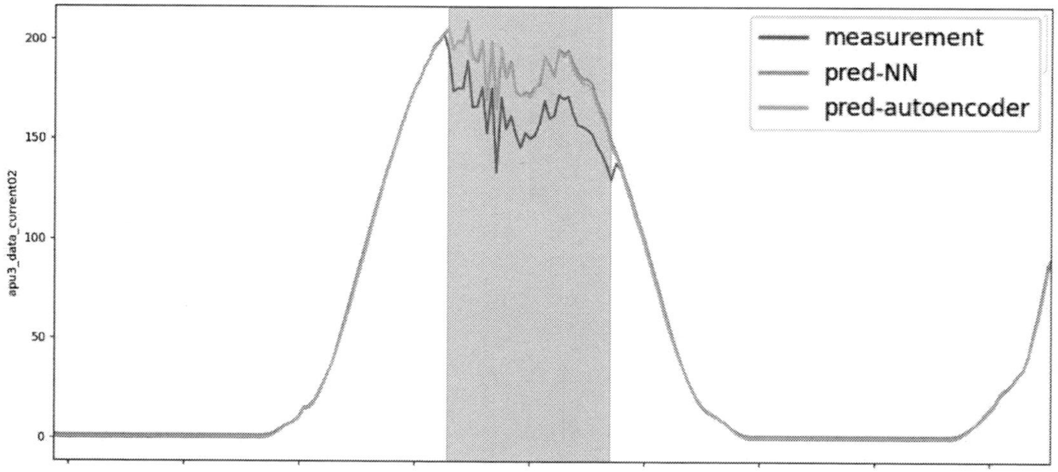

Summary

- The **complexity of large PV parks limits the feasibility** of algorithmic and physics based performance projections for monitoring and power forecasts.
- **AI based data models** are beeing developed for **string fault detection** addressing PV parks in Germany and France.
- **Field experiments with artificial faults** have been conducted to train, tune and evaluate different procedures for failure detection.
- Procedures based on **ANN models proved successful in detecting faults of 2 or more** strings connected to a combiner box.
- **Autoencoder type data models** are promising for increasing the **sensitivity of the anomaly detection** as well as easing the **transfer to other PV plants**.

Zentrum für Sonnenenergie- und Wasserstoff-
Forschung Baden-Württemberg

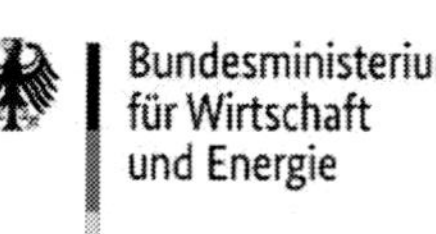

Energie Baden-Württemberg AG

ACKNOWLEDGMENT

The research was financially supported by the German Federal Ministry for Economic Affairs and Energy, contract code 03EE1177A.

Bundesministerium
für Wirtschaft
und Energie

Zentrum für Sonnenenergie- und Wasserstoff-
Forschung Baden-Württemberg

Energie Baden-Württemberg AG

THANK YOU FOR YOUR ATTENTION.

Dirk Stellbogen

E-Mail: dirk.stellbogen@zsw-bw.de

For further information, you may visit our booth C8 in the exhibition.

Stuttgart

Ulm

Ulm eLaB

Ulm HyFaB / Powder-Up!

Solar test field

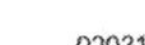

Wind test field

Fachhochschule Kiel University of Applied Sciences   Fraunhofer CSP   saferay   WATTMANUFACTUR Energie mit Mehrwert

A Comprehensive Framework for Accurate Power Degradation Estimation in Large Photovoltaic Systems using Machine Learning

Kak-Pong Cheung[1], Stephanie Malik[2], David Daßler[2], Carsten Hennig[3], Hauke Nissen[4], Patrick Hennig[1]

[1] Kiel University of Applied Sciences, Kiel, Germany;
[2] Fraunhofer CSP, Halle, Germany;
[3] saferay, Berlin, Germany;
[4] Wattmanufactur, Galmsbüll, Germany

Presented by
James Cheung

24.09.2025
EU PVSEC 2025 @ Bilbao, Spain

Motivation

Performance Degradation **Inevitable**

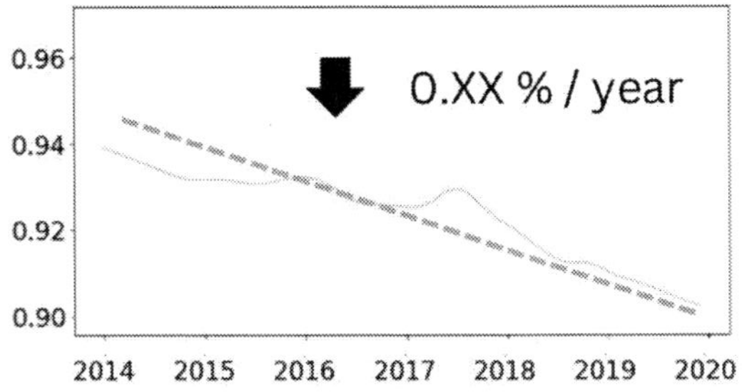

Challenges in Power Degradation Estimation

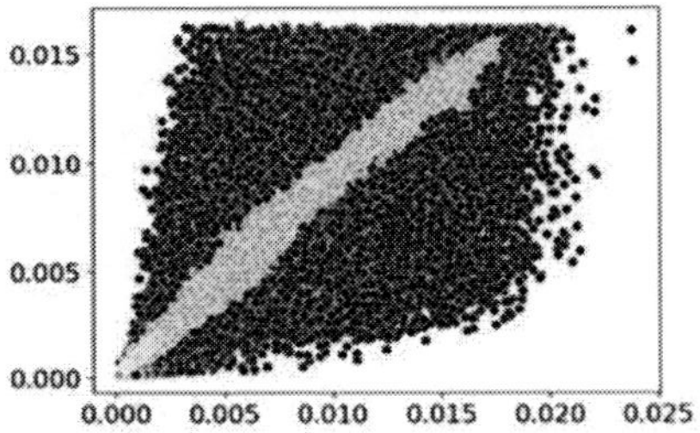

Noisy Dataset

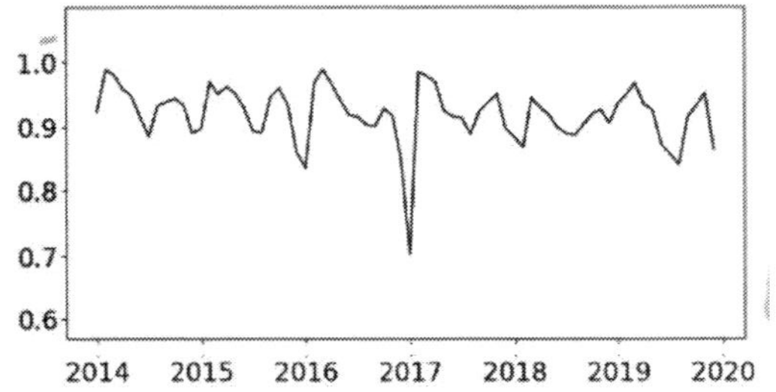

Seasonality

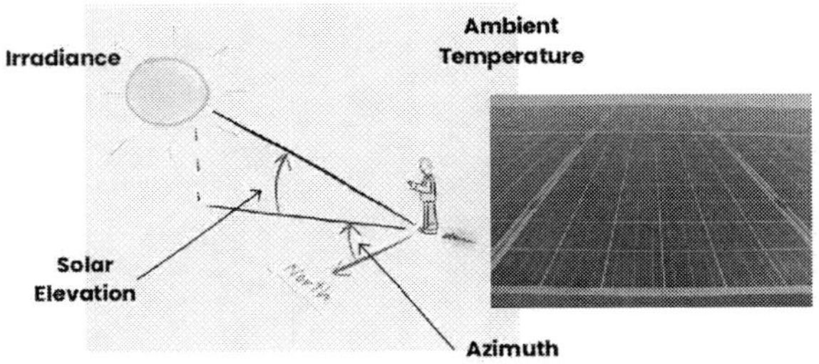

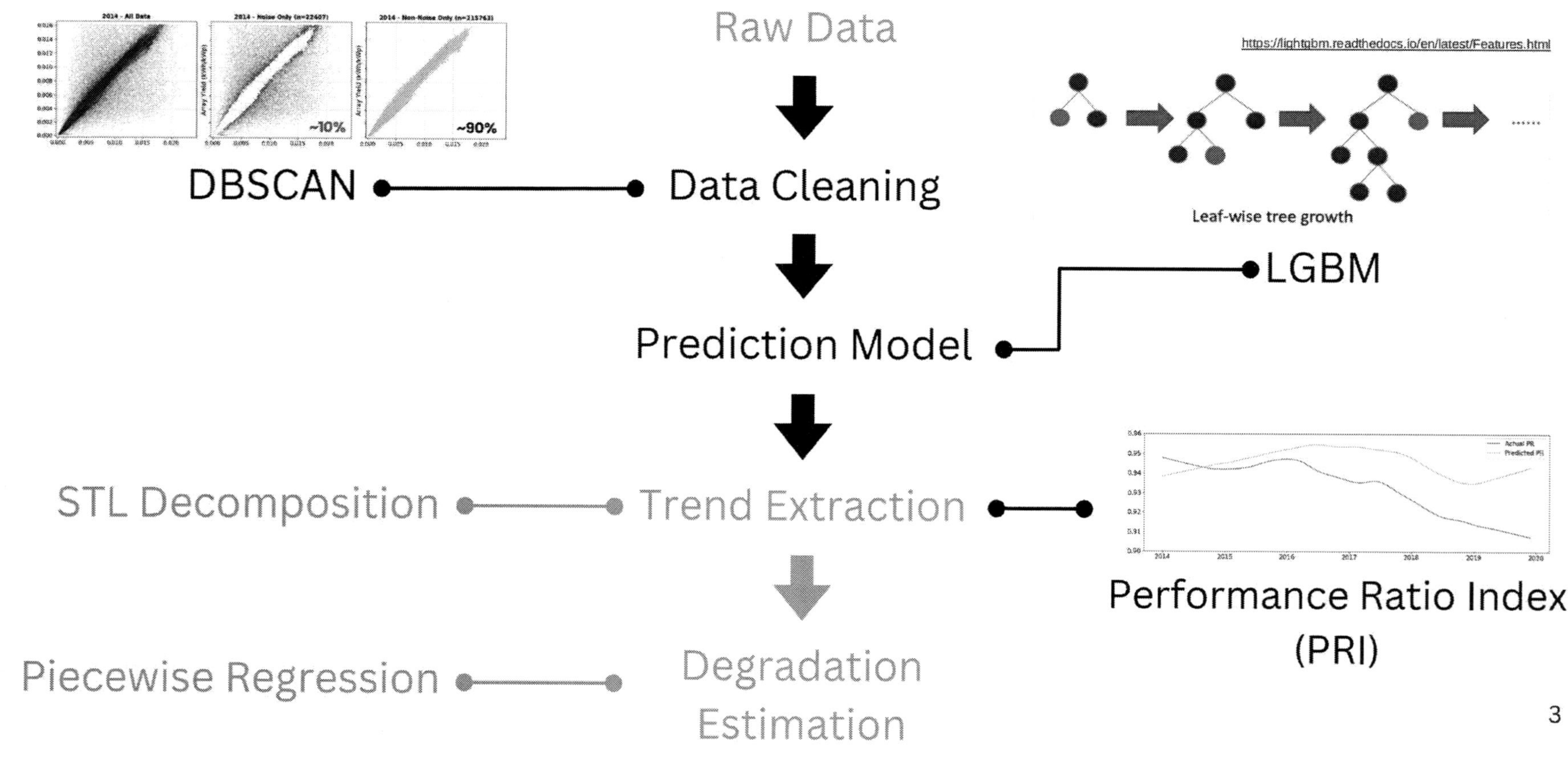

Environmental Factors

Proposed Framework

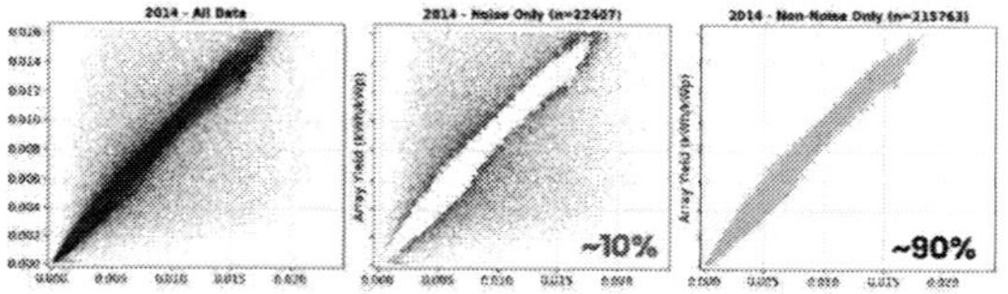

https://lightgbm.readthedocs.io/en/latest/Features.html

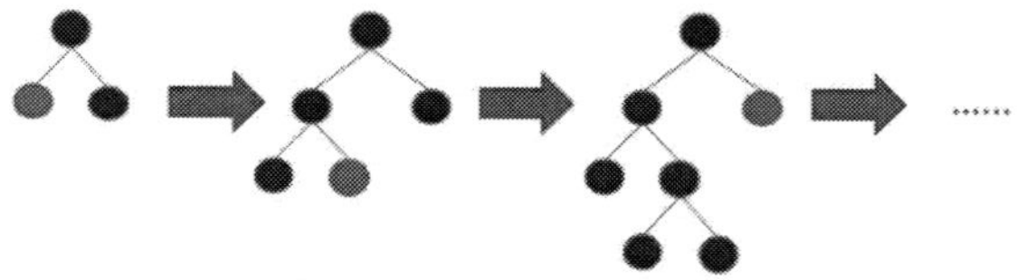

Raw Data

↓

Data Cleaning — DBSCAN

↓

Prediction Model — LGBM

↓

Trend Extraction — STL Decomposition

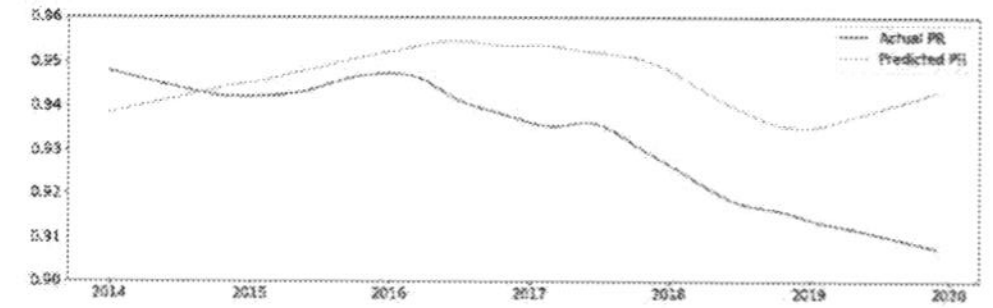

Performance Ratio Index (PRI)

↓

Degradation Estimation — Piecewise Regression

3

Raw Data | Cleaning | Predictive Model | Metric | Trend Extraction | Degradation Estimation

Data Description

SOURCE : Solar Energy Company

LOCATION : Germany (Single Site)

DATA POINT : over 12 millions from 3 central inverters

RESOLUTION : Minute

PERIOD : 2014 - 2019 (6 years)

DEVICES : Inverter, Pyranometer, Temperature Sensor

FEATURES : Date time, DC Power, Irradiance (POA), Ambient Temperature

GENERATED : Solar Elevation, Azimuth

DATA QUALITY : Less than 1% missing value / Time Gap / Abnormal Behaviour

Raw Data | **Cleaning** | Predictive Model | Metric | Trend Extraction | Degradation Estimation

Density-Based Spatial Clustering of Applications with Noise (DBSCAN)

Array Yield (kWh / kW)
DC side only

$$y_f = \frac{\Delta t}{P_{STC}} \cdot \sum_{i=1}^{N} P_i$$

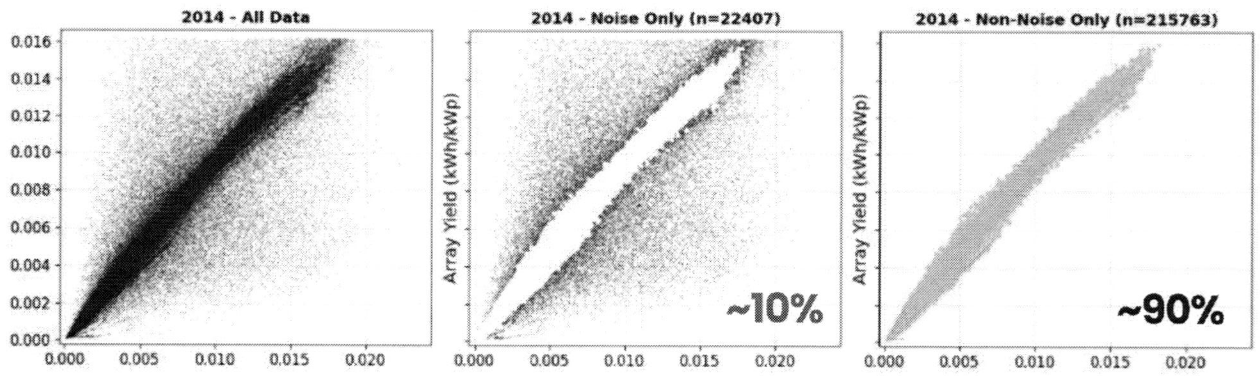

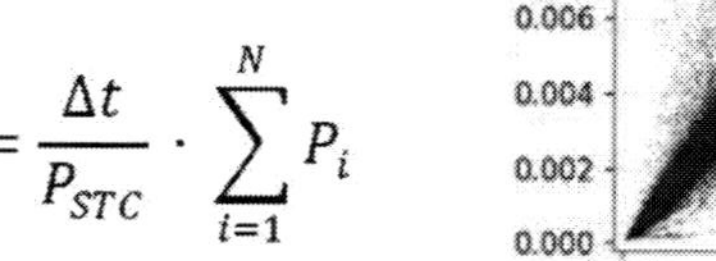

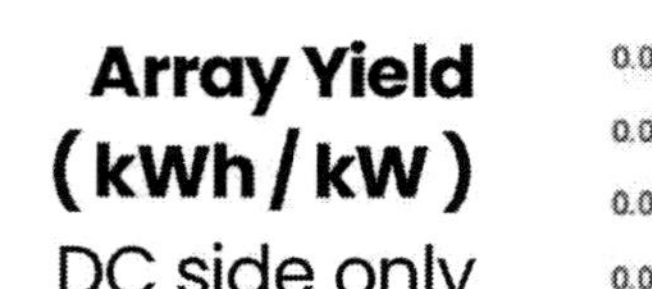

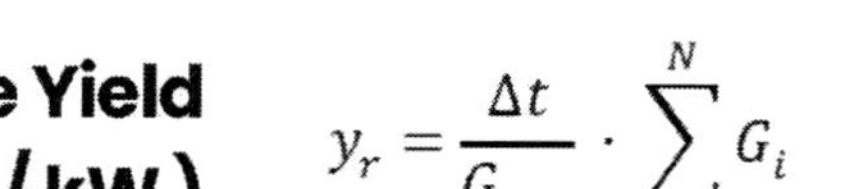

Reference Yield (kWh / kW)

$$y_r = \frac{\Delta t}{G_{STC}} \cdot \sum_{i=1}^{N} G_i$$

Light Gradient Boosting Machine (LGBM)

Input Features

Irradiance
Ambient Temperature
Solar Elevation
Solar Azimuth

Output Prediction

DC Power

Result : Mean Absolute Percentage Error (MAPE)

Year	MAPE (%)	
2014	5.46	Training
2015	9.78	Testing
2016	8.38	Testing
2017	13.83	Testing
2018	14.69	Testing
2019	7.52	Testing

Inverter 1001

Raw Data | Cleaning | **Predictive Model** | Metric | Trend Extraction | Degradation Estimation

LGBM Performance Evaluation

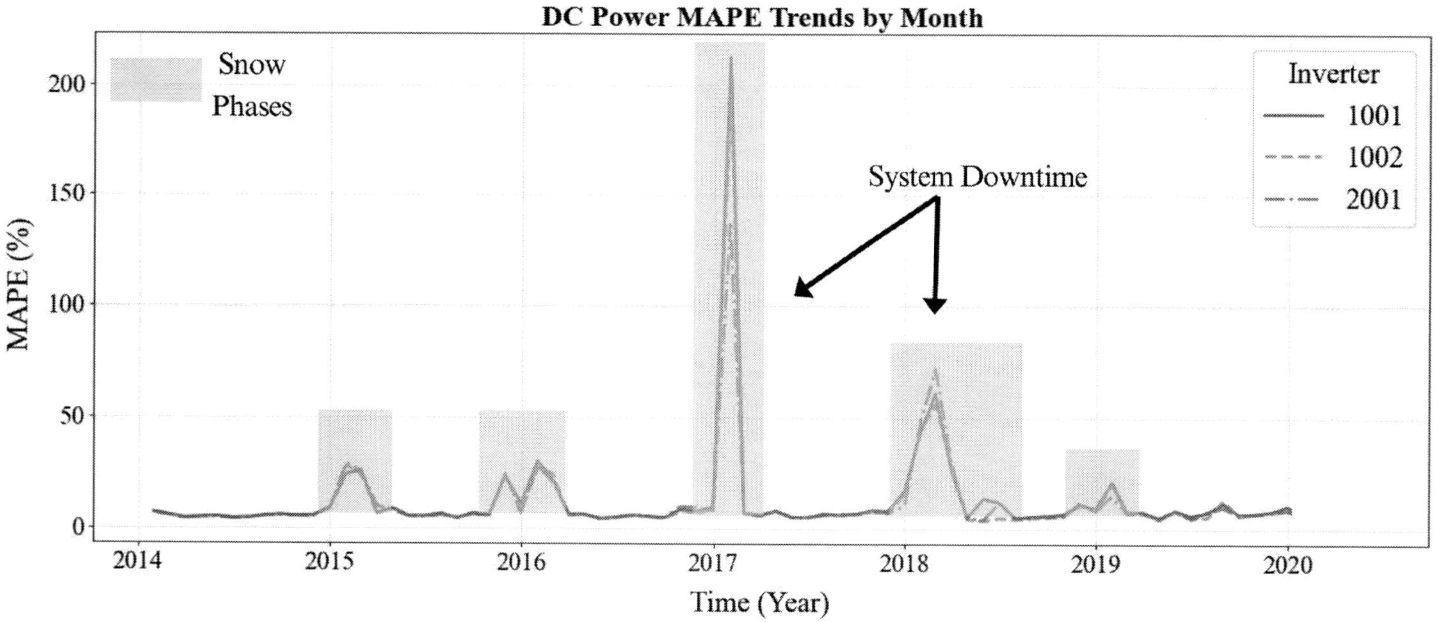

Monthly MAPE (%)

7

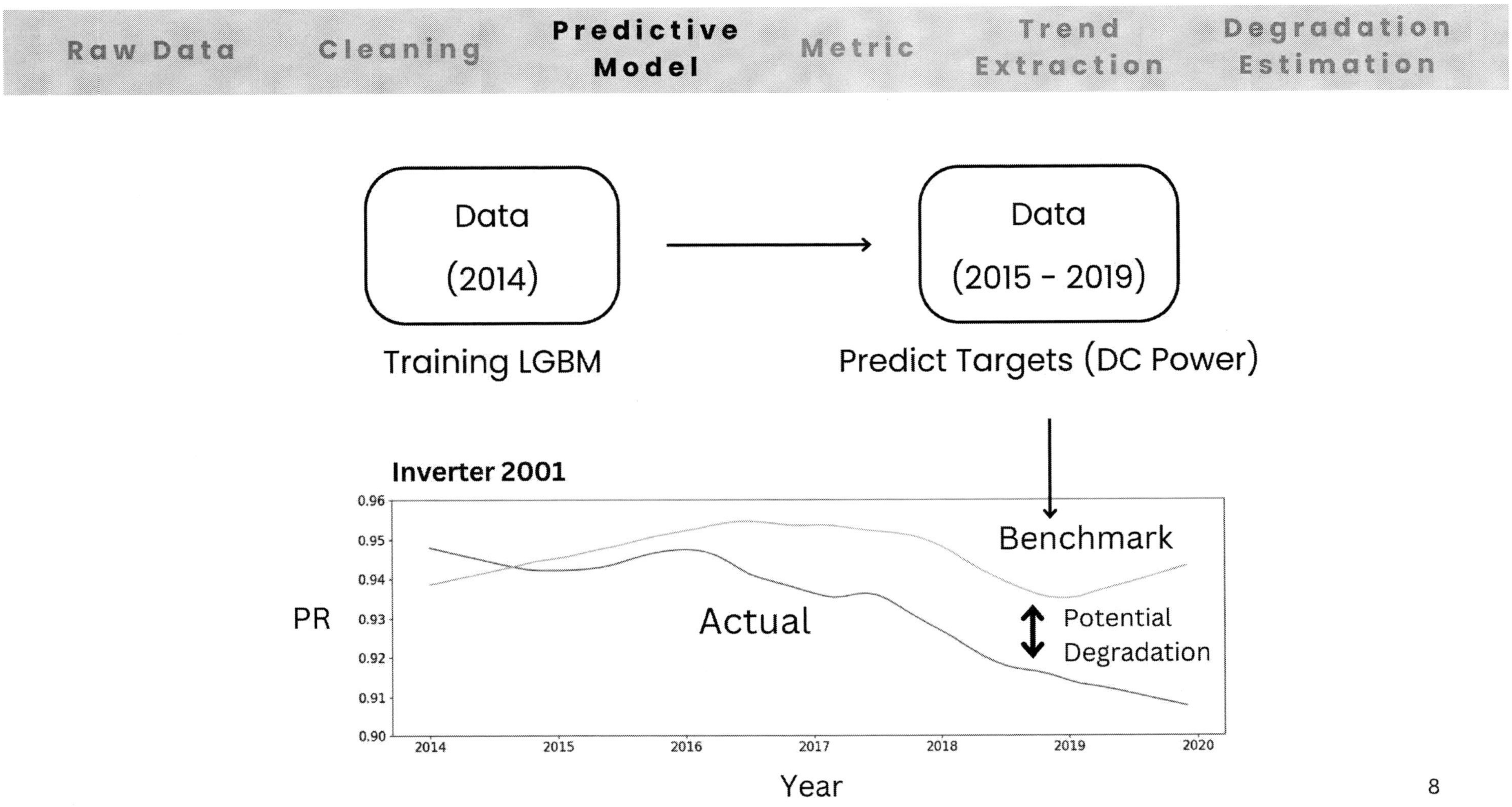
Raw Data
Cleaning
Predictive Model
Metric
Trend Extraction
Degradation Estimation
Data
(2014)
Training LGBM
Data
(2015 - 2019)
Predict Targets (DC Power)
Inverter 2001
PR
Year
Benchmark
Actual
Potential Degradation
0.96
0.95
0.94
0.93
0.92
0.91
0.90
2014
2015
2016
2017
2018
2019
2020
8

Proposed Metric

Performance Ratio Index (PRI) = $\frac{\text{Actual PR}}{\text{Predicted PR}}$

Seasonal Trend Decomposition using LOESS

PRI

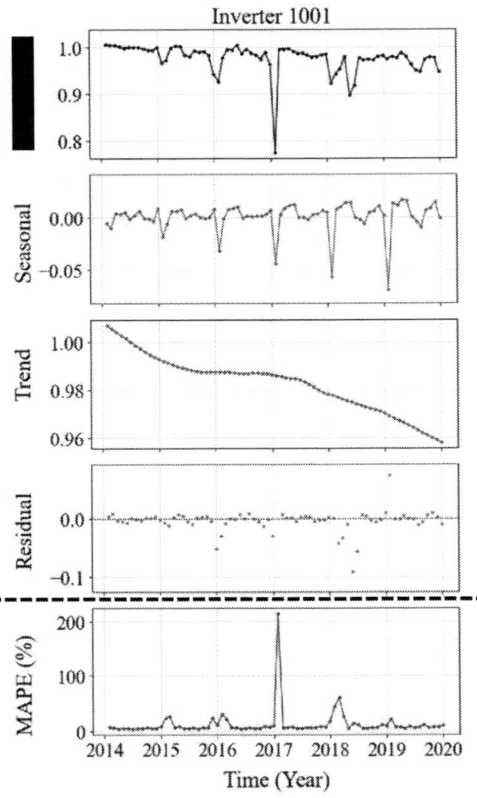

Trend Component

10

Raw Data | Cleaning | Predictive Model | Metric | Trend Extraction | **Degradation Estimation**

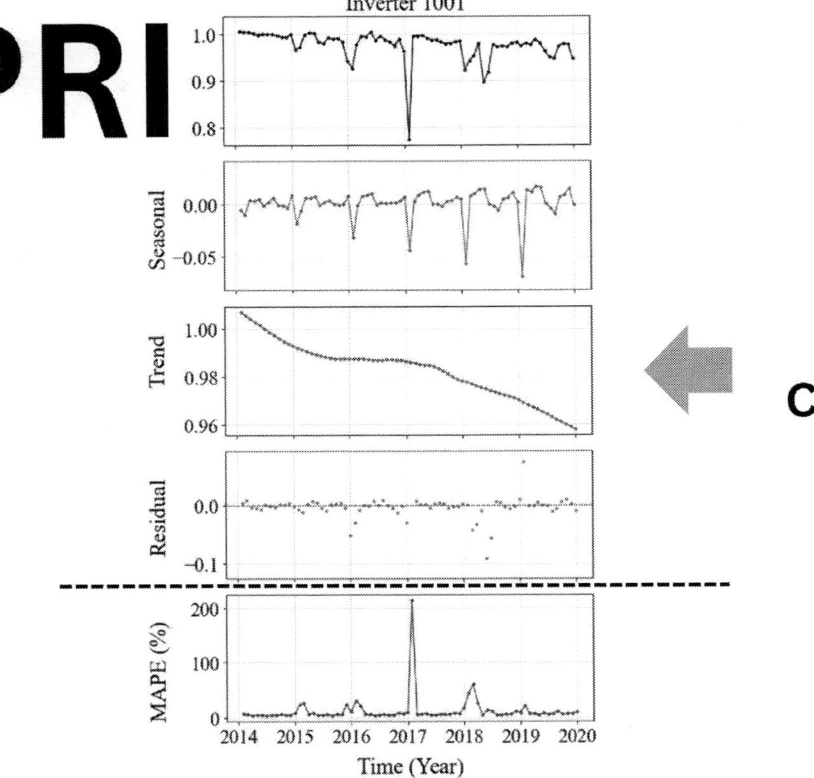

Piecewise Regression

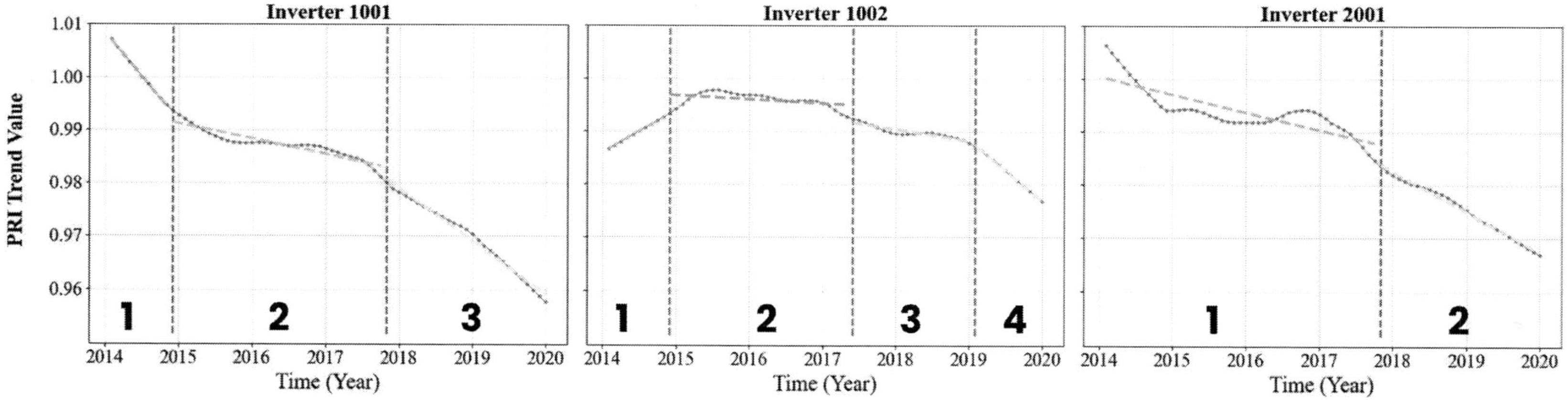

Inverter 1001	Inverter 1002	Inverter 2001
Phase 1: -1.65% / year	Phase 1: +0.81% / year	Phase 1: -0.33 % / year
Phase 2: -0.29% / year	Phase 2: -0.07% / year	Phase 2: -0.76 % / year
Phase 3: -0.99% / year	Phase 3: -0.22% / year	
	Phase 4: -1.22% / year	

PRI-Based Result

Our Result

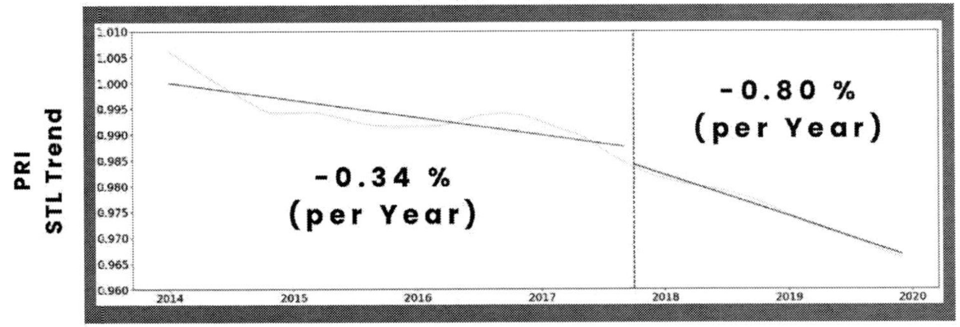

System	$\overline{PLR}$	System	$\overline{PLR}$	System	$\overline{PLR}$
EURAC	-0.85 %/a	NREL1	-0.33 %/a	US DOE luemkoy**	0.95 %/a
FOSS	-0.71 %/a	NREL2	-0.54 %/a	US DOE lwcb907	-0.03 %/a
RSE CdTe	-1.75 %/a	NREL3*	0.06 %/a	US DOE t3pg1sv	-0.75 %/a
RSE pc-Si	-0.96 %/a	NREL4	-0.25 %/a	US DOE wca0c5m***	-1.00 %/a
Pfaffstaetten A	-3.57 %/a	US DOE c10hov6	-0.50 %/a	US DOE wxysjaf	-0.97 %/a
Pfaffstaetten B	-3.96 %/a	US DOE kob-dpi8	-0.73 %/a	US DOE z0aygry***	-2.32 %/a
Pfaffstaetten C	-1.29 %/a				

Report IEA-PVPS T13-22:2021

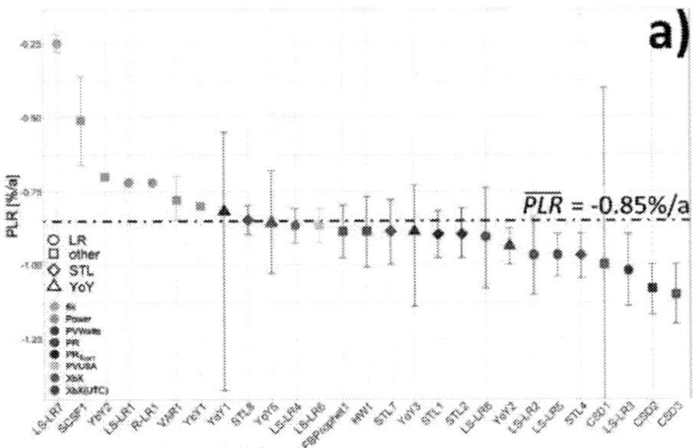

Report IEA-PVPS T13-22:2021

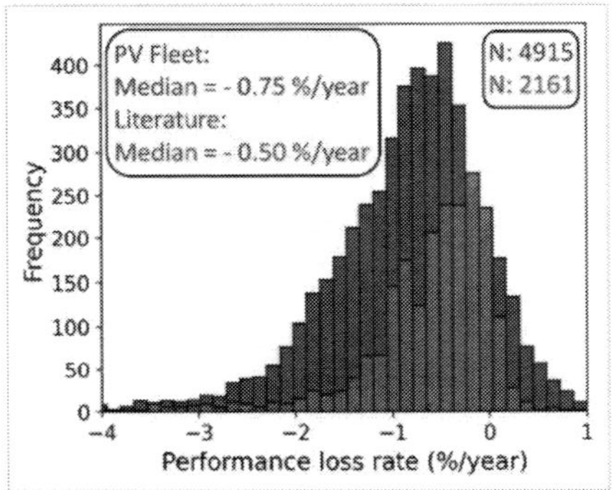

doi.org/10.1002/pip.3566

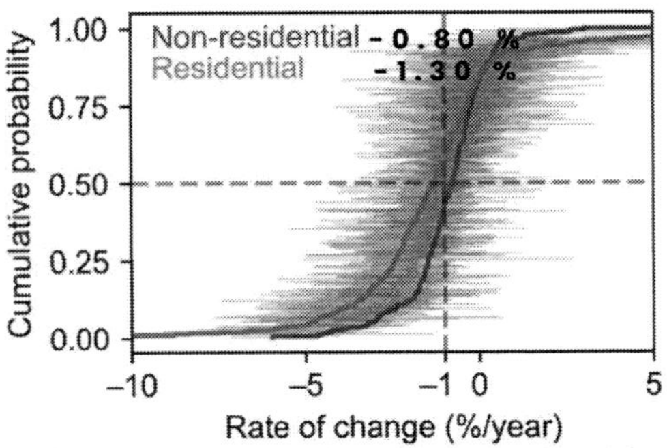

doi.org/10.1109/JPHOTOV.2018.2884948

Industry Benchmarking Results

Contribution

DBSCAN Noise Filtering

Data-driven - retain only the densest region, defined by the underlying relationship between array yield and reference yield

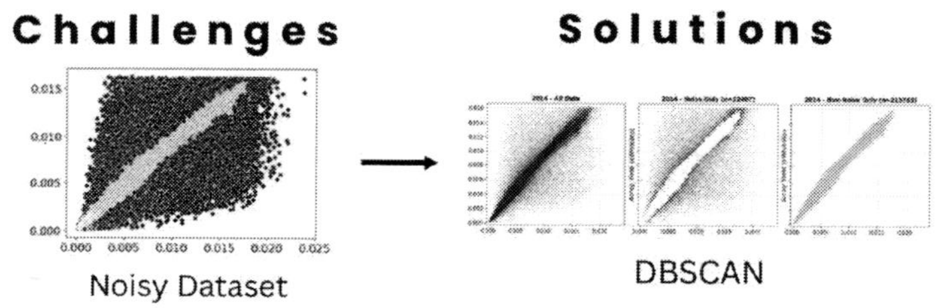

Performance Ratio Index (PRI) with LGBM Predictive Benchmarking

Environmental Independent Metric - Normalized performance by factoring out weather and solar factors

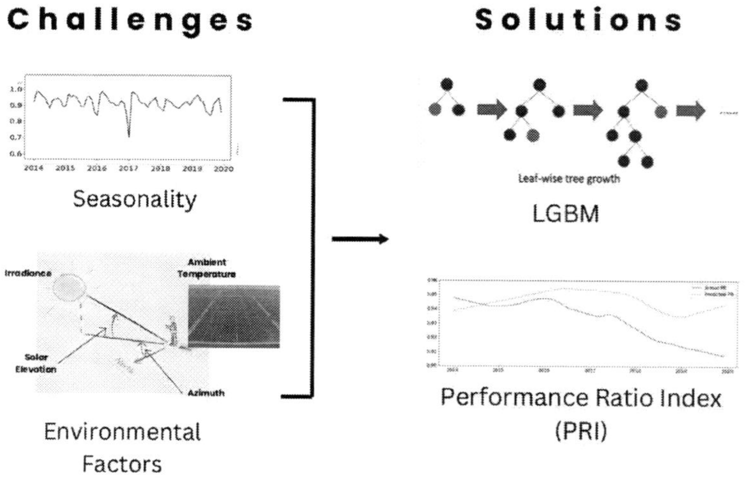

Future Work

Broaden Data Ecosystem

heterogeneous PV assets across climatic zones and manufacturers

Comparative Modeling Landscape Exploration

Systematically evaluate diverse A.I. predictive architectures

Model-Guided Data Curation

Leverage predictive model performance (e.g. MAPE-based filters)

14

THANK YOU

Contact Information

James Cheung

kak.p.cheung@fh-kiel.de

+49 176 8757 7924

Fachhochschule Kiel
University of Applied Sciences

15

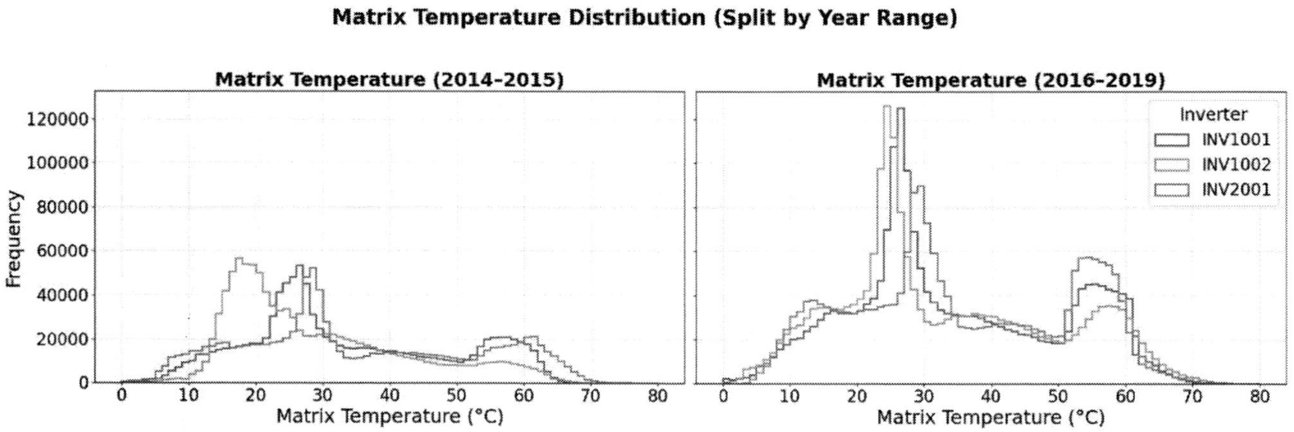
Matrix Temperature Distribution (Split by Year Range)
Matrix Temperature (2014-2015)
Matrix Temperature (2016-2019)
Frequency
120000
100000
80000
60000
40000
20000
0
0
10
20
30
40
50
60
70
80
Matrix Temperature (°C)
Inverter
INV1001
INV1002
INV2001

16

DBSCAN RESULTS

2014
2015
2016
2017
2018
2019

INVERTER: 1001

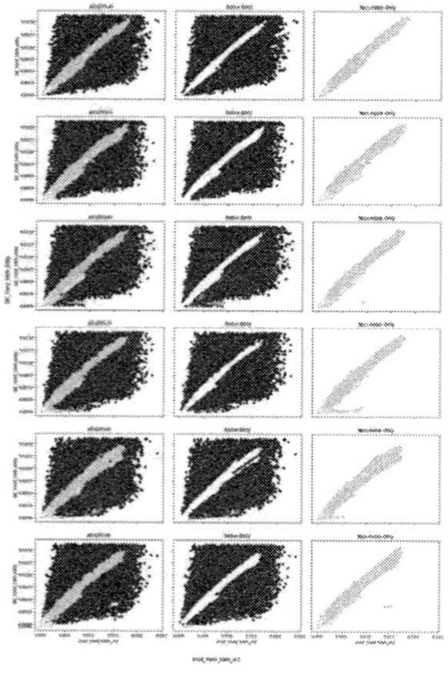

INVERTER: 1002

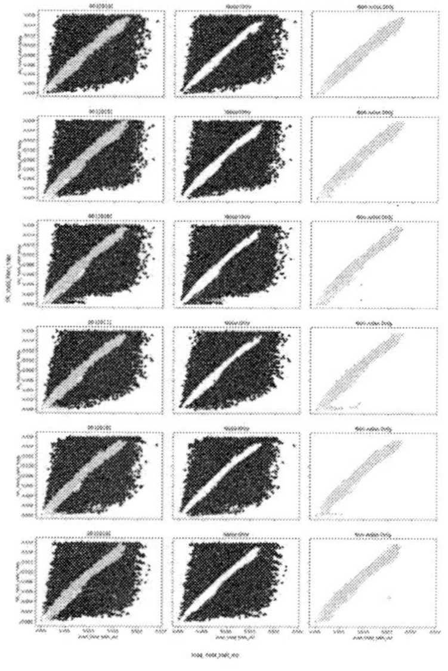

INVERTER: 2001

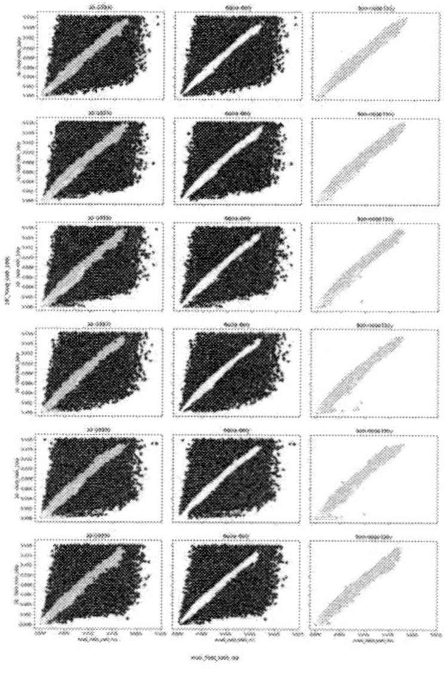

17

Seasonal Trend Decomposition using LOESS

PRI

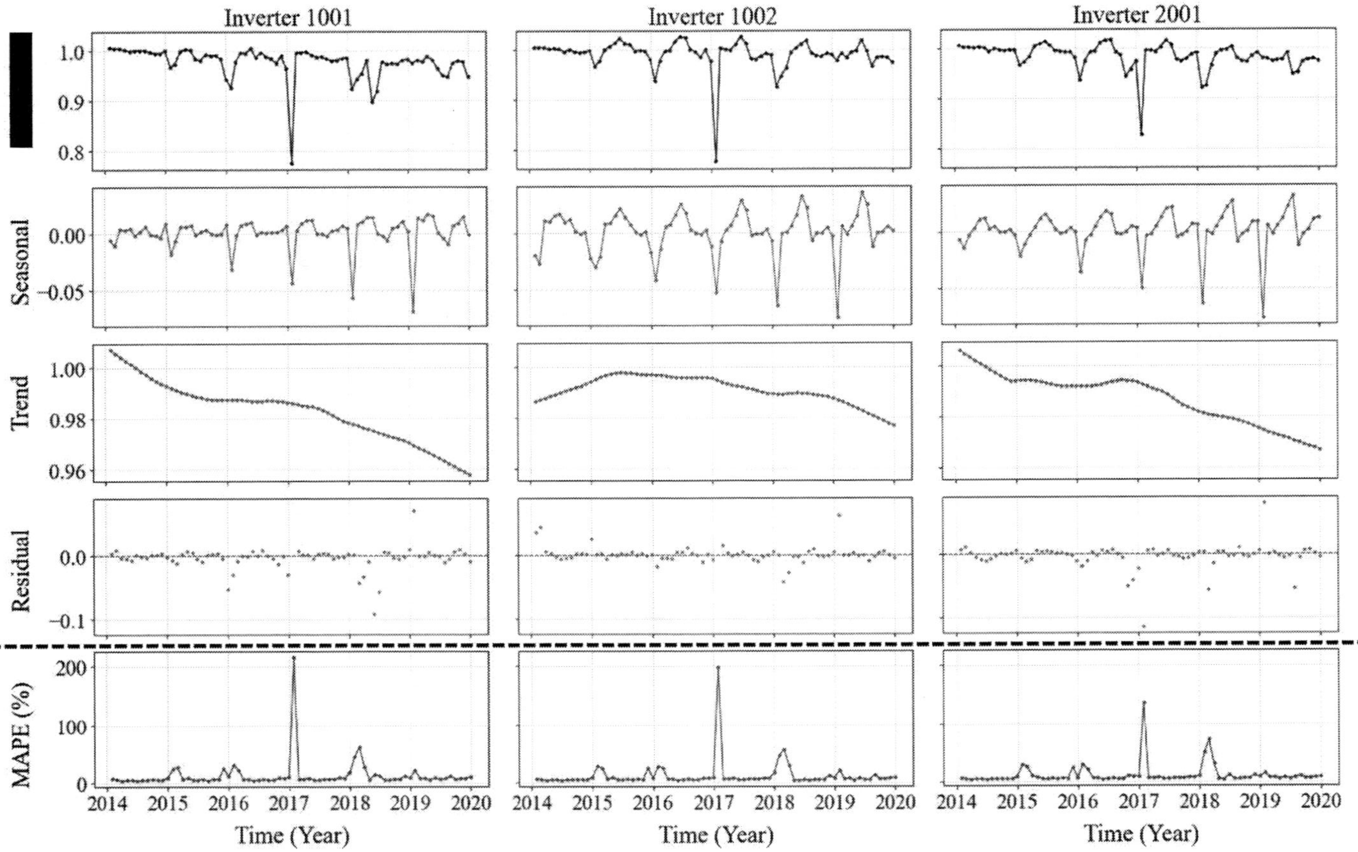

18

42nd European Photovoltaic Solar Energy Conference and Exhibition

This presentation was selected by the Sc. Committee of the EU PVSEC 2025 for submission of a full paper to one of the EU PVSEC's collaborating peer-reviewed journals.

Use of a digital twin to detect stalling tracker events in photovoltaic power plant with horizontal single-axis tracking systems

Riccardo Adinolfi Borea[1], Matthew Muller[2], Silvana Ovaitt[2], Vincenzo Cirimele[1], Francesco Melino[1]
[1] Alma Mater Studiorum – University of Bologna, Via Zamboni, 33, 40126 Bologna, Italy
[2] National Renewable Energy Laboratory – NREL, 15013 Denver West Parkway, Golden, CO 80401

ABSTRACT: Horizontal single-axis trackers are widely employed in photovoltaic power plants to enhance energy production. Despite their benefits, these systems encounter mechanical issues, such as stall events, which can lead to significant power losses. This work introduces a novel and broadly applicable methodology for detecting stalled tracker events through pairwise comparisons. The proposed algorithm operates directly on measured output power and requires minimal site-specific inputs. Validation was performed using both synthetic datasets – generated with physical models and randomized anomalies – and real field measurements from a photovoltaic array. Results from synthetic data demonstrate an F_1 score of 0.60, highlighting potential for further refinement. Applying a day clearness threshold of 0.60 improved performance substantially, raising the F_1 score to 0.96. When tested on field data under the same conditions, the algorithm achieved an F_1 score of 0.75, pointing to additional challenges caused by phenomena that mimic stalled behavior.

Keywords: single-axis tracker reliability, stall detection, synthetic dataset, performance losses

1 INTRODUCTION

In utility-scale photovoltaic (PV) plants, solar trackers are commonly used to increase energy yield and improve cost-effectiveness. The most widespread design is the horizontal single-axis tracker, which uses a simple torque tube and motor mechanism. Despite their simplicity, trackers vary in reliability due to differing mechanical solutions across manufacturers. Tracker-related issues rank among the top three causes of service tickets in PV plants – after inverters (~60%) and modules (~18%) – and account for about 11% of cases, with an average resolution time of 14 days [1]. To address these challenges, some manufacturers now include position sensors, but most systems still lack reliable angular data. This gap has motivated the development of methodologies for detecting stalled trackers. In [2], a method based on pairwise comparison is proposed, where each PV system is evaluated against its best-performing neighboring peers. Peers are identified using the variance and covariance of the ratio between the capacity utilization factors of neighboring systems. Days with correlations below a threshold are flagged, though the method does not name the cause of low correlation. On the same topic, [3] introduces a physics-informed deep learning approach to detect faulty tracker patterns. The validation dataset consists of string-level measurements from a 624-string PV field collected over one year, including 340,000 daily profiles (170,000 measured healthy and 170,000 faulty, synthetically generated via a convolutional neural network). The authors emphasize that embedding physics improves performance compared to a purely data-driven approach. However, both methods face practical challenges: [2] requires detailed system information such as capacity, maintenance records, and nearby plant data, while [3] relies on high-quality datasets with reliable maintenance records – conditions not always met in real-world PV operations.

It is therefore the aim of this work to tackle this topic from a different perspective. This work aims to evaluate a methodology for detecting stalled tracker events in datasets with limited information and availability. Therefore, it is proposed an agnostic approach, and the evaluation of the impact of such agnosticism. This work is an extension of the work presented in [4]. The following sections address firstly the detection algorithm, then the obtainment of synthetic and field data for validation, and lastly the score and limiting factors of the algorithm.

2 METHODOLOGY

2.1 Detection algorithm

The algorithm is based upon pairwise comparisons between measured and modeled output power. For each PV system, it simulates expected daily power under both regular tracking and fixed orientations along the tracker's rotation path, then selects the scenario that best matches the measured data. The inputs are minimal, namely the measured output power, the location, the global horizontal irradiance (ghi), and ground coverage ratio (GCR).

Modeled daily DC output power, P^*_{DC}, is generated using the Sandia view-factor model, the Sandia array performance model [5], and PVWatts [6]. These simulations represent three operating conditions: tracking, fully stalled (modules remain fixed at orientations), and partially stalled (where only a fraction of the array is fixed and the rest tracks properly). In the latter case, the output is expressed as

$$P^*_{DC}(\zeta,\theta) = \zeta \cdot P^*_{DC,stalled}(\theta) + (1-\zeta)\, P^*_{DC,tracking} \,,$$

where ζ is the stall fraction (1 represents a fully stalled tracker and 0 represents regularly operating tracker) and θ the orientation at which the tracker is stalled. θs are obtained dividing the range of motion of the tracker in 5° intervals, and ζ is set to 0.33 and 0.66.

Once all daily scenarios are produced, the algorithm normalizes modeled outputs by their daily maximum and measured output by the 96th quantile, then compares them using the coefficient of determination (R^2). The scenario yielding the highest similarity is considered equivalent to the measured system's operating condition.

2.2 Data obtainment for validation

The detection algorithm is validated on both synthetic and field data. Synthetic data are produced following the methodology in [7], which enables the creation of datasets that replicate the output power of photovoltaic systems under varying conditions. After selecting a location, weather data from the National Solar Radiation Database (NSRDB) are retrieved and used to simulate the output power of a reference PV array. The methodology then introduces physical anomalies and noise into the generation process, including effects such as soiling losses, stalled trackers, inverter clipping, string outages, and both random and irradiance-dependent noise. Because anomalies are modeled as discrete, configurable events and noise can be tuned, the approach allows for the generation of tailored datasets. Events are positioned randomly throughout the time span to avoid repetition, ensuring that running the script multiple times yields different datasets.

The detection algorithm is validated on multiple synthetic datasets. For each location, six variants of the same dataset are generated, differing only in the tracker stall fraction, S, which is set to 0.01, 0.1, 0.25, 0.50, 0.75, and 1.0. Output power profiles are obtained as

$$P_{DC} = S \cdot P_{DC,stalled}(0°) + (1 - S) \cdot P_{DC,tracking} \ ,$$

where $P_{DC,stalled}$ and $P_{DC,tracking}$ are simulated with identical noise but different orientations, representing stalled and normally operating trackers, respectively. Before being fed to the detection algorithm, each dataset is filtered using a clearsky classification method described in [8], which permits to discard non-clearsky timestamps.

Concerning field data, these are obtained from the National Renewable Energy Laboratory's (NREL) Bifacial Experimental Single-Axis Tracking Field, located at the South Table Mountain Campus in Golden, Colorado (39.74° N, −105.17° W), described in [9]). To generate the dataset, tests are carried out by fixing one tracker at 0° while the others continue normal operation.

3 RESULTS

The metric used to express and compare results is the F_1 score, given by

$$F_1 = \frac{2\,TP}{2\,TP + FN + FP} \ ,$$

where TP, FP, and FN, stand for true positive, false positive, and false negative, respectively. A TP is a stall event that is correctly flagged (regardless of the stall orientation suggested by the algorithm), a FP is a day that is wrongly flagged as a stalled event, and a FN is a stall event that is not flagged.

3.1 Validation on synthetic data

Merging the results of the 38 locations considered, the algorithm achieves an F_1 score of 0.60. Defining the day clearness as the fraction of daylight timestamps classified as clearsky, the algorithm tends to fail more frequently toward lower values of day clearness. Introducing a day clearness threshold permits to filter out predominantly overcast days hence improve the performance. Fig. 1 shows the algorithm's performance when different thresholds are applied. Even with no threshold, roughly 140 days per year are excluded due to the clearsky-only classification. Increasing the threshold improves performance, with the F_1 score rising from 0.60 to 0.97 as the minimum day clearness increases from 0 to 0.60. However, this also removes some potential stall events. These are considered less critical, since energy losses during partially cloudy days are smaller than during clear ones. For this reason, a minimum day clearness of 0.60 is adopted for reliable results and will be assumed in all subsequent analyses.

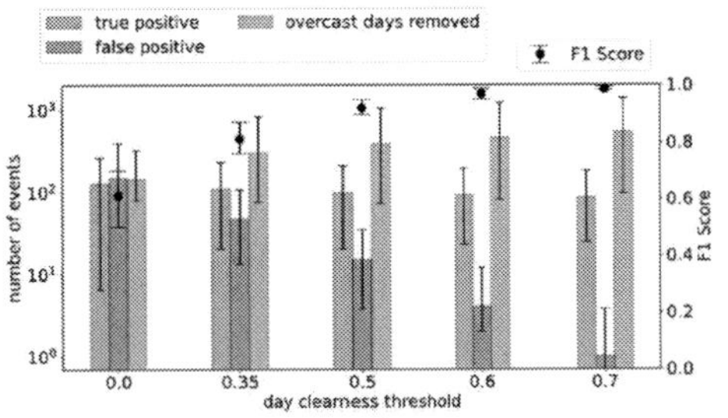

Fig. 1 True positive, false positive, overcast days removed, and F_1 score, when different values of minimum day clearness are imposed.

The algorithm's capability to identify partially stalled events is evaluated by running it on six dataset variants per location, each generated with a different stall fraction S. Results show a strong dependence on stall severity: lower S values lead to fewer true positives, more false negatives, and consequently lower F_1 scores. This outcome confirms that the algorithm is more reliable when stall events have higher stall fractions, with performance becoming appreciable when $S > 0.25$.

3.2 Validation on field data

The detection algorithm was run on six datasets, each containing 67 daily P_{DC} profiles with day clearness above 0.60, including three stall events. Given the small number of stall events, results from field data should be considered preliminary. During a stall event, row 3 was fixed at 0° while row 8 operated normally. Each dataset was constructed by combining the output of row 3 ($P_{DC,3}$) and row 8 ($P_{DC,8}$) using the stall fraction S, as in

$$P_{DC} = S\,P_{DC,3} + (1 - S)P_{DC,8} \ ,$$

with S set to 0.01, 0.1, 0.25, 0.50, 0.75, and 1.0. Fig. 2 summarizes performance across all S values: for $S < 0.1$ stall events are undetectable, whereas for $S > 0.25$ all stall events are correctly identified. Corresponding F_1 scores for S equal to 0.25, 0.75, and 1.0 are 0.67, 0.75, and 0.86, reflecting 3, 2, and 1 false negative days, respectively.

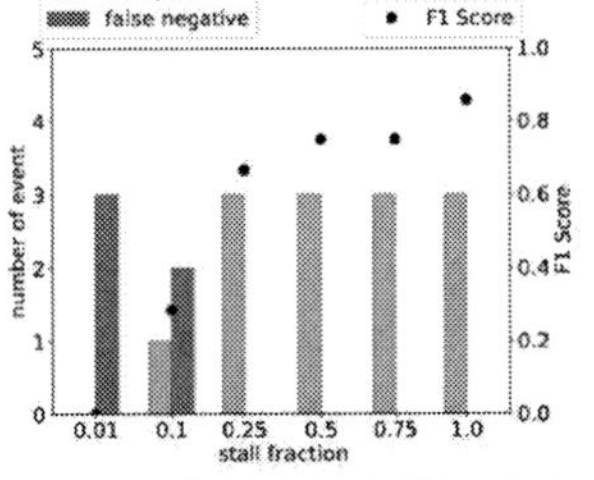

Fig. 2 algorithm's performance at different S values. The F1 changes accordingly to S.

Fig. 3 examines the three FNs days that make the F_1 score change. On February 9th, both trackers briefly exhibited a possibly stall condition that was later on corrected but still

10.4229/EUPVSEC2025/4CO.9.3

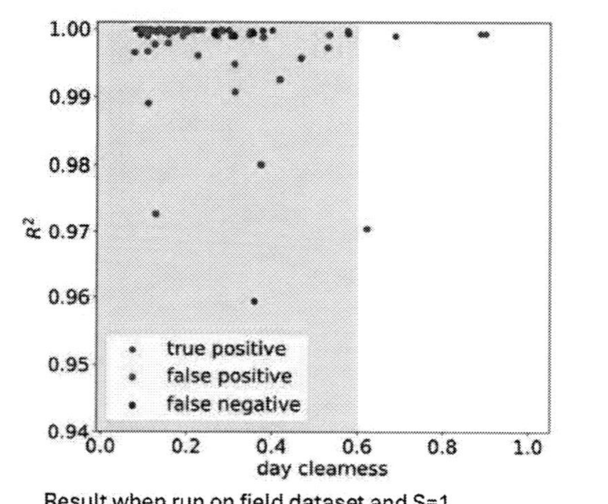

flagged by the algorithm. On January 8th, row 8 underperformed in the morning in a manner resembling a stalled tracker, despite tracking normally; further analysis of NREL meteorological data indicates that snow on the modules likely caused this temporary reduction, which cleared by midday. On May 20th, lastly, row 8 again underperformed in the evening. In both January and May cases, differing performances between rows 3 and 8 mean that variations in the stall fraction S produce different detection outcomes.

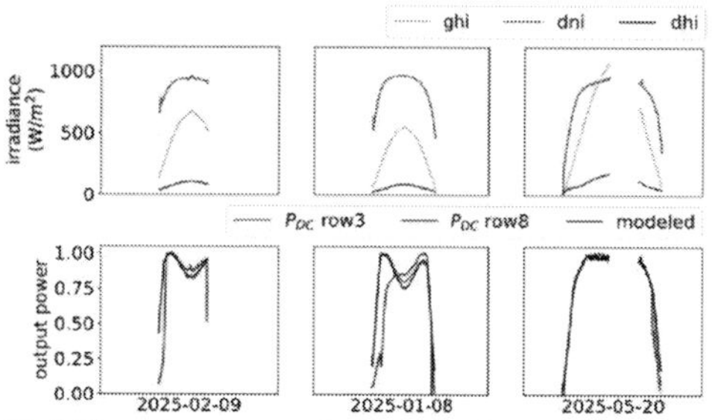

Fig.3 Three days that are flagged as stall events. February 9th is a day during which both trackers probably faced a tracker stall, hence is flagged regardless of S. January 8th and May 20th, instead, are days in which row no.8 has an issue and row no.3 is operating regularly, thus how the two are combined influences the result.

4 CONCLUSIONS

This study presented a broadly applicable algorithm for detecting stall events in PV power plants with horizontal single-axis trackers. The method relies on pairwise comparisons between measured and modeled output power and requires minimal site-specific information, making it suitable for scenarios with limited data. Validation on synthetic datasets showed that the algorithm effectively detects stall events when the stall fraction exceeds 0.25 and partially overcast days are excluded. Imposing a day clearness threshold of 0.6 increased the F_1 score from 0.60 to 0.97 for $S = 1$. Field data validation highlighted additional challenges: while all stall events were detected, three days are misclassified as partially stalled events. In two cases, temporary underperformance mimicked a stall, making the algorithm's classification reasonable. Due to the small dataset (67 days, only 3 stall events), further conclusions are preliminary. Ongoing field data collection is expected to enable more robust results in future work.

5 ACKOWLEDGEMENTS

This work has been supported by Ricerca per il Sistema Energetico Spa (RSE) through the Fondo di Ricerca per il Sistema Elettrico (RdS) within the framework of the Triennial Plan 2022-2024 (DM MITE n. 337, of 15.09.2022) and the project RdS 1.1 project "High-Efficiency Photovoltaics", supported by the Alma Mater Studiorum - Università di Bologna through the National Doctoral Program in "Photovoltaics" for the XXVIII cycle, as per article 3, paragraph 2 of DM 226/2021.

This work was also authored in part by the National Renewable Energy Laboratory (NREL) for the U.S. Department of Energy (DOE) under Contract No. DE-AC36-08GO28308. Partial funding is provided by the U.S. Department of Energy (DOE)'s Office of Energy Efficiency and Renewable Energy (EERE) from the Solar Energy Technologies Office (SETO), under CPS Agreement 52799. The views expressed in the article do not necessarily represent the views of the DOE or the U.S. Government. The U.S. Government retains and the publisher, by accepting the article for publication, acknowledges that the U.S. Government retains a nonexclusive, paid-up, irrevocable, worldwide license to publish or reproduce the published form of this work, or allow others to do so, for U.S. Government purposes. The funders had no role in study design, data collection and analysis, decision to publish, or preparation of the manuscript.

6 REFERENCES

[1]. "Past Proceedings | PVRW: Photovoltaic Reliability Workshop | NREL." Available: https://pvrw.nrel.gov/past-proceedings

[2]. J. Leloux, et. al, "Automatic fault detection on BIPV systems without solar irradiation data," 2014, doi: 10.13140/2.1.2280.3200.

[3]. J. Zgraggen, et. al, "Physics Informed Deep Learning for Tracker Fault Detection in Photovoltaic Power Plants," *Annu. Conf. PHM Soc.*, Oct. 2022, doi: 10.36001/phmconf.2022.v14i1.3235.

[4]. K. Anderson, et. al, "A Method for Estimating Time-Series PV Production Loss From Solar Tracking Failures," *IEEE J. Photovolt.*, Jan. 2022, doi: 10.1109/JPHOTOV.2021.3123872.

[5]. J. Kratochvil, et. al, "Photovoltaic array performance model.," SAND2004-3535, 919131, Aug. 2004. doi: 10.2172/919131.

[6]. A. Dobos, "PVWatts Version 5 Manual," NREL/TP-6A20-62641, Sep. 2014. doi: 10.2172/1158421.

[7]. M. Muller, et. al, "Generating Synthetic Time Series PV Data with Real-World Physical Challenges and Noise for Use in Algorithm Test and Validation,", Sep. 2023. doi: 10.21948/1999772.

[8]. D. C. Jordan and C. Hansen, "Clear-sky detection for PV degradation analysis using multiple regression," *Renew. Energy*, Jun. 2023, doi: 10.1016/j.renene.2023.04.035.

[9]. "BEST Field Data - DuraMAT Data Hub.", 2023, Available: https://datahub.duramat.org/dataset/best-field-data

ALMA MATER STUDIORUM
UNIVERSITÀ DI BOLOGNA

RSE

NREL
Transforming ENERGY

EU PVSEC

Use of a digital twin to detect stalling tracker events in photovoltaic power plant with horizontal single-axis tracking systems

Riccardo Adinolfi Borea, Matthew Muller, Silvana Ovaitt, Vincenzo Cirimele, Francesco Melino

Alma Mater Studiorum – University of Bologna, Bologna, Italy
National Renewable Energy Laboratory – NREL, Golden, Colorado
Ricerca sul Sistema Energetico S.p.a. – RSE

Overview

- Single-axis solar trackers in PV applications
- Is a stuck tracker something we should worry about?
- Detection algorithm layout
- Methodology to generate synthetic data for validation
- Test for field data obtainment
- Validation of the algorithm on synthetic data
- Validation of the algorithm on field data
- Conclusions & future works

Single-axis solar trackers in PV applications

Trackers are system that change the orientation of PV modules

The reasons to use solar trackers are multiple:

- Protect the infrastructure, in case of heavy wind
- Protect the PV modules, in case of hailstorm
- Increase the energy yield of PV modules

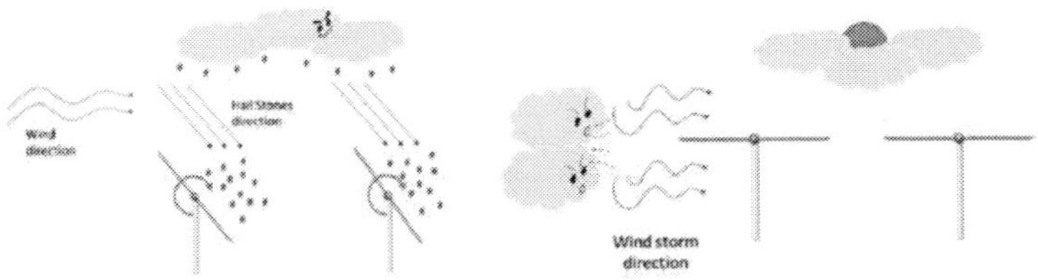

TRACKER FACE AWAY FROM WIND DIRECTION TRACKER WIND STORM POSITION

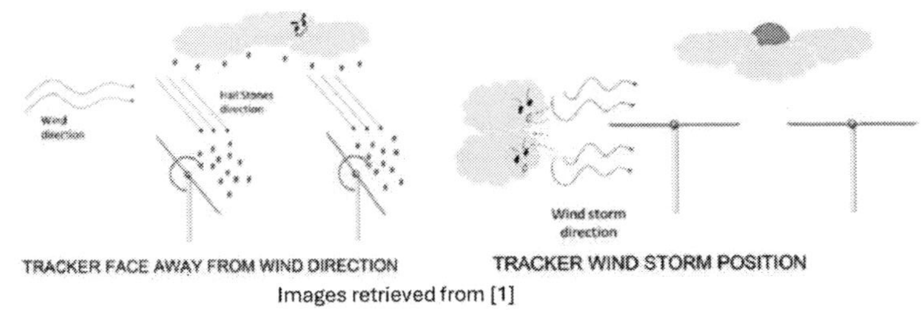

Images retrieved from [1]

[1] DOI: 10.69766/JOIK1919

Is a stuck tracker something we should worry about?

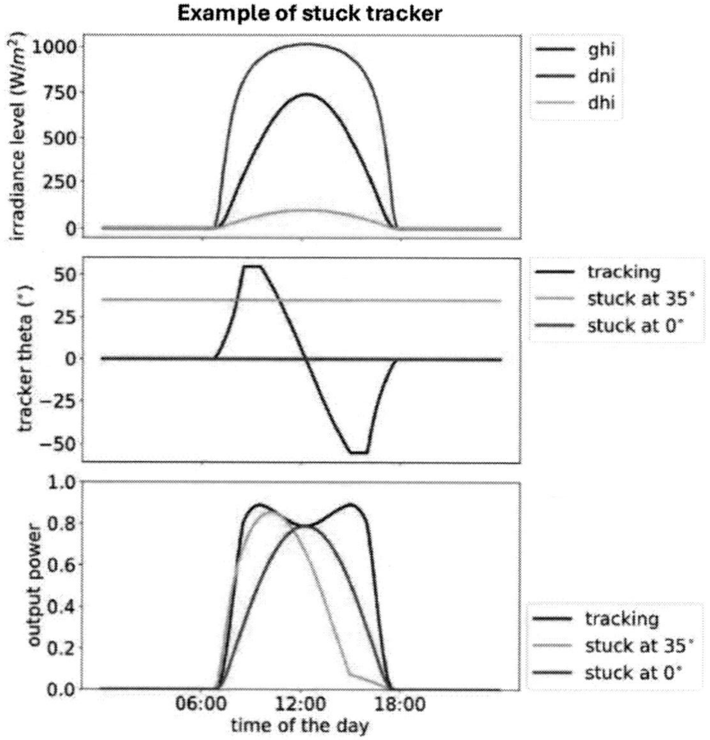

Irradiance conditions, tracker theta, and output power, in different tracking conditions: properly tracking, stuck at 35°, and stuck at 0°.

[1] "Past Proceedings 2024 | PVRW: Photovoltaic Reliability Workshop | NREL."

Is a stuck tracker something we should worry about?

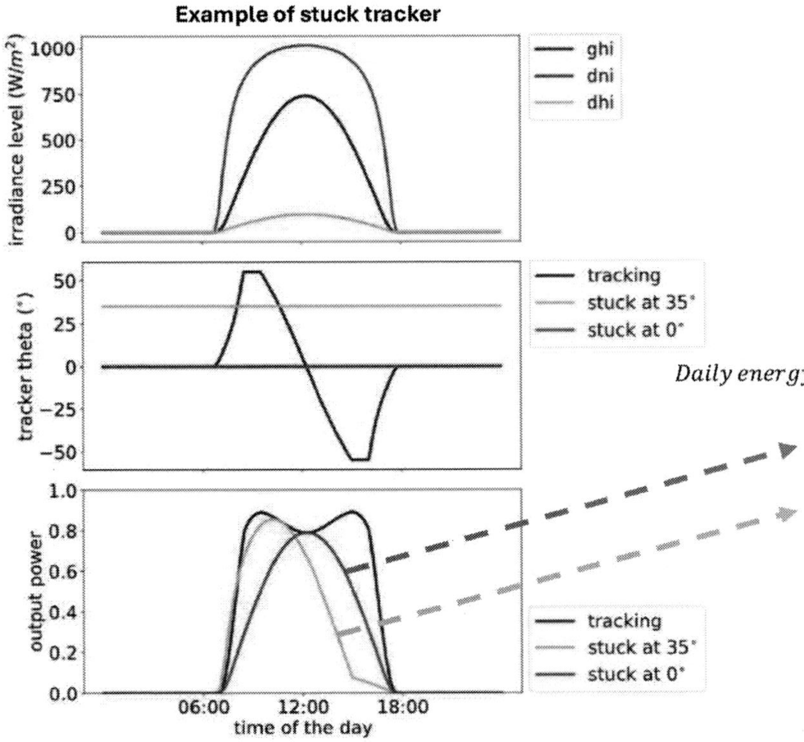

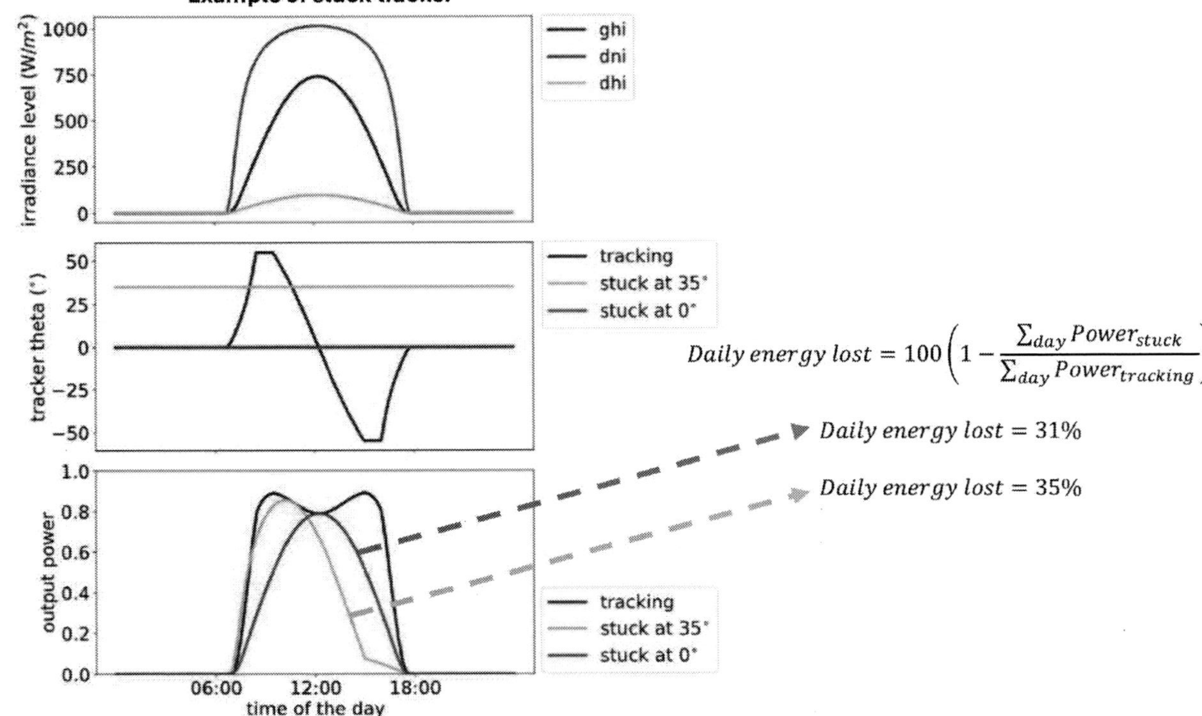

$$Daily\ energy\ lost = 100\left(1 - \frac{\sum_{day} Power_{stuck}}{\sum_{day} Power_{tracking}}\right)$$

$Daily\ energy\ lost = 31\%$

$Daily\ energy\ lost = 35\%$

Irradiance conditions, tracker theta, and output power, in different tracking conditions: properly tracking, stuck at 35°, and stuck at 0°.

[1] "Past Proceedings 2024 | PVRW: Photovoltaic Reliability Workshop | NREL."

Is a stuck tracker something we should worry about?

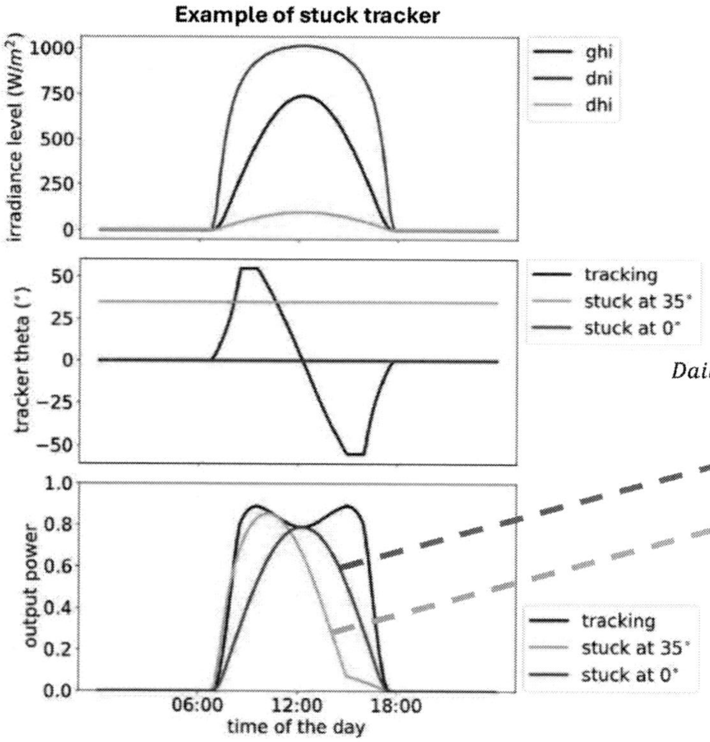

Irradiance conditions, tracker theta, and output power, in different tracking conditions: properly tracking, stuck at 35°, and stuck at 0°.

$$Daily\ energy\ lost = 100\left(1 - \frac{\sum_{day} Power_{stuck}}{\sum_{day} Power_{tracking}}\right)$$

$Daily\ energy\ lost = 31\%$

$Daily\ energy\ lost = 35\%$

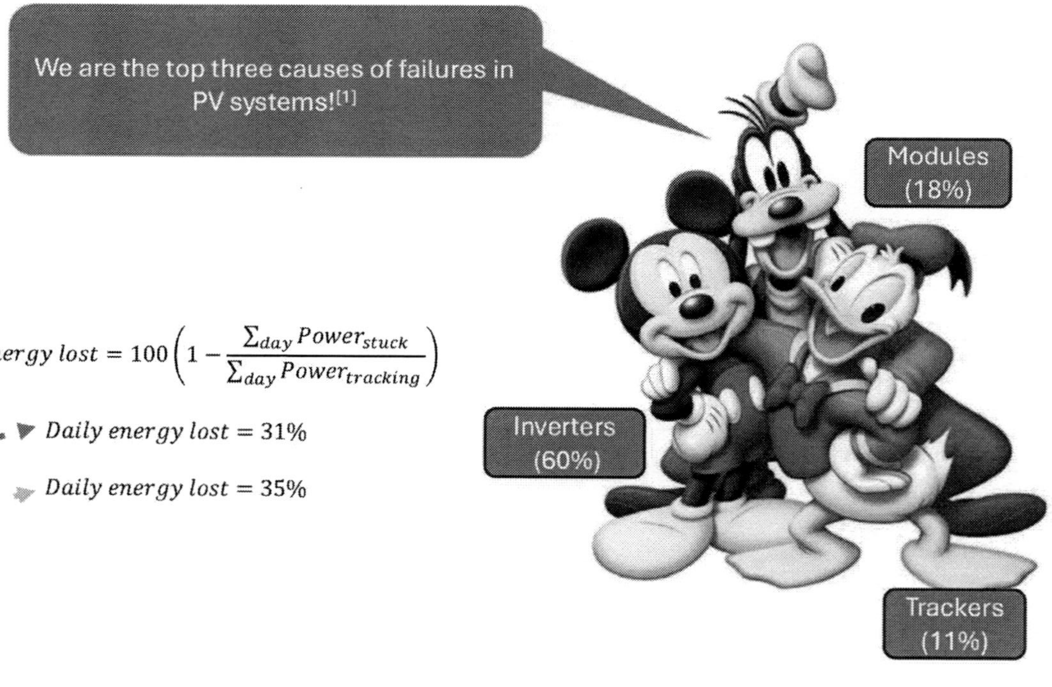

[1] "Past Proceedings 2024 | PVRW: Photovoltaic Reliability Workshop | NREL."

Is a stuck tracker something we should worry about?

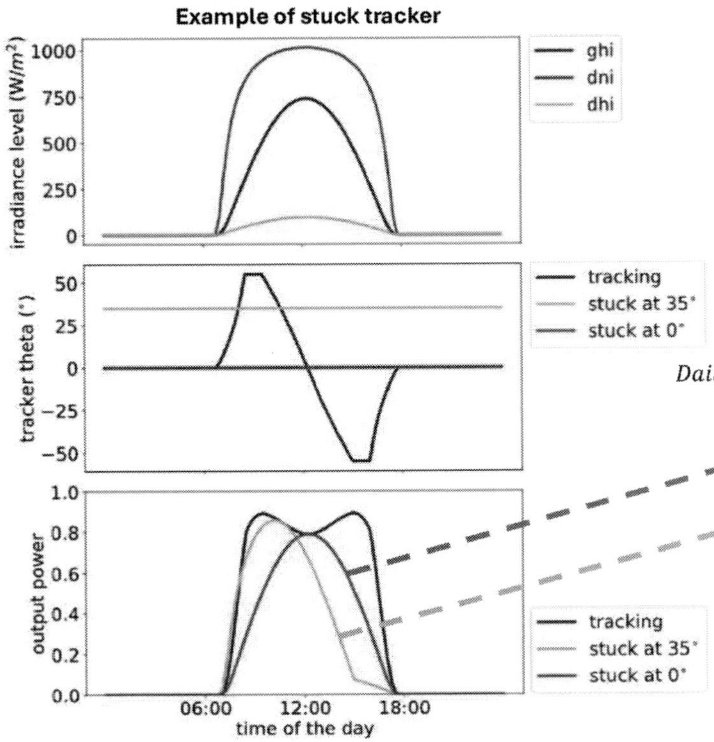

Irradiance conditions, tracker theta, and output power, in different tracking conditions: properly tracking, stuck at 35°, and stuck at 0°.

$$Daily\ energy\ lost = 100\left(1 - \frac{\sum_{day} Power_{stuck}}{\sum_{day} Power_{tracking}}\right)$$

$$Daily\ energy\ lost = 31\%$$

$$Daily\ energy\ lost = 35\%$$

TAKEAWAY

Yes, we need to address the detection of stuck trackers to avoid energy losses that reach up to 35% of the daily energy yield on sunny days. Doing so it possible to avoid accusing PV module degradation of this energy loss, hence have a clearer view about the benefits and costs of PV plants with trackers.

[1] "Past Proceedings 2024 | PVRW: Photovoltaic Reliability Workshop | NREL."

Detection algorithm layout

Detection algorithm layout

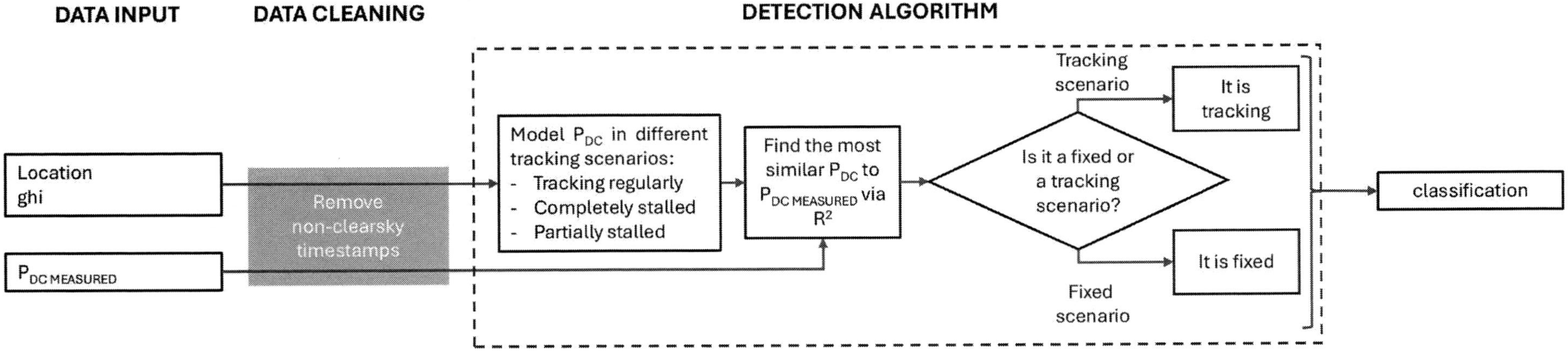

Detection algorithm layout

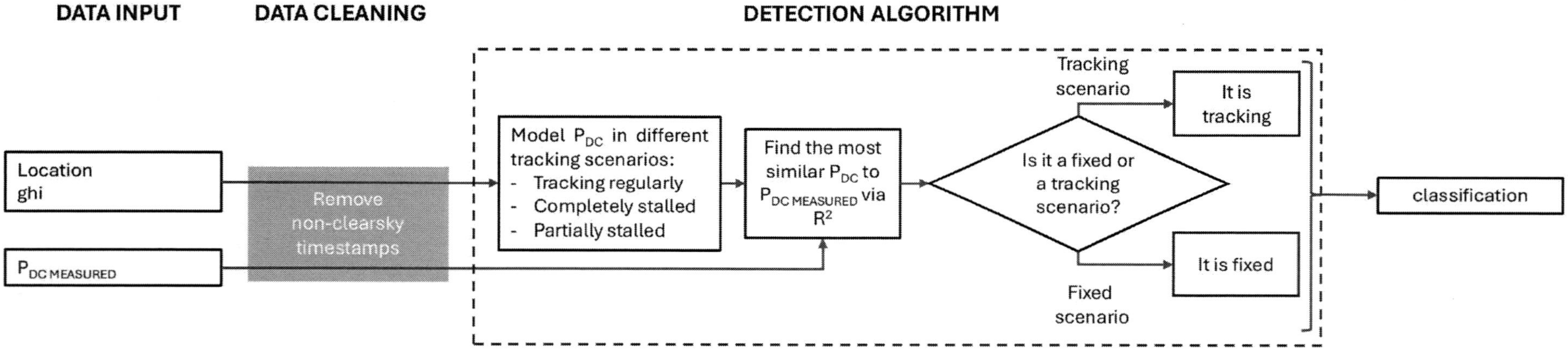

Visual explanation

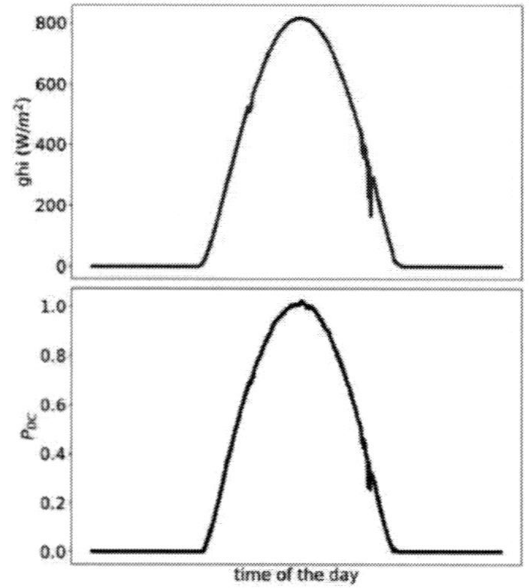

Detection algorithm layout

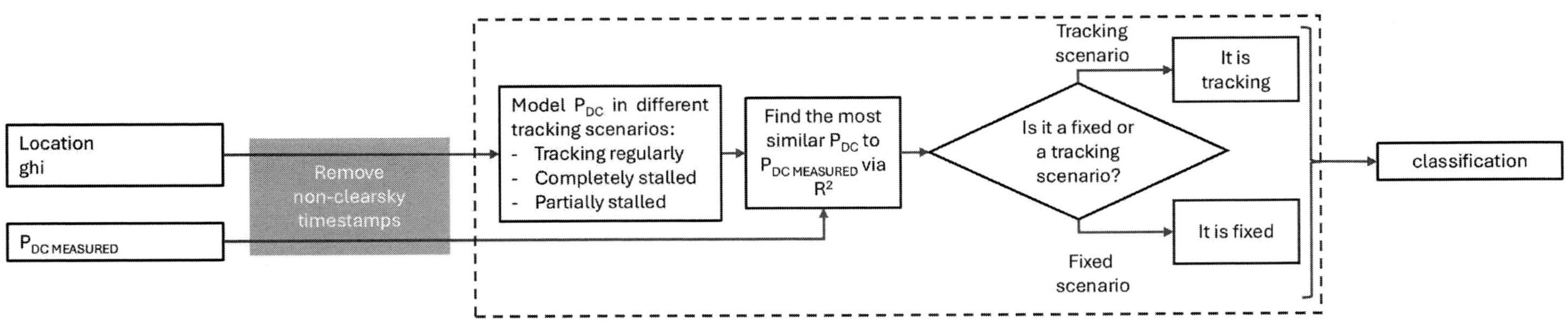

Visual explanation

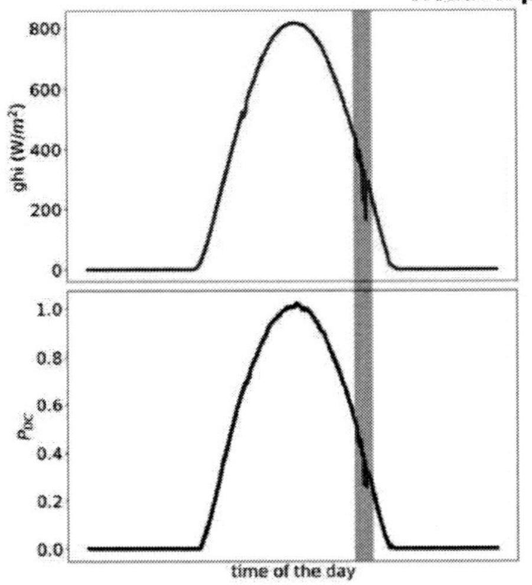

Detection algorithm layout

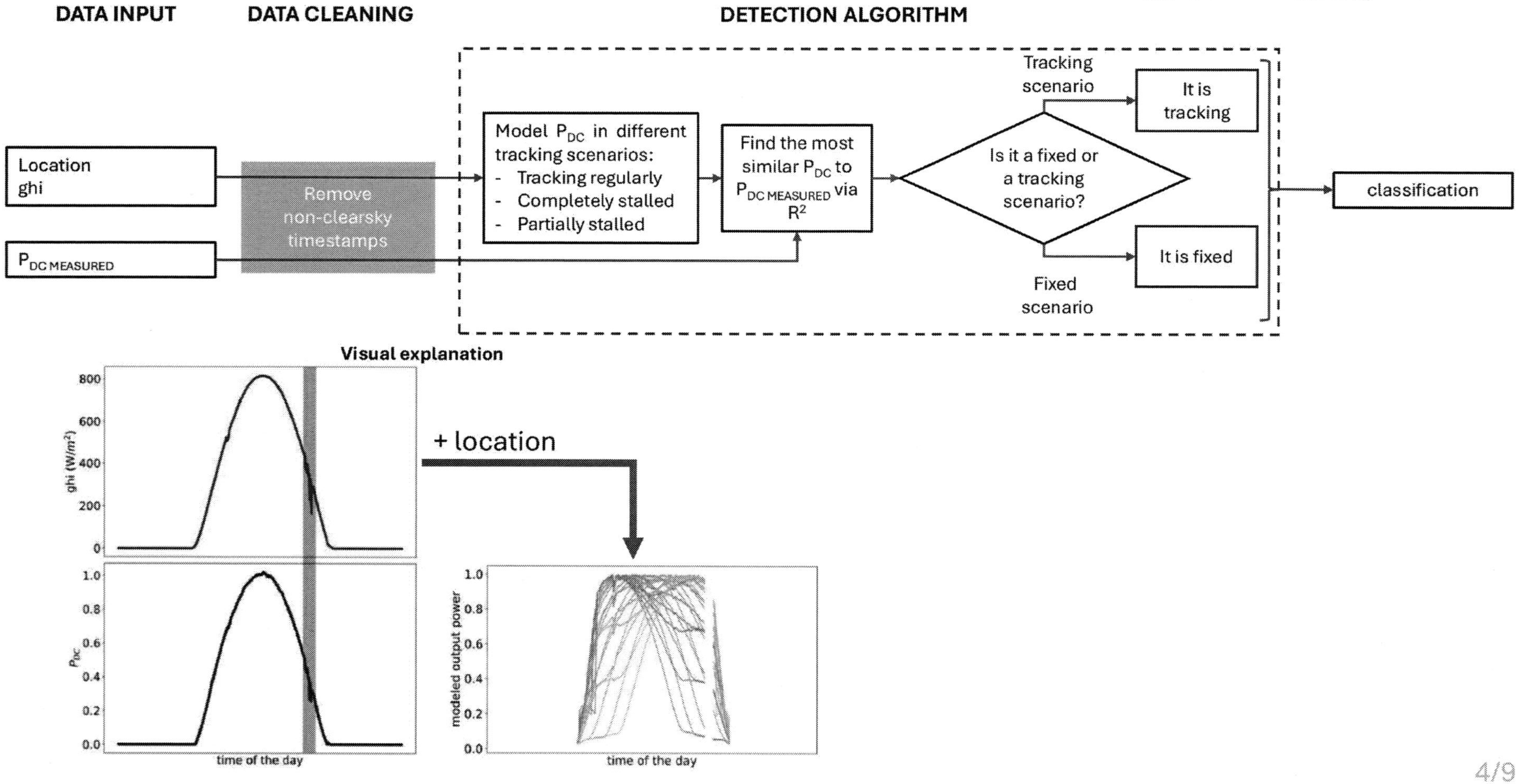

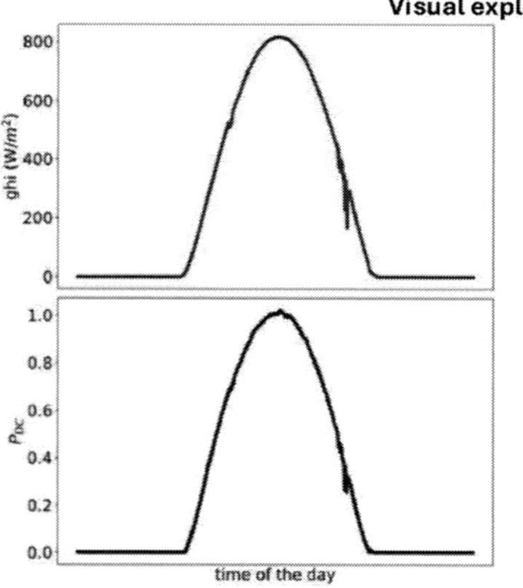

Detection algorithm layout

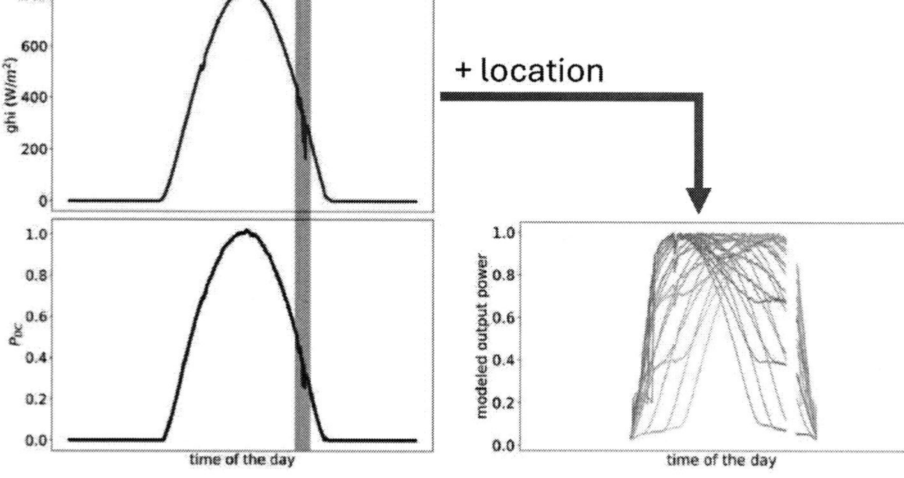

DATA INPUT DATA CLEANING DETECTION ALGORITHM

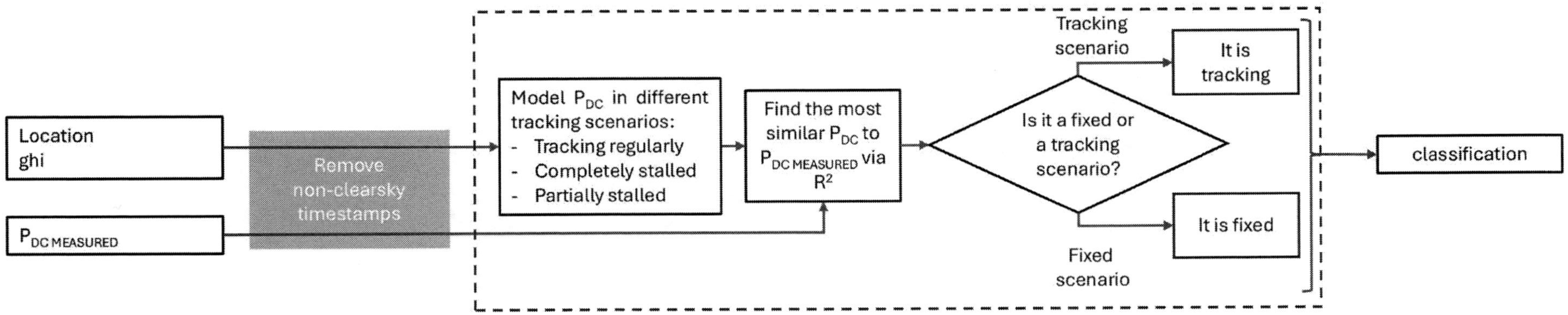

Visual explanation

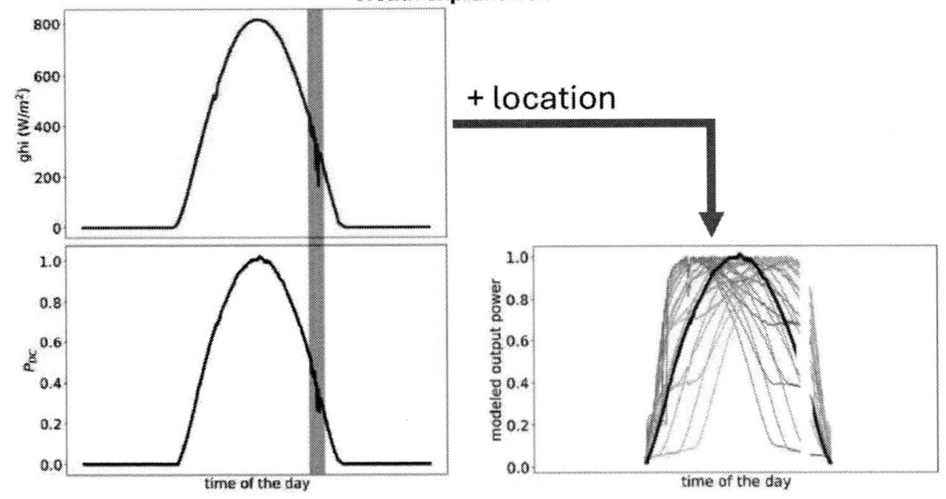

Detection algorithm layout

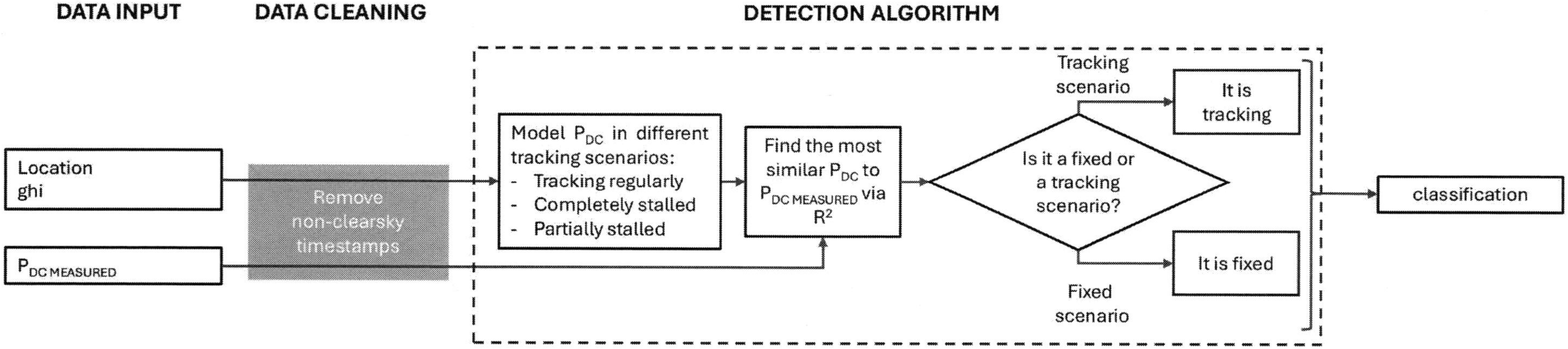

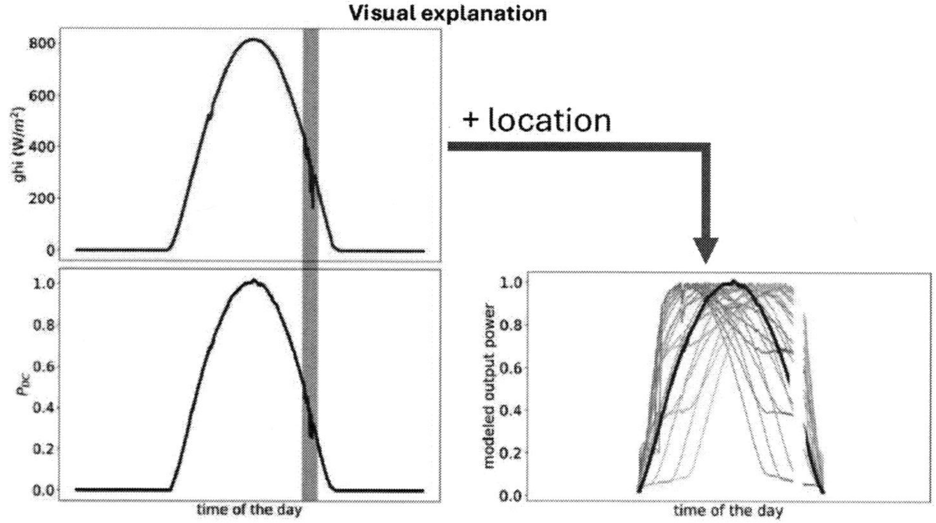

TAKEAWAY

The detection algorithm is used for data post-processing. It assumes that the gcr, the tracker algorithm, and the maximum tilt angle of the tracker, have all usual values/logics, as all of these are usually not available.

Methodology to generate synthetic data for validation

5/9

Methodology to generate synthetic data for validation

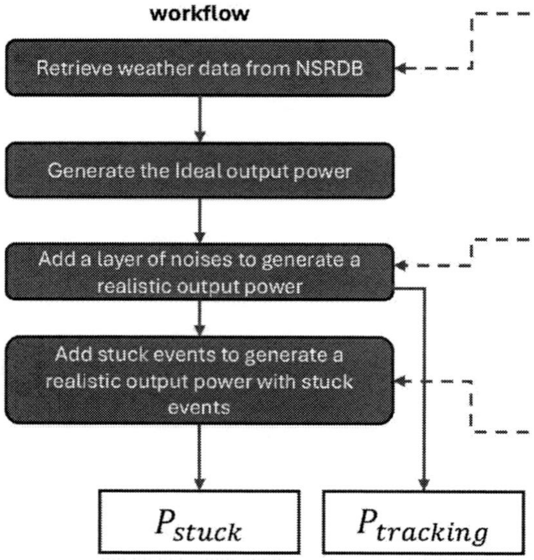

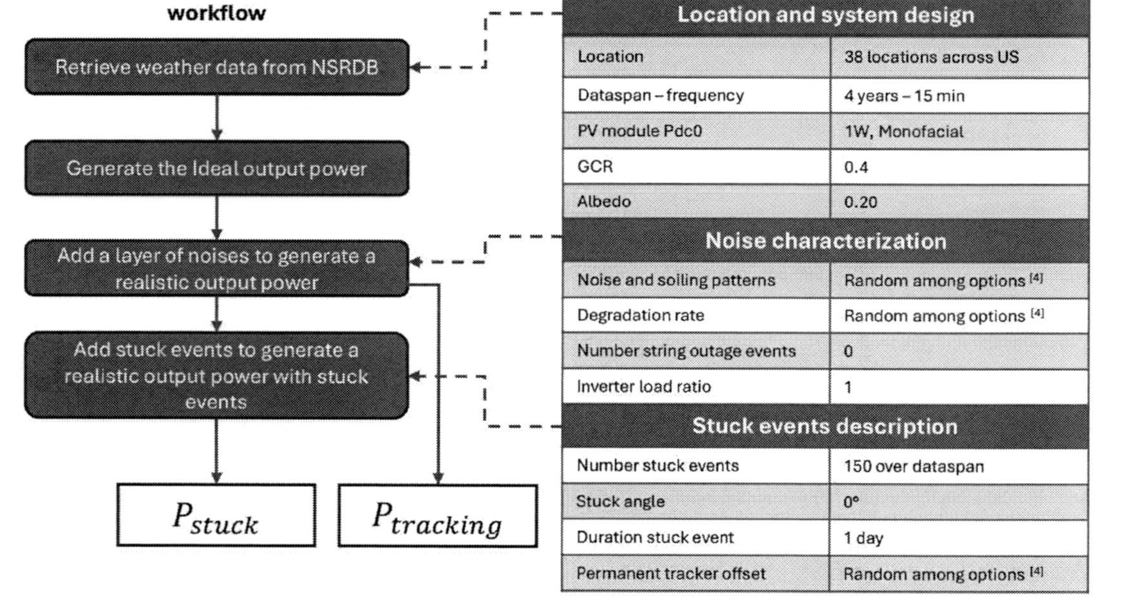

Location and system design	
Location	38 locations across US
Dataspan – frequency	4 years – 15 min
PV module Pdc0	1W, Monofacial
GCR	0.4
Albedo	0.20
Noise characterization	
Noise and soiling patterns	Random among options [4]
Degradation rate	Random among options [4]
Number string outage events	0
Inverter load ratio	1
Stuck events description	
Number stuck events	150 over dataspan
Stuck angle	0°
Duration stuck event	1 day
Permanent tracker offset	Random among options [4]

[4] NREL/TP-5K00-86459

Methodology to generate synthetic data for validation

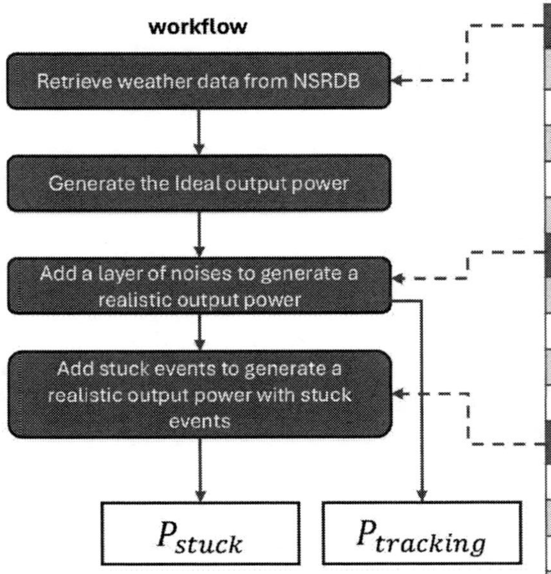

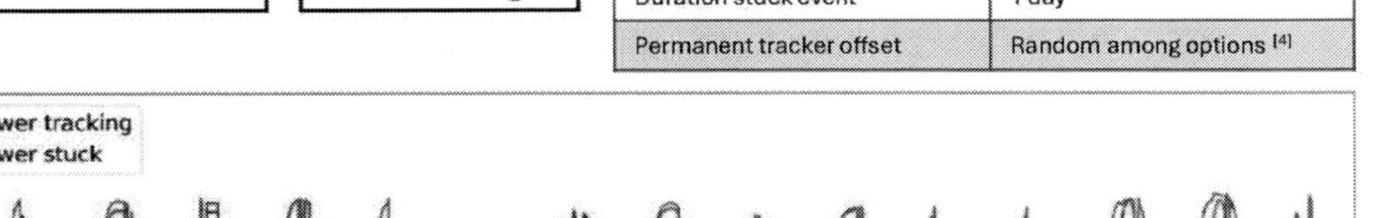

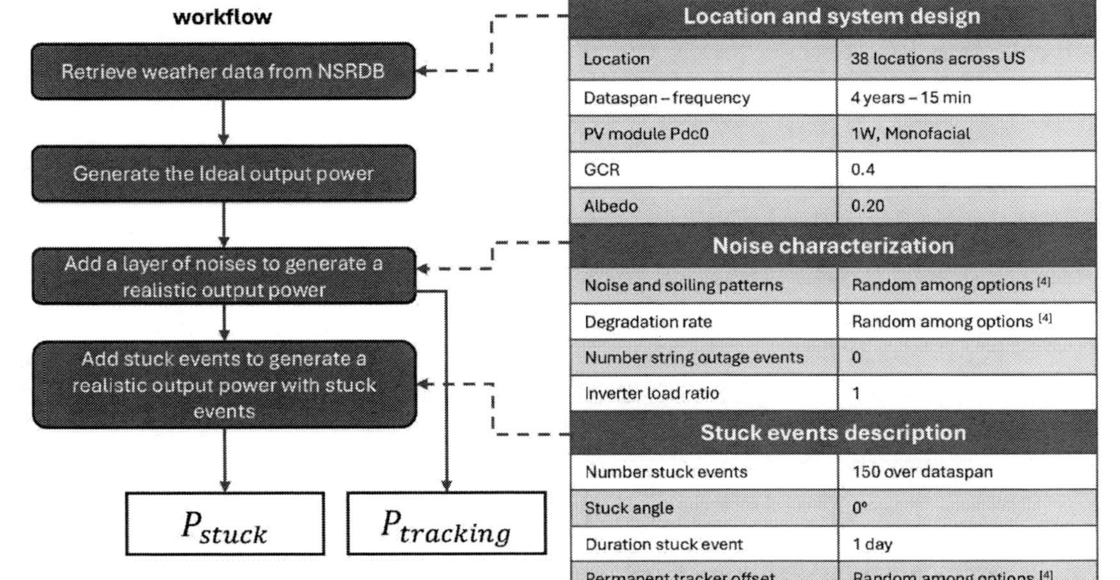

Location and system design	
Location	38 locations across US
Dataspan – frequency	4 years – 15 min
PV module Pdc0	1W, Monofacial
GCR	0.4
Albedo	0.20
Noise characterization	
Noise and soiling patterns	Random among options [4]
Degradation rate	Random among options [4]
Number string outage events	0
Inverter load ratio	1
Stuck events description	
Number stuck events	150 over dataspan
Stuck angle	0°
Duration stuck event	1 day
Permanent tracker offset	Random among options [4]

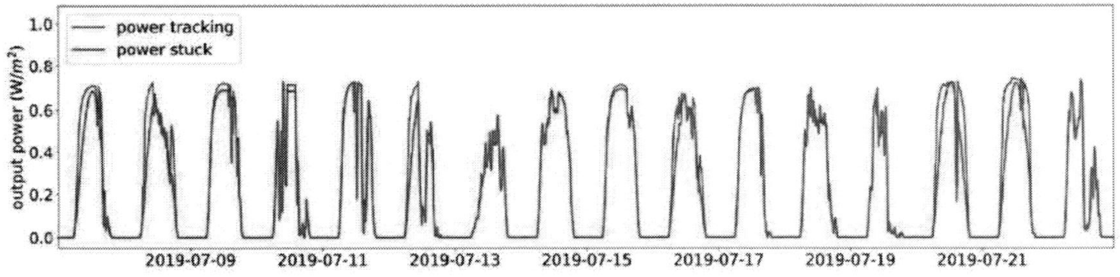

Realistic power output vs modeled power output for the case of Valdosta, Georgia

[4] NREL/TP-5K00-86459

Methodology to generate synthetic data for validation

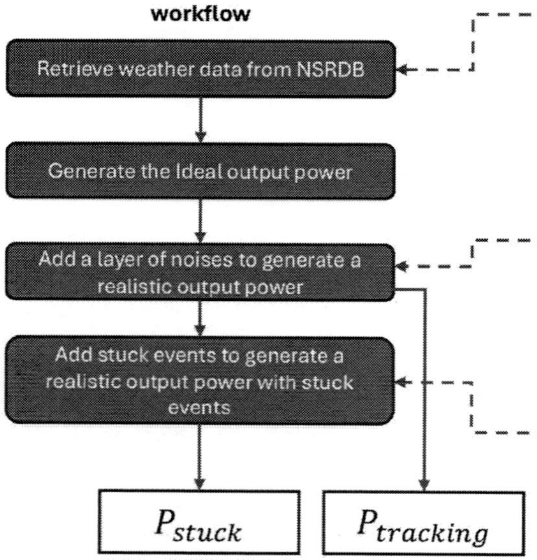

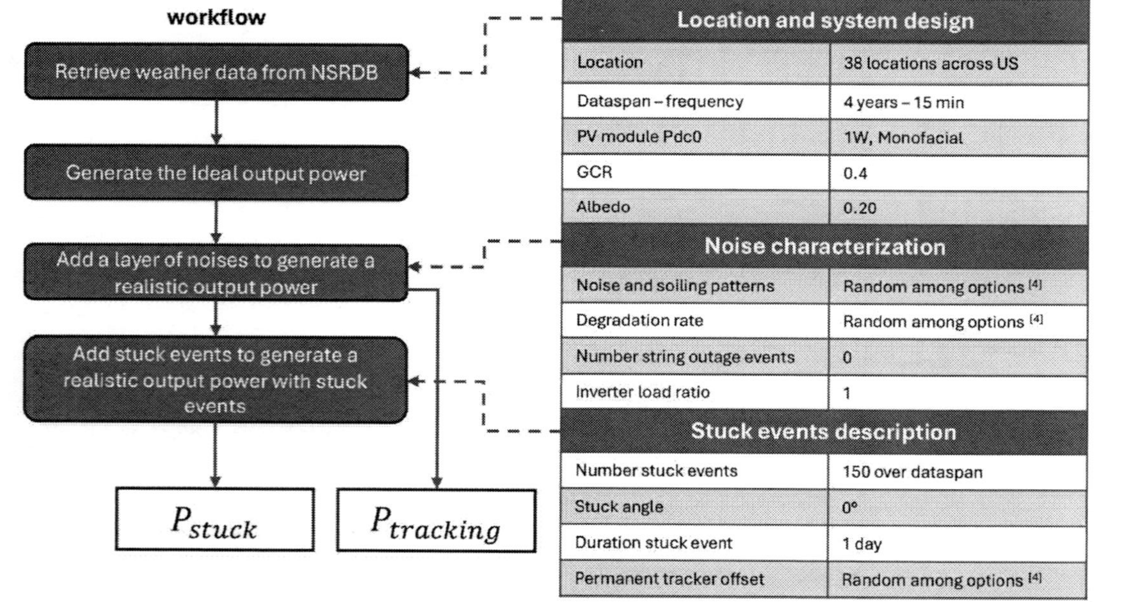

Location and system design	
Location	38 locations across US
Dataspan – frequency	4 years – 15 min
PV module Pdc0	1W, Monofacial
GCR	0.4
Albedo	0.20
Noise characterization	
Noise and soiling patterns	Random among options [4]
Degradation rate	Random among options [4]
Number string outage events	0
Inverter load ratio	1
Stuck events description	
Number stuck events	150 over dataspan
Stuck angle	0°
Duration stuck event	1 day
Permanent tracker offset	Random among options [4]

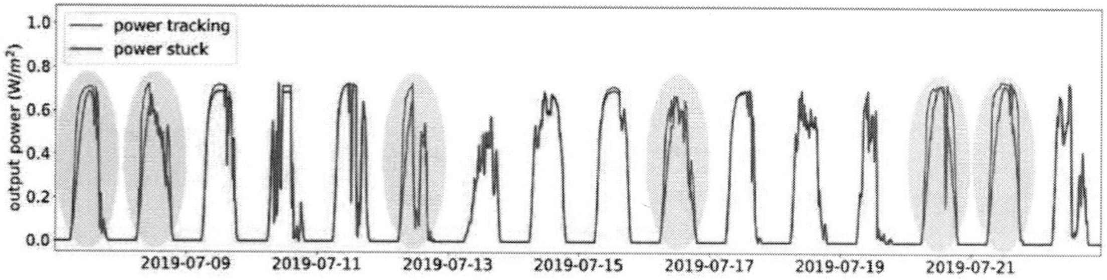

Realistic power output vs modeled power output for the case of Valdosta, Georgia

[4] NREL/TP-5K00-86459

Methodology to generate synthetic data for validation

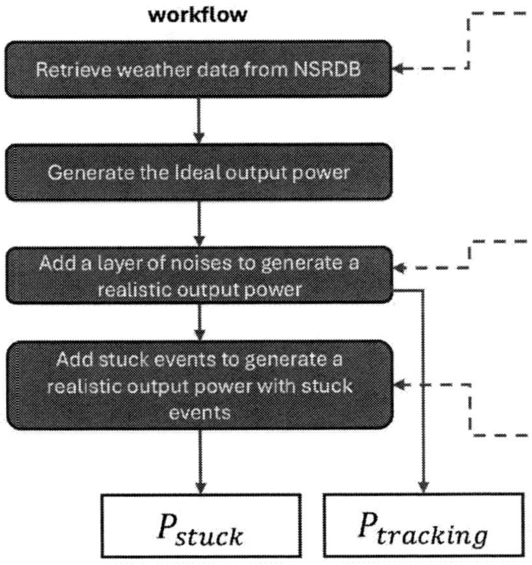

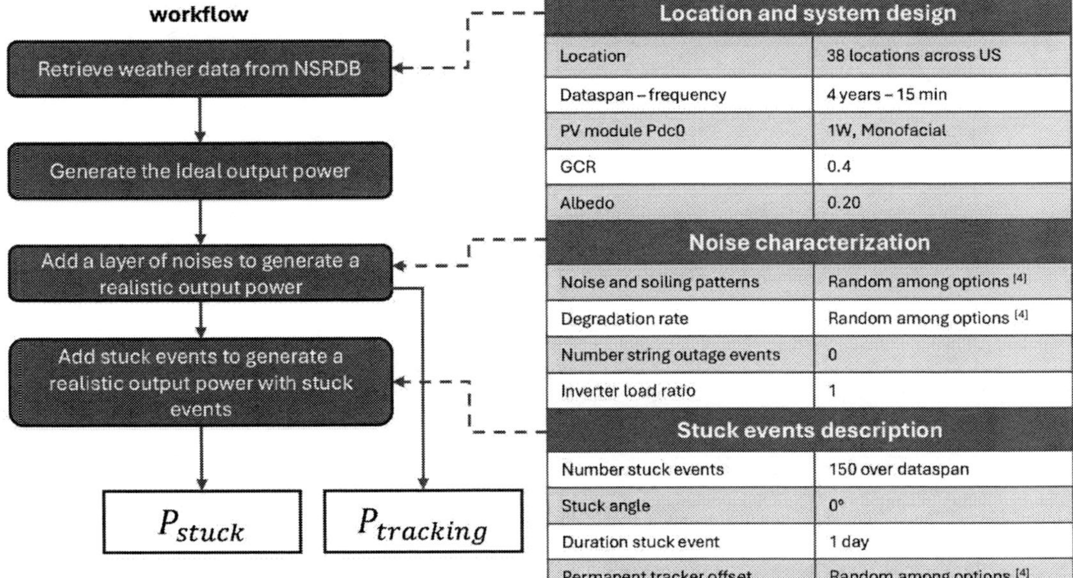

Location and system design	
Location	38 locations across US
Dataspan – frequency	4 years – 15 min
PV module Pdc0	1W, Monofacial
GCR	0.4
Albedo	0.20
Noise characterization	
Noise and soiling patterns	Random among options [4]
Degradation rate	Random among options [4]
Number string outage events	0
Inverter load ratio	1
Stuck events description	
Number stuck events	150 over dataspan
Stuck angle	0°
Duration stuck event	1 day
Permanent tracker offset	Random among options [4]

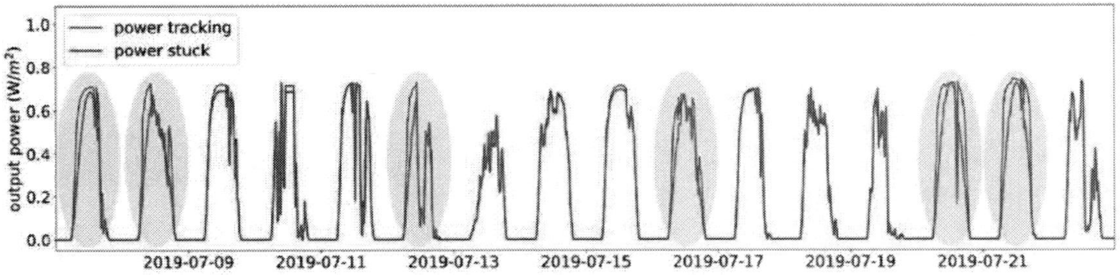

Realistic power output vs modeled power output for the case of Valdosta, Georgia

[4] NREL/TP-5K00-86459

Most of times, multiple strings feed the same combiner, so it is possible to have ''partially stuck events''. Those cases are modeled as

$$P_{out}(S) = S \cdot P_{stuck} + (1 - S)P_{tracking}$$

where S is the fraction of stuck rows, considered as

$$S = \frac{number\ of\ stuck\ rows}{total\ number\ of\ rows}$$

Methodology to generate synthetic data for validation

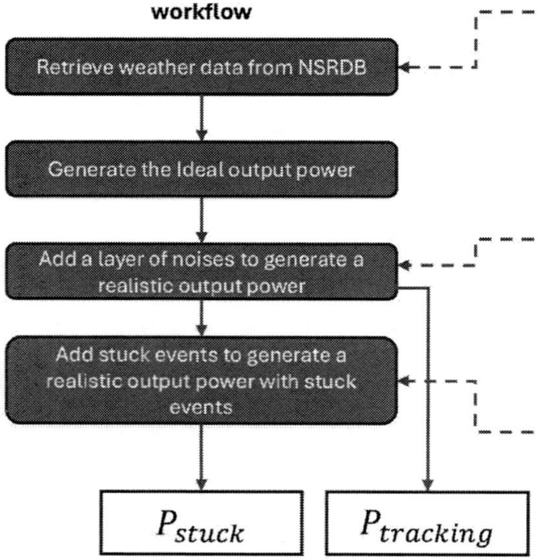

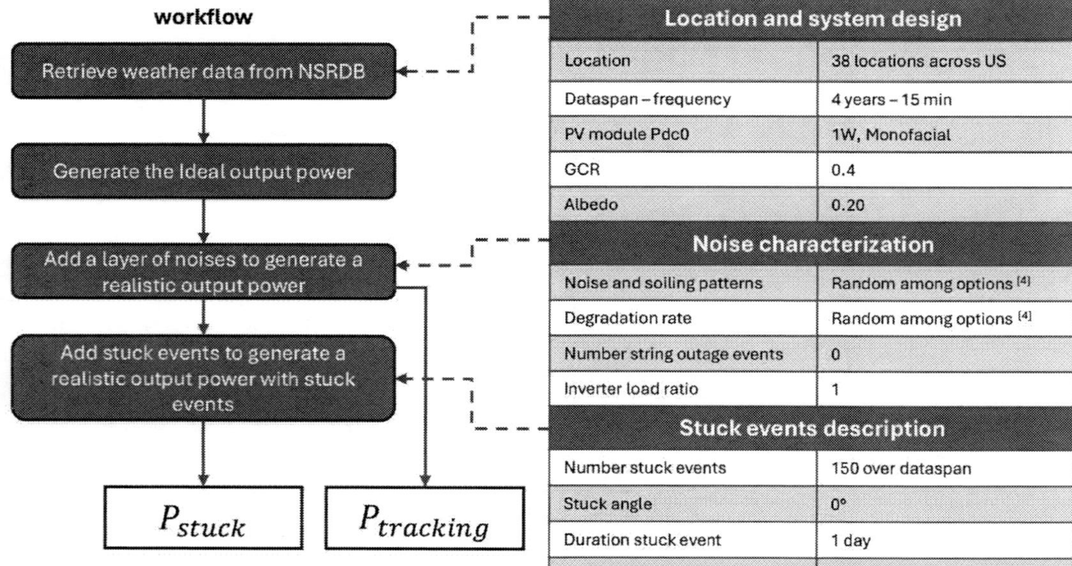

Location and system design	
Location	38 locations across US
Dataspan – frequency	4 years – 15 min
PV module Pdc0	1W, Monofacial
GCR	0.4
Albedo	0.20
Noise characterization	
Noise and soiling patterns	Random among options [4]
Degradation rate	Random among options [4]
Number string outage events	0
Inverter load ratio	1
Stuck events description	
Number stuck events	150 over dataspan
Stuck angle	0°
Duration stuck event	1 day
Permanent tracker offset	Random among options [4]

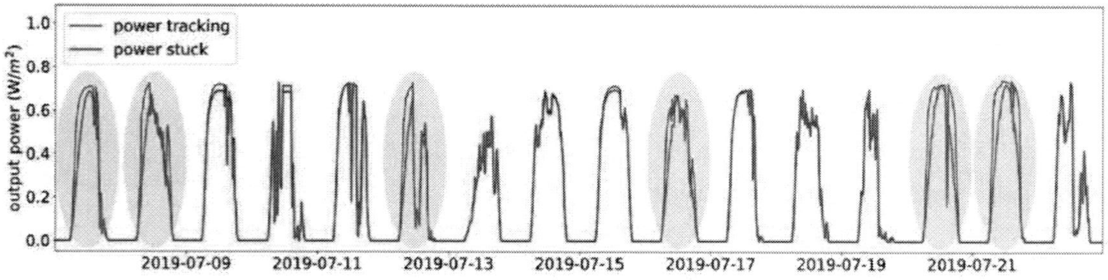

Realistic power output vs modeled power output for the case of Valdosta, Georgia

Most of times, multiple strings feed the same combiner, so it is possible to have ''partially stuck events''. Those cases are modeled as

$$P_{out}(S) = S \cdot P_{stuck} + (1 - S)P_{tracking}$$

where S is the fraction of stuck rows, considered as

$$S = \frac{number\ of\ stuck\ rows}{total\ number\ of\ rows}$$

TAKEAWAY

Given the location, the methodology generates a synthetic dataset that is used to create a set of variants thanks to S. This is done for 38 locations across US.

[4] NREL/TP-5K00-86459

Test for field data obtainment

RSE NREL Transforming ENERGY

System description
Ten rows individually measured and controlled
Current, voltage, and output power, are measured at the DC side

Experiments description
Row 3 is set at 0° for the entire day while row 8 is operating regularly.

Power combination
Power of row 3 and row 8 are first normalized per their nameplate power, than combined to create different stuck scenarios

Validation of the algorithm on synthetic data

7/9

Validation of the algorithm on synthetic data

$$Day\ clearness = \frac{num(clearsky\ timestamps)^{[3]}}{num(total\ timestamps)}$$

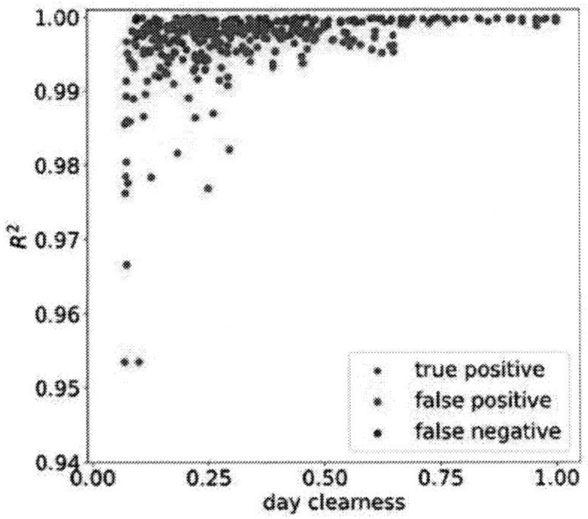

Result when run on dataset for Valdosta, Georgia, and S=1.

[3] DOI: 10.1016/j.renene.2023.04.035

Validation of the algorithm on synthetic data

$$Day\ clearness = \frac{num(clearsky\ timestamps)^{[3]}}{num(total\ timestamps)}$$

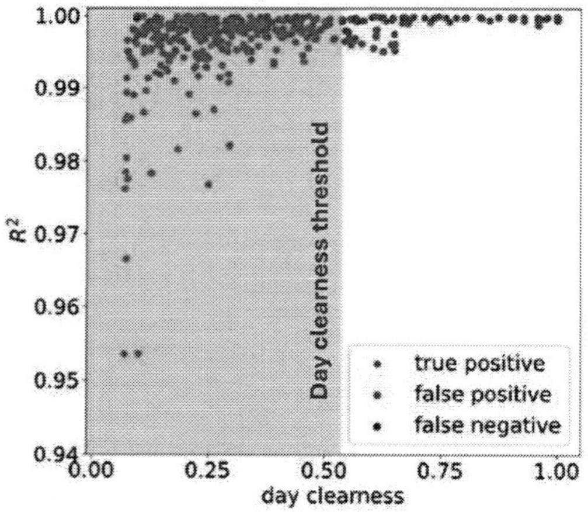

Result when run on dataset for Valdosta, Georgia, and S=1.

[3] DOI: 10.1016/j.renene.2023.04.035

Validation of the algorithm on synthetic data

$$Day\ clearness = \frac{num(clearsky\ timestamps)^{[3]}}{num(total\ timestamps)}$$

$$F_1 = \frac{2\,TP}{2\,TP + FN + FP}$$

TP True positive
FP False positive
FN False negative

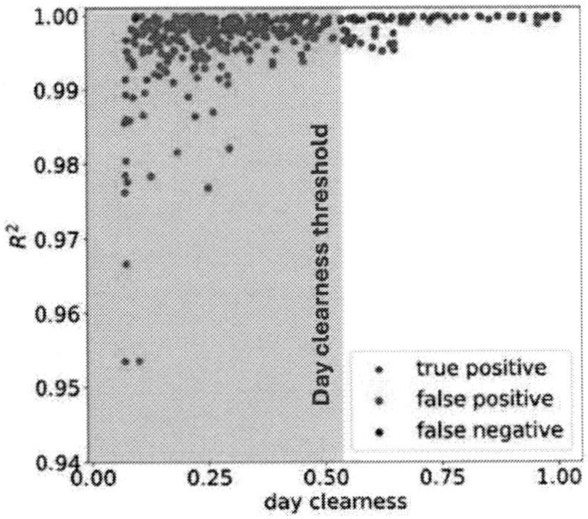

Result when run on dataset for Valdosta, Georgia, and S=1.

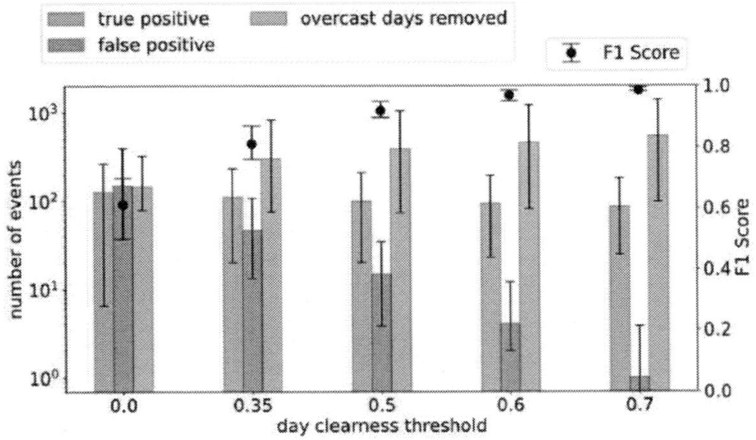

Result, averaged among all 38 locations, when S=1 and a day clearness threshold is implemented.

[3] DOI: 10.1016/j.renene.2023.04.035

Validation of the algorithm on synthetic data

$$Day\ clearness = \frac{num(clearsky\ timestamps)^{[3]}}{num(total\ timestamps)}$$

$$F_1 = \frac{2\,TP}{2\,TP + FN + FP}$$

TP True positive
FP False positive
FN False negative

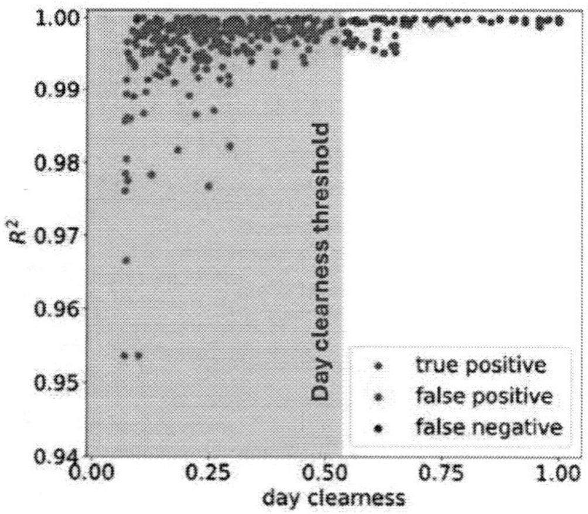

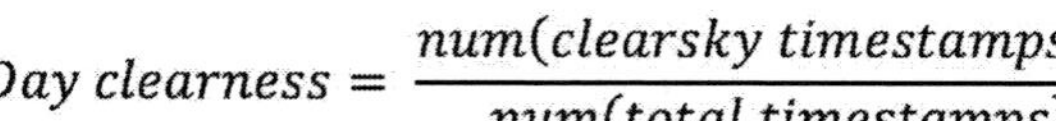

Result when run on dataset for Valdosta, Georgia, and S=1.

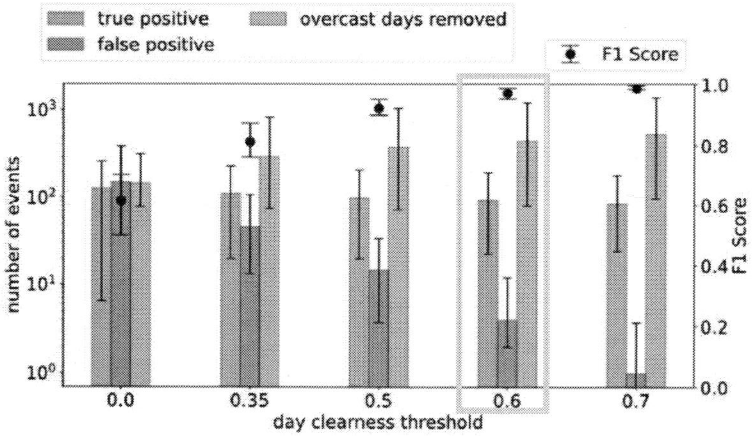

Result, averaged among all 38 locations, when S=1 and a day clearness threshold is implemented.

[3] DOI: 10.1016/j.renene.2023.04.035

Validation of the algorithm on synthetic data

$$Day\ clearness = \frac{num(clearsky\ timestamps)^{[3]}}{num(total\ timestamps)}$$

$$F_1 = \frac{2\,TP}{2\,TP + FN + FP}$$

TP True positive
FP False positive
FN False negative

$$S = \frac{number\ of\ stuck\ rows}{total\ number\ of\ rows}$$

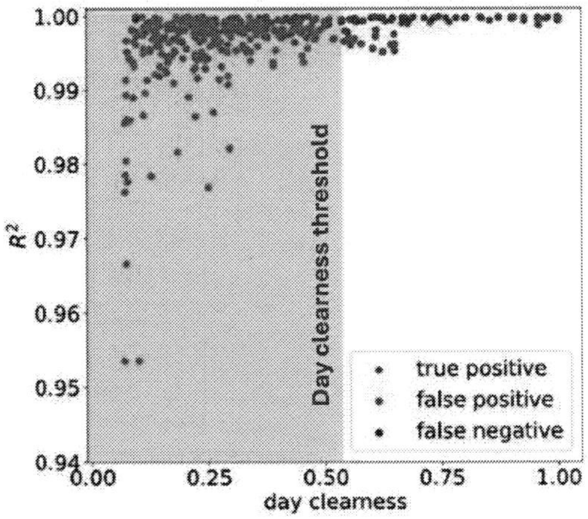

Result when run on dataset for Valdosta, Georgia, and S=1.

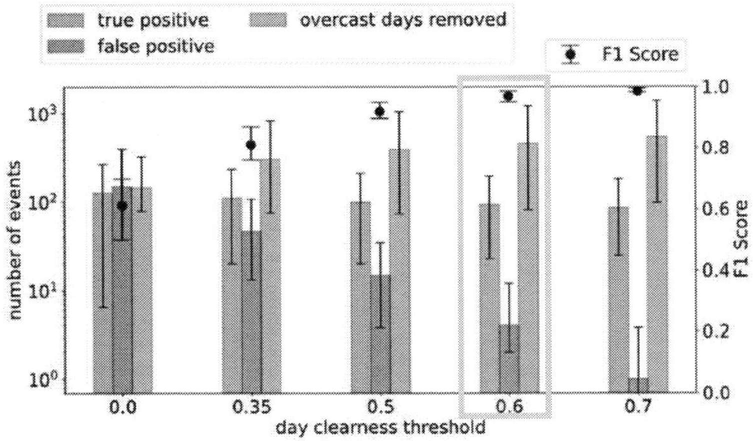

Result, averaged among all 38 locations, when S=1 and a day clearness threshold is implemented.

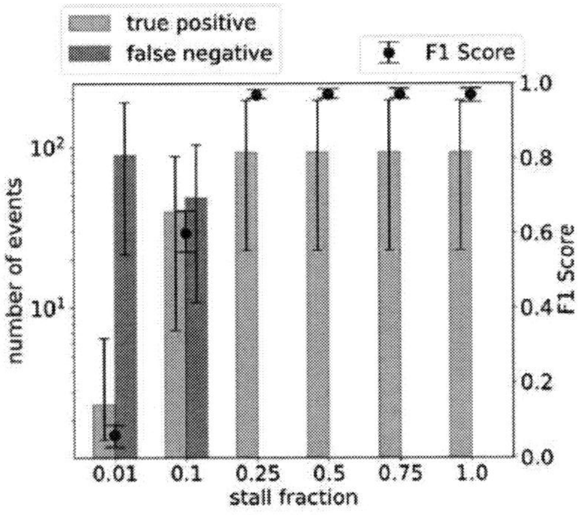

Result, averaged among all 38 locations, when a day clearness threshold of 0.6 is implemented, at varing S.

[3] DOI: 10.1016/j.renene.2023.04.035

Validation of the algorithm on synthetic data

$$Day\ clearness = \frac{num(clearsky\ timestamps)^{[3]}}{num(total\ timestamps)}$$

$$F_1 = \frac{2\,TP}{2\,TP + FN + FP}$$

TP True positive
FP False positive
FN False negative

$$S = \frac{number\ of\ stuck\ rows}{total\ number\ of\ rows}$$

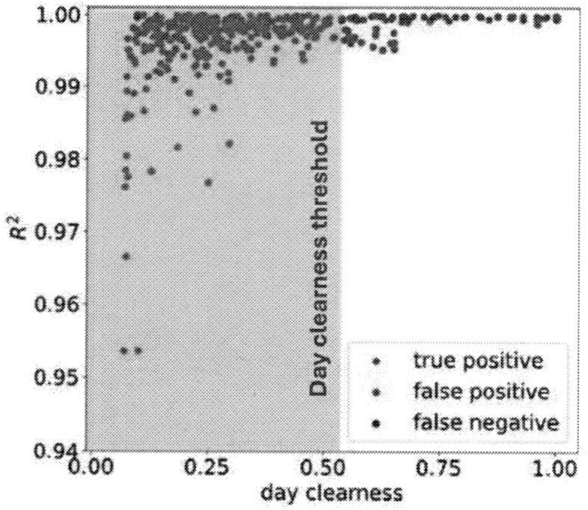

Result when run on dataset for Valdosta, Georgia, and S=1.

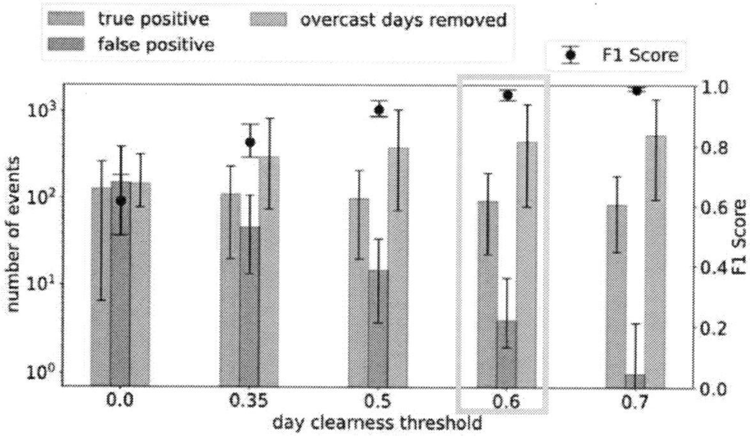

Result, averaged among all 38 locations, when S=1 and a day clearness threshold is implemented.

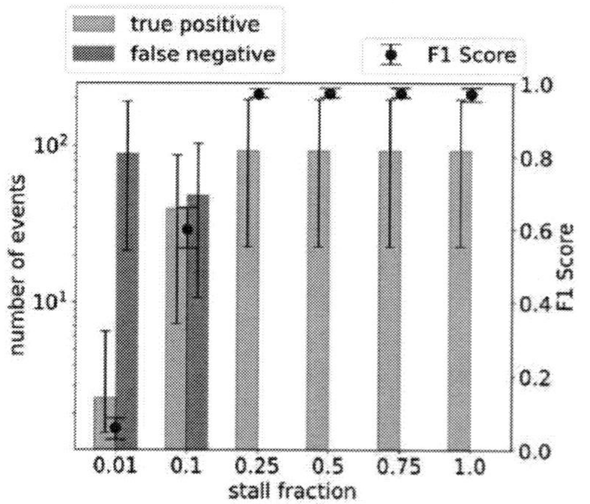

Result, averaged among all 38 locations, when a day clearness threshold of 0.6 is implemented, at varing S.

TAKEAWAY

The algorithm is sensitive to day clearness, when day clearness is low the algorithm has low amount of data to make a classification. Implementing a day clearness threshold improves drastically the performance. 0.60 is found to be a good trade off between evaluated days and F_1 score, enabling a F_1=0.96. Partially stuck scenarios are easier to detect the higher is the stuck fraction. Scenarios with stuck fraction below 0.25 cannot be detected.

[3] DOI: 10.1016/j.renene.2023.04.035

Validation of the algorithm on field data

8/9

Validation of the algorithm on field data

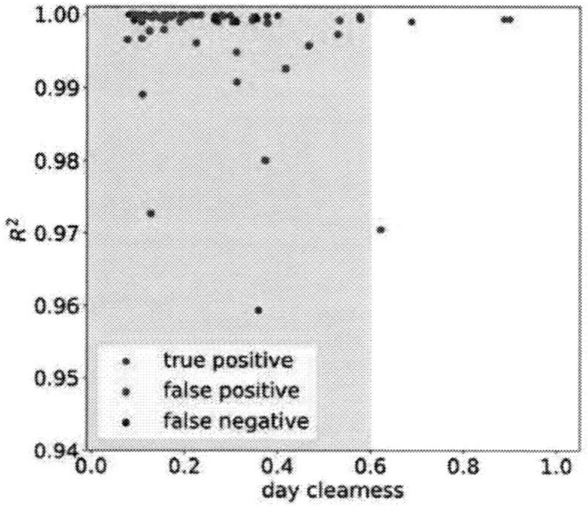

Result when run on field dataset and S=1.

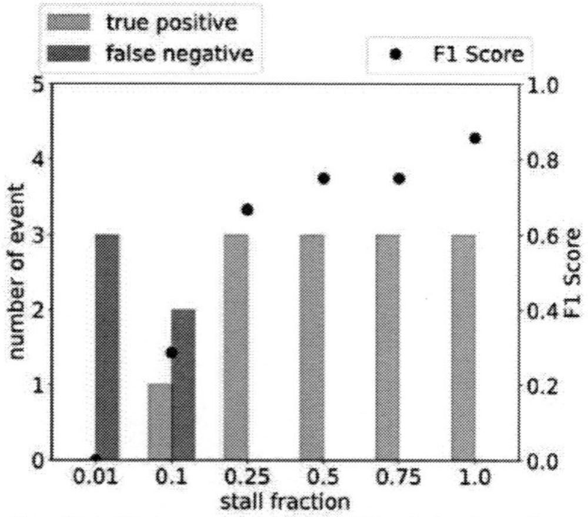

Result when run on field dataset and a day clearness threshold 0.6 is applied.

Validation of the algorithm on field data

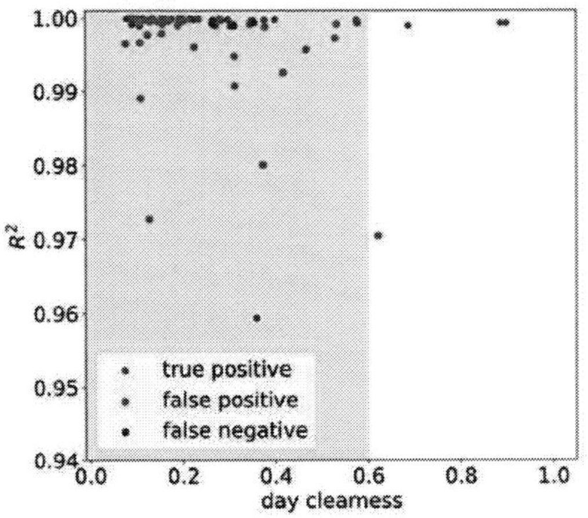

Result when run on field dataset and S=1.

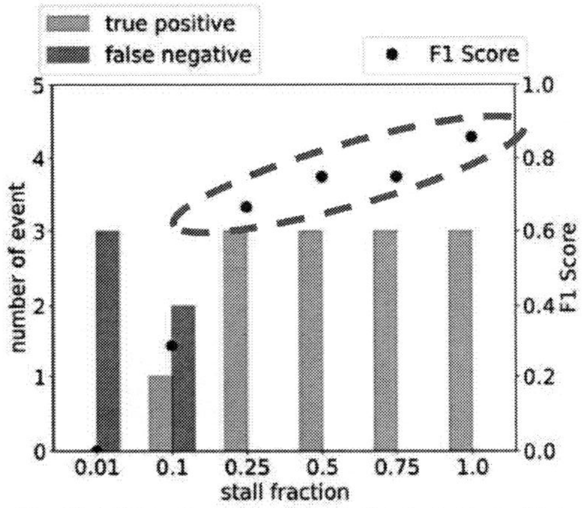

Result when run on field dataset and a day clearness threshold 0.6 is applied.

Validation of the algorithm on field data

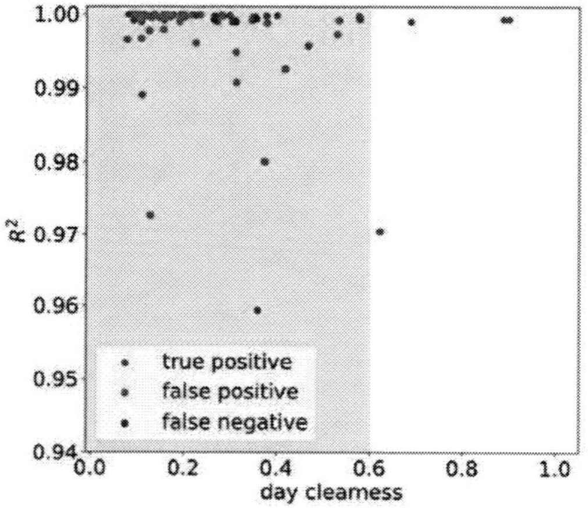

Result when run on field dataset and S=1.

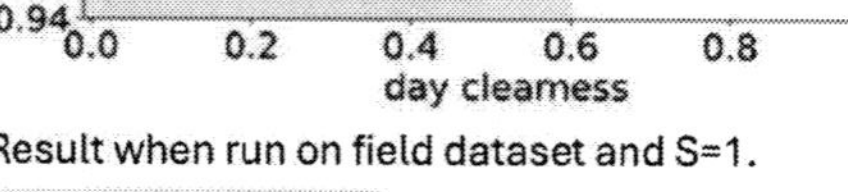

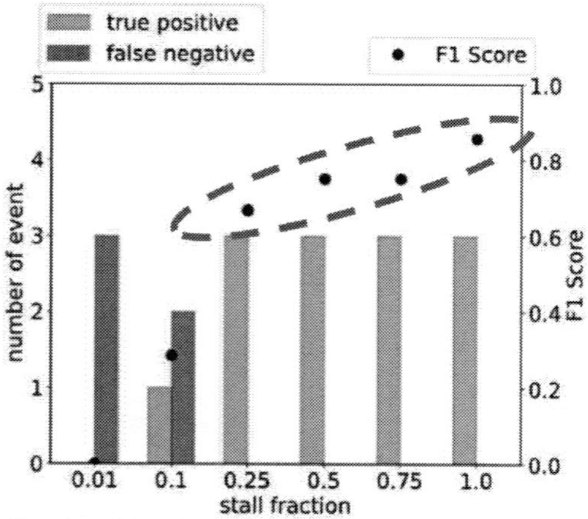

Result when run on field dataset and a day clearness threshold 0.6 is applied.

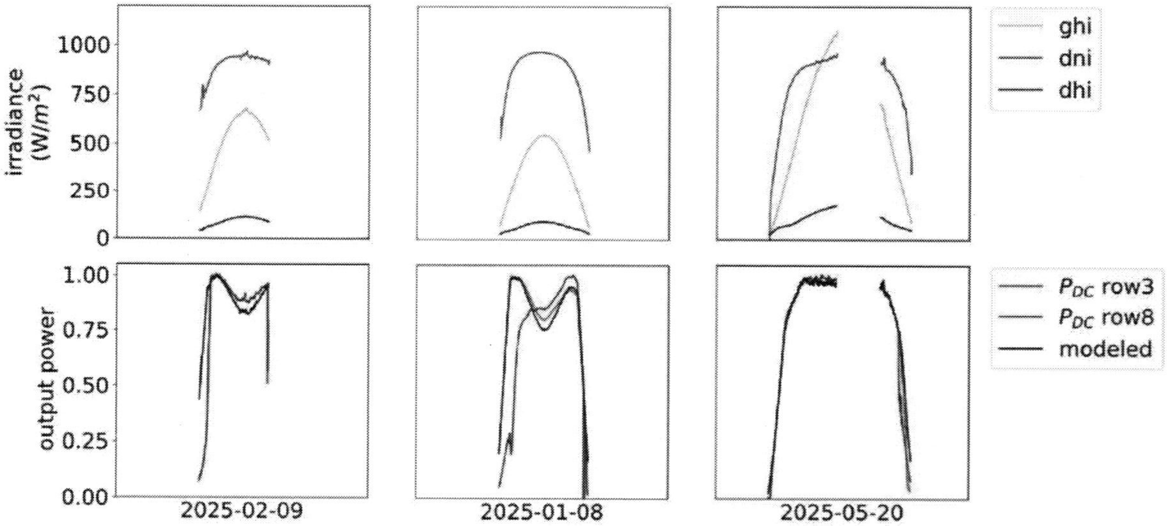

Days that make the algorithm reach a different F1 with different values of *S*.

Validation of the algorithm on field data

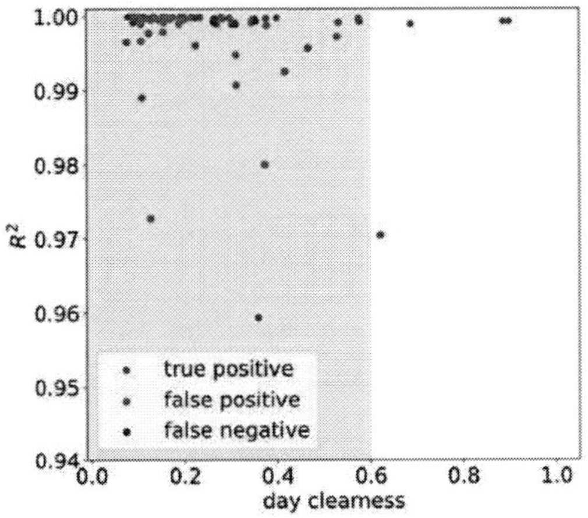

Result when run on field dataset and S=1.

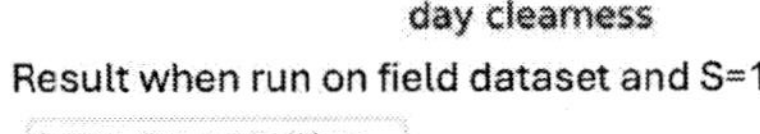

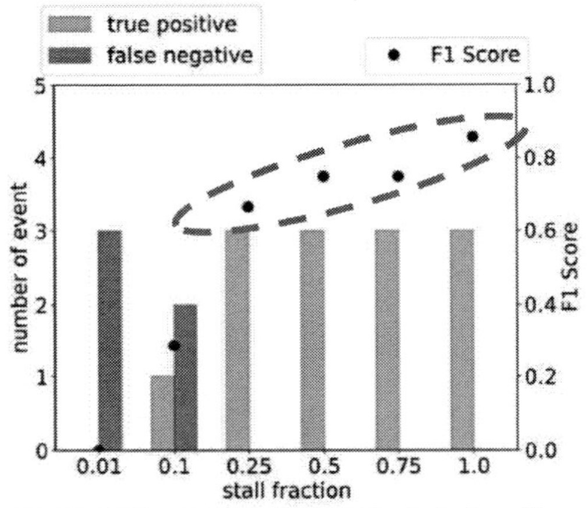

Result when run on field dataset and a day clearness threshold 0.6 is applied.

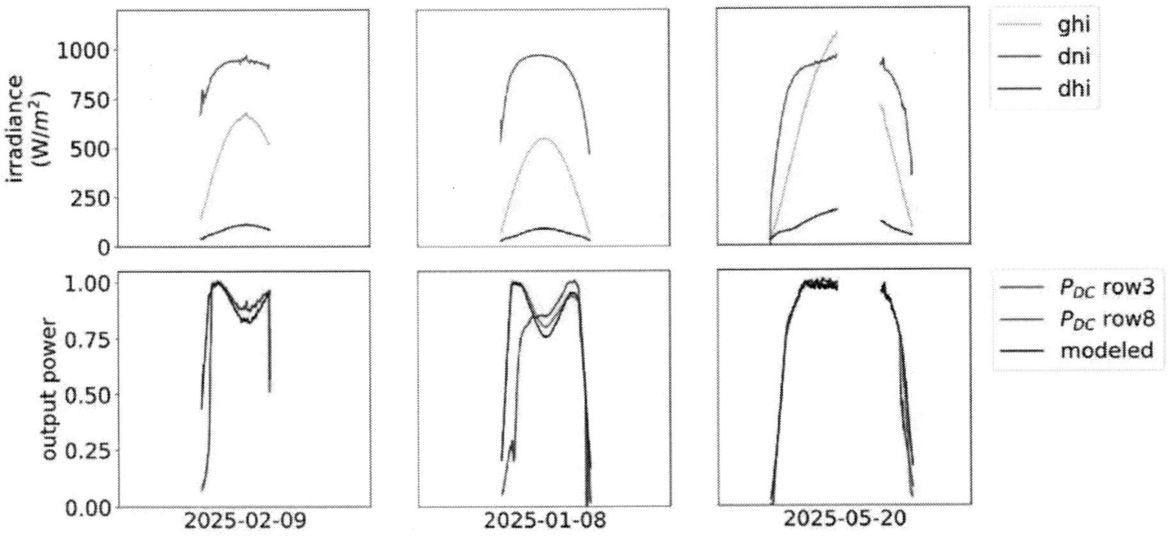

Days that make the algorithm reach a different F1 with different values of S.

TAKEAWAY

The algorithm is sensitive to cases in which underperformance is not related to weather conditions and appears to mimic a stuck condition. Although useful in some cases, January 8th and May 20th are not stuck events, thus are considered as FPs. Further claims per the field data are premature to make due to limited size of the data set (67 days with only 3 stalled events).

8/9

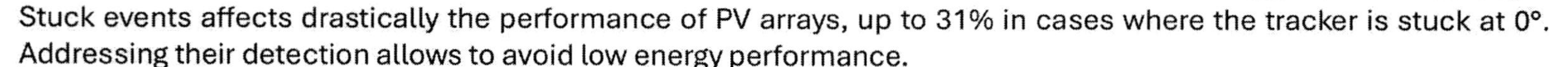

Conclusions

- Stuck events affects drastically the performance of PV arrays, up to 31% in cases where the tracker is stuck at 0°. Addressing their detection allows to avoid low energy performance.
- The detection algorithm's correctness is largely influenced by the day clearness: days with high day clearness are easier to classify.
- Implementing a day clearness threshold improves significantly the algorithm's performance. 0.60 looks like a sweet spot: improve the F1 from 0.60 to 0.96, and avoid removing the majority of days from the dataset.
- Partially stuck events can be detected with good performance if they are characterized by a stuck fraction above 0.25.
- The detection algorithm flags days when the underperformance is not related to weather conditions. For the aim of the algorithm these days are considered as FPs, but are days that should not be considered when addressing PV degradation analysis.

Future works

- Continue collecting field data to better address the performance in real conditions.
- Looking into more metrics that might improve the robustness of the algorithm.

Conclusions

- Stuck events affects drastically the performance of PV arrays, up to 30% in cases where the tracker is stuck at 0°. Addressing their detection allows to avoid low energy performance.
- The detection algorithm's correctness is largely influenced by the day clearness: days with high day clearness are easier to classify.
- Implementing a day clearness threshold improves significantly the algorithm's performance. 0.60 looks like a sweet spot: improve the F1 from 0,60 to 0,96, and avoid removing the majority of days from the dataset.
- Partially stuck events can be detected with good performance if they are characterized by a stuck fraction above 0.25.
- The detection algorithm flags days when the underperformance is not related to weather conditions. For the aim of the algorithm these days are considered as FPs, but are days that should not be considered when addressing PV degradation analysis.

Future works

- Continue collecting field data to better address the performance in real conditions.
- Looking into more metrics that might improve the robustness of the algorithm.

Thanks for the attention!!

Riccardo Adinolfi Borea

Alma Mater Studiorum – University of Bologna
National Renewable Energy Laboratory – NREL
Ricerca sul Sistema Energetico S.p.a. – RSE

riccardo.adinolfi2@unibo.it

9/9

Something helpful

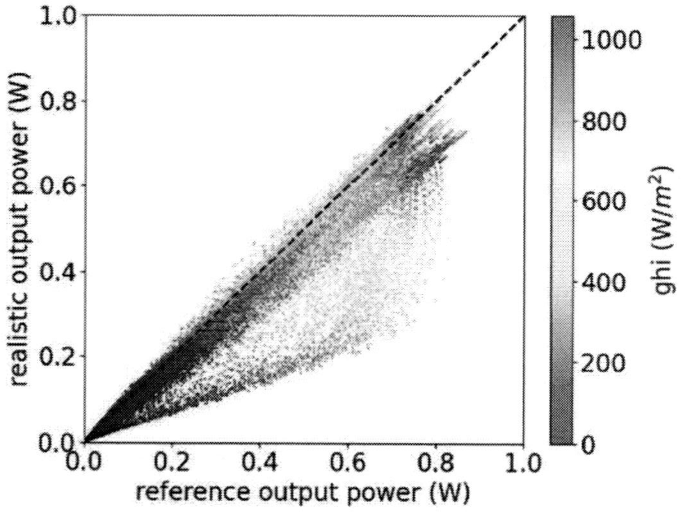

Fig. 5 Realistic power output vs modeled power output for the case of Valdosta, Georgia.

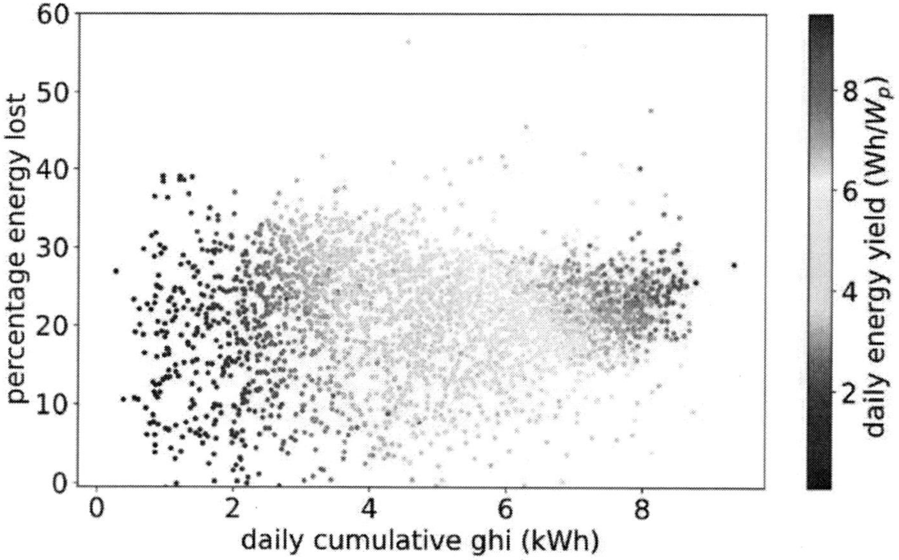

Example
25% stuck scenario

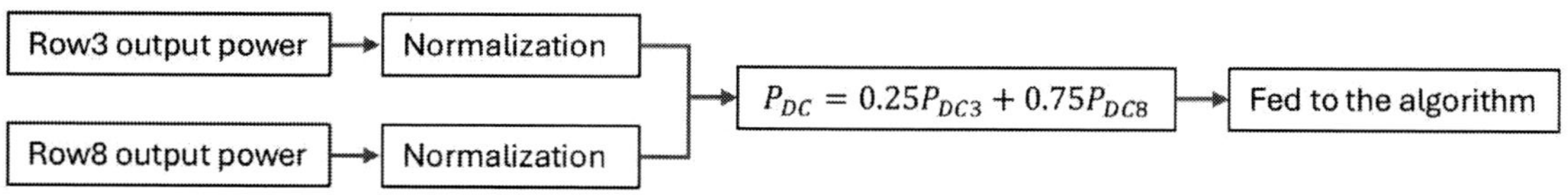

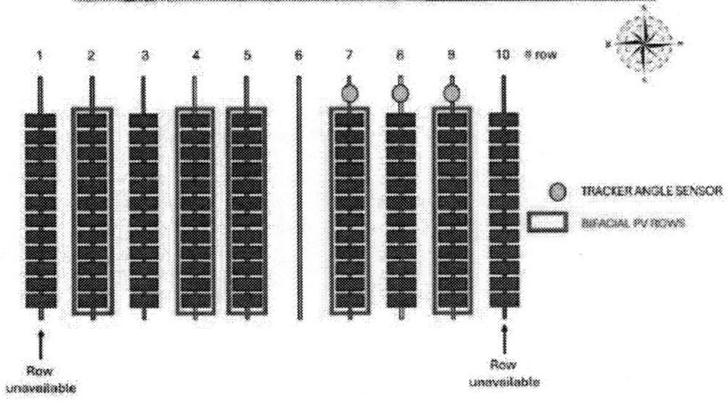

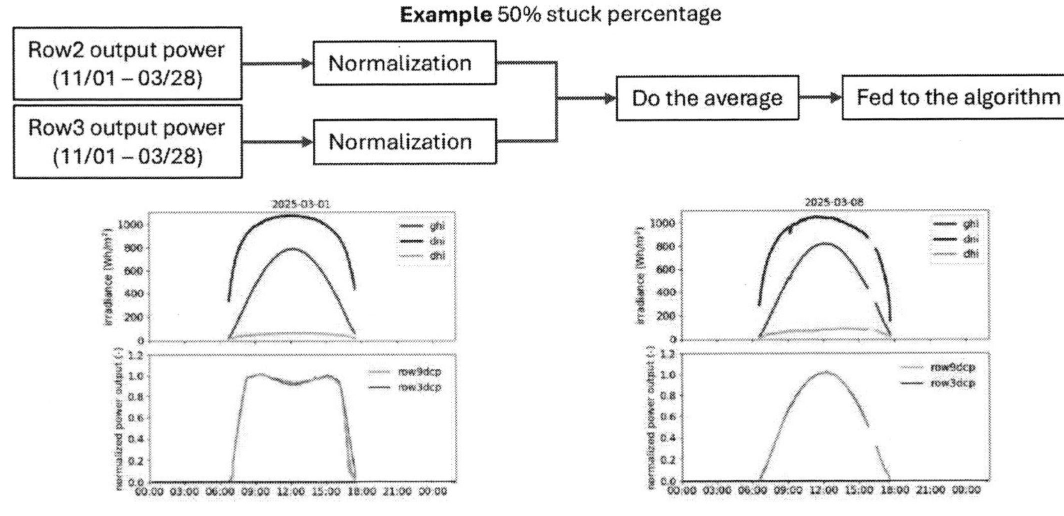

System description

Row 6 is unavailable due to changing modules.
Row 1 and row 10 are unavailable due to different electrical connection (i.e., directly with the grid).
For Row 2-9 it is measured operating current, voltage, and power at string level (at the DC side).
Row 1, 3, 8, and 10 are monofacial, while 2, 4, 5, 7, and 9, are bifacial.

Experiments description

Rows are stuck at 0° for the entire day because 0° is the most difficult angle to detect. Multiple rows are stuck at same time but, if that's the case, rows that are stuck are not adjunct.
To create the different stuck tracker percentages, we first normalize the output power of each string (each one by its own nameplate power) and than do the average of the rows taken into consideration.
To have the same ratio of "stuck days/total days" that was used with synthetic data, we included measurements from November 1st.
Monofacial and bifacial rows are treated as equal.

Example 50% stuck percentage

Row2 output power (11/01 – 03/28) → Normalization
Row3 output power (11/01 – 03/28) → Normalization
→ Do the average → Fed to the algorithm

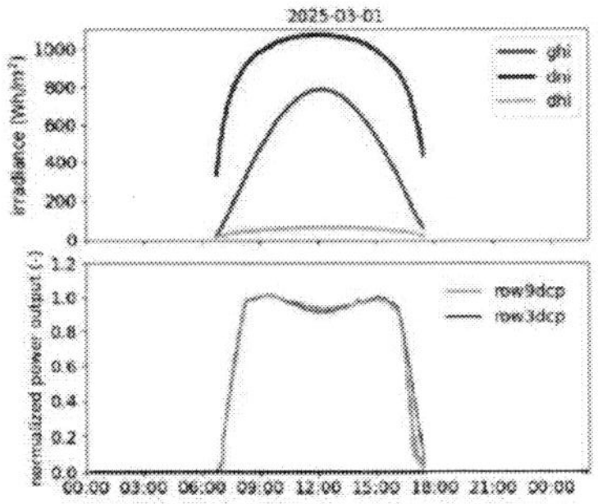

Comparison of the normalized power of a bifacial and monofacial rows when tracking.

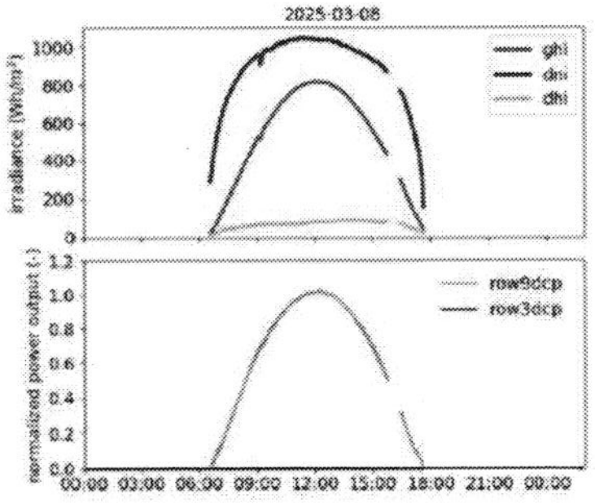

Comparison of the normalized power of a bifacial and monofacial rows when stuck.

BECQUEREL INSTITUTE
Strategy Consulting in Solar PV

Autonomous Multi-AI Agent System for PV Health Monitoring: a Fully Automated O&M Pipeline with Field Robotics Integration

M. Sondoqah, D. Moser
Becquerel Institute Italia

A. Louwen
RISE Research Institutes of Sweden

Formerly: Eurac Research

EUPVSEC 2025

Outline

1. Automation roadmap 2030
2. Challenges in data-driven O&M pipelines
3. O&M PV Ontology
4. Symptom detection through Multi-Modal Large Language Models
5. Multi-AI agent system for O&M
6. Medical doctor-like failure detection approach
7. Validation with ground truth

Becquerel Institute

Current and Projected Automation Levels by 2030

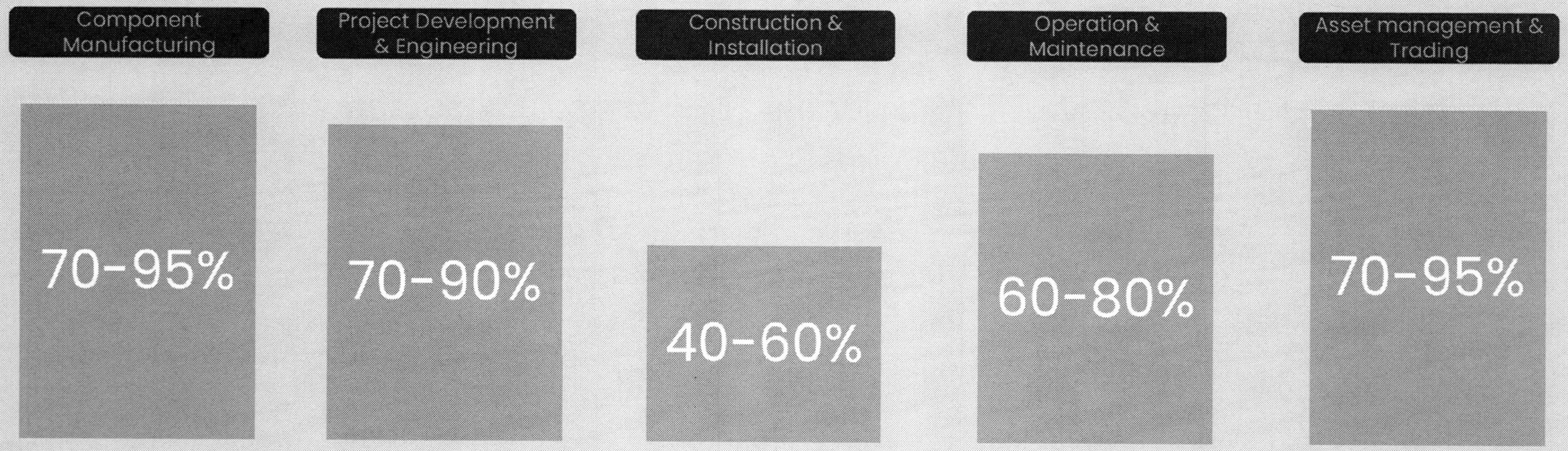

Source: Transforming the PV Sector: The AI & Robotics Revolution-Becquerel Institute

Becquerel Institute

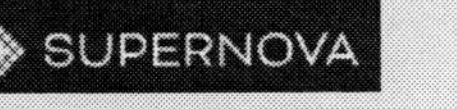

INGREDIENTS FOR AUTOMATION IN O&M and AM: State of the art

Management, sharing and federation of PV asset information throughout the lifecycle
DIGITAL TWIN AND UNIVERSAL MAPPING

TRUSTPV

SUPERNOVA

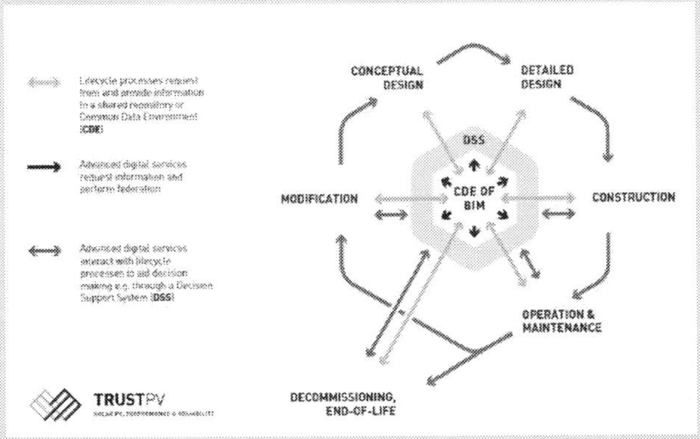

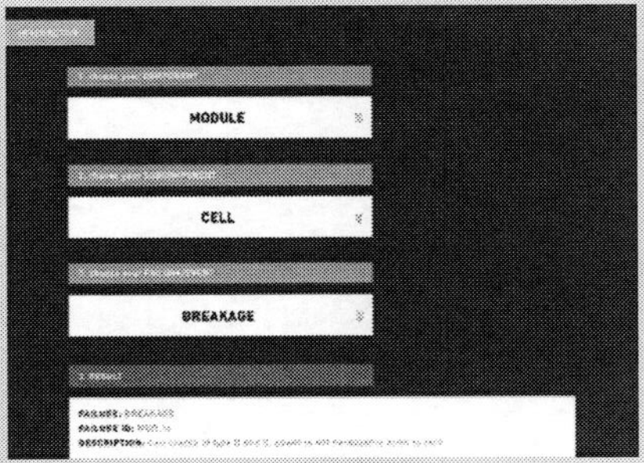

TRUSTPV

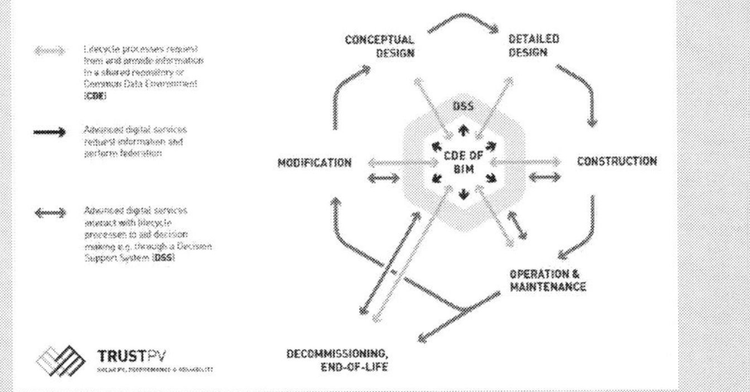

Implement a RISK MATRIX in the ticketing platform to harmonise data coming from the field (independent from operator)

Becquerel Institute

INGREDIENTS FOR AUTOMATION IN O&M AND AM: State of the art

Identify failure through for e.g. advanced monitoring and semiautomated inspection techniques, and resolve the issue (SOLUTION MATRIX)

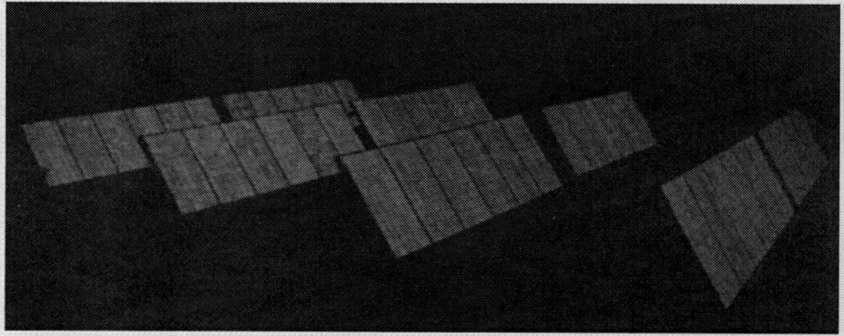

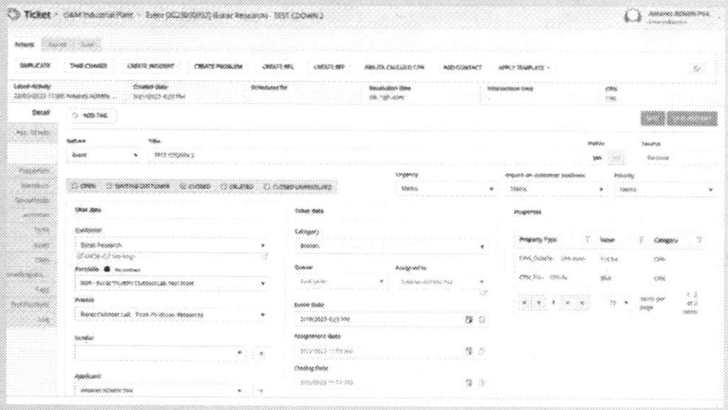

Calculate the final KPI and update a KNOWLEDGE BASE database

→ A **DSS** system can provide suggestions based on statistics and previous field experience for the most effective solution

TRUSTPV

Becquerel Institute

Challenges in classic data driven approaches

- **Limitations of Traditional Data-Driven O&M Pipelines:**
  - Failures in PV systems are many and tend to occur at different component levels
  - Multiple data streams with different format (numerical, images, unstructured data, etc.) are generated, but they are rarely exploited to their full potential (and rarely shared....)
  - Large labeled datasets are required to train data-driven models
  - Data-driven models are fragmented, and they deal with each modality on its own

Becquerel Institute

How to move on?

Becquerel Institute

O&M Ontology

- The ontology of O&M is where every element in the O&M pipeline is defined
- The elements of the O&M ontology are Failure, Symptom, Inspection, & Solution
- Each of these elements is represented via text
- These elements are connected through relationships
- The final structure of the ontology is introduced as knowledge graphs

Becquerel Institute

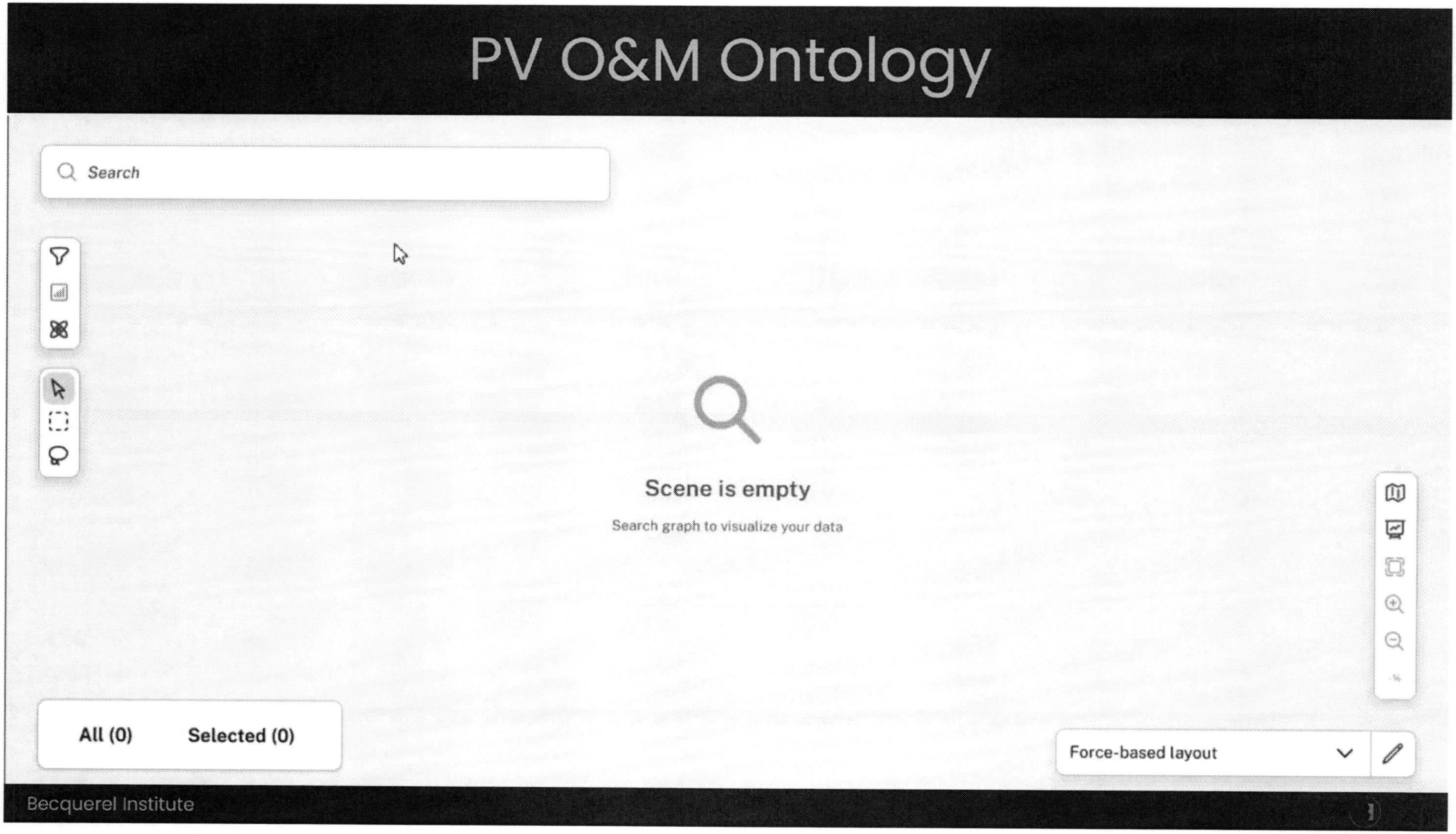
PV O&M Ontology
Search
Scene is empty
Search graph to visualize your data
All (0)
Selected (0)
Force-based layout
Becquerel Institute

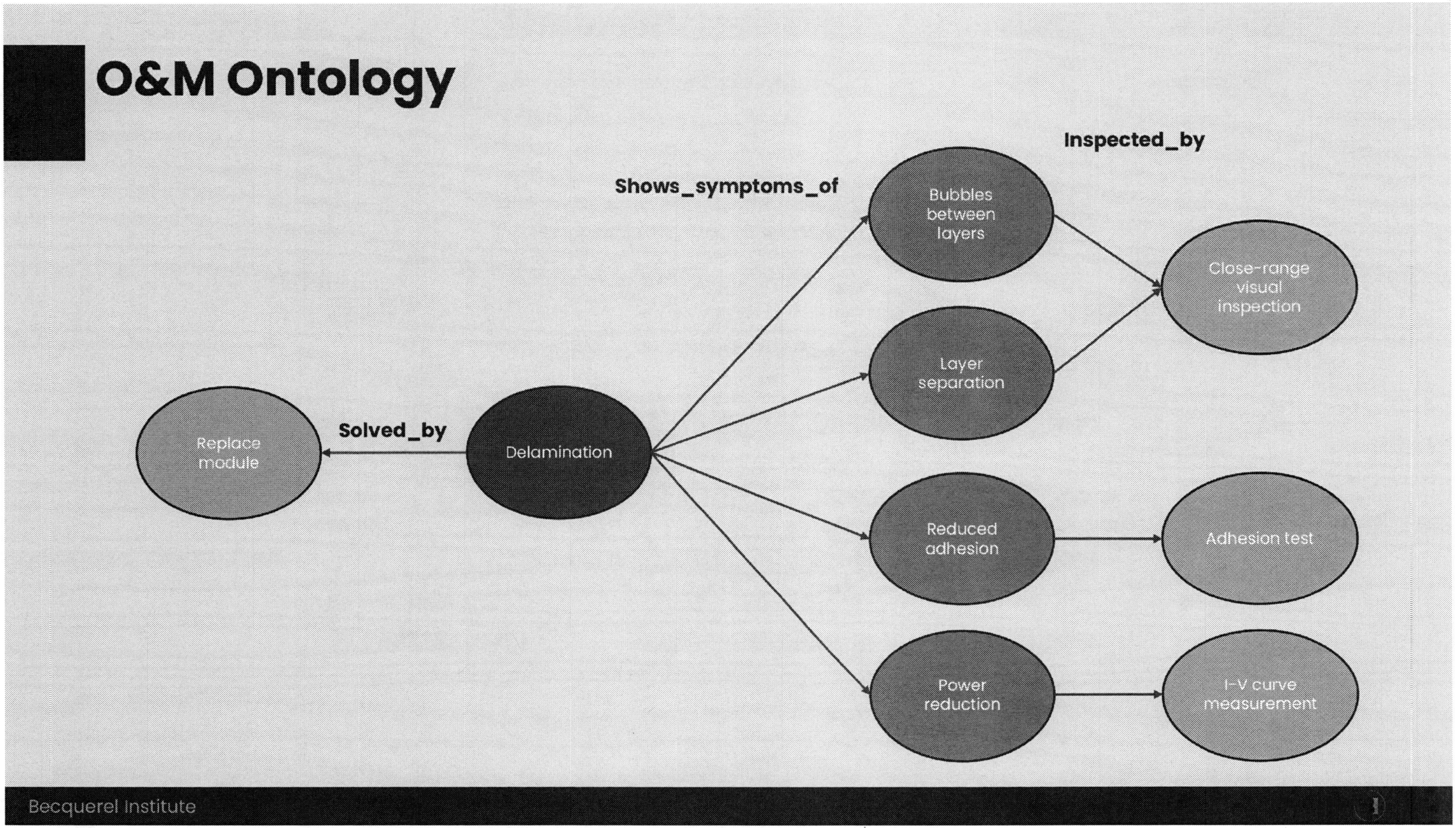
O&M Ontology
Inspected_by
Shows_symptoms_of
Bubbles between layers
Close-range visual inspection
Layer separation
Replace module
Solved_by
Delamination
Reduced adhesion
Adhesion test
Power reduction
I-V curve measurement
Becquerel Institute

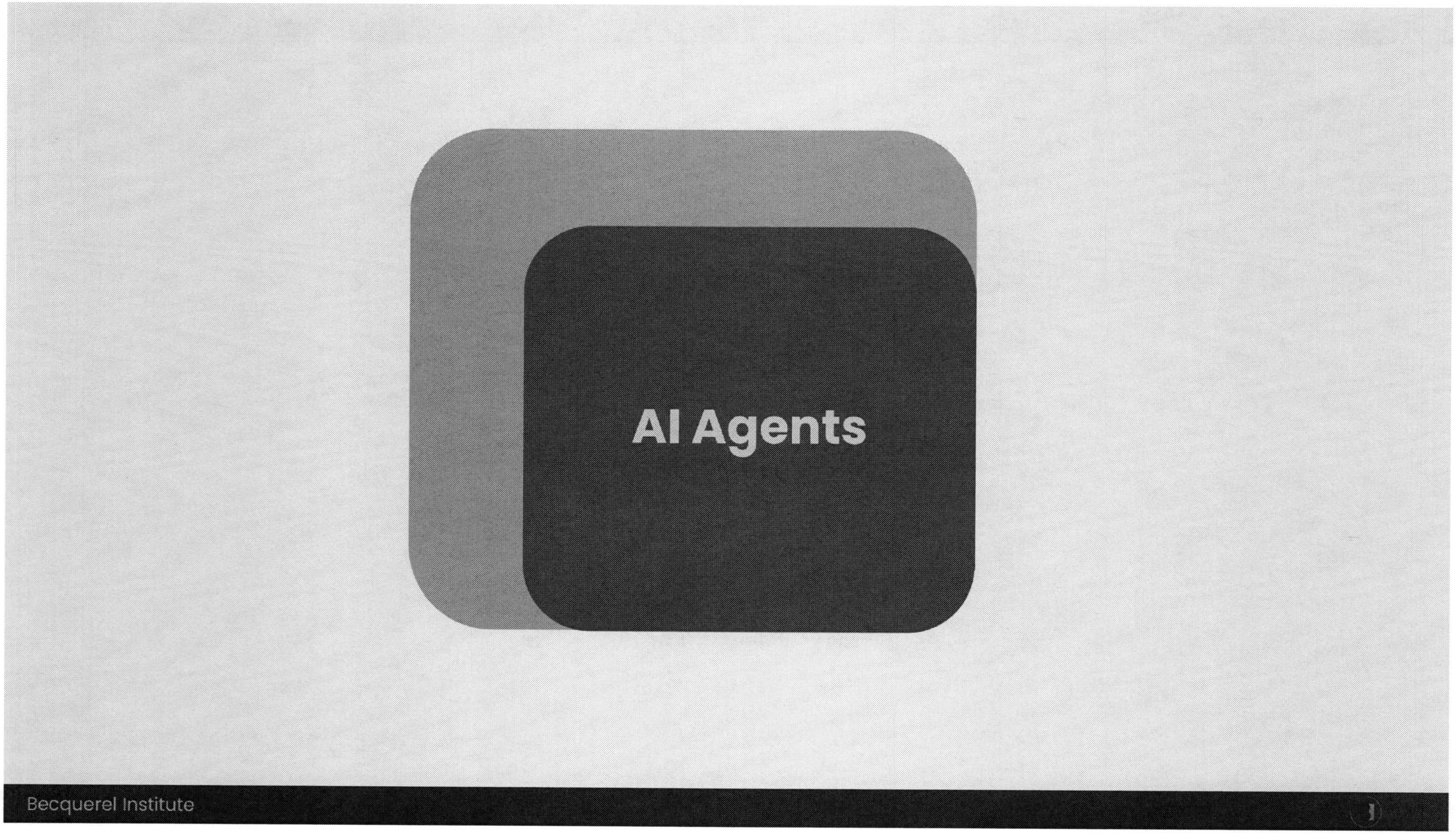
AI Agents
Becquerel Institute

Modality to context

- **Every element in the O&M ontology was translated into context**
- **AI agent wrapped on the top of a proper Multi-Modal Large-Language-Model (MLLM) were built to generate context**

- **Example:**

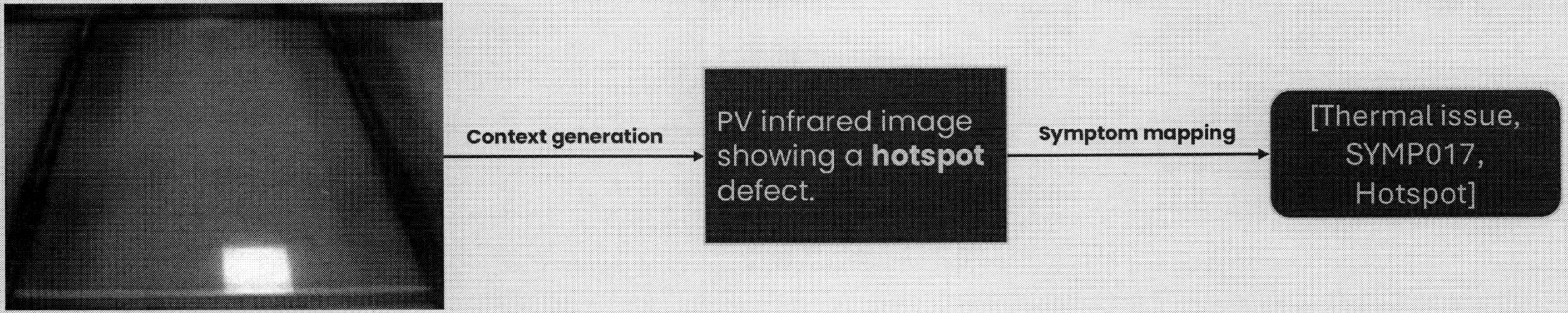

Becquerel Institute

Modality to context in the O&M ecosystem

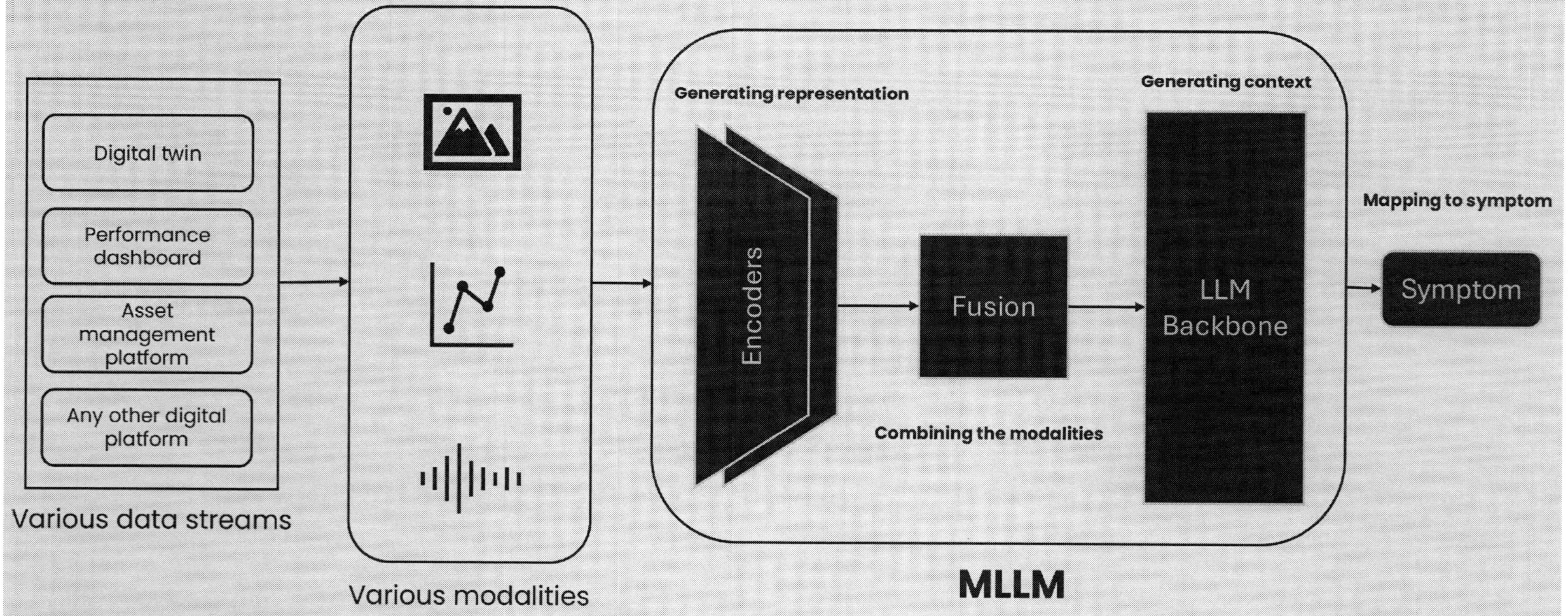

Becquerel Institute

MLLM engine

- Each **modality** (image, audio, video, text, sensor data, etc.) has a **specialized encoder** that can transform raw data into a numerical representation (vector embeddings).
- Once the encoders create modality-specific embeddings, these are **aligned and fused** into a shared space.
- After fusion, the combined representation is passed into a **Large Language Model backbone** (GPT).
- Then the **LLM** generates **textual outputs** (answers, captions, reasoning steps) or even **actions** in agentic frameworks.

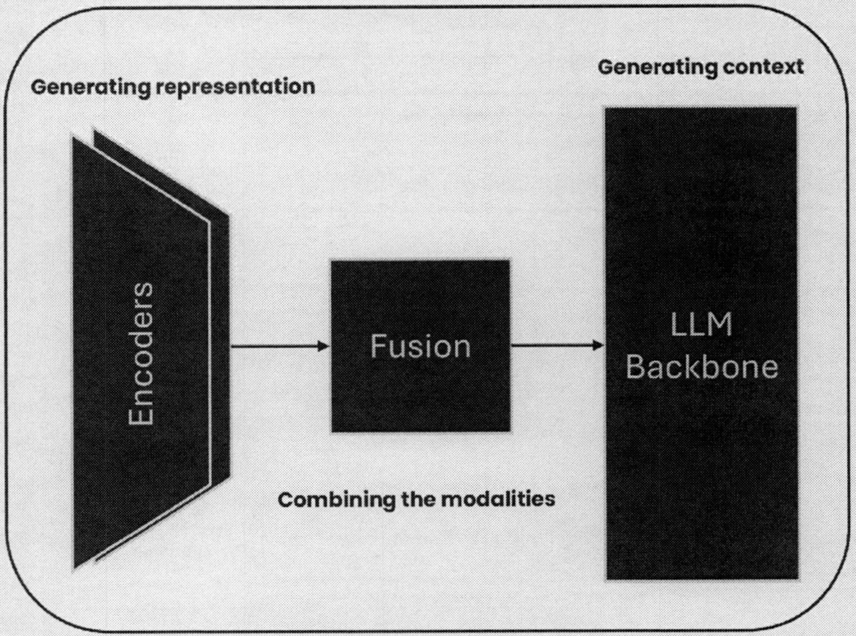

MLLM

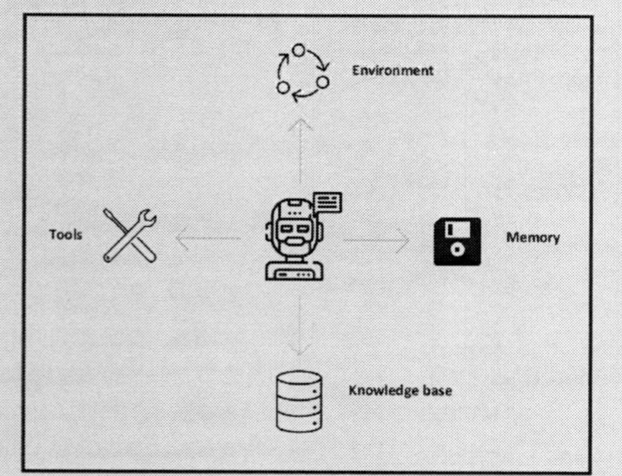

Becquerel Institute

Multi-agent system workflow

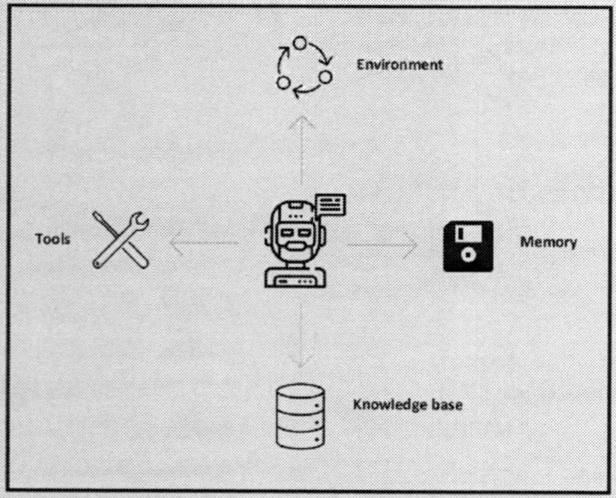

Figure 1: Proposed single agent architecture implementation & integration

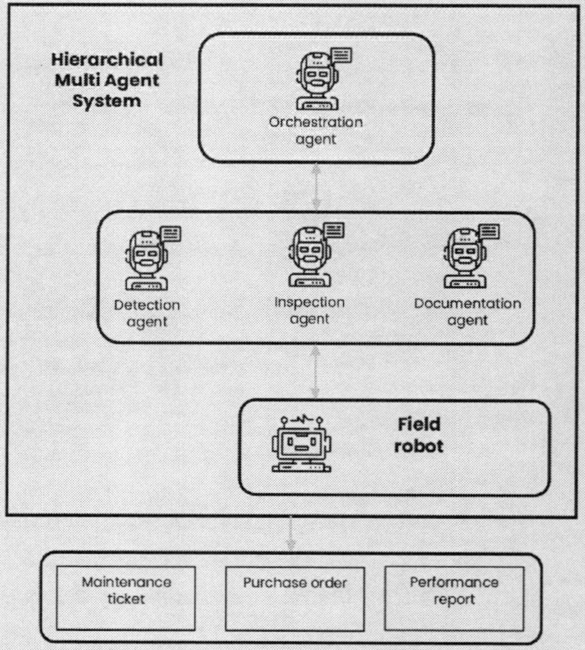

Figure 2: Proposed Multi-agent System Workflow Integrated with Field Robotics Layer

Becquerel Institute

Multi-agent system workflow: AI agents work profile

The **Orchestration Agent** acts as the central coordinator, managing interactions among all autonomous agents to ensure seamless collaboration, conflict resolution, and efficient execution of tasks.

The **Detection Agent** is a Multi Modal Large Language Model - based AI agent responsible for identifying symptoms in defective PV system components.

The **Inspection Agent** determines and executes the appropriate inspection method based on the symptoms identified by the detection agent and the instructions received from the orchestration agent.

The **Documentation Agent** records all relevant information and outputs from various stages of the pipeline, providing decision-makers with insights into system performance.

Becquerel Institute

Medicine-like workflow

Becquerel Institute

Medical diagnose-like approach

Becquerel Institute

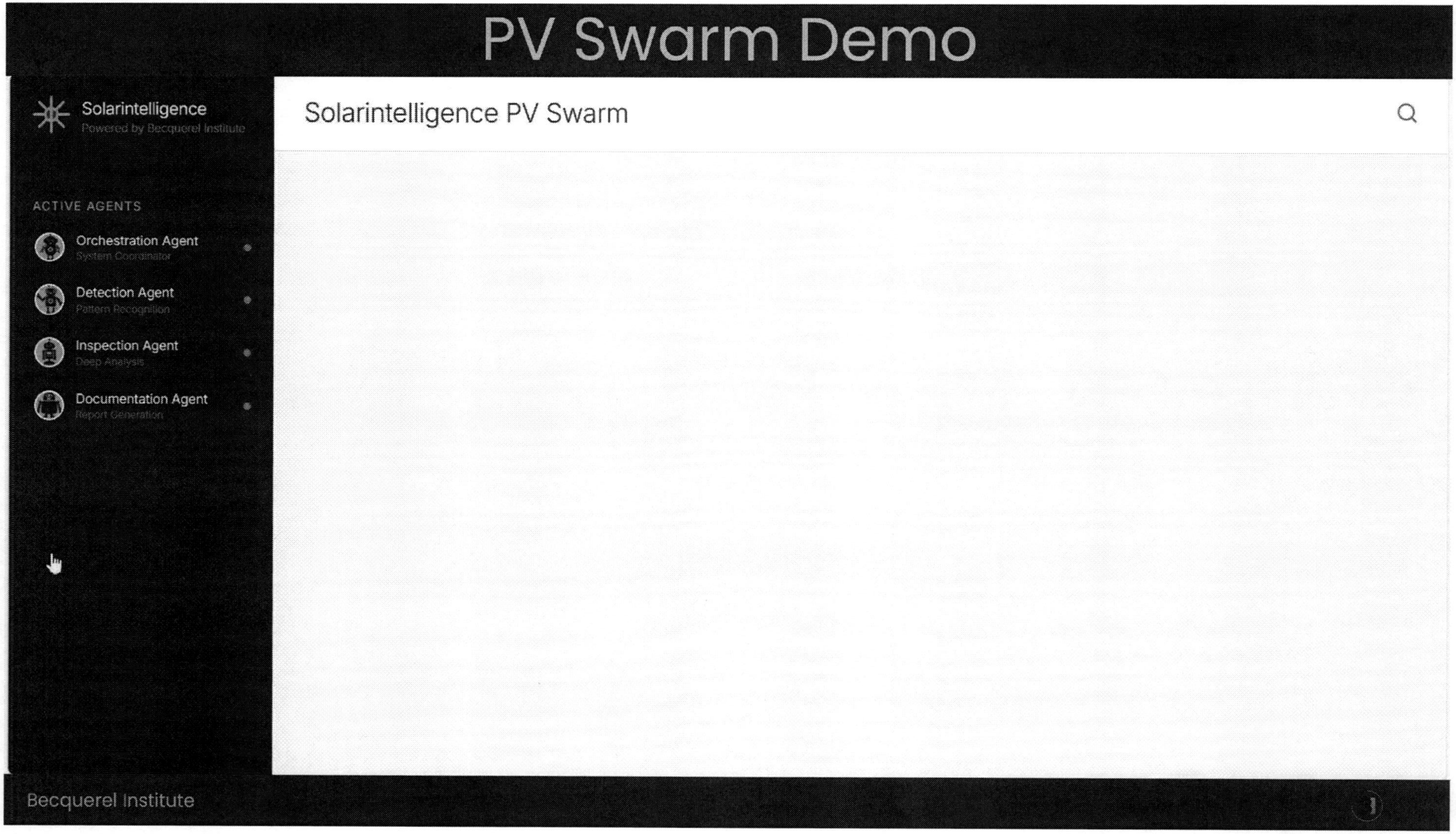
PV Swarm Demo
Solarintelligence
Powered by Becquerel Institute
Solarintelligence PV Swarm
ACTIVE AGENTS
Orchestration Agent
System Coordinator
Detection Agent
Pattern Recognition
Inspection Agent
Deep Analysis
Documentation Agent
Report Generation
Becquerel Institute

Symptom & failure detection experiments

- The system achieved an estimated accuracy of over 80% across 10 distinct failure types.
- In some cases, the final diagnosis may still be correct even if the symptom is not detected with full accuracy.
- The detection agent processes multiple data types as input to identify potential symptoms.
- Failure detection is based on a combination of the initial input data, the symptoms identified by the detection agent, and supplementary information obtained from additional inspections.

Case	Failure Type (Observed)	Symptom Prediction	Failure Prediction	Evaluation
1	White powdery surface	SYMP005 – White powdery surface	Mod.03 – Chalking	**Correct**
2	Encapsulant bubbling / delamination	SYMP011-Bubbles between layers	Mod.24-Delamination	**Correct**
3	Bypass diode failure	SYMP017 – Hot spots	Mod.54 – Defect bypass diode	**Incorrect**
4	Connector housing crack	SYMP031-Broken connectors	Not found	**Partially correct**
5	Encapsulant browning	SYMP003 - Discoloration	Mod.28-Yellowing or browning of encapsulation	**Correct**
6	Soiling	SYMP026 – Soiling	Mod.49 – Soiling	**Correct**
7	Cracked glass with burn marks	SYMP001 – Cracks + SYMP002 – Burn marks	Mod.46 – Glass breakage	**Correct**
8	Snail trails	SYMP001 – Visible cracks	Mod.27-snail trails	**Incorrect**
9	Cell crack/Frame crack	SYMP001 – Cracks	Mod.17 – Breakage (cell cracks)	**Partially correct**
10	Moisture ingress	SYMP024-Moisture ingress	Mod.26 – Moisture	**Correct**

Becquerel Institute

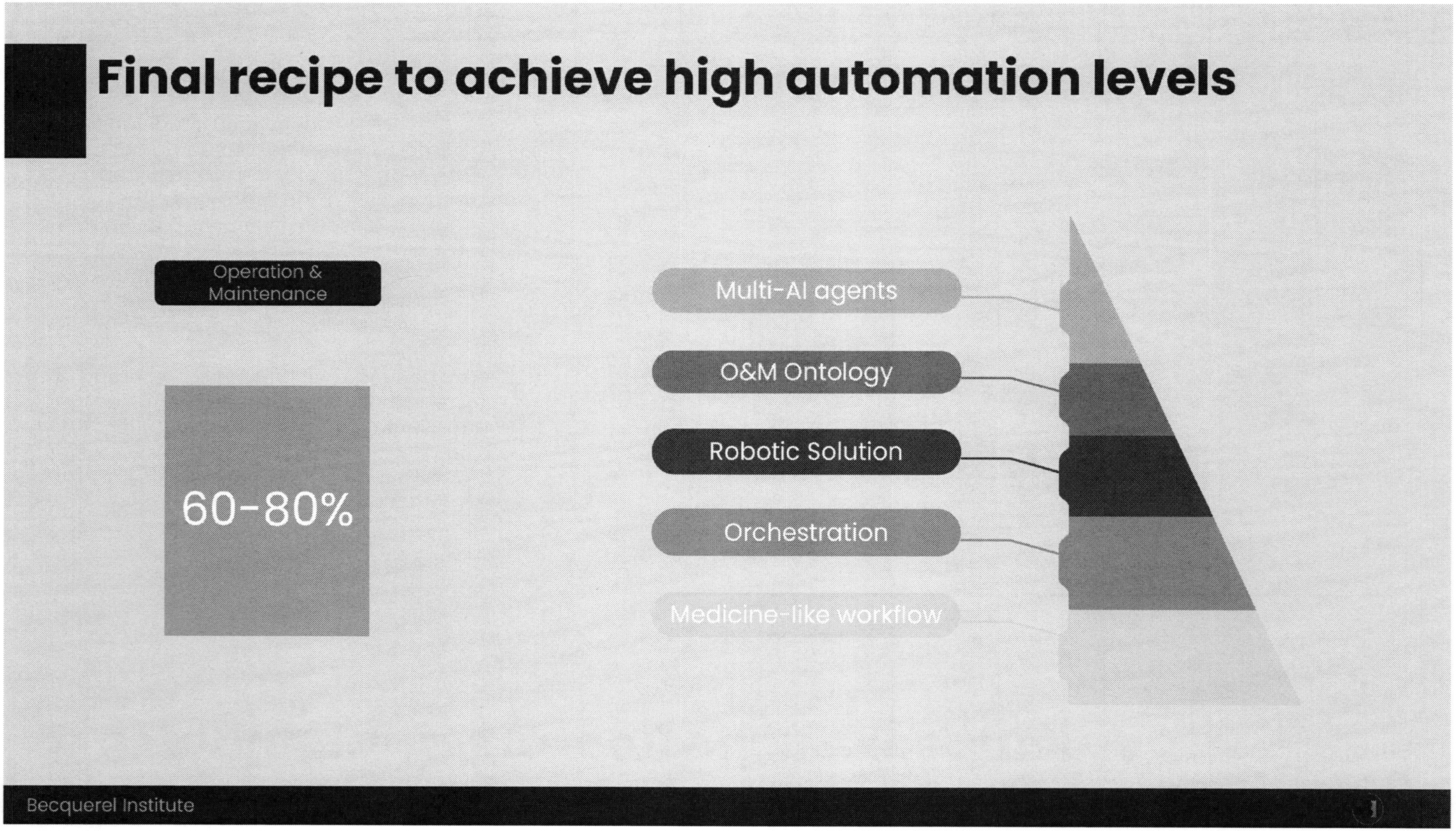
Final recipe to achieve high automation levels
Operation & Maintenance
60-80%
Multi-AI agents
O&M Ontology
Robotic Solution
Orchestration
Medicine-like workflow
Becquerel Institute

Not all that glitters is gold: new challenges to overcome

📍 Geographic Distribution vs. Economics: Robotics deployment faces massive logistics challenges.

🔧 The AI-Robotics Integration Gap: You need both AI systems AND human teams (another level of coordination).

🏗 Legacy System Compatibility Crisis: PV Plants are designed for human maintenance, not AI optimization or robotic access

⚡ The Reliability Requirements Reality: Autonomous maintenance systems must demonstrate exceptional reliability because failures could exceed automation benefits. The redundancy required may significantly increase costs beyond current projections.

📊 Data Quality Limitations: Legacy assets often lack sufficient monitoring, while fragmented systems create integration challenges that limit AI effectiveness to newer, data-rich installations.

Becquerel Institute

BECQUEREL INSTITUTE
Strategy Consulting in Solar PV

Becquerel Institute Italia

d.moser@becquerelinstitute.eu

m.sondoqah@becquerelinstitute.eu

42nd European Photovoltaic Solar Energy Conference and Exhibition

This presentation was selected by the Sc. Committee of the EU PVSEC 2025 for submission of a full paper to one of the EU PVSEC's collaborating peer-reviewed journals.

PREDICTIVE MODELLING AND ANALYSIS OF SOILING LOSSES IN PV PLANTS THROUGH A HYBRID DATA-DRIVEN APPROACH

Ioannis (John) A. Tsanakas[1*], E. Pilat[1], S. Arbaretaz[1], M.-T. Doi[1], F. Monteiro Martins[2], J. Veludo[2], C. Ménézo[3]
[1] CEA, Liten, Univ. Grenoble Alpes, Campus INES, 73375 Le Bourget du Lac, France
[2] Galp Energia S.A., 1349-065 Lisboa, Portugal
[3] Laboratoire Procédés Energie Bâtiment (LOCIE), Université Savoie Mont Blanc (USMB), 73375 Le Bourget du Lac, France

*corresponding author : ioannis.tsanakas@cea.fr

ABSTRACT: Photovoltaic (PV) system efficiency is significantly affected by soiling, leading to energy losses and increased operational costs. Within the SERENDI-PV project, this study refines soiling loss modeling through two complementary approaches: the Stochastic Quantifying Soiling Loss (SQSL) method and a machine learning (ML)-based predictive model. SQSL quantifies soiling losses using electrical performance data, independent of meteorological inputs, while the ML model forecasts losses using environmental parameters such as temperature, humidity, wind speed, and particulate matter concentration. The SQSL method identifies soiling phases—cleaning periods, stable periods, and soiling periods—by analyzing PV performance trends. Monte Carlo simulations generate probable soiling profiles, assessing uncertainty and informing maintenance strategies. Additionally, SQSL enables classification of soiling accumulation patterns, distinguishing between gradual and rapid soiling events. The ML-based approach integrates artificial neural networks and regression models to predict soiling losses, applying data pre-processing techniques to enhance accuracy. Regional climate variations and site-specific soiling characteristics are incorporated to improve predictive performance. Preliminary results validate the robustness of both methodologies. SQSL-generated profiles align closely with observed soiling trends, and ML models effectively capture seasonal variations. Field studies at a utility-scale PV plant in Spain further demonstrate the location dependency of soiling patterns. Comparative analysis of SQSL predictions and real soiling measurements shows prediction errors between 1% and 2.6% over an eight-day forecast period. These findings support the integration of predictive soiling models into PV monitoring platforms, optimizing maintenance strategies and minimizing energy yield losses.

Keywords: *PV systems; soiling loss modeling; machine learning (ML); PV performance, predictive modelling.*

1 INTRODUCTION: CONTEXT and AIM

Soiling, the accumulation of dust and particulate matter on photovoltaic (PV) modules, is a major factor in system performance degradation, causing significant energy losses and elevating operational expenses [1-3]. This makes its management crucial for optimizing PV output. As detailed in [1], research into soiling has evolved to encompass various assessment methods and mitigation strategies, including cleaning and anti-soiling coatings. The review in [2] emphasizes the severity of soiling losses in arid and polluted regions, noting the benefits of passive anti-soiling coatings—such as waterless operation, lower cost, and durability—over active cleaning methods. Furthermore, Bess et al. in [3] stress the importance of site-specific monitoring, evaluate different sensor technologies, and predict a rising global demand for thousands of sensors annually, while also providing economic analysis and experimental comparisons of mitigation techniques.

The economic impact is substantial, with global income losses from soiling-induced degradation estimated to surpass 10 billion EUR per year [4]. The severity of soiling is influenced by a combination of factors: local climate (rainfall, wind speed, humidity), airborne particulate composition (PM10, PM2.5), and site-specific conditions like proximity to deserts or urban areas. Consequently, soiling loss estimates vary widely, underscoring the necessity for accurate quantification, modeling, and prediction to optimize cleaning schedules, enhance energy yield forecasts, and enable proactive maintenance [5-7]. Experts from IEA PVPS Task 13, in both [5] and [6], have comprehensively summarized soiling, covering global dust distribution, particle types, measurement techniques, modeling, economic impacts, and mitigation strategies—including climate-specific maintenance and considerations for snow in higher latitudes. Meanwhile, the researchers in [7] developed innovative, calibration-free testing prototypes for accurate power loss estimation and provided new insights into soiling mechanisms through a lab protocol.

Accurately assessing soiling remains complex. Many existing models are validated on data from specific locations, raising concerns about their generalizability to diverse climates and sites. The dynamic nature of soiling, driven by multiple interacting environmental factors, demands robust modeling techniques capable of capturing these intricate relationships [8-9].

Soiling modeling approaches fall into three main categories: analytical/physics-based, empirical/statistical, and data-driven models. Analytical models use mathematical formulas with environmental data like rainfall and particulate matter concentration to estimate losses. A more detailed subset, physics-based models, simulate the fundamental mechanisms of dust deposition and removal by incorporating factors such as particle size, wind, and humidity.

One of the simplest analytical models is by Kimber [10], which assumes linear accumulation during dry periods and complete cleaning after a fixed rainfall threshold. However, it doesn't account for particulate matter concentration or partial cleaning. More advanced models address these limitations. The Humboldt State University (HSU) model [11] incorporates PM10/PM2.5 concentration, deposition velocity, and tilt angle. Toth et al. [12] proposed a model that differentiates between fine and coarse particles, better capturing the adhesive properties of fine dust. A comparative analysis on Spanish PV plants [13] found the Kimber model to be the simplest but least accurate. The HSU and Toth models improved accuracy by including particulate matter but were still limited by fixed thresholds. The SOMOSclean model [13] demonstrated the best performance with a mean absolute error of 0.694%; it uses an exponential growth function to simulate saturation and variable rainfall cleaning thresholds. A key limitation of physics-based models is their high demand for extensive, site-specific environmental and dust property data.

Empirical and statistical models use historical performance data to quantify losses. A standard method is the Soiling Ratio (SR), which compares a soiled module to a clean reference [7]. Other methods calculate a dirt derating factor [14] or analyze performance trends to infer soiling rates [15,16]. While straightforward, their accuracy can be compromised if a reliable clean reference is unavailable or if clean periods cannot be precisely identified.

The rise of large datasets has accelerated the use of machine learning (ML) models for soiling prediction. These data-driven methods excel at identifying complex, non-linear patterns that are difficult for traditional models to capture. Common techniques include linear regression and artificial neural networks (ANNs), with ANNs often delivering superior results. For instance, Laarabi et al. [17] and Chiteka et al. [18] used ANNs with environmental variables like rainfall and humidity to predict losses, showing improved accuracy despite being constrained by data availability and computational demands. Zitouni et al. [19] combined ML with regression, underscoring the potential of hybrid approaches. A notable data-driven method is the Stochastic Rate and Recovery (SRR) technique, which automatically detects soiling and cleaning events and models rates from a single system's data without a clean reference [15].

Research highlights the value of using hourly data to capture intra-day variations and training models over long periods to identify seasonal patterns. Common inputs include ambient temperature, relative humidity, wind, rainfall, particulate matter, and system tilt to extract "PV soiling profiles" for analysis, forecasting, and optimized cleaning [20]. Data processing involves standardization, cleaning, and filtering for specific conditions like snow. A recognized limitation is that many ML models are trained on data from a single location, underscoring the need for multi-environment training to improve generalizability. Future research directions include exploring advanced neural networks (e.g., Time-Series, Recurrent Neural Networks) and integrating considerations for bifacial PV systems.

Significant recent advancements have been made in soiling characterization and forecasting. Micheli et al. [20] created a framework for generating site-specific soiling profiles, showing that median-based annualized rates often miss seasonal variations. Their weighted average and Markov-chain algorithms achieved prediction errors below 1.3% and could identify optimal cleaning dates within three weeks, a major improvement over conventional methods. Kumar et al. [21] advanced empirical modeling by testing five variants of the Kimber and HSU models against sensor data. Their optimized models reduced RMSE by up to 23%, with all configurations keeping MAPE under 1%. They found that modified Kimber models excelled during extended dry periods and frequent rainfall, while their adapted HSU model was 12% more accurate than the original, highlighting the need for site-specific model selection based on local precipitation.

Alternative prediction methods have also emerged. Ballestrín et al. [22] showed the efficacy of ARMA time-series models, achieving a mean relative error of just 0.07% for seasonal forecasts, though they were less effective at predicting daily fluctuations. Smestad et al. [23] and Micheli et al. [24] pioneered spectral and image analysis techniques, respectively. In [23], researchers established that natural soiling follows consistent transmittance patterns and provided a cross-validation framework linking cleanliness standards to optical measurements (R^2 = 0.89). Meanwhile, work in [24] investigated image analysis thresholding uncertainties on a large micrograph dataset, finding methods like "percentile" and bimodal distributions to be inconsistent. They identified the "Triangle" method as the most reliable and recommended multiple micrographs per sample to account for non-uniformity and keep error low. The convergence of optical [23,24], statistical [22], and machine-learning enhanced [21] approaches points toward a new multi-method paradigm for soiling assessment.

Despite progress, challenges remain, including the incomplete integration of variables like wind and humidity, and sensor limitations. ML models require large datasets, restricting their use in data-sparse regions. Within the SERENDI-PV project, this study aims to refine soiling loss modeling and create predictive tools to enhance maintenance and yield forecasting. We present two complementary approaches: the Stochastic Quantifying Soiling Loss (SQSL) method for retrospective analysis from performance data, and a machine learning-based model for forward-looking predictions using environmental data. The ultimate goal is to integrate these into predictive tools for improved energy yield assessments, enabling data-driven decisions to minimize soiling-related losses.

2 METHODOLOGY – APPROACH

The SQSL method identifies soiling trends by analyzing PV performance metrics over time. Unlike traditional methods that require external environmental inputs such as rainfall data, SQSL relies entirely on variations in electrical performance, making it particularly useful in cases where meteorological data is unavailable or unreliable. In such approach, statistical thresholds are defined to segment performance variations into distinct "key" phases that make up the soiling profile: cleaning periods (CP), stable periods (StP), and soiling periods (SoP). Cleaning events are identified based on a significant increase in PV performance metrics, while stable periods are detected by analyzing fluctuations within a defined threshold. The transition into a soiling period is determined once PV performance metrics imply degradation beyond acceptable variation limits. A *theoretical* representation of these different phases is given in Fig. 1 (top), illustrating the transitions between cleaning, stable, and soiling periods. To contextualize such phases/classifications into real-life profiles of soiling losses, Fig. 1 (bottom) shows an example profile from *actual* real-case data, displaying how these phases are detected in practice.

We employ statistical analyses and Monte Carlo

simulations, to generate *probable* soiling profiles, enabling estimates of average soiling ratios and uncertainty ranges. This probabilistic approach helps define different soiling scenarios, ranging from worst-case to optimal conditions. The methodology also includes sensitivity analysis, examining how variations in input parameters, such as the frequency and effectiveness of cleaning events, influence the estimated soiling losses. Additionally, the SQSL method allows the classification of different soiling accumulation patterns by analyzing the rate of PV performance decline during soiling periods. This enables distinguishing between slow, gradual soiling accumulation and rapid degradation due to specific environmental conditions. Such "soiling profiling" capability provides valuable insights for optimizing maintenance strategies for PV plants.

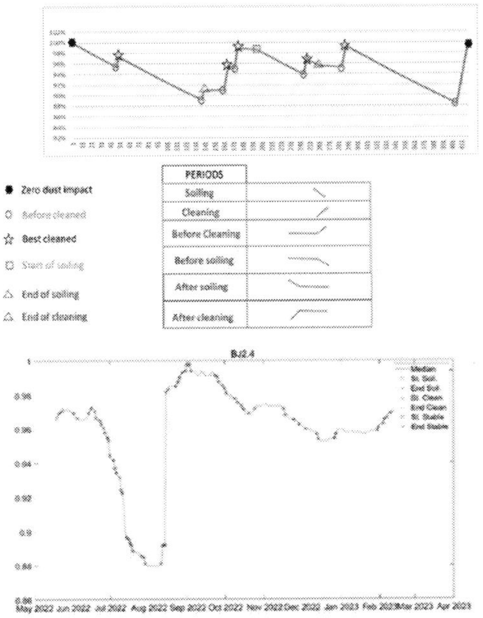

Figure 1: Top: Theoretical representation of the different key phases-variations in PV performance, considered for soiling profiling in the SQSL approach. Bottom: Identification of such phases within a real-case performance/soiling data from a utility-scale PV plant.

A complementary machine learning (ML)-based methodology (Fig. 2) integrates artificial neural networks and regression models to predict soiling losses from environmental parameters. These models process historical data, applying rigorous pre-processing steps such as data standardization, outlier removal, and missing data correction. The inclusion of wind speed, rainfall (precipitation) accumulation, and particulate matter levels improves model accuracy. A filtering process refines environmental datasets, correcting anomalies in precipitation records based on correlated meteorological variables, thereby ensuring better soiling loss estimations. Additionally, the developed methodology accounts for site-specific soiling characteristics by incorporating long-term data analysis. Soiling accumulation patterns vary significantly based on regional climate, local air pollution levels, and seasonal effects. The study emphasizes the importance of adapting soiling models to local conditions to improve predictive accuracy. To exclude snowy days from soiling ratio calculations, as also shown in Fig. 2, a filter is applied based on snow depth and albedo measurements. Since snow depth sensors can be noisy, only days with a significant albedo increase are considered snowy.

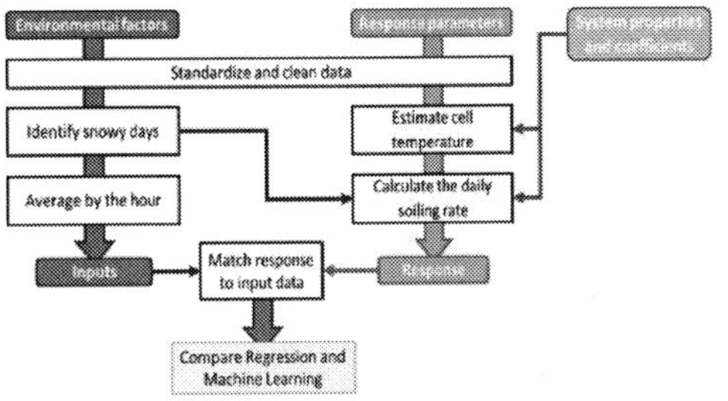

Figure 2: Architecture of the ML-based model for soiling loss prediction, assessed complementarily in this study.

3 RESULTS and DISCUSSION

Preliminary SQSL validation results indicate a high correlation between simulated and actual soiling profiles. The Monte Carlo-generated profiles effectively reconstruct historical soiling trends, confirming the robustness of the method. Figure 3 demonstrates this through a set of simulated PV performance (soiling loss) profiles, for the real-case study data of Fig.1-right, illustrating how uncertainty ranges are captured in the estimation. The post-cleaning PV performance jumps observed in field data validate the method's ability to estimate cleaning efficiencies under different operational conditions.

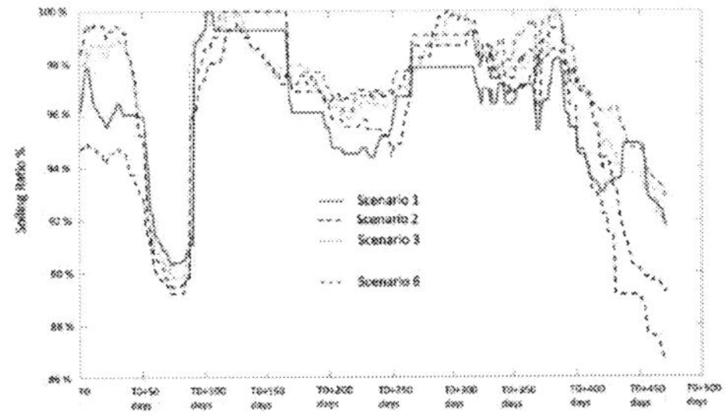

Figure 3: Example results of SQSL-based generation of various soiling loss profiles, based on the real-case data/curve shown in Fig.1.

Further, the ML-based models trained on datasets from NREL and CEA floating PV plant demonstrate a strong ability to capture seasonal soiling variations. The comparison of measured and predicted soiling ratios (Fig. 4) reveals that prolonged training periods improve predictive accuracy. However, the models require further refinement to account for location-specific environmental influences.

Further simulations, employing both our SQSL method and our ML modelling framework, were carried out for the case of a utlity-scale PV plant located in the Aragon region, northeastern Spain. The studied PV installation, with installed capacity of 62 MW_p, spans over 100 ha in a soiling prone site, influenced by climatic conditions (cold semi-arid climate (BSk)) that favor dust

10.4229/EUPVSEC2025/4CO.9.5
020317-003

accumulations. In the specific case, for employing the SQSL approach, we examined DC current measurements at PV strings level, for a full year, identifying different soiling periods based on performance output (PV production) patterns. Different PV string locations experience distinct soiling behaviors due to varying micro-climatic exposure conditions. Figure 5 presents indicative examples of resulting soiling profiles, generated through distinct "training", "validation" and "test" data. The modelling results are suggestive of considerable variations across soiling profiles for different strings, highlighting the location-dependency and influence of microclimatic conditions on soiling losses, particularly in the case of wide-area soiling-prone PV installations.

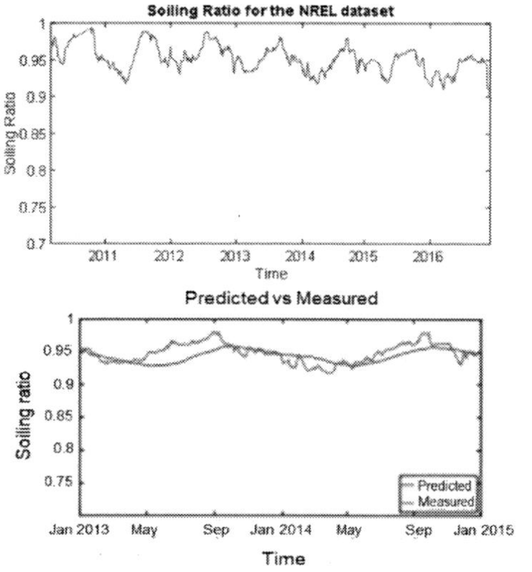

Figure 4: Top: Measured soiling ratio for the case of NREL dataset, over a 7-year period (01/2010-01/2017). Bottom: Measured vs. predicted (through the CEA ML-based model) soiling ratio, over two years (01/2013-01/2015) of the same NREL dataset.

Although the SQSL method does not rely on weather data as inputs for its computations, environmental parameters such as wind speed, humidity, and precipitation were analyzed to validate and interpret the soiling trends observed in the electrical data. This auxiliary analysis helps confirm whether environmental conditions align with SQSL-detected cleaning and soiling events. For instance, the correlation between increased humidity and dust adhesion, or the impact of heavy rainfall on natural cleaning, provides insights into the accuracy of SQSL-based estimations.

Finally, Fig. 6 presents example comparative results on the soiling ratio predicted (8 days ahead) by applying the SQSL method against actual soiling ratio measurements, for an indicative period of 3 months in 2024, for four different PV strings of the aforementioned PV plant. In this case, prediction errors range between 1% and 2.6%. Despite the short period of the training dataset (from 20/03/2023 to 05/03/2024), the results are encouraging. This limited period of measurement does not allow the model to learn much of the tendency in the long term, but the errors observed are sufficiently low to consider a reliable prediction/simulation of soiling losses in such real-life cases

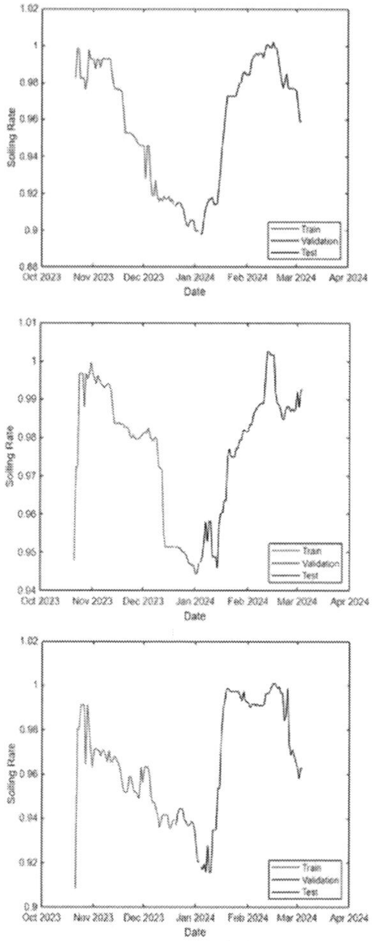

Figure 5: Soiling rate trends for different PV strings (three indicative examples) of the studied utility-scale PV plant in northeastern Spain. Labels 'train,' 'validation,' and 'test' indicate the data split used for model training and evaluation.

Next to the presented predictive modelling framework for PV soiling losses, CEA has also developed a virtual case study generator to support further soiling model development. This tool – which will be discussed in more details in the full version of this paper – simulates daily soiling rates based on multivariable regression models, considering wind speed, rainfall, and airborne dust concentration. It generates synthetic datasets useful for validating and improving soiling models under controlled conditions. The ability to predict daily soiling ratios provides valuable insights for optimizing maintenance strategies.

Further investigation reveals that soiling losses exhibit non-linear degradation patterns, influenced by meteorological anomalies. Periods of high relative humidity combined with low wind speeds create conditions that promote dust adhesion, significantly increasing soiling rates. Conversely, heavy precipitation events can lead to unexpected recovery in performance.

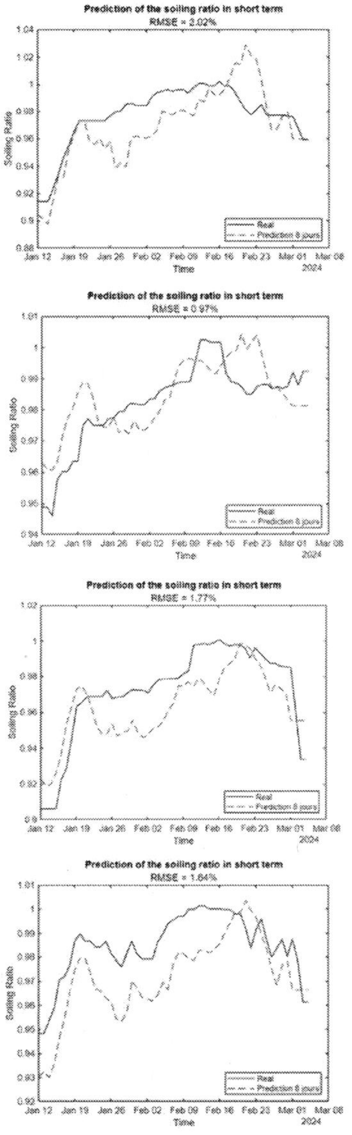

Figure 6: ML-based predictive modelling of the soiling ratio (SR) for four different PV strings of the studied PV plant in northeastern Spain: Comparative results of predicted SR vs real SR, 8-days ahead prediction, for a study period of 3 months.

4 CONCLUSIONS - OUTLOOK

The field of PV soiling modeling and prediction is rapidly evolving in response to the urgent need to mitigate energy losses and enhance operational efficiency. This study contributes to this objective by introducing two synergistic methodologies: the Stochastic Quantifying Soiling Loss (SQSL) method and a machine learning (ML)-based predictive model. Both approaches are designed for integration into existing PV monitoring platforms to refine maintenance planning and reduce energy yield degradation.

The SQSL method offers a robust framework for retrospective analysis, quantifying soiling impacts using exclusively electrical performance data, without dependence on external meteorological inputs. By examining performance trends, the method identifies and categorizes key soiling phases—such as cleaning intervals, stable performance periods, and soiling accumulation periods. Utilizing Monte Carlo simulations, it generates probabilistic soiling profiles that estimate average soiling ratios and associated uncertainty ranges. This stochastic methodology supports the definition of diverse soiling scenarios, from worst-case degradation to optimal conditions, thereby offering critical insights for maintenance optimization. It further enables the classification of accumulation patterns, distinguishing between gradual soiling buildup and rapid performance decline. Initial validation confirms the robustness of the SQSL approach, with generated profiles showing strong alignment with empirical observations. In field testing at a utility-scale PV plant in Spain, the model achieved soiling ratio predictions up to eight days in advance, with errors between 1% and 2.6%. Although currently focused on retrospective analysis, future development aims to incorporate weather forecasts and seasonal priors into the Monte Carlo simulations, enhancing predictive capability and improving the representation of seasonal variability for more reliable cleaning scheduling.

Complementing the SQSL method, the ML-based predictive model employs a forward-looking approach, leveraging an extensive set of environmental parameters. This model integrates artificial neural networks and regression techniques, augmented with advanced data pre-processing, to capture complex non-linear relationships and seasonal dynamics often missed by conventional models. Trained on hourly data over extended periods, the model accommodates regional climate variations and site-specific soiling behaviors, improving predictive accuracy. Validation using datasets from NREL and a CEA floating PV installation demonstrated the model's capacity to predict seasonal soiling trends, with performance improving as training duration increases.

Despite these advances, several challenges persist. Many ML models remain constrained by limited generalizability, having been trained and validated on data from single locations. The substantial data requirements of powerful ML algorithms also restrict their applicability in regions with sparse monitoring infrastructure. Additionally, discrepancies between pyranometer-based soiling estimates and electrical performance-based quantifications underscore the need for multi-source validation to improve assessment robustness. Future efforts will focus on enhancing model adaptability across diverse environments, refining input parameters, and investigating advanced ML architectures such as Time-Series Neural Networks and Recurrent Neural Networks. Further development will include adaptation for bifacial PV systems and validation against measurements from a dedicated CEA soiling sensor. A virtual case study generator will also be employed to produce synthetic datasets under controlled conditions, supporting ongoing model validation and refinement.

By uniting these two methodologies, this research establishes a comprehensive and reliable framework to support PV plant operators in making data-informed decisions, ultimately improving economic efficiency and strategic operational planning.

ACKNOWLEDGEMENTS

Part of this work has been carried out in the framework of the H2020 SERENDI-PV and Horizon Europe CACTUS projects. SERENDI-PV project has received funding from the European Union's Horizon 2020 research and innovation programme under grant agreement No. 953016. CACTUS project has received funding from the European Union's Horizon Europe research and innovation programme under grant agreement No. 101132182. For CEA team, part of this work was also supported by the French National Program "Programme d'Investissements d'Avenir - INES.2S" under Grant Agreement ANR ANR-10-IEED-0014 0014-01.

REFERENCES

1. Ricardo Conceição, José González-Aguilar, Ahmed Alami Merrouni, Manuel Romero, Soiling effect in solar energy conversion systems: A review, Renewable and Sustainable Energy Reviews, Volume 162, 2022, 112434. https://doi.org/10.1016/j.rser.2022.112434
2. Pooya Hooshyar, Hesam Moghadasi, Seyed Ali Moosavi, Ali Moosavi, Ali Nouri Borujerdi, Recent progress of soiling impact on solar panels and its mitigation strategies: A review, Applied Energy, Volume 379, 2025, 124979. https://doi.org/10.1016/j.apenergy.2024.124979
3. João Gabriel Bessa, Leonardo Micheli, Florencia Almonacid, Eduardo F. Fernández, Monitoring photovoltaic soiling: assessment, challenges, and perspectives of current and potential strategies, iScience, Volume 24, Issue 3, 2021, 102165. https://doi.org/10.1016/j.isci.2021.102165
4. L. Micheli et al. (2024). Modelling Performance and Maximum Allowed Costs for Anti-Soiling Coatings in Europe. 41th EUPVSEC, Vienna, Austria.
5. Schill, C., Anderson, A., Baldus-Jeursen, C., Burnham, L., Micheli, L., Parlevliet, D., Pilat, E., Stridh, B., & Urrejola, E. (2022). Soiling losses – Impact on the performance of photovoltaic power plants (Report No. IEA-PVPS T13-11:2022). International Energy Agency Photovoltaic Power Systems Programme. ISBN 978-3-907281-09-3.
6. Jahn, U., Herteleer, B., Tjengdrawira, C., Tsanakas, I., Richter, M., Dickeson, G., Astigarraga, A., Tanahashi, T., Valencia, F., Green, M., Anderson, A., Stridh, B., Alonso, A. R. L., & Sangpongsanont, Y. (2022). Guidelines for operation and maintenance of photovoltaic power plants in different climates (Report No. IEA-PVPS T13-25:2022). International Energy Agency Photovoltaic Power Systems Programme. ISBN 978-3-907281-13-0.
7. JA Tsanakas, R Moretón, E Pilat, J Solórzano, J Veludo, K Garcia. (2024). "Quality Assurance from Laboratory to Field: Novel Test Solutions for Soiling-Prone PV Systems". EUPVSEC 2024, DOI : 10.4229/EUPVSEC2024/4AO.9.4 (ISBN: 3-936338-90-6).
8. Micheli, L., and Muller, M. (2017) An investigation of the key parameters for predicting PV soiling losses. Prog. Photovolt: Res. Appl., 25: 291–307. doi: 10.1002/pip.2860.
9. Klemens K. Ilse, Benjamin W. Figgis, Volker Naumann, Christian Hagendorf, Jörg Bagdahn, Fundamentals of soiling processes on photovoltaic modules, Renewable and Sustainable Energy Reviews, Volume 98, 2018, Pages 239-254, https://doi.org/10.1016/j.rser.2018.09.015.
10. A. Kimber, L. Mitchell, S. Nogradi and H. Wenger, "The Effect of Soiling on Large Grid-Connected Photovoltaic Systems in California and the Southwest Region of the United States," 2006 IEEE 4th World Conference on Photovoltaic Energy Conference, Waikoloa, HI, USA, 2006, pp. 2391-2395, doi: 10.1109/WCPEC.2006.279690.
11. M. Coello and L. Boyle, "Simple model for predicting time series soiling of photovoltaic panels," IEEE J. Photovoltaics, vol. 9, no. 5, pp. 1382-1387, Sep. 2019.
12. Toth, S., Hannigan, M., Vance, M., & Deceglie, M. (2020). Predicting Photovoltaic Soiling From Air Quality Measurements. IEEE Journal of Photovoltaics, 10(4), 1142-1147. Article 9090155. https://doi.org/10.1109/jphotov.2020.2983990. https://doi.org/10.1109/JPHOTOV.2020.2983990
13. Redondo, M., Platero, C.A., Moset, A., Rodríguez, F., Donate, V. (2024). Review and Comparison of Methods for Soiling Modeling in Large Grid- Connected PV Plants. Sustainability, 16, 10998. https://doi.org/10.3390/su162410998
14. Jamil, W. J., Rahman, H. A., Shaari, S., & Desa, M. K. M. (2020). Modeling of soiling derating factor in determining photovoltaic outputs. IEEE Journal of Photovoltaics, 10(5), 1417-1424.
15. M.G. Deceglie, L. Micheli and M. Muller, "Quantifying Soiling Loss Directly From PV Yield," in IEEE Journal of Photovoltaics, vol. 8, no. 2, pp. 547-551, March 2018, doi: 10.1109/JPHOTOV.2017.2784682.
16. L. Micheli, D. Ruth, M/G. Deceglie and M. Muller, Time Series Analysis of Photovoltaic Soiling Station Data: Version 1.0, August 2017, Technical Report NREL/TP-5J00-69131.
17. B. Laarabi, O. May Tzuc, D. Dahlioui, A. Bassam, M. Flota-Bañuelos, A. Barhdadi, Artificial neural network modeling and sensitivity analysis for soiling effects on photovoltaic panels in Morocco, Superlattices and Microstructures, Volume 127, 2019, Pages 139-150. https://doi.org/10.1016/j.spmi.2017.12.037
18. Chiteka, K., Arora, R. & Sridhara, S.N. A method to predict solar photovoltaic soiling using artificial neural networks and multiple linear regression models. Energy Syst 11, 981–1002 (2020). https://doi.org/10.1007/s12667-019-00348-w
19. Houssain Zitouni, Alae Azouzoute, Charaf Hajjaj, Massaab El Ydrissi, Mohammed Regragui, Jesús Polo, Ayoub Oufadel, Abdellatif Bouaichi, Abdellatif Ghennioui,

Experimental investigation and modeling of photovoltaic soiling loss as a function of environmental variables: A case study of semi-arid climate, Solar Energy Materials and Solar Cells, Volume 221, 2021, 110874. https://doi.org/10.1016/j.solmat.2020.110874
20. Micheli, L., Fernández, E. F., Muller, M., & Almonacid, F. (2020). Extracting and generating PV soiling profiles for analysis, forecasting, and cleaning optimization. IEEE Journal of Photovoltaics, 10(1), 197-204.
21. Kumar, D., Ritter, K., III, Raush, J., Ferdowsi, F., Gottumukkala, R. and Chambers, T. (2025), Optimizing Photovoltaic Soiling Loss Predictions in Louisiana: A Comparative Study of Measured and Modeled Data Using a Novel Approach. Prog Photovolt Res Appl, 33: 560-579. https://doi.org/10.1002/pip.3891
22. Jesús Ballestrín, Jesús Polo, Nuria Martín-Chivelet, Javier Barbero, Elena Carra, Joaquín Alonso-Montesinos, Aitor Marzo, Soiling forecasting of solar plants: A combined heuristic approach and autoregressive model, Energy, Volume 239, Part E, 2022, 122442, https://doi.org/10.1016/j.energy.2021.122442 .
23. Smestad, G.P., Germer, T.A., Alrashidi, H. et al. Modelling photovoltaic soiling losses through optical characterization. Sci Rep 10, 58 (2020). https://doi.org/10.1038/s41598-019-56868-z
24. Micheli, L., Smestad, G. P., Khan, M. Z., Lange, K., Almughary, H. M. I., Abraim, M., Alamat, Y., Anderson, C. B., Bentouba, S., Figgis, B., Fuke, P., Hachicha, A. A., Karim, M., Kottantharayil, A., Martinez-Morales, A. A., Merrouni, A. A., Olivares, D., Picotti, G., Rabanal-Arabach, J., Wiesinger, F., & Ilse, K. (2024). Soiling in solar energy systems: The role of the thresholding method in image analysis. Solar RRL, 8(3). https://doi.org/10.1002/solr.202300654
25. Redondo, M., Platero, C. A., Moset, A., Rodríguez, F., & Donate, V. (2023). Soiling Modelling in Large Grid-Connected PV Plants for Cleaning Optimization. Energies, 16(2), 904. https://doi.org/10.3390/en16020904

CONSTRUCTION AND COMPARISON OF OUTDOOR PV TEST STANDS IN DIFFERENT CLIMATE ZONES

R. Ebner[1], M. Rennhofer[1], V. Neussl[1], B. Kubicek[1], M. Ankit[1], G. Ujvari[1], B. Azzopardi[2], A. Mignonac[3], Carlos Meza[4], Sebastian Dittmann[4], A. Gracia Amillo[5], J. M. Cuadra[5]
[1]AIT Austrian Institute of Technology, Center for Energy, 1210 Vienna, Austria, T +43 50550-6628, F +43 50550-6390, rita.ebner@ait.ac.at, www.ait.ac.at
[2]FIR The Foundation for Innovation and Research, Malta
[3]CEA Cadarache, Saint-Paul-Lez-Durance, France
[4]HSA Anhalt University of Applied Sciences, Köthen, Germany
[5]CENER National Renewable Energy Center, Sarriguren, Spain

ABSTRACT:
For the evaluation of the photovoltaic (PV) energy yield and potential investment decisions, the knowledge of the actual energy produced per year is far more important than the nominal peak power under standard test conditions (STC) in the laboratory. However, the actual energy yield strongly depends on the geographical location of the installation [1, 2, 3]. Therefore, within the PROMISE project, outdoor PV test stands were installed in different climate zones (Köppen climate classification): in the Humid Temperate zone (Germany), in the Mediterranean zone (Malta), in the Temperate zone (Austria), in the Mediterranean zone (France), and in Navarra, Spain, where the Alpine, Atlantic, and Mediterranean zones converge.

KEYWORDS: Different climate zones, PV test stand, Energy yield

1 INTRODUCTION

In the proposed work outdoor PV test stands were set up and compared in different climate zones in Austria (48.2081° N, 16.3713° E), Malta (35.9375° N, 14.3754° E), Spain (42.742 N, 1.629 W), France (43.6935° N, 5.7330° E) and Germany (51.9503° N, 11.6923° E).

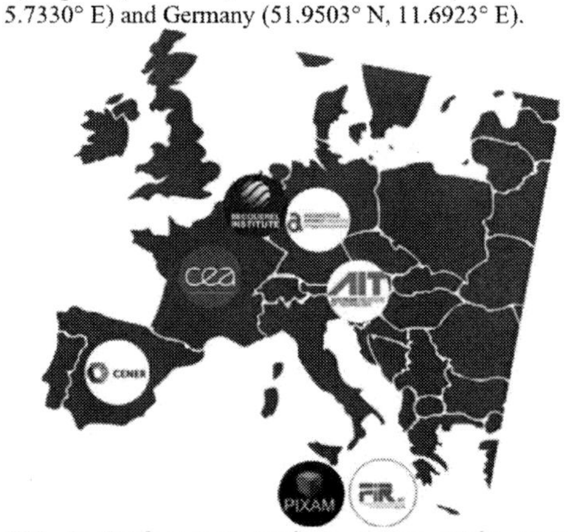

FIG. 1: Outdoor test stands in Austria, Malta, Spain, France, and Germany.

2 EXPERIMENTS

15 field-aged modules (10 years outside) (see Fig. 2) from Malta were subjected to STC performance measurements at the AIT PV laboratory (see Fig. 3 and Table 1).

Module type: Honey Module TSM-PD05 (see Fig. 2). These are polycrystalline modules with 60 cells. Their output ranges from 255–270 W, with a power density of up to 165 W/m² and a maximum efficiency of 16.5%. The cell size is 156 mm × 156 mm, and the module size is 1650 mm × 992 mm × 35 mm with a weight of 18.6 kg. The module has high-transparency, anti-reflective, tempered solar glass (3.2 mm thick) and an aluminum frame.

The current-voltage (IV) curves [6] of the PV modules nearly overlap, indicating that they exhibited similar degradation rates over time. This could be due to a variety of factors such as solar irradiation, temperature fluctuations, humidity, and other environmental influences. Since the modules show uniform degradation, it can be assumed that they age at roughly the same rate and that their performance decreases evenly throughout their lifetime.

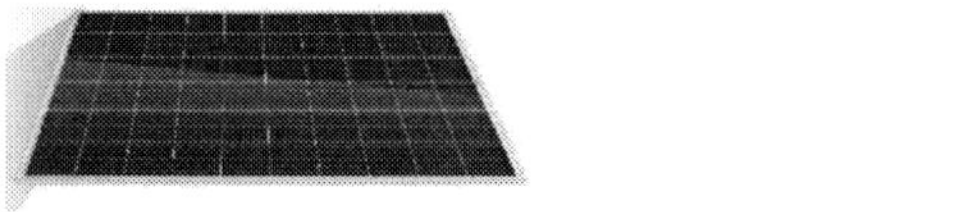

FIG. 2: Module.

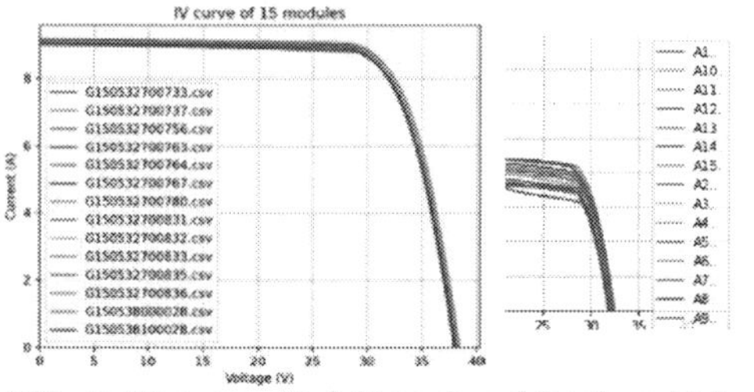

FIG. 3: IV-curves, 15 field-aged modules from Malta, initial characterization for this study, prior to installation in the different climates.

Table 1: IV measurement results at STC, 15 aged modules ("Out of the Box")

Sample	Voc[V]	Isc [A]	Fill Factor [%]	Pmax [W]	Efficiency [%]
A1	38,41	9,12	76,00	266,38	18,24
A2	38,47	9,16	75,75	267,09	18,29
A3	38,28	9,06	75,72	262,82	17,99
A4	38,10	9,09	75,63	262,08	17,94
A5	38,39	9,17	75,46	265,73	18,19
A6	38,28	9,10	75,99	264,82	18,13
A7	38,31	9,08	76,09	264,75	18,13
A8	38,08	9,05	75,52	260,55	17,84
A9	38,17	9,05	76,31	263,90	18,07
A10	38,02	9,09	75,84	262,38	17,96
A11	37,96	9,03	75,93	260,55	17,84
A12	38,00	8,98	76,16	260,12	17,81
A13	37,96	9,01	75,74	259,16	17,74
A14	38,10	9,03	75,66	260,61	17,84
A15	38,10	9,08	75,55	261,41	17,90

After recording the initial measurement results, the short-circuit current (Isc) was plotted against the open-circuit voltage (Voc). With respect to performance consistency, the diagram shows that the modules exhibit slightly different performance characteristics (see Fig. 4).

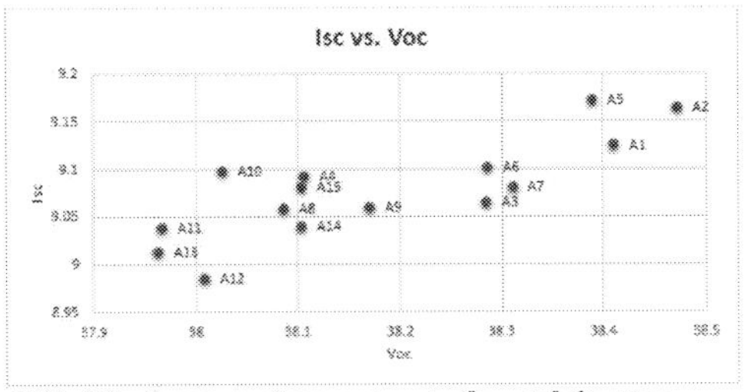

FIG. 4 Performance improvement after stabilization.

Next, a stabilization (preconditioning) procedure was carried out, followed by a second laboratory performance measurement under STC. This procedure not only determines the initial degradation and/or stable power generation, but also establishes a reliable "actual" wattage of the module, which then serves as the "baseline" (rather than the "nominal" nameplate value) for all energy yield data. All modules improved after stabilization (see Figs. 5 and 6).

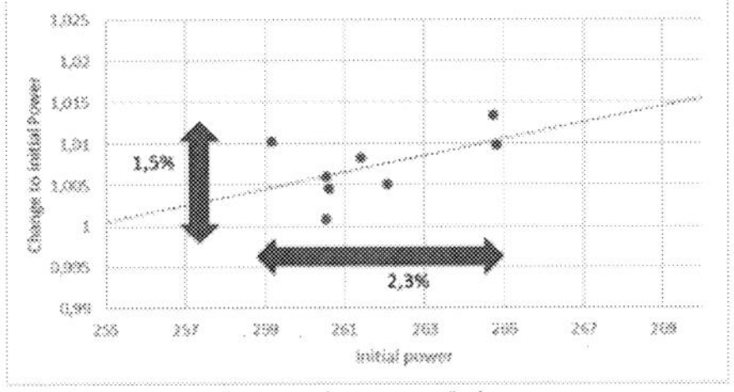

FIG. 5 Power change due to stabilization

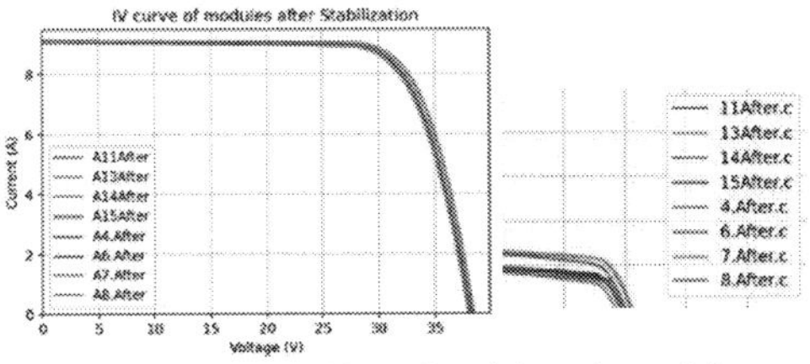

FIG. 6 IV curves, 15 field-aged modules, after stabilization

After stabilization, two modules were distributed to every PROMISE project partners FiR, CENER, CEA, and HSA for long-term outdoor measurements.

The following PV module and system data were recorded:

- Module temperature
- DC characteristics: Vmpp, Impp
- Irradiance
- Wind speed and direction
- Cumulative energy yield (DC side)

Most sits were additionally equipped with a state-of-the-art meteorological station, including:

- Pyranometer
- Pyrheliometer
- Spectroradiometer
- UV radiometer
- Ambient temperature sensors

3 RESULTS

All project partners (Malta, Germany, Spain, France and Austria) installed their two PV modules outdoors and conducted monitored throughout 2025.

3.1 Results of Austria

Module No. 1 (A1) and No. 2 (A2) were installed at the AIT outdoor test bench (see Fig. 7). The modules were oriented south at a tilt angle of 39°. Measurement results are logged every minute.

FIG. 7 AIT outdoor test stand

Fig. 8 shows the outdoor measurement system at AIT and which sensors were installed.

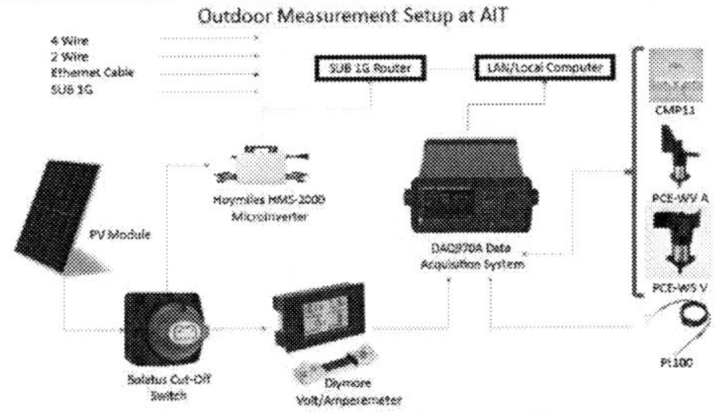

FIG. 8 Outdoor measurement system at AIT

The evaluation of the monitoring data (every minute) in Austria covers the period from March 2024 to August 2025. The monthly yield of Module No. 1 (A1) and Module No. 2 (A2) was determined and is shown in Fig. 9. Module No. 1 performs slightly worse than module No. 2. Therefore, further measurement results are only presented for Module 2.

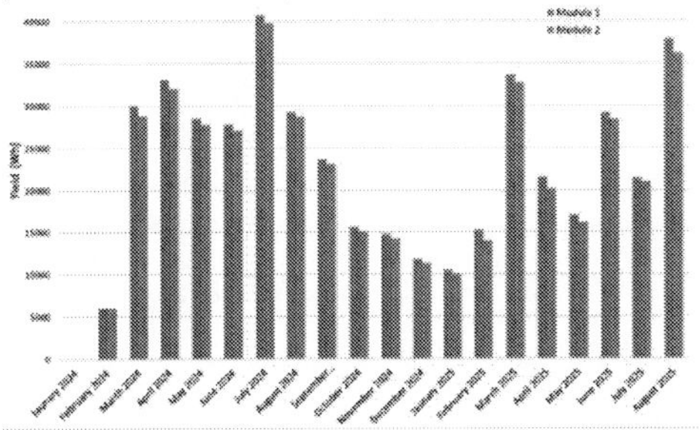

FIG.9 Monthly yield of Module No. 1 and Module No. 2 mounted in Austria from March 24 to August 25

10.4229/EUPVSEC2025/4CV.1.2
020318-002

Figures 10 and 11 show the daily irradiance, maximum power, module temperature, and wind speed in July, and September 2024 for the outdoor-mounted Module No. 2 (A2).

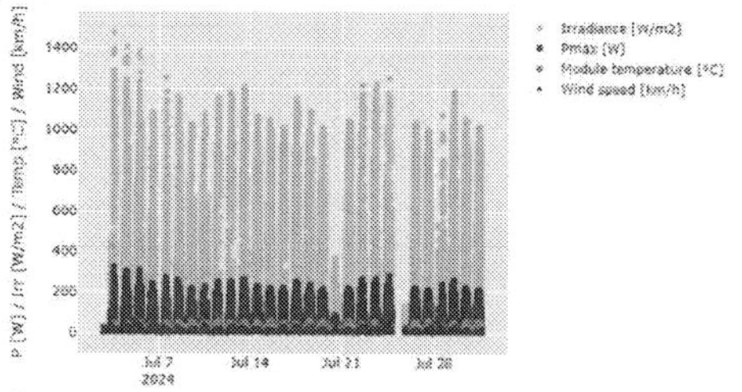

FIG. 10 Measurements results from Module 2 (A2), mounted outdoors: daily irradiation values, daily maximum output, daily module temperature, and daily wind speed in July 2024.

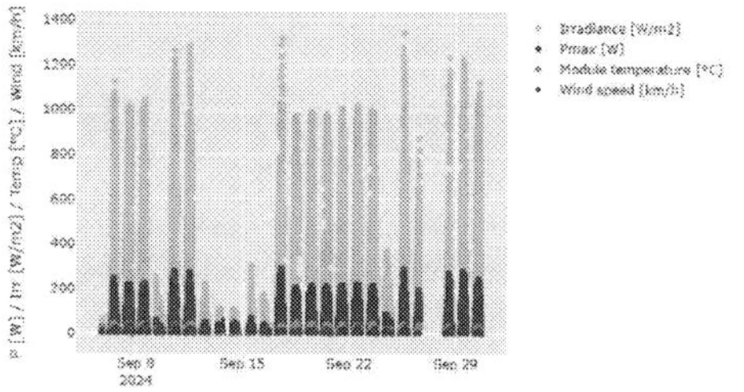

FIG. 11 Measurement results from Module 2 (A2), mounted outdoor: daily irradiation values, daily maximum power output, daily module temperature, and daily wind speed in September 2024.

In mid-September 2024, a sharp performance drop can be observed. This corresponds to the extreme bad weather and flooding that occurred at that time in Vienna and the surrounding area.

In order to illustrate the maximum output in September 2024 more clearly, the irradiation has been hidden in Fig. 12. The drop in output and a sharp decline in temperature (mid-September) can be seen again.

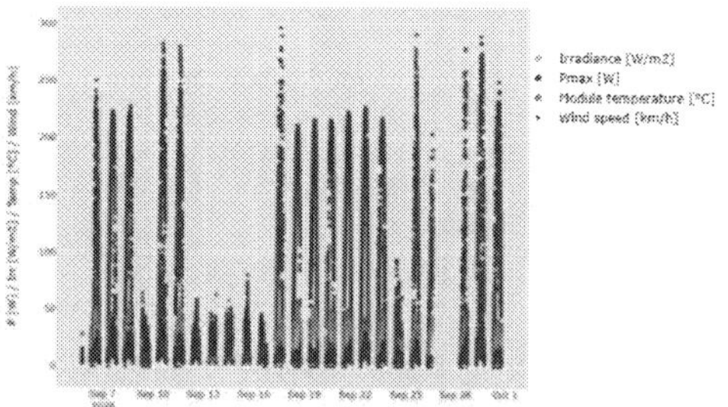

FIG. 12 Measurement results from Module 1, mounted outdoors: maximum dialy power output, daily module temperature, and daily wind speed in September 2024. The monthly irradiation values have been hidden.

In order to illustrate the module temperature and wind speed in September 2024 more clearly, the irradiation and maximum output have been hidden in Fig. 13. The increased wind speed and a sharp drop in temperature (mid-September) are again clearly visible.

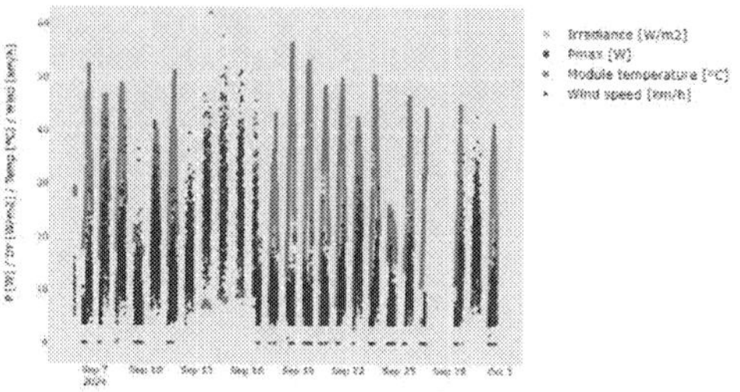

FIG. 13 Measurement results from Module 2 (A2), mounted outdoors: monthly daily temperature and daily wind speed in September 2024. The daily irradiation values and maximum output have been hidden.

The degradation over time (February 2024 to August 2025) was also analyzed. For Module 2, the following degradation rates were identified (see Fig. 14): −0.700 W/month at 600 W/m² irradiation, −0.630 W/month at 800 W/m² irradiation, and −0.703 W/month at 1000 W/m² irradiation.

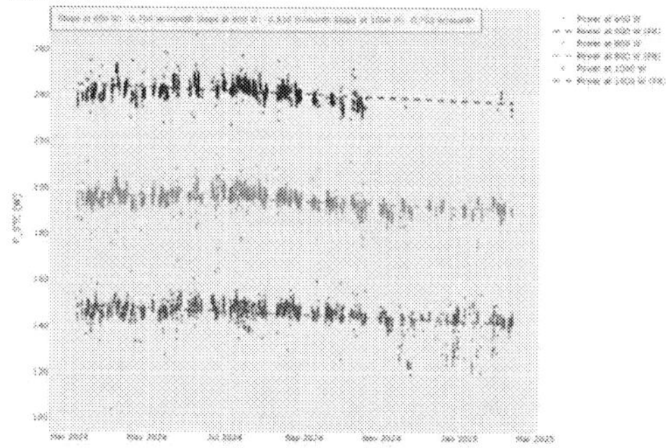

FIG. 14 Temperature corrected power over time at several irradiation values (600 W/m², 800 W/m² and 1000 W/m²) for Module 2.

3.2 Results of different climate zones

The PV yields of all modules installed across the different climate zones were evaluated and compared for the period from February to August 2025. The results are presented in Fig. 15. Due to technical issues at some partner sites, a significant portion of monitoring data was lost; consequently, not all partners were able to provide complete measurement results for the entire period.

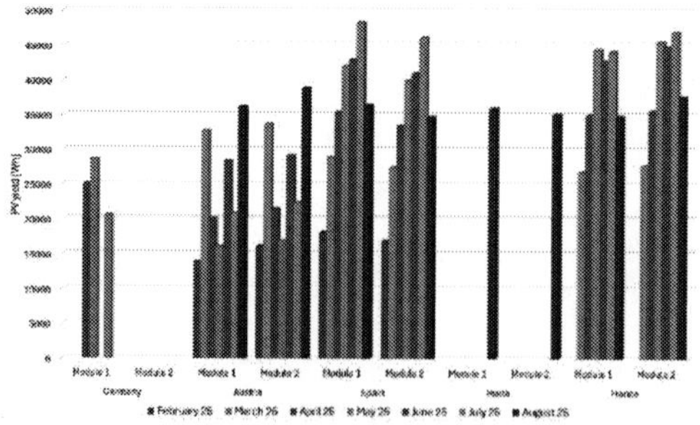

FIG. 15 PV yield results of PV modules in different climate zones from February 2025 to August 2025.

In Austria, the high PV yield observed in March 2025 can be explained by exceptionally sunny weather and higher

temperatures compared to April and May 2025, which were characterized by frequent rainfall. August 2025 was again very sunny and hot, whereas July was predominantly rainy.
In Spain, the results show a continuous increase in yield from February to July 2025. In France, the yield increased until May 2025, followed by a slight decrease in June, and then a renewed increase in July.

4 SUMMARY AND OUTLOOK

Over their lifetime, PV modules are prone to various degradation processes, including light-induced degradation, recombination losses, and material degradation. These processes can drastically affect the performance characteristics of the modules, such as open-circuit voltage (Voc), short-circuit current (Isc), fill factor (FF), and maximum power (Pmax). Understanding and mitigating these degradation effects is essential for maintaining and improving solar energy conversion efficiency.
In this study, 15 field-aged modules from Malta (10 years outdoor) were comprehensively characterized and stabilized. Subsequently, two modules each were installed at outdoor PV test benches located in different climate zones (Humid-Temperate zone: Germany; Mediterranean zone: Malta; Temperate zone: Austria; Mediterranean zone: France; and Navarra, Spain, where the Alpine, Atlantic, and Mediterranean zones meet).
The results from the AIT outdoor test bench were presented in this work and compared with the results of outdoor PV test benches established in the different climate zones.

5 REFERENCES

1. Statistical evaluation of PV system performance and failure data among different climate zones, M. Halwachs, L. Neumaier, N. Vollert, L. Maul, S. Dimitriadis, Y. Voronko, G.C. Eder, A. Omazic, W. Mühleisen, Ch. Hirschl, M. Schwark, K.A. Berger, R. Ebner; Renewable Energy, Elsevier, 2019. DOI: 10.1016/j.renene.2019.02.135
2. Photovoltaic Degradation Climate Zones, K. Todd, et all., 46th IEEE Photovoltaic Specialist Conference (PVSEC), 2019. DOI: 10.1109/PVSC40753.2019 .8980831
3. Descriptive statistics on the climate related performance and reliability issues from global PV installations; M. Halwachs, K. A. Berger, L. Maul, L. Neumaier, Y. Voronko, A. Mihaljevic, N. Vollert, W. Mühleisen, M. Schwark, R. Ebner, Ch. Hirschl, TIP, PV Conference "Quality and sustainability of PV systems" 2018.
4. Best Practices for Operation and Maintenance of Photovoltaic and Energy Storage Systems; 3rd Edition, NREL, Technical Report: NREL/TP-7A40-73822, 2018.
5. Guidelines for Operation and Maintenance of Photovoltaic Power Plants in Different Climates; Report IEA-PVPS T13-25:2022.
6. IEC 61215-1-1: Terrestrial photovoltaic (PV) modules – Design qualification and type approval - Part 1-1: special requirements for testing of crystalline silicon photovoltaic (PV) modules. Ed2 2021.

Acknowledgment
This work was funded by the Horizon Europe PROMISE Project (No. 101079469).

COMPARATIVE STUDY OF ENERGY YIELD IN PV SYSTEMS USING DIFFERENT MODULE TECHNOLOGIES AND INVERTER CONFIGURATIONS

Matevž Bokalič, Kristijan Brecl, Marko Topič
University of Ljubljana, Faculty of Electrical Engineering
Tržaška 25, SI-1000 Ljubljana, Slovenia
E-mail: Matevz.Bokalic@fe.uni-lj.si

ABSTRACT: The rapid development of photovoltaic (PV) technology has led to a broad variety of products in both the module and inverter markets, raising questions about long-term reliability and real-world performance. While new cell technologies such as TOPCon, SHJ, and IBC promise higher efficiency, recent field reports indicate higher degradation rates than expected, which could impact warranty stability and market confidence. Likewise, inverter configurations ranging from classical string inverters to optimizers and microinverters introduce trade-offs between compliance with grid regulations, system scalability, and final energy yield.

Within the Horizon 2020 project Aurora, five new PV power plants were installed within the renewable energy community at the Faculty of Electrical Engineering, University of Ljubljana, to evaluate performance of different inverter types and cell technologies under real operating conditions. Five new systems consist mostly of TOPCon modules alongside smaller strings of PERC, SHJ, and IBC technologies. Energy production data from February to August 2025 were analysed with a digital twin approach, combining pyranometer and temperature measurements with pvlib Python library based irradiance and thermal modelling. Performance evaluation relied on temperature-corrected AC performance ratio and energy yield for PV power plants, and on DC performance ratio for PV modules. Shading was identified and removed from the dataset to ensure comparability.

Results show that the new PV plants achieve shading and temperature corrected power ratio values between 0.85 and 0.9, while the 15-year-old reference power plant displayed expected degradation. String inverters performed best under unshaded conditions, optimizers were ~1% lower, and microinverters ~3% lower. Module-level comparison revealed similar performance across technologies, with IBC showing slightly reduced summer values. Initial degradation trends were not yet evident.

Overall, the study highlights the importance of shading correction, accurate thermal modelling, and multi-technology benchmarking for objective PV system evaluation.

Keywords: PV digital twin, performance modelling, Performance ratio, Shading removal

1 INTRODUCTION

Current photovoltaic (PV) market offers a huge variety of different products. This variety is present in both the PV module market and in the inverter market. In the PV module market several cell technologies are competing to offer either the best performance or the best price-performance ratio. In the price-performance arena, there are declining-share PERC cells which are being replaced by the more advanced TOPCon cells. In the high-performance arena, there are SHJ and IBC cells. The inverter market for residential and commercial applications varies not only between different manufacturers, but also between different types of inverters. There are conventional string inverters, string inverters with optimizers and easily scalable microinverters.

Recently, several contributions reported higher degradation rates in the field of new cell technologies [1,2]. The lower than expected real-life TOPCon module performance is a crucial research topic, especially because the TOPCon modules come with stricter warranty conditions. If the modules fail to produce energy within these conditions, that could potentially lead to a huge number of warranty claims possibly destabilizing module market. There were also publications on optimizers providing a lower final performance on homogeneously irradiated PV arrays [3,4]. This is also an important topic, as optimizers (or microinverters) are often required to meet the low voltage requirements of several net-metering regulations in place in Europe.

Within the Horizon 2020 funded European project Aurora [5] (*Achieving a new European Energy Awareness*) the goal was to establish a renewable energy community (REC) based around a photovoltaic power plants (PVPPs). The process of setting up the REC as a virtual community was presented at the EU PVSEC last year [6]. In addition to energy production, the power plants also have to provide educational benefit and research data, therefore we have designed the power plants comprised of different inverters, optimizers, microinverters and combinations thereof as well as a field of modules of different technologies.

The power plants were installed in 2024 and beginning of 2025 and were grid connected in February 2025. In this contribution we present performance evaluation of these power plants, together with an old power plant, focusing on different inverter configurations and on performance of modules with different solar cell technologies.

In the experimental section of this paper we first describe the analysed PV power plants and modules, followed by explanation of data analysis, digital twin and shading removal. In the results section applicability of shading removal and performance analysis of plants and modules is presented. The paper is finished by discussion and conclusion.

2 EXPERIMENTAL

2.1 PV power plants and modules

There are in total six power plants on the roofs of the Faculty of Electrical Engineering at University of Ljubljana, as depicted in Figure 1. The first power plant, named *A old* was installed in 2010 and we are including it in the study for comparison. This power plant consists of classical multi-crystalline Al BSF PV modules connected to classical string inverter. The new power plants, *A*, *B*, *C*, *D upper* and *D lower*, were installed within the Aurora Project. They are based on the same TOPCon modules to provide comparability between inverter types, however a smaller part of the power plant *B* is designed with single module optimizers and modules with cells of different technologies to provide variability between cell technologies. This part of the power plant will demonstrate the performance, reliability and long-term degradation of modules with cells of different technologies. The power plants are summarized in Table 1.

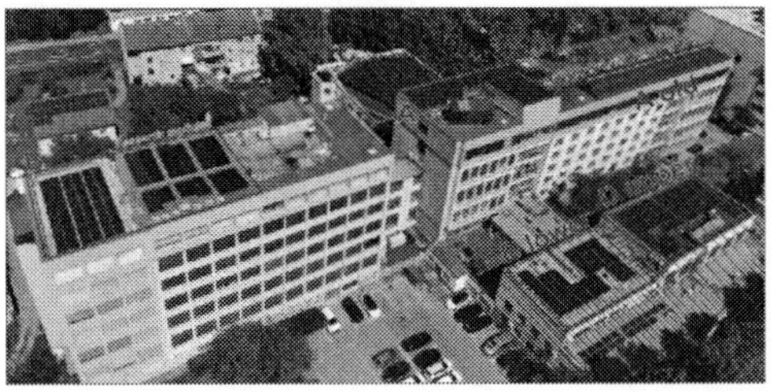

Figure 1: PV power plants installed on the Faculty of Electrical Engineering within the University of Ljubljana, Slovenia (46.07° N, 14.52° E).

Power Plant	Inverter type	Module type	P [kW]	Orientation	Inclination
A old	String	AL-Bsf	17.2	25°E	30°
A	String	TOP Con	45.8	25°E, 155°W	7°
B	Optimizers	TOP Con, ...	45.7	25°E, 155°W	7°,10°E-W
C	Optimizers	TOP Con	56.3	115°E, 65°W	14°
D upper	String	TOP Con	34.3	25°E	10°E-W
D lower	Microinverters	TOP Con	23.8	25°E	10°E-W
Total			223.1		

Table 1: List of power plants with basic details

To compare the differences due to different technologies, we tried to find the modules with the same bill of materials (frame/cover/cell size), while at the same time they had to be commercially available. We have selected modules with black frame, front glass and black backsheet cover, with two repeated cell technologies in glass/glass configuration, and half-cell module topology. Due to availability on the Slovenian market we have two different cell sizes. The installed modules are listed in Table 2.

Technology	Bill of materials	P_{STC} [W]	P_{flash} [W]
TOP Con a	g/bs, 108 M10 hcs	440	*432
TOP Con b	g/bs, 108 M10 hcs	420	406
PERC	PERCg/bs, 108 M10 hcs	405	396
SHJ a	g/bs, 120 M6 hcs	380	367
SHJ b	g/g, 120 M6 hcs	390	367
IBC	g/bs, 132 M6 hcs	420	394

*used P_{flash} = 415 W for PR_T comparison

Table 2: List of research PV modules with cells of different technologies with basic details.
(g/bs – glass/backsheet, g/g – glass/glass, hcs – half cells)

Orientation-wise we had to adapt to the available roof orientations and building configurations, which resulted in several final orientations and mounting fashions. Since the buildings are facing 25° from south toward east, please note that all orientations mentioned below are with a 25° offset to the east. On flat roofs, we used East-West triangle configurations with ballast mounting and a 10° module inclination. On other slightly pitched roofs, the angles range from 7° to 14°, while the mounting configuration is either anchoring to wooden or metal beams or standing seam mounting. The orientations are listed in Table 1.

2.2 Digital twin

For the purpose of this evaluation we have extracted production data from cloud-based services of inverters and optimizers. The global and diffused irradiance together with air temperature are obtained from pyranometers and air temperature sensors installed at our test sites.

We have evaluated the performance of the power plants during the first 6 months of operation. The evaluation is based on the calculation of temperature corrected AC performance ratio ($PR_{T,AC}$) and on calculation of energy yield (Ey). The data was analysed with python using the digital twin approach.

The digital twin granularity goes down to string level. It transforms general environmental parameters to parameters that the string experiences. Horizontal total and diffuse irradiance (G_{tot}, G_{dif}, respectively) are transformed to plane of array irradiance (G_{poa}) of respective strings of the same modules with the same orientations using Perez model in pvlib library. Back irradiance was not taken into account due to close proximity of the modules to the roof [7]. Air temperature (T_{air}) is transformed to module temperature (T_m) using the normal operating cell temperature (NOCT) of the module by

$$T_m = T_{air} + \frac{T_{m,NOCT} - 20°C}{800\,W/m^2} \cdot G_{poa}$$

The digital twin power of the string ($P_{DC,string}$) is calculated by:

$$P_{DC,string} = P_{STC,string} \cdot \frac{G_{poa}}{1000\,W/m^2} \cdot (1 + \gamma \cdot (T_m - 25°C))$$

Total plant DC power is the sum of all string powers:

$$P_{DC,twin} = \sum P_{DC,string}$$

Finally, $PR_{T,AC}$ is calculated as a ratio between measured and digital twin energies in given time interval:

$$PR_{T,AC} = \frac{E_{AC,measured}}{E_{DC,twin}}, \text{where } E = \int P\,dt$$

Energy yield (Ey) is calculated as energy produced ($E_{AC,measured}$) divided by sum of modules' rated power (P_{STC}):

$$Ey = \frac{E_{AC,measured}}{P_{STC}}$$

Performance evaluation of research modules of different types was based on the production data as measured by individual DC optimizer energy output and digital twin energy:

$$PR_{T,DC} = \frac{E_{DC,measured}}{E_{DC,twin}}$$

Therefore $PR_{T,DC}$ includes optimizer losses. However, since all the modules have similar rated and measured powers (Table 2), the results should be comparable nevertheless. Two remarks must be made here. First, instead of modules' rated power, an average of modules' measured power is taken as a reference, because the differences between rated and measured power were not negligible. Second, for *TOP Con a* PV modules, the measured power was further reduced from 432 W to 416 W to align the $PR_{T,DC}$ with *TOP Con b* modules.

Finally, for PR_T analysis, we only considered data points when total horizontal irradiance (G_{tot}) was higher than 500 W/m².

2.3 Shading removal

To allow objective evaluation of performance, shading must be excluded from the analysis. To achieve that we

10.4229/EUPVSEC2025/4CV.1.7

selected clear sky days throughout the analysed period between including March and August 2025. For each of those days we plotted $PR_{T,AC}$ over that day. An example is plotted in Figure 2 for March 7, 2025. Observing the shape of $PR_{T,AC}$ there is usually a midday plateau at a constants value between 0.85 and 0.9, and the $PR_{T,AC}$ drops off more or less abruptly from morning and towards evening hours. This drop is indicative of shading and can be corelated with the physical location of the power plants with respect to nearby buildings and trees that drop shadow on them. For example, looking at plant *C* (Figure 2, red curve) full shading is observed before 9 AM, with partial shading extending all the way to afternoon, only reaching expected $PR_{T,AC}$ at around half past 1 PM. For the times when plants are shaded, $PR_{T,AC}$ is plotted in dashed style, and for the unshaded times $PR_{T,AC}$ is plotted solid. We selected end and stop times of shading for all clear sky days and interpolated those times between clear sky days. Data points labelled as shaded were dropped from unshaded $PR_{T,AC}$ analysis.

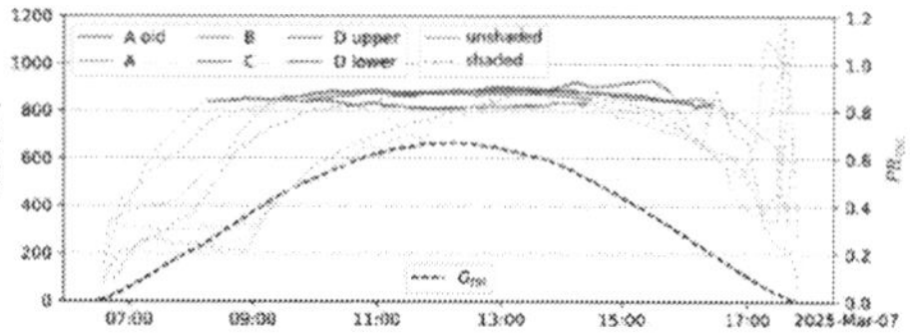

Figure 2: Temperature corrected AC performance ratio of power plants during early spring day. Solid lines represent unshaded time of the day, while dashed lines represent shaded time of the day for respective power plants.

3 RESULTS

3.1 PV power plant performance

Figure 3a shows monthly performance of PV power plants including shading, while subfigure b) displays the performance without shading, and subfigure c) displays environmental conditions.

Influence of shading is clearly observable for power plants *A* and *C* in March and April, with further reductions of performance for plant *A* throughout the summer. Less detrimental effects of shading can also be noted for other power plants.

Several observations can be made on monthly performance without shading (Figure 3b). Most notable is lower performance of *A old* power plant. This is expected, because the power plant is already 15 years old, and assuming initial $PR_{T,AC}$ between 0.85 and 0.9, shows degradation between 5 and 10%. There is a performance drop for most power plants in June. This can be attributed to determination of module temperature (T_m). Because the same air temperature (T_{air}) is used for all powerplants, effects of microclimate, which are different on different roofs, are ignored.

The drop is most noticeable on roofs *A*, *B* and *D lower*, which are all low tilt or flat (<7°) and highly insulated, thereby increasing local air temperature significantly. The opposite trend for *D upper* may be justified by worse insulation providing some cooling effect, and for *A old* the actual module temperature is probably overestimated due to higher tilt and considerable airgap below the modules.

The additional drop for *D lower* may be attributed to microinverter overheating. It can also be observed that the

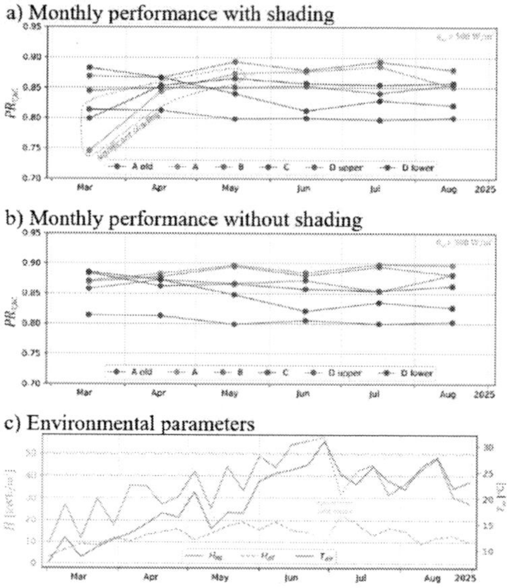

Figure 3: Temperature corrected AC performance ratio of power plants over monthly interval with shading (a) and without shading (b), and environmental parameters (c)

power plants with higher tilts (*A old* and *C*) result in more constant performance. Finally, based on the acquired data, initial degradation cannot be detected.

Aggregated performance data without shading over six months (Figure 4 and Table 3) reveals that $PR_{T,AC}$ of new power plants is between 0.84 and 0.9. Comparison between similar power plants with and without optimizers show about 1% lower performance for plants with optimizers (-1% $PR_{T,AC}$ *B* vs *A*, and *C* vs *D upper*). Power plant with microinverters perform slightly worse for about 3% (*D lower* vs *D upper*). As described above, performance of *A old* power plant is lower due to degradation.

Finally, the energy yield of all power plants per month is presented in Figure 5. Energy yield calculation considers total produced AC power without any filtering. In the case of *A old* power plant, there were three incidents. In April

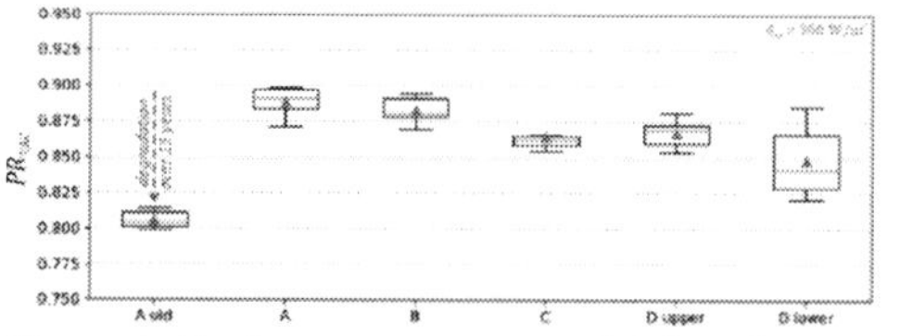

Figure 4: Total temperature corrected AC performance without shading of power plants over the 6-month period

Power Plant	Inverter type	Module type	$PR_{T,AC}$ G_{tot} > 500 W/m² All	w/o shading	*Ey* [kWh/kW] Mar-Aug
A old	String	AL-Bsf	0.80	0.80	*635
A	String	TOP Con	0.86	0.89	807
B	Optimizers	TOP Con, ...	0.88	0.88	800
C	Optimizers	TOP Con	0.86	0.86	764
D upper	String	TOP Con	0.85	0.87	771
D lower	Microinverters	TOP Con	0.84	0.84	732

*invalid due to missing production

Table 3: Final results of temperature corrected performance ration and energy yield of PV power plants.

10.4229/EUPVSEC2025/4CV.1.7

there was a monitoring data outage, while in May and August a safety electronic device failed. This results in production data and energy loss; therefore the energy yield of *A old* power plant is lower in these months. For other power plants, general energy yield trends match irradiation trends, but there are also some differences. Power plant *A* has the highest energy yield, despite significant shading, because it has the most optimal module orientation. Due to shading, energy yield drops in March and August for plants *A* and *C*. There is also a drop of energy yield observable for plant *D lower* during summer months, which may be due to higher temperatures of microinverters.

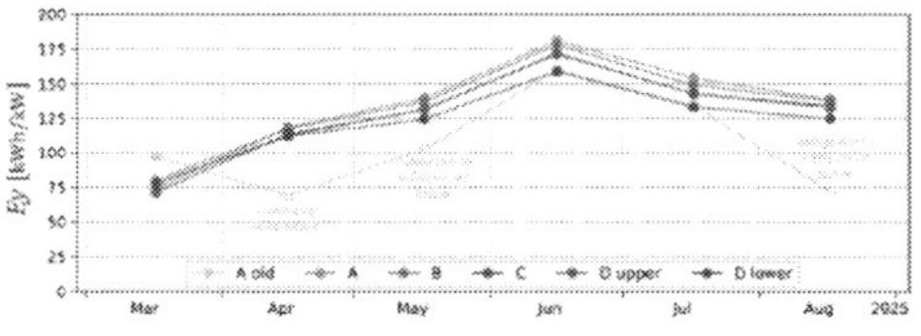

Figure 5: Energy yield of power plants over monthly interval with shading

3.2 Performance of modules of different technologies

Temperature corrected DC performance ratio ($PR_{T,DC}$) is presented in Figure 6 a) and b) for weekly and monthly intervals, respectively. As mentioned in the Methodology section, DC performance of modules is measured as DC output energy by single module optimizers. All the modules should experience similar environmental conditions, as they are all installed on the same roof, and measured STC power was used as a reference module power, with the exception of *TOP Con a*, where measured STC power was reduced for 4% to roughly match the *TOP Con b* performance ratio to ease the comparison. Finally, shading was not filtered out for this analysis as all the modules are on the same roof.

a) Weekly

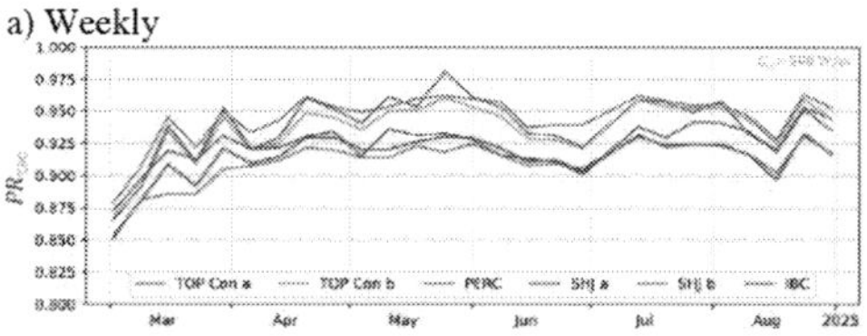

b) Monthly

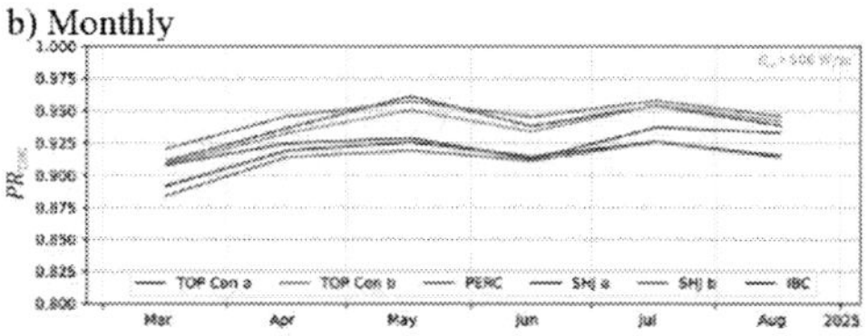

Figure 6: Temperature corrected DC performance ratio of PV modules of different technologies with shading over weekly (a) and monthly (b) intervals

Modules of the same technology perform similarly. In general, performance ratio is higher during summer, probably due to higher irradiance incident angle. There is however a notable drop in performance in June, which is due to very sunny weather and high temperatures that are amplified by insulated bitumen roof thereby deviating from the measured air temperature 2 m above the roof. In comparison to other module technologies, IBC modules show slightly lower performance during the sunny half of the year for yet unknown reasons. Based on the presented measurements it is not yet possible to draw conclusion on different degradation rates because all technologies perform quite similarly.

4 DISCUSSION AND CONCLUSION

Based on the analysis, we conclude that power plants operate as expected with temperature and shading corrected AC performance ratio between 0.85 and 0.9. For objective evaluation of performance of PV power plant components (i.e., modules, inverter and optimizers) shading correction is essential. Lower incident angles of direct sunlight on flat roofs reduce performance ratio in spring.

Regarding the efficiency of different inverter types, we have observed the best unshaded performance of classical string inverters, closely followed by string inverters with optimizers, while microinverters showed slightly lower performance.

During the analysis, we have learned several lessons and things that can be further improved. For correct prediction of module temperature, air temperature must be measured on the same roofs, and module temperature measurement would further increase model accuracy. Shading evaluation for research modules should be done. Since most of the inverters also provide DC data, further insights on inverter and module performance could be obtained from analysis of this data.

5 ACKNOWLEDGEMENT

This work has received funding from the European Union's Horizon 2020 research and innovation programme under grant agreement No 101036418 and from Slovenian Research and Innovation Agency (ARIS) research programme P2 0415.

6 REFERENCES

[1] Sen C, Wang H, Khan MU, Fu J, Wu X, Wang X, Hoex B. Buyer aware: Three new failure modes in TOPCon modules absent from PERC technology. *Solar Energy Materials and Solar Cells* **2024; 272**, pp. 112877. DOI:10.1016/j.solmat.2024.112877.

[2] Friesen G, Özkalay E, Caccivio M. Performance and Degradation Evaluation of C-Si Modules Under Different Open-Rack and Residential Mounting Configurations. In: *41st European Photovoltaic Solar Energy Conference and Exhibition* proceedings, Vienna, Austria: 2024, pp. 3DO.17.5.

[3] Baumgartner FP, Golroodbari S, Bucher C, Berwind M, Valencia F, Jahn U. Performance of Partial Shaded PV Generators Operated by Optimized Power Electronics an IEA PVPS T13 Activity. *41st European Photovoltaic Solar Energy Conference and Exhibition* **2024**, pp. 4CP.2.3. DOI:10.4229/EUPVSEC2024/4CP.2.3.

[4] Baumgartner FP, Klenk M, Widler A, Baumann L. MPP Tracking Losses of Module Level Power Electronics at Partial Module Shading. *41st European Photovoltaic Solar Energy Conference and Exhibition* **2024**, pp. 3EO.1.5. DOI:10.4229/EUPVSEC2024/3EO.1.5.

[5] AURORA Project. *AURORA H2020*; https://www.aurora-h2020.eu/ (accessed January 29, 2025).

[6] Bokalič M, Guštin M, Topič M, Belen Cristóbal A, Victoria M, Cavaco A, Fialho L, Gerber A. Challenges of Energy Communities at Universities – A Virtual Approach. In: *41st European Photovoltaic Solar Energy Conference and Exhibition* proceedings, Vienna, Austria: 2024, pp. 5DV.3.43.

[7] Brecl K, Cerón EM, de la Casa Higueras J, Topič M. Is an exact backside irradiance modelling essential for bifacial PV systems? *Renewable Energy* **2026; 256**, pp. 123942. DOI:10.1016/j.renene.2025.123942.

A HIGHLY ADAPTABLE PERFORMANCE EVALUATION METHOD FOR PV SYSTEMS USING REMOTE METEOROLOGICAL DATA AND ON-SITE REFERENCE COMPARISONS

WeiZhen Xiong, Jindan Cui, and Yuzuru Ueda
Tokyo University of Science, Japan
4324532@ed.tus.ac.jp

ABSTRACT: This study presents a highly adaptable, sensor-free framework for the performance evaluation of photovoltaic (PV) systems, aiming to address the limitations of traditional methods that rely on expensive on-site sensors. The proposed method includes a two-phase approach. In the training phase, data from 2018 to 2022 were used to derive a combined loss coefficient (K_o) that links global horizontal irradiance (GHIith power output. The evaluation phase uses this coefficient to infer local GHI and calculate the theoretical power output, which is then compared with actual power generation to assess system performance. The framework also employs a peer-comparison strategy as a contingency plan when remote meteorological data is unreliable. By using K-means clustering and the SHAP tool, the method can effectively diagnose the causes of performance degradation, such as shading. The results prove that the proposed framework is a workable and versatile approach for analyzing PV system performance. The peer-comparison method further provides a valuable reference for maintenance teams in data-scarce scenarios.
Keywords: Photovoltaic (PV) systems, Performance evaluation, Remote meteorological data, Sensor-free framework, Peer-comparison, Loss attribution, SHAP, K-means.

1 INTRODUCTION

In the context of achieving carbon neutrality by 2050, the introduction of photovoltaic (PV) power generation is expected to increase rapidly in Japan and worldwide. Traditional performance evaluation methods, such as Performance Ratio (PR), typically rely on expensive on-site sensors, making them difficult to apply to widely distributed PV systems. This study aims to address these challenges by proposing a highly adaptable, sensor-free performance evaluation framework for PV systems to identify systems with performance degradation and accurately quantifies losses attributed to shading

2 PROPOSED METHOD

This study presents a framework for photovoltaic system performance evaluation and loss attribution, which innovatively does not rely on localized solar irradiation data. The method is founded on a core hypothesis: under ideal conditions—without shading or system faults—a PV system's performance should exhibit a stable and predictable relationship with its environmental parameters. However, specific factors like partial shading may cause a system's actual performance to deviate from this ideal baseline or the behavior of a peer group.

2.1 Flow of Operation

The methodology of this study is primarily divided into two phases: the training phase and the evaluation phase.

In the training phase, data from 2018 to 2022 were used as proxies for local solar irradiation. All data were aligned to an hourly granularity, and the training dataset was curated by comparing power generation with solar irradiation data to identify consistent, clear-weather days. Subsequently, the data were grouped by module type (monocrystalline or polycrystalline) and month. A physical model, which incorporates temperature loss, was then used to train and derive a combined loss coefficient (K_o), which links the global horizontal irradiance (GHI) and power output P_{PV}.

In the evaluation phase, clear-weather days in 2023 were first identified based on power output curves. The derived loss coefficient (K_o) was used to invert the model and deduce the local GHI for those days. This inferred GHI data was subsequently applied to calculate the theoretical power output of other PV systems under ideal conditions. A system's performance was evaluated by comparing this theoretical value with its actual power generation. Additionally, when remote solar irradiation data is unreliable, a peer-comparison strategy is employed. This approach uses the real-time power generation data from multiple systems with similar parameters to identify the densest data point, which serves as the ideal performance benchmark for the group.

2.2 Step.1: Similar Day Screening

Initially, this study normalizes a full day's worth of power generation data and remote solar irradiation data by their respective maximum values, treating them as two vectors. Cosine similarity is used to measure the consistency of the shape and trend between these two vectors, while the DTW (Dynamic Time Warping) algorithm corrects for potential time shifts. Days with an average cosine similarity of 0.985 or higher are selected, ensuring a high degree of trend consistency between the power generation and solar irradiation data vectors for that day.

$$similarity = \sum_{t=1}^{24} \cos\theta$$

$$= \frac{\sum_{t=1}^{24} P_{PV_t} \times GHI_t}{\sqrt{\sum_{t=1}^{24}(P_{PV_t})^2} \times \sqrt{\sum_{t=1}^{24}(GHI_t)^2}} \geq 0.985 \qquad (1)$$

Where θ is calculated by taking the mean of the cosine values of the angles between the power generation data vector and the solar irradiation data vector for each hour throughout the entire 24-hour period. Specifically, as shown in Figure 1, the horizontal axis represents the time t of the day, and the vertical axis represents a dimensionless value after aligning the maximum value of

10.4229/EUPVSEC2025/4CV.1.8

the solar radiation data to the power generation data curve. Then, the cosine values of the two vectors at the corresponding time points are calculated, and the average of these cosine values within the day is calculated.

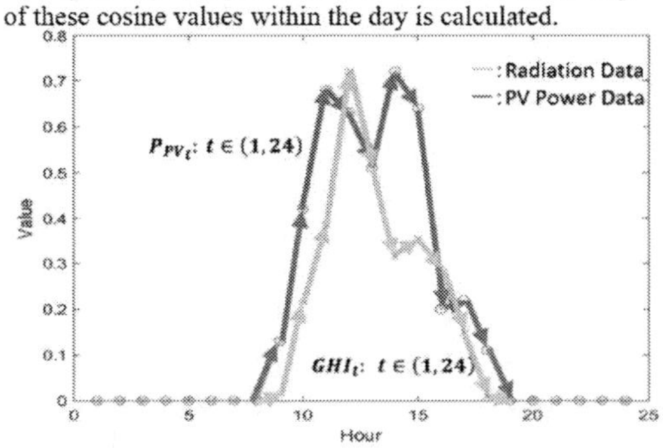

Figure 1: Normalized Comparison of Solar Irradiation and PV Power Data

2.3 Step2: Model Training and Solar Irradiation Inversion

In the model training and solar irradiation inversion phase, data were classified and trained based on both module type (monocrystalline/polycrystalline) and month. For instance, all filtered clear-day data from January for selected monocrystalline systems serving as on-site sensors were collected and used for training to derive a combined loss coefficient (K_o). This coefficient is obtained using the following physical model, which links the global horizontal irradiance (GHI) and power output (P_{PV}):

$$P_{DC}(t) = K_o \times \frac{PoA(t)}{G_{STC}} \times [1 + \gamma(T_c(t) - T_{STC})] \times P_{STC}^{tot} \quad (2)$$

Where:

$\boldsymbol{K_o}$ is the parameter to be trained, representing various combined losses.

$\boldsymbol{PoA(t)}$ is the tilted-surface solar irradiation

$\boldsymbol{G_{STC}}$ is the standard solar irradiation

$\boldsymbol{\gamma}$ is the system's temperature parament.

$\boldsymbol{T_c(t)}$ is the PV module temperature

$\boldsymbol{T_{STC}}$ is the standard temperature.

$\boldsymbol{P_{STC}^{tot}}$ is the rated capacity of the PV system

The tilted-surface solar radiation is decomposed by the Perez model[1].

$$F_1' = F_{11}'(\varepsilon) + F_{12}'(\varepsilon) \cdot \Delta + F_{13}'(\varepsilon) \cdot \theta_Z \quad (3)$$

$$F_2' = F_{21}'(\varepsilon) + F_{22}'(\varepsilon) \cdot \Delta + F_{23}'(\varepsilon) \cdot \theta_Z \quad (4)$$

$$\varepsilon = \frac{H_d + H_b}{H_d} \quad (5)$$

$$\Delta = AM_A \cdot \frac{H_d}{H_0} \quad (6)$$

The direct and diffuse components of solar irradiation are separated using the Erbs model [1].

$$CI \leq 0.22 \qquad H_d = (1.0 - 0.09 \cdot CI) \cdot H_g \quad (7)$$

$$0.22 \leq CI \leq 0.80$$

$$H_d = (0.9511 - 0.1604 \cdot CI + 4.388CI^2 - 16.638 \cdot CI^3 + 12.336 \cdot CI^4) \cdot H_g \quad (8)$$

$$CI > 0.80 \qquad H_d = 0.1650 \cdot H_g \quad (9)$$

After obtaining the K_o coefficient, this study solves for the local GHI value as an inverse problem with a linear equation, utilizing the filtered clear-day power generation data and the trained K_o.

2.4 Step3: Contingency Plan for Unreliable Solar Irradiation Data

When remote meteorological data fails to accurately represent local weather conditions due to geographical factors, this study employs a peer-comparison method as a contingency plan to assess whether individual PV systems are experiencing significant performance degradation. This approach begins by classifying systems based on their type, tilt angle, and azimuth, followed by a performance comparison among a group of similarly configured and closely located systems.

Specifically, at any given moment, the ratio of each system's power output to its rated capacity is calculated, defining the performance utilization rate. These rates are then plotted on a number line. To find the densest point (the ideal performance benchmark), we calculate the sum of the absolute differences in power output between each system k and all other systems j in the group. The system with the minimum D_k is selected as the densest point, and its power output P_{PV_k} is defined as the baseline power value for that moment. By comparing each system's performance utilization rate to this benchmark, a performance deviation value is obtained, which allows us to observe the deviation between the target system's performance and that of the group.

$$D_k = Min \sum_{j=1, j\neq k}^{sys} \left| \boldsymbol{P_{PV_k}} - \boldsymbol{P_{PV_j}} \right| \quad (10)$$

Step4: Analysis of Loss Causes

This study uses K-means clustering to analyze the following data points: solar altitude h, solar azimuth ψ, tilt angle θ, internal surface temperature of the PV system t, clearness index(CI), timestamp, and the residual $\Delta P_{resi}(t)$ between the actual and predicted power output. The predicted power output is calculated using a physical model based on the inverted solar irradiation data obtained from the preceding steps.

Subsequently, the SHAP (Shapley Additive Explanations) tool is utilized for an importance analysis of the residuals, which quantifies and determines which factors have the most significant impact on the power output loss under various conditions.

Residuals refer to the difference between the theoretical value, which is inversely estimated using inverted on-site solar irradiance data, and the actual observed value. Specifically, it is calculated using the following formula:

$$Residuals = P_{PV} - P_{inverted} \quad (11)$$

3 USED DATA

The data for this study was sourced from a large-scale photovoltaic power plant located in Hokuto City, Yamanashi Prefecture, Japan, covering an analysis period from January 1, 2018, to December 31, 2023. The dataset primarily consists of two types:

PV System Data: This includes data from 6 monocrystalline silicon systems and 7 polycrystalline silicon systems. All systems share a 30° tilt angle, a due-south azimuth, and an approximate rated capacity of 10 kW each. Additionally, internal panel surface temperature data for each system was utilized.

Meteorological Data: Solar irradiation data was obtained from the Japan Meteorological Agency's AMeDAS (Automated Meteorological Data Acquisition

10.4229/EUPVSEC2025/4CV.1.8
020320-002

System), with a granularity of one hour.

4 RESULTS AND DISCUSSION

4.1 Data filtering results

Figure 2 presents the cosine similarity curve, with red circles indicating data points below 0.985. It was observed that during the winter months (November to January), there was an increase in the number of mismatched days, which may be attributed to microclimates caused by local terrain.

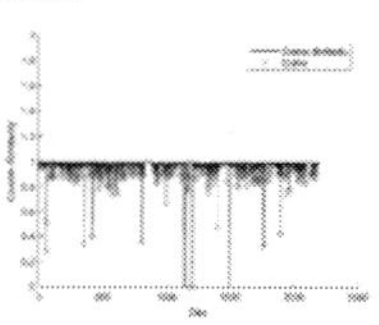

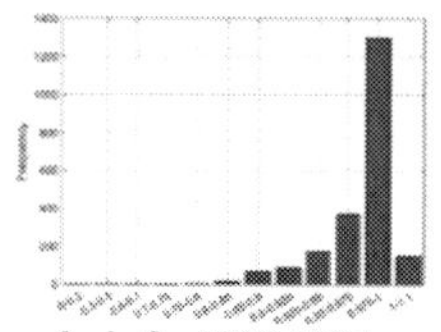

Figure 2: Cosine similarity analysis for 2018-2024year
Figure 3: Cosine similarity Distribution for 2018-2024 year

Cosine similarity, which measures the trend consistency between power generation and remote solar irradiation data vectors, approaches 1 for highly similar trends. Statistical results show that most values fall within the range of 0.95 to 1, as presented in

Figure 3. This filtering process, which exclusively selects clear and meteorologically similar days, allows approximately 52% of the year's days to be utilized for model training. The average prediction error for these clear days is currently between 5.2% and 8.6%.

4.2 Analysis Using Remote Solar Irradiation Data

This study calculated loss parameters for converting solar irradiation to power using a similarity filter, with the parameters specific to different system types, months, and times of day. For predictions, we first compared the daily power data to an ideal solar curve to ensure the data was suitable for analysis.

K-means cluster analysis was then employed to diagnose the causes of performance decline by analyzing the relationship between power output errors and solar altitude and azimuth. This analysis revealed two distinct scenarios:

Scenario 1: One system exhibited a significant performance drop during the winter months (November to January) between 10 a.m. and 2 p.m. Cluster analysis revealed that the Residuals occurred at low solar altitudes and azimuths between -20° and 20°, which aligned with shading from a forest to the south.

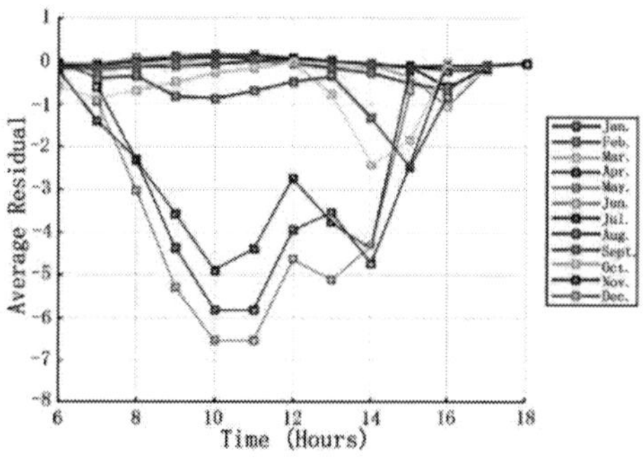

Figure 4: Monthly Performance Trends and Residuals of the Systems affected by shadows

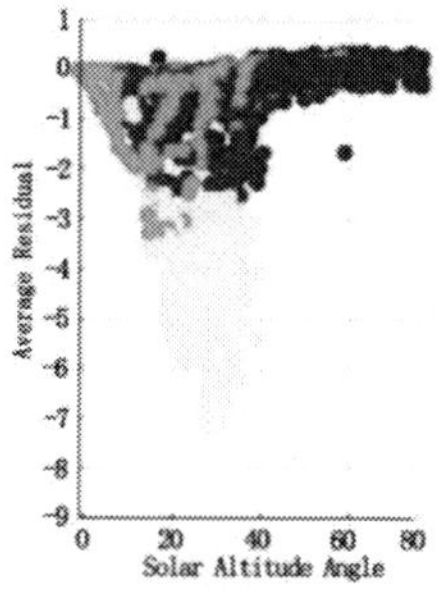

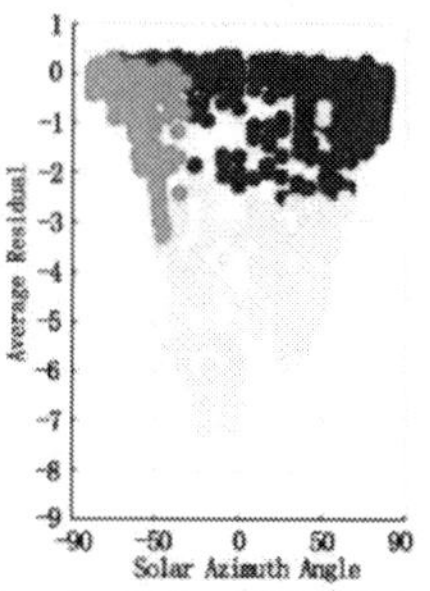

Figure 5: K-Means Clustering Analysis of Residuals vs. Solar Altitude Angles of the Systems affected by shadows
Figure 6: K-Means Clustering Analysis of Residuals vs. Solar Azimuth Angles of the Systems affected by shadows

Scenario 2: Another system remained stable year-round with only a minor drop in December. Cluster analysis showed no patterns linked to specific solar angles, indicating that the issue was not due to long-term shading.

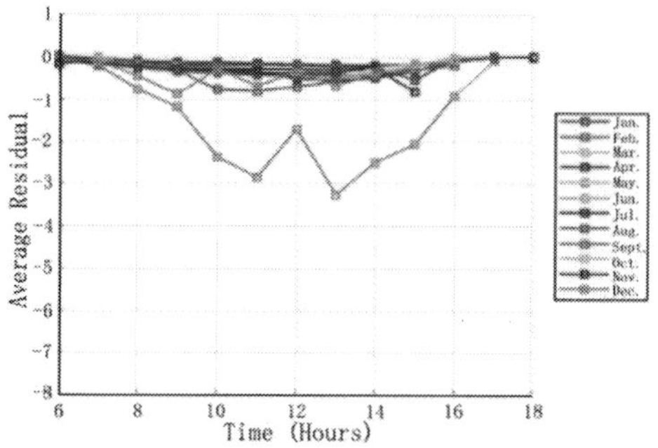

Figure 7: Monthly Performance Trends and Residuals of the Normal System

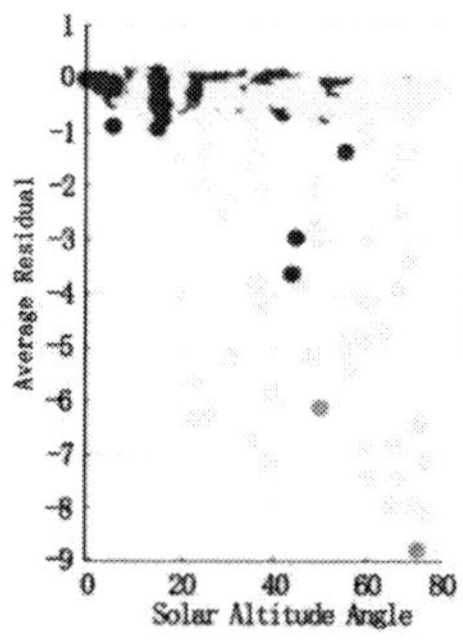

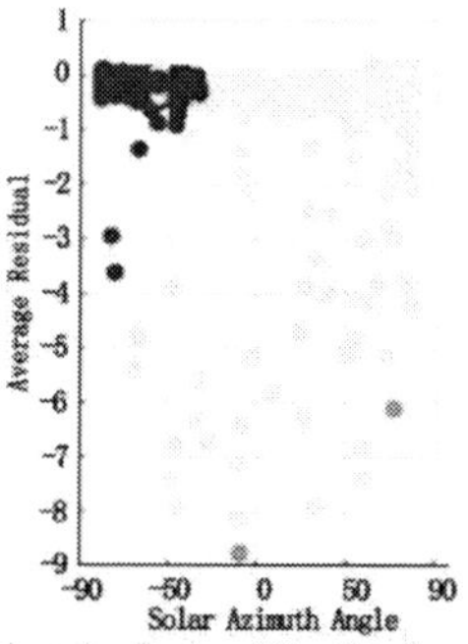

Figure 8: K-Means Clustering Analysis of Residuals vs. Solar Altitude Angles of the Normal System
Figure 9: K-Means Clustering Analysis of Residuals vs. Solar Azimuth Angles of the Normal System

4.3 SHAP Importance Analysis

Using the SHAP tool, we assessed the importance of various factors contributing to power output residuals. The factors analyzed included zenith angle, angle of incidence, altitude angle, azimuth, solar irradiation, month, time, and clearness index.

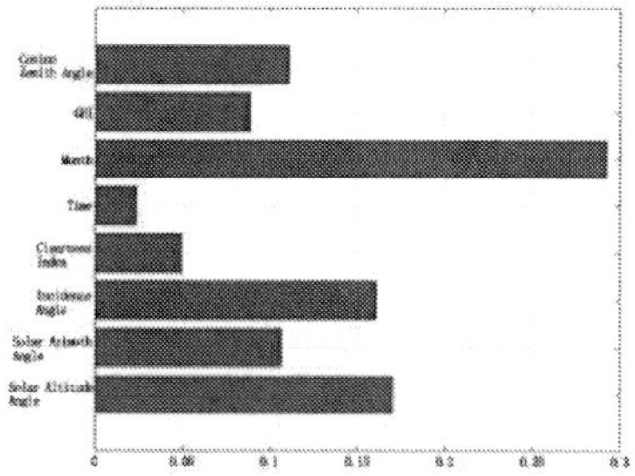

Figure 10: SHAP Importance Analysis of Power Output Residuals of Systems affected by shadows

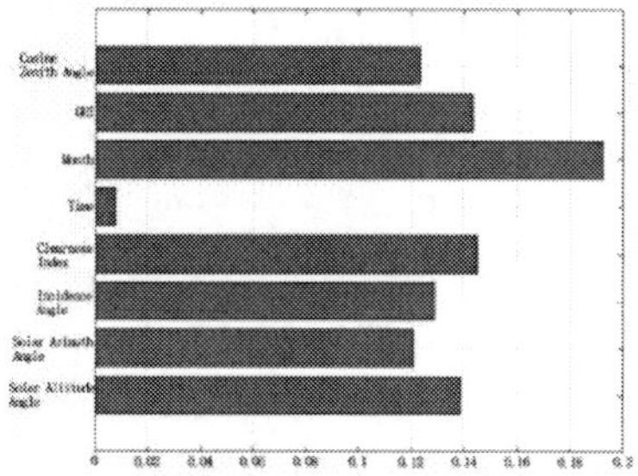

Figure 11: SHAP Importance Analysis of Power Output Residuals of Normal System

For systems with clear seasonal influences, the angle of incidence and altitude angle showed significant importance in the SHAP analysis, which aligns with the presence of fixed directional shading. In contrast, for systems without fixed shading, the contribution of each factor to the residual was nearly identical. The minor influence of time on the residual is likely due to its overlap with the monthly factor.

4.4 On-site Reference Comparison

When solar irradiation data is unavailable, a quick on-site reference comparison method can be used to observe a system's power generation performance relative to a group of systems with similar parameters. For instance, in a group of polycrystalline silicon systems with identical capacity, tilt angles, and azimuth angles, we applied the on-site comparison method.

As shown in Fig. 11, we observed that the system's performance was lower than the group average during spring and winter. Although this method cannot pinpoint the specific cause of the performance degradation, it effectively reveals a clear seasonal pattern. In contrast, Fig. 12 shows a system with normal performance and minimal fluctuation, indicating that its performance remains consistent with its peers.

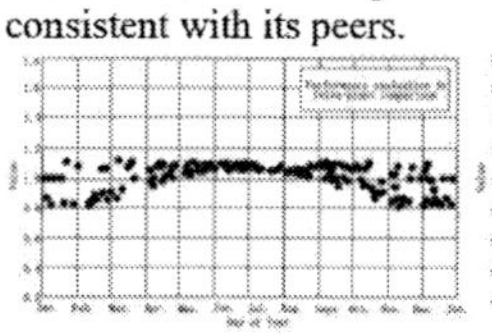

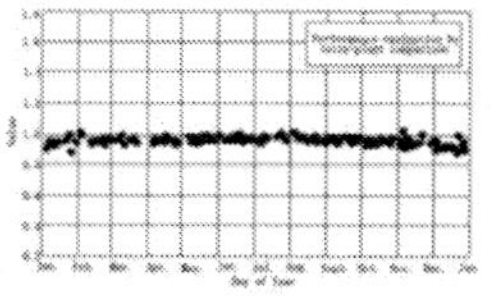

Figure 12: Performance Evaluation by Peer-Comparison of Systems affected by shadows

Figure 13: Performance Evaluation by Peer-Comparison of Normal System

5 CONCLUSIONS

This study demonstrates the feasibility of using remote meteorological data for analyzing PV system performance. The proposed method offers several key advantages:

Sensor-Free Operation: By utilizing hourly remote data, the method eliminates the need for expensive on-site measurement instruments, making it highly versatile for widespread application.

Accurate Shading Loss Quantification: The framework provides a clear and effective means to analyze and quantify the specific effects of shading on power generation.

Contingency Plan for Data Scarcity: The peer-comparison method serves as a valuable contingency plan when data is scarce, providing maintenance crews with a reliable reference for performance trends

6 FUTURE WORK

Future work will focus on the following three key areas to further enhance the functionality and practicality of the proposed framework:

Developing an Automated Reference System Selection Algorithm: We plan to develop a fully automated algorithm to intelligently identify and select an ideal reference system. The goal is to create a virtual PV system free of defects that can serve as an on-site solar irradiation sensor, thereby enhancing the algorithm's functionality.

Quantifying Performance Loss Attribution: We will quantitatively estimate the contribution of each cause of performance degradation to determine its specific share of the total loss.

Enhancing Overall Algorithm Functionality: These planned improvements are aimed at further enhancing the overall functionality and robustness of the algorithm.

7 REFELENCES

[1]. Ueda, Yuzuru. A study on an advanced performance analysis method for PV systems using monitoring data. PhD diss., Tokyo University of Agriculture and Technology, 2007.

[2]. Wataru Yasuhara, Kenji Hirata, and Jun Toyotani, "Solar irradiance nowcasting by LightGBM with cloud information from sky images," Journal of the Japan Information Directory Society, vol. 21, 2023.

[3]. Theristis, Marios, et al. "Blind photovoltaic modeling intercomparison: A multidimensional data analysis and lessons learned." IEEE Journal of Photovoltaics, 21 July 2023, https://doi.org/10.1002/pip.3729.

[4]. Elsinga, Boudewijn, Wilfried van Sark, and Lou Ramaekers. "Inverse photovoltaic yield model for global horizontal irradiance reconstruction." Energy Science & Engineering, vol. 5, no. 5, 7 Aug. 2017, pp. 882–891, https://doi.org/10.1002/ese3.162.

[5]. Martín-Martínez, S., Cañas-Carretón, M., Honrubia-Escribano, A., & Gómez-Lázaro, E. (2019). Performance evaluation of large solar photovoltaic power plants in Spain. *Energy Conversion and Management*, *183*, 515–528.

EU PVSEC
42nd European Photovoltaic Solar Energy Conference and Exhibition
Session Reference No.: 4CV.1.8

A Highly Adaptable Performance Evaluation Method for PV Systems Using Remote Meteorological Data and On-Site Reference Comparisons

Author: Weizhen Xiong*[1], Jindan Cui [1], Yuzuru Ueda [1]
[1]Tokyo University of Science, Japan
Contact: 4324532@ed.tus.ac.jp

東京理科大学
TOKYO UNIVERSITY OF SCIENCE

Introduction

As large-scale PV systems are integrated into the grid,
Traditional performance evaluation methods rely on on-site sensors.

- Propose a versatile and cost-effective framework that is independent of on-site data, to quantify and separate losses from factors like shading.
- Enable loss attribution, supporting refined operation and maintenance decisions.

Framework

Step1: Data Preparation

- **Historical Power Generation and Panel Temperature** — P_{PV} , T (From multiple PV systems)
- **Remote Meteorological and Astronomical data** — GHI_t (From AMeDAS - Japan Meteorological Agency)

Step2: Processing & Baseline Construction

- **Data Validation & Intelligent Filtering**
  - Cosine Similarity
  - DTW(Dynamic Time Warping)
- **Segmented Baseline Model Construction** — Output: Segmented model parameters K_{o_t}

Step3: Loss Quantification & Attribution

- **Loss Quantification**
  - Total Loss
- **Loss Attribution & Pattern Analysis** — Segregating Shading Loss
- **Shading Patterns** — By Time Segment, Season, Azimuth Angle

Proposed method

Remote Data Reliability Assessment

Assess the consistency between the on-site power generation curve $P_{PV}(t)$ and the remote meteorological station's irradiance curve $GHI(t)$ using two core metrics.

- Cosine Similarity

$$similarity = \sum_{t=1}^{24} \cos\theta = \frac{\sum_{t=1}^{24} P_{PV_t} \times GHI_t}{\sqrt{\sum_{t=1}^{24}(P_{PV_t})^2} \times \sqrt{\sum_{t=1}^{24}(GHI_t)^2}} \geq 0.985$$

- DTW

The time difference is corrected by systematically shifting one curve to find the offset that gives the best fit between the two curves.

Loss Quantification

- Select the data from system with the highest $P_{PV}(t)$ as the optimal sample for that time point t

$$P_{PV}(t) = K_{o_t} \times \frac{PoA(t)}{G_{STC}} \times [1 + \gamma\ (T_c(t) - T_{STC})\ ] \times P_{STC}^{tot}$$

※The POA here is the solar radiation data of the remote meteorological data filtered by similarity.

- Using the trained K_{o_t} value, the solar radiation data is inverted based on the measured value of power generation on that day, thus obtaining highly reliable local solar radiation data.
- Quick Estimation

When remote meteorological data is unreliable, we use a quick, on-site comparison method. Choose P_{PV_k} which makes D_k minimum as sample data

$$D_k = \sum_{m=i, m\neq k}^{N} |P_{PV_k} - P_{PV_m}|$$

By contrasting the performance of similar PV systems within the same plant, to identify the "highest density point" that best represents the overall performance and use it as the performance indicator for the target system.

Pattern Analysis

- Clustering

Utilizing the K-means algorithm to cluster features such as residuals, solar angles, and clearness index.

$$\Phi_{f_i} = \sum_{S \subseteq F \setminus \{f_i\}} \frac{|S|!\,(M - |S| - 1)!}{M!} [f_{loss}(S \cup \{f_i\} - f_{loss}(S))]$$

- Feature Importance

to quantify the influence of each feature on the loss, providing deeper insights into the causes of shading.

Objective

- ✓ To establish a framework for quantifying and segregating PV system losses caused by partial shading.
- ✓ The goal is to identify and analyze the impact of shading on power generation performance without the need for on-site meteorological data.

Dataset

Target location: Nagasakacho Natsuaki, Hokuto, Yamanashi City, Japan
Simulation data: From 2018 to 2023
Time Grain: 1hour
For PV output forecasts, solar radiation, temperature, and solar radiation data from the distant meteorological station are used

Table.1 Equipment Configuration

	Setting
Number	6 Monocrystalline 7 Polycrystalline
Capacity	Approximately 10kW
Tilt Angle	30°
Azimuth Angle	South-facing

Results and discussion

◆Remote Data Validation Results

Fig.1 Solar Radiation Sensor Performance

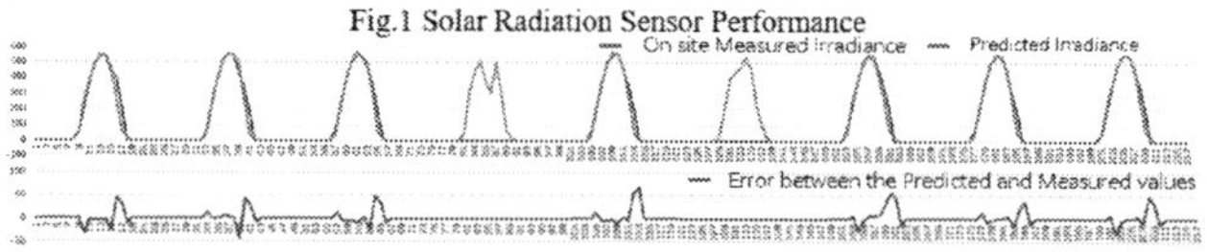

Through this data filtering, performed exclusively on clear and meteorologically similar days, approximately 52% of the year's days can be utilized for training. The average prediction error for clear days at the present time is between 5.2% and 8.6%.

◆On-site Reference Comparison Results

Fig.2 Performance Trend without meteorological data

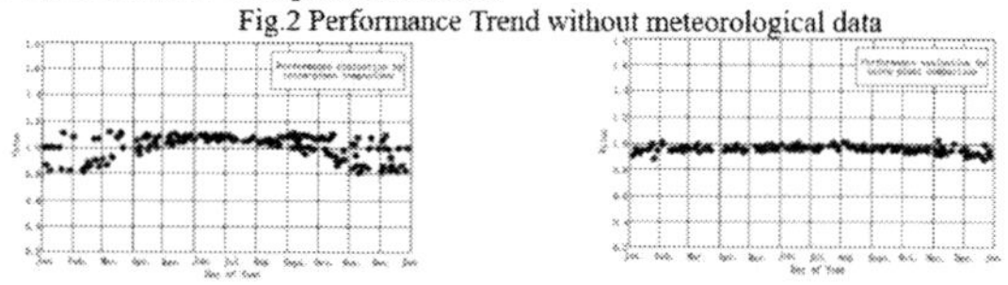

The systems unaffected by shading exhibit stable performance, consistent with the group average. In contrast, systems with fixed shading show clear degradation patterns, especially in winter when the solar altitude angle is low.

◆Loss Pattern Analysis

Fig.3 Seasonal System Loss Comparison Chart

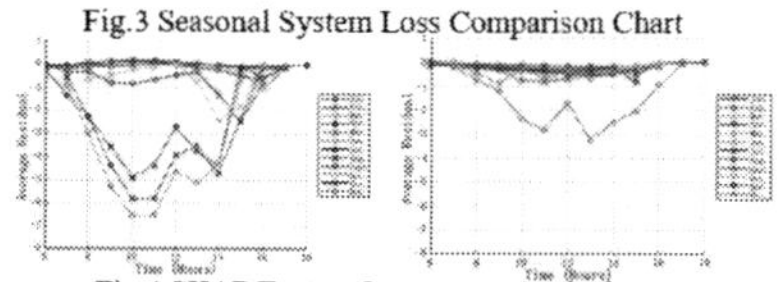

Left Chart: Indicate the most significant impact in winter.
Right Chart: With low losses in most of months.

Fig.4 SHAP Feature Importance Analysis

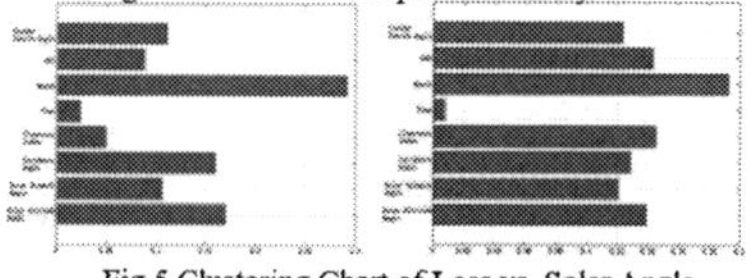

Left Chart: The"Month" parameter has the highest contribution to the loss, confirming a strong seasonal dependency for shading-induced losses.

Fig.5 Clustering Chart of Loss vs. Solar Angle

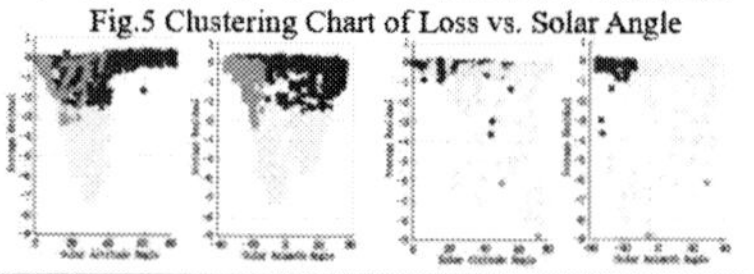

The loss clusters are concentrated at specific solar altitude and azimuth angles.
This can be used to determine the location of the shading object.

Conclusions

- ✓ Propose and validate a performance evaluation framework for PV systems that does not rely on on-site meteorological sensors.
- ✓ Identify systems with performance degradation and reveals the patterns of power generation changes caused by shading

42nd European Photovoltaic Solar Energy Conference and Exhibition

PV-Reliability.ch

EU PVSEC 2025, 22.-26. September 2025, Bilbao (Spain)
Matthias Hügi[1], Christof Bucher[1], Leo Hofer[1], Fabio Panduri[1]
[1]Bern University of Applied Sciences (BFH), School of Engineering and Computer Science (TI), Institute for Energy and Mobility Research (IEM), Laboratory for Photovoltaic Systems (PV-Lab), Burgdorf (Switzerland)
christof.bucher@bfh.ch

"The life expectancy of inverters is around 15 years and therefore need to be replaced once during the service life of a photovoltaic system". This statement is being analysed in the "PV Reliability" research project. The platform processes data entered by users in order to calculate the survival probability of inverters and optimisers depending on time, installation location, manufacturer and other parameters and to create comparisons.

Objectives and approach

The aim of this research project is to quantify the service life of inverters and power optimisers. It is analysed whether time, installation location and manufacturer influence the service life and how important the respective factors are.

In order to achieve this goal, we are looking for private individuals and companies, both nationally and internationally, who are willing to provide basic data and operating data on their PV systems. Private individuals can independently record systems and events on the website pv-reliability.ch. For companies with large data sets, an individualised import is possible.

Innovation and relevance

This project contributes to a better understanding of the effects of ageing on inverters, which can be influenced by the users. In contrast to previous research work, this project does not investigate the cause of the damage, but rather the stress factors that can be influenced.

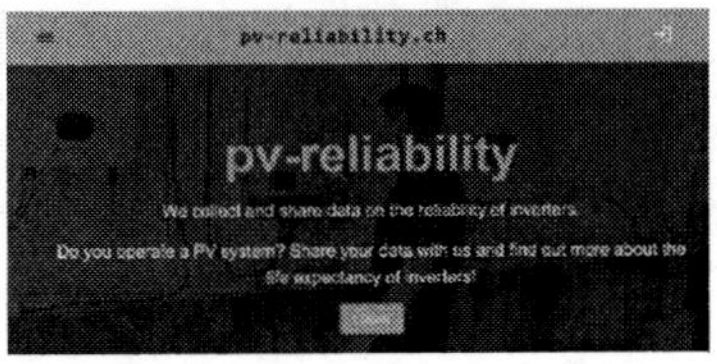

Figure 1: Home page pv-reliability.ch

Today, millions of PV systems are connected to monitoring portals. However, these portals do not provide any information about the load factors that can be influenced and generally do not know the age and condition of the components used. In particular, when an inverter is repaired or replaced 1:1, this is often not recorded by the portals. The platform aims to close this research gap.

Recording of installations

The pv-reliability.ch platform utilises the crowd data sourcing approach. In a first step, users of the platform create a login and enter master data on their PV system. This data includes the location, product types used and basic characteristics of the PV system, such as

- Number of modules per string
- Number of modules per inverter
- Installation location of the inverter
- Use of optimisers

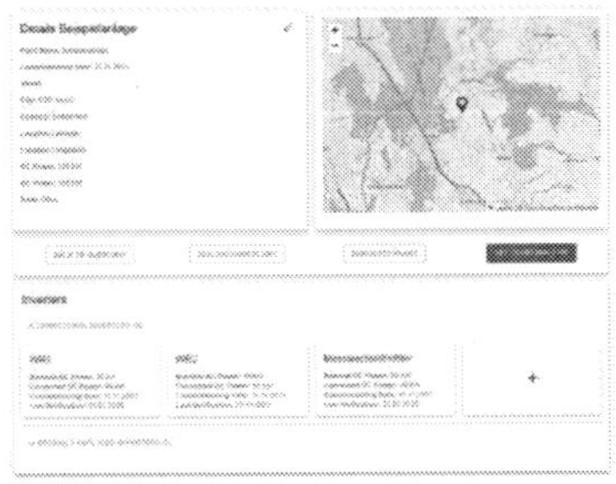

Figure 2: Overview page of an installation

Inverter commissioning data is also recorded in order to determine the service life. The data is recorded using simple input masks. All data is then clearly displayed.

Verification process

In order to calculate the service life of the various inverters, faults, defects or even the replacement of devices must be recorded/updated regularly. This is done in the Verification section. On this page, the status of each inverter can be defined at a specific point in time. The following statuses can be selected :

- Operational
- Replaced without failure
- Broken

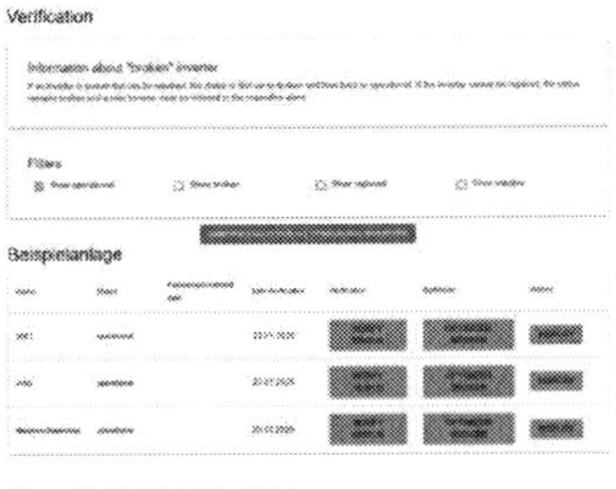

Figure 3: Verification page

Defective optimisers can also be recorded. Verification can be carried out individually for each inverter or directly for all recorded devices. The data should be updated once a year, for which purpose a corresponding request is sent to the users.

Results

The pv-reliability.ch platform was only recently put into operation. It was created on the basis of a survey and publication with an identical scope from 2022.

Automatic analyses are currently implemented in the internal area, but have not yet been activated, as there are currently too few data sets available for a statistically relevant evaluation. For initial statements on the service life of inverters, please refer to the 2022 study [1].

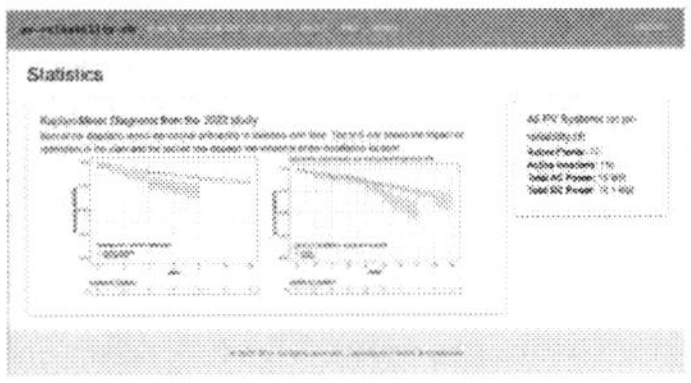

Figure 4: Results of the 2022 study

Support the research!

We are looking for companies and individuals who are willing to share their data on inverter failures with us. Individual systems can be entered at pv-reliability.ch, larger portfolios (e.g. of installation companies) can be sent to the PV laboratory with an Excel list. matthias.huegi@bfh.ch will be happy to provide further details.

https://pv-reliability.ch/

Thanks to

A big thank you goes to all those who agree to make their data available for this project and to update it regularly.

References

[1] Christof Bucher, Jasmin Wandel, David Joss, Life expectancy of PV inverters and optimizers in residential PV systems, 29.09.2022, WCPEC-8 https://www.bfh.ch/de/forschung/referenzprojekte/lebenserwartung-photovoltaik-wechselrichter/

Berner Fachhochschule
Haute école spécialisée bernoise
Bern University of Applied Sciences

▸ Department of Engineering and Computer Science (TI)
▸ Institute for Energy and Mobility Research (IEM)

Laboratory for Photovoltaic Systems
3400 Burgdorf | Jlcoweg 1
www.bfh.ch/pvlab | christof.bucher@bfh.ch

Applied Photovoltaic Research
Swiss Solar Competence

020322-001

Investigation and Discuss of Failures during Operation and Maintenance in Floating Photovoltaic

EU PVSEC 2025

* Jieun Lee, Hyunsik Jo, Jungi Jeong , Donggeon Yang
Water Energy research, Korea Water Resources corporation (K-water)

K water

INTRODUCTION

- For Low Carbon, Need to be improved the Capa. Of photovoltaic which have portion 70% in renewable energy of South Korea
- FPV(Floating photovoltaic) is actively used to overcome the topography feature of PV on ground.
- For stable power supply, operation and maintenance are essential, in which diagnosis with type of degradation and effect of power with different type of environment are also importance for effectively managing of PV system
- In this research, we will analysis the status of failure during diagnosis and operating with long term and discuss about way to manage of FPV for a future.

FLOATING PHOTOVOLTAIC IN K-WATER

- FLOATING PV
  - ➢ Photovoltaic mounted on a structure that floats on a body of water

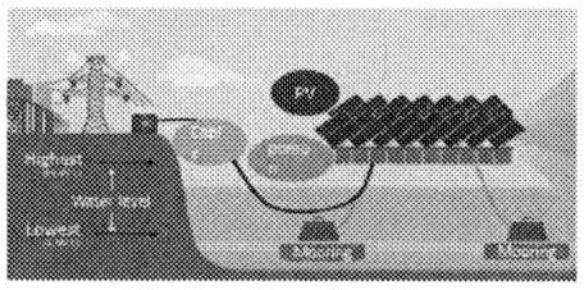

<Floating PV configuration>

<Floating PV system>

- Status of FPV in K-water
  - ➢ Research and business FPV are 58.4MW in K-water

('11.11) Hapchun Dam 100kW ('12.10) Hapchun Dam 500kW ('13.05) Hapchun Dam 100kW ('16.03) Boryung 2MW

('17.02) Soyanggan Dam110kW ('17.12) Chungju Dam 3MW ('18.06) Chungju Dam 200kW ('21.04) Siwha 200kW (offshore)

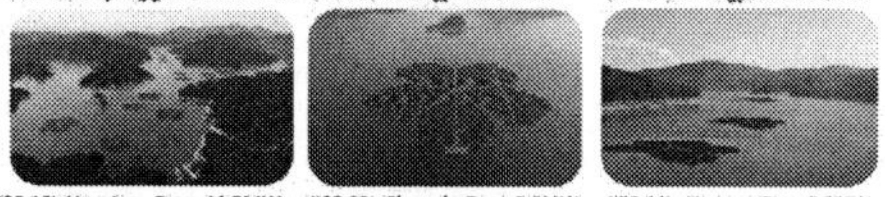

('22.12) Hapchun Dam 41.5MW ('22.08) Chungju Dam 2.6MW ('23.11) Yanggu Dam 8.8MW

MAINTENANCE AND INSPCETION IN A FIELD

- Maintenance Task in FPV system[1]

Component	Task Description	Periodicity	Recommended Documentation
Tasks specific to FPV			
Buoyant structure	Inspection for buoyancy issues, damage, and biofouling	Monthly	DNVGL-RP-0584, Manufacturer's manual
	Clean the floaters if algae or any other auatic growth is observed on their surface.	Quarterly	
Anchors	Inspection for general conditions (wear, degradation), risk of lifting and proper positon	2.5year	ISO 1990-7, DNVGL-ST-0119
Mooring system	Check for wear, corrosion, marine growth Inspect the integrity of connecting points (fairleads, shackles and frayed crimp points) Tension adjustments	yearly and every 2.5years for under water sections	DNVGL-RP-0584 ISO 199101-7
Tasks similar to GPV but more challenging			
Structural components	Inspect for rust on frame supports, cable clips and fasteners	Quarterly	DNVGL-RP-0584, manfacturer's manual
	Verify strength, tightness, and integrity of bolt and other connectors Inspect the structural integrity and galvanic corrosion in dissimilar metals	Yearly	
PV module	Vrify the cleanliness and integrity of module sufaces and check for objects causing shading Visual inspection for defects in both front and aback sides Conduct performance tests and IR, PL and EL scanning	Monthly Quarterly Yearly	IEC 62446-3, IEC 61215, Manufacturer's manual
Cables	Inspect for signs of damages and degraded insulation	Monthly	IEC 62446-1, IEC 60364
	Verify mechanical and watertight integrity of cable conduits/cable trays	Quarterly	
	Perform tests to check continuity, insulation resistance and hot spots	Yearly	
Inverter	Check error log files from inverter database	Monthly	IEC 62109-1, IEC 62109-2, IEC 62093, Manufacturer's manual
	Inspect for water ingress, physical damages and corrosion Clean inverter fans and inspect ventilation	Quarterly	
	Test the operational efficiency and check anti-islanding fuction of the inverter	Yearly	
Transformer	Inspection for water ingress, physical damages and corrosion	Quarterly	IEC 60076 series, Manufacturer's manual
	Check oil level, oil temperature, dielectric strength and tap changer temperature	Quarterly	
	Test the operational efficiency and check hot spots	Yearly	
Electrical protective system	Inspect for visual damages and verify integrity of equipotential bonding Inspect the condition of the main grounding cable	Monthly	IEC 62561-2, IEC 62305-2, IEEE 81-2012, IEC 62548, Manufacturer's manual
	Conduct continuity and earth resistance test	Biannually	
	Verify any defects in the protective switchgears(circuit breakers, residual current breakers surge protective devices) Check earth pit and its resistivity if earth cable returns to shore Check the earthing material for corrosion if earthing is done through water body	Yearly	
Data monitoring system	Verify operations of sensors, data loggers, and communication modules	Biannually	IEC 62676, IEC 61724-1, Manufacturer's manual

1.Hemha Limel Wasiala et al., Operation and Maintenance of Floating PV System: A review, IEEE Journal of Photovoltaics (Volume: 13, Issue: 3, May 2023)

DIAGNOSIS AND INSPECTION IN K-water

- Diagnosis in a Field (Progress once a 2~4year, periodically)

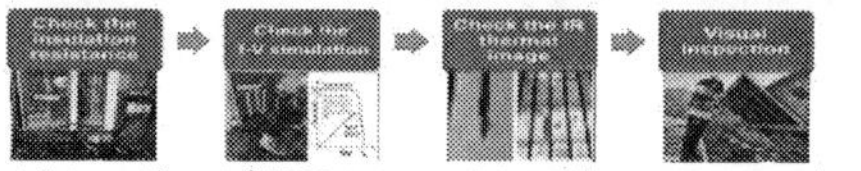

- Inspection of FPV system (Monthly or Frequently

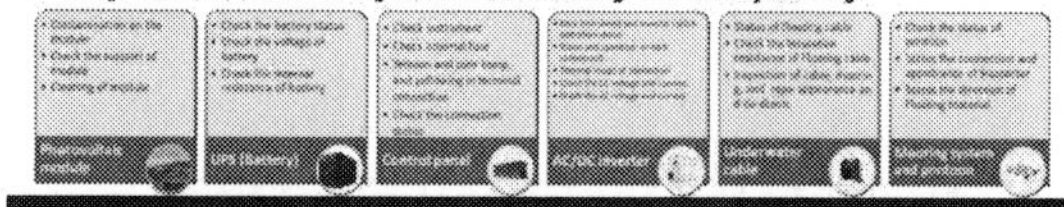

RESULT AND DISCUSSION

- Diagnosis result in FPV
  - ➢ The Most of issue Floating 56.4% and Electric room 29% in FPV system
  - ➢ Floating : Mounting system(21.8%), Mooring (7.1%), Module(5.6%), Underwater cable(3.0%)

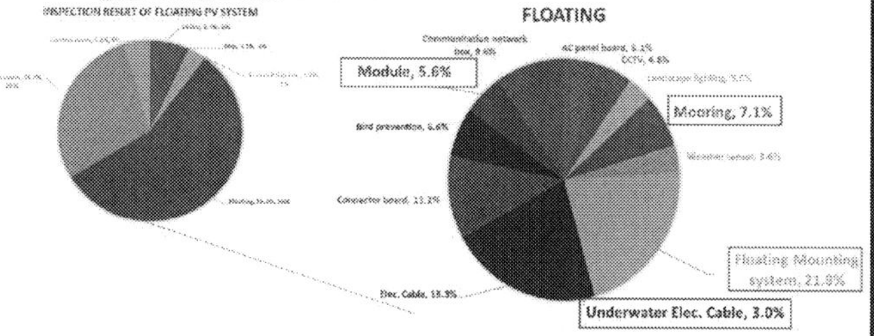

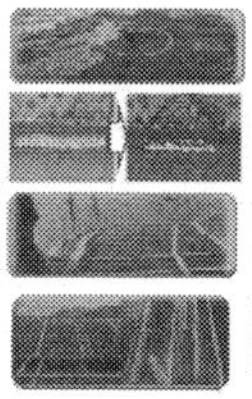

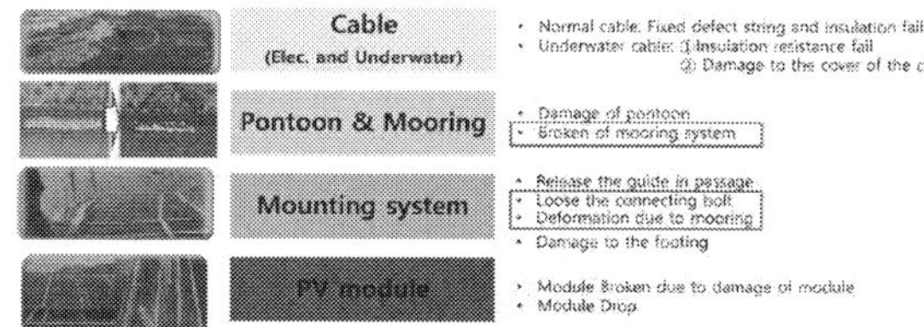

Cable (Elec. and Underwater)	• Normal cable: Fixed defect string and insulation failure • Underwater cable: ① Insulation resistance fail ② Damage to the cover of the clamp joint due to tension
Pontoon & Mooring	• Damage of pontoon • Broken of mooring system
Mounting system	• Release the guide in passage • Loose the connecting bolt • Deformation due to mooring • Damage to the footing
PV module	• Module Broken due to damage of module • Module Drop

- Analysis of impact from Fault and Defect
  - ➢ Mooring and Floating Mount system for Floating

Cause	Effect	
Broken of mooring	Broken underwater cable	Degradation of power generation
	Damage the module (Penetration of water & corrosion)	
Loose the connect bolt	Module Drop	
Deformation of mounting	Cell & Backsheet crack and snail track	

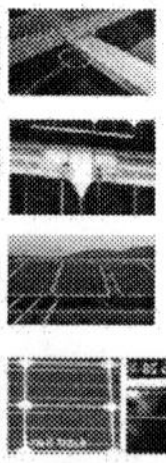

SUMMARY AND CONCLUSION

- Short term : Mounting structure Fault due to micro wave on water
- Long term : BS and cell crack due to unstable mounting structure and corrosion due to moisture in FPV
- Additional inspection for improving safety and reliability in K-water
  - Inspection of Mooring system (water level and GPS), Mounting system(Connecting)

Corrosion for mounting system

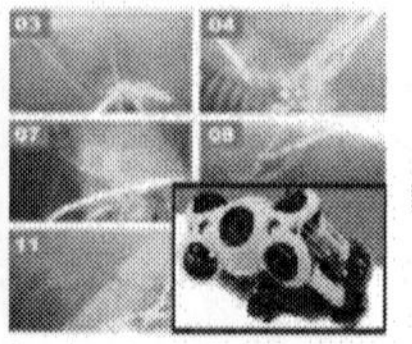

Mooring with underwater drone

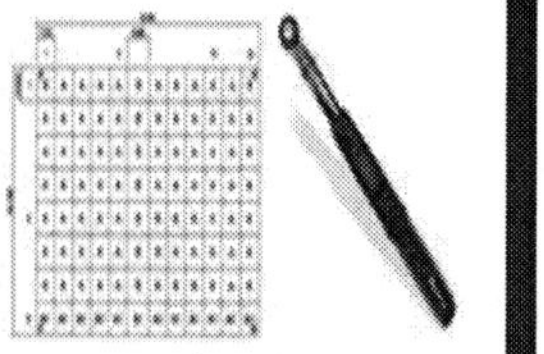

Inspect for connection

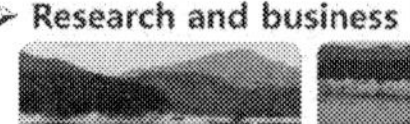

This work was supported by the Korea Institute of Energy Technology Evaluation and Planning(KETEP) and the Ministry of Trade, Industry & Energy(MOTIE) of the Republic of Korea [illegible]

Study on Power Generation Estimation Model using Inverter Data and Machine Learning

Suk whan Ko[1], Young Chul JU[1], Hye Mi HWANG[1], Jin-Seok Lee[1], Woo Gyun Shin[1]

Korea Institute of Energy Research, Korea

presenting author (korea19@kier.re.kr)

Abstract

Globally, efforts are being made to overcome the climate change crisis by reducing carbon-based power sources and adopting renewable energy-based power sources through initiatives such as RE100 and ESG management. The most widely utilized renewable energy source is photovoltaic (PV) energy, with the cumulative installed capacity surpassing 2 TW in 2024. This marks a doubling of capacity in just two years, compared to 1 TW in 2022. Notably, PV installations are expected to continue increasing in the coming years. As the installation of PV plants increases, the market for operation and maintenance (O&M) is also growing. According to the related report, the global PV O&M market is estimated to grow at a compound global annual rate (CAGR) of 14.49 % during the forecast period 2022-2027 and reach $7,339.60 million by 2027, from around $3,330.73 million in 2021. In recent years, advancements in big data and artificial intelligence technologies have brought changes to PV operation and maintenance (O&M) activities. Traditional PV O&M activities are evolving into more efficient operations through the application of digital technologies.

In this paper, we proposes a method and model for estimating power generation by using PV inverter data as training data for machine-learning models. First, the data for training the machine learning model is preprocessed using a physical model to remove outliers. The physical model calculates voltage and current data based on irradiance and module temperature. Next, irradiance, module temperature, voltage, and current data are used as input variables, while the measured voltage and current data are used as output variables to train the machine learning model. After training seven different regression models, the ensemble (bagging tree) model achieved the lowest root mean square error (RMSE) values for voltage and current, at 2.1158 (V) and 0.1406 (A), respectively.

Background

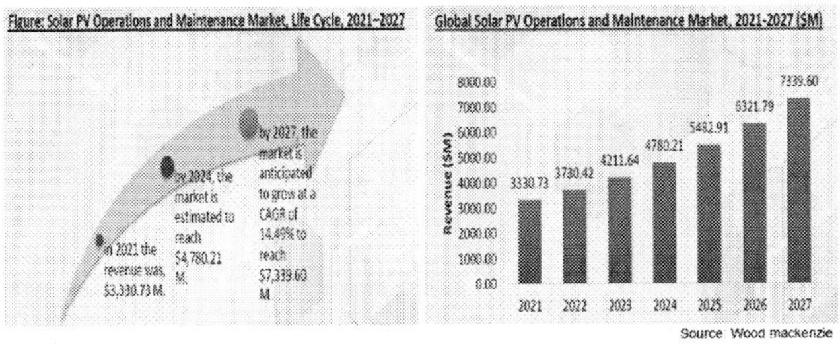

O&M market expansion from PV growth and aging systems

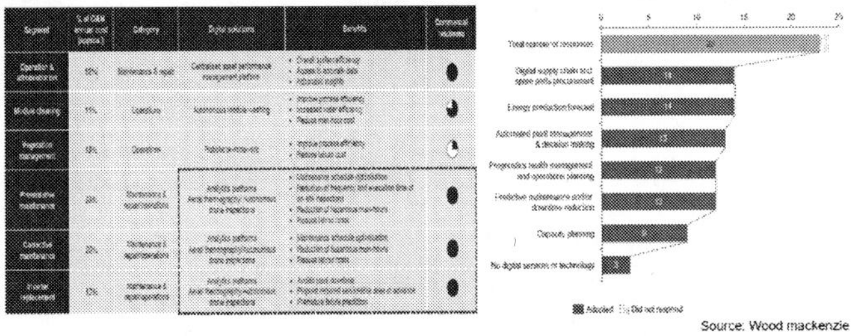

Growing demand for PV O&M technologies utilizing AI and data

Experiment and Result

◆ Preprocessing method of collected inverter data

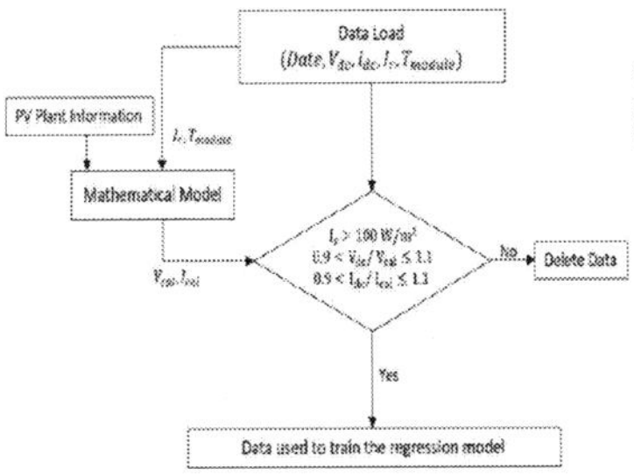

Data preprocessing procedure

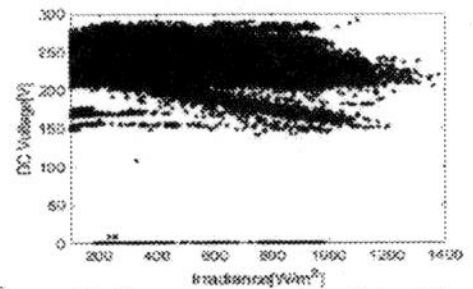

Before preprocessing data (V)

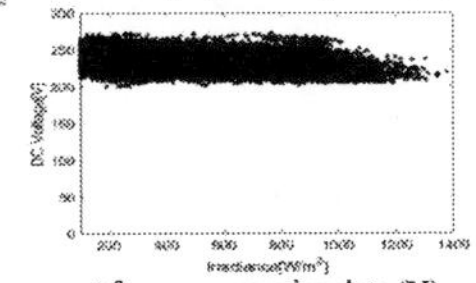

After preprocessing data (V)

- For the operation and maintenance (O&M) of photovoltaic power plants, data is essential, and inverter data is the most easily accessible source. Inverter data collects various parameters (voltage, current, power, frequency, power factor, etc.) that can be used to assess plant conditions.
- Among these, voltage, current, and power data represent the output performance of the PV system; however, abnormal values may occur due to inverter shutdowns or MPPT malfunctions.
- If such abnormal values are included in the training dataset for machine learning, the results cannot be considered reliable. Therefore, as shown in the figure, the collected data were preprocessed using a mathematical model and measured irradiance as reference.
- As illustrated in the figure, the raw data contained scattered abnormal values before preprocessing. Through data preprocessing, these outliers were removed, and the training dataset was consolidated within a consistent range.

◆ Validation results using trained machine learning model (Bagging Tree)

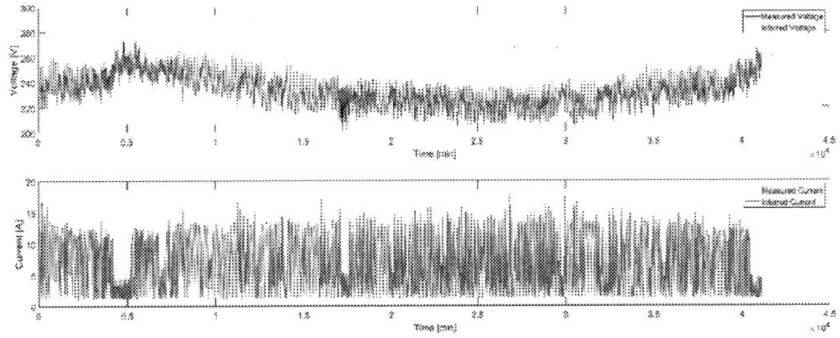

Comparison of measured and Inferred DC voltage and current (Machine Learning)

- Using the preprocessed data, seven machine learning models were trained as shown in the table below.
- Among the trained models, the Bagging Tree model demonstrated the best performance, achieving R^2 values of 0.9666 (voltage) and 0.9987 (current), and NRMSE values of 0.0294 (voltage) and 0.0202 (current).

Results for DC Voltage (V)

Model	R^2	NRMSE	RMSE
Linear	0.9450	0.0377	2.7134
Neural	0.9519	0.0352	2.5380
Tree	0.9564	0.0336	2.4206
LSK	0.9462	0.0373	2.6841
GPR	0.9573	0.0332	2.3902
Boosted	0.9501	0.1419	10.2179
Bagging	0.9666	0.0294	2.1158

Results for DC Current (A)

Model	R^2	NRMSE	RMSE
Linear	0.9977	0.0266	0.1852
Neural	0.9985	0.0216	0.1503
Tree	0.9984	0.0218	0.1513
LSK	0.9967	0.0317	0.2203
GPR	0.9986	0.0203	0.1410
Boosted	0.9977	0.0559	0.3882
Bagging	0.9987	0.0202	0.1406

Conclusion

- PV inverter data is the most easily accessible dataset for O&M purposes. However, for performance analysis in O&M, input data such as irradiance and temperature must also be collected.
- In addition, abnormal values may occur due to data collected during the MPPT process, inverter shutdowns, or restarts, which are not measured under steady-state conditions.
- Since training data containing such abnormal values reduces the reliability of the model, this study applied a data preprocessing method to remove outliers.
- The machine learning model trained with the preprocessed data achieved excellent performance, with R^2 values of 0.9666 (voltage) and 0.9987 (current).
- Furthermore, future work will focus on fault diagnosis by analyzing performance through comparison between measured and inferred values using the trained model.

This work was conducted under the framework of the research and development program of the Korea Institute of Energy Research (Project No: C5-2427) and was supported by the Korea Environmental Industry and Technology Institute (Project No: C5-6707).

Application of Multivariate Data Analysis and NIR Spectroscopy in Evaluating PV System Performance and Packaging Degradation

B. A. Belferkous[1], C. Barretta[1], G. Oviedo Hernandez[2], L. Koester[3], G. Oreski[1,4]

[1] Polymer Competence Center Leoben GmbH (PCCL), Sauraugasse 1, 8700 Leoben, Austria – brahim.anis.belferkous@pccl.at
[2] BayWa r.e. Operation Services S.r.l., 00139 Rome, Italy
[3] Eurac Research, 39100 Bolzano, Italy
[4] Chair of Material Science and Testing of Polymers, Montanuniversitaet Leoben, 8700 Leoben, Austria

PCCL
Polymer Competence Center Leoben

INTRODUCTION AND OBJECTIVES

The operational performance of photovoltaic (PV) systems is impacted by the degradation of their packaging materials. Such degradation manifests through both visible and invisible phenomena, including corrosion, micro-cracking, macro-cracking, delamination, discoloration, and so on [1, 2].

Non destructive testing combined with multivariate data analysis (MVDA) such as Principal Component Analysis (PCA) and Uniform Manifold Approximation and Projection (UMAP), are remarkably more effective at detecting early stage degradation of Bill of Materials (BOMs), making it a valuable combination for evaluating PV system performance.

The aim of the study is to:

- Identify the BOMs of PV modules with unknown compositions through the application of Near Infrared (NIR) spectroscopy.
- Detecting signs of material degradation.

EXPERIMENTAL

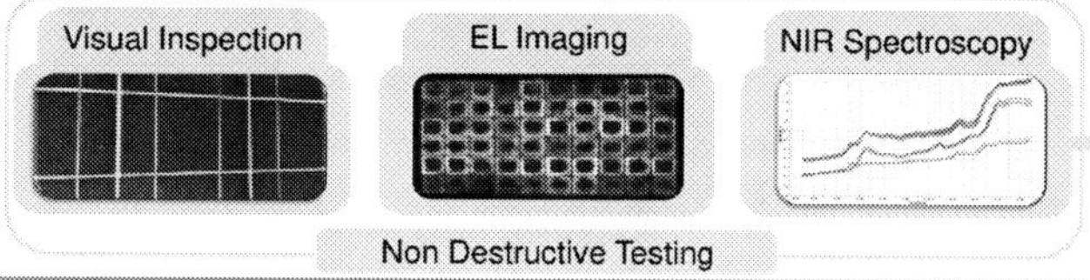

NIR Spectroscopy

- ❖ Potential for automation.
- ❖ Rapid response time.
- ❖ Detecting material property changes.
- ❖ Complementary to visual inspection and Electroluminescence (EL).
- ❖ Suitability for field deployment.
- ❖ Determining BOM composition.

12 modules, installed in 2011

The modules showed encapsulant discoloration, backsheet cracks, corrosion, delamination, etc.

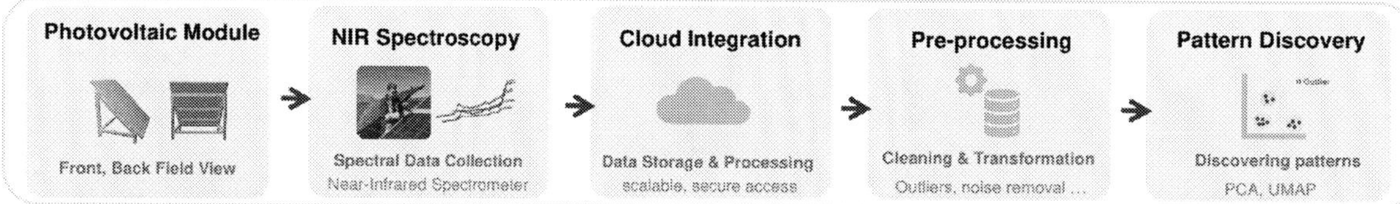

RESULTS AND DISCUSSION

ENCAPSULANT

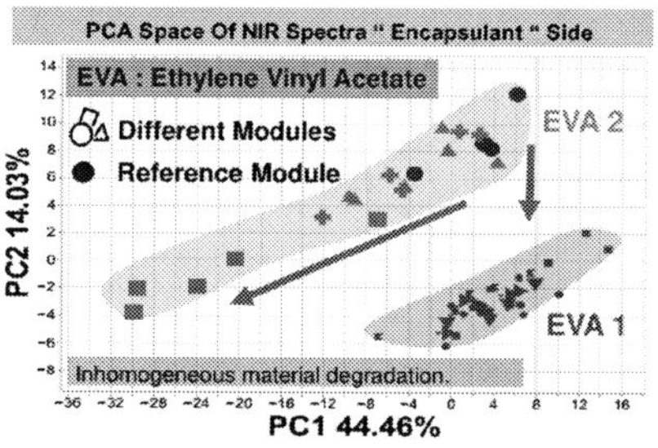

- ❖ Data shows notable **differences between** the Reference (**unexposed**) and **exposed** modules.
- ❖ **Differences** between **encapsulants types** (EVA 1 and EVA 2) due to **non-uniform additives**, identifies variations in material authenticity.
- ❖ **UMAP** was used alongside PCA as it provided **clearer and tighter clustering** of EVA 1 and EVA 2.
- ❖ **UMAP** can **uncover complex**, non-linear **patterns** in the data that **PCA might overlook**.

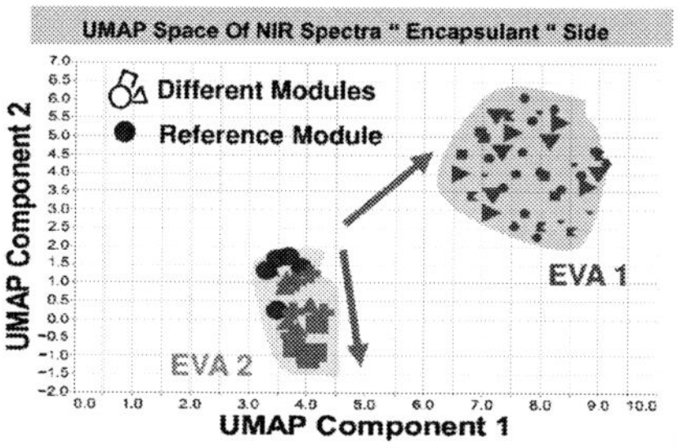

PC Loadings interpretation / additive composition

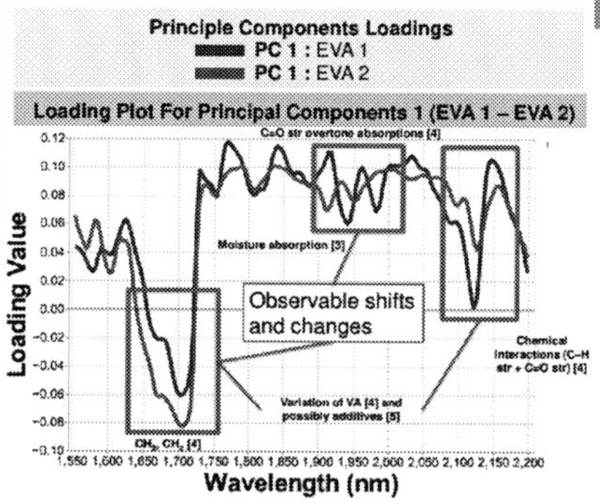

- ❖ **PC1: EVA 1 vs EVA 2** differ mainly in the region between 1600 and 1750 nm and in the region between 2000 and 2200 nm, most associated with **VA content** [4, 6], also confirmed by FTIR ATR spectroscopy.
- ❖ **PC2:** Amplitudes and sign of the peaks and valleys are very different for most wavelengths.
- ❖ Differences relate to **vinyl acetate content** and **chemical structure (including additives).**
- ❖ **Most attention** on **PC1** for the main conclusions, **PC2** to interpret secondary trends with **limited** additional **information.**

Thermal Desorption Gas Chromatography coupled to Mass Spectrometry (TD-GC/MS)

Additives	EVA 1	EVA 2
Antioxidant	None	Butylated hydroxytoluene
UV absorber	2-Hydroxy-4-n-octyloxybenzophenone	2-hydroxy-4-methoxy benzophenone
Light stabilizer (HALS)	Bis(2,2,6,6-tetramethyl-4-piperidyl) sebacate	

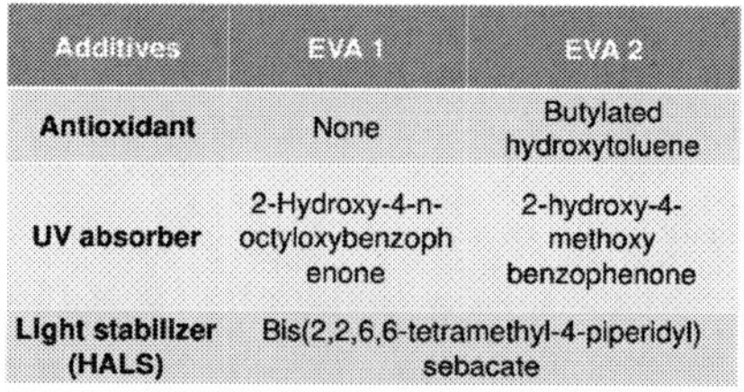

EVA 2 has more VA

CONCLUSIONS AND OUTLOOK

- ❖ **NIR** spectroscopy is highly **effective and rapid** in detecting material changes.
- ❖ **Non uniform BOM** structures for both **encapsulant** and **back-sheet** materials.
- ❖ PCA and UMAP provide complementary views of high-dimensional NIR data PCA shows variance trends, **UMAP improves cluster separation**.
- ❖ **Loadings plot** differences, reinforcing that the encapsulants types are **distinguishable through NIR & MVDA analysis.**

❑ Integrating PV performance metrics Data.
❑ Predictive modelling for material performance.

REFERENCES
[1] [illegible]
[2] [illegible]
[3] [illegible]
[4] [illegible]
[5] [illegible]
[6] [illegible]

ORCID ID

Learn more at 3AV.2.25

SUPERNOVA
supernova-pv.eu
Co-funded by the European Union

The work was carried out within the project SUPERNOVA, co-funded by the European Union under Horizon Europe Grant Agreement No 101146883. Views and opinions expressed are however those of the author(s) only and do not necessarily reflect those of the European Union or CINEA. Neither the European Union nor the granting authority can be held responsible for them.

AUTOMATED IDENTIFICATION OF OPEN CIRCUITS IN PHOTOVOLTAIC ARRAYS VIA MASK-RCNN, THERMOGRAPHIC SIGNAL PROCESSING AND HYBRIDIZED REGION-GROWTH ALGORITHMS

Daniel J. Castillo Patton*, Lucas Viani, Mario Martínez González, Sergio Suárez Sánchez, Fernando García, Sofía Rodríguez-Conde, José Manuel Rivas Rodríguez
Enertis Applus+, Parque Empresarial Las Mercedes, C/ de Campezo, 1, 28022 Madrid, Spain
Carlos III University of Madrid, Av. de la Universidad, 30, 28911 Leganés, Madrid, Spain
*e-mail: daniel.castillo.p@enertisapplus.com

ABSTRACT: We present a hybrid workflow for the automated detection of open circuits (*open strings*) in utility-scale photovoltaic (PV) plants using aerial infrared thermography. The approach combines three stages: (i) module localization via instance segmentation to delineate each panel, (ii) temperature profiling to compute per-module statistics and identify gradient breaks along strings, and (iii) a region-propagation algorithm that expands from anomalous seeds to recover entire strings, even when occlusions or partial detection errors occur. This design ensures robustness under heterogeneous environmental conditions and does not rely exclusively on large training datasets. The system outputs both quantitative indicators (per-module temperature profiles and string-level labels) and qualitative evidence (binary masks and annotated thermal images), enabling scalable fault localization across thousands of modules. Validation on multiple PV plants demonstrates consistent performance, with accurate detection of open strings, reduced false positives compared to purely deep-learning approaches, and processing times compatible with large-scale aerial inspections.

1 INTRODUCTION

Photovoltaic (PV) generation has grown explosively over the past decade, with global installed capacity expected to surpass 1.5 TW by the mid-2020s, playing a central role in the transition to renewable, emission-free energy [1]. Yet, this growth is still accompanied by significant production losses caused by operational defects, material degradation, shading, soiling, and electrical faults, which can reduce expected yield by 10–25% according to recent studies [2].

Among these faults, open circuits at cell, module, or string level are particularly critical: they interrupt current flow, cause immediate performance losses, and may trigger secondary defects (e.g., overheating in redistributed module areas) if undetected [3]. Given the scale of modern PV plants—millions of modules spread across large sites—and the variability of environmental conditions, manual inspection is impractical and error-prone.

Deep learning has therefore become a cornerstone for automating defect detection in aerial thermography. Lightweight CNNs provide efficient fault recognition, while hybrid models have validated the inclusion of open-circuit detection among multiple defect classes, achieving accuracy levels above 99% in certain tasks [4].

Building on these advances, this work proposes a hybrid workflow that integrates deep-learning-based module segmentation, temperature profiling, and a novel region-propagation strategy. The goal is to provide a robust and scalable system for automated open-circuit detection at string level, reducing energy losses, enabling predictive maintenance, and improving operational efficiency in utility-scale PV plants.

2 RELATED WORKS

2.1 Module detection and segmentation with deep learning

Reliable module localization is the first step toward diagnosing open strings. Two dominant families exist: bounding-box detectors (e.g., YOLO variants) and semantic/instance segmentation models applied to RGB/TIR aerial imagery. In PV applications, YOLO-based detectors trained with domain-specific datasets have reached high precision and recall (e.g., ST-YOLO [5]), while segmentation approaches such as Mask2Former have demonstrated accurate delineation of modules in heterogeneous aerial and satellite imagery [6], supported by curated datasets of very high resolution [7]. Collectively, recent reviews confirm that DL has become the standard for module and defect detection, with growing deployment in UAV-based and semi-automated O&M workflows [8].

2.2 Thermography and open-string detection

An open string manifests as a group of modules with uniformly elevated thermal signatures compared to adjacent strings, reflecting abnormal dissipation and lack of power delivery. This phenomenon is well documented in field thermography [3], and aerial IR inspections (aIRT) have been validated as effective for detecting string-level anomalies in utility-scale plants [4,9]. Technical literature (IEA-PVPS Task 13, IEC TS 62446-3, and subsequent reviews [1,10,11]) establishes the link between thermal patterns and electrical failure modes (open, short, mismatch, PID, shading), supporting workflows that combine: module segmentation, string-level aggregation, and thermal classification to distinguish open strings from other anomalies.

2.3 Tracking systems and yield impact

Single and dual-axis trackers improve energy yield by 10–25% compared to fixed-tilt systems, with further gains in bifacial configurations [12,13,14]. However, tracker

10.4229/EUPVSEC2025/4CV.1.15
020326-001

performance depends on proper string operation: even isolated open strings can offset expected yield and affect the levelized cost of electricity (LCOE). Best-practice reports (IEA-PVPS, Sandia PVPMC [15,16,17]) emphasize the importance of disaggregated monitoring at string/tracker level to prioritize corrective actions. Comparative studies further highlight parasitic loads and variability of performance in tracking systems [18,19], reinforcing the need for precise and automated open-string detection.

3 METHODOLOGY

In this section, we present the proposed hybrid workflow for the automated detection of open-circuit strings in utility-scale photovoltaic (PV) plants. The approach combines deep learning–based segmentation with thermographic signal processing and a region-propagation algorithm, enabling robust performance under variable operating conditions. The workflow is designed to segment individual PV modules from aerial infrared imagery, enrich these modules with pixel-level temperature data to construct temperature profiles, identify gradient discontinuities that indicate potential open circuits, and propagate the detection across neighboring modules to delineate entire strings.

The following subsections describe each component of the methodology in detail: dataset preparation and preprocessing (3.1), module segmentation with Mask RCNN (3.2), temperature profiling (3.3), module mapping of strings (3.4), gradient break detection (3.5), and region-propagation (3.6).

3.1 Dataset and preprocessing

The dataset consists of infrared images collected by Enertis Applus+ during inspections of multiple utility-scale photovoltaic plants. These images provide an authentic source of thermal data and were deliberately selected to ensure realism and representativeness. Grounding the dataset in real field conditions rather than controlled, the proposed workflow is designed to extend beyond purely scientific experimentation and demonstrate applicability to practical PV field inspections.

Table I: Dataset for module images.

Data	Images	Objects
Solar Panel	2867	120653

In addition to its size, the dataset captures a wide spectrum of operational scenarios, including variations in irradiance, ambient temperature, and module typologies across plants. Such diversity ensures that the evaluation of the proposed workflow is not restricted to uniform or idealized cases, but instead reflects the complexity and variability encountered in real PV assets. This makes the dataset a reliable benchmark for validating automated approaches to open-circuit detection.

3.2 Module segmentation – Mask RCNN

For the first stage of the workflow, we employ a neural network dedicated to the identification of photovoltaic modules in infrared imagery. An instance segmentation architecture based on Mask R-CNN was selected for this task due to its ability to:

A. Localize objects with pixel-level precision.
B. Handle overlapping or partially occluded modules.
C. Flexible integration with downstream temperature analysis.

While alternative approaches such as YOLO-based detectors and semantic segmentation networks have been explored in the literature [20], Mask R-CNN was preferred given its superior preliminary performance on our dataset. The overall architecture of the network is illustrated in Figure 1:

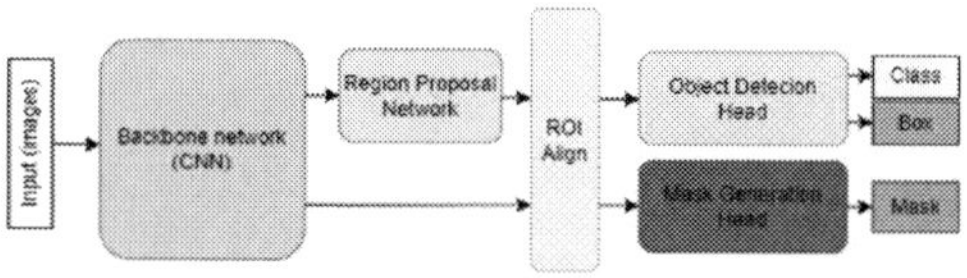

Figure 1: Basic architecture for a Mask RCNN model, showing the different steps performed to realize a segmentation.

This model was implemented using the Detectron2 library and was chosen over pure object detection approaches because instance segmentation is required to precisely delineate all pixels belonging to each module. Unlike bounding-box detectors that only provide coarse localization, instance segmentation assigns a unique mask to every object instance, enabling pixel-level analysis of thermal values within each module. This level of granularity is critical for constructing accurate temperature profiles and detecting subtle anomalies across strings. The architecture follows the Mask R-CNN framework introduced in [21].

3.2.1 Mask RCNN training

For the training stage, the model was configured with the parameter settings summarized in Table II. These settings define the backbone architecture, initialization strategy, and the most influential hyperparameters for convergence and detection accuracy:

Table II: Training selection.

	Parameters settings
Backbone	ResNet FNP
Model Weights	ImageNet MSRA R-50
Learning Rate	0.002
Anchor Generator	32, 64,128, 256
Weight Decay	1×10^{-4} (L2)
Activation Function	ReLU

The configuration follows the standard Detectron2 implementation, with ResNet-50 and FPN providing multi-scale feature extraction. Pretrained ImageNet weights were used to accelerate convergence. A base learning rate of 0.002 with L2 regularization (1×10^{-4}) was applied. Anchor scales were set to [32, 64, 128, 256], covering a wide range of receptive fields so that modules could be detected at different resolutions. In particular, smaller anchors capture distant or partially visible modules, while larger anchors allow the network to detect panels that dominate the field of view. This design ensures that the detector remains robust across images with varying ground sampling distances and module scales. All other parameters, such as ROI head structure and pooling resolutions, were kept at Detectron2's default values to ensure reproducibility and comparability with prior work.

3.2.2 Evaluation Metrics

Model performance was assessed using standard evaluation metrics widely adopted in computer vision: Precision, Recall, and the F1-score [22]. Precision (Eq. 1) quantifies the reliability of positive detections by measuring the proportion of true positives among all predicted positives, while Recall (Eq. 2) evaluates the ability of the model to recover all relevant instances. In large-scale PV inspections, maximizing Recall is particularly critical, as even a small omission rate (<1%) may correspond to thousands of undetected modules. To balance these complementary aspects, we also report the F1-score (Eq. 3), which represents the harmonic mean of Precision and Recall. This metric offers a more comprehensive assessment by penalizing both false positives and false negatives, and is especially relevant under class imbalance conditions, providing a balanced view of the model's detection capability.

$$(1)\ Precision = \frac{TP}{TP+FP}$$

$$(2)\ Recall = \frac{TP}{TP+FN}$$

$$(3)\ F1\ Score = 2 \cdot \frac{Precision \cdot Recall}{Precision+Recall}$$

Having established the evaluation metrics, we now proceed to analyze the results obtained from our experiments.

3.2.3 Evaluation Results

For model evaluation, we employed a dedicated test set that was never exposed during training. This separation guarantees that the reported metrics reflect the model's ability to generalize to previously unseen data. Presented below are the performance metrics for each class for the detection models (see Table III):

Table III: Evaluation Results for Segmentation Model.

Class	Precision	Recall	F1-Score
Solar Panel	99,98%	99,99%	99,98%

The results demonstrate promising performance, with consistently high precision and recall values. While perfect accuracy is not reached, the residual errors are primarily associated with rare and extreme environmental conditions, which are expected in a dataset of this scale. Figure 2 illustrates qualitative examples of the detection outputs, highlighting the ability of the model to correctly identify modules across diverse scenarios.

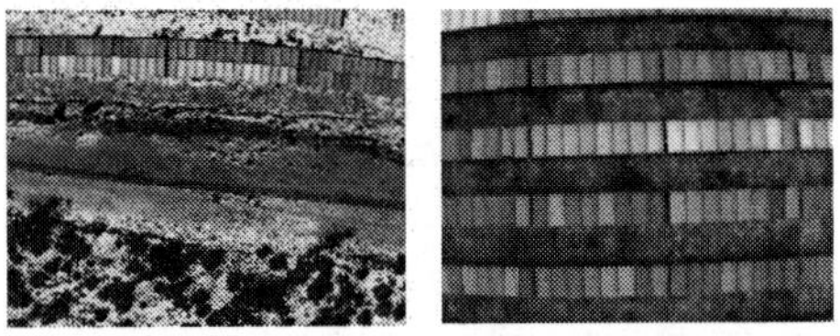

Figure 2: Illustration of the segmentation results, showing that PV modules are successfully detected in two completely different scenarios, demonstrating the robustness of the Mask R-CNN approach.

3.3 Temperature profile generation

Infrared images are first decoded to recover the true pixel-level temperature values rather than relying on the false-color visualizations typically provided by the cameras. This allows us to work directly with calibrated thermal data in degrees Celsius, ensuring that the analysis is grounded in real physical measurements rather than approximations. These arrays are then preserved in a lossless format so that no information is lost in subsequent stages of the workflow.

Figure 3: Example of an infrared frame represented with encoded pixel-level temperature values, replacing the conventional false-color colormap with the actual thermal data.

Once the temperature field is obtained, it is combined with the segmentation masks to retain only the pixels that belong to the photovoltaic modules. In practice, this means that all irrelevant background information is discarded, leaving a clean and precise temperature profile for each panel. To improve interpretability, contrast is adapted to the median values of the scene so that subtle variations become visible without being dominated by outliers. At the same time, robust statistical descriptors such as the median are extracted, providing reliable inputs for the detection of gradient changes and, ultimately, the identification of open circuits.

3.4 Module Mapping of Strings

After segmentation, modules are not analyzed in isolation but grouped into strings, understood as contiguous rows of panels arranged along the same horizontal alignment. This grouping is necessary to study collective thermal behavior, since modules placed adjacently in the same row typically exhibit similar operating conditions. Ordering them left-to-right provides a consistent spatial reference that allows temperature profiles to be compared across the entire row.

Formally, given a set of modules $M = \{m_1, m_2, \dots, m_n\}$ with centroid coordinates (x_i, y_i), modules belonging to the same string are identified by applying a tolerance on their vertical coordinates:

$$(4)\ S_k = \{m_i \in M : |y_i - \overline{y_k}| < \epsilon\}$$

Where $\overline{y_k}$ is the mean vertical position of string k and ϵ is a threshold that controls row alignment. Once grouped, each string S_k is ordered by increasing x_i:

$$(5)\ S_k^{\text{ordered}} = \text{sort}(S_k,\ \text{key} = x_i)$$

This procedure yields a sequence of modules per string, ensuring that subsequent profiling steps follow the natural spatial arrangement of the array, giving us a detailed mapping of each string:

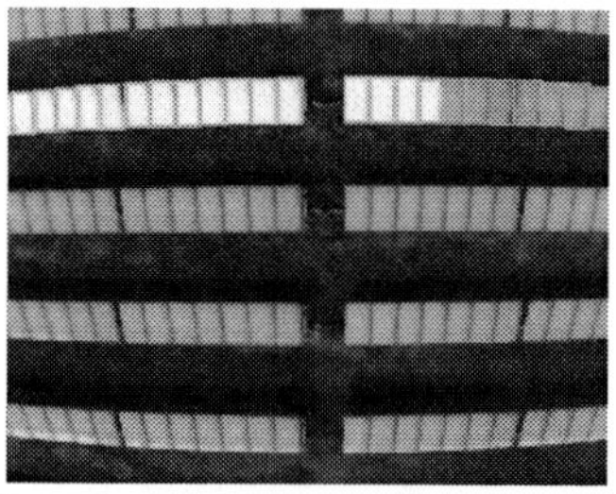

Figure 4: Example of module mapping into strings. Each module is indexed and ordered left-to-right within its row, allowing consistent profiling of the string structure

3.5 Gradient break

Once modules are grouped into ordered strings, their median temperatures are assembled into sequential profiles. Under normal conditions, these profiles remain relatively uniform, reflecting consistent thermal behavior across panels in the same row.

A gradient break is defined as a significant discontinuity in this sequence, where the temperature of one or more consecutive modules deviates abruptly from the trend of the string. Detecting such breaks allows the system to flag potential anomalies that extend beyond individual panels. Formally, given a string profile $T = \{t_1, t_2, \dots, t_n\}$, a break is identified whenever:

$$(6)\ |t_{i+1} - t_i| > \delta,$$

Where δ is an adaptive threshold that accounts for the expected thermal variability under field conditions. Figure 5 illustrates an example, where a sharp drop in temperature marks the onset of a string-level anomaly.

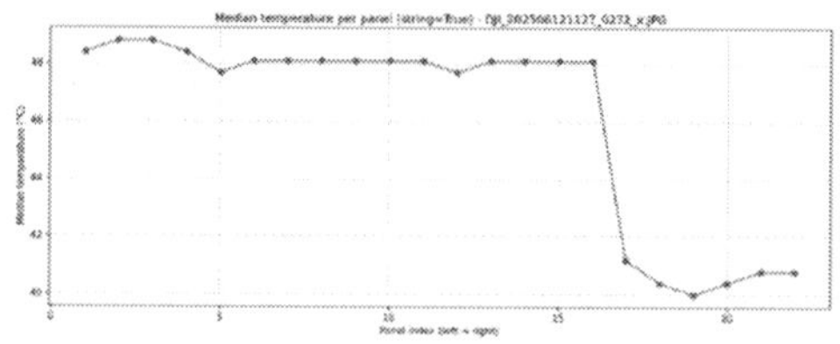

Figure 5: Median temperature profile along the modules of a single string. A sudden drop around panel 17 clearly indicates the onset of an open-circuit anomaly.

This profiling step transforms raw temperature values into an interpretable sequence, allowing anomalies to emerge clearly as deviations from the expected uniform pattern. Such representation provides a robust foundation for the subsequent region-propagation stage.

3.6 Region propagation for string propagation

In some cases, intermediate panels within a string may be missing from the profile, either due to detection failures or partial occlusions in the image. This can disrupt the continuity of the gradient-based analysis, leading to incomplete identification of the affected string.

To address this issue, we introduce a region-propagation algorithm where the basic units are not pixels but entire modules. Starting from the panels identified at the gradient break, the method iteratively extends the region to neighboring modules that share consistent thermal behavior. In this way, missing or occluded panels are incorporated into the open-circuit group, ensuring that the resulting string remains complete and representative of the underlying fault.

$$(7)\ R = \bigcup_{m_i \in B} \{m_j \in N(m_i) : |t_j - t_i| < \delta\}$$

Here in (Eq. 7) is where we define the region propagation step. Starting from the set B of modules identified at the gradient break, the algorithm expands the region by including neighboring modules $m_j \in N(m_i)$ whenever their median temperature t_j is sufficiently similar to that of the seed module t_i, with the similarity controlled by a threshold δ. The union operator ensures that all propagated neighbors are aggregated into a single contiguous region R, thereby recovering panels that may have been missed due to occlusion or detection errors.

4 USE CASE RESULTS

To illustrate the complete workflow, we present a representative case where the methodology is applied step by step until the final open-string detection is obtained. Each stage is shown in the figures below, with its corresponding explanation.

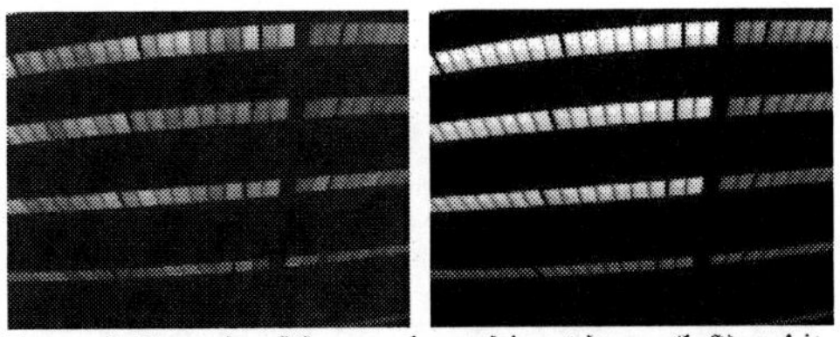

Figure 6. Example of the raw thermal input image (left) and its corresponding segmentation mask of detected modules (right). These provide the basis for subsequent analysis and allow the extraction of per-panel temperature values.

Once the modules are segmented, the system computes the median temperature of each panel along the string. By plotting these values sequentially, it becomes possible to identify sudden changes in the temperature profile, referred to as gradient breaks.

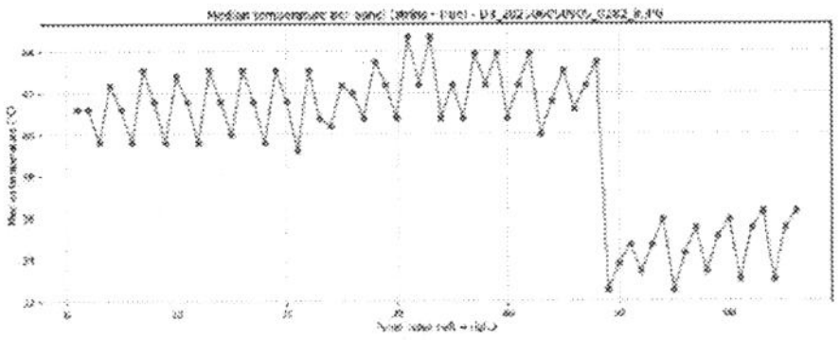

Figure 7. Temperature profile of the analyzed string. The plot reveals a sharp discontinuity that indicates the presence of an open-circuit anomaly.

Using this information, the affected region is isolated by generating a binary mask that highlights only the modules belonging to the abnormal string. This step enables precise localization of the fault while discarding unaffected modules.

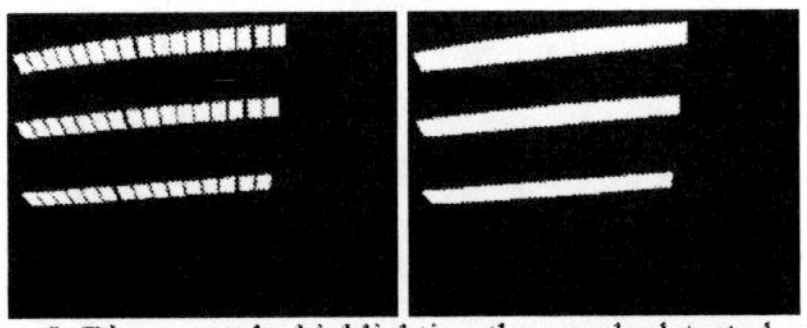

Figure 8. Binary masks highlighting the panels detected as part of the open string.

Finally, the binary masks are combined with the original thermal image, and a region-propagation algorithm is applied to ensure that all modules belonging to the same string are included—even if some were partially occluded or missed in earlier stages. This produces a complete visualization of the open-circuit defect.

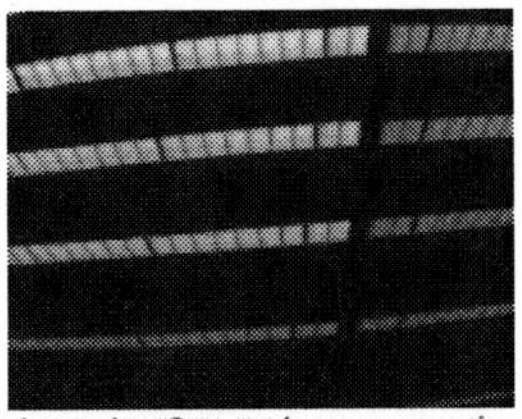

Figure 9. Final result after region propagation, showing the identified open-string modules superimposed on the original thermal image.

As shown in the final visualization, the open strings are clearly highlighted, while the panels at the far left are deliberately discarded. This exclusion is necessary because partially cropped modules at the image boundaries could otherwise lead to false positives in the analysis.

5 CONCLUSIONS AND FUTURE WORKS

This work introduced a hybrid methodology for the automated detection of open strings in utility-scale PV plants using aerial infrared thermography. By integrating module segmentation, thermal profiling, and a region-propagation algorithm, the system achieves reliable identification of string-level faults under diverse operating conditions.

Compared to purely deep-learning models, the proposed workflow reduces false positives and remains scalable to large inspection campaigns. From an operational perspective, the method provides actionable outputs that can directly support O&M strategies, enabling early fault localization and contributing to reduced energy losses. Literature reports indicate that undetected string-level faults can increase the levelized cost of electricity (LCOE) by 3–7% depending on plant topology and irradiance [23], suggesting that systematic adoption of automated detection workflows such as the one presented here can yield tangible financial benefits for asset owners.

Nonetheless, the current methodology still depends on the accuracy of the segmentation stage, which may degrade under strong occlusions or image artifacts. In addition, extreme environmental conditions (very low irradiance, rapidly changing cloud cover, or excessive wind) can distort thermal gradients and affect anomaly propagation.

Future research will therefore focus on expanding the dataset with additional climatic and technological scenarios, integrating complementary data sources (e.g., IV curves, SCADA signals, EL imaging) for cross-validation, and refining the propagation logic for cases of highly irregular degradation. Further work will also explore optimization for real-time deployment on UAV platforms, facilitating on-site decision-making during inspections.

6 REFERENCES

[1] IEA-PVPS Task 13. (2018). *Review on Infrared and Electroluminescence Imaging for PV Field Applications.* Report T13-10:2018. International Energy Agency – PVPS.

[2] Islam, M. T., Almutairi, A., & Rahman, S. (2023). *Artificial Intelligence in Photovoltaic Fault Identification and Monitoring.* Energies, 16(21), 7417. https://doi.org/10.3390/en16217417

[3] Muttillo, M., Pantoli, L., Stornelli, V., & Ferri, G. (2020). *On-Field Infrared Thermography Sensing for PV System Characterization.* Sensors, 20(21), 6051. https://doi.org/10.3390/s20216051

10.4229/EUPVSEC2025/4CV.1.15

[4] de Oliveira, A. C., Pereira, R., & Andrade, L. (2023). *Automatic fault detection of utility-scale PV power plants and physical location inside the site.* Solar Energy, 258, 124–135. https://doi.org/10.1016/j.solener.2023.01.058

[5] Xie, H., Yuan, B., Hu, C., & Chen, H. (2024). *ST-YOLO: A defect detection method for photovoltaic modules based on infrared thermal imaging and machine vision technology.* PLOS ONE, 19(12), e0310742. https://doi.org/10.1371/journal.pone.0310742

[6] García, G., Aparcedo, A., Nayak, G. K., Ahmed, T., Shah, M., & Li, M. (2024). *Generalized deep learning model for photovoltaic module segmentation from satellite and aerial imagery (Mask2Former).* Solar Energy, 274, 112539. https://doi.org/10.1016/j.solener.2024.112539

[7] Clark, M., & Pacifici, F. (2023). *A solar panel dataset of very high-resolution satellite imagery.* Scientific Data, 10, 636. https://doi.org/10.1038/s41597-023-02761-0

[8] Gallardo-Saavedra, S., Lillo-Saavedra, M., Cortés, J. A., & Peña, R. (2020). *Infrared Thermography for the Detection and Characterization of Photovoltaic Defects: Comparison between Illumination and Dark Conditions.* Sensors, 20(16), 4395. https://doi.org/10.3390/s20164395

[9] de Oliveira, A. K. V., Aghaei, M., & Rüther, R. (2020). *Aerial infrared thermography for low-cost and fast fault detection in utility-scale PV power plants.* Solar Energy, 211, 712–724. https://doi.org/10.1016/j.solener.2020.09.066

[10] IEC. (2017). *IEC TS 62446-3:2017. Photovoltaic (PV) systems – Part 3: Outdoor infrared thermography.* International Electrotechnical Commission.

[11] IEA-PVPS Task 13. (2022). *Guidelines for Operation and Maintenance of Photovoltaic Power Plants in Different Climates.* Report T13-25:2022. International Energy Agency – PVPS.

[12] Pelaez, S., Marion, B., Deline, C., & Stein, J. (2018). *Model and Validation of Single-Axis Tracking with Bifacial PV — Benefit in Addition to 15–25% vs Fixed-Tilt.* NREL/TP-5K00-72039. National Renewable Energy Laboratory.

[13] PV-Tech. (2015). *Motivation for single-axis trackers versus fixed tilt.* PVTech Power, (23), 46–51.

[14] Barbón, A., Fernández, D., & López, J. (2025). *Fixed Tilt vs. Horizontal Single-Axis Tracker: Comparative Study.* Applied Sciences, 15(8), 4571. https://doi.org/10.3390/app15084571

[15] IEA-PVPS Task 13. (2024). *Best Practices for the Optimization of Bifacial Photovoltaic Tracking Systems.* Report T13-26:2024. International Energy Agency – PVPS.

[16] IEA-PVPS / Sandia PV Performance Modeling Collaborative. (2024). *Task 13 notes on KPIs, partial shading and O&M.* Available at: https://pvpmc.sandia.gov

[17] Sandia PV Performance Modeling Collaborative. (2024). *Subsystem analysis resources and modeling guide.* Available at: https://pvpmc.sandia.gov

[18] Sadeghi, A., Moradi, M., & Hejazi, M. (2025). *Review and Comparative Analysis of Solar Tracking Systems.* Energies, 18(10), 2553. https://doi.org/10.3390/en18102553

[19] Tan, W., Li, H., & Xu, Z. (2021). *Comprehensive Methodology to Evaluate Parasitic Energy Consumption for Dual-Axis Sun-Tracking Systems.* International Journal of Photoenergy, 2021, 6654321. https://doi.org/10.1155/2021/6654321

[20] Jia, Y., Chen, G., & Zhao, L. (2024). *Defect detection of photovoltaic modules based on improved VarifocalNet.* Scientific Reports, 14, 15170. https://doi.org/10.1038/s41598-024-66234-3

[21] He, K., Gkioxari, G., Dollár, P., & Girshick, R. (2017). *Mask R-CNN.* Proceedings of the IEEE International Conference on Computer Vision (ICCV), 2961–2969. https://doi.org/10.1109/ICCV.2017.322

[22] Powers, D. M. W. (2011). *Evaluation: From Precision, Recall and F-measure to ROC, Informedness, Markedness & Correlation.* Journal of Machine Learning Technologies, 2(1), 37–63.

[23] Rivai, A., Abd Rahim, N., Mohamad Elias, M. F., & Jamaludin, J. (2020). *Analysis of Photovoltaic String Failure and Health Monitoring with Module Fault Identification. Energies*, **13**(1), 100. DOI: 10.3390/en13010100

10.4229/EUPVSEC2025/4CV.1.15
020326-006

AUTOMATED IDENTIFICATION OF OPEN CIRCUITS IN PHOTOVOLTAIC ARRAYS VIA MASK-RCNN, THERMOGRAPHIC SIGNAL PROCESSING AND HYBRIDIZED REGION-GROWTH ALGORITHMS

uc3m | Universidad Carlos III de Madrid

AMPL | Autonomous Mobility and Perception Lab

Daniel J. Castillo Patton [1*], Lucas Viani [1], Fernando García[2], Mario Martínez[1], Sergio Suárez[1], Sofía Rodríguez-Conde [1], José Manuel Rivas[1]

****email: daniel.castillo.p@applus.com***

[1] Enertis Applus S.L. – Business Development Department

[2] Autonomus Mobility and Perception Lab (AMPL), UC3M

ENERTIS Applus®

INTRODUCTION

- Open-circuit defects remain a critical source of performance loss in PV arrays.
- Infrared thermography enables fault detection, but manual analysis is unfeasible at scale.
- Conventional deep learning approaches often struggle in unseen environments or with limited data, raising a challenge in some situations.
- In this work, we propose a hybrid workflow combining segmentation, temperature profiling, and region propagation to ensure robust detection of open strings.

Detection of open circuits in PV panels

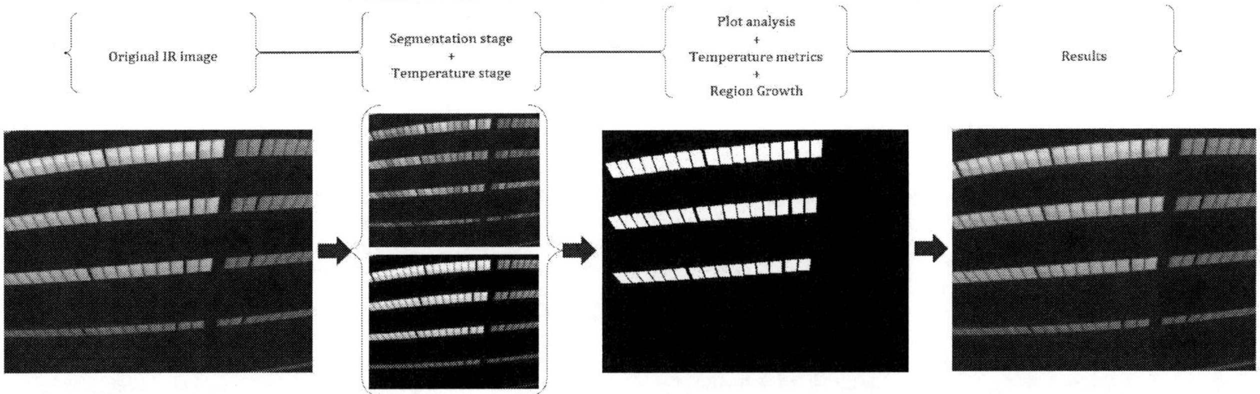

The proposed workflow is based on the combination of different technologies with the goal of automatically detecting open circuits in thermographic images. The aim of this work is to provide an alternative methodology for identifying these defects that does not rely on conventional neural networks, allowing adaptation to unfamiliar environments or situations with limited data availability.

Proposed system

Modules are segmented with Mask R-CNN and enriched with pixel-level temperature data to generate profiles that reveal gradient changes along strings. A region-growing algorithm then merges neighboring panels, enabling full open-circuit string detection.

Module mapping of strings

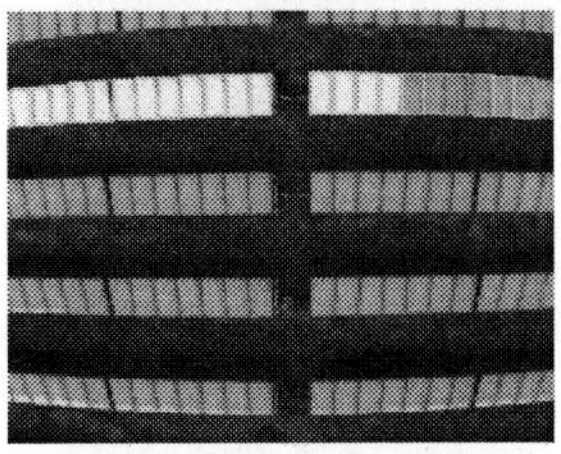

Identifying each module individually allows us to calculate temperatures per panel and then group them to analyze string-level behavior.

This approach provides a clearer view of how local anomalies propagate across the string.

Region-propagation of panels

After detecting a gradient break in the temperature profile, neighboring modules with similar values are propagated in the similar series value, ensuring physically separated panels and intermediate anomalies are included in the open string.

Conclusions

- Hybrid workflow with segmentation, temperature profiling and region-propagation detects open circuits without large datasets.
- Robust across environmental conditions, outperforming purely deep-learning approaches.
- Scalable for automated PV inspections, enabling faster fault detection and reduced energy losses.

Deep Learning Model – Mask RCNN

Modules are segmented using a Mask R-CNN, providing individual identification for each panel.

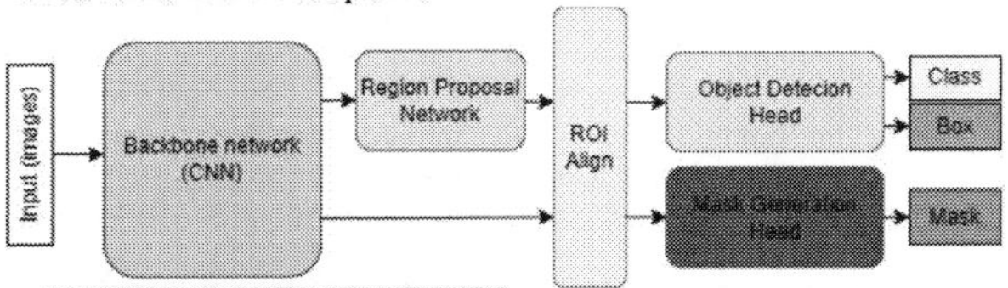

Temperature profiling

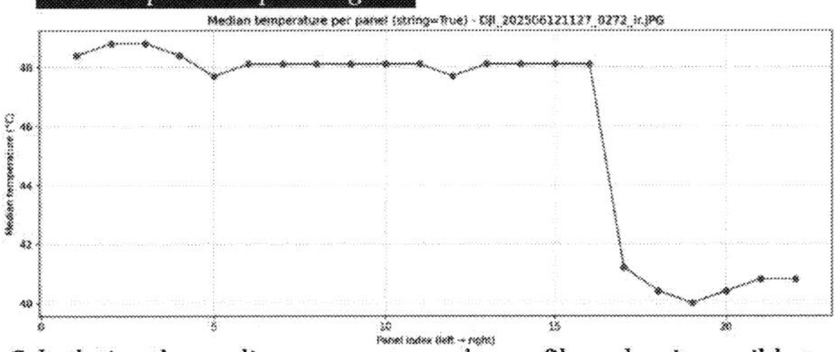

Calculating the median temperature, the profile makes it possible to observe uniform sections as well as sudden drops or shifts that indicate anomalies in the temperature behavior of the string.

References

- El-Banby, G. M., Moawad, N. M., Abouzalm, B. A., Abouzaid, W. F., & Ramadan, E. A. (2023). *Photovoltaic system fault detection techniques: a review.* Neural Computing and Applications, 35, 24829-24842. https://doi.org/10.1007/s00521-023-09041-7
- Jia, Y., Chen, G., & Zhao, L. (2024). *Defect detection of photovoltaic modules based on improved VarifocalNet.* Scientific Reports, 14, 15170. https://doi.org/10.1038/s41598-024-66234-3

UNDERPERFORMANCE OF PV PLANTS. AN ANALYSIS IN OVER 3.3GW

Quiroz, Mónica and Solórzano, Jorge
Qualifying Photovoltaics S.L., 102 Caleruega Street, 10th Floor. 28033 Madrid, Spain.
Tel.: +34 644 72 51 74
m.quiroz@qpv.es, j.solorzano@qpv.es

ABSTRACT: The rapid growth of solar energy and shrinking project margins highlight the need to optimize photovoltaic (PV) plant operation and maintenance (O&M). However, a growing number of installations show deviations between expected and actual production, jeopardizing profitability. This paper presents results from the PhotoVoltaics Evaluation Tool (PVET), developed by Qualifying Photovoltaics S.L. (QPV), applied to over 3.3GW of peak capacity PV plants and 4.2 GW.year of operational data. PVET performs real-time monitoring, data filtering, and in-depth analysis; considering irradiance, module temperature, and electrical performance. Recurrent operational failures—such as inverter shutdowns, tracking failures, open strings, etc—were identified, causing annual energy losses of 1–3% and up to 7.9% in critical cases. Non-recoverable losses, such as grid restrictions, were also identified. PVET's filtering module enhances fault detection, quantifies energy losses more accurately, and mitigates biases in production assessments. Results demonstrate that advanced data-driven diagnostic tools in PV O&M enable significant loss reduction, improve system reliability and increase project profitability, thus supporting large-scale solar deployment.

Keywords: Photovoltaics Failures, O&M, Failures, Big Data.

1 INTRODUCTION

As the need to mitigate emissions and address climate change becomes more urgent, solar energy plays an increasingly decisive role in the international energy matrix. The solar industry is experiencing continuous growth, having surpassed 2 TW of global installed capacity, with expectations to reach 3.5 TW by 2027. [1]

Due to the rapid evolution of the sector and the reduction in project costs and economic margins, optimizing the operation, performance, and maintenance (O&M) of photovoltaic systems is presented as a critical challenge and a key element for their long-term sustainability. However, plant productivity often falls short of expectations. According to the Solar Risk Assessment 2025 by kWh Analytics, published as part of their industry report series, PV plants underperform against P50 expectations by an average of 8.6%, confirming a persistent gap between financial models and real-world production. [2]

Our internal analyses estimate that recurrent operational failures can account for up to 7.9% of annual energy production losses. These losses are mainly associated with inverter shutdowns, open strings, other system-level malfunctions and external factors. Their magnitude, however, is not uniform: it varies depending on the geographical location of the plant, the presence or absence of solar tracking systems, and the availability and reliability of the local power grid. To systematically address these challenges and reduce their impact, Qualifying Photovoltaics S.L. has developed the PhotoVoltaics Evaluation Tool (PVET), an advanced analytics platform designed to detect, classify, and quantify failures across diverse PV portfolios.

2 PVET

2.1 Function

The primary objective of PVET is to serve as an automated analysis tool designed to optimize the performance of photovoltaic (PV) plants. This is achieved by improving the accuracy of initial estimates and enhancing Operations and Maintenance (O&M) tasks, thereby reducing losses and increasing profitability.

PVET operates through four integrated stages. First. SCADA monitoring collects real-time data on irradiance, temperature, current, voltage, and other key variables from plant sensors. This information is then securely transmitted and centralized in the PVET Cloud. Next, data filtering algorithms remove incomplete or inconsistent records, ensuring reliable inputs for analysis. Finally, advanced data analytics are applied to detect, diagnose, and quantify failures across the plant's operation.

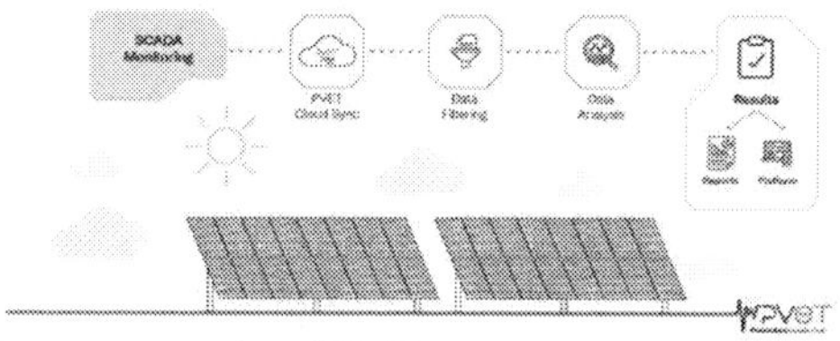

Figure 1: Operation of PVET.

2.2 Data filtering and augmentation

Reliable failure detection in PV plants requires complete and accurate data to properly evaluate device performance and ensure generation efficiency. In practice, however, communication errors or interruptions in data transmission are common, often limiting the correct assessment of the operational status of inverters, stringboxes, and trackers. To address these issues and minimize false positives. PVET integrates a dedicated data filtering and augmentation module.

Data filtering removes incoherent or inconsistent values, ensuring that only high-quality information is used in the analysis, for example, negative irradiance values or those over 1.300 W/m2. Data augmentation complements this process by inferring and reconstructing missing values when devices are offline or data is missing—for example, when an inverter is stopped, a string or stringbox is disconnected, or a tracker has no communication with its RTU. By analyzing historical records and operational trends, QPV's algorithms generate reliable estimates for

10.4229/EUPVSEC2025/4CV.1.19

critical variables at both device and plant level. This enables more accurate identification of inverter stops, open strings, or tracker malfunctions, enhancing the robustness of performance analysis.

Applying this method to the plant portfolio revealed significant differences. Table VI summarizes these results, demonstrating that inverter-related losses increased from 12.4 GWh to 24.3 GWh after data augmentation, representing a difference of +96%. Similarly, tracker-related losses increased from 46.8 GWh to 53.0 GWh, corresponding to a +12% difference. These findings confirm that raw datasets tend to underestimate the actual impact of operational failures, whereas data augmentation reveals hidden losses with greater accuracy.

Table I: Comparison of inverter- and tracker-related losses before and after data augmentation.

Category	Losses (GWh)	Losses _ Augmentation (GWh)	% of Difference
Inverter	12.4	24.3	96
Tracker	46.8	53.0	12

2.3 Failure detection, diagnosis and quantification algorithms

PVET employs advanced algorithms to detect, diagnose, and quantify failures that affect PV plant performance across all operational levels. At the plant level, external factors such as grid restrictions can be identified; at the inverter level, shutdowns, overheating, or curtailments are detected; at the stringbox level, disconnected strings and imbalances are revealed; and at the tracker level, misalignments and tracking errors are monitored where applicable.

The system not only identifies failures but also quantifies the associated energy losses, providing precise estimates that can be used for performance assessment or claims. Tested in real PV plants. PVET's algorithms have demonstrated false positive rates below 1%. ensuring reliability in operational environments. In addition, the module is capable of diagnosing, evaluating, and predicting performance anomalies by distinguishing between data acquisition errors, generation failures, and predictive indicators of malfunction.

3 QUANTIFICATIONS OF FAILURES AND LOSSES

The study analyzed 37 photovoltaic (PV) plants from QPV's portfolio, totaling 3.2 GW of installed capacity and 4.2 GW.year of operational data. This metric converts installed capacity and operation time into an annual power equivalent, allowing for consistent comparison across plants, even when their operational periods differ. Table II summarizes the key characteristics of the evaluated plants.

Table II: PV plants analyzed by continent and installed peak power.

Continent	Number of Plants	Total Peak Power (MWp)
Africa	3	189
Oceania	1	429
Europe	14	597
North America	7	755
South America	12	1332

Among these, 18 plants are equipped with trackers, while 19 operate without tracking systems.

3.1 Recoverable and Non-Recoverable Failures

To achieve a more accurate assessment of failures in photovoltaic plants, a classification into two main categories is proposed: recoverable failures and non-recoverable failures. These failures are detected through QPV's proprietary algorithms and are described below.

3.1.1 Recoverable failures

These failures are production losses that can be mitigated through timely O&M interventions. With effective monitoring platforms such as PVET and proper maintenance execution, these energy losses can be recovered. Typical recoverable failures relate to O&M efficiency, equipment condition, control system performance, or components requiring calibration or replacement. Early detection plays a crucial role in minimizing their impact on energy generation. Table III presents this classification, organized into three categories according to the affected device.

Table III: Recoverable failures.

Category	Recoverable Failures
Inverter	Inverter stop, MPPT failure, MPPT temperature and MPPT VDC
Generator	Open string, open stringbox, defective string and defective diode
Tracker	Tracking stop, misalignment, flag position, target position error and wind alarm

3.1.2 Non-Recoverable failures

Non-recoverable failures are beyond the scope of O&M and originate from external factors or inherent design limitations. Table III summarizes these failures in two categories: grid and inverter. Among them, grid-related failures have the greatest impact, as they represent the most significant share of energy losses.

Table IV: Non-Recoverable failures.

Category	Non-Recoverable Failures
Grid	Grid constrictions, grid shutdown and grid saturation
Inverter	Saturation

3.2 Results

The total production reached 8,299 GWh, with 3.8% attributed to non-recoverable losses, 2.6% to recoverable

10.4229/EUPVSEC2025/4CV.1.19

losses, and an additional 1.5% from other factors such as vegetation, soiling, and excessive module degradation. These results highlight the importance of considering all three categories of losses when assessing operational performance and profitability. Non-recoverable failures represent permanently lost energy, primarily caused by grid-related constraints, and thus remain an unavoidable limitation that directly reduces the maximum achievable yield of PV plants.

Table V: Overall energy production and distribution of recoverable and non-recoverable losses.

Category	Energy (GWh)	% of Total Energy Production
Total production	8,299	100
Non-Recovareble losses	326	3.8
Recoverable losses	223	2.6
Other losses	125	1.5

Table VI provides a breakdown of failures by category. Plant-level incidents, mainly related to grid restrictions, represent the largest share with 59.3% of total failures (3.8% of production). Inverter-related failures contribute 14% (0.9% of production), generator-related issues account for 15.8% (1.0% of production), while tracker failures have the lowest impact with 10.6% of failures (0.7% of production).

The results indicate that tracker-related losses are comparatively smaller in the mixed portfolio than in plants composed exclusively of tracker-based systems. This is because the presence of non-tracking plants dilutes the overall contribution of tracker-specific issues—such as misalignment, wind alarms, or position errors—when aggregated at portfolio level. In contrast, portfolios consisting entirely of tracker-equipped plants exhibit a higher sensitivity to these operational failures, leading to a larger relative impact on total losses.

Table VI: Breakdown of operational losses by category and contribution to total energy production with and without tracker.

Category	Energy (GWh)	% of Total Failures	% of Total Energy Production
Plant	325	59.3	3.8
Inverter	76	14	0.9
Generator	87	15.8	1.0
Tracker	59	10.6	0.7

Finally, a sub-classification was performed between plants with and without trackers.

3.2.1 PV plants with tracking systems

Table VII summarizes the 18 photovoltaic plants in the study equipped with solar tracking systems. The table reports their distribution by continent, the number of installations, and the corresponding total peak power. Europe accounts for the largest number of plants with trackers, while Oceania contributes the single largest plant in terms of peak capacity.

Table VII: PV plants with tracking systems by continent and installed peak power

Continent	Number of Plants	Total Peak Power (MWp)
Oceania	1	429
Europe	9	448
North America	2	296
South America	5	252

Figure 2 illustrates the share of recoverable and non-recoverable failures across the analyzed PV plants. Non-recoverable failures account for 62.93% of total losses, while recoverable failures represent 37.07%. This distribution is largely explained by the concentration of PV plants with tracking systems in Europe, a continent where grid restrictions remain a significant challenge. In contrast, in North and South America, these restrictions are less severe, as the installed renewable capacity in terms of MW peak is comparatively lower, resulting in fewer non-recoverable losses.

According to Jäger-Waldau [3], the total installed solar photovoltaic capacity exceeded 1.6 TWp at the end of 2023, with an annual newly installed capacity of more than 420 GWp. Europe contributed over 260 GWp, North America around 170 GWp, and South America approximately 40 GWp. This indicates a significant global expansion of solar energy, with Europe contributing a substantial share. In comparison, North and South America have lower installed capacities, which may correlate with fewer grid-related restrictions and, consequently, fewer non-recoverable failures in PV plants.

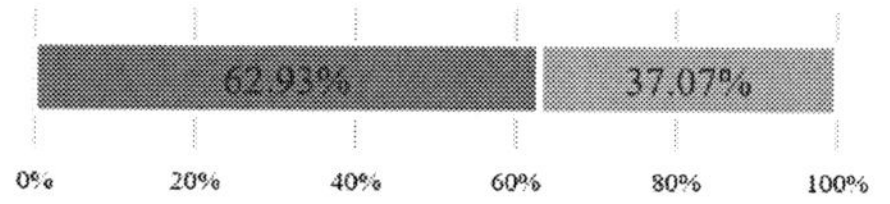

Figure 2: Distribution of recoverable and non-recoverable failures in PV plants with tracker

The presented percentages of recoverable and non-recoverable failures represent the share of losses relative to the annual energy production of all evaluated plants. Among non-recoverable failures presented in Figure 3, grid-related issues are the most significant, with grid constrictions having the highest impact (5.80%), followed by grid shutdowns (0.72%) and grid saturation (0.26%). Inverter saturation was negligible (0.001%). These results highlight the structural influence of grid availability on PV plant performance, in contrast to equipment-level failures.

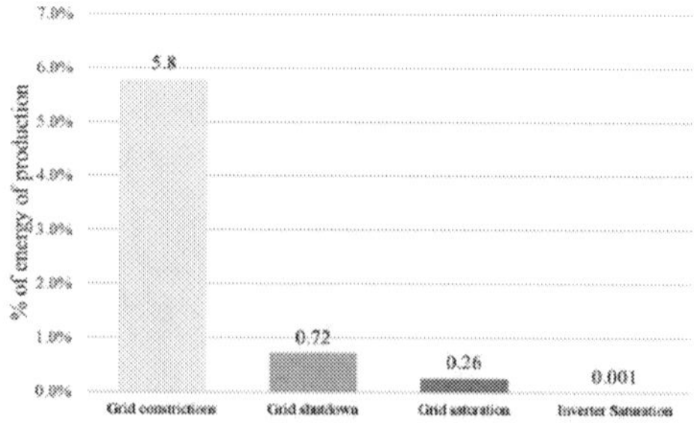

10.4229/EUPVSEC2025/4CV.1.19
020328-003

Figure 3: Distribution of non-recoverable failures in PV plants with tracker.

In contrast, of recoverable failures, the most frequent events are inverter stops (1.2%), misalignment (1.1%), open strings (0.8%). and open stringboxes (0.5%). Additional recoverable issues include tracking stops (0.3%), flag position errors (0.2%), MPPT failures (0.06%), and other minor failures (0.13%) like defective strings, defective diodes, target position error, wind alarm, MPPT Temperature and MPPT VDC.

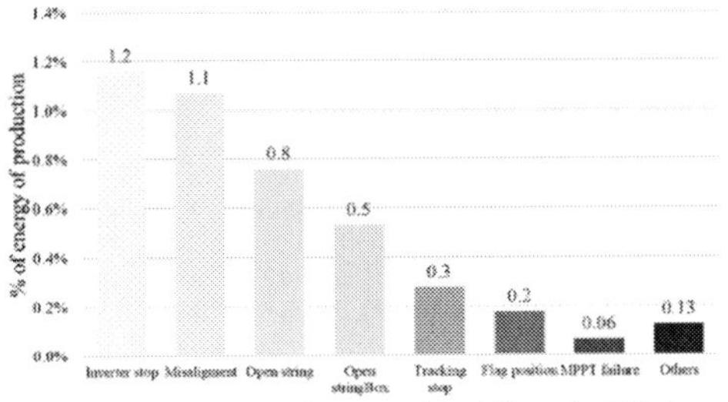

Figure 4: Distribution of recoverable failures in PV plants with tracker.

Table VIII presents the breakdown of operational losses in plants equipped with trackers. Plant-level incidents, mostly related to grid restrictions, dominate with 63% of total failures, representing 6.7% of annual energy production. Inverter and generator failures contribute similarly, each accounting for around 12% of failures (≈1.3% of production). Tracker-specific issues, such as misalignment or wind alarms, represent 14% of failures, with an impact of 1.5% on production. Overall, these results confirm that grid-related restrictions remain the primary structural limitation, while tracker-related losses, although smaller, are still relevant in portfolios fully dependent on tracking systems.

Table VIII: Breakdown of operational losses by category and contribution to total energy production with tracker

Category	Energy (GWh)	% of Total Failures	% of Total Energy Production
Plant	272	63	6.7
Inverter	59	11	1.3
Generator	52	12	1.3
Tracker	59	14	1.5

3.2.2 PV plants without tracker

Table IX summarizes the 19 photovoltaic plants analyzed in this study that operate without solar tracking systems. Their distribution across countries shows variability in the number of installations and installed peak power. Notably, South America accounts for the highest installed capacity 1,044 MWp while Europe contributes the smallest share with 148 MWp. This heterogeneity reflects different deployment strategies across regions, where countries with high solar resources but lower grid saturation tend to host larger non-tracking systems.

Table IX: PV plants without tracking systems by continent and installed peak power

Continent	Number of Plants	Total Peak Power (MWp)
Africa	3	189
Europe	5	148
North America	5	459
South America	6	1044

Figure 5 illustrates the distribution of failures in these plants. In contrast to plants equipped with tracking systems, recoverable failures dominate with 53.77% of total losses, while non-recoverable failures account for 46.23%. This distribution suggests that non-tracking plants face a higher proportion of faults that can be mitigated through O&M interventions, such as inverter stops and open strings, which represent major opportunities for performance recovery. Just like in plants with trackers, non-recoverable failures in these plants are mainly linked to grid limitations, although their relative impact is lower than in countries with high renewable penetration such as Europe.

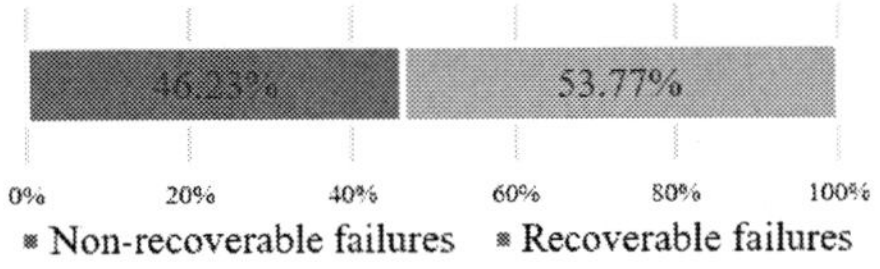

Figure 5: Distribution of recoverable and non-recoverable failures in PV plants without tracker.

Non-recoverable failures are mainly related to grid limitations, with grid constrictions representing 0.9%, grid shutdowns 0.2%, and grid saturation 0.1%. Inverter saturation contributes only marginally 0.004%.

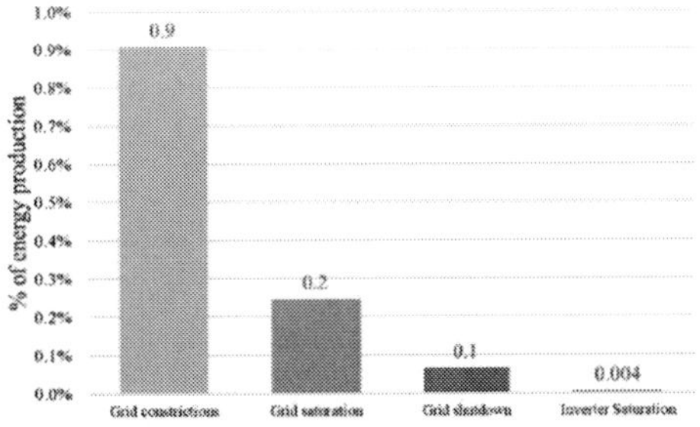

Figure 6: Distribution of non-recoverable failures in PV plants with tracker.

On the other hand, of recoverable failures, the most common events are open strings (0.69%) and inverter stops (0.59%), which together represent the majority of recoverable issues. Additional failures include open stringboxes (0.07%), MPPT failures (0.03%), defective diodes (0.02%), defective strings (0.01%), and other minor issues (0.01%).

10.4229/EUPVSEC2025/4CV.1.19
020328-004

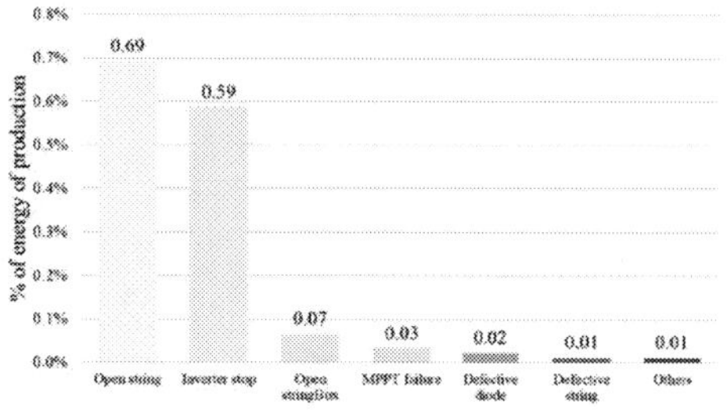

Figure 7: Distribution of recoverable failures in PV plants without tracker.

Table X summarizes the breakdown of operational losses in plants without trackers. Plant-level incidents, mainly linked to grid restrictions, account for 46% of total failures, corresponding to 1.2% of annual production. Inverter-related issues represent 24% of failures (0.6% of production), while generator failures contribute 30% (0.8% of production). Compared to plants with trackers, the overall impact of losses is lower, particularly at the plant level, reflecting reduced exposure to tracker-specific issues and a more balanced distribution of failures across components.

Table X: Breakdown of operational losses by category and contribution to total energy production without tracker

Category	Energy (GWh)	% of Total Failures	% of Total Energy Production
Plant	54	46	1.2
Inverter	28	24	0.6
Generator	35	30	0.8

Overall, the comparison between plants with and without trackers shows that tracker plants are more exposed to additional recoverable failures, but these can be better quantified through data augmentation. Conversely, in plants without trackers, recoverable failures dominate and represent a major opportunity for O&M-driven mitigation.

4 DEVIATIONS FROM INITIAL EXPECTATIONS

The PV plant operational chain illustrates how resource availability, environmental conditions, and equipment performance contribute to deviations from initial yield expectations. In the first assessment, based on raw measurements, global horizontal irradiation (GHI) presented a deviation of –7.4%, partially offset by a gain of +3.1% in the global tilted irradiation (GTI). However, after applying data filtering and removing incorrectly measured values, the results converged to more consistent deviations of –2.0% for GHI and –2.3% for GTI.

Figure 8 shows the loss chain using unfiltered irradiance values, while Figure 9 illustrates the loss chain after data filtering. The comparison between both figures highlights the importance of data preprocessing: filtering reduces uncertainty, corrects measurement errors, and provides a more reliable basis for assessing PV plant performance and expected production gaps.

Beyond irradiance corrections, global effective irradiation (GEI), which accounts for module spectral and reflection losses, showed a deviation of –1.1%. Temperature effects were also unfavorable, with an additional loss of –0.8%. The combined deviation of irradiance and temperature resources, relative to initial expectations, reached –3.9%. At the equipment level, inverters and generators contributed –0.9% and –1.0% losses, respectively, while trackers added another –0.7%. Additional factors such as soiling, vegetation, and excessive module degradation accounted for 1.5%, while grid-level restrictions contributed –3.8%. Altogether, operational losses amounted to –7.9% of expected production.

When combined with the irradiance and temperature deviations, the total underperformance reached –11.9% compared to initial expectations. These results highlight two key insights: (i) initial yield assessments tend to be systematically optimistic, and (ii) resource variability and equipment underperformance remain the dominant contributors to energy gaps. Incorporating these deviations into predictive models and long-term planning can significantly improve risk assessment, strengthen forecasting accuracy, and ultimately ensure more resilient investment strategies for large-scale PV deployment.

Figure 8: Loss chain without filtering data of GHI and GTI.

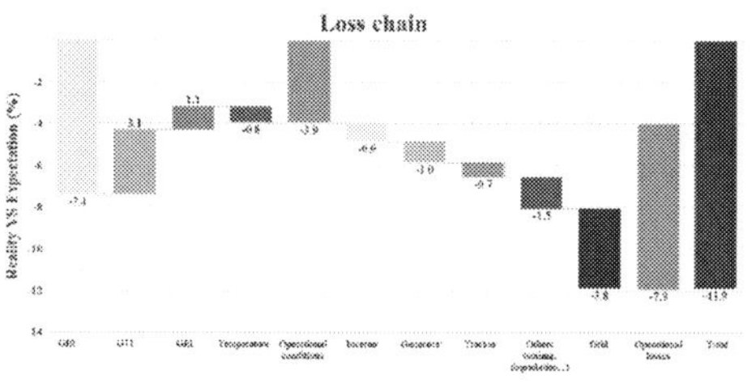

Figure 9: Loss chain with filtering data of GHI and GTI.

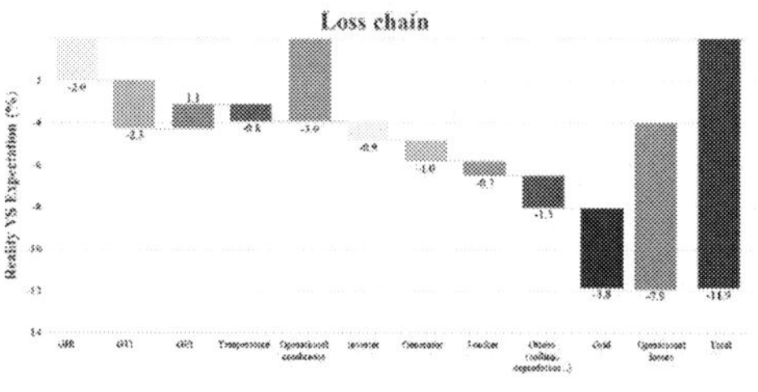

5 CONCLUSIONS

The analysis provides a detailed understanding of energy losses and performance deviations in utility-scale PV portfolios. Recoverable failures, such as inverter stoppages, MPPT issues, generator string faults, and tracker misalignments, represent around 2.6% of annual production losses and can be mitigated through timely O&M interventions supported by monitoring platforms like PVET, emphasizing the value of proactive maintenance.

Non-recoverable failures, accounting for approximately 3.8% of annual losses, are mainly caused by grid restrictions, shutdowns, and inverter saturation. This highlights the importance of considering regional grid conditions when planning new PV projects.

The use of data filtering and augmentation enhanced

failure detection by removing erroneous measurements, normalizing missing operational periods, and uncovering previously hidden recoverable losses. This approach allows for better-informed O&M strategies and contributes to improving plant reliability and profitability.

Performance deviations were primarily driven by solar resource variability and generator performance. Efficiency and temperature effects provided only a partial offset to these losses. On average, actual production was 11.9% below expectations, 3.9% from lower-than-expected available resource and 7.9% coming from operational losses.

Overall, combining failure classification, data augmentation, and analysis of performance deviations provides a comprehensive framework for optimizing PV portfolio operations. This approach not only supports targeted maintenance and energy recovery but also guides strategic planning to maximize reliability and economic performance across diverse geographic regions.

6 ACKNOWLEDGEMENTS

The authors gratefully acknowledge the financial support provided by the Institute for Energy Diversification and Saving (IDAE), within the framework of the Recovery, Transformation and Resilience Plan – funded by the European Union – Next Generation EU, under grant agreement PR-NMN-01-2023-000162. The authors also wish to thank Qualifying Photovoltaics (QPV) for granting access to the portfolio data and for their collaboration, which made this research possible.

7 REFERENCES

[1] Raptor Maps. (2025). 2025 Global Solar Report: The State of PV Performance. https://raptormaps.com/solar-tech-docs/global-solar-report-2025

[2] kWh Analytics, "Solar Risk Assessment 2025," Industry Report, San Francisco, CA, USA, 2025. Accessed: Sept. 20, 2025: https://www.kwhanalytics.com/solar-risk-assessment

[3] A. Jäger-Waldau, "Snapshot of Photovoltaics February 2024," *EPJ Photovoltaics*, vol. 15, 2024. Accessed: Sept. 20, 2025: https://doi.org/10.1051/epjpv/2024018

10.4229/EUPVSEC2025/4CV.1.19
020328-006

BASELINE EFFICIENCY: A NEW KEY PERFORMANCE INDICATOR FOR PV SYSTEMS

Anastasios Kladas, Bert Herteleer, Jan Cappelle
KU Leuven Research Group ELECTA Ghent, Gebroeders De Smetstraat 1, 9000 Ghent, Belgium
anastasios.kladas@kuleuven.be

ABSTRACT: This work introduces Baseline Efficiency (BE), a novel key performance indicator (KPI) for photovoltaic (PV) systems. BE quantifies system degradation and serves as a reference to identify thermal losses, faults, and other performance deviations. Calculated through PV output modeling, instantaneous efficiency calculations, filtering, and daily aggregation, BE captures changes in maximum power point (MPP) current, voltage, and power, and can incorporate open- and short-circuit data to reflect changes across the entire IV curve. By integrating BE, long-term PV output estimations become more accurate compared to static models, which degrade in precision due to system aging. BE also enhances fault detection and power forecasting when paired with weather forecasts. Results from a 6-year dataset demonstrate that BE stabilizes estimation accuracy for power and current, with voltage showing minimal degradation.

Keywords: PV output estimation, PV degradation, PV KPI

1 INTRODUCTION

Accurate estimation of photovoltaic (PV) system output is critical for effective fault detection and performance monitoring. Traditional KPIs, such as Performance Ratio (PR) and Energy Performance Index (EPI) [1], along with their instantaneous counterparts, normalized efficiency (η_N) [2] and Power Performance Index (PPI) [3], aggregate energy values to assess PV efficiency. However, these metrics incorporate all losses (e.g., faults, degradation, and low-light conditions), making them unsuitable as direct inputs for precise PV output estimation models. This work proposes Baseline Efficiency (BE) as a new KPI to address these limitations. BE focuses on capturing degradation and soiling patterns, enabling dynamic adjustments to PV output models for improved long-term accuracy. By serving as a reference for non-degradation-related losses, BE enhances fault detection, performance loss quantification, and power forecasting, particularly for aging PV systems.

2 METHODOLOGY

The calculation of Baseline Efficiency (BEx) for PV output parameters (e.g., maximum power point power [P_{MPP}], voltage [V_{MPP}], or current [I_{MPP}]) involves a multi-step process:

1. PV Output Model Development
   A Multi-Layer Perceptron (MLP) regressor [4], implemented using Python's scikit-learn library, predicts P_{MPP}, I_{MPP}, and $V_{MP}P$ based on plane-of-array irradiance (G_{PoA}) and PV cell temperature (T_{PV}). Hyperparameters are adjusted (hidden_layer_sizes=(20,), learning_rate_init=0.05, batch_size=200), and training data are resampled to 10-minute resolution using averages. For V_{MPP}, inputs are pre-processed by taking the natural logarithm of normalized G_{PoA} and its square to account for its sensitivity to temperature.
2. Data Filtering
   A two-layer filtering process ensures data quality:
   - Outlier Removal: Anomalous data points are excluded.
   - Daily Filters:
     - Correlation Filter: Days with a coefficient of determination (R^2) between I_{MPP} and G_{PoA} below 0.95 are removed.
     - Performance Ratio Filter: Days with a current-based Performance Ratio (PR_I), defined as $PR_I = (\int I_{MPP} / I_{Ref}) / (\int G_{PoA} / 1000)$, below 0.6 are excluded. The first 180 days of filtered data, where degradation effects are minimal, are used for training.
3. Baseline Efficiency Calculation
   - Instantaneous Performance Index (xPI): Calculated as xPI = x / x_EST, where x is the measured parameter and x_EST is the estimated value from the MLP model.
   - Daily Aggregation: A dataset of xPI values is created, excluding early morning and late afternoon data. This is resampled to daily resolution using the median (MED(xPI)). Days with a standard deviation (STD) > 0.1 or MED(xPI) outside 0.3 to 1.1 are discarded.
   - Outlier Removal: Linear regression between system age and MED(xPI) generates a regression line (xPIlinear). Values are retained if their deviation (DEV = MED(xPI) – xPIlinear) falls within AVG(DEV) ± 2*STD(DEV). Discarded values are filled via linear interpolation, and a 7-day rolling window smooths the signal to produce BEx.
   - Dynamic Output Estimation: BEx is used as a weighting factor for G_{PoA} to re-estimate x using the MLP models, making predictions dynamic.

3 DATA USED

The methodology was applied to a 6-year, 1-minute

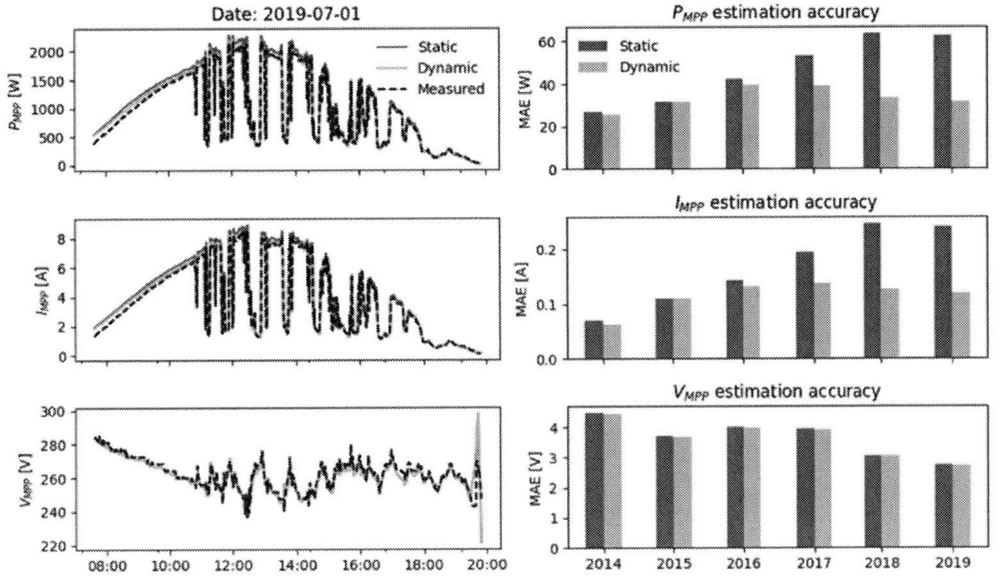

Figure 1 Comparison of measured PV output with estimations from static and dynamic models (using BE-weighted irradiance) (left). Comparison of Mean Absolute Error (MAE) between estimated and measured values for each model (right).

resolution dataset from a fixed-tilt 2.4 kWdc PV system at the Southeastern Solar Research Center (SSRC) in Birmingham, Alabama, USA. The dataset, sourced from an open-source repository, includes measurements of P_{MPP}, I_{MPP}, V_{MPP}, G_{PoA}, and T_{PV}, enabling the calculation of BE, BE_I (I_{MPP}-based), and BE_V (V_{MPP}-based).

4 RESULTS

Figure 2 illustrates the step-by-step transformation of the instantaneous Voltage Performance Index (VPI), Current Performance Index (CPI), and Power Performance Index (PPI) into daily baseline efficiency values: BE_V, BEI, and BE, respectively. While BE and BE_I exhibit mild degradation over time, BE_V remains relatively stable.

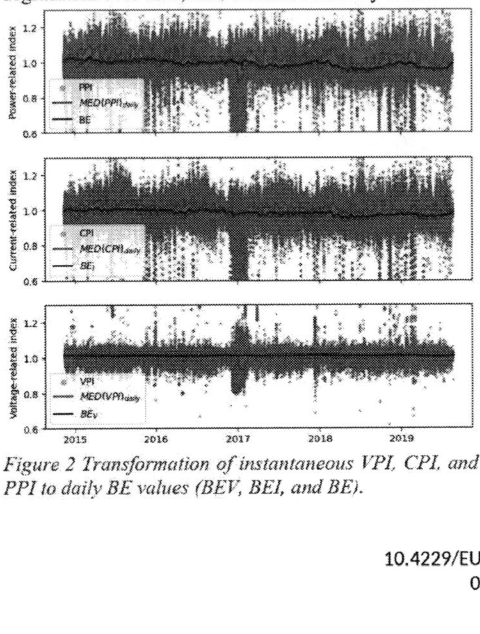

Figure 2 Transformation of instantaneous VPI, CPI, and PPI to daily BE values (BEV, BEI, and BE).

Figure 1 compares model precision using both the static PV output model and its dynamic counterpart, which incorporates baseline efficiency as a dynamic weight to irradiance. The left-hand plots show time series estimations for instantaneous values. The right-hand plots compare the Mean Absolute Errors (MAE) between estimated and measured values. The BE approach demonstrably stabilizes accuracy over time for P_{MPP} and I_{MPP} estimations. In contrast, static and dynamic V_{MP}P estimations show no significant difference, consistent with the minimal degradation observed in V_{MPP}.

The use cases of this KPI are the following:

o Improved Long-Term PV Output Estimations: Enhances the accuracy of long-term PV output predictions.

o Quantification of Performance Deviations: Enables precise quantification of performance losses caused by thermal effects, low-light conditions, or system faults.

o Performance Loss Rate Assessment: Facilitates accurate determination of the system's degradation rate.

o Power Forecasting: Improves power forecasting accuracy when coupled with corresponding weather forecasts.

o PV Diagnostics: Supports comprehensive diagnostics of PV system health and performance.

Future work will extend this analysis to diverse PV systems, including bifacial, dual-orientation, and agrivoltaic installations, to further validate BE's utility.

5 REFERENCES

[1] IEC 61724-1, Photovoltaic system performance – Part 1: Monitoring, " Edition 1.0. 2017.

[2] B. Herteleer, B. Huyck, F. Catthoor, J. Driesen, and J. Cappelle, "Normalised efficiency of photovoltaic systems: Going beyond the performance ratio," Solar Energy, vol.

10.4229/EUPVSEC2025/4CV.1.22

157, pp. 408–418, Nov. 2017, doi: 10.1016/J.SOLENER.2017.08.037.
[3] G. G. Kim, J. H. Hyun, J. H. Choi, S.-H. ahn, B. G. Bhang, and H.-K. Ahn, "Quality Analysis of Photovoltaic System Using Descriptive Statistics of Power Performance Index," IEEE Access, vol. 11, pp. 28427–28438, 2023, doi: 10.1109/ACCESS.2023.3257373.
[4] M. W. Gardner and S. R. Dorling, "Artificial neural networks (the multilayer perceptron)—a review of applications in the atmospheric sciences," Atmos Environ, vol. 32, no. 14–15, pp. 2627–2636, Aug. 1998, doi: 10.1016/S1352-2310(97)00447-0.
[5] F. Pedregosa et al., "Scikit-learn: Machine learning in Python," Journal of machine learning research, vol. 12, no. Oct, pp. 2825–2830, 2011.
[6] J. O. Allen and W. B. Hobbs, "The effect of short-term inverter saturation on modeled hourly PV output using minute DC power measurements," Journal of Renewable and Sustainable Energy, vol. 14, no. 6, Nov. 2022, doi: 10.1063/5.0130265.

KU LEUVEN GENT

Faculty of Technology Engineering

Baseline efficiency: A new key performance indicator for PV systems

Anastasios Kladas, Bert Herteleer, Jan Cappelle
Research group ELECTA Ghent

- PV degradation determines output
- Prediction models should highlight unexpected loss causes
- Linear degradation assessments may miss non-linear losses
- Historical EPI trends can misrepresent module health due to (unexpected) faults
- Robust KPI proposed for PV output estimation models

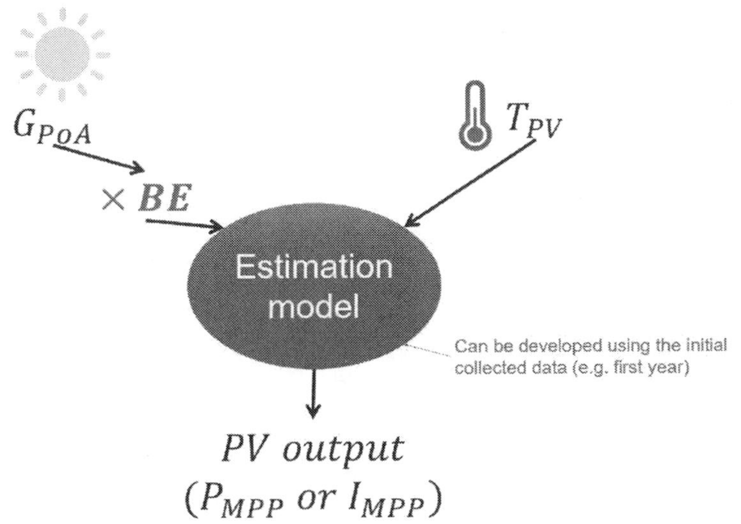

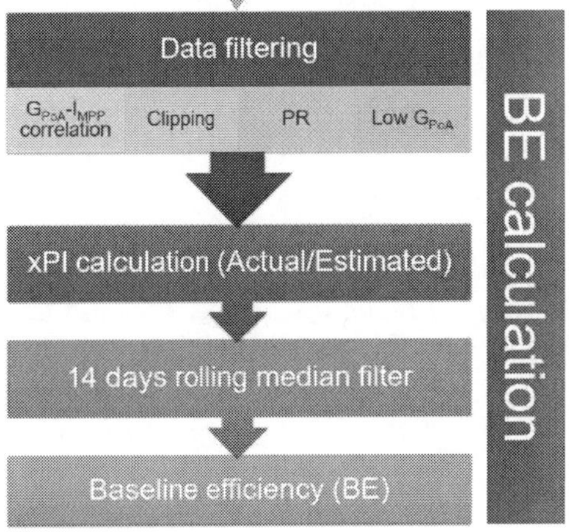

Results

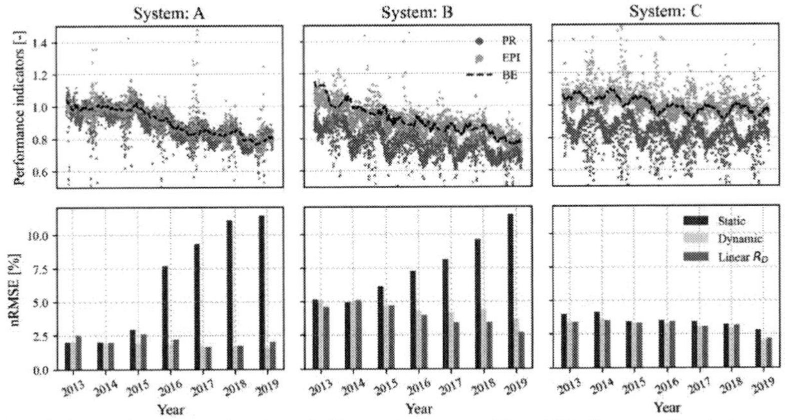

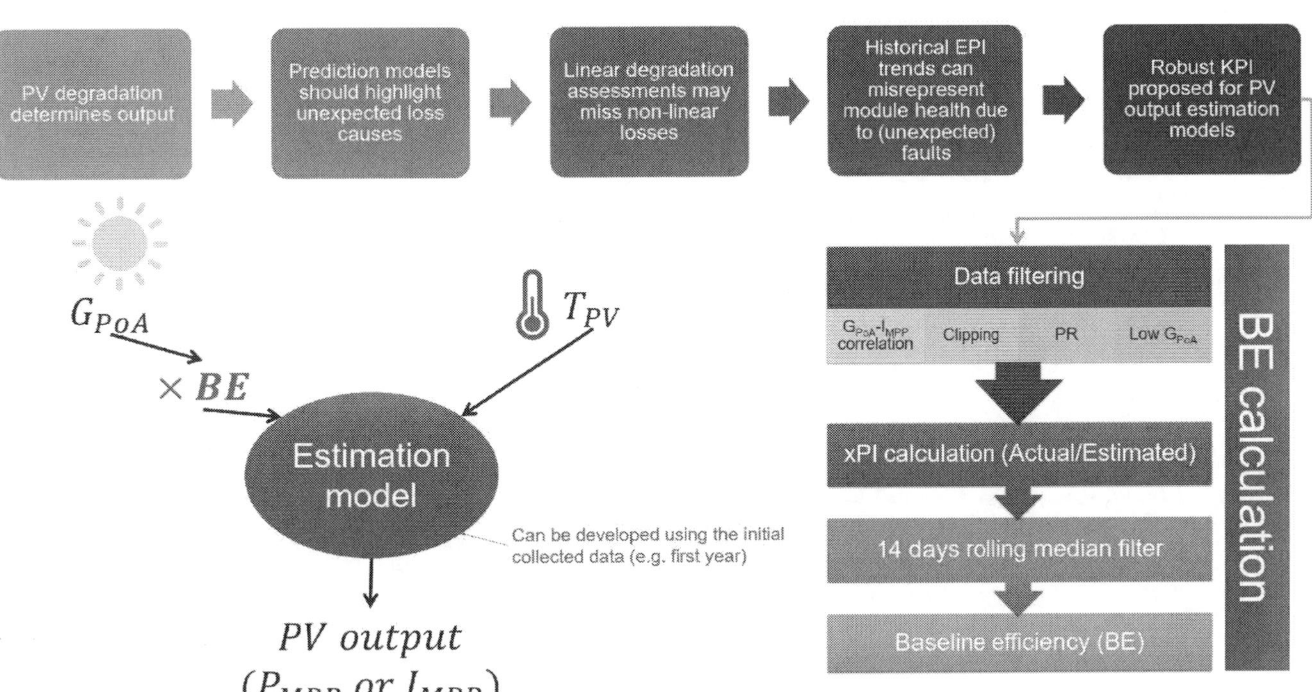

Results of P_{MPP} estimation using the BE (Dynamic approach) and the linear estimated degradation using YoY (Linear R) against using a static model on Pfaffstaetten PV systems [1]

Notes

- Stabilizes the estimation accuracy over time
- Can be calculated for power or current, enabling more detailed degradation analysis
- The PLR estimated by applying linear regression to the BE and the respective values published from Task 13 [2] are closely matching [3]
- Suggested as irradiance weight to prevent lowering the clipping point during estimations

References

[1] K. Rath *et al.*, "Pfaffstaetten," Sep. 2020, *OSF*. doi: 10.17605/OSF.IO/R34P7
[2] R. H. French et al., "Task 13 Assessment of Performance Loss Rate of PV Power Systems," 2021. Accessed: Dec. 03, 2024. [Online]. Available: https://iea-pvps.org/research-tasks/performance-operation-and-reliability-of-photovoltaic-systems/
[3] A. Kladas, B. Herteleer & J. Cappelle, "A Degradation-Responsive Framework for Long-Term PV Power Estimation." Advanced Theory and Simulations, 2025, https://doi.org/10.1002/adts.202500631

https://www.linkedin.com/in/anastasioskladas
AnastasiosKladas@kuleuven.be
+30 6975718485

Soiling forecasts for cleaning scheduling optimization

Fernanda Norde Santos[1], Stefan Wilbert[1*], Carl Becker[1], Elena Ruiz Donoso[1], Laura Campos Guzman[1], Álvaro Fernández Solas[1], Luis Zarzalejo[2], Anne Forstinger[3], David Helten[3], Veith Pietsch[4], Robert Pitz-Paal[5]

[1]DLR Institute for Solar Research, Almeria, Spain, [2]CIEMAT Energy Department – Renewable Energy Division, Madrid, Spain, [3]CSP Services GmbH, Cologne, Germany, [4]Aquila Capital, Hamburg, Germany, [5]DLR Institute of Solar Research, Cologne, Germany. *stefan.wilbert@dlr.de

Motivation

- Soiling = Accumulation of particles + other objects (e.g. leaves, bird droppings) on solar collectors
- Soiling causes a loss of 3%–4% of potential global solar energy production[1], therefore cleaning is important

Soiling measurement at the West African Power Pool (WAPP) network station in Malanville, Benin[2]

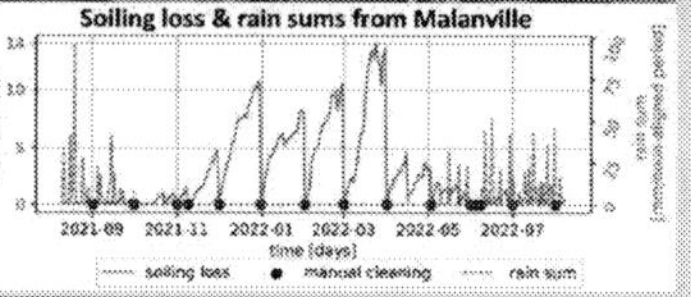

Objectives

- Create soiling loss forecasts to
  - Predict solar energy yield accurately & to
  - Optimize cleaning to reach the best trade-off between the soiling losses & cleaning costs
    - Not only frequency of cleaning, but also the selection of the cleaning dates must be optimized
    - Avoid unnecessary cleanings just before strong rainfalls or strong soiling events
- Evaluate soiling forecasts based on the most recent soiling measurements & different weather forecasts & long-term meteorological data

Soiling forecasting approaches

- **Soiling & rain cleaning models**
  - Various options of semi-physical soiling models incl. deposition & natural cleaning tested
  - **Soiling rate models** for days without rain cleaning:
    - *a) Persistence*[3]: soiling rate is predicted as the average of the last 20 days without cleaning
    - *b) Kimber*[4]: fixed soiling rate of 0.435%/d[5]
    - *c) HSU*[6]: soiling rate depending on PM & tilt with settling velocities of 0.0009 m/s for PM2.5 & 0.004 m/s for PM10
  - **Rain cleaning models**
    - *a) Full cleaning above threshold of 1 mm daily rain sum; no cleaning otherwise*
    - *b) Partial cleaning*[7] *effect with logarithmic rain sum dependence*
- **Input data:**
  - Parameters: particulate matter, precipitation, collector orientation
  - Two input data options:
    - *I. MERRA2 data*[8] *of 40 years used as ensemble prediction*
    - *II. combination of MERRA2, ECMWF*[9] *and CAMS*[10] *data*
      - First 6 days:
        - all weather parameters except for PM: ECMWF forecast (50 ensemble members)
        - PM: 1st to 5th day: CAMS PM forecast, 6th day: PM from 5th day
      - From day 7 to day 365: MERRA2 data
      - Creation of 200 ensemble members as concatenations of 40 MERRA2 years & 5 members from ECMWF (rain sum closest to avg, lowest, highest, 25- & 75-percentile)

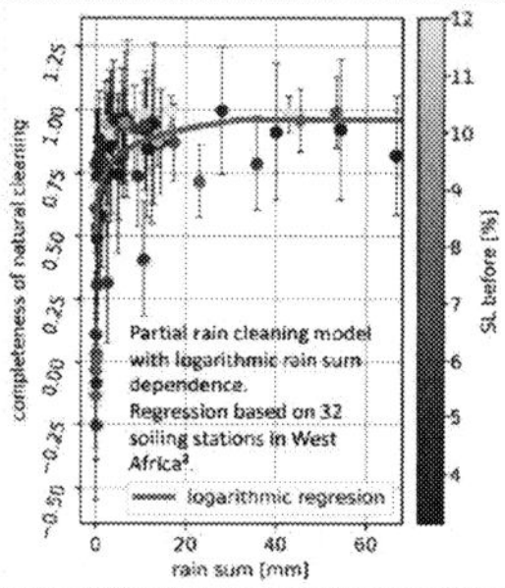

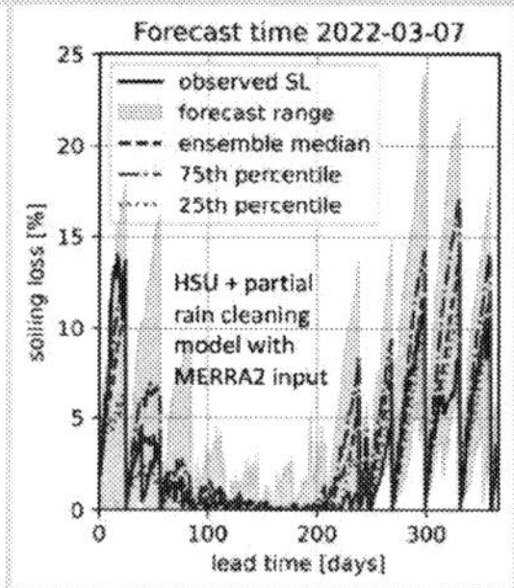

- **Case study**
  - Apply & evaluate the forecasts for Malanville (Benin)
  - There, soiling was measured for more than one year
  - Forecasts for the case study were created with a horizon of one year

Soiling forecast validation in Malanville

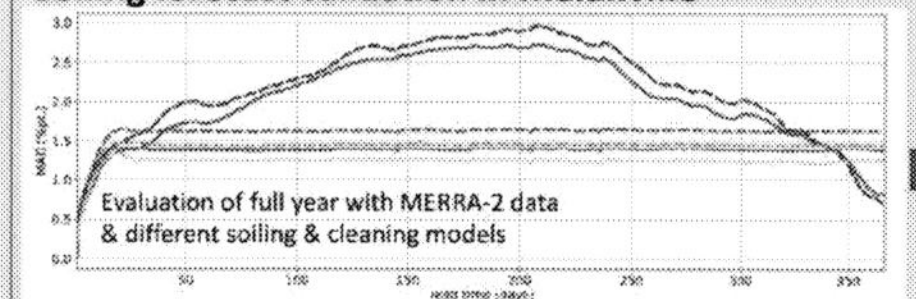

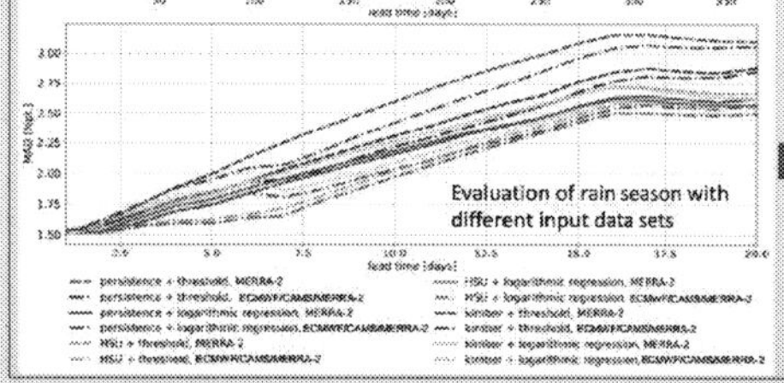

Evaluation of different soiling & cleaning models with MERRA2 data:

- *Kimber & HSU models outperform persistence most of the time*, except:
  - with forecast lead time of ~1 year (persistence benefits from seasonal effect)
  - during the first days (all forecasts benefit from application of latest measurement data)
- Kimber combined with logarithmic regression achieves the best performance for many lead times
  - This can change if the Kimber model's fixed soiling rate is less adequate for the site of interest
- In the first days, HSU + logarithmic rain cleaning model performs best
- Using *the logarithmic rain cleaning model improves the soiling forecast* compared to using the same models with a cleaning threshold

Evaluation of the effect of using additional CAMS PM & ECMWF precipitation data:

- *CAMS & ECMWF data can reduce the forecast errors in some cases*, e.g. rainy period (April - September)
- Considering also the dry period, an overall increase of the errors was found using the additional data. The MERRA2 ensemble seems to describe the weather conditions quite well.
- Especially in the first 7 days, the HSU model using CAMS and ECMWF performs considerably better than the other combination of models and datasets.

Cleaning optimization

- Cleaning schedule optimizer based on a Markov Decision Chain (MDC) approach[11,12] for an exemplary PV plant in Malanville, Benin.
- Optimizer is executed every day in the morning with most recent forecasts (MERRA2, partial cleaning)
  - It derives the time plan of cleaning tasks for the next year resulting in the largest economical yield
  - Only the suggested cleaning tasks that have to be ordered on the current day are actually considered
  - The actually scheduled cleaning tasks form the cleaning timeseries that is used for the evaluation of the economic and energetic effect of the optimization
- Compared to a PV system that is not cleaned
  - 9.7 % net income increase
  - 12.1 % energy generation increase

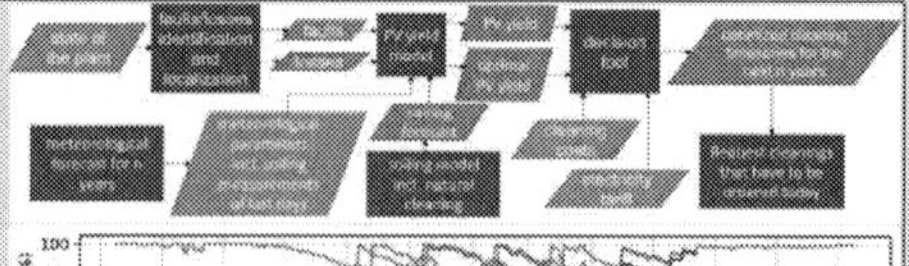

Conclusion & outlook

- Results highlight the potential of soiling forecasts and cleaning schedule optimization to improve yield predictions, and the actual economic & energetic yield of PV systems
- Calibration of soiling models to site or soiling type is important for accuracy
- More complex models and further data sets may be useful depending on the data quality and season. However, this is not guaranteed as the 40 year ensemble from MERRA2 already provides valuable information, and all data/model uncertainties are high
- If a PV system is meant to be cleaned less frequently than once per year the forecast horizon would have to be increased. Additionally, the soiling model would have to include the long-term build-up of soiling due to particles that cannot be easily removed by rain.

References

Acknowledgement

The authors would like to thank Yandalux Solar GmbH, the World Bank, the West African Power Pool and the WAPP station responsible for providing the measurement data used in this study. We also thank the European Centre for Medium-Range Weather Forecast (ECMWF), the Copernicus Atmosphere Monitoring Service (CAMS) and NASA's Global Modeling and Assimilation Office (GMAO) for providing the forecast and reanalysis data.
The authors further thank the European Union for funding the CAMEO project (grant agreement 101082125) and the German Ministry of Economic Affairs and Energy for funding the PVOptDigital project (grant 03EE1107).

Federal Ministry for Economic Affairs and Energy

Funded by the European Union

020331-001

ADAPTING PV PANEL CLEANING STRATEGIES TO MARKET DYNAMICS: THE IMPACT OF VARIABLE PRICING AND REGULATORY MARKET PARTICIPATION

Marta Redondo Cuevas[1,2], Carlos A. Platero Gaona[1]
[1]Universidad Politécnica de Madrid, [2]ENDESA Generación
e-mail address(es) marta.redondo.cuevas@alumnos.upm.es, marta.redondo@enel.com, carlosantonio.platero@upm.es

ABSTRACT: The profitability of photovoltaic (PV) panel cleaning is increasingly shaped by external market dynamics rather than technical thresholds alone. This study analyzes how evolving electricity market conditions in Spain—characterized by price volatility, midday price collapses, and growing participation in ancillary service markets—affect the timing and economic viability of cleaning operations.
Using real data from 47 PV plants (2020–2025) and the SOMOSclean decision model, we demonstrate that identical soiling levels can lead to different cleaning strategies depending on market context. Factors such as the solar capture price factor (CPF), curtailments, and regulatory participation significantly influence whether recovered energy can be monetized.
We propose a context-aware framework that integrates soiling dynamics, market signals, and operational constraints to optimize cleaning schedules. The results highlight the need for flexible, market-responsive strategies to enhance profitability while maintaining operational agility.

Keywords: soiling, cleaning, photovoltaic, electricity market, curtailment, ancillary services, decision framework

1 INTRODUCTION

The operational efficiency of PV plants is increasingly influenced by external market factors. Traditional cleaning strategies, based solely on technical or environmental criteria, may no longer be sufficient. This study explores how evolving market conditions between 2020 and 2025 affect the profitability and timing of panel cleaning operations.

Figure 1: Dirty and clean panel in PV plant.

This paper is structured as follows:
- Section 2 reviews the evolution of the electricity market (2020-2025).
- Section 3 discusses cleaning decisions in a market context.
- Section 4 presents the main results.
- Section 5 summarizes the conclusions.

2 MARKET EVOLUTION (2020-2025)

In recent years, the electricity market has undergone significant transformations that have directly impacted the operation and profitability of photovoltaic solar plants. Although this study focuses on Spain, it is important to note that many of these dynamics are also common in other European markets. The figures presented in this section are the authors' own elaboration, based on data provided by REE (ESIOS [1] and I3DIA files [2]).

2.1 Day-ahead market prices

The Spanish day-ahead electricity market has undergone a significant change, as illustrated in Figure 2.

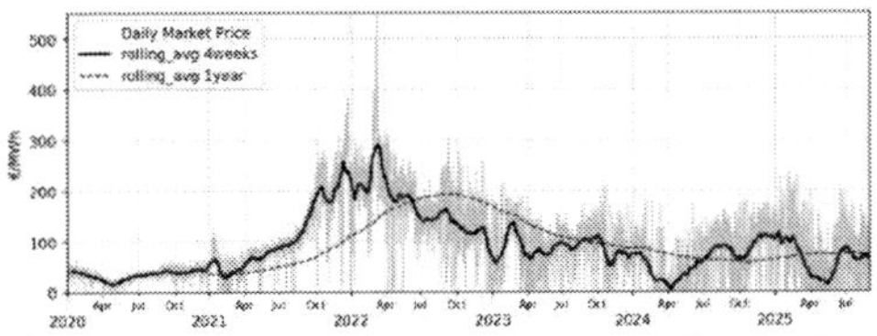

Figure 2: Evolution of daily market prices (€/MWh) from 2020 to 2025

During the first months of 2020, day-ahead electricity prices in Spain remained relatively stable, mostly ranging between 30 and 60 €/MWh. This pattern, typical of the previous decade, reflected a balanced supply-demand scenario supported by a diversified generation mix and the absence of major external disruptions.

However, from the second half of 2021 onwards, a sharp upward trend emerged, with sustained price increases and a marked rise in volatility. This shift was driven by several international factors, including the surge in natural gas prices across European wholesale markets, higher CO_2 emission allowance costs, and geopolitical tensions related to the conflict in Ukraine. As a result, daily average prices frequently exceeded 200 €/MWh for several months, with occasional peaks approaching 500 €/MWh.

From mid-2022, regulatory measures implemented in Spain and Portugal—most notably the so-called "Iberian mechanism" to cap the price of gas used for electricity generation—helped to partially moderate prices. Nevertheless, volatility remained high, with pronounced short-term fluctuations, sharp peaks, and abrupt drops.

In 2023 and especially in 2024, the rapid increase in renewable generation capacity, combined with episodes of high wind and solar output, led to the recurrent appearance of near-zero and even negative hourly prices in the day-ahead market. This unprecedented situation in the recent history of the Spanish power system reflects periods of temporary oversupply from non-dispatchable renewable sources.

2.2 Solar Capture Price Factor

The capture price factor (CPF) measures the ratio between the weighted average price obtained by solar PV generation and the average day-ahead market price:

$$CPF_{solar} = \frac{\sum_h P_h \cdot E_{solar,h}}{\sum_h E_{solar,h}} \cdot \frac{1}{\sum_h P_h} \quad (1)$$

where P_h is the market price in hour h, and $E_{solar,h}$ the energy generated by solar technology in that hour.

As shown in Figure 3, the CPF for solar in Spain remained close to 100% until 2022, indicating that PV captured prices similar to the market average. However, from 2022 onwards, the CPF has declined steadily due to the increasing share of solar generation, which often coincides with periods of lower demand and reduced prices. This trend has become more pronounced in 2023 and 2024, with prolonged periods where the CPF dropped below 70%, especially during episodes of high renewable output and low demand, occasionally resulting in zero or negative hourly prices.

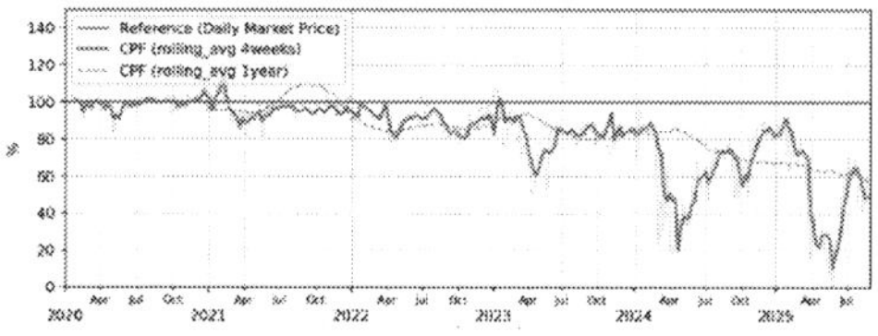

Figure 3: Capture Price Factor (CPF) for solar technology.

2.3 Increase in solar production and deviations from day-ahead schedule

Throughout the period analyzed, solar PV generation in Spain has increased significantly, particularly from 2022 onwards, in line with the rapid growth of installed capacity in the national power system. This expansion has been driven mainly by the steady connection of large-scale PV plants. The actual increase would be even greater if self-consumption installations (excluded from REE publications) were taken into account.

However, this rise in production has been accompanied by a growing gap between the scheduled energy and the actual energy injected into the grid. As shown in Figure 4, this discrepancy is represented by the shaded area between the two curves. It reflects situations where solar energy is not delivered to the system, mainly due to factors such as technical grid limitations, system security constraints, or the activation of balancing services

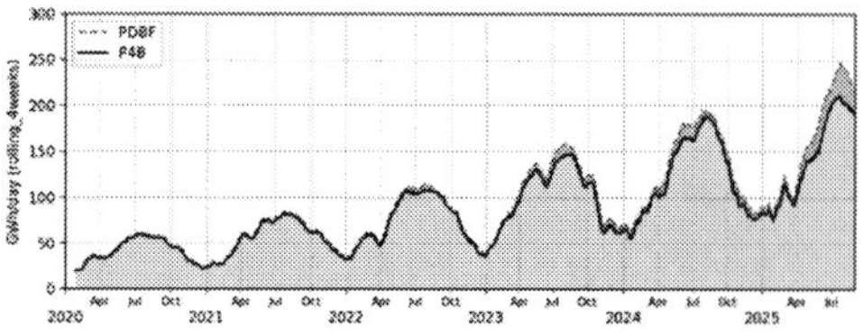

Figure 4: Scheduled vs. actual solar PV generation in Spain. The shaded area indicates curtailed energy due to grid or market constraints.

2.4 Participation in balancing services

Figure 5 illustrates the evolution of solar PV participation in secondary regulation markets in Spain, measured through the contracted regulation band. Initial participation began in 2022, but remained marginal. In 2023, participation increased progressively, driven by the growth in installed PV capacity.

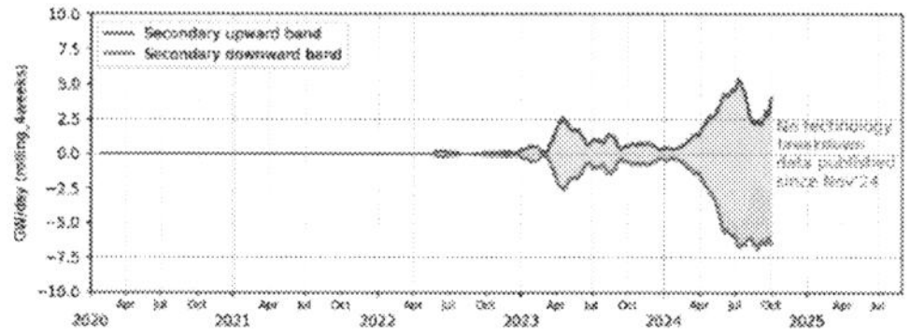

Figure 5: Participation of PV plants in secondary regulation markets

A significant regulatory change introduced in April 2024 [3] allowed for asymmetric bidding—enabling different offers for upward and downward regulation. This adjustment particularly benefited solar PV technology, which can more easily reduce output (i.e., offer downward regulation). As a result, participation in secondary regulation markets surged.

However, since November 2024, REE has discontinued the publication of secondary regulation band data disaggregated by technology. Therefore, it is no longer possible to quantify the exact level of solar PV participation in these markets.

3 CLEANING DECISIONS IN A MARKET CONTEXT

Accurate prediction of soiling levels (%) is essential for optimizing cleaning schedules in PV plants. In this study, the SOMOSclean model [4][5] was applied to 47 PV power plants in Spain, representing a total installed capacity of over 2 GWp.

It is important to note that the percentage of soiling does not directly translate into an equivalent energy loss. The actual impact of soiling depends on the market context, including factors such as grid curtailments or participation in secondary regulation markets. For example, a 5% soiling level may not result in a 5% reduction in output if the plant is already curtailed due to grid constraints. Therefore, cleaning actions should be scheduled only when real energy gains are expected, rather than simply responding to high soiling levels.

A simplified decision flow is presented in Figure 6, which illustrates the main variables and data sources considered when assessing whether panel cleaning is economically justified.

10.4229/EUPVSEC2025/4CV.1.24

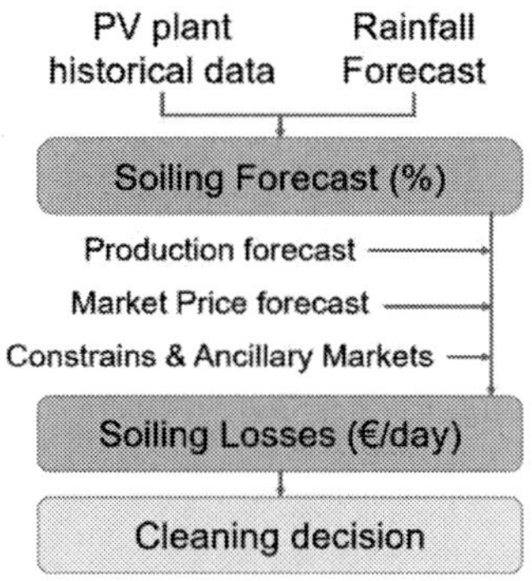

Figure 6: Decision flow for PV panel cleaning based on technical and market variables (SOMOSclean)

4 RESULTS: ONE SOILING LEVEL, MANY STRATEGIES

The application of the SOMOSclean model with real market data reveals that identical soiling levels can lead to very different cleaning decisions depending on the market context. Table I summarizes how cleaning strategies have evolved from 2020 to 2025, reflecting variations in daily market prices, capture price factors, grid constraints, and participation in ancillary services.

Table I: Evolution of cleaning strategies for PV plants in Spain (2020–2025), with similar soiling levels (%) and considering market conditions. (*) Data for 2025 include values up to August only.

Year	Market Price €/MWh	Solar CPF	Curtail.	Balancing Service	Strategy (cleanings /summer)
2020	34	97%	Neglig.	No	1-2
2021	112	92%	Neglig.	No	2-3
2022	168	90%	Medium	Neglig.	1-2
2023	87	84%	High	Low	0-1
2024	63	67%	High	Sec. Reg.	0-1
2025 (*)	64 (*)	53% (*)	Medium	Extended	TBD

Despite similar soiling levels across the years, the number of summer cleanings has significantly decreased. In 2021, most plants required two to three cleanings during the summer period. By contrast, in recent years many plants have reduced this to just one or even none.

These results highlight that cleaning decisions cannot rely solely on technical indicators such as soiling percentage. Instead, they must consider whether the recovered energy can be monetized under current market conditions.

Importantly, the strategies shown in Table I refer to PV plants without storage systems (BESS). In plants equipped with battery storage, recovered energy can be stored and dispatched later, potentially shifting the optimal cleaning timing to align with higher market prices.

Additionally, contractual obligations such as Power Purchase Agreements (PPA) may impose further constraints, making a one-size-fits-all approach ineffective.

4 CONCLUSIONS

Optimizing PV panel cleaning is no longer solely a technical or environmental matter. The increasing complexity of electricity markets—characterized by price volatility, curtailments, and participation in ancillary services—requires a more integrated and adaptive approach.

Future cleaning strategies must be supported by context-aware decision frameworks, such as the SOMOSclean model, which combine:

- Soiling dynamics (%)
- Market price signals
- Grid curtailments and operational constraints
- Participation in balancing and ancillary service markets

In this evolving landscape, PV cleaning strategies must be smart, flexible, and market-responsive to ensure both operational efficiency and economic viability.

5 ACKNOWLEDGEMENTS

The authors would like to thank Enel Green Power and Endesa Generación SA for enabling the implementation of the SOMOSclean model in their PV plants. Special thanks are also extended to the entire O&M solar team for their valuable expertise and insightful discussions throughout this project.

6 REFERENCES

[1] Red Eléctrica de España, "API ESIOS: datos del sistema eléctrico", 2025 [Online]. Available: https://api.esios.ree.es/
[2] Red Eléctrica de España, "I3DIA: archivos agregados por tecnología del mercado eléctrico", 2025. [Online]. Available: https://www.esios.ree.es/en/downloads
[3] Comisión Nacional de los Mercados y la Competencia (CNMC), "Resolution of 25 April 2024, amending the conditions relating to balancing and the operating procedures for the participation of the Spanish peninsular electricity system in the European balancing platforms MARI and PICASSO", Boletín Oficial del Estado, no. 137, pp. 66281–66524, Jun. 6, 2024.
[4] M. Redondo et al, "Soiling Modelling in Large Grid-Connected PV Plants for Cleaning Optimization" Energies, 2023. https://doi.org/10.3390/en16020904
[5] M. Redondo et al, "Review and Comparison of Methods for Soiling Modeling in Large Grid-Connected PV Plants" Sustainability, 2024. https://doi.org/10.3390/su162410998

ADAPTING PV PANEL CLEANING STRATEGIES TO MARKET DYNAMICS: THE IMPACT OF VARIABLE PRICING AND REGULATORY MARKET PARTICIPATION

Marta Redondo Cuevas [1,2], Carlos A. Platero Gaona [1]

[1] Universidad Politécnica de Madrid / [2] ENDESA GENERACIÓN

Motivation & Objectives. *Why rethink PV cleaning strategies?*

Cleaning PV panels is essential to minimize soiling losses and maximize energy yield. However, the **evolving market conditions** in recent years —such as price volatility and midday price collapses— have introduced **new challenges and opportunities** for optimizing this process. Additionally, the increasing participation of solar plants in regulatory markets adds further complexity to operational decision-making.

This study proposes a framework that integrates market conditions, revenue projections, and operational constraints to optimize cleaning schedules. The findings highlight the need for flexible, market-responsive cleaning strategies to enhance profitability while maintaining operational agility.

Market Evolution (2020-2025)

How have market conditions changed?

- Daily Market Prices:

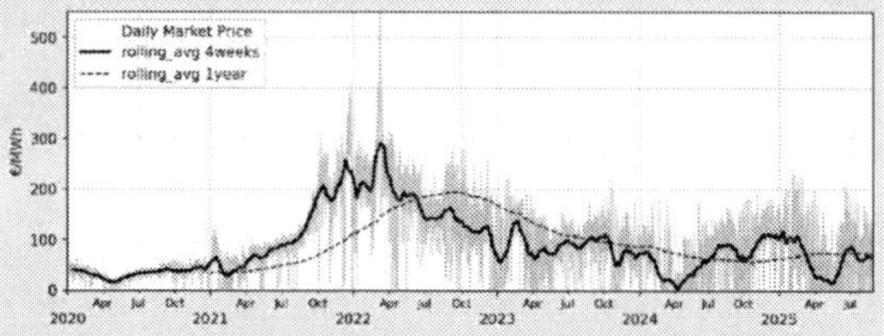

- Capture price factor (CPF) for solar technology:

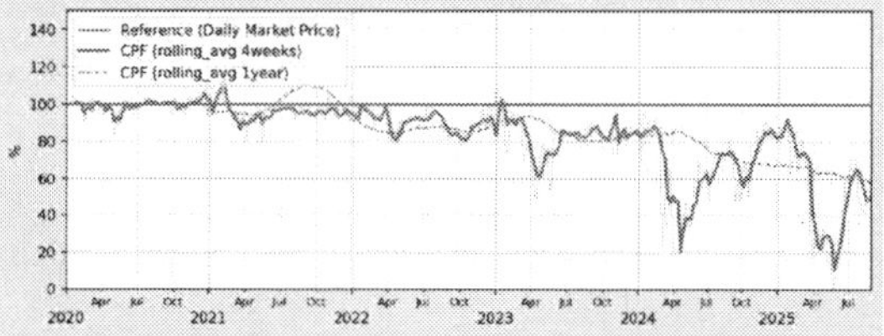

- PV Generation & Deviations from day-ahead operating program:

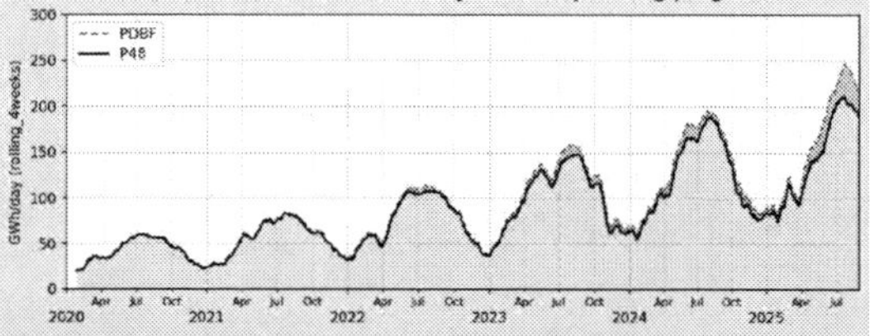

- Participation of PV plants in secondary ancillary services:

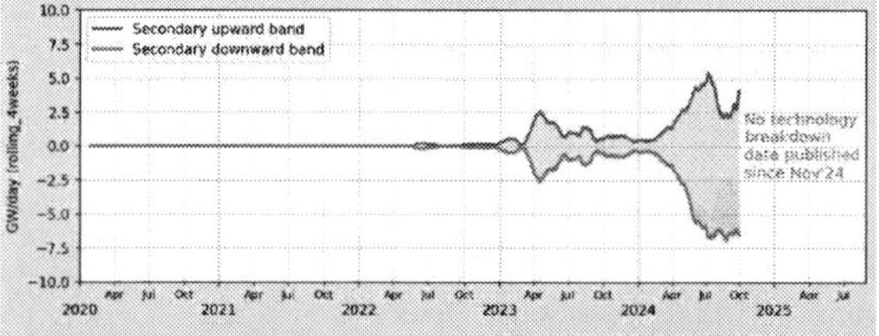

Source: Spain, REE (ESIOS and i3DIA files)

Cleaning Decisions in a Market Context

When is cleaning really worth it?

- Necessary to **predict** soiling levels (%):
  → **SOMOSclean model** [1] [2]
  → Applied to 47 PV power plants in Spain (>**2GWp**)
- Soiling in % ≠ direct energy loss
  → Impact depends on market context (e.g., curtailments or secondary regulation)
  → e.g., a 5% soiling level may not reduce output by 5% if the plant is already curtailed
  → Clean only when energy gains are real — not just when soiling is high.

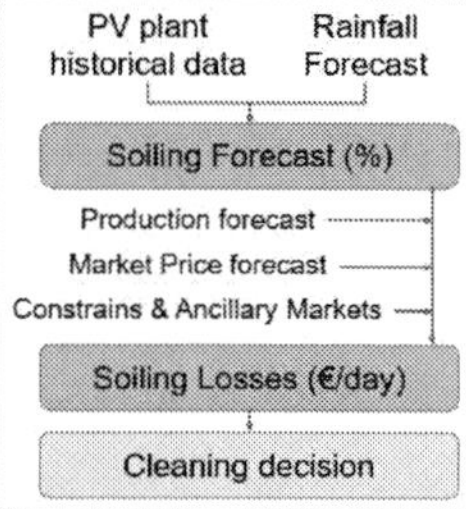

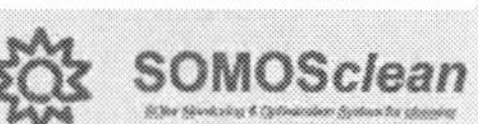

Results. *One Soiling Level, Many Strategies*

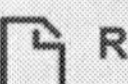

Applying the SOMOSclean model with real market data shows that **identical soiling levels** can lead to **very different cleaning decisions**:

Year	Daily Market Prices	Capture Prices for solar technology	Grid curtailment / constrains	Balancing Service (Secondary & Tertiary Markets)	Typical cleaning strategy
2020	34 €/MWh	97%	Negligible	No	1-2 cleanings /summer
2021	112 €/MWh	92%	Negligible	No	2-3 cleanings /summer
2022	168 €/MWh	90%	Medium	Negligible	1-2 cleanings /summer
2023	87 €/MWh	84%	High	Low	0-1 cleanings /summer
2024	63 €/MWh	67%	High	Secondary regulation markets (upward/downward bids since April'24)	0-1 cleanings /summer
2025	64 €/MWh (up to Aug)	53% (up to Aug)	Medium	Extended participation	¿?

The strategies shown above refer to PV plants **without storage (BESS)**; in BESS-integrated plants, recovered energy can be stored, shifting the optimal cleaning timing.

Additionally, contractual obligations as PPAs may impose further constraints, making a **one-size-fits-all approach ineffective**.

Conclusions

What should future strategies look like?

Optimizing PV panel cleaning is **no longer just a technical or environmental issue**.

It requires a **context-aware framework**, such as the SOMOSclean model, that integrates:

- Soiling dynamics (%)
- Market price signals
- Curtailments and grid constraints
- Participation in ancillary services

To remain competitive, PV cleaning strategies must be **smart, flexible, and market-aware**.

References

[1] M. Redondo et al, "Soiling Modelling in Large Grid-Connected PV Plants for Cleaning Optimization" *Energies*, 2023. https://doi.org/10.3390/en16020904

[2] M. Redondo et al, "Review and Comparison of Methods for Soiling Modeling in Large Grid-Connected PV Plants" *Sustainability*, 2024. https://doi.org/10.3390/su162410998

ADVANCING PHOTVOLTAIC PERFORMANCE THROUGH DIGITALISATION IN LIVING LABORATORIES: INSIGHTS FROM THE PROMISE PROJECT

Brian Bartolo[1,2], Brian Azzopardi[1,2,3,4 *], Carmel Azzopardi[1], Austeja Mockeviciute-Azzopardi[1], Alexandre Mignonac[5], Marcus Rennhofer[6], Bernhard Kubicek[6], Rita Ebner[6], Carlos Meza[7], Melodie de l'Epine[8], Eugenia Zugasti[9], Steve Zerafa[2,3,10], Kenneth Scerri[1,3]

[1]The Foundation for Innovation and Research – Malta (FiR.mt); [2]Malta College of Arts, Science and Technology (MCAST); [3]The University of Malta; [4]Azzopardi & Associates, Malta; [5]Commissariat à l'Energie Atomique et aux Energies Alternatives (CEA), France; [6]AIT Austrian Institute of Technology GMBH, Austria; [7]Anhalt University of Applied Sciences, Germany; [8]Becquerel Institute, Belgium; [9]Fundación CENER - National Renewable Energy Centre, Spain; [10]PIXAM Ltd.

* Brian.Azzopardi@FiR.mt

ABSTRACT: The growing demand for renewable energy continues to drive the large-scale deployment of photovoltaic (PV) systems. However, ensuring the sustained performance of existing installations remains essential, particularly in regions such as Malta, where elevated temperature, humidity, and salinity accelerate component degradation. This paper presents the next phase of the PROMISE project (Photovoltaics Reliability Operations and Maintenance Innovative Solutions for Energy Alliance), which advances the harmonised multi-site PV monitoring framework introduced in 2024 into a fully digitalised, cloud-integrated infrastructure. The upgraded system now encompasses ten rooftop laboratories and three dedicated test sites, each equipped with high-precision Class A sensors operating at 3-second acquisition intervals in accordance with IEC 61724-1:2021. The monitoring network is supported by an end-to-end Microsoft Azure pipeline—comprising IoT Hub, Function Apps, Cosmos DB, and Power BI—that enables real-time data streaming, anomaly detection, and predictive analytics across all locations. Moreover, the establishment of the PROMISE Open PV Reliability Repository provides public access to harmonised datasets, promoting transparency and collaboration within international PV reliability programmes. The results demonstrate a scalable, research-grade digital framework that strengthens system interoperability, enhances data quality, and supports the broader goals of smart monitoring and sustainable energy transition in the Mediterranean and beyond.

Keywords: Photovoltaic System Monitoring, Multi-Site Measurements, IoT Cloud Architecture, Mediterranean Climate PV Performance

1 INTRODUCTION

The European Green Deal and "Fit for 55" package continue to drive Europe's decarbonisation pathway toward net-zero emissions by 2050, with photovoltaic (PV) technologies remaining a cornerstone of this transition [1], [2] . Beyond rapid capacity expansion, sustained attention must be given to optimising the performance of existing PV assets to maximise energy yield and reliability under real-world conditions, as highlighted in numerous studies and reports [3] [4], [5],.

In the Mediterranean region, particularly in island nations such as Malta, photovoltaic (PV) installations are exposed to challenging environmental conditions, including elevated temperature, humidity, dust, and atmospheric salinity [6], all of which accelerate component degradation and reduce system efficiency. In addition to these stressors, rapid weather fluctuations [7] and limited available land area demand tailored monitoring strategies with higher measurement granularity and accuracy to capture environmental uncertainties and ensure optimal system performance. The combination of abundant solar resources and spatial constraints further underscores the need for precise, high-resolution monitoring to maximise energy yield. Within this context, the PROMISE project (Photovoltaics Reliability Operations and Maintenance Innovative Solutions for Energy Alliance) [8] established the Malta Living Laboratories as a distributed experimental platform for advanced PV performance monitoring.

The framework introduced in Bartolo *et al.*[9] (EU PVSEC 2024) demonstrated the feasibility of harmonising multi-site PV measurements using open-source platforms and standardised data protocols. While that study successfully validated the concept of a unified IoT-based monitoring architecture, it was primarily intended as a rapid-deployment solution to ensure data continuity on initially installed systems and provide temporary public access to performance information through a dedicated data repository [10]. Operational experience with this configuration revealed several technical limitations associated with the *ThingSpeak* [11] IoT Analytics platform used for data ingestion, storage, and basic visualisation, complemented by *Grafana Cloud* [12] for advanced dashboards. These limitations included the restriction to eight data fields per channel, which led to fragmented time-series records for systems featuring more than eight measurement parameters, thereby complicating subsequent data analysis. Additional challenges involved interoperability constraints between independent cloud ecosystems and the absence of real-time data-stream access between the ingestion and storage layers, which hindered the implementation of live performance monitoring and subsequent tasks such as real-time anomaly detection techniques.

To overcome these bottlenecks, this study introduces a fully digitalised, cloud-integrated infrastructure pipeline that, rather than functioning as a monolithic closed system, is composed of segregated yet interoperable consumer services within a unified ecosystem. The upgraded framework leverages *Microsoft Azure IoT Hub* [13], *Azure Function Apps* [14], *Cosmos DB*,[15] and *Power BI* [16] to ensure seamless data flow from the sensory layer to visualisation or application layer. In parallel, the data-acquisition frequency has been enhanced and refined in accordance with the updated IEC 61724-1:2021 standard requirements [17].

The current configuration also reflects a major expansion of the Living Laboratories network—from six operational sites in 2024 to a total of ten PV laboratories and three dedicated test facilities. These additional testings sites support benchmarking, degradation analysis, and multi-orientation configurations analysis of PV systems, providing a comprehensive dataset for performance comparison across diverse operational and environmental conditions. This evolution transforms the PROMISE framework from a rapid-deployment demonstrator into a scalable, analytics-ready digital platform capable of real-time diagnostics, predictive maintenance, and multi-site benchmarking across the Malta Living Laboratories.

1.1 Aim and Scope

This paper presents the continued development of the PROMISE monitoring framework, aimed at improving the efficiency, reliability, and interoperability of photovoltaic (PV) systems through digitalisation and real-time data analysis and therefore exploiting additional results.

The study focuses on optimising system scalability and enhancing data-sharing mechanisms to support open scientific collaboration. Through the establishment of a publicly accessible data repository, as demonstrated in [10], stakeholders and the public can visualise key measurements and evaluate performance in real-time while download historical data for further analysis and modelling, reinforcing transparency and supporting benchmarking activities across different sites.

The key objectives of this framework are:

i. To monitor and analyse PV system performance and evaluate degradation across an expanded network of laboratories and benchmark testing sites under local environmental Mediterranean conditions.
ii. To strengthen the interoperability and scalability of the PROMISE digital infrastructure, enabling multi-site data aggregation and comparison.
iii. To promote open data sharing through a structured repository that facilitates collaboration among researchers, policymakers, and industry partners.
iv. To demonstrate how harmonised data standards and improved acquisition practices contribute to higher traceability and comparability across sites.
v. To provide a scalable monitoring model that can be replicated in other regions with similar environmental and operational challenges, while exploiting the additional key results described in Section 5.

By achieving these objectives, the PROMISE framework advances from a national proof-of-concept to a pan-European digital platform that supports transparent, standardised, and collaborative research on PV system performance and reliability.

1.2 PROMISE PV Living Laboratories

The PROMISE project (*Photovoltaics Reliability Operations and Maintenance Innovative Solutions for Energy Alliance*) is a three-year research initiative funded by the European Commission that establishes a distributed platform for studying the reliability and optimisation of PV systems in real operating conditions. Initially centred in Malta, the network has now expanded to ten PV laboratories and three specialised test sites across Europe, supporting large-scale data collection, benchmarking, and degradation analysis.

PROMISE integrates digitalisation techniques, predictive analytics, and optimisation tools to enhance PV performance and accelerate the clean-energy transition. Alongside its technical goals, the project promotes capacity building and knowledge transfer through workshops, internships, and open-data initiatives.

The project is structured around two complementary pillars:

i. A research platform to study the reliability of PV systems and develop innovative solutions for optimisation.
ii. A knowledge transfer platform that supports training, internships, and workshops to enhance the research and engineering capabilities within Malta's PV sector.

1.3 Data Monitoring Constraints

A key challenge in photovoltaic (PV) system monitoring lies in distinguishing true system faults from data anomalies introduced by measurement noise or environmental variability. Previous studies have shown that filtering noise without suppressing meaningful fault signatures remains difficult, as factors such as transient shading or irradiance fluctuations can mimic real system defects and lead to misleading performance evaluations [18],[19].

To improve fault detection accuracy, effective data-filtering strategies must be applied [8]. Threshold-based filtering—such as excluding measurements taken under irradiance levels below 20 W/m² [18]—helps remove low-signal noise while retaining relevant operating data. Similarly, restricting analysis to peak irradiance periods (typically 10:00–16:00 h) reduces the uncertainty associated with shading and low-angle solar conditions [9].

Although post-processing filters are useful, a more robust approach is to minimise noise at the source. This can be achieved using high-quality, Class A sensors capable of operating in demanding climatic environments and conforming to OEM, ISO/IEC 17025 [20], ISO 9001 [21] and IEC 61724-1 standards [17]. Additionally, implementing granular, high-frequency data acquisition enables the capture of short-term fluctuations, improving the system's ability to identify transient anomalies and early-stage faults.

This paper is organised into six main sections. This section introduces the PROMISE project and outlines its objectives, while Section 2 describes the configuration of the expanded monitoring network. Section 3 details the edge-device data acquisition and processing framework, and Section 4 presents the Azure-based cloud architecture pipeline. Section 5 discusses the exploitable results and key outcomes of the upgraded infrastructure, and Section 6 concludes the study, highlighting future directions for real-time anomaly detection, system expansion, and predictive analysis for grid-integration forecasting.

2. SYSTEM OVERVIEW

This section introduces the configuration of the PROMISE PV Living Laboratories and provides an overview of the monitoring infrastructure deployed across the Malta Living Laboratory sites. The rooftop systems and test sites installed on public and institutional buildings are equipped with high-precision sensors and data-acquisition units that monitor real-world PV operation under diverse urban and coastal environments.

The three specialised test sites complement these installations by supporting advanced research functions. One site is dedicated to degradation analysis and forms part of a round-robin study coordinated within the European network to assess how PV modules degrade under different climatic conditions in different countries within the EU. Another facility hosts multiple irradiance reference cells mounted at various orientations and tilt angles to evaluate the influence of array geometry on system output and grid-integration behaviour. A third site is equipped with a high-accuracy pyranometer array used for benchmarking, reference calibration, and validation of the field-deployed sensors.

2.1 Sensor and Device Selection

The monitoring system employs high-precision electrical and meteorological sensors designed for continuous, real-time data capture. Measurements are recorded at 3-second intervals, providing high-resolution insight into short-term system behaviour and environmental variability. Data acquisition is implemented using the Modbus RTU protocol over RS-485 [22] wiring system , ensuring robust and cost-effective data transfer between field instruments and the central controller.

Key operational parameters—including DC current and voltage, plane-of-array irradiance, ambient temperature, module and cell temperature—are monitored using Class A-rated sensors compliant with the latest requirements of IEC 61724-1:2021. These devices are also calibrated and certified in accordance with ISO/IEC 17025 and ISO 9001 standards, guaranteeing measurement traceability, quality assurance, and long-term stability.

This high-accuracy instrumentation ensures reliable performance monitoring and supports real-time analysis and early fault detection within the PROMISE framework.

3. EDGE DEVICE DATA PROCESSING

This section outlines the sensor integration and data processing framework locally on each site adopted for real-time and historical PV system monitoring.

3.1 Data Processing

The sensors are managed by a *Raspberry Pi* controller [23], which functions as both the *Modbus RTU* master for the sensors and the edge device bridging the sensory and cloud layers. Each sensor is assigned a unique Modbus ID, and data are collected via *RS-485* wiring system, providing high robustness against electrical noise and transmission errors. The communication network follows strict specifications for baud rate, shielding, and terminating resistors, ensuring signal integrity and reliability [22],[24].

The *Raspberry Pi* operates on a Linux-based platform for stability and long-term performance, using *Python* libraries such as *PyModbus* [25] for device communication and data handling. This open-source configuration offers full customisation and scalability while avoiding the costs associated with proprietary systems.

Acquired data are securely transmitted to the Microsoft Azure Cloud, which provides the IoT architecture pipline for data ingestion and storage and visualation. Communication with the Azure IoT Hub is authenticated via connection strings, and telemetry messages are sent in JSON format through the MQTT protocol, enabling real-time monitoring and live data synchronisatio. Remote access via *RealVNC* [26] supports post-deployment configuration and diagnostics. To enhance resilience, a *Cron Job* [27] automatically restarts the acquisition script following power outages or communication interruptions, thereby preventing data loss.

3.2 Data Treatment

In the earlier PROMISE configuration (Bartolo et al., 2024) [9], data acquisition was performed at 10-second intervals, and the data were transmitted without a local timestamp, relying instead on irregular timestamps assigned upon receipt in *ThingSpeak*. In accordance with the updated IEC 61724-1:2021 Class A monitoring guidelines, the new system now samples data every 3 seconds, which are then aggregated and averaged over 30-second intervals to define the official recording cadence. This approach captures high temporal resolution and ensures compliance with IEC 61724-1 standards, while optimising cloud upload frequency, storage efficiency and related uploaded messages and storage costs. The average for each 30-second record is calculated from the number of valid entries captured within the aggregation window. When no valid data are recorded during a given interval, a null value is uploaded to the cloud to preserve dataset continuity.

Each data package is timestamped according to the Raspberry Pi's local clock rather than the arrival time at the *IoT Hub*. This method ensures consistent, synchronised timestamping for every monitored site by avoiding time stamp inconsistencies due to network latency effects.

Unlike the previous framework all implausible or corrupted values—typically arising from communication errors or temporary sensor malfunctions—are uploaded to the cloud as raw data. This strategy offloads computational tasks from the Raspberry Pi, allowing it to focus exclusively on accurate data acquisition while minimising processing overhead at the edge. Subsequent data validation, filtering, and further data analysis are performed within the Azure cloud pipeline, leveraging the real-time data stream between the IoT Hub and the Cosmos DB storage container. This architecture ensures continuous live access to unfiltered measurements for diagnostic purposes, while centralising data treatment and quality control within the cloud environment. Fig. 1 shows the comprehensive framework showing the transmission of data from the perception layer to the cloud environment.

4. . CLOUD ARCHITECTURE PIPLINE

The PROMISE digital-monitoring framework employs a fully integrated Microsoft Azure cloud architecture for IoT applications to manage real-time telemetry, data processing, storage, analytics, and visualisation. This pipeline ensures scalability, security, interoperability, and continuous availability within a unified ecosystem, while maintaining compliance with IEC 61724-1 data-handling principles and filtering practices.

Telemetry generated by the Raspberry Pi edge devices is transmitted to the Azure IoT Hub using the MQTT protocol, with each payload encoded in JSON and tagged with its local timestamp. Within the cloud pipeline, the IoT Hub forwards the data to Azure Function Apps, where they are automatically validated, organised, and routed to the appropriate containers in Cosmos DB database for storage. The stored data are then synchronised with the *Analytical Store* [28]and made accessible through *Azure Synapse Link* [29]for analysis in *Synapse Analytics* [30]. Finally, processed and aggregated results are visualised through interactive dashboards in Power BI, enabling real-time monitoring and long-term performance evaluation.

This end-to-end configuration provides historical real-time visibility, long-term reliability, and seamless data flow from the edge or fog layer to the cloud and application layers. The individual components of the cloud architecture pipeline are described in the following sections.

4.1 Azure IoT Hub (Ingressor)

The *IoT Hub* acts as the secure gateway between the edge device and other downstream cloud services. Telemetry messages, encoded in JSON and transmitted via the MQTT protocol, are authenticated through device-specific connection strings. The Hub supports communication, ensuring reliable message delivery and enabling remote diagnostics when required. All incoming data are timestamped and queued for downstream processing by the Function Apps, guaranteeing loss-tolerant transmission even under intermittent connectivity.

4.2 Azure Function Apps (Streamer)

Azure Function Apps perform the event-driven processing of telemetry within the cloud pipeline and can be coded in various programming languages. Each Function App acts as a container for one or more functions that are automatically triggered by incoming events, such as IoT Hub messages or scheduled timer executions. Serving as the bridge—or streamer—between the *IoT Hub* and downstream services, they parse, validate, and route

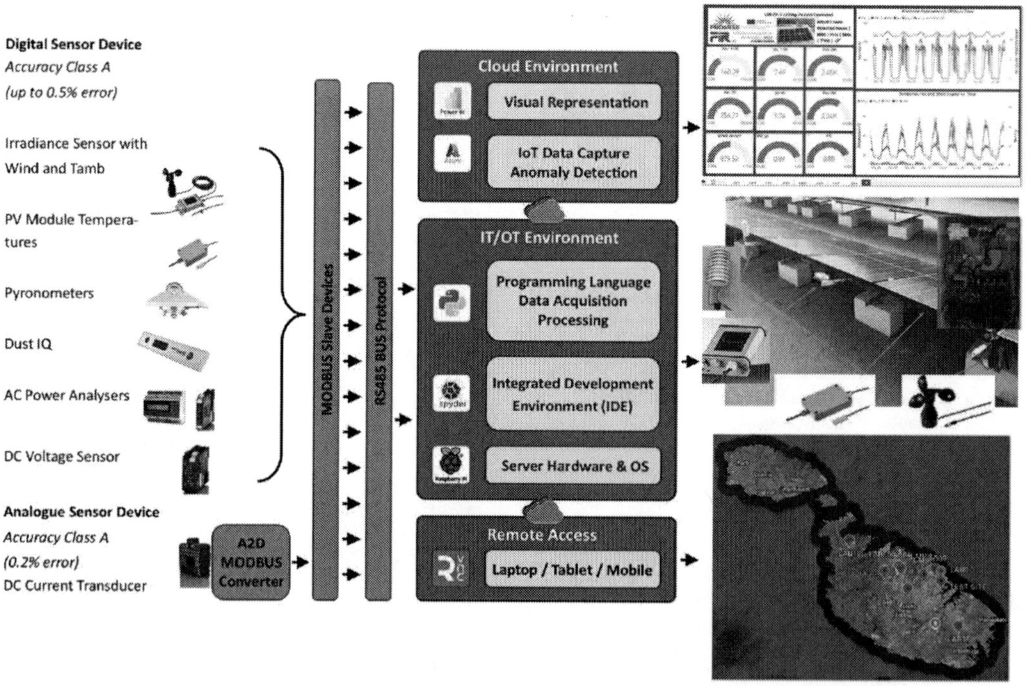

Figure 1: Sensory Edge and Cloud Comprehensive Framework for the Malta Living Laboratories

10.4229/EUPVSEC2025/4CV.1.25
020334-004

incoming data to the appropriate storage container in *Cosmos DB* database. When telemetry from an unrecognised device ID is detected, the system automatically creates a new storage container in Cosmos DB, enabling the seamless integration of newly added sites. These functions can be developed directly through the Azure portal or locally on a PC and then deployed to Azure as serverless applications, allowing flexible development, integration, and scalability

Beyond basic routing, the Functions perform both light and advanced pre-processing, including removal of malformed packets, assignment of laboratory identifiers, and automatic creation of new storage containers for newly deployed. They also generate status flags and send notifications to users when null or implausible values are detected, typically arising from sensor or communication errors. In addition, the Functions continuously monitor incoming telemetry to perform performance-driven anomaly detection and support downstream analytics within the PROMISE monitoring framework.

4.3 Azure Cosmos DB and Analytical Store (Storage)

The *Cosmos DB (NoSQL)* [15] database provides the primary storage layer for all monitoring data. Telemetry is written to the Transactional Store as JSON documents, ensuring millisecond-level ingestion and global redundancy. Data are then mirrored automatically to the Analytical Store, where they are restructured into a columnar format optimised for large-scale queries and analytical workloads. This dual-store mechanism separates operational and analytical traffic, preserving ingestion performance while enabling efficient querying for research analysis and dashboarding. Historical data can be downloaded in both CSV and JSON formats

4.4 Azure Synapse Link and Analytics, and *Power BI*

The Synapse Link bridges *Cosmos DB's Analytical Store* with *Azure Synapse Analytics*, providing a direct, near-real-time connection to analytical and visualisation services without Extraction, Loading and Transformation processes (ELT). Within *Synapse Analytics*, data can be queried using serverless SQL or processed with Spark for machine-learning tasks.

The processed and aggregated datasets feed directly into *Power BI*, which serves as a front-end unified visualisation and dissemination platform. Dashboards built in *Power BI Desktop are* deployed through the *Power BI Service*, offering both private, capacity-backed access through different tiers for project partners and public dashboards embedded on the PROMISE website. These visual dashboard interfaces deliver real-time operational awareness and retrospective performance analysis across all Living Laboratories and test facilities, as illustrated Fig. 1.

5. . EXPLOITABLE RESULTS

Following the digital upgrade of the PROMISE monitoring infrastructure, the system has now expanded from the initial six PV Living Laboratories reported in Bartolo et al. (2024) to a total of ten monitoring sites and three dedicated test facilities across Malta. Electrical and meteorological sensors, continue to ensure high reliability under Mediterranean climatic conditions. Data acquisition now occurs at 3-second intervals, enabling enhanced temporal resolution and adherence to the IEC 61724-1:2021 standard.

One of the most significant developments of this phase is the establishment of the PROMISE Open PV Reliability Repository, which provides public access to real-time and historical datasets from all laboratories. This open-data initiative promotes transparency, collaboration, and reproducibility, aligning the PROMISE project with European directives on open science and enabling Malta's active participation in international PV reliability and benchmarking programmes.

The multi-site configuration now includes:

i. Ten rooftop PV monitoring sites across institutional and industrial locations, covering diverse microclimates and system architectures.
ii. Three dedicated test sites, each with a specific role:
iii. A PV Degradation Test Site forming part of a round-robin international study to benchmark long-term degradation across European climates.
iv. A BIPV reference facility equipped with a multi-orientation, multi-inclination angle-optimised reference sensor array for grid-integration and energy-yield studies.
v. A PV calibration site, equipped with secondary-standard pyranometers, serving as a second-level calibration reference laboratory for benchmarking and calibration of other monitoring nodes.

5.1 Developed Key Exploitable Results (KERs)

The expanded infrastructure and digitalisation framework have produced a series of exploitable research, technical, and capacity-building outcomes:

1. Malta PV Living Laboratories – Monitoring Infrastructure: a national, cloud-integrated, real-time monitoring network for distributed PV systems.
2. Smart PV Insights – AI Prediction Models for Islands: machine-learning models for forecasting PV performance and grid interaction under insular conditions.
3. Malta PV Calibration Lab – Second-Level Reference Facility: establishes traceability and calibration procedures for sensors and instruments across the Living Labs.
4. PV Module Degradation Test Site – Global Benchmark Node: contributes to a Europe-wide round-robin initiative for comparative degradation analysis.
5. BIPV Angle-Optimised Reference Sensor Array Enables evaluation of tilt- and orientation-dependent irradiance effects on PV yield and grid stability.
6. Mediterranean PV Schools – Capacity-Building Flagship: training programmes, internships, and educational outreach to strengthen local expertise.
7. First-Check App – Real-Time PV Health Snapshot: a lightweight mobile interface providing quick visualisation of laboratory and system health indicators.

8. PV ThermalScan – Drone-AI Fault Detection Service: an aerial inspection tool integrating thermography and AI analytics for field fault detection.
9. Advanced PV Diagnostics – EL & IV Testing Setup: laboratory infrastructure for detailed characterisation of PV modules.
10. PROMISE Open PV Reliability Repository: a fully public, cloud-hosted data repository promoting transparency and collaborative research.
11. Postgraduate Framework with Anhalt University: Academic collaboration enabling joint supervision and research exchange in PV reliability and digitalisation.
12. Reactive Power Control Testbed for PV–EV Scenarios: Experimental platform for assessing PV–EV grid interaction and smart-inverter control strategies

6. CONCLUSION

The 2025 phase of the PROMISE project marks a major advancement in the digital transformation of PV system monitoring. The transition from a hybrid ThingSpeak–Grafana setup to a unified Microsoft Azure-based architecture has addressed previous limitations related to scalability, data synchronisation, and interoperability. Through the integration of IoT Hub, Function Apps, Cosmos DB, and Power BI, the framework now supports real-time analytics, predictive maintenance, and cross-site benchmarking. The expansion to ten monitoring laboratories and three dedicated test sites establishes a comprehensive platform for studying PV degradation behaviour, orientation effects, and grid-integration dynamics under diverse environmental conditions.

The introduction of the PROMISE Open PV Reliability Repository further reinforces transparency and open collaboration by providing public access to harmonised, high-quality datasets readily available on the project website Malta PV Living Laboratories – PROMISE. [8] These developments position PROMISE as a replicable model for intelligent, cloud-integrated PV monitoring aligned with the objectives of the European Green Deal and the digital energy transition.

Future work will focus on implementing real-time performance and anomaly detection frameworks within the cloud pipeline, expanding the monitoring network to additional European sites with similar climatic challenges, and performing multi-site irradiance correlation analyses to support short-term weather transition forecasting. This capability will enable utilities to anticipate the impact of atmospheric changes on PV generation, contributing to smarter, more resilient grid operation.

ACKNOWLESGEMENTS

Funded by the European Union

UK Research and Innovation

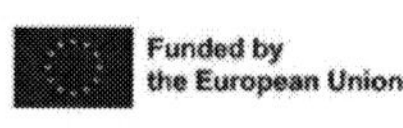

Partly funded by the European Union under Grant 101079469 PROMISE "Photovoltaics Reliability Operations and Maintenance Innovative Solutions for Energy Alliance" project, under Grant 101075747 and UK Research and Innovation (UKRI) TRANSIT "TRANSITion to sustainable future through training and education" project, European Union, Xjenza Malta under Grant REP-2023-061 RoOFPEVs "Robust Optimization Framework for PVs and EVs Integration at Low Voltage Network" project.

Views and opinions expressed are, however, those of the author(s) only and do not necessarily reflect those of the granting authorities/agencies nor that the granting authorities/agencies can be held responsible for them. Furthermore, the authors would like to thank the owners of the PV systems deployed as FiR.mt Living Laboratories in Malta.

REFERENCES

[1] 'EU Fit for 55: Navigate emissions management | LR'. Accessed: Sep. 27, 2025. [Online]. Available: https://www.lr.org/en/expertise/maritime-energy-transition/fit-for-55/

[2] 'The European Green Deal - European Commission'. Accessed: Sep. 27, 2025. [Online]. Available: https://commission.europa.eu/strategy-and-policy/priorities-2019-2024/european-green-deal_en

[3] 'Performance of New Photovoltaic System Designs'. Accessed: Oct. 10, 2025. [Online]. Available: https://isfh.de/en/reports/performance-of-new-photovoltaic-system-designs

[4] D. L. King, 'More "efficient" methods for specifying and monitoring PV system performance', in *2011 37th IEEE Photovoltaic Specialists Conference*, Jun. 2011, pp. 000219–000224. doi: 10.1109/PVSC.2011.6185884.

[5] 'Technical Specifications for On-site Solar Photovoltaic Systems', Energy.gov. Accessed: Oct. 10, 2025. [Online]. Available: https://www.energy.gov/femp/technical-specifications-site-solar-photovoltaic-systems

[6] M. A. Cassar, 'A study on the salinity of Maltese Soils in relation to their distance from the coast', bachelorThesis, University of Malta, 2016. Accessed: Sep. 29, 2025. [Online]. Available: https://www.um.edu.mt/library/oar/handle/123456789/22065

[7] R. J. Whittaker and J. M. Fernández-Palacios, 'Island environments', in *Island Biogeography: Ecology, evolution, and conservation*, R. J. Whittaker and J. M. Fernández-Palacios, Eds., Oxford University Press, 2006, p. 0. doi: 10.1093/oso/9780198566113.003.0002.

[8] 'Malta PV Living Laboratories – PROMISE'. Accessed: Sep. 30, 2025. [Online]. Available: https://pv-promise.eu/malta-pv-living-laboratories/

[9] B. Bartolo *et al.*, 'Harmonising Multi-Sites Measurement of Photovoltaic Systems: Comprehensive Framework for Real-Life Test Conditions in a Maltese Environment', *41st Eur. Photovolt. Sol. Energy Conf. Exhib.*, pp. 020340-001-020340–004, 2024, doi: 10.4229/EUPVSEC2024/4BV.3.26.

[10] B. Bartolo, B. Azzopardi, and K. Scerri, 'Development and implementation of a public data

repository for photovoltaic systems: Case study malta's living laboratories', *Sol. Energy Adv.*, vol. 5, p. 100100, Jan. 2025, doi: 10.1016/j.seja.2025.100100.
[11] 'IoT Analytics - ThingSpeak Internet of Things'. Accessed: Sep. 30, 2025. [Online]. Available: https://thingspeak.mathworks.com/
[12] 'Grafana Cloud | Observability platform overview', Grafana Labs. Accessed: Sep. 30, 2025. [Online]. Available: https://grafana.com/products/cloud/
[13] SoniaLopezBravo, 'Azure IoT Hub Documentation'. Accessed: Sep. 30, 2025. [Online]. Available: https://learn.microsoft.com/en-us/azure/iot-hub/
[14] ggailey777, 'Azure Functions documentation'. Accessed: Sep. 30, 2025. [Online]. Available: https://learn.microsoft.com/en-us/azure/azure-functions/
[15] markjbrown, 'Understand Distributed NoSQL Databases - Azure Cosmos DB'. Accessed: Sep. 30, 2025. [Online]. Available: https://learn.microsoft.com/en-us/azure/cosmos-db/distributed-nosql
[16] 'Power BI'. Accessed: Sep. 30, 2025. [Online]. Available: https://app.powerbi.com/home?experience=power-bi
[17] 'IEC 61724-1:2021'. Accessed: Sep. 04, 2025. [Online]. Available: https://webstore.iec.ch/en/publication/65561
[18] 'The Use of Advanced Algorithms in PV Failure Monitoring'. Accessed: Oct. 10, 2025. [Online]. Available: https://isfh.de/en/reports/the-use-of-advanced-algorithms-in-pv-failure-monitoring
[19] S. Vergura, 'A Statistical Tool to Detect and Locate Abnormal Operating Conditions in Photovoltaic Systems', *Sustainability*, vol. 10, no. 3, p. 608, Mar. 2018, doi: 10.3390/su10030608.
[20] 'ISO/IEC 17025:2017', ISO. Accessed: Oct. 10, 2025. [Online]. Available: https://www.iso.org/standard/66912.html
[21] 'ISO 9001:2015', ISO. Accessed: Oct. 10, 2025. [Online]. Available: https://www.iso.org/standard/62085.html
[22] 'Modbus_Application_Protocol_V1_1b3.pdf'. Accessed: Sep. 30, 2025. [Online]. Available: https://www.afs.enea.it/project/protosphera/Proto-Sphera_Full_Documents/mpdocs/docs_EEI/Modbus_Application_Protocol_V1_1b3.pdf?utm_source=chatgpt.com
[23] 'raspberry-pi-4-product-brief.pdf'. Accessed: Sep. 30, 2025. [Online]. Available: https://datasheets.raspberrypi.com/rpi4/raspberry-pi-4-product-brief.pdf?utm_source=chatgpt.com
[24] 'Application Note ModBus Rev B.pdf'. Accessed: Sep. 30, 2025. [Online]. Available: https://www.electrokit.com/upload/product/41020/41020847/Application%20Note%20ModBus%20Rev%20B.pdf?utm_source=chatgpt.com
[25] *pymodbus: A fully featured modbus protocol stack in python*. Python. Accessed: Sep. 30, 2025. [MacOS :: MacOS X, Microsoft, OS Independent, POSIX :: Linux, Unix]. Available: https://github.com/pymodbus-dev/pymodbus/
[26] 'Download VNC Viewer by RealVNC®', RealVNC®. Accessed: Sep. 30, 2025. [Online]. Available: https://www.realvnc.com/en/connect/download/viewer/
[27] Emmet, 'Beginners Guide to Cron Jobs and Crontab', Pi My Life Up. Accessed: Oct. 10, 2025. [Online]. Available: https://pimylifeup.com/cron-jobs-and-crontab/
[28] jilmal, 'What is Azure Cosmos DB analytical store?' Accessed: Sep. 30, 2025. [Online]. Available: https://learn.microsoft.com/en-us/azure/cosmos-db/analytical-store-introduction
[29] im-microsoft, 'What is Azure Synapse Link for SQL? - Azure Synapse Analytics'. Accessed: Sep. 30, 2025. [Online]. Available: https://learn.microsoft.com/en-us/azure/synapse-analytics/synapse-link/sql-synapse-link-overview
[30] juluczni, 'Azure Synapse Analytics - Azure Synapse Analytics'. Accessed: Sep. 30, 2025. [Online]. Available: https://learn.microsoft.com/en-us/azure/synapse-analytics/

AUTHORS CONTRIBUTIONS

Conceptualisation (BB, BA, AM, MR, BK), Data curation (BB), Formal analysis (BB), Hardware/Software (BB, BA, CA), Funding acquisition (BA), Investigation (BB, BA), Methodology (BB, BA, KS), Project administration (BA), Resources (BA), Supervision (BA, KS), Validation (BA), Visualisation (BB, BA), Writing – original draft (BB, BA), Writing – review and editing (RE, CM, ME, EZ, SZ).

UAV-BASED AUTONOMOUS MONITORING AND REAL-TIME THERMAL ANOMALY DETECTION OF PHOTOVOLTAIC MODULES

G. Taghipour Kani [1], S.M. Esmailifar [1], A. Ghahremani[1], and M. Aghaei[2,3*]

[1]Department of Aerospace Engineering, Amirkabir University of Technology, Tehran 15119-43943, Iran
[2]Department of Ocean Operations and Civil Engineering, Norwegian University of Science and Technology (NTNU), 6009 Ålesund, Norway
[3]Department of Sustainable Systems Engineering (INATECH), University of Freiburg, 79110 Freiburg, Germany

*mohammadreza.aghaei@ntnu.no

ABSTRACT: This study presents an end-to-end autonomous monitoring framework for photovoltaic (PV) modules using unmanned aerial vehicles (UAVs), integrating thermal anomaly detection, boundary segmentation, and adaptive coverage path planning. The proposed system utilizes deep learning-based YOLO classifiers to identify nine different thermal faults in PV arrays, ensuring accurate and efficient real-time fault detection during flight. YOLOv8l achieved the highest classification performance (83.02% Top-1 accuracy), and YOLOv8n demonstrated exceptional computational efficiency with an inference time of just 8 ms and a compact model size of 2.94 MB, making it ideal for resource-constrained UAVs. To guide the UAV flight inside a solar farm, YOLO segmentation models were trained to extract PV plant boundaries from aerial images. YOLOv8l, selected for its high segmentation accuracy (mAP@50 = 0.952), provided precise navigable zone delineation critical for the next planning stage. These boundaries were used to generate a grid-based representation of the inspection area, supporting a deterministic sweep coverage algorithm with real-time obstacle avoidance and fallback handling. The coverage path planning system dynamically adapts to the layout of each PV installation, ensuring all accessible areas are inspected while minimizing flight distance and energy consumption. This multi-component framework enhances UAV autonomy and inspection completeness, reduces manual effort, and supports scalable real-time maintenance strategies for large-scale solar farms.

Keywords: UAV-based monitoring; photovoltaic modules; thermal anomaly detection; YOLO classifiers; real-time monitoring; coverage path planning

1 INTRODUCTION

As photovoltaic (PV) deployment expands globally, maintaining performance through efficient monitoring is increasingly critical. Traditional inspections—manual walk-throughs or ground-based thermal imaging—are slow, labor-intensive, and impractical for large PV farms. They are also prone to human error and limited visibility, often missing anomalies such as hot spots, diode failures, or cracks [1-4].

UAVs equipped with thermal cameras offer a scalable, contactless, and rapid alternative for large-area PV inspection. Yet achieving fully autonomous, real-time operation remains challenging, particularly for fault classification under limited onboard resources, navigable area segmentation, and energy-efficient path planning [2, 5, 6].

Moradi Sizkouhi et al. [7] introduced RoboPV, an autonomous UAV monitoring system with 93% inspection accuracy, combining boundary detection, path planning, and fault detection via a deep learning encoder-decoder. However, RoboPV lacks robust real-time detection across diverse PV faults. Addressing this gap, this study proposes a comprehensive UAV-based framework integrating:

- Grid-based path planning with adaptive logic for full coverage and energy efficiency
- Boundary segmentation for precise inspection area extraction
- Thermal anomaly classification using optimized YOLO models across nine PV conditions

Figure 1 shows the workflow of the proposed system.

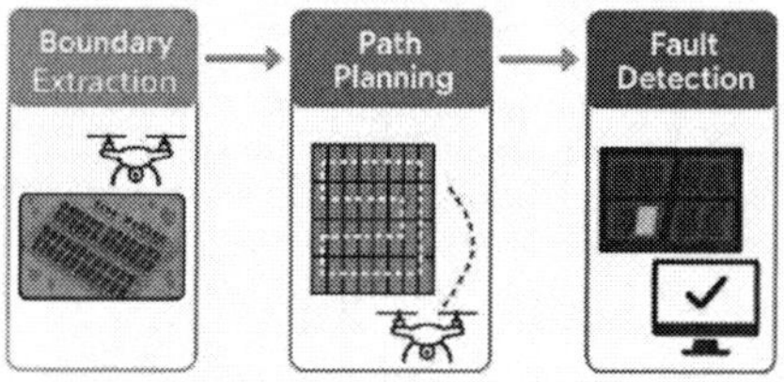

Figure 1. Workflow of the proposed UAV-based PV monitoring framework.

This work builds upon earlier efforts such as RoboPV, which demonstrated effective UAV-based inspection workflows but lacked real-time anomaly detection and lightweight path intelligence. By addressing these limitations, our proposed system offers a robust, real-time solution for autonomous monitoring and maintenance of solar farms, contributing to higher operational uptime, reduced maintenance cost, and improved energy output.

2 EMPLOYED DATASET

To enable real-time fault classification and autonomous navigation in UAV-based solar farm monitoring, this study uses a dataset of 20,000 aerial thermal images [8], each at 24×40 resolution and representing diverse PV module conditions.

Images are labeled into nine classes: eight common thermal anomalies and one nominal (defect-free) state. The anomaly classes include hot-spot heating, cracking, bypass diode failures (single/multiple), shading, vegetation overgrowth, soiling, and offline modules, which are key indicators of PV performance degradation.

10.4229/EUPVSEC2025/4CV.1.26
020335-001

Table 1. Thermal Images Dataset Description

Class Name	Number of Images	Description
Hot-Spot	3,663	High-temperature regions caused by faults.
Cracking	941	Surface cracks visible in thermal imaging.
Shadowing	1,056	Obstructions caused by vegetation or nearby structures.
Diode	1,499	Activation of bypass diodes affecting module efficiency.
Diode-Multi	175	Multiple activated bypass diodes reducing performance.
Vegetation	1,639	Panels blocked by vegetation growth.
Soiling	205	Dirt or debris reducing energy output.
Offline-Module	828	Entire module disconnected or malfunctioning.
No-Anomaly	10,000	Nominal solar modules with no visible defects.

The data were collected using piloted aircraft and UAVs equipped with midwave and longwave infrared (MWIR/LWIR) sensors covering 3–13.5 µm. Depending on sensor type and altitude, the ground sampling distance (GSD) ranged from 3.0 to 15.0 cm per pixel, providing sufficient thermal resolution for defect detection.

For focused analysis, anomaly instances were manually cropped from larger mosaics to isolate individual PV modules. The final dataset reflects a semi-realistic anomaly distribution, with 50% of samples representing nominal conditions. This intentional imbalance simulates real-world scenarios where functional modules dominate but early-stage faults must still be detected.

3 YOLO CLASSIFIERS TRAINING AND TUNING

YOLO (You Only Look Once) classifiers are well-suited for real-time vision tasks due to their unified architecture, which enables detection or classification in a single forward pass. In this study, three YOLO variants (YOLOv8n, YOLOv8l, and YOLOv8x) were employed for multi-class thermal anomaly classification. These models were selected to represent a range of trade-offs between accuracy, speed, and model size, which are crucial when deploying inference pipelines onboard UAVs.

3.1 Training and Optimization Process

All models were implemented using the Ultralytics YOLOv8 framework, supporting streamlined training and hardware optimization. Input images were standardized to 96×96, and augmentations (random flips, scaling, HSV shifts, mosaic) were applied to improve generalization under varied UAV imaging conditions.

Models were trained for up to 600 epochs with a batch size of 32, using early stopping (patience of 100). A grid search–based hyperparameter tuning refined performance, exploring:

- Initial and final learning rates (lr0, lrf)
- Momentum and weight decay
- Warmup epochs for training stability
- Mosaic and HSV probabilities for augmentation control

These steps maximized classification accuracy while maintaining real-time responsiveness and low computational overhead.

3.2 Tuning Results and Model Performance

The tuned models demonstrated precious achivements in both accuracy and inference performance. YOLOv8l achieved the highest Top-1 classification accuracy of 83.02%, while YOLOv8n offered the best efficiency, requiring only 8 ms per inference with a minimal 2.94 MB model size. The results are summarized in the following tables.

Table 2. Tuned YOLO Models Hyperparameter Configurations.

Model	lr0	lrf	Momentum	Weight Decay	Warmup Epochs	HSV-H	Scale	Mosaic
YOLOv8x	0.01	0.01	0.937	0.0005	3.0	0.015	0.5	1.0
YOLOv8n	0.0101	0.01112	0.91359	0.00047	2.78907	0.015	0.6	0.99306
YOLOv8l	0.00939	0.01112	0.92606	0.00044	3.01336	0.014	0.488	0.977

Table 3. YOLO Model Performance After Tuning

Model	Top-1 Accuracy	Top-5 Accuracy	Inference Time (ms)	Model Size (MB)
YOLOv8n	82.25%	99.23%	8.0	2.94
YOLOv8l	83.02%	99.17%	11.0	70.92
YOLOv8x	82.13%	99.37%	21.0	109.88

- **YOLOv8n**: Lightweight with 82.25% Top-1 and 99.23% Top-5 accuracy, 8 ms inference, and 2.94 MB size, which is ideal for real-time UAV deployment in large solar farms.

- **YOLOv8l:** Most accurate (83.02% Top-1, 99.17% Top-5), with 11 ms inference and 70.92 MB size, balancing precision and efficiency for mid-resource platforms.

- **YOLOv8x:** 82.13% Top-1 and 99.37% Top-5 accuracy, but its 109.88 MB size and 21 ms inference limit suitability for UAVs, though effective in precision-focused tasks.

10.4229/EUPVSEC2025/4CV.1.26
020335-002

3.3 Insights and Interpretations

All YOLO variants achieved over 99% Top-5 accuracy, confirming their ability to distinguish subtle thermal patterns across nine anomaly classes. YOLOv8n, the most compact and fastest, suits edge UAV deployment where speed and power are critical, while YOLOv8l balances accuracy and efficiency for mid-tier platforms. Learning and validation curves (Figure 2) indicate stable convergence and minimal overfitting, validating the training pipeline and hyperparameter design.

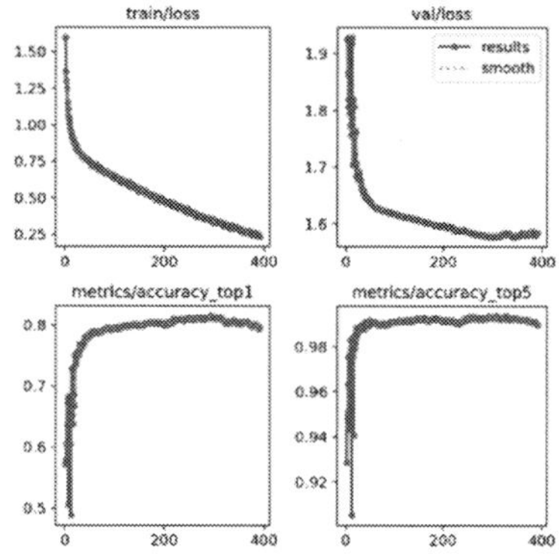

(a)

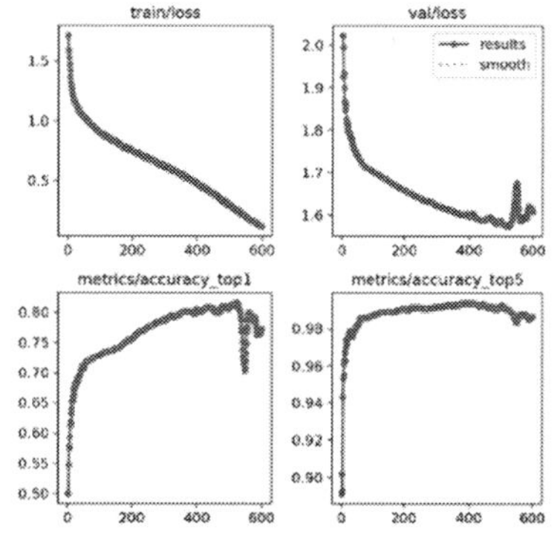

(b)

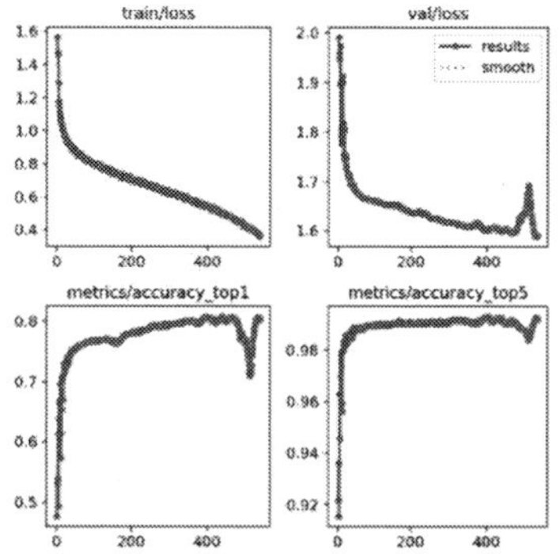

(c)

Figure 2. Obtained loss and accuracy curves for YOLO classifiers: a) yolov8x-cls.pt training process, b) yolov8l-cls.yaml and c) yolov8n-cls.pt during the training process.

The results demonstrate that YOLO models are highly effective for UAV-based PV anomaly detection, providing a reliable, efficient, and scalable solution for real-time thermal monitoring of solar farms. Their ability to balance accuracy and computational efficiency makes them perfect choices for enhancing solar farm productivity through UAV-integrated monitoring systems.

4. SOLAR FARM BOUNDARY DETECTION

Accurate boundary extraction is essential for autonomous UAV inspection, ensuring navigation remains within operational areas, avoiding non-functional zones, and conserving energy. It also forms the basis for structured grid maps needed in path planning.
Two YOLO segmentation models were evaluated using the Amir dataset [9, 10], which contains 3,548 high-resolution aerial images of large-scale PV installations worldwide with precisely annotated PV masks for supervised training.
Models were trained with the Ultralytics YOLO segmentation framework for 200 epochs, batch size 64, on an NVIDIA GeForce RTX 4070 Ti GPU, enabling fast cycles and scalability for large datasets.

4.1 SEGMENTATION TRAINING AND METRICS

The segmentation process employed a multi-part loss function, which includes components for bounding box regression, segmentation masks, class prediction, and distribution focal loss (DFL). The segmentation loss was computed using binary cross-entropy, penalizing pixel-wise deviation from ground truth masks. This structure allows the model to simultaneously learn object presence, boundary shapes, and spatial alignment.

Model performance was measured using:

- Precision: ratio of correctly segmented areas to total predicted segments,
- Recall: proportion of ground truth regions that were successfully segmented,
- mAP@50: mean Average Precision at IoU threshold 0.5, summarizing precision-recall balance across confidence thresholds.

A prediction was considered correct if its segmentation mask overlapped with ground truth by at least 50% using Intersection over Union (IoU).

4.2 Results And Model Comparison

Both YOLOv8l and YOLO11l achieved smooth convergence with rising precision and recall across epochs. As shown in Table 4, YOLOv8l reached a mAP@50 of 0.952, outperforming YOLO11l at 0.911, demonstrating higher segmentation reliability and suitability for accurate navigability maps.
YOLO11l, though less accurate, offered faster inference (46 ms vs. 55 ms), making it a viable option for highly resource-constrained UAVs where speed is prioritized.

10.4229/EUPVSEC2025/4CV.1.26
020335-003

However, due to the importance of boundary precision for navigation safety and grid accuracy, YOLOv8l was chosen as the final model. Figure 3 shows successful boundary extraction under diverse aerial conditions.

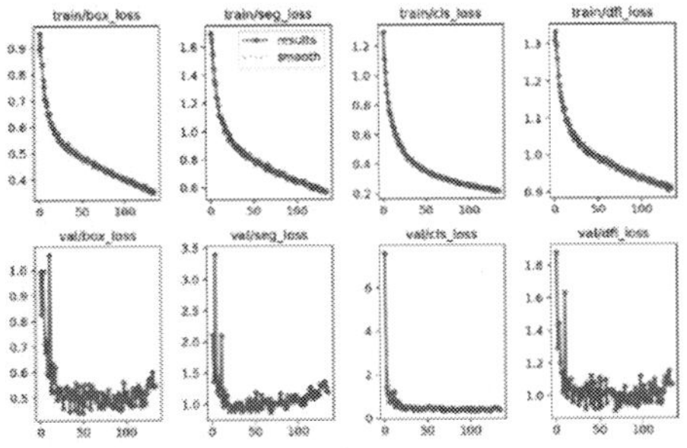

(a)

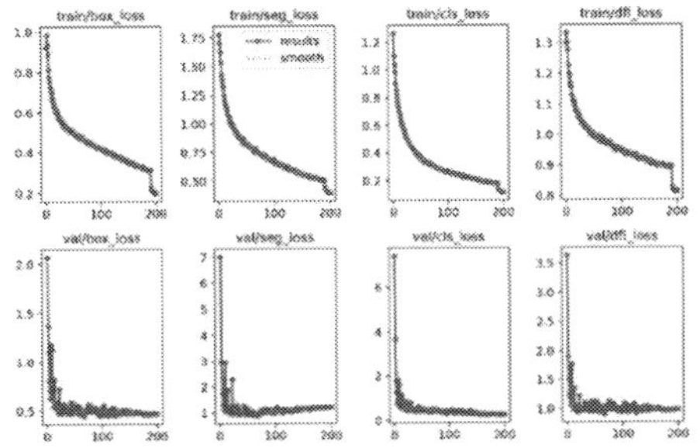

(b)

Figure 3. Cost function for train and validation sets for a) YOLOv8l segmentation model, b) YOLO11l segmentation model

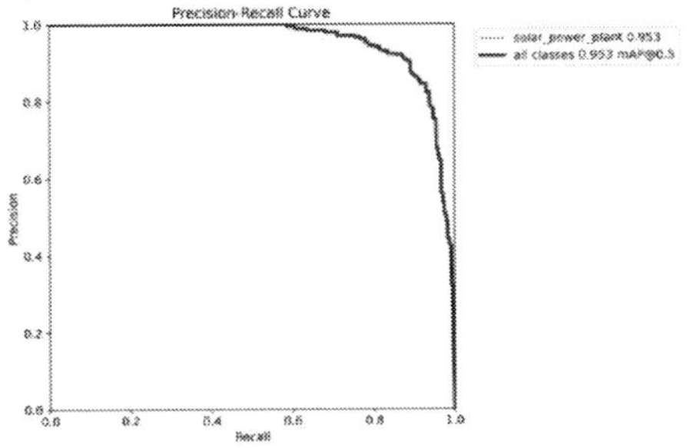

(a)

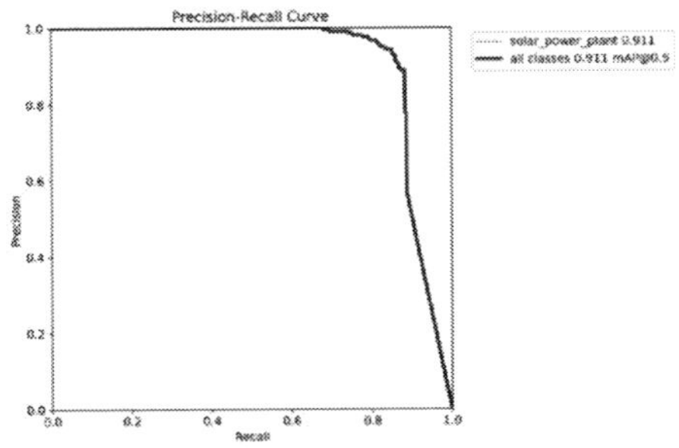

(b)

Figure 4. Precision versus recall graph for a) YOLOv8l segmentation model, b) YOLO11l segmentation model.

Table 4. Boundary Detection Results

Segmentation Model	Inference Time (ms)
YOLOv8l	55.00
YOLO11l	46.00

The boundary extraction model result is shown in Figure 4. By incorporating accurate and real-time boundary extraction using YOLOv8l, the system ensures precise mapping of navigable areas for UAVs, laying the groundwork for the path planning module described in the following section.

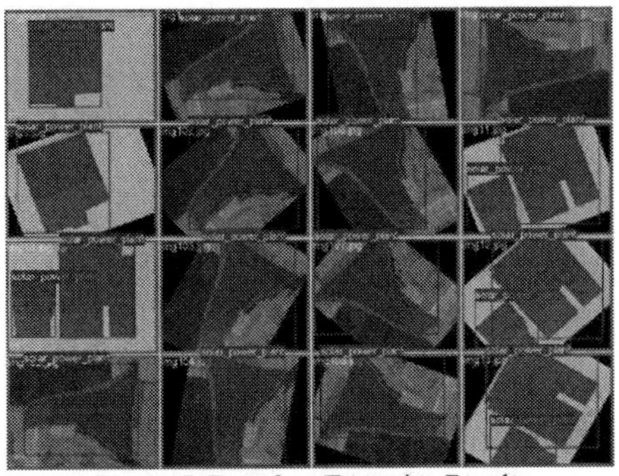

Figure 5. Boundary Extraction Results

5. PATH PLANNING FOR UAV NAVIGATION

Following boundary extraction, an adaptive navigation strategy is required to ensure complete inspection of the solar farm. This section introduces a grid-based path planning algorithm for UAVs, designed to deliver systematic and energy-efficient coverage. By utilizing aerial imagery and segmentation-derived navigable zones, the method ensures every operational cell of the solar array is inspected, even in complex or obstructed environments.

The planner divides the farm into a grid, with each cell representing a discrete inspection zone based on the UAV's thermal camera field of view. Cells are classified as navigable (safe for flight) or non-navigable (obstacles or irrelevant areas) using YOLOv8l segmentation. This spatial mapping enables optimized path execution with minimal overlap and adaptive redirection.

5.1 Methodology and Coverage Mechanism

The segmented aerial image is transformed into a 2D navigability grid, where each cell corresponds to part of the solar field:

- Navigable cells: safe for traversal
- Non-navigable cells: physical obstacles (e.g., trees, buildings, inaccessible terrain)

10.4229/EUPVSEC2025/4CV.1.26
020335-004

Classification is derived from YOLOv8l segmentation. The UAV begins inspection from a defined starting point and follows a deterministic raster sweep: scanning rows horizontally, shifting vertically, and reversing direction. This minimizes angular turns, simplifies control logic, and adapts to both compact and dispersed PV arrays. The grid abstraction generalizes across various geometries, while navigability masks prevent unsafe entry. Figure 6 illustrates the grid environment and UAV sweep zones.

5.2 Obstacle Handling and Adaptive Navigation

Solar plants often include incomplete rows, irregular layouts, and unexpected obstacles. To address these, the algorithm integrates real-time detection and fallback strategies. When the UAV reaches a boundary or non-navigable cell, it:

- Searches for adjacent unvisited navigable cells
- If none exist, applies a Euclidean distance heuristic to locate the nearest unvisited cell

This ensures no segment is skipped and prevents entrapment in concave areas. If isolated by obstacles, the UAV autonomously reroutes, reorients, and resumes sweeping, maintaining mission continuity without manual input. The fallback mechanism avoids dead-ends and supports uninterrupted coverage even after detours.

5.3 Full Coverage and State Tracking

To ensure complete inspection, the system maintains a binary state matrix marking each navigable cell as visited or unvisited. The UAV queries this matrix to:

- Prioritize unvisited cells
- Avoid redundant revisits
- Confirm mission completion via global coverage status

This mechanism supports both regular arrays and irregular layouts with missing or concave sections. Unlike conventional planners assuming convex farms, it accommodates fragmented, discontinuous installations. Through fallback repositioning and local re-alignment, the UAV systematically inspects all reachable zones. If any area remains uncovered due to obstacles or flight limits, the planner redirects the UAV until the matrix confirms completion or termination criteria are met.

5.4 Energy Efficiency and Path Optimization

With UAVs constrained by limited flight autonomy, minimizing energy use is essential. The planner enhances efficiency by:

- Reducing turns in sweep patterns
- Cutting backtracking through nearest-cell fallback logic
- Streamlining transitions between rows

These measures lead to fewer motor actuations, shorter inspection times, and higher coverage per battery cycle. Ultimately, optimized paths extend flight duration and enable broader inspection, improving scalability for utility-scale solar plants.

5.5 Visualization and Monitoring

The framework provides a real-time interface that tracks:

- UAV position on the grid
- History of visited cells
- Remaining unvisited regions

This gives operators a live view of progress and coverage. Post-flight, the module enables analytics such as heatmap generation, coverage validation, and detection of missed zones, supporting mission improvement and targeted re-inspection.

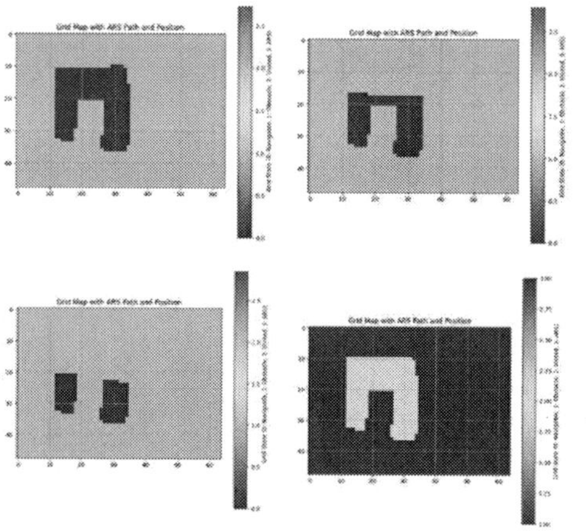

Figure 6. Automated path planning system phases during coverage process

5.6 Summary

This path planning system combines:

- Rule-based sweeping,
- Intelligent obstacle avoidance,
- Fallback logic,
- Energy-aware movement strategies, and
- Live inspection state tracking,

to deliver a robust, scalable, and fully autonomous UAV coverage algorithm. Unlike rigid route planners, this method adapts dynamically to environmental complexity, ensuring completeness and efficiency under real-world constraints. It forms the foundation of a reliable UAV-based PV monitoring pipeline, capable of operating without human intervention in large, irregular, or obstacle-dense solar farms.

10.4229/EUPVSEC2025/4CV.1.26

6 CONCLUSIONS

his paper presents an autonomous framework for real-time UAV inspection of photovoltaic (PV) modules, addressing fault detection, boundary mapping, and navigation. Unlike prior approaches treating classification and coverage separately, the proposed system integrates optimized deep learning with adaptive path planning into a deployable pipeline.

In classification, YOLO-based models were evaluated across nine thermal anomaly types. YOLOv8l achieved the highest Top-1 accuracy (83.02%) with moderate computational demand, while YOLOv8n offered the best efficiency, providing 8 ms inference and a 2.94 MB size suitable for resource-limited UAVs. For navigation, segmentation-based boundary extraction with YOLOv8l reached a mAP@50 of 0.952, reliably distinguishing navigable from non-navigable regions in complex PV layouts.

The core contribution is the adaptive grid-based path planner, which:

- Converts aerial segmentation into a navigability grid
- Uses deterministic sweep logic for row-wise traversal
- Integrates obstacle avoidance and fallback logic
- Tracks visited cells with a state matrix
- Optimizes path length and turns for energy efficiency

This ensures systematic inspection of all zones, including irregular or fragmented arrays. The combined logic and adaptive redirection enable autonomous operation across diverse solar farm conditions.

Overall, the framework delivers a scalable and robust solution that minimizes downtime, reduces manual labor, and enhances monitoring accuracy. By coupling real-time anomaly detection with intelligent flight coordination, it marks a step toward fully autonomous solar farm maintenance.

5 REFERENCES

1. Phungket, C. and P. Nangthin. *Deep Convolutional Neural Networks for Accurate Solar Module Classification in Thermal Images*. in *2024 12th International Electrical Engineering Congress (iEECON)*. 2024.
2. Zefri, Y., et al., *Developing a deep learning-based layer-3 solution for thermal infrared large-scale photovoltaic module inspection from orthorectified big UAV imagery data*. International Journal of Applied Earth Observation and Geoinformation, 2022. **106**: p. 102652.
3. Segovia Ramírez, I., B. Das, and F.P. García Márquez, *Fault detection and diagnosis in photovoltaic panels by radiometric sensors embedded in unmanned aerial vehicles*. Progress in Photovoltaics: Research and Applications, 2022. **30**(3): p. 240-256.
4. Wang, B., et al., *PVF-10: A high-resolution unmanned aerial vehicle thermal infrared image dataset for fine-grained photovoltaic fault classification*. Applied Energy, 2024. **376**: p. 124187.
5. Nie, J., T. Luo, and H. Li, *Automatic hotspots detection based on UAV infrared images for large-scale PV plant*. Electronics Letters, 2020. **56**(19): p. 993-995.
6. Sizkouhi, A.M.M., et al. *Autonomous Path Planning by Unmanned Aerial Vehicle (UAV) for Precise Monitoring of Large-Scale PV plants*. in *2019 IEEE 46th Photovoltaic Specialists Conference (PVSC)*. 2019.
7. Moradi Sizkouhi, A.M., et al., *RoboPV: An integrated software package for autonomous aerial monitoring of large scale PV plants*. Energy Conversion and Management, 2022. **254**: p. 115217.
8. Millendorf, M., E. Obropta, and N. Vadhavkar. *Infrared solar module dataset for anomaly detection*.
9. Sizkouhi, A.M.M., et al., *Automatic Boundary Extraction of Large-Scale Photovoltaic Plants Using a Fully Convolutional Network on Aerial Imagery*. IEEE Journal of Photovoltaics, 2020. **10**(4): p. 1061-1067.
10. M. Aghaei, et al, *Autonomous Intelligent Monitoring of Photovoltaic Systems: An In-Depth Multidisciplinary Review*, Progress in Photovoltaics: Research and Applications, 2024, https://doi.org/10.1002/pip.3859.

PHOTOVOLTAIC POWER OUTPUT ESTIMATION WITH DIGITAL VISIBLE CAMERAS

Abad-Alcaraz, V.[a,b], García-Campos, E.[a], Álvarez, J.D.[a,b], Pérez-García, M.[a,c], Carballo, J.A.[a,d], Castilla, M.M.[a,b], Alonso-Montesinos, J.[a,c]

[a] CIESOL, Solar Energy Research Centre, University of Almería ceiA3, Ctra. Sacramento s/n, La Cañada de San Urbano, Almería 04120, Spain.

[b] Department of Informatics, University of Almería- ceiA3, Ctra. Sacramento s/n, La Cañada de San Urbano, Almería 04120, Spain.

[c] Department of Chemistry and Physics, University of Almería – ceiA3, Ctra. Sacramento s/n, La Cañada de San Urbano, Almería 04120, Spain.

[d] Centro de Investigaciones Energéticas, Medioambientales y Tecnológicas-Plataforma Solar de Almería (CIEMAT-PSA), Ctra. de Senés, km. 4,5, Tabernas 04200, Spain

vabadalcaraz@ual.es, ecampos@ual.es, jhervas@ual.es, mperez@ual.es, jcarballo@psa.es, mcastilla@ual.es, joaquin.alonso@ual.es

ABSTRACT: Monitoring and estimating the production of a photovoltaic (PV) system is crucial to optimise energy efficiency, detect performance problems and improve its financial viability. Monitoring allows the operator to detect faults early, improve maintenance planning and maximise energy production, thus improving return on investment and sustainability. On the other hand, estimating PV field production helps to plan energy consumption and integrate it into the grid. This study aims to explore a deep learning approach to estimate power generation in real time using images captured every ten minutes by three fixed cameras positioned at different perspectives (left, lateral and right) of the PV field at CIESOL research center. A hybrid neural network combining convolutional neural networks (CNN) and long-term memory networks (LSTM) is used to analyse the images and establish correlations with the actual power production. The results show that an accuracy of up to 8% (NRMSE) can be achieved in production estimation, as well as adequately capturing power variations and environmental influences. These findings underscore the potential of image-based monitoring as a non-intrusive and efficient method for improving PV system management and maintenance.

Keywords: Photovoltaic production, forecasting, monitoring, computer vision, deep learning.

1 INTRODUCTION

The growing global energy demand and the negative environmental impacts associated with fossil fuels have spurred increasing interest in renewable energy sources as a clean and sustainable alternative [1]. In this context, photovoltaic (PV) solar energy has consolidated itself as one of the most promising options due to its widespread availability, implementation flexibility, and the continuous cost reductions associated with technological advances [2]. PV systems offer major advantages by directly harvesting solar radiation to generate electricity, thereby minimizing pollutant emissions and contributing effectively to global climate-change mitigation targets [3].

However, the efficiency and operational reliability of these systems largely depend on advanced and accurate techniques for monitoring and predicting energy performance [4]. Continuous monitoring enables the prompt detection of operational issues, appropriate planning of preventive maintenance, and the optimization of energy production [5]. Among the factors that can significantly affect the efficiency of PV plants, dust accumulation—or soiling—stands out, especially in arid and semi-arid regions affected by Saharan dust intrusions. Soiling reduces incident irradiance and adversely impacts energy yield and system profitability [6,7]. Hence, developing effective methods for the timely detection and precise quantification of these losses is essential [8].

Traditionally, PV performance monitoring has relied on direct measurements using specialized instrumentation such as pyranometers, temperature sensors, and other environmental devices [9,10]. Although these methods are generally accurate, they present drawbacks related to high cost, the need for frequent maintenance, and sensitivity to harsh environmental conditions, which undermines long-term reliability [11].

In response to these limitations, innovative non-intrusive approaches based on computer vision have emerged, employing digital visible cameras to capture real-time information on the surroundings and the condition of the solar modules [12]. Automated image analysis makes it possible to detect critical environmental phenomena—such as cloud cover, module shading, and dust accumulation—without the need for additional direct instrumentation [13].

In parallel, the development of deep learning algorithms has revolutionized the ability to extract and analyse complex patterns present in visual and sequential datasets. Artificial Neural Networks (ANNs) are computational models inspired by the functioning of the human brain, capable of learning abstract, non-linear representations from large volumes of data. Within this family, Convolutional Neural Networks (CNNs) are particularly effective for analysing and recognizing patterns in images, while Long Short-Term Memory networks (LSTMs) model and predict temporal dependencies in sequential data [14,15]. The combination of these hybrid CNN–LSTM architectures has delivered excellent results in complex tasks such as energy prediction, clearly outperforming conventional approaches and other statistical machine-learning techniques [16,17]. In particular, recent architectures such as EfficientNet-B0 have demonstrated superior capability for extracting relevant visual features with high computational efficiency for practical applications [18,19].

This study proposes to explore the capability of different visual viewpoints captured by digital cameras (oriented toward the left side, lateral side, and right side of the field) to accurately estimate, in real time, the energy production of a PV system. To this end, a hybrid CNN–LSTM architecture based on EfficientNet-B0 is employed with the aim of evaluating which perspective provides the most representative and accurate information. The results obtained are expected to substantially improve current monitoring strategies, optimize predictive maintenance, and enhance the overall efficiency of PV systems.

The remainder of this article is organized as follows: after this introduction, Section 2 details the methodology, including the characteristics of the PV system, the image acquisition and preprocessing. Section 3 presents a description of the proposed CNN–LSTM model. Section 4 reports the results and their comparative analysis across the different camera viewpoints. Finally, Section 5 summarizes the main conclusions, offering recommendations for the practical implementation of the proposed method and suggestions for future research.

2 METHODOLOGY

2.1 Location and photovoltaic system

The study is conducted at the CIESOL[1] building (Solar Energy Research Centre), a joint research facility of the University of Almería and the Plataforma Solar de Almería, located on the northern side of the University of Almería campus (Spain) and in operation since 2006. CIESOL is a bioclimatic building conceived as a living laboratory for research and technological demonstration in solar energy. Notable features include a solar-driven HVAC system (heating and cooling via an absorption chiller supplied by solar thermal collectors), automated windows and solar shading devices, and distributed instrumentation with more than 300 sensors for monitoring indoor variables and controlling thermal comfort. The roof integrates a PV array that supplies part of the building's electricity demand and solar thermal collectors that feed the cooling system based on solar energy, as shown in Fig. 1.

Figure 1: CIESOL building

The building was part of the ARFRISOL project (Bioclimatic Architecture and Solar Cooling), aimed at validating passive strategies and active solar systems in tertiary buildings; within this framework, envelope and control solutions were implemented to minimize demand and cover a significant fraction of thermal loads with solar energy.

From a functional and construction standpoint, CIESOL consists of two floors with a built area of approximately 1,070 m², housing eight laboratories and prototyping areas, in addition to workspaces and technical rooms. Several laboratories are north-facing, which supports stable daylight conditions and reduces direct solar gains during research activities. As part of its active integration of renewables and to meet building demand, the facility includes a grid-connected PV plant of $\approx$ 9.3 kWp (covering building electrical uses), alongside roof-mounted solar thermal collectors linked to the absorption-based HVAC system.

Additionally, the site is equipped with a comprehensive set of meteorological and radiometric sensors that record global, direct, and diffuse irradiance on the plane of array, together with environmental variables such as wind speed and relative humidity. These measurements document operating conditions and support dataset quality control (physical consistency checks and filtering of unsuitable periods). They are not used as predictors; in the setup, the target variable is the PV plant's measured electrical power.

The combination of this instrumentation with the building's renewable-energy infrastructure and high-cadence monitoring and control system makes CIESOL an effective testbed for the development and validation of power-estimation methodologies.

2.2 Image acquisition system

a) Left camera vision

b) Right camera vision

c) Lateral camera vision

Figure 2: Vision of the three cameras installed in the CIESOL PV plant.

[1] https://ciesol.com/

10.4229/EUPVSEC2025/4CV.1.28
020336-002

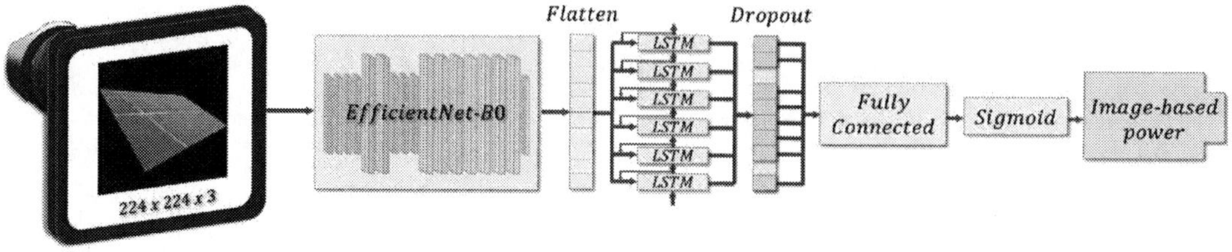

Figure 4: Model with CNN–LSTM using the EfficientNet-B0 framework

To enable power estimation based on visual information, three low-cost fixed digital cameras were installed with complementary perspectives on the PV generator:

- Left camera, with a view of the left wing of the field.
- Right camera, facing the right wing.
- Lateral camera, positioned to provide an overall view of the field from the side.

As seen in Fig. 2, the cameras operate in the RGB (visible) spectrum and capture an image every 10 minutes, generating a time series that can be synchronized with the power records.

2.3 Image preprocessing and mask generation

The final dataset used in this work consisted of 6,324 images, after an initial filtering process that eliminated those captured during nighttime, when electricity production is not active. A binary mask was systematically applied to each image to delimit exclusively the surface of the photovoltaic modules, thereby removing the sky, ground, and any other elements unrelated to the generator. Pixels within the panel area were assigned the logical value 1, while the rest of the scene was assigned 0. Overlaying this mask on the original image generated an effective crop that focused entirely on the PV field, ensuring that the visual information provided to the model corresponded only to the area of interest.

This segmentation process was found to be essential for reducing background noise and directing the learning process toward patterns directly related to system behaviour. Preliminary tests confirmed that the use of this segmentation step contributed to more accurate results in power prediction from images.

As illustrated in Fig. 3, the final image format is fed into the neural network. The original images had a slightly rectangular resolution of 3072 × 2028 pixels. Regardless of the input origin, whether lateral, left or right, all images were resized to a square format of 224 × 224 pixels to meet the input requirements of EfficientNet-B0 (CNN architecture). Although this resizing entails some loss of visual detail, the dimension was deemed sufficient for the network to operate efficiently while maintaining a manageable computational load.

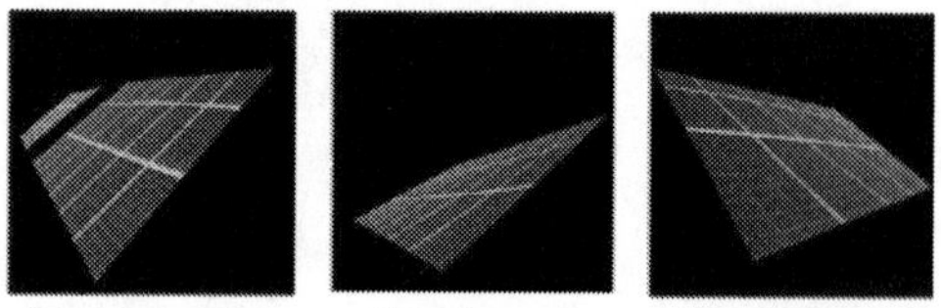

a) Lateral camera b) Left camera c) Right camera

Figure 3: Final preprocessed input images

The images are stored in RGB colour, which makes it easy to spot surface changes like dust accumulation or shading patterns. As the figure illustrates, the lateral perspective captures the largest visible area of the photovoltaic modules, providing a broader representation of the generator surface compared to left or right views.

In addition to the visual preprocessing, an exhaustive review of the power data used as the model output was carried out. First, all observations in which the recorded power was equal to zero at times when production was expected were discarded, as well as negative values generated by instrumental or logging errors. A selection procedure based on robust percentiles was also applied: the 0.5th and 99.5th percentiles of the power distribution were set as reference thresholds. Any value below the lower percentile was replaced by this limit, and similarly, any value above the 99.5th percentile was replaced by that threshold. After this process, which helps to remove erroneous data not detected manually, it was confirmed that the power was within the expected range, with a maximum value of 7,012.2 W. This ensures the consistency of the time series and prevents the model from being affected by spurious values. The procedure guarantees that the data fed into the neural network are clean, consistent, and physically plausible.

3 THE PROPOSED MODEL

3.1 CNN–LSTM architecture

In this work, meteorological and radiometric variables are used exclusively for dataset quality control and traceability; they are not used as predictors (e.g., discarding nighttime data, outliers under shading, or sensor faults). The supervised task is defined with the measured electrical power of the PV plant as the target variable, time-aligned with the images (see section 2.3 for data cleaning and filtering details). Power measurements and images were aligned by timestamp; samples without paired image or power record were discarded.

The predictive framework adopted in this work is based on a hybrid neural network that combines a CNN with an LSTM network, as illustrated in Fig. 4. This design leverages the ability of CNNs to extract spatial features from images and the capacity of LSTMs to capture temporal dependencies in sequential data. The synergy between both models enables the integration of visual and temporal information, which is essential when dealing with the short-term variability of PV power generation.

Solar radiation can undergo significant fluctuations even over short intervals, primarily due to cloud dynamics and atmospheric variability. In this context, extending the input sequences beyond a certain length not only adds little value to immediate prediction but also considerably increases computational cost and training complexity.

10.4229/EUPVSEC2025/4CV.1.28
020336-003

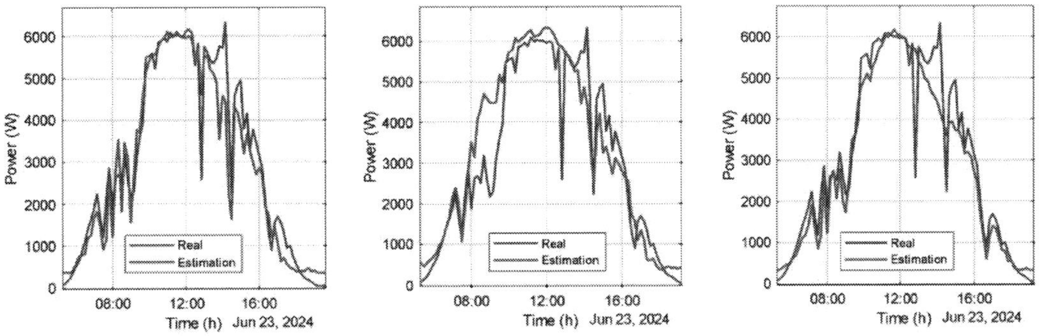

a) Lateral camera (b) Left camera (c) Right camera

Figure 5: Estimation of PV field power from the three camera viewpoints

Based on experimental evaluation, a one-hour interval was identified as the most suitable choice, as it strikes an optimal balance between capturing the relevant dynamics of solar variability and maintaining the computational efficiency of the model.

The convolutional branch of the network is based on EfficientNet-B0, an architecture that combines computational efficiency and accuracy through balanced scaling of depth, width, and resolution. This model has around 82 layers, among which the Mobile Inverted Bottleneck Convolutions (MBConv) blocks stand out.

The features generated by EfficientNet-B0 are flattened into one-dimensional vectors and are then fed into the LSTM branch. These recurrent networks allow temporal dependencies to be captured through a set of internal gates that regulate the flow of information: the forget gate decides which previous information is discarded, the update gate controls the incorporation of new input data, and the output gate determines which part of the updated internal state influences the hidden state transmitted to the next temporal step.

Finally, the combined output of the CNN and LSTM is connected to a fully connected dense layer, which is responsible for integrating the information extracted by both branches. The estimates are normalised in the range [0, 1] using a sigmoid activation function, which proved to be more suitable than classical standardization for this case.

3.2 Training and validation of prediction models

The model was trained using the Stochastic Gradient Descent with Momentum (SGDM) algorithm. This technique, an extension of traditional stochastic descent, incorporates a momentum term that smooths oscillations during optimization and accelerates convergence. In this work, the usual value of 0.9 was adopted, which has been shown to offer a good compromise between speed and stability. Compared to other optimizers such as Adam, SGDM exhibited more consistent behaviour and lower memory requirements.

The learning rate was set at 0.05, regulating the magnitude of weight updates in each iteration. A batch size of 64 was used, with the aim of balancing computational performance and memory utilisation. To avoid overfitting, a dropout layer was applied, which randomly deactivates 30% of the neurons during training, thus promoting the extraction of more robust features and reducing dependence on specific patterns.

In order to build and validate the model, complete days were randomly selected from the dataset, which is composed of a total of 93 days. The partition was divided into three subsets: 70% for training, 20% for validation, and 10% for testing. This strategy, the result of an experimental adjustment process, ensures a balanced distribution and favors the generalization of the model, while allowing its final performance to be evaluated on an independent dataset.

4 RESULTS AND DISCUSSION

In order to evaluate some statistical criteria, the measured power values of the CIESOL PV plant have been compared with the values estimated by the hybrid neural network. The results obtained demonstrate the efficacy of the deep learning model in estimating the power of the PV field from images captured from different perspectives. To assess the accuracy of the estimation, several statistical indices have been utilized, like the Mean Bias Error (MBE) to study the behaviour of the model in over/sub estimation; whereas the Root Mean Square Error (RMSE) and the normalised RMSE (NRMSE), calculated as the RMSE divided by the range of the observed data, were used to quantify the accuracy of the prediction:

$$RMSE = \sqrt{\frac{1}{n}\sum_{i=1}^{n}(\hat{y}_i - y_i)^2}\,; \quad NRMSE = \frac{RMSE}{y_{max} - y_{min}}$$

where, $\hat{y}_i$ is the predicted value, y_i is the observed value, n is the number of observations and y_{max}, y_{min} the maximum and minimum of y_i in the evaluation set.

Table I summarizes the statistical indices, offering a clear comparison of the model's performance across the different camera perspectives.

Table I: Statistical indices obtained from the power estimation

Camera position	MBE (W)	RMSE (W)	NRMSE(%)
Lateral camera	-55.48	552.30	7.92
Left camera	-131.58	736.79	10.57
Right camera	-217.59	849.49	12.19

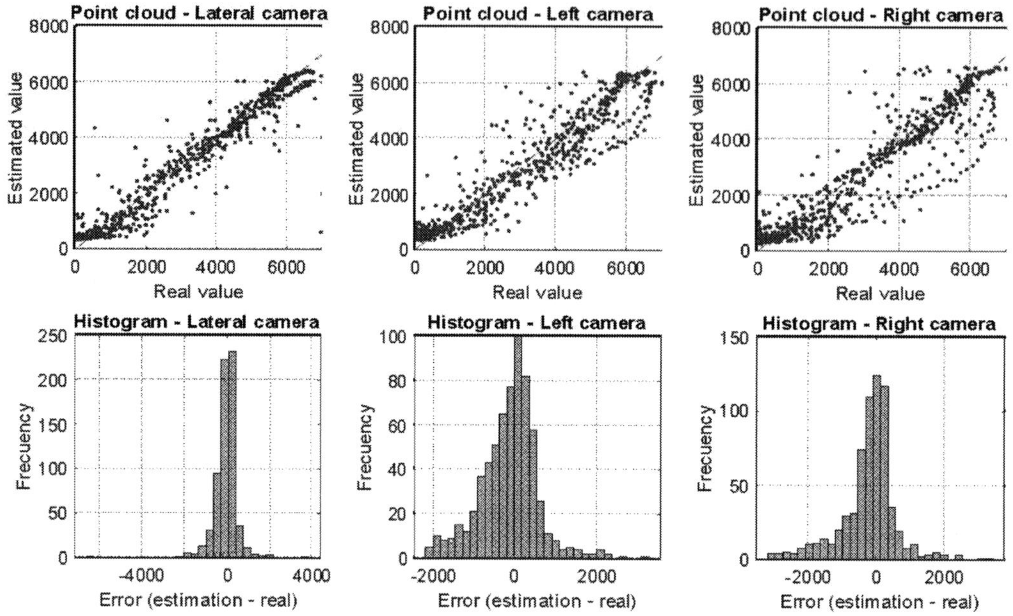

Figure 6: Dispersion diagram and error histogram for the CIESOL PV power estimation

According to this metric, the images captured by the lateral camera provide better results, with an NRMSE value of 7.92% and a subestimation of about 55 W, while the left and right cameras present values of 10.57% and 12.19%, respectively. This suggests that the lateral perspective provides a more accurate characterisation of power generation compared to the other two camera positions.

Analyzing the power estimation plots, one can see these findings, as shown in Fig. 5. Comparing the estimation curves with the actual measurements, the lateral camera shows the best fit, capturing more accurately the daily evolution of energy production, even in the case of external interferences such as clouds or fluctuations in solar radiation. The right camera also shows a good fit in this example, although with some discrepancies. As for the left camera, although its estimates are close to the real ones, a slight subestimation is noted at certain times. Although this graph represents a specific case, it reinforces that the lateral perspective is the most robust for power estimation.

In addition to the results presented in Table 1 and Fig. 5, Fig. 6 shows the error histograms for the lateral, left and right cameras. In the lateral camera, the estimates closely follow the line of identity, and its error histogram shows a highly concentrated distribution around zero, indicating low dispersion. The left camera shows more variability in the estimate, with some values far from the identity, and its histogram reflects a wider distribution. On the other hand, the right camera shows the highest dispersion in the estimation. Its histogram indicates greater variability, although it is relatively centred. Taken together, these results suggest that the lateral camera provides the most accurate estimates. The left and right cameras, moreover, have a larger spread in errors, which is consistent with their higher NRMSE values.

5 CONCLUSION AND FUTURE WORK

In conclusion, it has been possible to estimate the power output of a solar photovoltaic plant from visible-band images captured by digital cameras. This work presents the results of three cameras that have been placed in different positions of the CIESOL building with the aim of estimating the electrical power of a photovoltaic plant. The images were included in a convolutional neural network, to estimate the PV electricity production. In this sense, it has been possible to estimate the PV production with an NRMSE value of less than 8% for different sky conditions, supporting image-based monitoring as a practical, non-intrusive alternative for real-time performance assessment.

A complementary objective of the study was to assess the influence of the camera viewpoint on predictive quality. Using three fixed perspectives (left, right, and lateral), the analysis indicates that the lateral viewpoint—which naturally encompasses a larger portion of the array—provides the most informative representation for the proposed task, delivering the lowest NRMSE. The results thus highlight how viewpoint selection can enhance the relevance of the visual signal used by the network, while all three configurations remain fully compatible with the proposed pipeline.

Looking ahead, several directions are especially promising. First, extending the approach from immediate nowcasting to short- and longer-horizon forecasting would expand its operational value for planning and grid integration. Second, incorporating numerical inputs available at the site (e.g., irradiance on the plane of array, wind speed, relative humidity) as additional predictors—together with the image stream—may further improve accuracy by providing complementary context. Finally, exploring strategies that process simultaneous inputs from multiple cameras could capitalize on the complementary information present in the different perspectives to enhance the robustness and precision of the predictions.

6 ACKNOWLEDGEMENTS

This work is part of the I+D+i TED2021-131655B-I00 project, and has been carried out thanks to funding from AEI/10.13039/501100011033/ and "Unión Europea NextGenerationEU". Also, this work has been partially funded by the National R+D+i Plan Projects PID2021-126805OB-I00 (HELIOSUN project) of the Spanish Ministry of Science and Innovation funds.

7 REFERENCES

[1] IEA, World Energy Outlook 2024, IEA, Paris (2024).
[2] IRENA, Renewable power generation costs in 2024, International Renewable Energy Agency, Abu Dhabi (2025).
[3] F. Creutzig, P. Agoston, G. Nemet, J.C. Goldschmidt, G. Luderer, R.C. Pietzcker, The underestimated potential of solar energy to mitigate climate change, Nature Energy, Vol. 2 (2017) 17140. DOI: 10.1038/nenergy.2017.140.
[4] F. Touati, A. Khandakar, M.E. Chowdhury, A. J. S. Gonzales, C. K. Sorino, K. Benhmed. Photo-Voltaic (PV) monitoring system, performance analysis and power prediction models in Doha, Qatar. In Renewable Energy-Technologies and Applications. IntechOpen (2020). DOI: 10.3390/en18143786.
[5] M. Yazdi. Maintenance Strategies and Optimization Techniques. In: Advances in Computational Mathematics for Industrial System Reliability and Maintainability. Springer Series in Reliability Engineering. Springer, Cham (2024). DOI: 10.1007/978-3-031-53514-7_3.
[6] K. Ilse, L. Micheli, B. W. Figgis, K. Lange, D. Daßler, H. Hanifi, F. Wolfertstetter, V. Naumann, C. Hagendorf, R. Gottschalg, J. Bagdahn. Techno-economic assessment of soiling losses and mitigation strategies for solar power generation. Joule, Vol. 3.10 (2019) 2303-2321.
[7] J. Alonso-Montesinos, F.R. Martínez, J. Polo, N. Martín-Chivelet, F.J. Batlles. Economic effect of dust particles on photovoltaic plant production. Energies, Vol. 13.23 (2020) 6376. DOI: 10.3390/en13236376.
[8] W. Zhang, V. Archana, O. Gandhi, C.D. Rodríguez-Gallegos, H. Quan, D. Yang, H. Quan, D. Yang & D. Srinivasan. SoilingEdge: PV soiling power loss estimation at the edge using surveillance cameras. IEEE Transactions on Sustainable Energy, Vol. 15.1 (2023) 556-566. DOI: 10.1109/TSTE.2023.3320690.
[9] F. Touati, M.A. Al-Hitmi, N.A. Chowdhury, J.A. Hamad, A.J.S.P. Gonzales. Investigation of solar PV performance under Doha weather using a customized measurement and monitoring system. Renewable Energy, Vol. 89 (2016) 564-577. DOI: 10.1016/j.renene.2015.12.046.
[10] D. Dabou, A. Bouraiou, A. Ziane, A. Necaibia, N. Sahouane, M. Blal, S. Khelifi, A. Rouabhia, A. Slimani. Development of autonomous monitoring and performance evaluation system of grid-tied photovoltaic station. International journal of hydrogen energy, Vol. 46.59 (2021) 30267-30287. DOI: 10.1016/j.ijhydene.2021.06.204.
[11] J. L. Lorente, X. Liu, & D. J. Morrow. Worldwide evaluation and correction of irradiance measurements from personal weather stations under all-sky conditions. Solar Energy, Vol. 207 (2020) 925-936. DOI: 10.1016/j.solener.2020.06.073.
[12] S. Daliento, A. Chouder, P. Guerriero, A. M. Pavan, A. Mellit, R. Moeini, P. Tricoli. Monitoring, diagnosis, and power forecasting for photovoltaic fields: A review. International Journal of Photoenergy, Vol. 1 (2017) 1356851.
[13] E.A. Setiawan, M. Fathurrahman, R. F. Pamungkas, S. Ma'arif. Fast partial shading detection on PV modules for precise power loss ratio estimation using digital image processing. Journal of Electrical and Computer Engineering, Vol. 1 (2024), 9385602. DOI: 10.1155/2024/9385602.
[14] I. M. Mustaqeem, S. Kwon. A CNN-assisted deep echo state network using multiple time-scale dynamic learning reservoirs for generating short-term solar energy forecasting. Sustain Energy Technol Assess, Vol. 52. C (2022) 102275. DOI: 10.1016/j.seta.2022.102275
[15] Z. Garip, E. Ekinci, A. Alan. Day-ahead solar photovoltaic energy forecasting based on weather data using LSTM networks: a comparative study for photovoltaic (PV) panels in Turkey. Electrical Engineering, Vol. 105.5 (2023) 3329-3345. DOI: 10.1007/s00202-023-01883-7.
[16] D. Venkateswaran, Y. Cho. Efficient solar power generation forecasting for greenhouses: A hybrid deep learning approach. Alexandria Engineering Journal, Vol. 91 (2024) 222-236. DOI: 10.1016/j.aej.2024.02.004.
[17] A. Jakoplić, D. Franković, J. Havelka, H. Bulat. Short-term photovoltaic power plant output forecasting using sky images and deep learning. Energies, Vol. 16.14 (2023) 5428. DOI: 10.3390/en16145428.
[18] R. U. Rani, J. Kakarla, B. Sundar. Weather image classification using EfficientNet and dual attention block. 2nd International Conference on Smart Technologies and Systems for Next Generation Computing (ICSTSN). IEEE, (2023) 1-4. DOI: 10.1109/ICSTSN57873.2023.10151564.
[19] V. Abad-Alcaraz, M. Castilla, J. A. Carballo, J. Bonilla, J. D. Álvarez. Multimodal deep learning for solar radiation forecasting. Applied Energy, Vol. 393 (2025) 126061. DOI: 10.1016/j.apenergy.2025.126061.

AUTOMATIC FAULT DETECTION AND DIAGNOSIS IN PHOTOVOLTAIC PLANTS BASED ON CONVOLUTIONAL NEURAL NETWORKS

Javier Martín-Rueda, Javier R. Ledesma, Celena Lorenzo, Pablo Merodio, L. Narvarte
Instituto de Energía Solar, Universidad Politécnica de Madrid
javier.martin@upm.es, javier.ledesma@upm.es, c.lorenzon@upm.es, pablo.merodio@upm.es, luis.narvarte@upm.es

ABSTRACT: This work aims to discover efficient and reliable machine-learning architectures and models for highly automated fault detection, diagnosis and predictive maintenance using the real-time flow of operational data generated at utility-scale photovoltaic plants. Our models consists of Convolutional Neural Networks which are trained on datasets which have been assembled from several years of operational data from about a dozen PV plants located in Europe and Latin America, with an approximate overall generation power of 1 GW, and different types of modules, tracking and terrain. We do minimal data preprocessing to construct our models. We use both 1-D and 2-D convolutional neural networks. For 2-D convolutional neural networks, we transform the time series into images by using Markov Field Transform, Recurrence plots, and Gramian Angular Fields. The performance of our models so far does not show significant improvements over other systems published in the literature, but it must be taken into consideration that the use of real operational data entails a significant challenge, when compared to simulated environments and small plant scenarios. We are improving the architectures and algorithms for higher reliability, a wider catalog of scenarios, and concurrent faults. We are also working on knowledge transfer among PV plants.
Keywords: Photovoltaic systems, Fault detection, Machine learning

1 INTRODUCTION

Sustained and significant growth of large photovoltaic (PV) plant portfolios demands smart automation of many operational aspects to achieve efficient plant operation. Fault detection and diagnosis are areas which can greatly benefit from advanced automated monitoring.

Utility-scale PV plants are extensively sensorised and produce large amounts of detailed operational data. Nowadays these data are used to detect faults using relatively rigid and simple methods, such as threshold crossing, statistical analysis, comparison between measured and simulated yields, and various heuristics. However, the unsophisticated nature of these methods means that many subtle faults go unnoticed, and that it is not uncommon to generate operational alarms which are unreliable or misdirected. Preventive maintenance, that is, early detection and diagnosis of conditions which do not currently impact operation but may do so in the short or mid-term, is even more of a *rara avis*.

Many AI techniques have recently been proposed for PV plant fault detection and diagnosis, but they tend to concentrate in specific problem cases, and in most cases have been evaluated with small and synthetic datasets. [1] shows a review of several previous work that use machine learning (ML) techniques for photovoltaic fault detection. [2] and [3] show the use of deep learning (DL) models based on artificial neural networks (ANN) combined with a digital twin (DT) to detect and diagnose faults in a simulated environment.

Such previous works show that applying ML and DL techniques can improve fault detection and diagnosis processes, by using images of PV modules and/or PV plant sensorisation data as their inputs. But they have mostly been tested in simulated scenarios, where many sources of environmental noise which are present in real PV plants are not taken into account, such as different electrical characteristics of the devices, aging, weather conditions, sensing variability and inaccuracies, concurrence of multiple faults, etc.

Our work aims to apply ML and DL techniques inspired by those which have shown their potential in simulated or small scale environments to real utility-scale PV plant sensorisation data. We intend to discover efficient and reliable machine learning architectures and models for the purpose of highly automated fault detection, diagnosis, and predictive maintenance, inspecting in real-time the data flow generated by sensors available at utility-scale PV plants. This will allow to optimize the operation of utility-scale PV plants, and to create the foundations for a reference description of data flow, fault classification and fault diagnosis.

2 DATASET DESCRIPTION

We have assembled a dataset of real utility-scale PV plant operational data, which covers several years of operation in about a dozen PV plants located in Europe and Latin America, with an approximate overall generation power of 1 GW. These PV plants also have different characteristics (monofacial vs bifacial, single-axis tracking vs fixed, flat vs uneven terrain…). The dataset includes detailed electrical sensorisation, as well as weather and irradiance data, with a time resolution in the order of 5-15 minutes.

These PV plants have suffered different faults and anomalies over the years, and we have carefully reviewed the data to construct a high-quality labelled dataset which can be used for AI model creation and performance evaluation. Over 30 types of faults and anomalies have been identified, although some of the cases are so rare that they are hardly useful for model training.

Among the different scenarios that we are addressing, in this paper we present three illustrative cases (the first two for fault detection, and the last one for predictive maintenance). They are:

Tracker target error: when the actual tracker position (continuous blue line) differs from the optimal objective position (dotted orange line), as shown on Figure 1.

10.4229/EUPVSEC2025/4CV.1.33

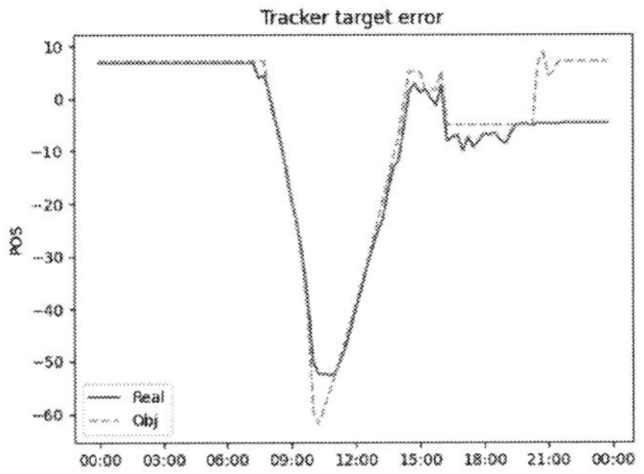

Figure 1. Example of tracker target error

Open string: when a string is disconnected, and its production is therefore lost. Causes could be open fuses, burned out connectors, manual operations, etc. Figure 2 shows yield differences between two stringboxes, where the one corresponding to the continuous blue line has an open string.

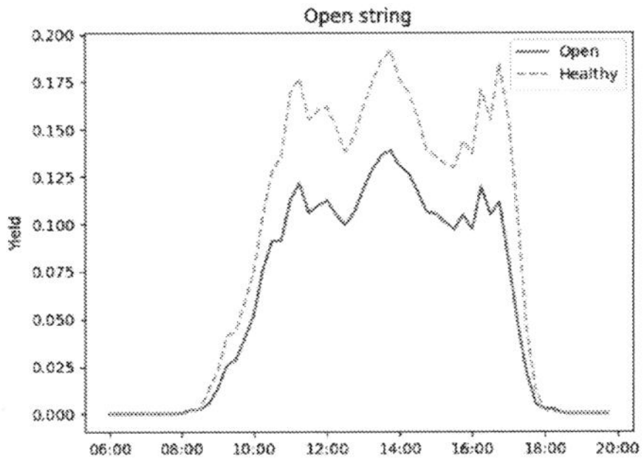

Figure 2. Example of open string

Anomalous element temperature: when temperature monitoring shows a pattern that does not comply with the correct operation of an element, such as an inverter or a transformer. This anomaly does not initially affect operation, but early identification and preventive maintenance will prevent future major problems. Figure 3 shows anomalous temperature in the inverter plotted with a continuous blue line.

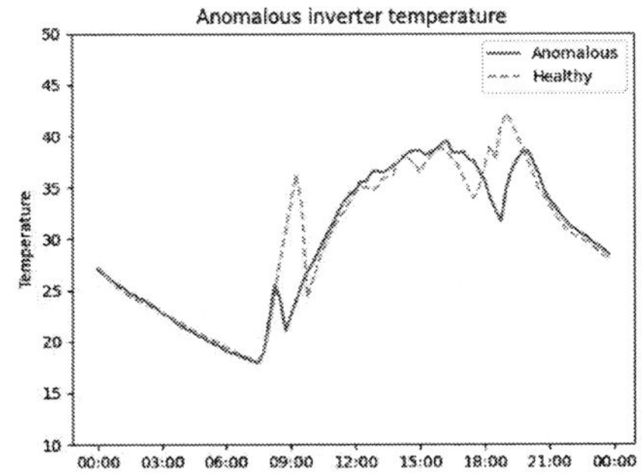

Figure 3. Example of anomalous inverter temperature

3 SYSTEM DESCRIPTION

We are using Convolutional Neural Networks (CNN) to create fault detection and diagnosis models, trained and validated with the datasets described in the previous section. CNNs are frequently used for image processing applications, while sensor data are typically time series of real values. We are using both 1-D and 2-D CNNs.

Convolutional neural networks have been frequently employed for image processing applications, where they have excelled at pattern recognition and classification, even in the presence of various types of noise. Most sensor data from PV plants are time series of real values, but some techniques, such as those described in [2] and [3], can be used to convert them into 2D matrices, which provide a visual representation suitable for effective analysis with a CNN. This will also allow us to confirm whether this approach is as effective with real operational data as with synthetic simulated data.

We are avoiding elaborate raw data preprocessing, as we intend to build models that can be efficiently applied and transferred among PV plants without the need of significant customization. So far, we are using simple preprocessing steps, such as cleaning unavailable sensorisation, normalizing measurements, grouping time series of similar devices, and selecting significant variables.

For 1-D CNNs, we are using mono and multi-variate time series which have been preprocessed as described above.

For 2-D CNNs, we are transforming mono and multi-variate time series data into 2-D images with several preprocessing techniques: Markov Transition Field, Recurrence Plots, and Gramian Angular Field. These techniques preserve temporal structure information and can be effectively processed by 2-D CNNs.

A Markov Transition Field transform (MTF) first discretizes continuous values in a times series using quantization techniques. Subsequently a Markov transition matrix is computed, where each element represents the probability of transitioning between two discrete states. That matrix is used to construct an image where each pixel corresponds to the transition probability between two states over time.

A Recurrence Plot is a 2-D matrix representation of time series in dynamic systems where each point (i,j) represents whether the system's state at time i is similar to the state at time j, that is, the phase space trajectory visits roughly the same area at both times.

A Gramian Angular Field transform (GAN) first maps the time series data into polar coordinates and then builds a corresponding Gram matrix. Essentially, each time point is mapped to a vector in polar coordinates where the temporal index is treated as the radius and the normalized magnitude as the inverse angle. The Gram matrix is a 2-D matrix where point (i,j) is computed from the inner product of vectors at times i and j.

4 RESULTS AND CONCLUSIONS

We have trained a validated several 1-D and 2-D CNN architectures with the datasets described in previous sections. The architecture hyperparameter sets have been optimized with KerasTuner [4]. Figure 4 shows the f1-score achieved by our CNNs for the three example fault and anomaly scenarios described in a previous section.

10.4229/EUPVSEC2025/4CV.1.33

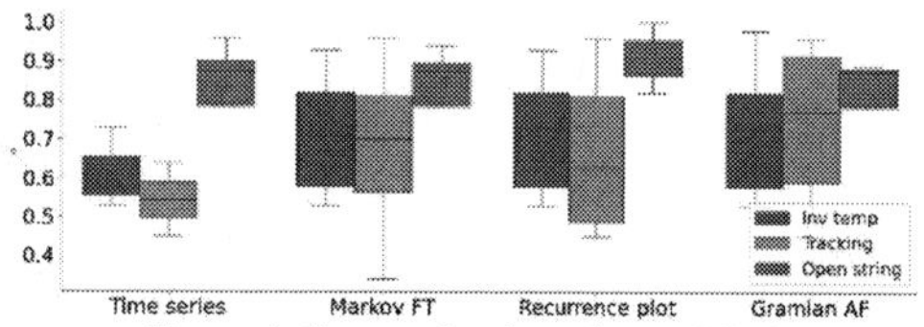

Figure 4. f1-score by algorithm and fault

These results so far do not show significant improvements over other systems published in the literature. However, it must be taken into consideration that our approach is working on real data from utility-scale PV plants, which is proving to be harder because real data typically contains more noise than those generated by simulation, and the amount of training examples is much more limited.

This work is ongoing and our next steps are:

- Use other improved DL architectures and ML algorithms. For instance, we are planning to experiment with ConvMixer architectures and pre-trained image classification models.
- Apply our models to a wider catalog of faults and anomalies, in particular to concurrent faults.
- Use synthetically generated samples to train our models where real data is scarce, and determine its usability to real conditions.
- Study the feasibility and procedure of transferring knowledge and models obtained from some PV plants to new PV plants, with as little customization as possible.

5 ACKNOWLEDGEMENTS

This work is funded by the European Union under the PVOP European Project, doi: 10.3030/101147000. Views and opinions expressed are however those of the author(s) only and do not necessarily reflect those of the European Union or CINEA. Neither the European Union nor the granting authority can be held responsible for them.

REFERENCES

[1] Et-taleby, A., Yassine Chaibi, Benslimane, M., & Boussetta, M. (2023). Applications of Machine Learning Algorithms for Photovoltaic Fault Detection: a Review. Statistics, Optimization & Information Computing, 11(1), 168-177, doi: 10.19139/soic-2310-5070-1537.

[2] Ying-Yi Hong, Rolando A. Pula, Diagnosis of PV faults using digital twin and convolutional mixer with LoRa notification system, Energy Reports, Volume 9, 2023, Pages 1963-1976, ISSN 2352-4847, doi: 10.1016/j.egyr.2023.01.011.

[3] Ying-Yi Hong, Rolando A. Pula, Diagnosis of photovoltaic faults using digital twin and PSO-optimized shifted window transformer, Applied Soft Computing, Volume 150, 2024, 111092, ISSN 1568-4946, doi: 10.1016/j.asoc.2023.111092.

[4] KerasTuner, O'Malley, Tom and Bursztein, Elie and Long, James and Chollet, François and Jin, Haifeng and Invernizzi, Luca and others, 2019. Accessed: Sep. 18, 2025 [Online]. Available: https://github.com/keras-team/keras-tuner

TEMPORAL GRAPH NEURAL NETWORKS FOR EARLY ANOMALY DETECTION AND PERFORMANCE PREDICTION VIA PV SYSTEM MONITORING DATA

S. Mukherjee [1,2], L. Vuillon[2], L. Bou Nassif[4], S. Giroux-Julien[5], H. Pabiou[4], D. Dutykh[3], I. Tsanakas[1]

[1]Univ. Grenoble Alpes, CEA, Liten, 73375 Le Bourget du Lac, France
[2]Univ. Savoie Mont Blanc, CNRS, LAMA, Chambéry, 73000, France
[3]Mathematics Department, Khalifa University, Abu Dhabi, PO Box 127788, United Arab Emirates
[4]INSA Lyon, CNRS, CETHIL, UMR5008, Villeurbanne, 69621, France
[5]Université Claude Bernard Lyon 1, CNRS, LAGEPP, UMR5007,Villeurbanne, 69100, France

*Corresponding author: Srijani.Mukherjee@univ-smb.fr Ph.: +33698703684

ABSTRACT: The rapid growth of solar photovoltaic (PV) systems necessitates advanced methods for performance monitoring and anomaly detection to ensure optimal operation. In this study, we propose a novel approach leveraging Temporal Graph Neural Network (Temporal GNN) to predict solar PV output power and detect anomalies using environmental and operational parameters. The proposed model utilizes graph-based temporal relationships among key PV system parameters, including irradiance, module and ambient temperature to predict electrical power output. This study is based on data collected from an outdoor facility located on a rooftop in Lyon (France) including power measurements from a PV module and meteorological parameters.

The Temporal GNN model integrates Graph Convolutional Networks (GCN) and Gated Recurrent Units (GRU) to capture spatial and temporal dependencies effectively. The model is trained to minimize Mean Squared Error (MSE) loss and is evaluated using Mean Absolute Error (MAE). Anomalies are identified by computing absolute errors and setting a threshold. The proposed framework achieves a MAE of 0.0707 on normalized output power prediction, outperforming traditional methods (e.g., Random Forests, SVMs) and advanced deep learning models (e.g., LSTMs) reported in recent literature, highlighting its potential to set a new benchmark for solar PV performance prediction and anomaly detection. The proposed method holds significant promise for real-world applications, providing actionable insights for maintenance and optimization in solar PV installations.

KEYWORD: Graph neural network; Spatio-temporal analysis; Power output prediction; Early anomaly detection.

1 INTRODUCTION

The increasing global reliance on solar energy has underscored the critical need for robust and reliable monitoring systems for photovoltaic (PV) installations. Effective performance prediction and timely anomaly detection are paramount to ensuring the long-term efficiency, reliability, and economic viability of these systems. Traditional monitoring methods, often based on simple thresholds or statistical rules, frequently fail to account for the complex interplay of environmental and operational variables that affect PV performance. These methods may lead to high rates of false positives or, more critically, miss subtle but significant anomalies that can indicate underlying system faults.
To overcome these limitations, advanced data-driven approaches are essential. Machine learning and deep learning models have shown promise in this field, offering the ability to learn complex, non-linear relationships from vast datasets. However, many of these models, such as Long Short-Term Memory (LSTM) networks or Support Vector Machines (SVMs), primarily focus on temporal dependencies, treating individual data points as independent sequences. This overlooks the inherent spatial relationships among different system parameters—such as the correlation between irradiance, temperature, and power output—which are crucial for a comprehensive understanding of system behaviour. Recent advances in Graph Neural Networks (GNNs) provide a powerful way to learn from structured data. By representing PV system parameters as graph nodes, and their interdependencies as edges, GNNs can capture both spatial (between parameters) and temporal (across time) correlations.
This study introduces a novel Temporal Graph Neural Network (T-GNN) that integrates Graph Convolutional Networks (GCNs) and Gated Recurrent Units (GRUs) for PV system analysis. Our model is designed to capture both the spatial dependencies between various PV system parameters and their temporal evolution. By representing the PV system as a dynamic graph, where each parameter is a node and its relationships over time are captured by edges, the T-GNN can model intricate dependencies more effectively than traditional methods. The primary objective is to develop a robust framework for accurate power output prediction and early anomaly detection, thereby providing actionable insights for PV system maintenance and optimization. This work represents a significant contribution to the field of PV performance analysis by demonstrating the superior capabilities of a spatiotemporal deep learning model in a real-world application.

2 METHODOLOGY

The proposed methodology for PV performance prediction and anomaly detection is a multi-step process centered on the T-GNN model. The workflow begins with data collection and preprocessing, followed by the model architecture design, training, and a two-stage process for prediction and anomaly detection.

2.1 DATA COLLECTION AND PREPROCESSING

Real-world monitoring data was collected from a PV system located on a rooftop in Lyon, France (latitude 45.783055° N, longitude 4.873611° E). The system consists of a central PV module (1675x992x35 mm) within a 12° tilted east-west array. Data from 10 sunny days per season (Spring: March-May 2023; Summer: June-August 2023; Autumn: September 2023) was used for this study. The data was recorded at 2-second intervals and includes four key input parameters:

- Global shortwave irradiation (G_sw)
- Global longwave tilted irradiation (G_lw)
- PV module temperature (T_pv)
- Ambient air temperature (T_air)

The target variable for prediction is the electrical power output (P_out). Prior to model training, all input features and the target variable were normalized using MinMax scaling to ensure a consistent range and prevent parameters with larger magnitudes from dominating the learning process. The dataset was then split into an 80-20 training and testing at random.

2.2 TEMPORAL GRAPH NEURAL NETWORK ARCHITECTURE

The core of our model is the Temporal GNN, which integrates two primary components to handle both spatial and temporal dependencies. To model the complex dependencies among PV system parameters, we construct a directed temporal graph $G=(V,E)$ where each node $v_i \in V$ represents a system parameter (e.g., irradiance, temperature, power output) at a given time step. Spatial relationships are encoded by directed edges $(v_i^t, v_j^t) \in E$, capturing causal influence between parameters at the same time step, such as irradiance affecting module temperature and temperature influencing power output[1]. Temporal dependencies are modeled by directed edges (v_i^t, v_i^{t+1}), linking each node to its future state, thereby preserving the sequential dynamics of the system. The adjacency matrix A of this graph is thus time-indexed, forming a sequence $\{A^t\}_{t=1}^{T}$. The node feature matrix at time t, denoted $X^t \in \mathbb{R}^{|V| \times d}$, stores the observed values of all parameters. During message passing, node embeddings are updated as

$$h_i^{t+1} = \sigma\left(\sum_{j \in \mathcal{N}(i)} \frac{1}{c_{ij}} W h_j^t + U h_i^t\right)$$

Here, $h_i^{(t+1)}$ represents the hidden state of node i at time $t+1$. Where $N(i)$ denotes the neighborhood of node i, W and U are learnable weight matrices, and c_{ij} is a normalization factor. The formula effectively combines a Graph Convolutional Network (GCN) layer for spatial information aggregation and a Gated Recurrent Unit (GRU) for temporal evolution[2]. The GCN layer aggregates information from a node's neighbors, while the GRU processes the sequential data to learn temporal patterns. The full model architecture consists of a Graph Convolution Layer, a GRUCell, and a final Fully Connected Layer (*Fig 1*) to produce the predicted power output, $\hat{P}\ out$. The model was trained using the Mean Squared Error (MSE) loss function with the Adam optimizer, with a learning rate of 0.01 and 100 epochs (*Fig 2*).

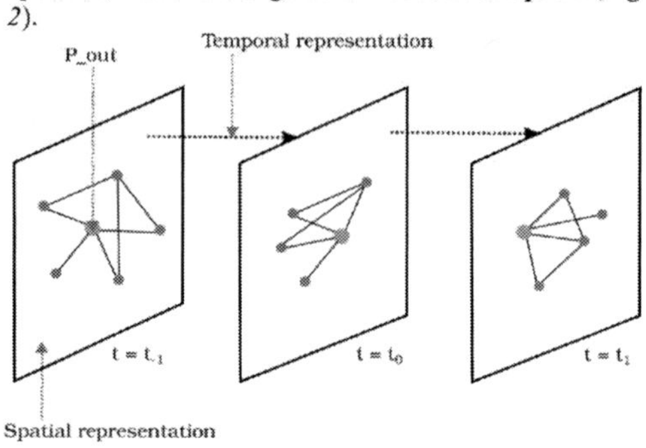

Fig 1: Schematic diagram of the evolution of the spatio-temporal graph prediction

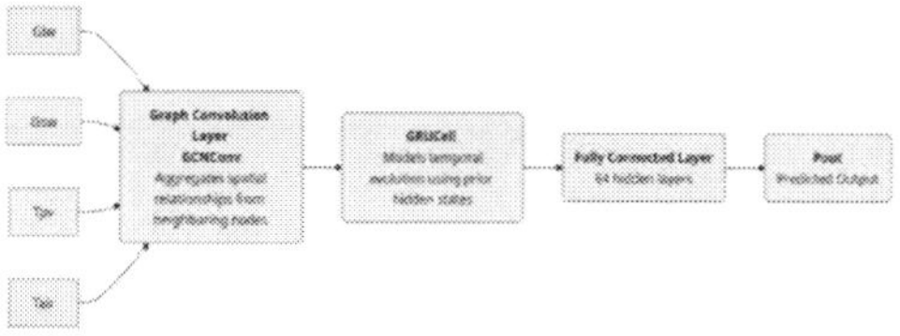

Fig 2: The architecture of the proposed model

2.3 ANOMALY DETECTION

Our framework for anomaly detection is a two-step process based on the model's prediction residuals.

Step 1: Power Prediction:
The T-GNN model predicts the power output, $\hat{P}\ out$.

Step 2: Residual Error Calculation:
The residual error, e, is computed as the absolute difference between the actual power output and the predicted power output:

$$e = |P\_out - \hat{P}\_out|$$

Step 3: Z-score Anomaly Detection:

Anomalies are identified using the Z-score of the residuals, which measures how many standard deviations an observation is from the mean of the residuals.

$$Z = \frac{e - \mu\_e}{\sigma\_e}$$

Here, μ_e is the mean of the residual errors and σ_e is the standard deviation. A point is flagged as an anomaly if its Z-score magnitude exceeds a predefined threshold, τ. For this study, the anomaly thresholds were set using the Interquartile Range (IQR) method, with a lower bound of ($Q1-1.5*IQR$) and an upper bound of ($Q3+1.5*IQR$). Outliers falling outside this range are considered anomalies.

3. RESULTS AND DISCUSSION

10.4229/EUPVSEC2025/4CV.1.35

The T-GNN model demonstrated strong predictive performance on the test set, effectively capturing the diurnal patterns of PV power generation as presented in *Fig 2*.

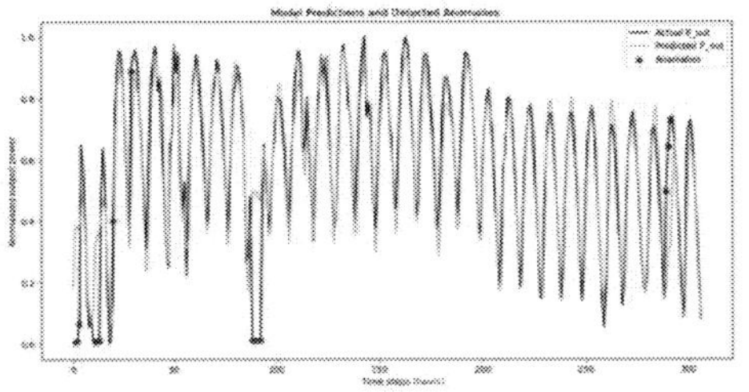

Fig 2

The model achieved a Mean Absolute Error (MAE) of 0.0707 for normalized power output prediction and a Mean Percentage Error (MPE) of 2.26. These results represent a significant improvement over existing state-of-the-art methods[3]. A comparison of our model's performance with other methods is summarized in *Table 1*.

Model	Notes	MAE
T-GNN (ours)	Spatio-temporal	0.0707
LSTM	Temporal only	0.09–0.10
RF / SVM	Traditional ML	0.10–0.15

Table 1: Comparison of Model Performance by Mean Absolute Error (MAE)

The T-GNN's superior performance can be attributed to its unique ability to learn from both the spatial relationships among input parameters and their temporal evolution, a capability that traditional models lack. As shown in the figure comparing actual and predicted power output, the model's predictions closely track the actual data, even during periods of rapid change.

The anomaly detection component of the model successfully identified some inconsistent power readings, which constituted 5.21% of the dataset. These anomalies were flagged as points where the model's prediction significantly deviated from the actual measured power output. A box plot in *Fig 3* of the absolute errors with anomaly thresholds clearly visualizes these outliers.

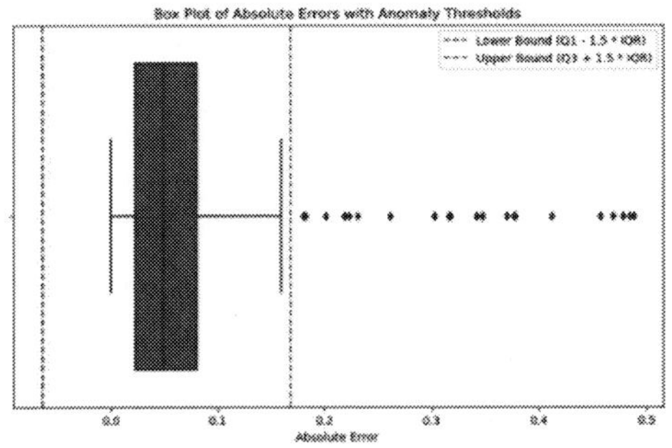

Fig 3

Cross-validation of the detected anomalies confirmed that they corresponded to genuine inconsistencies in the measured data, such as sudden and unexplainable drops in power output, which may indicate a measurement fault or an operational irregularity. The low percentage of detected anomalies suggests that the model is highly selective and robust[4], minimizing the risk of false positives. This makes the framework a valuable tool for real-time monitoring, as it can alert operators to potential issues without generating excessive noise.

4. CONCLUSION AND FUTURE RESEARCH

This study successfully demonstrates the effectiveness of a Temporal Graph Neural Network for both predicting PV power output and detecting anomalies in real-time. By leveraging a T-GNN, our model can effectively capture the complex spatiotemporal dependencies inherent in PV system data, leading to significantly higher predictive accuracy compared to traditional machine learning and deep learning methods. The low MAE and MPE achieved by our model, combined with its ability to precisely identify anomalies, positions it as a promising solution for enhancing the reliability and efficiency of solar PV systems.

The insights gained from this work provide a clear path toward developing more intelligent and resilient PV monitoring systems. Future work will focus on expanding the model's capabilities by incorporating additional data sources, such as electrical parameters (e.g., voltage and current) and infrared (IR) thermal images. This multi-modal approach is expected to further enhance the model's ability to detect more subtle and complex types of anomalies, providing a more comprehensive diagnostic tool for PV system maintenance and optimization.

4.3 References

[1] Mukherjee Srijani, Vuillon Laurent, Dutykh Denys, Tsanakas Ioannis.
Scalable weather data reduction for solar PV analysis using graph-based approach. *Energy Syst* (2025). https://doi.org/10.1007/s12667-025-00767-y

[2] Guangyin Jin, Yuxuan Liang, Yuchen Fang, Zezhi Shao, Jincai Huang, Junbo Zhang, and Yu Zheng.
Spatio-Temporal Graph Neural Networks for Predictive Learning in Urban Computing: A Survey .
IEEE Transactions on Knowledge & Data Engineering, 36(10):5388–5408, October 2024.

[3] Theocharides, Spyros, Makrides, George, and Georghiou, George E.
PV generation forecasting utilizing a classification-only approach.
EPJ Photovolt., 15:12, 2024.

[4] Jagbir Singh, Owais Ahmad Shah, Sujata Arora,
Smart Grid Cybersecurity: Anomaly Detection in Solar Power Systems Using Deep Learning.
Energy Storage and Saving, 2025.

OPTIMIZATION OF MAINTENANCE OF PV MODULE ARRAYS BASED ON ASSET MANAGEMENT STRATEGIES: CASE OF STUDY

L. Alejandro Cárdenas, Andrés Figueroa, Fernando Herrera, Ernesto Pérez and David Nova
Universidad Nacional de Colombia
Carrera 45 No. 26-85, Bogotá, Colombia
Corresponding autor: L. Alejandro Cárdenas, luacardenasga@unal.edu.co

ABSTRACT: This paper presents a methodology to optimize the maintenance of grid-connected photovoltaic (PV) systems by defining cleaning intervals within an asset management framework. The approach combines analysis of energy production, feed-in tariffs, and cleaning costs to maximize overall revenue. The proposed approach was evaluated through a case study of a 5.6 kWp PV system located on the Bogotá campus of the Universidad Nacional de Colombia. Experimental results showed that modules without cleaning accumulated performance losses above 25–30% after five years, while those cleaned annually exhibited controlled losses of around 5–10% per year. Furthermore, the variability of the loss rate (LR) highlights the importance of adapting soiling models to local climates. In Bogotá, where rainfall is frequent, precipitation contributes to partial self-cleaning, reducing soiling accumulation compared to arid climates. The study concludes that incorporating local environmental factors into predictive models and maintenance planning improves both the technical performance and economic profitability of PV systems.
Keywords: photovoltaic systems, soiling, cleaning optimization asset management

1 INTRODUCTION

In line with global decarbonization efforts stimulated by the Paris Agreement, Latin America is undergoing a significant energy transition, with solar photovoltaics (PV) at the forefront. Within this regional context, Colombia has established ambitious national targets, aiming for solar PV to represent 12% of the country's installed power capacity by 2037 [1]. This rapid expansion of solar infrastructure introduces an urgent need for advanced operational strategies. The successful integration and long-term profitability of these new assets are contingent not on their installation alone, but on ensuring they perform optimally throughout their lifecycle [2]. Consequently, developing data-driven asset management frameworks tailored to specific local conditions is important to safeguarding these national investments and realizing their full potential.

Performance losses in PV systems are mainly caused by soiling, degradation, and failures. Soiling reduces the irradiance reaching solar cells through soft shading (e.g., pollution) or hard shading (e.g., dust), affecting current and voltage output differently [3]. Over time, PV systems also experience degradation, though recent analyses report annual rates as low as 0–0.29%, lower than the commonly assumed 0.5%, reflecting improvements in technology and maintenance [4]. Failures contribute less significantly, typically below 1% of net energy yield losses, while inefficiencies represent over 20%, emphasizing the need for optimized design and operation [5].

Asset management has emerged as a holistic strategy to maximize both revenue and the operational lifetime of photovoltaic (PV) plants. By integrating design optimization, advanced maintenance practices, and computerized management systems, asset management contributes to reducing capital costs, improving risk management, and ensuring long-term plant profitability [2]. However, large-scale PV plants face increasing challenges due to stricter environmental regulations, growing energy demand, and the lack of structured strategic frameworks. Addressing these issues through well-defined asset management approaches not only enhances plant performance but also strengthens the competitiveness of solar energy against conventional generation [6].

This paper proposes a maintenance optimization methodology framed within a broader asset management strategy, with a detailed case study on soiling and cleaning optimization in Bogotá. While performance losses in PV systems may also arise from degradation and failures, soiling represents a more immediate and significant challenge due to its direct impact on irradiance and energy yield. By focusing on cleaning strategies and their integration into asset management, this work aims to enhance operational efficiency, extend plant lifetime, and maximize revenue.

2 METHODOLOGY

To illustrate the application of the asset management strategy in real conditions, a 5.6 kWp photovoltaic plant located at the Universidad Nacional de Colombia, Bogotá campus, was selected as a case study. This plant is located in an urban environment with high variability in dust and precipitation, making it a representative scenario for analyzing the impact of soiling on energy performance. The methodology developed combines the analysis of experimental data from the plant with a model for estimating daily soiling deposition, from which the associated energy losses are calculated. Finally, a validation process is carried out and a cost optimization stage is incorporated, which allows for the definition of cleaning period adapted to the local context. The general flow of the methodology is summarized in Fig, 1.

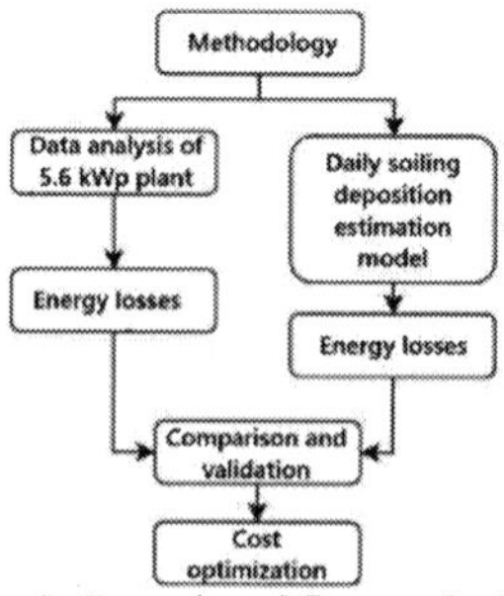

Figure 1: General workflow methodology

10.4229/EUPVSEC2025/4CV.1.36
020339-001

2.1 Case of study

The photovoltaic installation is located on a building at the Universidad Nacional de Colombia in Bogotá, as shown in Fig. 2. The system is located on the roof and consists of 14 pv modules with a nominal power of 400 W each one, giving a total installed peak power of 5.6 kWp. Seven modules face east and the remaining seven face west. The layout and numbering of the modules is shown in Fig. 3. In both orientations, one module has been designated for cleaning and another for never being cleaned, forming three pairs per orientation, which are cleaned at intervals of 6, 12, and 18 months. Additionally, modules 7 and 8 have not been cleaned since their installation.

Figure 2: Photovoltaic System 5.6 kWp

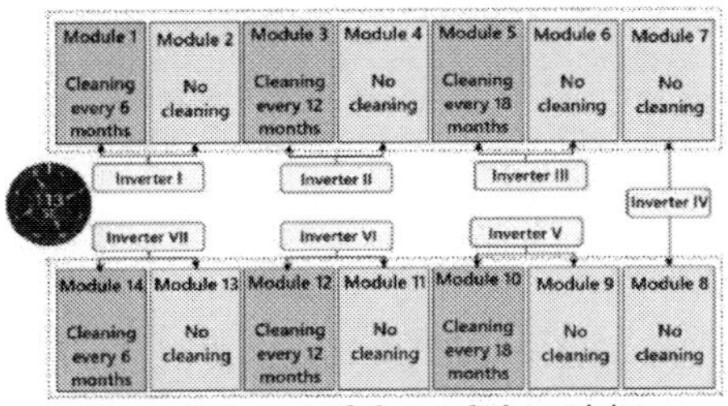

Figure 3: Layout of photovoltaic modules

The electrical parameters of the modules are acquired through microinverters, each connected to two pv modules. The technical characteristics of the modules are shown in Table I.

Since meteorological data is required to estimate the theoretical energy produced by a photovoltaic module, this data is obtained from the Davis Instruments weather station. This station is in the LIATER building of the Universidad Nacional de Colombia, approximately 100 meters from the photovoltaic installation at the North-est. It measures irradiance, ambient temperature, wind speed and direction, among other factors in a frequency of 5 minutes, which are of interest to us. The information from the weather station is shown in Table III.

Since there was no weather station available when the photovoltaic system was installed, additional data was obtained from NREL's National Solar Radiation Database (NSRDB) and include global horizontal irradiance, ambient temperature, wind speed and direction. This meteorological data was collected at 60-minute intervals.

Table I: Technical specifications of photovoltaic modules

Characteristic	Value
Cell type	N-type monocrystalline
Maximum power (STC)	400 W
Open circuit voltage (Voc)	49.3 V
Short-circuit current (Isc)	10.47 A
Module efficiency	19.3%
Temperature coefficient	-0.36%/°C

2.2 Estimation of the System's Daily Theoretical Energy

The energy expected to be generated under ideal conditions (without soiling) is calculated based on solar irradiance, cell temperature, and the system's nominal power according to the IEC 61724 [7]. First, the hourly power of the system is estimated because the meteorological data interval is hourly:

$$P_{teo}(t) = P_{STC}\left(\frac{G_{POA(t)}}{\frac{1000W}{m^2}}\right)[1+\gamma\,(T_{mod}(t)-25)] \quad (1)$$

Additionally, considering degradation:

$$P_{teo}(t) = P_{teo}(t)(1+\delta\cdot n) \quad (2)$$

Where:

- P_{teo}: Theoretical power of the system [kW].
- P_{STC}: Nominal power under standard conditions [kW].
- $G_{POA}(t)$: Hourly irradiance on the module plane [kW/m2].
- γ: Temperature correction coefficient for module power [%/◦C].
- $T_{mod}(t)$: Average daily photovoltaic module temperature during operation [◦C].
- δ: Annual degradation of the module [0.5%/year].
- n: Number of years elapsed [year].

The temperature of the cell module can be estimated from the ambient temperature [7]:

$$T_{mod}(t) = T_{amb}(t) + \frac{G_{POA}}{\frac{800W}{m^2}}(T_{NOCT}-20) \quad (3)$$

Where:

- P_{amb}: Ambient temperature [◦C].
- P_{mod}: Module temperature [◦C].

The theoretical daily energy intake corresponds to [8]:

$$E_{teo} = \int_0^{24} P_{teo}(t)dt \quad (4)$$

2.3 Soiling rate

The degree of soiling is quantified by the Soiling Ratio (SR) index, defined as the ratio between the energy

10.4229/EUPVSEC2025/4CV.1.36

generated under real conditions (under soiling) and that which would be generated under clean conditions [8]:

$$SR_i = \frac{E_{mod_i}}{E_{teo}} \cdot 100\% \qquad (5)$$

Where:

- E_{mod_i}: Energy generated by module i (kWh).
- E_{teo}: Estimated theoretical energy (kWh).

Then, energy losses due to dirt are determined as follows[8]:

$$LR_i = 100\% - SR_i \qquad (6)$$

This accumulation depends on variables such as the rate of soiling deposition, water precipitation, and wind speed [9].

2.4 Comparison of particulate matter estimates

A. Calculation of Daily Dust Deposition:

Daily dust deposition (DDep) is calculated using an empirical model based on key meteorological factors, such as wind speed and particulate matter concentration. This model is derived from the work of [10], that established a quantitative relationship between these parameters and the accumulation of dust on module surfaces.

$$DDep = (10.6 - 4.99WS + 247PM - 73.4WS \cdot PM)0.00144 \qquad (7)$$

The factor 0.00144 converts μg/(m²·min) to g/(m²·day).

- WS: Average daily wind speed (m/s).
- PM: Average daily particulate matter concentration (g/m²).

B. Adjustment for Environmental Conditions:

To account for the effects of humidity and soiling adhesion in arid climates, a calibration factor α = 0.1 is introduced when AP > 2.7 mm (heavy rain that wash away dust) [8]:

$$DDep' = \begin{cases} DDep, if\ AP < 2.7mm \\ \alpha \cdot DDep,\ if\ AP \geq 2.7mm \end{cases} \qquad (8)$$

When rainfall exceeds 2.7 mm, it is considered that dust is reduced by 10% due to natural rainfall.

Finally, the daily accumulation of soiling is expressed as the addition of the previous day's accumulation and the soiling from the current day.

$$Acc(t) = Acc(t-1) + DDep' \qquad (9)$$

2.5 Minimum Residual Modeling (β)

To simulate realistic conditions where soiling is not completely removed, a minimum residue β is introduced after cleaning events. This approach follows the observations of [8].

$$Acc(t)' = f(x) = \begin{cases} Acc(t),\ without\ cleaning \\ \beta,\ cleaning\ date \end{cases} \qquad (10)$$

Where:

- $Acc(t)$: Soiling accumulation on day t (g/m2).
- β = 0.01 g/m2: Minimum residue.

This means that when cleaning events happen, the accumulation of soiling is not completely zero. There is a minimum residue β that remains on the surfaces of the module.

2.6 Calculation of Energy Loss ($E_{loss}(t)$)

Daily energy loss is modeled as [11]:

$$E_{loss}(t) = E_{teo} \cdot \left(Eff_{mod} - Eff(t)\right) \qquad (11)$$

Where:

- E_{teo}: Theoretical daily energy [kWh].
- Eff_{mod}: Module efficiency [19.3%].
- $Eff(t)$: Module efficiency reduced due to dirt [%].

This reduced module efficiency is calculated based on the daily accumulation of soiling. This expression is based on the observations in [8]:

$$Eff(t) = -0.0026Acc(t)'^3 + 0.032Acc(t)'^2 - 0.1369 \cdot Acc(t)' + Eff_{mod} \qquad (12)$$

$$LR_{teo} = \frac{E_{loss}}{E_{teo}} \cdot 100\% \qquad (13)$$

2.7 Economic Model

Economic energy losses due to dirt are estimated as [12]:

$$C_{loss}(\$) = LR_{average}(\%) \cdot E_{teo}(kWh) \cdot CU_{rate}\left(\frac{\$}{kWh}\right) \qquad (14)$$

$$C_1(d) = \frac{365}{d}(1 + 2 + \cdots + d) \cdot C_{loss} \qquad (15)$$

$$C_1(d) = \frac{365}{2}(d+1) \cdot C_{loss} \qquad (16)$$

$$C_2(d) = \frac{365}{d} \cdot C_{clean} \qquad (17)$$

As presented in [13], an optimization function for cleaning photovoltaic modules is developed, which considers the average percentage of daily energy losses and parameters such as peak sun hours, system capacity, efficiency, and costs, defining the cleaning days as the optimization variable.

Where CUtarifa is the unit cost of energy per kWh. On the other hand, the cleaning cost corresponds to:

$$C_{clean} = C_{labor} + C_{water} + C_{product} \qquad (18)$$

This includes labor costs, water costs, and cleaning product costs, if used. The minimum wage was considered as a benchmark for determining labor costs[14].

2.8 Optimization Function

The objective is to minimize the total annual cost associated with energy losses by soiling and cleanup costs. Also, for the analysis, the average electricity rate for stratum 4, a category that does not receive subsidies, was considered throughout the study period [15][16].

If T is the cleanup interval:

$$C_{\text{water}}(\$) = V(m^3) \cdot C_{rate}\left(\frac{\$}{m^3}\right) \quad (19)$$

$$C_2(d) = \frac{365}{d} \cdot C \quad (20)$$

$$C_T(d) = \frac{365}{2}(d+1) \cdot C_{loss} + \frac{365}{d} \cdot C_{clean} \quad (22)$$

$$d(C_T) = 0 \quad (23)$$

Where nT = ⌊ 365/T ⌋. The value T that minimizes Ctotal is the optimal frequency desired for cleaning the photovoltaic modules[17].

$$C_T(d) = \sum_{d=1}^{365} \frac{365}{2}(d+1) \cdot C_{loss} + \frac{365}{d} \cdot C_{clean} \quad (24)$$

3 RESULTS AND DISCUSSION

Figures 4 and 5 show the daily experimental loss rate of modules 3 (west) and 12 (east), which are cleaned every 12 months and modules 7 (west) and 8 (east), which never have been cleaned. The time series of modules 3 and 12 exhibits gradually increase of LR throughout each year, reaching values close to 10–15%. When analyzing the average slope across the different years, the effective loss rate corresponds to an average increase of approximately 5 % per year. This value can be considered a representative measure of the natural soiling accumulation within a 12-month period under the experimental conditions. The variability of the slopes also reflects that external factors such as rainfall, dust events, or local microclimate conditions significantly influence soiling accumulation.

The LR in uncleaned modules reaches values above 25% by mid-2022. The absence of cleaning produces a much stronger trend, with the slope expected to be consistently positive around 8–12%/year. This suggests that modules exposed without cleaning undergo progressive and irreversible optical and efficiency losses, severely compromising their performance over time. Moreover, the data dispersion suggests that, beyond the average trend, the instantaneous LR can vary widely, which may be attributed to short-term environmental factors such as rain cleaning events, dust storms, or shading.

The variability of LR indicates that soiling models must adapt to local climates. In Bogotá, a city with frequent rainfall, precipitation both cleans and influences dust deposition on PV modules. Models developed for arid regions may overestimate losses, so Bogotá's rainy conditions should be explicitly considered to improve prediction accuracy and optimize maintenance strategies.

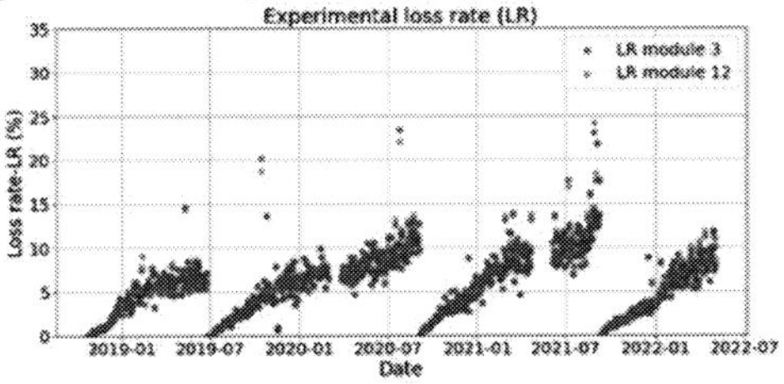

Figure 4: Results of experimental LR modules with 12-month cleaning cycles (Mod3, Mod12)

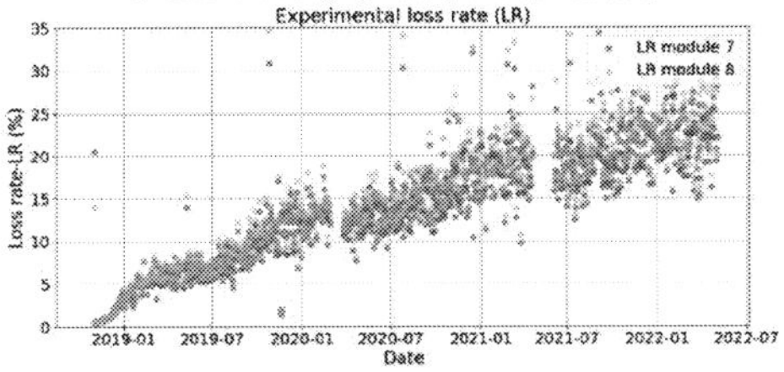

Figure 5: Results of experimental LR modules with no cleaning cycles (Mod7, Mod8)

Figure 6 shows the theoretical LR, both as accumulated values and as per-cycle increases, indicating a cumulative degradation rate of 9.2% per year. Figure 7 contrasts this theoretical behavior with the actual LR measured in different modules, showing good agreement during the initial years but deviations at later stages, where experimental LR exceeds the theoretical prediction. This divergence highlights that, although the theoretical model captures the general trend of soiling accumulation, real conditions introduce additional variability due to environmental effects and differences in cleaning efficiency.

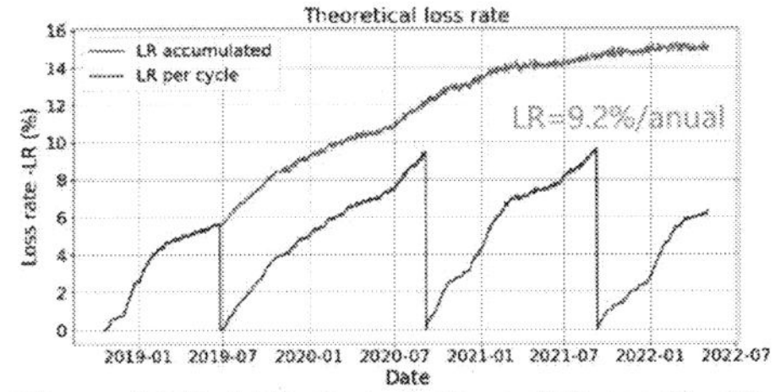

Figure 6: LR results theoretical cumulative and by 12-month cycles

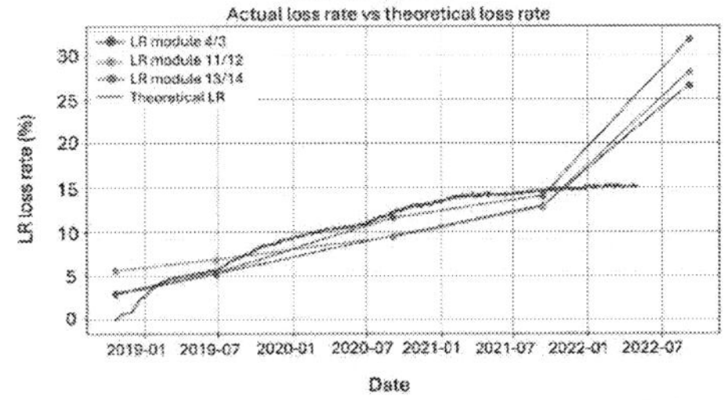

Figure 7: Comparison results between theoretical LR and actual LR of modules on cleaning dates

Figure 8 presents the relationship between experimental and theoretical soiling rate (SR) under a 12-month cleaning cycle, together with the impact of water precipitation. The experimental SR curves of module 3 (west) and module 12 (east) follow the general decreasing pattern predicted by the theoretical model, confirming the validity of the accumulation–cleaning framework. However, deviations appear around rainy periods, where higher precipitation correlates with partial natural cleaning of the modules, temporarily reducing SR. This demonstrates that rainfall plays a significant role in mitigating soiling accumulation, effectively complementing scheduled manual cleanings. The results highlight that integrating precipitation data into theoretical models improves the accuracy of LR/SR predictions and provides a more realistic basis for designing optimized cleaning strategies in PV systems.

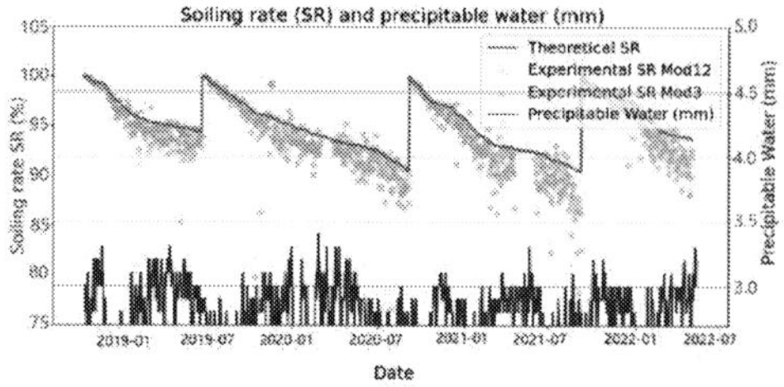

Figure 8: Comparison of experimental and theoretical SR in Impact of water precipitation 12-month cycle

Figure 9 shows the long-term experimental LR for modules without cleaning, updated with data collected in May 2025. LR3_4 (blue) shows the LR of module 3 compared to 4 (west), LR12_11 (red) shows the LR of module 12 compared to 11 (east) and LR14_13 (blue) shows the LR of module 14 compared to 13 (east). The results confirm a continuous accumulation of losses, with LR values stabilizing between 25–30% after about six years of exposure. Although the rate of increase slows down after 2022, the accumulated soiling remains high, indicating that a saturation effect occurs once the surface reaches a maximum dust coverage, beyond which additional deposition has a reduced incremental effect on optical losses. The comparison among different modules suggest a higher impact of soiling to modules orientated to the west (green). These findings reinforce the importance of cleaning interventions, as long-term soiling results in persistent high-performance losses that cannot be naturally reversed.

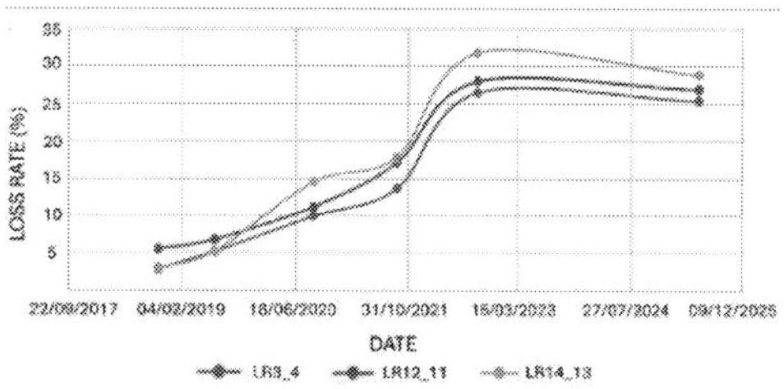

Figure 9: Experimental LR for modules without cleaning

Figures 10 and 11 present the optimization of PV module cleaning frequency under different economic conditions, considering both the price of electricity (Figure 10) and labor costs (Figure 11). The results clearly show that the optimal cleaning period is not fixed, but shifts depending on the balance between energy revenues and cleaning expenses. At higher electricity prices, the optimal strategy is to clean more frequently, since the revenue loss from soiling exceeds the additional labor costs. Conversely, at lower electricity prices the optimal point occurs earlier, as the economic penalty of soiling is less severe. Similarly, when labor costs are low the model suggests more frequent cleanings.

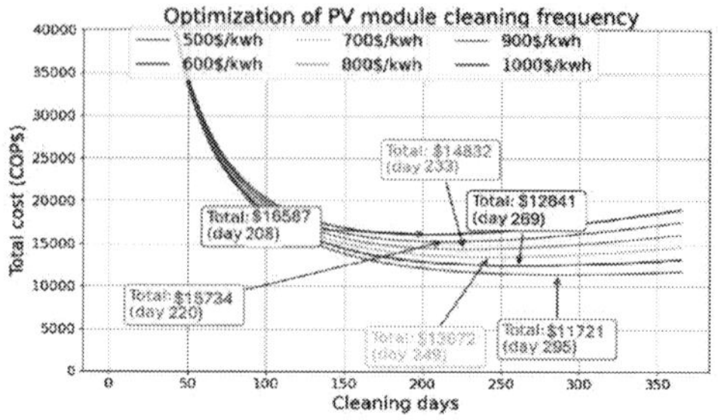

Figure 10: Annual cost optimization by varying energy rates

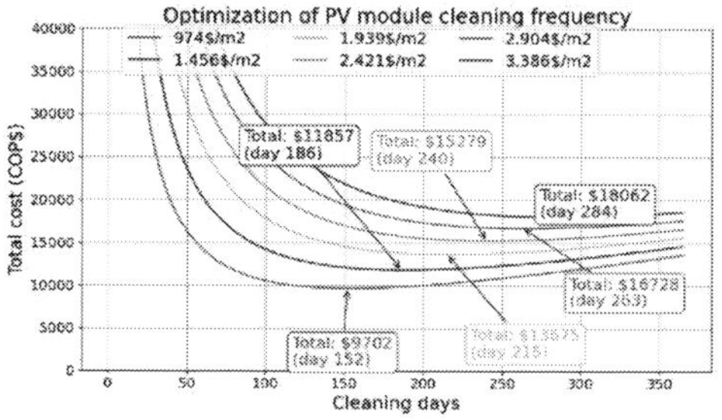

Figure 11: Annual cost optimization by varying labor

4 CONCLUSIONS

The results highlight the critical role of maintenance strategies in photovoltaic performance. While annual cleaning controls the loss rate within manageable bounds 9.2% per year, no cleaning results in more than 25–30% cumulative loss in less than five years, which can considerably reduce energy yield and profitability. The comparison between theoretical models and experimental data confirmed that rainfall events partially mitigate soiling, but not enough to replace scheduled cleaning. These findings underscore the relevance of integrating environmental parameters, such as precipitation, into predictive models for more accurate estimation of performance degradation.

Overall, these results emphasize the need to adapt cleaning frequency to the environmental soiling conditions. In climates with moderate dust deposition, annual cleaning may be sufficient, while in harsher conditions, shorter cycles or alternative mitigation measures would be required to avoid excessive losses.

From an economic perspective, the optimization analysis revealed that the optimal cleaning frequency depends strongly on both electricity tariffs and labor costs. At higher energy prices or lower labor costs, more frequent cleaning is economically justified, while lower tariffs or high labor expenses shift the optimal point toward longer intervals between cleanings. These results provide PV system operators with a practical framework to adapt cleaning strategies to local conditions, ensuring maximum profitability. Overall, the study confirms that combining experimental monitoring with cost-based optimization enables data-driven decision-making, improving both the technical and economic performance of photovoltaic systems.

5 ACKNOWLEDGMENTS

This project has received funding from the European Union's Horizon Europe research and innovation programme under grant agreement No. 101132182

6 REFERENCES

[1] Unidad de Planeación Minero Energética, "Plan Indicativo de Expansión de la Generación 2023-2037," Bogotá, Colombia, Oct. 2023.

[2] M. N. AlMallahi, B. Yousef, Y. C. Tan, H. Al Jaghoub, and K. Obaideen, "The role of asset management in solar PV systems and its linkage to sustainable development goals," 2023, p. 040001. doi: 10.1063/5.0165207.

[3] M. R. Maghami, H. Hizam, C. Gomes, M. A. Radzi, M. I. Rezadad, and S. Hajighorbani, "Power loss due to soiling on solar panel: A review," Jun. 01, 2016, *Elsevier Ltd*. doi: 10.1016/j.rser.2016.01.044.

[4] A. Boretti and S. Castelletto, "Annual relative performance degradation in photovoltaic solar plants," *Solar Energy Advances*, vol. 4, Jan. 2024, doi: 10.1016/j.seja.2024.100074.

[5] I. Lillo-Bravo, P. González-Martínez, M. Larrañeta, and J. Guasumba-Codena, "Impact of energy losses due to failures on photovoltaic plant energy balance," *Energies (Basel)*, vol. 11, no. 2, Feb. 2018, doi: 10.3390/en11020363.

[6] S. W. Ali Shah, M. Nateque Mahmood, and N. Das, "Strategic Asset Management Framework for the Improvement of Large Scale PV Power Plants in Australia," in *Australasian Universities Power Engineering Conference- AUPEC2016*, IEEE, 2016.

[7] "The IEC 61724-1:2021 standard for PV monitoring systems: a quick explanation | Hukseflux." Accessed: Aug. 16, 2025. [Online]. Available: https://www.hukseflux.com/applications/solar-energy-pv-system-performance-monitoring/iec-61724-12021-standard-for-pv

[8] A. G. S. Matar and H. An, "Optimal Scheduling of PV Panel Cleaning and Policy Implications Considering Uncertain Dusty Weather Conditions in the Middle East," *Systems*, vol. 12, no. 10, p. 418, Oct. 2024, doi: 10.3390/SYSTEMS12100418/S1.

[9] T. Sarver, A. Al-Qaraghuli, and L. L. Kazmerski, "A comprehensive review of the impact of dust on the use of solar energy: History, investigations, results, literature, and mitigation approaches," *Renewable and Sustainable Energy Reviews*, vol. 22, pp. 698–733, Jun. 2013, doi: 10.1016/J.RSER.2012.12.065.

[10] B. Figgis, B. Guo, W. Javed, S. Ahzi, and Y. Rémond, "Dominant environmental parameters for dust deposition and resuspension in desert climates," *Aerosol Science and Technology*, vol. 52, no. 7, pp. 788–798, Jul. 2018, doi: 10.1080/02786826.2018.1462473/ASSET/AFC25938-0081-4327-B868-F9F99B93C0B9/ASSETS/IMAGES/LARGE/UAST_A_1462473_F0016_OC.JPG.

[11] A. Sayyah, M. N. Horenstein, and M. K. Mazumder, "Energy yield loss caused by dust deposition on photovoltaic panels," *Solar Energy*, vol. 107, pp. 576–604, Sep. 2014, doi: 10.1016/J.SOLENER.2014.05.030.

[12] Z. A. Darwish, H. A. Kazem, K. Sopian, M. A. Alghoul, and H. Alawadhi, "Experimental investigation of dust pollutants and the impact of environmental parameters on PV performance: an experimental study," *Environ Dev Sustain*, vol. 20, no. 1, pp. 155–174, Feb. 2018, doi: 10.1007/S10668-016-9875-7/TABLES/8.

[13] M. Mani and R. Pillai, "Impact of dust on solar photovoltaic (PV) performance: Research status, challenges and recommendations," *Renewable and Sustainable Energy Reviews*, vol. 14, no. 9, pp. 3124–3131, Dec. 2010, doi: 10.1016/J.RSER.2010.07.065.

[14] "El salario mínimo para 2025 aumentó en 9,5% y quedará en $1'423.500." Accessed: Aug. 16, 2025. [Online]. Available: https://www.presidencia.gov.co/prensa/Paginas/El-salario-minimo-para-2025-aumentara-el-9-54-porciento-y-queda-en-1423500-presidente-Gustavo-Petro-241224.aspx

[15] "Tarifas de energía | Enel Colombia." Accessed: Aug. 16, 2025. [Online]. Available: https://www.enel.com.co/es/personas/tarifas-energia-enel-distribucion.html

[16] "Tarifas 2024." Accessed: Aug. 16, 2025. [Online]. Available: https://www.acueducto.com.co/wps/portal/EAB2/Home/atencion-al-usuario/tarifas/tarifas_2024

[17] M. Abu-Naser, "Solar Panels Cleaning Frequency for Maximum Financial Profit," *Open Journal of Energy Efficiency*, vol. 06, no. 03, pp. 80–86, 2017, doi: 10.4236/OJEE.2017.63006.

A SPATIALLY RESOLVED CLEAR-SKY FILTER USING PHOTOVOLTAIC MODULES AS CLOUD DETECTORS

Elin Dypvik Sødahl, Magnus Moe Nygård, and Marie Syre Wiig
Department of Solar Power Systems, Institute for Energy Technology (IFE), NO-2007 Kjeller, Norway
elin.sodahl@ife.no

ABSTRACT: Operation and maintenance of photovoltaic (PV) power plants is essential to mitigate performance losses. Time series of the temperature corrected performance ratio (*PR*) can be used to monitor system performance or as input to advanced algorithms that estimates degradation and soiling. However, these algorithms are sensitive to the signal-to-noise level in *PR* time series, and might struggle if there are much missing data. Traditional clear-sky filters often discard large amounts of data, particularly during shifting weather conditions. This study introduces a novel clear-sky detection method that retains more data by using PV modules as cloud detectors, yielding a spatially resolved clear-sky index. The method proposed here is compared to the one by Reno and Hansen which is included in the open-source python library PVAnalytics. The results show that the new filter retains more data, especially on partially cloudy days, leading to more reliable performance metrics for the PV system.

Keywords: Clear-sky detection, geospatial PV analytics, operations and maintenance

1 INTRODUCTION

Operation and maintenance (O&M) of photovoltaic (PV) power plants is necessary to limit performance losses, such as degradation and soiling. [1], [2] Mitigations of faults and losses can increase energy yield, and thus also return of investments. For example, Iftikhar et al. found that an 18 MWp PV power plant had 4% underperformance due to tracker system faults, and resolving the issue could increase earnings with 175 000 Euro per year.[3]

The total effect of losses in a PV system can be assessed using the temperature adjusted performance ratio (*PR*), [4] which is defined as

$$PR = \frac{\sum_t P_t}{\sum_t c_{t,25°C} P_{STC}\, G_{POA,t} / G_{STC}}. \tag{1}$$

In Eq. (1), P_t is the power output in a time interval t, P_{STC} is the rated power at standard test conditions, $G_{POA,t}$ the plane-of-array (POA) irradiance received during t, and G_{STC} is the standard test condition irradiance of 1000 W/m^2. $c_{t,25°C}$ is a temperature correction term which depends on the module temperature, T_t and the module temperature coefficient, γ,

$$c_{t,25\,°C} = 1 + \gamma(T_t + 25\,°C). \tag{2}$$

While *PR* is a measure of the total losses, it cannot provide information about the root causes of reduced power output. This means that permanent losses, such as degradation, and transient losses, such as curtailment or cloud cover will have a similar effect on *PR*. Thus, using *PR* as a meaningful assessment of PV system health is only valuable when datapoints affected by transient losses are removed from the dataset. Furthermore, transient losses yields noise in the *PR* timeseries, which can make data analysis challenging. [5]

There are several established approaches for identifying timestamps where the PV system is experiencing clear-sky conditions. This enables improved *PR* calculations by removing data when the production is reduced due to shading by clouds. Reno and Hansen have suggested an algorithm that evaluates the shape of the irradiance curve measured at site. [6] This method assesses the mean and maximum global horizontal irradiance (GHI), the line-length of the GHI vs. time curve, the standard deviation in the rate of change of GHI, in addition to the maximal changes between measured GHI and estimated clear-sky time series to detect timestamps with clear-sky conditions. The method have also been extended to POA irradiance, and relies on setting threshold values for five parameters. The threshold values are also dependent on the time resolution of the measured irradiance data. Ellis et al. have suggested a similar approach that only relies on measured irradiance data. [7] Neither of these methods account for the spatial resolution of the irradiance data. This can lead to discarding large fractions of the dataset, particularly in large PV assets where a passing cloud only will affect a small subset of the PV production at a given time. Excessive removal of data will affect days with changing cloud-cover to a larger extent than days with consistent clear-sky conditions or overcast. Yi et al. recently published a clear-sky identification method based on machine-learning aimed on identifying clear days.[8] Even with a large detection rate, this method will also discard large amounts of data due to classification of whole days instead of clear-sky timestamps. Furthermore, machine-learned methods tend to be more involved than direct data analysis and often demands tuning to capture site-specific conditions.

Achieving spatial resolution in PV plant monitoring have seen increased interest. For O&M, this is for example relevant for drone imaging. [9] IR imaging using drones can be a powerful tool to identify module faults, such as hotspots and connection failures, but relies on robust mapping of string positions to enable maintenance actions. Furthermore, spatial resolution is also important in the field of power production forecasting, [10], [11] where tracking the movement of clouds over a large PV asset can yield more accurate short-term production predictions.

This work present a new procedure for clear-sky identification by using PV modules as cloud detectors. The cloud detection can be extended to the pyranometer data as the relative positions of pyranometers and strings are known for the site studied. By leveraging a dataset with a high temporal resolution we achieve a clear-sky filtering method that can retain a larger fraction of the production data than the conventional approaches. The large data retention also allows for clear-sky filtering on string-level, where conventional methods relies on filtering the measured irradiance. We demonstrate the performance of the clear-sky identification approach suggested here by computing *PR* on string level, and compare with the established method of Reno and Hansen.

2 METHODS

2.1 PV system data and cloud detection

This work relies on a 1-minute resolution dataset from a 150+ MWp PV power plant located in a tropical wet and dry climate ("As" in the Köppen–Geiger climate classification system) with a rainy season between January and July. The current of the monofacial PV modules is measured per string-set, which consist of two parallel connected strings of on average 31 modules each. The plant consist of in total 8088 string-sets. The 12 pyranometers at the site are mounted at the tracker of 12 different strings. The relative position of all strings-sets and pyranometers are stored in the site metadata. Initial data filtering is carried out prior to any analysis where all timestamps with curtailment are omitted. Timestamps where the tracker angle deviates from the setpoint angle are also filtered out.

The PV modules are used as cloud detectors through the calculation of a clear-sky index, $k_{i,t}$ for each string-set in the power plant through the following equation,

$$k_{i,t} = \frac{P_{i,t}\,/P_{i,STC}}{c_{t,25\,°C}G_{POA,CS,i,t}/G_{STC}}. \quad (3)$$

In Eq. (1), $P_{i,t}$ is the power output of the *i*-th string-set during *t*. $G_{POA,CS,i,t}$ is the modelled clear-sky POA irradiation. This value is obtained using the simplified Soilis model to estimate the global horizontal, direct normal, and diffuse horizontal contributions to the clear-sky irradiance for the PV system location.[12] Next, the angle-of incidence (AOI) is computed using the measured tracker angle for each string-set to obtain the incident-angle modifier by applying the De Soto model.[8] Finally, $G_{POA,CS,i,t}$ is obtained by transposing the clear-sky irradiance contributions to the POA using the Perez model,[13] and adjusting for the AOI by multiplying with the incident angle-modifier. Version 0.11.2 of pvlib is used to apply all models leveraged in this work, where default settings are used throughout.[14]

2.2 Proposed clear-sky filter

In this study, we leverage the clear-sky indices obtained with Eq. (3) to identify the strings shaded by clouds. Fig. 1 displays the calculated clear-sky indices for all string-sets in the power plant for a given timestamp. Note that the pyranometer positions are indicated by red circles in the plot. The figure shows that several of the sensors are shaded by clouds, while most of the string-sets have large clear-sky indices and can be assumed to experience clear-sky conditions.

The $k_{i,t}$ values are computed on a sting-set level. This means that while we now have a measure for when each string is shaded, it still remains to filter the irradiance data. As the pyranometers are mounted on trackers, we map the clear-sky indices to the pyranometers by assuming that the irradiance conditions are equal for the string and pyranometer mounted to the same tracker. This spatial mapping allows for detection of clear-sky conditions for

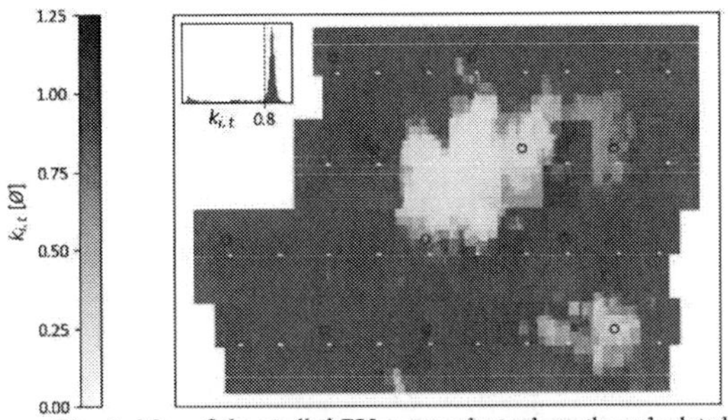

Fig. 1: Map of the studied PV power plant where the calculated clear-sky index for each string-set is indicated. The red circles indicate pyranometer positions. The inset displays a histogram of the clear-sky values for all string-set for this particular time

each individual string-set and pyranometer, rather than for the power plant as a whole. Furthermore, the high temporal resolution of the dataset ensures minimal cloud movement during each time step *t*. Thus, we can assume that the clear-sky index is an appropriate measure of the instantaneous irradiation conditions. The clear-sky POA irradiance can be assumed to be a linear average of all non-shaded measurements for each timestamp.

Finally, to enable clear-sky filtering, it is necessary to define a threshold value for $k_{i,t}$ that separates clear-sky from cloudy conditions. By assessing the distribution of $k_{i,t}$, we define clear-sky conditions as datapoints with $k_{i,t} > 0.8$, see the histogram in the inset of Fig. 1. There is an unavoidable mismatch when mapping the string-set $k_{i,t}$ values to pyranometers due to the physical extent of the strings and the positional mismatch between string and pyranometers. Thus, two datapoints are removed before and after each instance of $k_{i,t} < 0.8$ to limit the effect of the mismatch on the identification of clear-sky timestamps.

3 RESULTS AND DISCUSSION

The proposed methodology for clear-sky identification is assessed by computing *PR* on string-set level and compared with the results obtained by applying the clear-sky filter by Reno and Hansen. [6] Fig. 2 presents the calculated *PR* time series and irradiance received in the POA during five days of November 2022. The top panel of Fig. 2 displays the *PR* calculated without applying any clear-sky filter. The obtained *PR* values are very noisy, which highlights the need of an effective clear-sky filter to achieve reliable *PR* assessment and loss identification.

The two panels in the middle of Fig. 2 display the *PR* timeseries obtained using our suggested filter (second from the top) and the filter of Reno and Hansen (second from the bottom). While the filter of Reno and Hansen retain a sizable fraction of the data on days with longer time intervals of clear-sky conditions, the bulk of the data is discarded for days with changing cloud cover, such as the 20th and the 23rd of November. No data is retained for the 20th. The approach suggested here retains a larger fraction of the data for all days. This is particularly evident

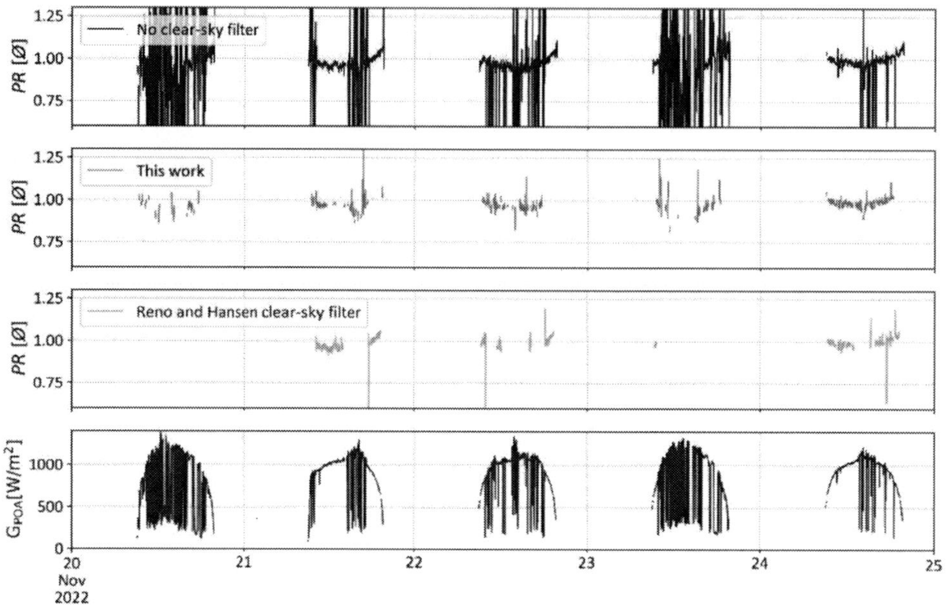

Fig. 2: Calculated *PR* time series for a selected string-set for five days in November 2022 (top) without clear-sky filtering, (second from the top) with the clear-sky filter proposed here, (second from the bottom) using Reno and Hansens's clear-sky filter. The bottom panel displays the measured irradiance received in the POA. The *PR*-values are normalized relative to the first value in the timeseries to avoid publishing business sensitive information

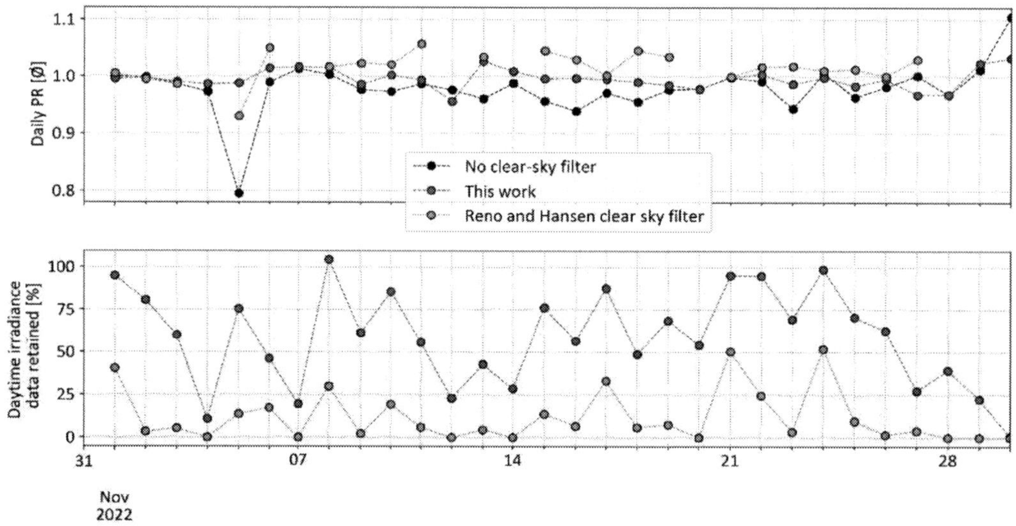

Fig 3: Daily *PR* values for a selected string-set computed using our proposed filter and the clear-sky detection of Reno and Hansen. The *PR*-values are normalized relative to the first value in the timeseries to avoid publishing business sensitive information. The bottom panel displays the percentage of string-set data retained for each day using the two clear-sky filters.

for days with frequent changes in cloud cover, and enables *PR* and loss assessment for periods where clouds are moving over the power plant. The noise in the *PR* values are also reduced compared to the unfiltered data in the top, meaning that timestamps affected by cloud shading are efficiently filtered out.

To further evaluate the performance of our clear-sky filter, we also compute the daily *PR* values for the same string-set for the month of November 2022. Fig. 3 shows the daily *PR* values (top panel) and the fraction of daytime data retained (bottom panel) using both the suggested clear-sky filter and that of Reno and Hansen. The calculated daily *PR* values show that there are several missing days for the data filtered using the method of Reno and Hansen. There are also a larger variation in the *PR* using this approach, which is the behavior expected if there was a variation in the power losses in the PV power plant. The *PR* values obtained used the method suggested here are more stable, and there are no days where sll daytime data is filtered out The bottom panel further highlights the difference in daytime data retention using the two clear-sky filters. Daytime data are defined here as timestamps where the solar elevation angle is above 10°. The new approach discards a smaller fraction of data for each day in the studied period, meaning that the calculated daily *PR* values are backed by more data. An increased data retention yields a higher confidence in computed *PR*, and can thus enable more reliable PV loss estimation.

Filtering on both string and pyranometer-level separates this method from the conventional approaches that only assesses the irradiance curve shape. Typically, clear-sky filters are applied by filtering the mean or median of all irradiance measurements at site. Thus, clear-sky timestamps are only moments when there are no clouds over the PV site.

Here, we construct a clear-sky irradiance time series by averaging the irradiance measured by all pyranometers that experience clear-sky conditions for a given time stamp. Furthermore, the filtering on string level ensures that only clear sky timestamps are included in the consecutive *PR* assessment.

In addition to construct a clear-sky irradiance time series that is valid for the whole site, we also ensure that

The focus of this work is to identify clear-sky timestamps. However, the suggested method can also be leveraged to find timestamps with overcast conditions. This requires setting a low threshold value for $k_{i,t}$, where values beneath the threshold are assumed to indicate significant cloud shading. This approach can for example be beneficial for PV power plants in the Nordic, which tend to experience significant shading by clouds. Using only overcast timestamps can in these instances also be a measure to reduce noise in *PR* time series.

4 CONCLUSIONS

We have presented a new clear-sky filter that leverages data with a high temporal resolution where the relative positions of string-sets and pyranometers are known. The suggested method effectively filters out timestamps affected by cloud cover by assessing calculated clear-sky indices that compare measured production with expected clear-sky power production. Furthermore, this approach only relies on defining a single threshold value, where we defined clear-sky conditions as timestamps with $k_{i,t} > 0.8$. By assessing the *PR* timeseries with a 1-minute resolution and daily *PR* we demonstrated that the new approach achieves a higher data retention than the established filter proposed by Reno and Hansen.

The new method can thus enable better loss estimation and string-level *PR* assessments.

ACKNOWLEDGEMENTS

This work was supported by the Norwegian Research Council through project number 355871.

5 REFERENCES

[1] D. C. Jordan og C. Hansen, «Clear-sky detection for PV degradation analysis using multiple regression», *Renew. Energy*, bd. 209, s. 393–400, jun. 2023, doi: 10.1016/j.renene.2023.04.035.

[2] D. C. Jordan, T. J. Silverman, J. H. Wohlgemuth, S. R. Kurtz, og K. T. VanSant, «Photovoltaic failure and degradation modes», *Prog. Photovolt. Res. Appl.*, bd. 25, nr. 4, s. 318–326, apr. 2017, doi: 10.1002/pip.2866.

[3] H. Iftikhar, E. Sarquis, og P. J. C. Branco, «Why Can Simple Operation and Maintenance (O&M) Practices in Large-Scale Grid-Connected PV Power Plants Play a Key Role in Improving Its Energy Output?», *Energies*, bd. 14, nr. 13, s. 3798, jan. 2021, doi: 10.3390/en14133798.

[4] *IEC 61724-1:2021 photovoltaic system performance - Part 1: Monitoring*, Geneva, Switzerland., 2021.

[5] M. M. Nygård, Å. F. Skomedal, M. S. Wiig, og E. S. Marstein, «Combined Degradation and Soiling With Validation Against Independent Soiling Station Measurements», *IEEE J. Photovolt.*, bd. 13, nr. 2, s. 296–304, mar. 2023, doi: 10.1109/JPHOTOV.2023.3239752.

[6] M. J. Reno og C. W. Hansen, «Identification of periods of clear sky irradiance in time series of GHI measurements», *Renew. Energy*, bd. 90, s. 520–531, mai 2016, doi: 10.1016/j.renene.2015.12.031.

[7] B. H. Ellis, M. Deceglie, og A. Jain, «Automatic Detection of Clear-Sky Periods From Irradiance Data», *IEEE J. Photovolt.*, bd. 9, nr. 4, s. 998–1005, jul. 2019, doi: 10.1109/JPHOTOV.2019.2914444.

[8] C. Yi *mfl.*, «Anomaly detection of photovoltaic power generation based on quantile regression recurrent neural network», *Electr. Power Syst. Res.*, bd. 238, s. 111132, jan. 2025, doi: 10.1016/j.epsr.2024.111132.

[9] E. Sovetkin, A. Gerber, B. Kubicek, og B. Pieters, «Single Image Geospatial Referencing», Proceedings of the 41st EUPVSEC (2024).

[10] M. M. Nygård, E. W. Eriksen, og H. N. Riise, «Photovoltaic power plants as efficient cloud motion detectors», Proceedings of the 41st EUPVSEC (2024).

[11] M. Lipperheide, J. L. Bosch, og J. Kleissl, «Embedded nowcasting method using cloud speed persistence for a photovoltaic power plant», *Sol. Energy*, bd. 112, s. 232–238, feb. 2015, doi: 10.1016/j.solener.2014.11.013.

[12] P. Ineichen, «A broadband simplified version of the Solis clear sky model», *Sol. Energy*, bd. 82, nr. 8, s. 758–762, aug. 2008, doi: 10.1016/j.solener.2008.02.009.

[13] R. Perez, P. Ineichen, R. Seals, J. Michalsky, og R. Stewart, «Modeling daylight availability and irradiance components from direct and global irradiance», *Sol. Energy*, bd. 44, nr. 5, s. 271–289, 1990, doi: 10.1016/0038-092X(90)90055-H.

[14] W. F. Holmgren, C. W. Hansen, og M. A. Mikofski, «pvlib python: a python package for modeling solar energy systems», *J. Open Source Softw.*, bd. 3, nr. 29, s. 884, sep. 2018, doi: 10.21105/joss.00884.

Elin Dynvik Sødahl*, Magnus Moe Nygård, and Marie Syre Wiig
Solar Power Systems
Institute for Energy Technology, Kjeller, Norway
**elin.sodahl@ife.no*

IFE

A spatially resolved clear-sky filter: photovoltaic modules as cloud detectors

Operation and maintenance of photovoltaic (PV) power plants is essential to mitigate performance losses due to degradation and soiling. Traditional clear-sky filters often discard large amounts of data, particularly during shifting weather conditions. Using the PV modules as cloud detectors enables clear-sky filtering on string-level and a spatially resolved filtering approach. This is beneficial in large PV system, as it allows retaining data for one part of the park while another area is shaded by clouds.

Data filtering is crucial to achieve a reliable performance ratio

The performance ratio takes measured irradiance and produced power as input and is used as a measure of the health of a PV system.

$$PR = \frac{\sum_t P_t}{\sum_t c_{t,25°C} P_{STC}\, G_{POA,t}\, / G_{STC}}$$

PR values does not separate between permanent losses (i.e., degradation) and temporary losses (i.e., soiling, changing cloud cover). Temporary losses should be filtered out to evaluate permanent losses.

String-set resolved clear-sky index

A clear sky index can be computed for each string (*i*) for each timestep (*t*) of the production data by modelling the clear-sky plane-of-array irradiance ($G_{POA,CS,i,t}$):

$$k_{i,t} = \frac{P_{i,t}\, / P_{i,STC}}{c_{t,25\,°C} G_{POA,CS,i,t} / G_{STC}}$$

This allows for mapping of the clouds over the PV plant. The position of strings and pyranometers in the PV system are known, meaning that the clear-sky indices of the strings can be mapped to the adjacent pyranometers.

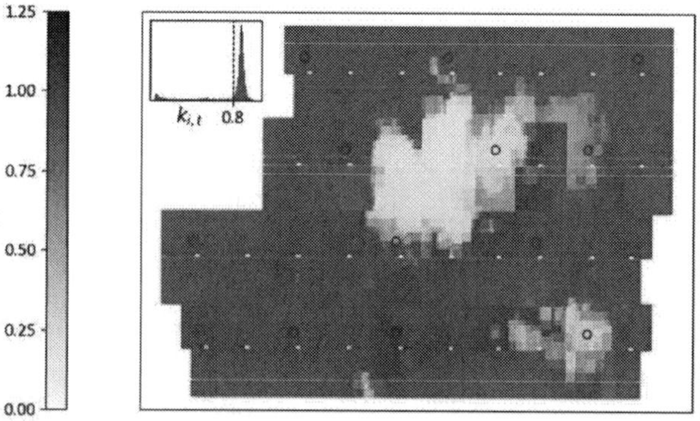

Figure 1: Map of the PV power plant where the clear-sky index of each string-set is indicated. The circles indicates the position of the irradiance sensors. The inset displays a histogram of the clear-sky values for all strings for this timestamp.

References:
[1] Reno. and Hansen. Renewable Energy, 2016, 90: p. 520-531.
[2] Holmgren et al. Journal of Open Source Software, 2018. 3(29).

Acknowledgements:
This work was supported by the Norwegian Research Council through project number 355871.

Proposed clear-sky filter

A high time-resolution is required to capture reduced $k_{i,t}$ as clouds moves above the PV system. Data is retained if $k_{i,t} > 0.8$. There are differences in the physical position and extent of the pyranometers and string, and two datapoints are removed before and after each timestep with $k_{i,t} < 0.8$ to limit the effect of this mismatch. The data can be filtered on string-level.

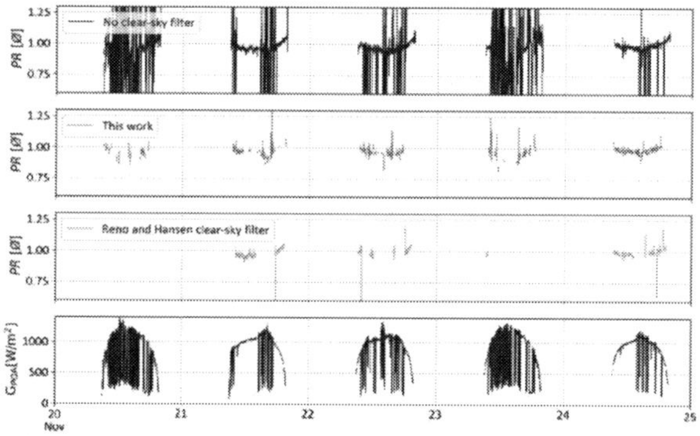

Figure 2: PR values for a selected string, including filtering Reno and Hansen[1] which is implemented in `pvlib`[2] and the method suggested here. The PR values are normalized.

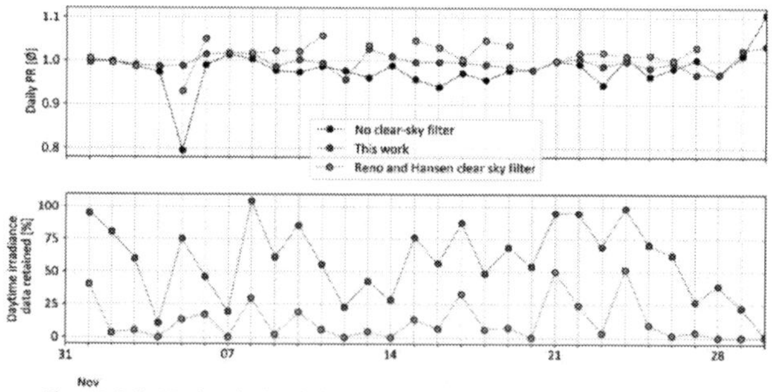

Figure 3: Daily PR values (top), and the percentage of data retained (bottom) using both the proposed clear-sky filter and that of Reno and Hansen[1]. The PR values are normalized.

Conclusions

The new clear-sky filter retains a larger fraction of data than that of Reno and Hansen on most days, and particularly for days with frequent changes in cloud-cover. This results in more reliable calculation of PR-values. Using the new filter results in PR values for all days in November 2022 for a single string and yields less noisy values compared with unfiltered data and the filter of Reno and Hansen.

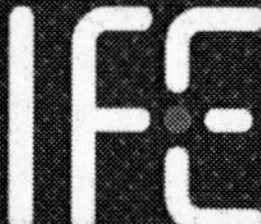

DEVELOPMENT OF COMPUTATIONAL MODELS FOR ENERGY PRODUCTION ESTIMATION IN BIFACIAL MODULES UNDER DIFFERENT CONFIGURATIONS AT THE ATACAMA DESERT SOLAR PLATFORM (PSDA)

Mauricio Trigo-Gonzalez [1, 3,*], Sebastián Rodríguez-Romero[1], Jorge Rabanal-Arabach[1,3], Jorge Vega-Herrera[1,3], Felipe Valencia[2] and Edward Fuentealba[1,3]

[1] University of Antofagasta, Av. Angamos 601, 1270300 Antofagasta, Chile.
[2] AtamosTec, Pérez Valenzuela 1635, 7500028 Providencia, Chile.
[3] Solar Energy Research Center, Tupper 2007, 8370451 Santiago, Chile.

* Corresponding Author: mauricio.trigo@uantof.cl

ABSTRACT: The Atacama Desert, located in the Antofagasta Region of Chile, has the highest levels of solar radiation and albedo worldwide. These conditions are ideal for bifacial photovoltaic (PV) technologies, as they maximize efficiency and energy generation. To assess the potential installable PV capacity in this region under extreme desert conditions, a machine learning-based estimation model is proposed. This model will provide approximate energy generation values based on climatic variables such as solar radiation, ambient temperature, and wind speed. With this approach, it will be possible to more accurately plan the optimal locations for bifacial PV plant installations in the Antofagasta region, reducing investment uncertainty and improving energy planning.

For this study, monofacial and bifacial PV modules were installed at the Atacama Desert Solar Platform (PSDA) in Chile to compare different technologies. Two mounting configurations were evaluated: a fixed system with a 20° tilt (TFE20°) and a single-axis horizontal tracking system (HSAT). The modules used were of the PERC (Passivated Emitter Rear Contact) type, and data was collected between June 2022 and September 2023. For the analysis, two estimation models were trained: an Artificial Neural Network (ANN) and a Multiple Linear Regression (MLR) model, aiming to compare different statistical approaches. The results showed that, in all cases, the models achieved RMSE% values below 6% and MBE values close to 0%. Notably, the ANN demonstrated slightly better performance compared to the MLR, for both monofacial and bifacial modules in both mounting configurations.

In conclusion, ANN models are an effective tool for estimating photovoltaic power and optimizing mounting configurations, especially in regions with extreme environmental conditions such as the Atacama Desert.

Keywords: Photovoltaic Power Estimation, Artificial Neuronal Network, Multiple Linear Regression, Bifacial Technology, Machine Learning, Atacama Desert , Bifacial Technology

1 INTRODUCTION

Photovoltaic (PV) systems represent one of the most promising solutions for sustainable energy generation, particularly in regions with high solar potential. Among these, the Atacama Desert in northern Chile stands out as a natural laboratory, offering the highest global horizontal irradiance and albedo levels worldwide. These extreme environmental conditions create both an opportunity for maximizing PV generation and a challenge for accurate energy yield assessment [1]–[3].

Recent advances in PV technologies highlight the growing role of bifacial modules, which capture irradiance from both the front and rear sides, significantly enhancing energy yield in high-reflectance environments. However, the accurate estimation of their performance remains complex, especially when using conventional linear models. Multiple Linear Regression (MLR) approaches have been widely employed, yet their capacity to represent the non-linear interactions between climatic variables and power generation is limited.

In this context, Artificial Neural Networks (ANN) have emerged as a powerful tool capable of modeling non-linear dependencies and improving predictive accuracy [4]. Previous studies have reported the potential of ANN for PV performance estimation under various conditions [5], but limited research has validated these models in environments as extreme as the Atacama Desert

The objective of this study is to evaluate and compare the predictive performance of ANN and MLR models in estimating the energy production of monofacial and bifacial PERC modules under two mounting configurations: a fixed-tilt system with 20° inclination (TFE20°) and a horizontal single-axis tracking system (HSAT). By analyzing experimental data collected at the Atacama Desert Solar Platform (PSDA, Spanish acronym)), this work aims to provide a reliable methodological framework for energy yield estimation, contributing to the reduction of uncertainty in the design and operation of PV plants in high-irradiance regions.

2 MATERIALS AND METHOD

2.1 MOUNTING CONFIGURATION

The fixed-tilt configuration (TFE20°) consisted of PERC-type PV modules installed with a 20° inclination facing north, in accordance with conventional design parameters for desert latitudes. This setup represents a baseline system, allowing the evaluation of photovoltaic behavior under static operating conditions. The configuration is particularly relevant in the Atacama Desert due to the high ground-reflected irradiance (albedo), which enhances the rear-side contribution in bifacial technologies.

The horizontal single-axis tracking (HSAT) system enabled modules to follow the solar trajectory along the east–west axis, maintaining a near-normal incidence of irradiance throughout the day. This configuration maximizes daily energy yield and provides a robust framework for comparing static and dynamic tracking strategies. The HSAT setup also minimizes angular losses and improves correlation between irradiance on the module plane and measured energy, which is critical for the calibration and validation of computational models. In Figure1, the mounting configurations of the photovoltaic modules for the TFE20° system and the HSAT are shown.

Fig. 1: Facilities studied in the PSDA. a) TFE20, b) HSAT

2.2 EXPERIMENTAL DATA

The experimental campaign was conducted on the Atacama Desert Solar Platform (PSDA), see figure 2, located at 24.09° S, 69.93° W, during the period June 2022 to September 2023. PSDA is characterized by a global horizontal irradiance (GHI) that exceeds 8 $\mathrm{kWh\,m^{-2}\,day^{-1}}$ day and a mean albedo of approximately 0.25.

Data acquisition included:

- Meteorological variables: frontal and rear irradiance, global horizontal irradiance, ambient temperature, module surface temperature, and wind speed. Horizontal irradiance peaks reached values close to 1200 W/m^2, while rear-side irradiance approached 300 W/m^2 on clear days. see figure 3
- Electrical variables: DC power and energy yield from monofacial and bifacial modules.

Fig. 2: Natural laboratory:Atacama Desert Solar Platform (PSDA, Spanish acronym)

Measurements were recorded at 5-minute intervals. Prior to model development, the dataset underwent a data preprocessing pipeline involving outlier detection and removal, missing value imputation, and input variable normalization. These preprocessing steps ensured numerical stability during training and reduced the risk of systematic biases in model estimation.

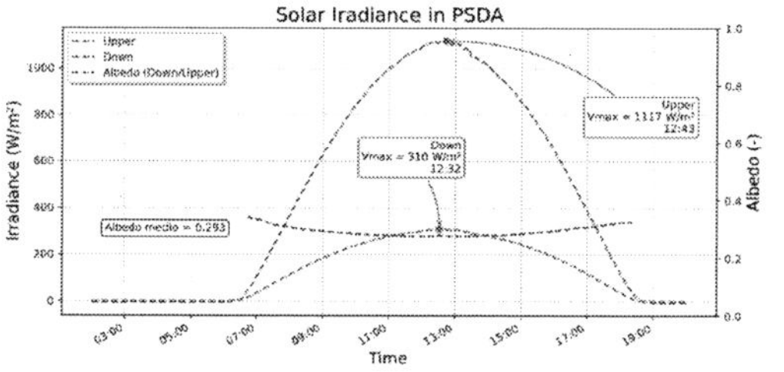

Fig. 3: Albedo

2.3 ESTIMATION MODEL

Two computational approaches were implemented to estimate the energy production of the PV systems: an Artificial Neural Network (ANN) and a Multiple Linear Regression (MLR) model.

2.31 ANN model

The ANN architecture was based on a multilayer perceptron (MLP), see figure 4. Input neurons represented the measured climatic variables (irradiance, temperatures, and wind speed), while the output neuron corresponded to the predicted PV power. For bifacial modules, the rear irradiance was explicitly included as an additional input. The architecture consisted of two hidden layers with 16 and 4 neurons, respectively, and sigmoid activation functions. The dataset was randomly partitioned into training (67%) and validation (33%) subsets. Weight optimization was performed using a backpropagation algorithm, with RMSE and MBE as performance indicators. This configuration was selected to capture the non-linear relationships between environmental conditions and PV energy production.

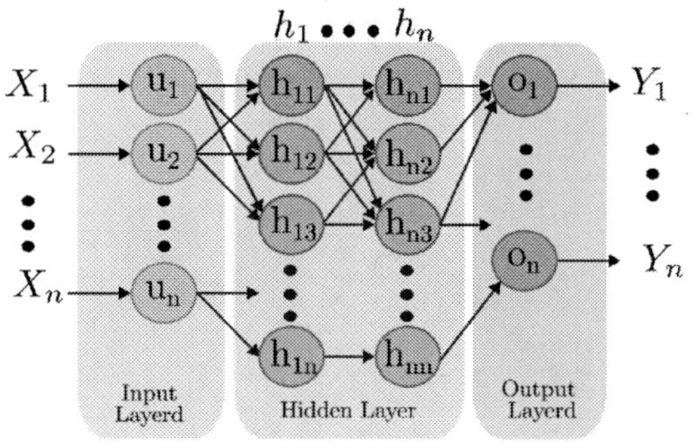

Fig. 4: Model ANN

2.32 MLR Model

The Multiple Linear Regression (MLR) model, see figure 5, was developed as a baseline for comparison. This model assumes a linear dependency between predictor variables (irradiance, temperature, wind speed) and the response variable (energy yield). Despite its simplicity, MLR provides insight into the degree of linearity of the system response and serves as a benchmark for validating the added value of non-linear ANN approaches under extreme desert conditions.

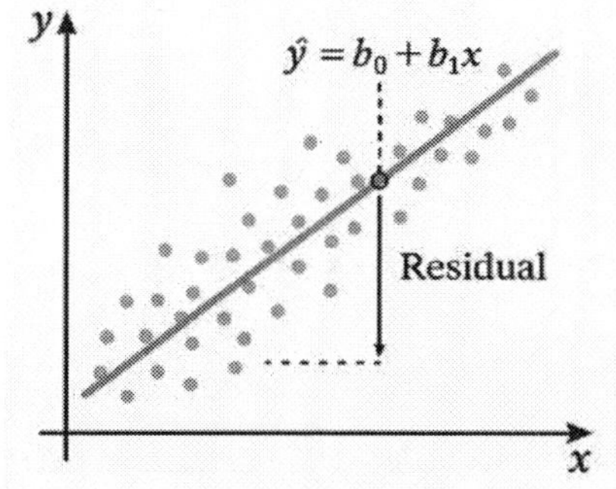

Fig. 5: Model MLR

3 RESULTS AND DISCUSSION

The predictive performance of the ANN and MLR models was analyzed for both mounting configurations (TFE20° and HSAT) and module technologies (monofacial and bifacial). Figure 6 shows the scatter plots of measured versus predicted energy, where ANN results are displayed in blue and MLR results in red. The dashed line corresponds to the ideal 1:1 correlation.

For the TFE20° configuration, the ANN model exhibits a higher level of accuracy compared to MLR. In the monofacial case (Fig. 6a), ANN predictions are more tightly aligned with the reference line, reducing dispersion and systematic deviations. The improvement is even more evident for bifacial modules (Fig. 6b), where ANN maintains RMSE values below 6%, outperforming MLR, which reaches approximately 8%. The MBE values remain close to zero for both models, although MLR shows slightly larger variability, suggesting a tendency to underestimate under certain irradiance ranges.

For the HSAT configuration, both models benefit from the improved irradiance correlation achieved by the tracking system. In the monofacial case (Fig. 6c), ANN achieves RMSE values of approximately 4.23%, while MLR remains near 4.65%. The bifacial case (Fig. 6d) confirms this trend, with ANN predictions closely following the ideal line and providing RMSE values of 4.16%, compared to 5.29% for MLR. The reduction in error dispersion highlights the capability of HSAT to minimize angular losses and stabilize the relationship between climatic variables and energy yield.

Summarizes the statistical indicators obtained for all scenarios. In every configuration, both models achieved RMSE% below 6% and MBE% values within ±1%. However, the ANN consistently provided lower RMSE% values, demonstrating its robustness in capturing non-linear interactions between irradiance, temperature, and energy production. MLR presented slightly lower dispersion in MBE in some cases, but at the expense of higher RMSE values.

Overall, the results confirm that the combination of ANN models with bifacial modules under HSAT configuration delivers the most accurate predictions. This synergy reflects both the technological advantage of bifacial modules in high-albedo environments and the ability of ANN models to adapt to the complex variability of desert climatic conditions.

4 CONCLUSIONS

This work presented a comparative analysis of Artificial Neural Networks (ANN) and Multiple Linear Regression (MLR) models for the estimation of photovoltaic energy production in monofacial and bifacial PERC modules under two mounting configurations, a fixed-tilt at 20° (TFE20°) and a horizontal single-axis tracker (HSAT), using experimental data collected at the Atacama Desert Solar Platform (PSDA). The results confirmed that both models provide reliable estimations, with RMSE% values below 6% and MBE% values close to zero across all scenarios. However, ANN consistently outperformed MLR, particularly in capturing the non-linear interactions between climatic variables and energy output, achieving RMSE values as low as 4% in the HSAT monofacial case. Furthermore, bifacial modules demonstrated superior performance under the desert's high irradiance and albedo conditions, while tracking systems reduced angular mismatch and improved the stability of model predictions. Overall, the combination of ANN with bifacial modules un-

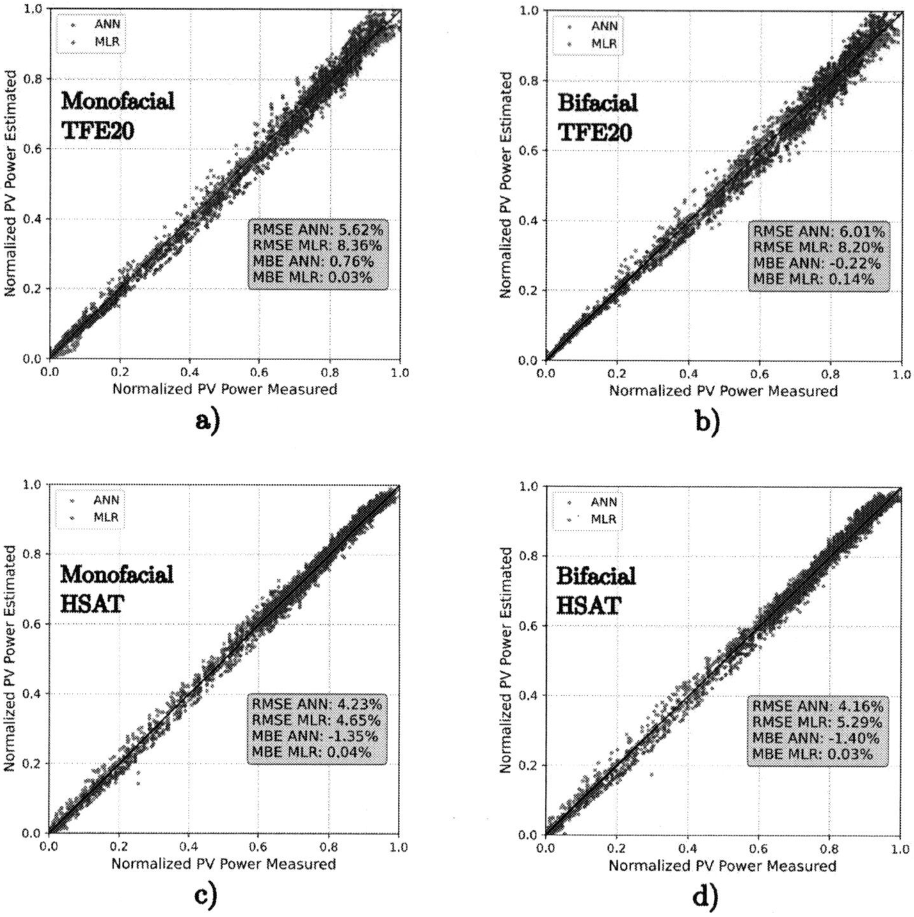

Fig. 6: Comparison between measured and predicted energy using MLR (red) and ANN (blue) for PERC modules under different configurations: (a) monofacial TFE20°, (b) bifacial TFE20°, (c) monofacial HSAT, and (d) bifacial HSAT

der HSAT configuration represents the most accurate approach, providing a robust methodology to reduce uncertainty in PV energy yield assessment and offering a transferable framework for the design and operation of photovoltaic plants in other high-irradiance regions worldwide.

ACKNOWLEDGMENTS

This work was supported by the Chilean Solar Energy Research Center (SERC Chile) through the FONDAP Grant 1523A0006, and by the Atacama Module and Systems Technology Consortium (ATA-MOSTEC) under the CORFO Program 17PTECES-75830. Agencia Nacional de Investigación y Desarrollo de Chile (ANID) a través del Programa de Doctorado Nacional, bajo el financiamiento ANID/Subdirección de Capital Humano/Doctorado Nacional/2024-21241192.

References

[1] J. D. Clarke, "Antiquity of aridity in the chilean atacama desert," *Geomorphology*, vol. 73, no. 1, pp. 101–114, 2006. [Online]. Available: https://www.sciencedirect.com/science/article/pii/S0169555X05002023
[2] A. Marzo, P. Ferrada, F. Beiza, P. Besson, J. Alonso-Montesinos, J. Ballestrín, R. Román, C. Portillo, R. Escobar, and E. Fuentealba, "Standard or local solar spectrum? implications for solar technologies studies in the atacama desert," *Renewable Energy*, vol. 127, pp. 871–882, 2018.
[3] J. Rabanal-Arabach, "Development of a c-si photovoltaic module for desert climates," Ph.D. dissertation, Universität Konstanz, Konstanz, 2019.
[4] A. Marzo, M. Trigo, J. Alonso-Montesinos, M. Martínez-Durbán, G. López, P. Ferrada, E. Fuentealba, M. Cortés, and F. J. Batlles, "Daily global solar radiation estimation in desert areas using daily extreme temperatures and extraterrestrial radiation," *Renewable Energy*, vol. 113, pp. 303–311, 2017.
[5] M. Trigo-González, M. Cortés-Carmona, A. Marzo, J. Alonso-Montesinos, M. Martínez-Durbán, G. López, C. Portillo, and F. J. Batlles, "Photovoltaic power electricity generation now-casting combining sky camera images and learning supervised algorithms in southern spain," *Renewable Energy*, vol. 206, pp. 251–262, 2023.

Universidad de Antofagasta

DEVELOPMENT OF COMPUTATIONAL MODELS FOR ENERGY PRODUCTION ESTIMATION IN BIFACIAL MODULES UNDER DIFFERENT CONFIGURATIONS AT THE ATACAMA DESERT SOLAR PLATFORM (PSDA)

Mauricio Trigo-Gonzalez[1,3], Sebastián Rodríguez-Romero[1,3], Jorge Rabanal-Arabach[1,3], Jorge Vega-Herrera[1,3], Felipe Valencia[2], and Edward Fuentealba-Vidal[1,3].

[1] Universidad de Antofagasta, Av. Angamos 601, 1270300 Antofagasta, Chile. [2] AtamosTec, Pérez Valenzuela 1635, 7500028 Providencia, Chile. [3] Solar Energy Research Center, Tupper 2007, 8370451 Santiago, Chile.

EU PVSEC 2025

INTRODUCTION

This study assesses the prediction of power output for monofacial and bifacial PV systems operating under the environmental conditions of the Atacama Desert, in Chile. Two mounting configurations were evaluated: a fixed one with a 20° tilt (TFE20°) and another with horizontal single-axis tracking (HSAT). The power of each of them is predicted by two estimation models: (1) Artificial Neural Network (ANN) and (2) Multiple Linear Regression (MLR).

METHODOLOGY

The experimental campaign was carried out at the Atacama Desert Solar Platform (PSDA), Chile (24.09° S; 69.93° W), between June 2022 and September 2023. The site is characterized by a global horizontal irradiance (GHI) exceeding 1100 W/m² at solar noon and a daily average albedo, under clear-sky conditions, of approximately 0.29.

The training methodology confirmed that the most representative input variables are the global horizontal irradiance (GHI), the module temperature (Tmod), and both the front and rear module irradiance (GI front and GI rear, respectively), all showing a Pearson correlation coefficient greater than 0.8.

Atacama Desert Solar Platform (PSDA)

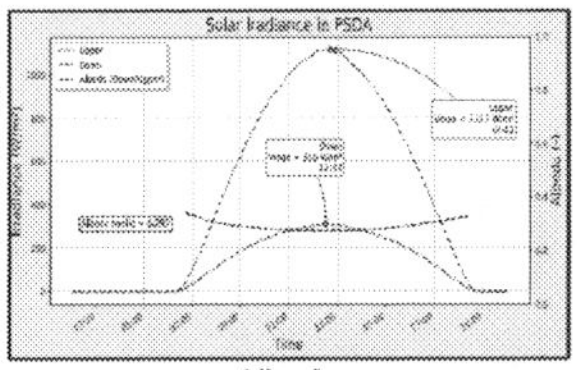

Albedo

South America, Chile

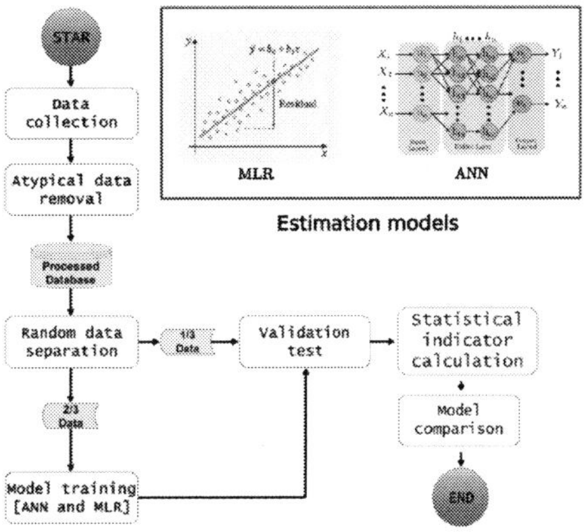

Estimation models

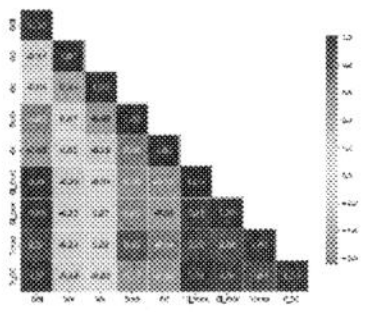

Pearson coefficient of TFE 20

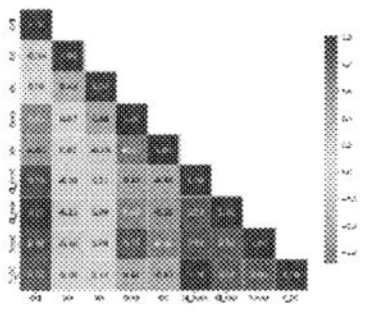

Pearson coefficient of HSAT

RESULTS

The ANN and the MLR models applied to monofacial and bifacial modules, under fixed (TFE20) and HSAT configurations showed high accuracy. In all cases, ANN achieved RMSE% values below 6%, slightly outperforming MLR (with 8%).

TFE20 Type Mounting

HSAT Type Mounting

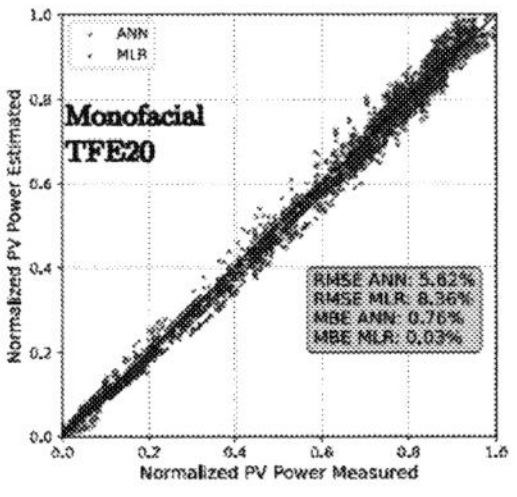

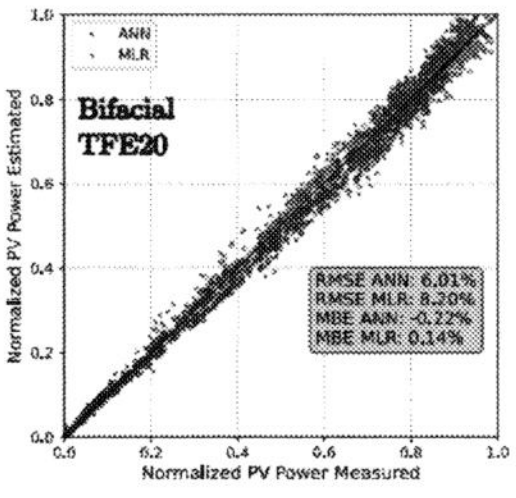

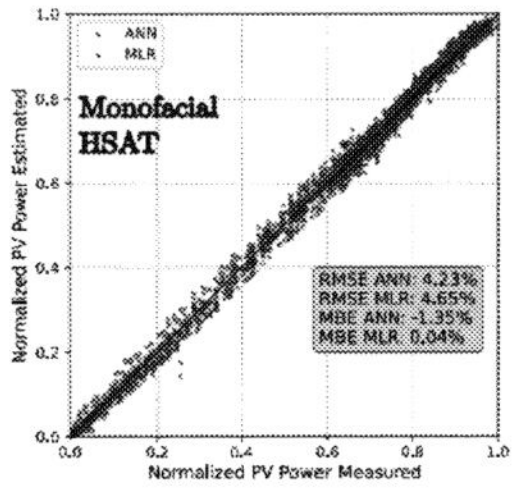

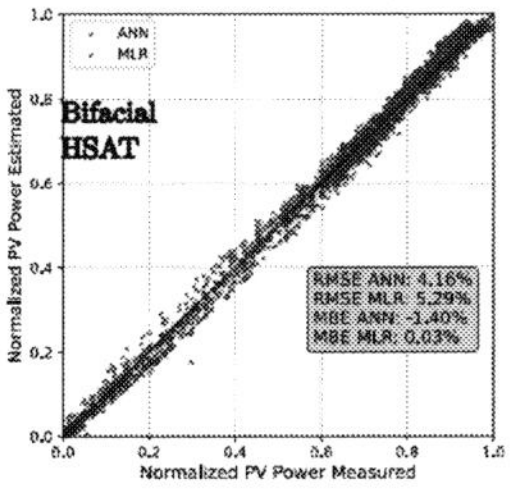

CONCLUSION

Estimation models for PV power under high solar irradiance desert conditions were compared, with ANN proving to be the most effective approach. Using only input variables such as irradiance and module temperature enables accurate predictions, supporting the planning of PV plants in high-irradiance environments.

This work was supported by SERC Chile under FONDAP 1523A0006 grant, and by the Atacama Module and Systems Technology Consortium, ATAMOSTEC, under CORFO 17PTECES-75830 program.

020343-001

CDEA CENTRO DESARROLLO ENERGÉTICO ANTOFAGASTA

SERC CHILE SOLAR ENERGY RESEARCH CENTER

ASSESSING PV MODULE QUALITY RISKS IN SOUTH AFRICA: PERFORMANCE INSIGHTS ACROSS UTILITY, COMMERCIAL AND INDUSTRIAL, AND RESIDENTIAL SECTORS

JL Crozier McCleland[1,2*], M Vumbugwa[1,2], NW Mngomezulu[2], FJ Vorster[1,2] , EE van Dyk[1,2]

[1]Nelson Mandela University, Nelson Mandela Bay, 6019, South Africa
[2]PVinsight (Pty) Ltd, Nelson Mandela Bay, 6019, South Africa
*Corresponding Author: Jacqueline.CrozierMcCleland@mandela.ac.za

ABSTRACT: South Africa's Solar Photovoltaic (PV) sector has expanded rapidly across utility, commercial and industrial (C&I), and residential markets, yet concerns about PV module quality remain. This paper presents insights from over a decade of accredited testing of PV modules across these sectors, highlighting how quality assurance (QA) practices shape performance outcomes. Utility-scale projects that applied QA frameworks consistently outperformed manufacturer specifications, with modules initially underspecified and remaining above warranty thresholds after ten years of operation. In the C&I sector, modules sourced directly from the market performed slightly below nameplate values but within measurement uncertainty, indicating variable reliability. In contrast, residential systems showed the highest risks with the focus on costs rather than quality. These results demonstrate that performance risks are not uniformly distributed across the market, and that sectors lacking QA are most exposed to underperformance and safety concerns. The findings support the principle that *"the best module is the tested module"* and make the case for extending QA practices beyond utility projects to safeguard investments, system yields, and consumer confidence across all PV market segments in South Africa.
Keywords: Module Degradation, Quality Assurance, Testing

1 INTRODUCTION

The Photovoltaic (PV) module makes up a significant portion of the cost of a PV system or utility-scale PV plant. The quality of a PV module can critically impact the performance, reliability, and longevity of these installations. In recent years, dramatic cost reductions in PV module manufacturing have helped accelerate the energy transition to renewables by making solar power increasingly affordable. However, these price declines have also coincided with design and material changes that raise concerns about performance reliability and durability. For investors, insurers, engineers, and system owners, the question is no longer just how cheap solar can become, but how reliably it can deliver electricity across its expected 25-year lifetime.

International studies have shown that modules can fail prematurely due to a range of issues, including cracks, encapsulant delamination, backsheet chalking, glass breakage, and hotspot formation [1]. These defects reduce system yield and, in severe cases, can pose fire and safety hazards. Real-world installations expose modules to stress factors such as high irradiance, thermal cycling, humidity, dust, windy conditions, and varying installation practices. These external factors, together with manufacturing quality variations and bill of materials (BOM) decisions, mean that actual field performance can diverge significantly from manufacturer specifications.

South Africa provides a particularly important context for examining these risks. Since the launch of the Renewable Energy Independent Power Producer Procurement Programme (REIPPPP) in 2011 [2], the country has developed a large portfolio of utility-scale PV plants. More recently, commercial and industrial (C&I) systems and residential rooftop installations have grown rapidly, driven by persistent electricity shortages and load-shedding. As a result, PV modules are now deployed across diverse settings, from rigorously procured multi-megawatt projects to small rooftop systems purchased directly by consumers. This creates a fragmented landscape in which quality assurance practices vary widely between sectors.

Utility-scale projects in South Africa typically apply quality assurance (QA) frameworks during procurement and operation, including independent laboratory testing of modules before and after installation [3]. Many projects implement annual testing programmes to monitor degradation and ensure performance warranties are met. By contrast, C&I and residential markets are characterised by limited or no QA practices. Modules in these segments are often sourced through distributors and rebranding channels, with little verification of manufacturer claims. This raises the risk of underperformance and early failure, particularly in residential systems where system owners lack the technical expertise or contractual leverage to demand testing.

The rapid pace of technological innovation in the PV industry compounds these risks. Module designs are trending towards larger formats, glass-glass constructions, bifacial architectures, and higher-efficiency cell technologies such as PERC and TOPCon [4]. While these innovations can reduce levelised cost of electricity (LCOE) by improving efficiency and lowering balance-of-system costs, their long-term reliability remains unproven in the field [5]. For a market like South Africa, which combines challenging operating environments varying levels of quality assurance and regulatory complience across sectors, this creates uncertainty that may undermine investor confidence and system performance.

This paper addresses these challenges by presenting empirical evidence of PV module quality risks across South Africa's utility, C&I, and residential sectors. Drawing on more than a decade of accredited testing performed by PVinsight (Pty) Ltd and the Nelson Mandela University Photovoltaics Research Group, we analyse case studies that highlight sector-specific trends in module performance relative to nameplate values and warranty conditions. The findings show clear differences between sectors: while utility-scale modules subjected to QA testing consistently outperform manufacturer specifications, commercially sourced modules show mixed results, and residential systems exhibit significant underperformance and manufacturing defects.

2 METHODOLOGY

The study looks at specific PV module quality risks that are common in PV modules in South Africa. PV plants that have been operational since 2014 have the risk of early failures and lower than expected performance. New module technologies have improved efficiencies, but their long-term reliability remains untested. The Quality assurance process is only adopted in the Utility scale sector and PV modules entering the Residential and Commercial and Industrial (C&I) market are seldom tested. This study presents case studies on PV module quality's effect on performance in the Utility, C&I and Residential sectors. The results are compiled from test projects performed by PVinsight and the Nelson Mandela University PV research group.

3 RESULTS

PV module quality risks include micro-cracks, encapsulant delamination, backsheet chalking, glass breakages and Hotspots which result in burn marks. These can result in module failures or decreased module performance and lower return on investment.

3.1 Case Study – Utility Scale

As part of the QA procurement process many Utility-scale projects implemented an annual testing programme to ensure that module degradation is monitored. Every year, the same sample of modules are removed and tested at the laboratory. Results of these types of projects have shown that modules provided to Utility-scale projects are underspecified. The initial power can be up to 8 % higher than the nominal power. Figure 1 shows a histogram of PV module power deviation from specification measured for a sample of modules after 10 years in the field. After 10 years, most modules are still above nominal power, and all are above warranty power. This ensures that the performance warranty is met, but product defects can still occur.

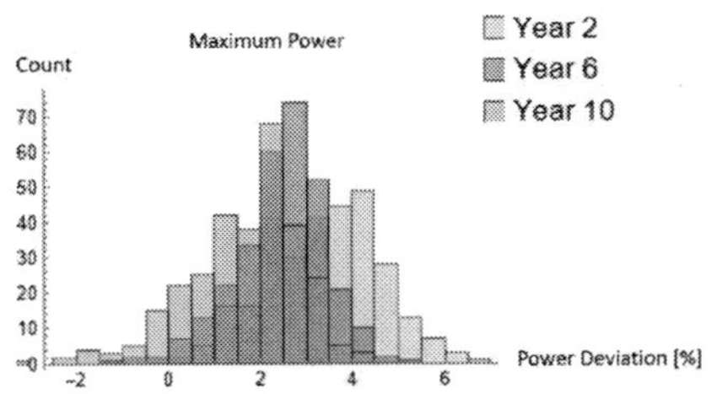

Figure 1: The Deviation of power from the specification of a sample of modules from a Utility-scale project.

3.2 Case Study – Commercial and Industrial Market

PVinsight lab purchased 15 commercially available modules from local electrical distributors in 2024 and 2025. The sample included modules from Canadian Solar, JA Solar and Trina Solar and a mix of mono-facial and bifacial modules of different sizes and technologies.
Figure 2 shows the deviation of power as % of specified power for the 15 modules. Also shown in the figure is the specified tolerance and the equipment measurement uncertainty. The results show that the initial power is lower than the nominal power for all modules, ranging from a deviation of -1.9 % to -2.7%. These results are acceptable based on measurement uncertainty of test equipment. Modules are new but equivalent to one-year outdoor exposure. This sample indicates that modules in the commercial market may be overspecified.

3.3 Case Study – Residential Market

PVinsight was approached by a residential PV system owner for testing of PV modules in an underperforming system. A sample of four modules were tested. These are modules that are rebranded in South Africa, and the modules have been installed for 22 months.

Figure 3 shows the deviation of power as % of specified power for the modules. The warranty value and the equipment measurement uncertainty are also shown in the figure. The results show that all modules have measured power below the expected value for the age, with measurement uncertainty accounted for. The deviation from specification ranged from -10% to -22% and the performance of the modules is below the expected or warranty power output for their age. Additional testing such as EL imaging, figure 4, indicted significant product manufacturing issues. The hail damage cannot be the sole cause of the power losses as the undamaged modules also have reduced power output.

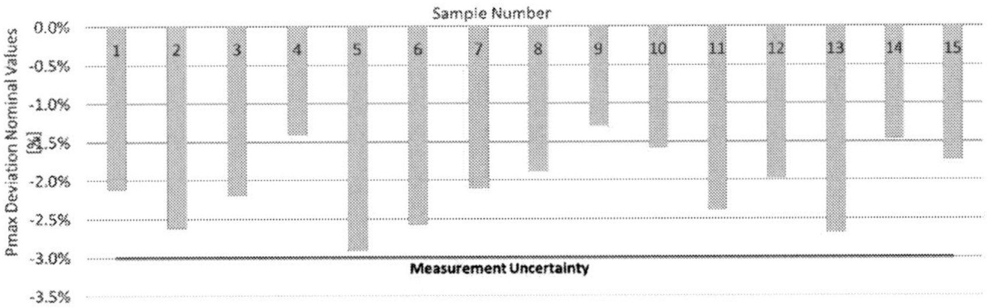

Figure 2: The Power deviation from nominal power of a sample of new modules.

10.4229/EUPVSEC2025/4CV.1.43
020344-002

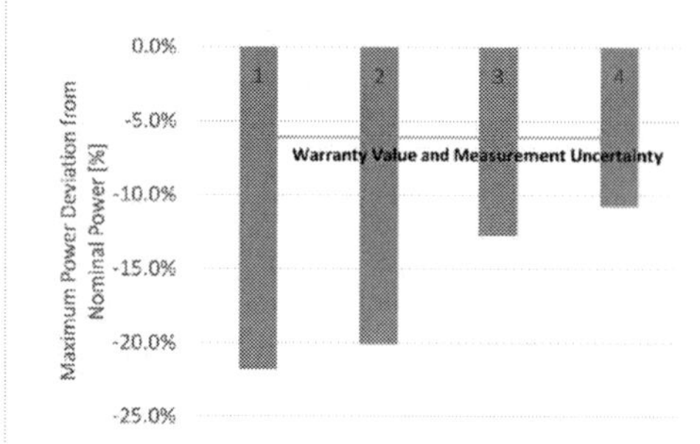

Figure 3: Power measurements indicated that the module's power was below the expected value based on the age accounting for measurement uncertainty [±3%].

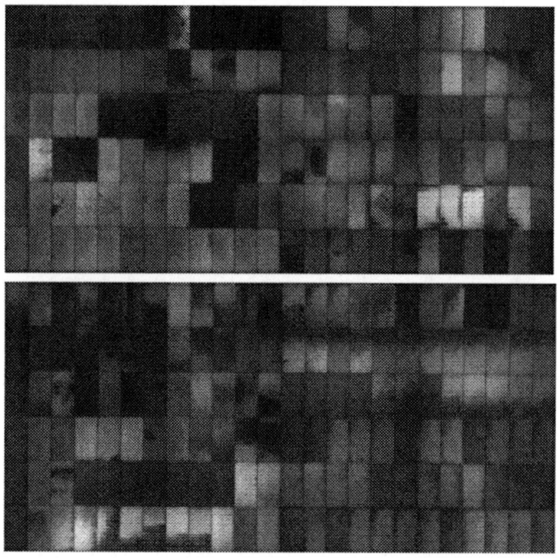

Figure 4: EL imaging of PV modules indicate critical cracks caused by a hail storm and product manufacturing concerns such as mismatched cells, solder abnormalities and accelerated degradation.

4 CONCLUSIONS

The rapid growth of the South African PV sector has created a dynamic but uneven quality landscape across utility, commercial and industrial, and residential markets. The case studies presented demonstrate that module quality and performance outcomes are strongly influenced by the presence or absence of quality assurance measures.

Utility-scale projects, which had implemented QA testing as part of procurement and operation, show robust performance: modules are often underspecified at installation and continue to deliver above warranty levels after more than a decade of operation. In contrast, commercially sourced modules in the C&I segment exhibited modest but consistent underperformance relative to nameplate values, remaining within measurement uncertainty but raising questions about the accuracy of manufacturer specifications. The residential case study revealed the highest risks, with rebranded modules showing severe early underperformance and evidence of manufacturing defects within just two years of operation.

These findings underscore three central insights. First, PV modules in South Africa are not uniformly reliable, and the risks of underperformance increase significantly in segments where QA practices are absent. Second, while underperformance in the C&I segment may appear minor, systematic deviation from specification erodes confidence in manufacturer claims and highlights the need for independent verification. Third, the failures observed in residential modules demonstrate the potential consequences of untested imports, including reduced energy yield, financial losses for system owners, and heightened safety risks.

Taken together, the evidence strongly supports the principle that "the best module is the tested module." Extending QA frameworks beyond the utility sector to include C&I and residential systems will be critical to sustaining investor confidence, protecting consumers, and ensuring that the rapid expansion of PV in South Africa delivers reliable, long-term value.

4 REFERENCES

[1] M. Aghaei et al., "Review of degradation and failure phenomena in photovoltaic modules," Renewable and Sustainable Energy Reviews, vol. 159, p. 112160, May 2022, doi: 10.1016/j.rser.2022.112160.

[2] A. Eberhard and R. Naude, "The South African Renewable Energy IPP Procurement Programme: Review, Lessons Learned & Proposals to Reduce Transaction Costs", Available Online: https://www.gsb.uct.ac.za/files/EberhardNaude_REIPPPPReview_2017_1_1.pdf, Accessed: 2025/09/01.

[3] VDE, "VDE SPEC 90038-2 V1.0 (en): Solar Module Quality Standard (SMQS) Part 2 – Measurements on PV Modules", VDE Association for Electrical, Electronic & Information Technologies, 2024.

[4] A. Metz, M. Fischer, and J. Trube, "International Technology Roadmap for Photovoltaics (ITRPV) 16th edition:," 2025.

[5] W. Gu, T. Ma, S. Ahmed, Y. Zhang, and J. Peng, "A comprehensive review and outlook of bifacial photovoltaic (bPV) technology," Energy Conversion and Management, vol. 223, p. 113283, Nov. 2020, doi: 10.1016/j.enconman.2020.113283.

10.4229/EUPVSEC2025/4CV.1.43
020344-003

ASSESSING PV MODULE QUALITY RISKS IN SOUTH AFRICA: PERFORMANCE INSIGHTS ACROSS UTILITY, COMMERCIAL AND INDUSTRIAL, AND RESIDENTIAL SECTORS

JL Crozier McCleland, M Vumbugwa, FJ Vorster, EE van Dyk | Nelson Mandela University, South Africa
NW Mngomezulu | PVinsight (Pty) Ltd, South Africa

NELSON MANDELA UNIVERSITY

Abstract

South Africa's Photovoltaic (PV) power generation installed capacity has increased exponentially in recent years. PV plants that have been operational since 2014, have a risk of early failures and lower than expected performance.
The study collects data and specific case studies of PV modules from operational PV systems in **South Africa** over the past decade to identify underperformance, common failures and quality risks[1].

South Africa PV Landscape

Growth in the South African PV market at utility scale has been driven by the Renewable Energy Independent Power Producer Procurement Programme (**REIPPPP**), and across other sectors by **rising electricity prices**, **falling solar PV technology costs**, and **increased load shedding.**

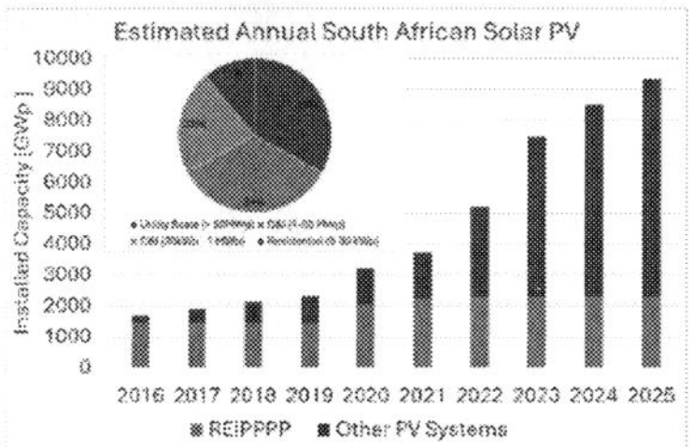

Figure 1: Estimated Installed capacity of Solar PV in South Africa. Source: CRSES- Stellenbosch University; Eskom, SAPVIA[2]

PV Module Quality Testing

POWER MEASUREMENTS

Output maximum power of the PV modules at standard test conditions (STC), using an A+A+A+ LED solar simulator.

ELECTROLUMINESCENCE

Electroluminescence (EL) imaging of photovoltaic modules to identify cracks, disconnected busbars, shunting and other cell defects.

VISUAL INSPECTION

Visual inspection is used to detect quality issues. The front and back sheet, frame and external circuitry of the modules are inspected for a set of known defects.

Overview of PV Module Quality Testing in South Africa

The PV Testing Laboratory was established by the PV Research group in the Nelson Mandela University Physics Department in 2014. PVinsight was established as a spinout company in 2017.

11 years In Operation

> 7.5 GW Tested

> 70 000 Tests conducted

PVinsight

Case Study: Utility-Scale Projects

A few Utility-scale projects in South Africa implemented an annual testing programme to ensure that annual module degradation was monitored.
Every year, the same sample of modules are removed and tested at the lab.
Results indicate that the modules tested are **underspecified** and the initial power is higher than the nominal power.
After 10 years, the majority of modules are still above nominal power, and all are above warranty Power.

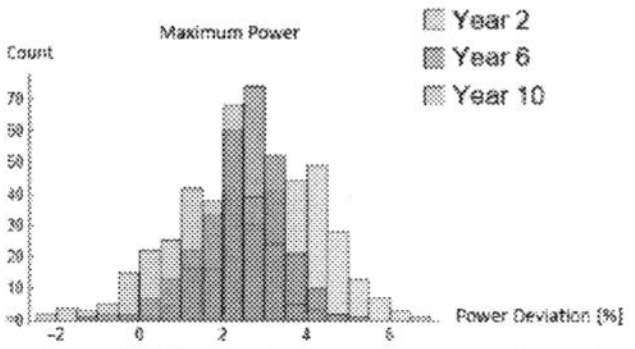

Figure 2: The Deviation of power from the specification of a sample of modules from a Utility-scale project.

Case Study: Commercial & Industrial (C&I) and Small-scale Embedded Generation

PVinsight lab purchased 15 commercially available modules from local electrical distributors in 2024 and 2025. The sample included modules from Canadian Solar, JA Solar and Trina Solar and a mix of mono-facial and bifacial modules of different sizes and technologies.
The results show that the initial measured power is lower than the nominal power for all modules, ranging from a deviation of **-1.3 % to -2.7%.**

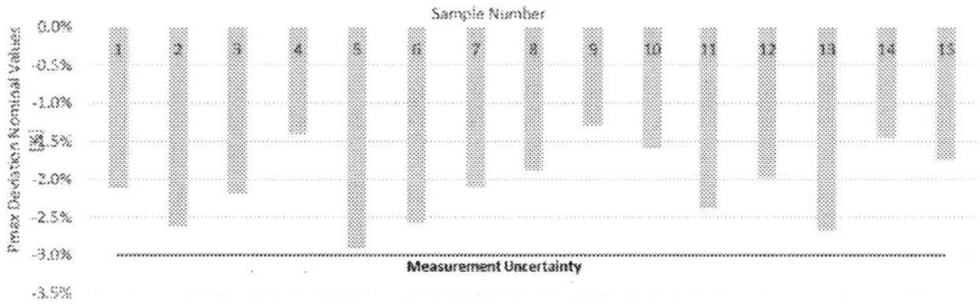

Figure 3: The Power deviation from nominal power of a sample of new modules.

Case Study: Residential Rooftop

PVinsight was approached by a residential PV system owner for testing of PV modules in an underperforming system. A sample of four modules were tested. These are rebranded modules, available in South Africa, and the modules have been installed for 22 months.

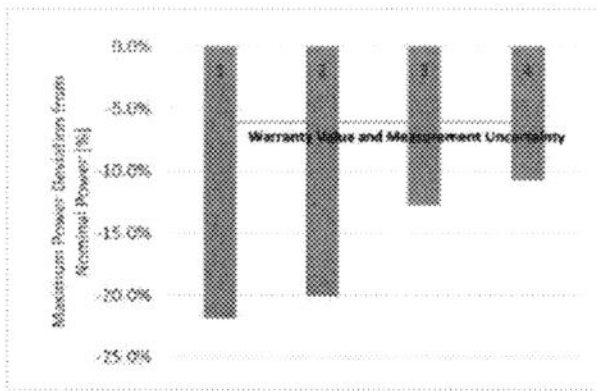

Figure 4: Power measurements indicated that the module's power was below the expected value based on the age accounting for measurement uncertainty [±3%].

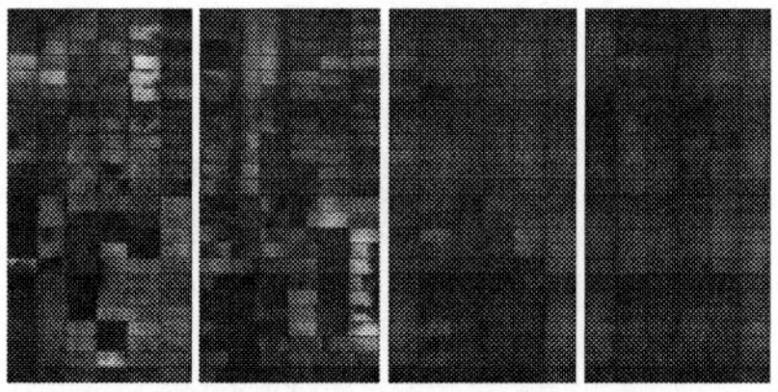

Figure 5: EL imaging of PV modules indicate critical cracks caused by a hail storm and product manufacturing concerns such as mismatched cells, solder abnormalities and accelerated degradation.

Conclusions

- Fast growth in the South African PV sector requires the support of a Quality Assurance Programme to ensure performance and reliability.
- The three case studies briefly discussed highlight the importance of PV module quality verification to ensure that the modules are performing at a warranted level.

References

1. M. Aghaei et al., "Review of degradation and failure phenomena in photovoltaic modules," Renewable and Sustainable Energy Reviews, vol. 159, p. 112160, May 2022, doi: 10.1016/j.rser.2022.112160.
2. Visualisation of South African Electricity Data, The Centre for Renewable and Sustainable Energy Studies (CRSES) – Stellenbosch University, https://www.crses.sun.ac.za/sa-energy-stats/, Accessed: 2025/09/01 .

Acknowledgements
The authors would like to thank the Nelson Mandela PV Research Group and PVinsight (Pty) Ltd for their financial support and input into the study.

Please connect with us using this QR code. We would love to have your feedback.

CAN REGULAR STRING IV MEASUREMENTS COMPLEMENT MPP MONITORING DATA?

Martin Bartholomäus, Fernando Román Vecino, Peter B. Poulsen, Mahmoud Dhimish, Sergiu V. Spataru
Technical University of Denmark, Department of Electrical and Photonics Engineering, Roskilde, 4000, Denmark
mabart@dtu.dk, s233168@student.dtu.dk, ppou@dtu.dk, mahdh@dtu.dk, sersp@dtu.dk

ABSTRACT: Existing operation and maintenance strategies for PV farms rely on maximum power point (M_{PP}) monitoring data. Meanwhile, current-voltage (IV) curve measurements deliver additional diagnostic information about the state of health of the PV system and inverter based IV scanning enables recording large data at minimal labor and monetary cost. In this work, we investigate the additional value of string IV-curve measurements complementing M_{PP} monitoring to enhance the accuracy for fault detection strategies. We record M_{PP} data along with frequent IV scans from PV strings in Denmark with and without faults such as PID, cell cracks, ribbon damage and bypass diode failures. Observing the IV scan function of a string inverter with high-frequency measurement equipment, we observed an initial sharp power drop, followed by a period of open circuit operation, sequential IV sweeps on each MPPT and slow ramping back to normal operation. The entire IV scan event lasts about 23 seconds for a 4-MPPT inverter. An energy loss estimation shows a maximum 0.087% energy loss per year for daily IV scans. Comparing fault detection accuracy of IV versus M_{PP} monitoring-based features, the IV showed superior accuracy of 96% compared to 82%. Minimal data requirement analysis showed that even at minimal data set size, the accuracy did not fall below 91%, which is still significantly better than the M_{PP} based fault detection. The findings suggest that regular inverter based IV scans can enhance current O&M strategies for improved fault detection at very little energy loss.

Keywords: IV, fault detection, inverter, photovoltaic, monitoring

1 INTRODUCTION

Existing operation and maintenance (O&M) strategies for PV systems mostly rely on maximum power point monitoring data [1, 2]. Specific action is taken in case the monitoring data is found suspicious, an alert is raised, and an O&M ticket is issued. M_{PP} data can be monitored without power loss at high time resolution, allowing for analysis of fault events over time. However, inverter-based current-voltage (IV) curves can provide diagnostic information at low cost, which may assist with and complement existing O&M strategies to reduce the need for labor-intensive field measurements such as electroluminescence or infrared imaging. Currently, inverter-based IV are rarely used because of concerns about power down time, missing evidence of usefulness, and guidelines on how to utilize them best. In the literature, M_{PP}-based methods are well established. For example, Filho et al. developed an automated fault detection system based on analytical data [3]. Jones et al. showed that inclusion of IV data in addition to M_{PP} monitoring data can improve the classification accuracy of fault detection from 90% to 98% percent, considering weak solder bonds, shade and soiling as fault classes [4]. In previous work, we have shown that the V_{mp}/V_{oc} ratio and series resistance are sensitive to shade and that the shunt resistance is sensitive to PID and may therefore be used as diagnostic markers for fault detection [5]. However, most studies focus on either M_{PP} or IV data for fault classification and rarely assess the combination of M_{PP} and IV monitoring data.

In this work, we assess how string IV scans can be utilized to complement M_{PP} monitoring. First, we measure M_{PP} monitoring data as well as regular IV scans from PV strings with known faults. We employ IV-based fault detection strategies and compare the accuracy to M_{PP}-based methods. Additionally, we monitor central inverter-based IV scans with high frequency measurement equipment and use the results to conduct an energy loss estimation. This allows to formulate recommendations to improve current O&M strategies.

2 METHODS

2.1 String IV tracing and M_{PP} monitoring at DTU

In the first stage, we utilized a fault detection test setup at DTU Risø consisting of four PV strings, with 22 305Wp monofacial modules of type Trina TSM-305DD05A.08 each. The test setup consists of healthy strings and strings that were modified to include faulty modules. Figure 1 shows a single line diagram of the strings. The outdoor strings are monitored with a Huawei KTL 185 inverter, measuring M_{PP} data every minute. The inverter also performed regular IV scans every half hour during daytime. Additionally, plane-of-array irradiance and backside module temperature conditions are measured every minute.

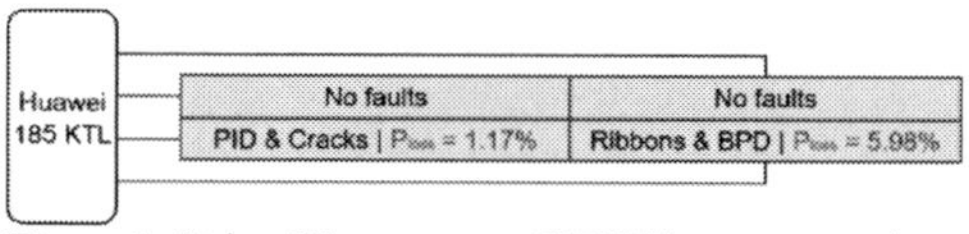

Figure 1: String IV test setup at DTU Risø campus, where an inverter measures M_{PP} monitoring data and IV curves of each PV string separately. The 22 module strings use identical PV modules, but two strings contain planted faults. Adapted from [5].

The test setup and the introduction of faults is described in detail in previous work [5], where we characterize the artificial faults and describe the methods used to introduce them into the PV module strings. In short, two strings contain no faults, one string contains modules with PID and cell cracks (about 1.2% power loss) , and one string contains modules with ribbon damage and short-circuited bypass diodes (BPD, about 6% power loss).

10.4229/EUPVSEC2025/4CV.1.44

Figure 2: Measurement setup for high-frequency sampling of inverter-based IV scan events. Central IV scans were triggered at the Huawei inverter. A Keithley oscilloscope with two voltage probes (one used for reference measurements) and one current probe was used for DC side measurements (~100Hz). A Gantner measurement box reports AC power (1Hz). The inverter also reported its IV curve measurement and monitoring data (1/min).

2.2 Fault detection approach

This setup is used to compare fault detection methods based on M_{PP} data against IV data. We recorded 3 months of data recorded between May 12, 2025 and August 12, 2025. Light filtering was applied to remove failed measurements and physically impossible data. The final IV curve data set includes 10,320 observations, with 5,689 data points for the healthy strings, 2,670 for PID & cracks and 1,961 for ribbon damage and BPD. Due to the higher sampling frequency, the M_{PP} data set is about 30 times larger at 309,325 observations, 155,729 for the healthy strings, 81,680 for PID & cracks and 71,916 for ribbon damage and BPD. Next, we derived 18 features from the IV data, which are the features discussed in [6]. Five features were extracted from the M_{PP} data, namely I_{MPP}, V_{MPP}, G_{POA}, T_{MOD} and the maximum power point factor M_{PPF}. An XGBoost machine learning classifier [7] was trained on these features and then used to classify the faults. For this purpose, we split the data sets, using 80% for training and 20% for testing. The XGBoost classifier trains a decision tree model with 200 trees each limited to a maximum depth of 5, using a learning rate of 0.1, a random state of 42 for reproducibility and optimizes based on the log-loss score. We compared the resulting accuracy in detecting the faults in the PV strings for each data set. Additionally, minimal data requirements for classification were assessed by reducing the size of the test data set to a minimum of 1.

2.4 Current, voltage and power observations during an inverter-based IV measurement event

Many commercial PV inverters offer IV sweep functions, at which all connected strings are measured in one IV sweep event, triggered centrally at the inverter. To observe this process, high resolution current, power and voltage sensing was done during an inverter-based IV measurement event on a Huawei 40KTL inverter featuring four maximum power point tracker (MPPT) with two PV string inputs each (see Figure 2). Five strings were connected, PV1 on MPPT1, PV3 on MPPT2, PV5 on MPPT3 and PV7 and PV8 on MPPT4. A 4-channel Keithley oscilloscope was utilized to monitor the output of one current probe and two Pico Technology voltage probes, which were connected to the PV strings on the DC side of the inverter and record data samples at ~100 Hz. We kept one voltage probe as a reference to measure the voltage of PV1, later used to align the different measurement events. The other voltage and current probe were used to measure the PV strings sequentially. For this purpose, a new IV scan was triggered at the inverter for each measurement on a PV string before the probes were moved to the next string.

Measurements were repeated at least once per string to check repeatability and to ensure redundancy in case of measurement failure or unwanted irradiance ramping events. The reference voltage measurement was used to align measurements at the minimum voltage point of the reference measurement, which is a unique and distinct point during PV1's IV trace. Parallel to the oscilloscope measurements, AC side active power was recorded with a Gantner AC measurement box at 1Hz. Lastly, the inverter also reports regular M_{PP} current and voltage monitoring data at 1 data point per minute as well as the IV traces, which contain 64 I-V points per IV curve.

The measurements enable an analysis of the energy loss caused by inverter-based IV scans in PV farms. We integrate the lost power compared to normal operation and extrapolate the results to large-scale PV farm operation using yearly PV performance data from PVGIS. The measurements also allow to assess power output ramps and fluctuations occurring during large scale PV string IV traces, which could cause negative impact on the stability of the power grid.

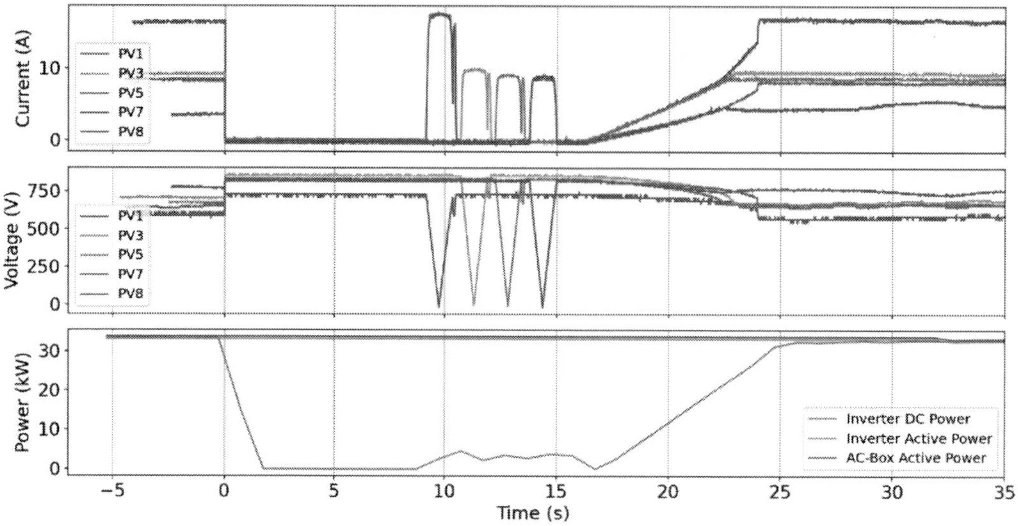

Figure 3: Oscilloscope measurements showing current, voltage and power measurements over time. PV1 to PV8 denote one PV string each. When an IV sweep is triggered, the inverter first switches all strings to open circuit, then measures each MPPT in sequential order (PV7 and PV8 are on the same MPPT input), after which the current/power is slowly ramped back to normal operation. The entire process lasts about 23 seconds. In the inverter monitoring data, the power is shown at a constant output which does not reflect the reality of the IV sweeps. AC-measurement box data sampled at 1 second reveals reduced power output on the AC side during the IV scan.

3 RESULTS AND CONCLUSIONS

3.1 Oscilloscope measurements

The experiments (Figure 3) reveal that when a central IV scan is triggered, the inverter first switches all strings to open circuit, then measures each MPPT in sequential order (PV7 and PV8 are on the same MPPT input), after which the current/power is slowly ramped back to normal operation. The entire IV scanning event lasts about 23 seconds. In the inverter monitoring data, power is shown at a constant output which does not reflect the reality of the IV sweeps. AC-measurement box data sampled at 1 second reveals reduced power output on the AC side during the IV scan.

Ramp rates are steep when the inverter first switches to open circuit, resulting in a complete power loss withing 0.1 second. The IV sweeps themselves also show fast power ramping from zero to maximum within 0.6 seconds, but only on a portion of the connected strings (1/4 for this inverter). After the IV sweeps, ramping is much slower and gradual than at the beginning, lasting about 7-10 seconds.

The total duration of an IV scan event may be greater for string inverters with more MPPTs but only by about 1.2 seconds per additional MPPT.

3.2 Energy loss analysis

An energy loss analysis was carried out based on the oscilloscope-based IV sweep observations described above. We found that an IV scan event triggered centrally at the string inverter took around 23 seconds to complete, during which time the power output was greatly reduced. For simplicity, in the following energy loss analysis, we assume zero power output for the entire 23 second IV scan. Utilizing a one-year hourly dataset from PVGIS [8] for a fixed tilt 25-degree 1MWp PV installation located in Risø, Denmark, we investigated the energy loss by reducing the output energy by 23/3600 in each hour in which an IV sweep was performed. Two scenarios were considered; First, daily IV scans at solar noon, representing a worst-case scenario, in which energy loss should be greatest. The energy loss was calculated to be 0.087% of yearly energy output for this case. Second, we consider a scenario in which IV sweeps are performed daily in the morning as soon as irradiance reaches 100W/m2, which represents the best-case scenario in terms of energy loss and amounted to 0.03% lost energy. If other IV measurement frequencies are assumed, the energy loss can approximately be linearly scaled up or down. For example, weekly IV scans should only amount to about one seventh of the energy loss, monthly IV scans to one thirtieth, etc.

While some inspection methods require no interruption of normal operation (such as infrared imaging, night-time electroluminescence or photoluminescence), others disrupt normal operation for longer periods at a time, for example manual IV tracing or daylight EL. Given the above analysis, inverter-based IV measurements therefore rank in the midfield of PV inspection methods at a non-zero but very low energy loss. Further on, we show that accurate fault detection from IV measurements does not necessarily require large test data sets, likely allowing lower testing frequency than daily.

3.3 IV-based versus MPP-based fault detection accuracy

The fault detection accuracy (Figure 4) using IV/ MPP features and an XGBoost classifier is greater for the full IV features, registering at 96%. If only MPP-related features derived from the IV curves are used, accuracy drops to 66%. Using the same MPP features on the MPP monitoring dataset increases the accuracy to 82% due to the greater amount of data originating from the higher sampling frequency of the M_{PP} monitoring. The results underline that inverter-based IV curve tracing can be useful for more advanced fault detection in PV strings.

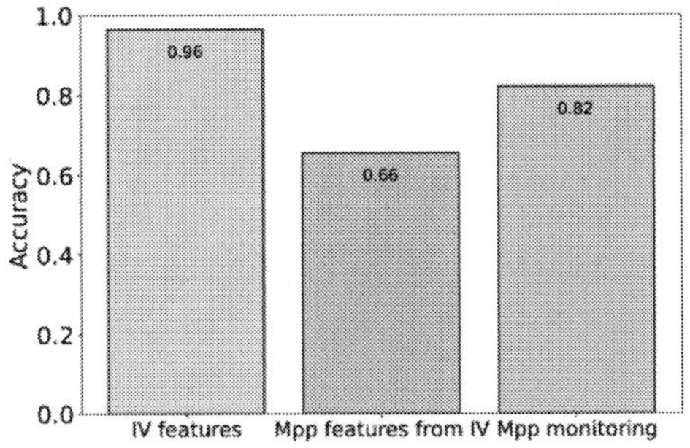

Figure 4: Fault detection accuracy of an XGBoost model classifying healthy PV strings versus PID & cell cracks versus ribbon damage & short-circuited bypass diodes. The highest accuracy of 96% was achieved using features derived from the inverter-based IV curves. Using M_{PP}-only features from these IV curves yielded an accuracy of 66%. Using higher-frequency M_{PP} monitoring data yielded an improved accuracy of 82%, still lower than from IV curve measurements.

An investigation of the minimal data requirement for IV-derived fault detection (Figure 5) showed that at very low test data numbers, the accuracy score oscillates. In the present case, the maximum deviation is around 5% from the stable level (91% instead of 96% accuracy). However, in all cases, even at a small data set, the accuracy is better than the M_{PP}-based method which has the benefit of much higher sample size. Other testing scores including precision, recall and f1-score behave similarly. The results show that as fault detection is usually non-perfect, a few IV scans should be taken to improve the validity of the results and robustness against misclassification due to outliers.

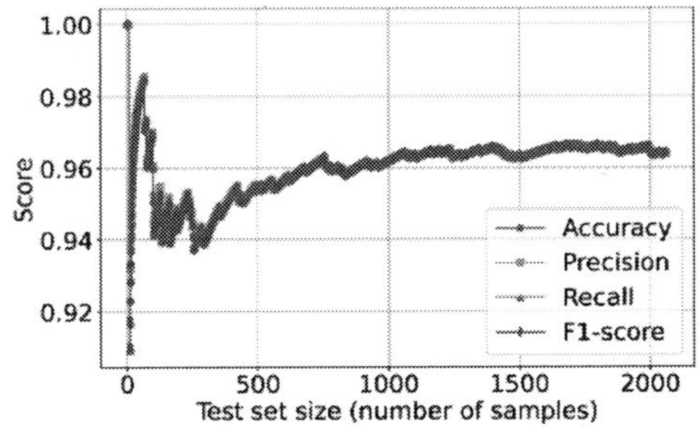

Figure 5: Observing model accuracy as a function of test data set size. We decreased the size from 2000 to 1 and calculated the model accuracy for each size. At lower test data set sizes, the accuracy starts oscillating around the true value of ~96%. Deviations do not exceed 5%.

4 CONCLUSIONS

Closely observing a centrally triggered IV scan event on a string inverter showed a sudden power loss when the inverter switches all strings to open circuit, followed by sequential IV curve tracing of all MPPT channels. Same-MPPT strings are measured simultaneously. After the IV traces, the inverter slowly ramps up the produced power. The energy loss connected to IV scans was shown to be in the order of less than 0.1% energy loss considering daily IV measurements. On the other hand, IV-based fault detection showed to be much more accurate than M_{PP}-based fault detection, even at a lower sampling rate. A minimal data requirement investigation showed that the accuracy oscillates at low sampling, but always performs better than M_{PP}-based methods.

Based on these findings, implementing regular IV traces into existing O&M strategies seems beneficial to PV operators, as inverter-based IV scans require no additional hardware, lead to minimal power loss and greatly enhance fault detection accuracies compared to M_{PP}-based methods.

5 ACKNOWLEDGEMENTS

This project has received funding from the European Union under grant agreement no. 101146377 as part of the SOLARIS project – Solar Operational Lifecycle and Asset Reliability Intelligence System.

6 REFERENCES

[1] U. Jahn, B. Herteleer, C. Tjengdrawira, I. Tsanakas, and M. Richter, "Guidelines for Operation and Maintenance of Photovoltaic Power Plants in Different Climates 2022," International Energy Agency, IEA-PVPS-Report-T13, 2022.

[2] Rob Andrews *et al.*, "Operation & Maintenance Best Practice Guidelines/Version 4.0." 2019.

[3] E. A. S. Filho, K. Kiefer, N. Holland, B. Kollosch, B. Müller, and P. J. C. Branco, "Analysis of automatic fault detection methods for commercially operated PV power plants".

[4] C. B. Jones, M. Theristis, J. S. Stein, and C. Hansen, "Feature Selection of Photovoltaic System Data to Avoid Misclassification of Fault Conditions," in *2020 47th IEEE Photovoltaic Specialists Conference (PVSC)*, Calgary, AB, Canada: IEEE, June 2020, pp. 1357–1362. doi: 10.1109/PVSC45281.2020.9300786.

[5] M. Bartholomäus, P. B. Poulsen, and S. V. Spataru, "Comparative analysis of string IV measurement methods for fault detection in photovoltaic systems," presented at the 41st European Photovoltaic Solar Energy Conference and Exhibition, 2024, p. 6. doi: 10.4229/EUPVSEC2024/4BV.3.18.

[6] M. Bartholomäus, P. B. Poulsen, M. Dhimish, and S. V. Spataru, "Evaluating IV curve derived features for fault detection," presented at the 2025 IEEE 52nd Photovoltaic Specialists Conference (PVSC), Montreal: IEEE, June 2025. doi: 10.1109/PVSC59419.2025.11132910.

[7] T. Chen and C. Guestrin, "XGBoost: A Scalable Tree Boosting System," in *Proceedings of the 22nd ACM SIGKDD International Conference on Knowledge Discovery and Data Mining*, San Francisco California USA: ACM, Aug. 2016, pp. 785–794. doi: 10.1145/2939672.2939785.

[8] T. Huld, R. Müller, and A. Gambardella, "A new solar radiation database for estimating PV performance in Europe and Africa," *Solar Energy*, vol. 86, no. 6, pp. 1803–1815, June 2012, doi: 10.1016/j.solener.2012.03.006.

Bernhard Kubicek[1], Marcus Rennhofer[1], Thomas Hutterer-Tik[2], Christian Ottl[2]
1: AIT Austrian Institute of Technology GmbH, Center for Energy bernhard.kubicek@ait.ac.at
2: Watt Analytics GmbH, Austria

AGGREGATION ERRORS BASED ON PV PRODUCTION DATA IN THE TIMESCALE OF SECONDS

AUSTRIAN INSTITUTE OF TECHNOLOGY
TOMORROW TODAY

Motivation

In PV system monitoring, typical logging intervals are in the range of 5 to 15 minutes. The question rises, how much information is lost by not logging at higher speeds. Using PV production data logged at sub-second sample rates, the variability is investigated over short time scales.

Sub-Second production data

During the data acquisition of PV monitoring data, mainly two strategies can be applied to aggregate time series to reasonable data size: time averaging, or single-sampling. Inverters e.g. typically perform averaging in the reporting of powers, while quantities such as currents or voltages are taken as the most current individual measurement. Hence, e.g. reported power does not equal voltage times current, as expected. However, for affordable weather stations, time averaging is seldomly performed.

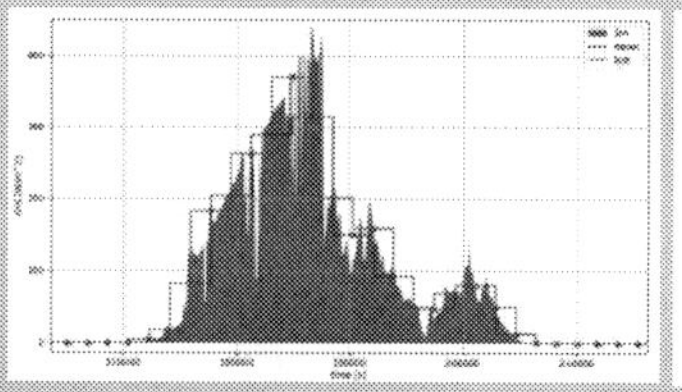

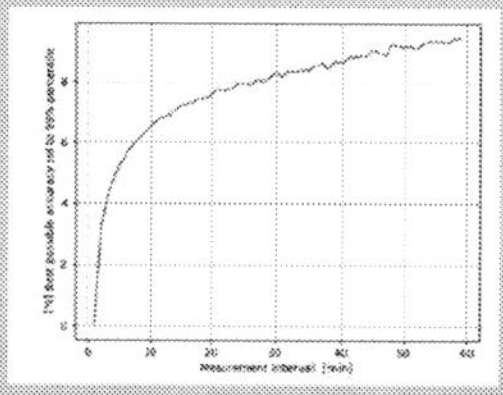

This leads to a basic error due to the deviation of time averaged power compared to single shot irradiation, that can be used to define how big of a principal error happens on which time scale [1].

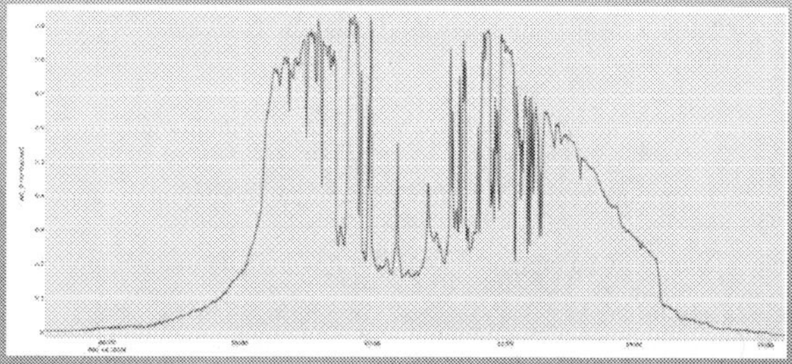

Using sub-second resolved power measurements of smart meter data of Watt Analytics, a new time regime can be looked at:

- How do clouds change irradiance at seconds timescales
- How much does the inverters' MPP tracking and grid stabilization change that?

To remove inverter effects, the data was resampled to 10 second intervals, as many inverter effects should be in the regime of a few 50Hz intervals.

Wavelet Analysis

To evaluate the intensity of changes in given frequency regimes, wavelet analysis is of better use than short time Fourier analysis: the timescale is adopted to the investigated frequency. The spectrograms thereby are more diffuse in time at lower frequencies.

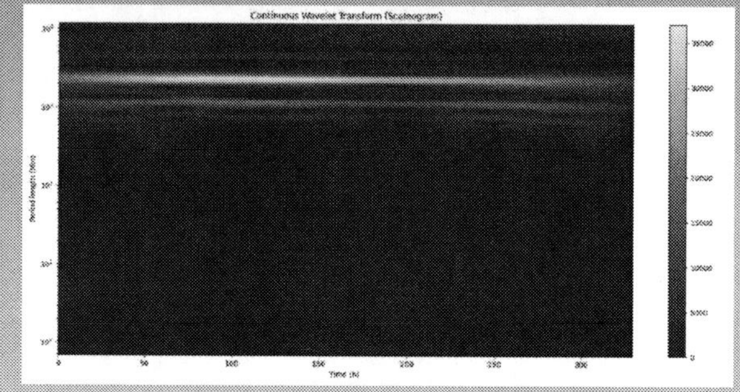

Above: The linear intensity scales shows a peak at a periodicity of 24h. Below: the log-color scale exhibits finer details during the day.

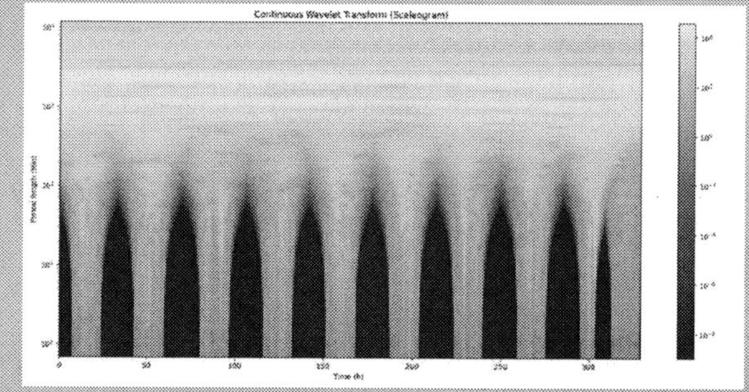

By integrating the intensity over time, a log-log plot of how the intensity changes by period length/frequency:

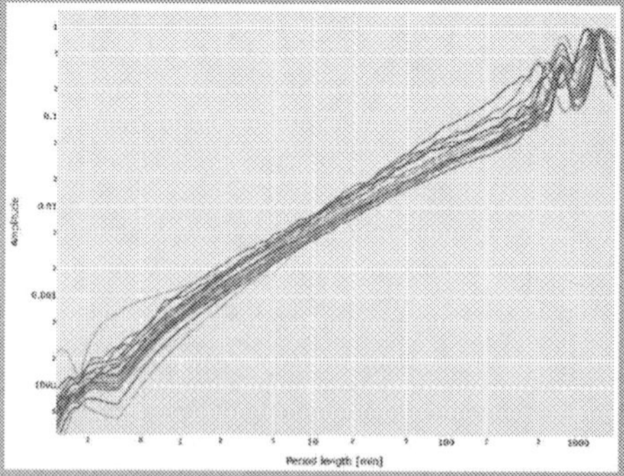

Conclusion

A 10-minute logging interval captures changes to typically 0.5% of the peak amplitude, a 5-minute interval halves that. To only ignore frequencies that contribute below 0.1 % of the peak amplitude, a 1-minute logging interval is recommended. Hower, to also decrease one-shot vs. averaging errors [1], a one-minute interval can be recommended.

[1] B.Kubicek, M. Steinbrecher, M. Rennhofer, „ERROR SOURCES IN PV PROGNOSIS", EU-PVSEC 2023.
This content was created within the „Fledged" Austrian national project.

IN-FIELD ASSESSMENT OF SOILING EFFECTS ON A FLOATING PHOTOVOLTAIC SYSTEM IN A HUMID SUBTROPICAL URBAN AREA

Renzo Vargas, Givaldo dos Reis, Rodrigo P. Maruyama, Alex Manito, Marcelo Pinho Almeida, Roberto Zilles
Institute of Energy and Environment, University of São Paulo

Corresponding author – Renzo Vargas, e-mail: renzovargas@usp.br

ABSTRACT: Floating photovoltaic (FPV) systems provide an alternative to land-based PV by deploying modules on reservoirs and other water bodies, using underutilized surfaces and benefiting from water-mediated passive cooling that mitigates heat-related efficiency losses. Nevertheless, important knowledge gaps remain, particularly at utility scale. In this study, we analyze soiling at a 7 MWp FPV plant (10,500 modules rated at 665W) operating in a humid subtropical urban environment. We quantify how cleaning frequency affects module-level plane-of-array (POA) irradiation and assess the feasibility of using reservoir water for cleaning. Modules cleaned monthly recorded up to 6.27% higher POA irradiation than those cleaned less frequently.
Keywords: Floating Photovoltaics; Soiling Losses; Utility-Scale Photovoltaics; Cleaning Frequency; Plane-of-Array Irradiation

1 INTRODUCTION

Soiling in photovoltaic (PV) systems refers to the accumulation of dust, dirt, organic material, bird droppings, and other particulates on the surface of solar modules. This layer attenuates the incident sunlight reaching the PV cells, thereby lowering the system's overall energy output and potentially accelerating module degradation.

In floating photovoltaic (FPV) systems installed on bodies of water—such as reservoirs, lakes, or offshore sites—soiling behavior can differ from that of land-based arrays. Although the water surface cools modules and may slightly reduce dust deposition [1]–[6], FPV installations remain vulnerable to airborne particulates, bird droppings, and, in some climates, biofouling or splash-borne mineral and algal residues. Several studies report that average soiling rates can be lower over water; nevertheless, the performance impact—especially in arid, dusty regions or near agricultural activity—can still be substantial [7], [8]. Moreover, evidence from utility-scale FPV systems remains limited.

Soiling losses often manifest as a reduction in the short-circuit current due to decreased transmissivity of the module glass, though the extent varies by dust composition and climate [9]. Additionally, tilt angles notably influence soiling rates; low-tilt or horizontal FPV configurations may trap more dust due to reduced rain wash-off and lower self-cleaning [10].

This study evaluates how soiling accumulation affects the performance of a utility-scale FPV plant located in an urban, humid subtropical environment. For achieving this evaluation, we compare module-level plane-of-array (POA) irradiation across modules subjected to distinct cleaning intervals and different cleaning-water sources.

1.1 Organization of the paper

This paper is structured as follows: Section 2 presents the material and methods employed for the soiling assessment of the FPV power plant; Section 3 presents the obtained results for different cleaning schedules and type of water; and Section 4 presents the conclusions of the work.

2 MATERIAL AND METHODS

2.1 Floating photovoltaic system

The study site is a 7.5-hectare floating photovoltaic (FPV) plant installed on a reservoir in a humid subtropical urban setting. The array employs monocrystalline-silicon PV modules, all north-facing and mounted at a 12° tilt. It is configured as a relatively open platform, with buoyancy provided by polyethylene pontoons and access walkways between each row to facilitate operation and maintenance. The FPV system is grid-connected.

2.2 Equipment and cleaning schedule

Six modules are selected and calibrated according to IEC 60904-2:2023–Item 14. After installation, dataloggers are deployed to monitor the modules short-circuit currents to record the irradiation data throughout the study period. Figure 1 illustrates the modules used in the experiment. Figure 2 depicts the datalogger connections.

Figure 1: Six modules used in the experiment

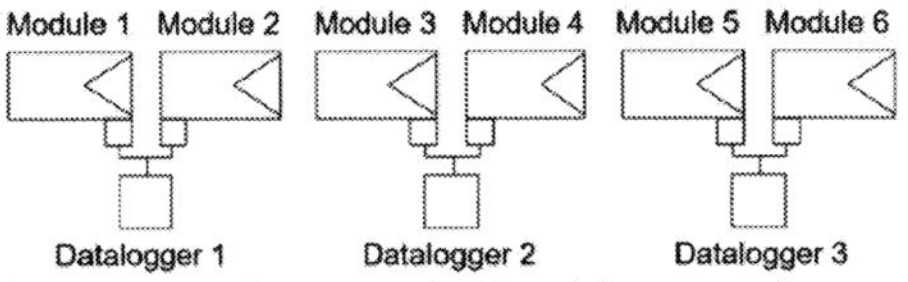

Figure 2: Dataloggers and PV modules connections

Table I summarizes the cleaning schedule and water properties used to clean the photovoltaic modules.

10.4229/EUPVSEC2025/4CV.1.48

Table I: Cleaning schedule and type of water

Item	Cleaning schedule	Type of water
Module 1	Every month	Clean water
Module 2	Every month	Reservoir water
Module 3	Every three months	Clean water
Module 4	Every three months	Reservoir water
Module 5	Every six months	Clean water
Module 6	No cleaning	Clean water

As shown in Table I, modules 1 and 2 are cleaned monthly with clean water and reservoir water, respectively, while modules 3 and 4 follow the same procedure every three months. Module 5 is cleaned every six months using clean water, while module 6 remains uncleaned throughout the study. These intervals are selected to assess both the impact of cleaning frequency on performance and the overall necessity of cleaning. Additionally, the choice of the water source for cleaning is crucial: while using clean water entails transport costs, reservoir water faces issues regarding its suitability and potential effects on module performance warrant careful evaluation.

For the manual cleaning process, the following equipment is used: 1) a mop, 2) a water container and, 3) a water pump. Figure 3 shows these items. Figure 4 presents the manual cleaning procedure.

Figure 3: Cleaning equipment

Figure 4: Manual cleaning procedure

Each clean-water module requires approximately six liters of water per cleaning. When using reservoir water, one end of the water pump is immersed in the reservoir while the other end directs the flow onto the module surfaces.

3 RESULTS

3.1 Soiling in the floating photovoltaic system

We documented several soiling modes on the FPV array; representative examples are shown in Figures 5 – 8.

Figure 5: Particulate deposition

Figure 6: Bird droppings

Figure 7: Residue from avian foraging

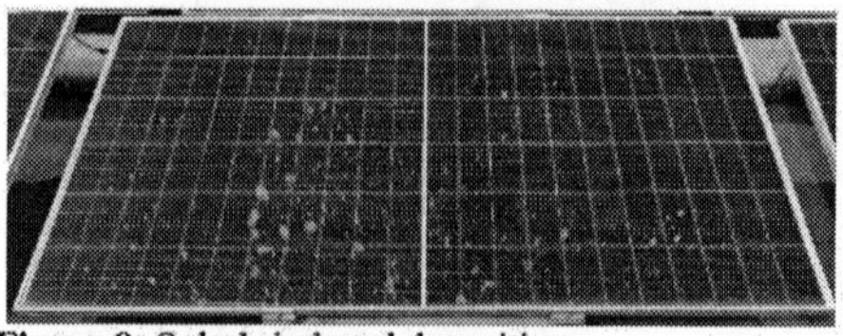

Figure 8: Splash-induced deposition

Figure 5 presents soiling due to particulate deposition; Figure 6 shows bird droppings; Figure 7 presents residue from avian foraging (organic matter after feeding); and Figure 8 depicts splash-induced deposition from the surrounding water body, characterized by algae. These categories capture the dominant mechanisms observed on site and frame the subsequent analysis.

3.2 Initial assessment of soiling based on the first two months of analysis

This subsection offers an early look at soiling using data from the study's first two months. For each month, the module with the highest monthly irradiation was used as the reference and normalized to 100%. Figure 9 shows each module's monthly irradiation as a percentage of this reference.

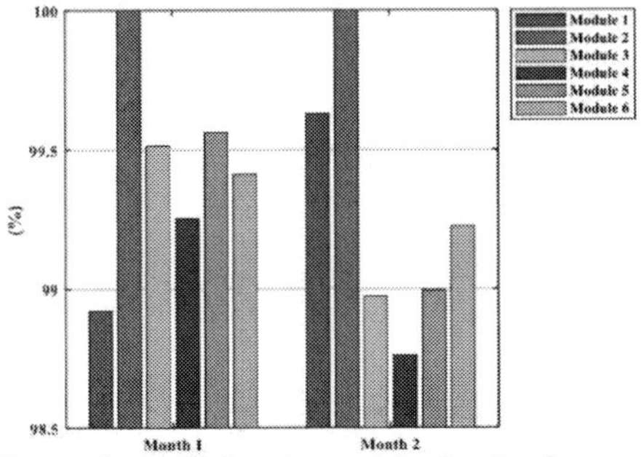

Figure 9: Irradiation by module for the first two months (% of reference module)

Across both months, module 2 achieved the highest irradiation and therefore defines the 100% reference in Figure 9. The corresponding numerical values are reported in Table II.

Table II: Assessment of soiling based on months 1 and 2

Item	Month 1	Month 2
Module 1	98.92 %	99.63 %
Module 2	100.00 %	100.00 %
Module 3	99.51 %	98.97 %
Module 4	99.25 %	98.76 %
Module 5	99.56 %	99.00 %
Module 6	99.41 %	99.23 %

In Table II, after the first month, inter-module differences were minimal. By the end of the second month, modules cleaned monthly produced up to 1.24% and 1.01% higher irradiation than modules cleaned every three and six months, respectively. Although we anticipated that module 1 would yield the highest irradiation, module 2, the unit cleaned with reservoir water, recorded the maximum value.

3.3 Results after five and six months of analysis

This subsection presents the soiling assessment for months five and six. For each month, the module with the highest monthly irradiation is taken as the reference (normalized to 100%), and all other modules are expressed as a percentage of this value; Figure 10 summarizes these results.

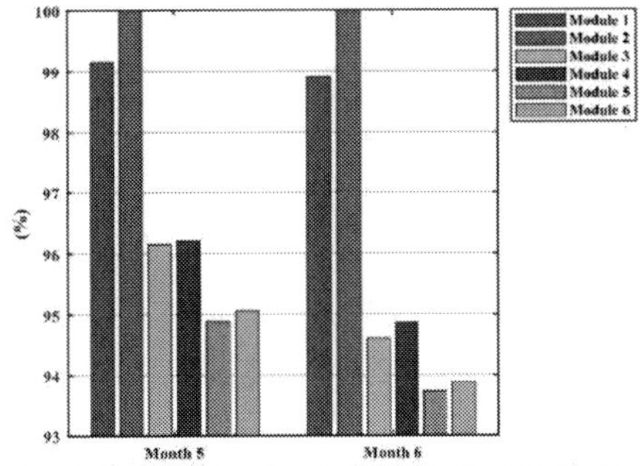

Figure 10: Irradiation by module after months five and six (% of reference module)

In both months, module 2 achieved the highest irradiation value and therefore defines the 100% reference in Figure 10. The corresponding numerical values are listed in Table III.

Table III: Assessment of soiling after months 5 and 6

Item	Month 5	Month 6
Module 1	99.15 %	98.91 %
Module 2	100.00 %	100.00 %
Module 3	96.15 %	94.60 %
Module 4	96.21 %	94.86 %
Module 5	94.89 %	93.73 %
Module 6	95.07 %	93.88 %

As shown in Table III, by the end of month six the monthly-cleaning regimen delivered up to 5.40% and 6.27% higher irradiation than the three-month and six-month cleaning regimens, respectively. The small difference in measured irradiation between modules 1 and 2 indicates that cleaning with reservoir water is a viable option from an energy-capture standpoint.

4 CONCLUSIONS

This study quantified the impact of soiling on a 7 MWp floating photovoltaic (FPV) plant in an urban, humid subtropical environment. Six representative modules were maintained under different cleaning frequencies and water sources, and their monthly plane-of-array (POA) irradiation was compared. Over the six-month observation window, monthly cleaning yielded up to 6.27% higher POA irradiation relative to less-frequent schedules. Contrary to expectations for module 1 (cleaned monthly with clean, non-reservoir water), the highest irradiation was recorded for module 2, which was cleaned using reservoir water.

The observed gain is consistent with two reinforcing drivers: (i) design—FPV arrays often employ low tilt angles to enhance mechanical robustness, which reduces rain-driven self-cleaning and promotes deposition; and (ii) environment—urban aerosol loading and frequent bird activity accelerate both particulate and organic fouling. From an operational standpoint, reservoir water proved viable for cleaning in this study; however, maintenance must follow manufacturer guidance to safeguard performance and warranty coverage. Some manufacturers prohibit the use of untreated reservoir water, which can necessitate logistics that are non-trivial: if 6 liters are required per module, a 7 MWp floating system with

10,500 modules would demand 63,000 liters transported by boat. Installing a pumping line from shore can mitigate transport needs but increases upfront costs and may introduce permitting and reliability considerations.

Finally, the optimal cleaning cadence is site-specific. Frequent rainfall can extend intervals by providing natural washing, whereas arid or dusty microclimates—and locations with high bird presence—typically require more frequent cleaning to sustain performance.

ACKNOWLEDGMENTS

This work was supported by the São Paulo Research Foundation (FAPESP), under grants #2023/00597-9, and #2023/17658-0.

REFERENCES

[1] M. A. Koondhar, L. Albasha, I. Mahariq, B. B. Graba, and E. Touti, "Reviewing floating photovoltaic (FPV) technology for solar energy generation," *Energy Strateg. Rev.*, vol. 54, no. June, p. 101449, Jul. 2024, doi: 10.1016/j.esr.2024.101449.

[2] R. C.J., K. H. Lim, J. C. Kurnia, S. Roy, B. J. Bora, and B. J. Medhi, "Towards sustainable power generation: recent advancements in floating photovoltaic technologies," *Renew. Sustain. Energy Rev.*, vol. 194, no. May 2023, p. 114322, Apr. 2024, doi: 10.1016/j.rser.2024.114322.

[3] A. Garrod, S. Neda Hussain, A. Ghosh, S. Nahata, C. Wynne, and S. Paver, "An assessment of floating photovoltaic systems and energy storage methods: a comprehensive review," *Results Eng.*, vol. 21, no. December 2023, p. 101940, Mar. 2024, doi: 10.1016/j.rineng.2024.101940.

[4] L. Essak and A. Ghosh, "Floating photovoltaics: a review," *Clean Technol.*, vol. 4, no. 3, pp. 752–769, Aug. 2022, doi: 10.3390/cleantechnol4030046.

[5] R. Zahedi, P. Ranjbaran, G. B. Gharehpetian, F. Mohammadi, and R. Ahmadiahangar, "Cleaning of floating photovoltaic systems: a critical review on approaches from technical and economic perspectives," *Energies*, vol. 14, no. 7, p. 2018, Apr. 2021, doi: 10.3390/en14072018.

[6] E. Cuce, P. M. Cuce, S. Saboor, A. Ghosh, and Y. Sheikhnejad, "Floating PVs in terms of power generation, environmental aspects, market potential, and challenges," *Sustainability*, vol. 14, no. 5, p. 2626, Feb. 2022, doi: 10.3390/su14052626.

[7] A. K and V. K, "A comparative study of floating and ground-mounted photovoltaic power generation in Indian contexts," *Clean. Energy Syst.*, vol. 9, no. June, p. 100140, Dec. 2024, doi: 10.1016/j.cles.2024.100140.

[8] S. A. Mohammed *et al.*, "Performance of passivated emitter and rear cell, tunnel oxide passivated contact, and heterojunction solar cells in floating photovoltaic systems across climatic zones," *Phys. status solidi*, vol. 2500354, Aug. 2025, doi: 10.1002/pssa.202500354.

[9] J. J. S. Souza, P. C. M. Carvalho, and G. C. Barroso, "Analysis of the characteristics and effects of soiling natural accumulation on 2 photovoltaic systems: a systematic review of the literature," *J. Sol. Energy Eng.*, vol. 145, no. 4, pp. 1–99, Dec. 2022, doi: 10.1115/1.4056453.

[10] G. M. Tina *et al.*, "PVSails: harnessing innovation with vertical bifacial PV modules in floating photovoltaic systems," *Prog. Photovoltaics Res. Appl.*, vol. 32, no. 12, pp. 872–888, Dec. 2024, doi: 10.1002/pip.3841.

IN-FIELD ASSESSMENT OF SOILING EFFECTS ON A FLOATING PHOTOVOLTAIC SYSTEM IN A HUMID SUBTROPICAL URBAN AREA

Renzo Vargas[1], Givaldo dos Reis[1], Rodrigo P. Maruyama[1], Alex Manito[1], Marcelo Pinho Almeida[1], Roberto Zilles[1]

INTRODUCTION

Floating photovoltaic (FPV) systems offer an alternative to land-based PV by deploying modules on reservoirs and other water bodies, repurposing underutilized surfaces and benefiting from water-mediated passive cooling that mitigates heat-related efficiency losses. Nevertheless, important knowledge gaps remain—especially at utility scale. In this study, we investigate soiling at a ~7 MWp FPV plant (10,500 modules, north-oriented, 12° tilt) operating in a humid subtropical, urban environment. We quantify the effects of alternative cleaning schedules on module-level irradiance capture and evaluate the feasibility of using reservoir water for cleaning.

METHODOLOGY

We select and calibrate six modules according to IEC 60904-2:2023–Item 14. After installation, dataloggers are deployed to monitor the modules short-circuit currents to record the irradiation data. The modules used in the experiment, the cleaning process, and the datalogger connections are presented in Figure 1.

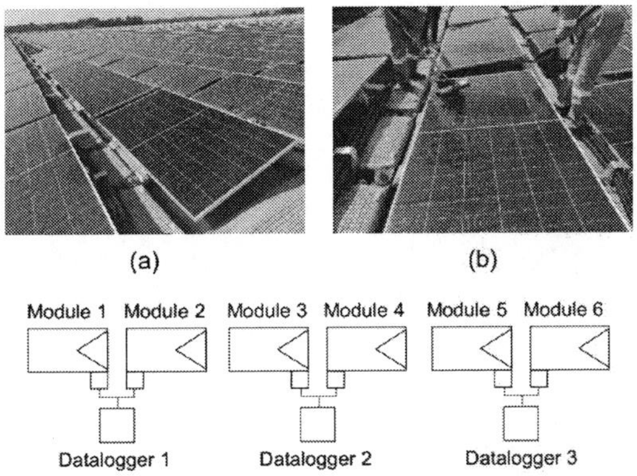

(c)

Figure 1. (a) Six modules used in the experiment, (b) manual cleaning procedure, (c) dataloggers and PV modules connections.

The cleaning schedule and the type of the water used for PV module cleaning are as follows:

Table I: Cleaning schedule and type of water

Item	Cleaning schedule	Type of water
Module 1	every month	clean water
Module 2	every month	reservoir water
Module 3	every three months	clean water
Module 4	every three months	reservoir water
Module 5	every six months	clean water
Module 6	no cleaning	—

Each clean-water module requires approximately six liters of water per cleaning. When using reservoir water, one end of the water pump is immersed in the reservoir while the other end directs the flow onto the module surfaces.

RESULTS

We documented several soiling modes on the FPV array. Representative examples are shown in Figure 2.

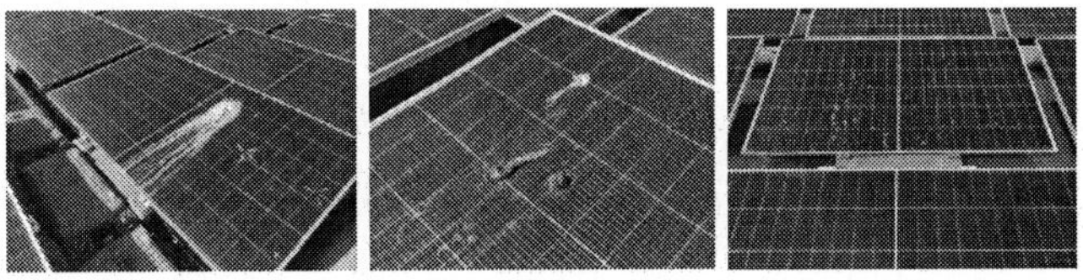

(a) (b) (c)

Figure 2. (a) Avian droppings, (b) residue from avian foraging, (c) splash-induced deposition.

We present an initial appraisal of soiling based on the first two months of analysis. For each month, the module with the highest monthly irradiation is used as the reference and normalized to 100%. Figure 3 shows each module's monthly irradiation as a percentage of this reference.

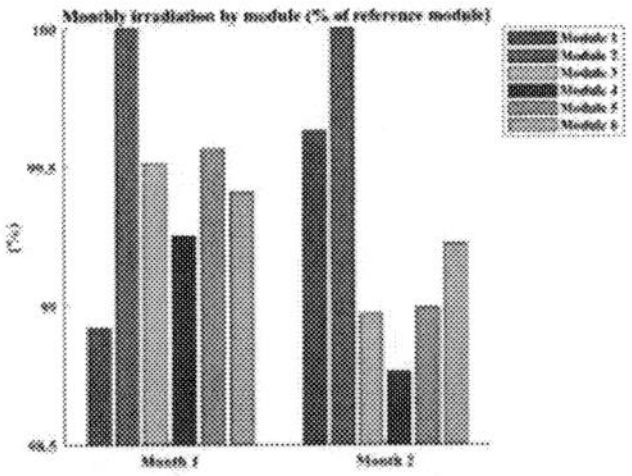

Figure 3. Irradiation by module for the first two months (% of reference module)

Comments for the first two months:
i) Module 2, the unit cleaned with reservoir water, recorded the maximum value of irradiation;
ii) After one month, there is minimal variation in measured irradiation among the modules;
iii) By the end of the second month, monthly cleaned modules exhibit up to 1.25% and 1.01% higher irradiation compared to those cleaned every three and six months, respectively.

Next, we present the soiling assessment for months five and six. For each month, the module with the highest monthly irradiation is taken as the reference (normalized to 100%).

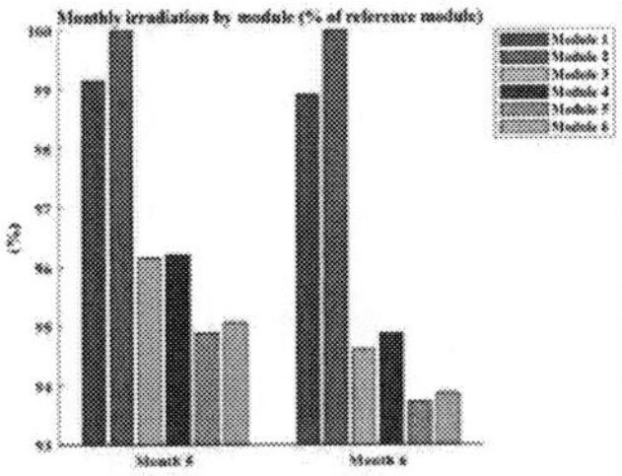

Figure 4. Irradiation by module after months five and six.

Comments after the sixth month:
i) By the end of the sixth month, monthly cleaned modules show up to 5.40% and 6.27% higher irradiation than those cleaned every three and six months;
ii) The small difference in measured irradiation between Module 1 and Module 2 suggests that using reservoir water for cleaning is a viable option from an energy capture perspective.

CONCLUSIONS

Modules cleaned monthly delivered up to 6.27% higher module-plane irradiation than less-frequently cleaned modules. Two factors explain this: (1) Design—FPV arrays typically adopt low tilt angles to enhance mechanical robustness, but low tilt reduces rain-driven self-cleaning and increases soiling; and (2) Environment—urban aerosol pollution and frequent bird activity accelerate particulate and organic deposition. Reservoir water proved viable for cleaning in this study, but it should be used only with manufacturer approval and documented water-quality controls to avoid warranty issues.

EU PVSEC

LSF IEE USP USP FAPESP

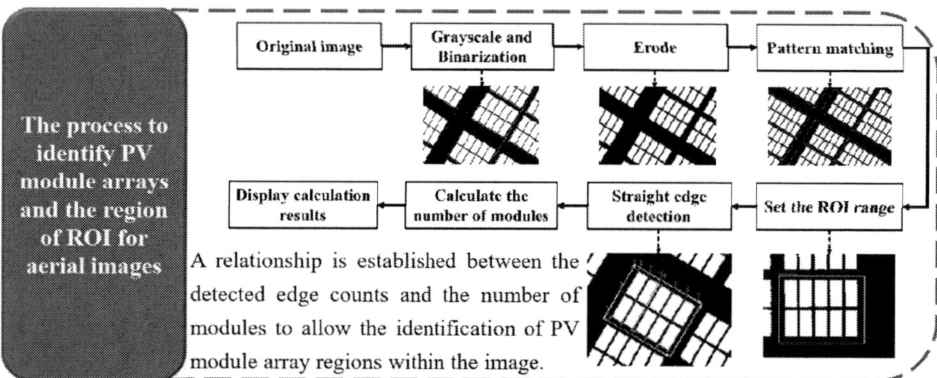

[1]Instituto de Energia e Ambiente
Universidade de São Paulo

EU PVSEC European Photovoltaic Solar Energy Conference and Exhibition

國立勤益科技大學 National Chin-Yi University of Technology

PI Website Here

The Panoramic Reconstruction Images to Photovoltaic Modules for Solar Power Plant Management

Demo Here

Chao-Wei Ou[1], Han-Chang Liu[2], Cheng-Yu Peng[1]*
[1] *National Chin-Yi University of Technology, R.O.C.*
[2] *Industrial Technology Research Institute, Hsinchu, Taiwan, R.O.C.*
*Corresponding author: peng@ncut.edu.tw

工業技術研究院 Industrial Technology Research Institute

ABSTRACT

This study simulates the scenario of an unmanned aerial vehicle (UAV) capturing images of a large-scale solar power plant to generate a panoramic reconstruction for maintenance and inspection management. By analyzing the panoramic image and comparing the characteristics of PV modules, it is possible to identify modules contaminated with bird droppings or dirt and estimate the optimal timing for maintenance and cleaning.

EXPERIMENTAL SETUP

The aerial images are stitched using the SIFT and RANSAC algorithms, utilizing feature extraction and feature matching techniques to identify overlapping regions and perform full image with seamless stitching. Semantic segmentation is applied to detect PV module arrays and extract background information with segmentation accuracy evaluated based on the average error. The Hough Transform is then employed for PV module edge detection. Finally, multiple regional images are stitched together to generate a complete panoramic view of the solar power plant.

Identify PV module arrays and the region of ROI for aerial images

The aerial images are the process of binarized and erosion applied to enhance the edge contours of the photovoltaic modules. The pattern matching is then used to identify PV module arrays and a region of interest (ROI) defined for further analysis. Within this ROI, the edge detection is performed twice using the Hough Transform and separately detecting edge counts in the X and Y directions.

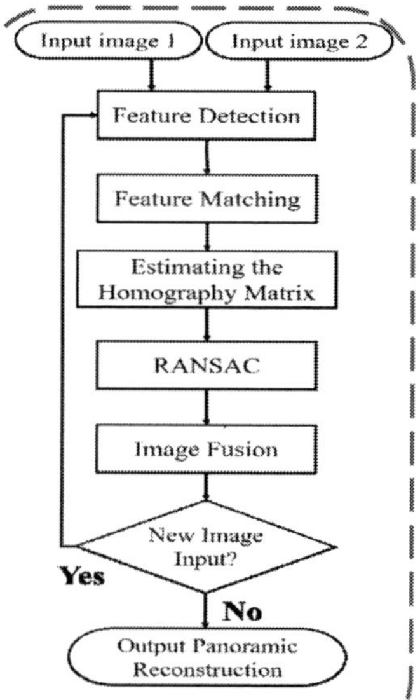

The flow chart of image stitching

The process to identify PV module arrays and the region of ROI for aerial images

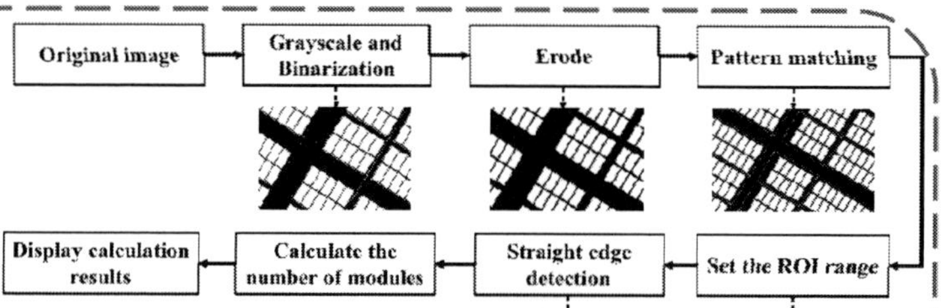

A relationship is established between the detected edge counts and the number of modules to allow the identification of PV module array regions within the image.

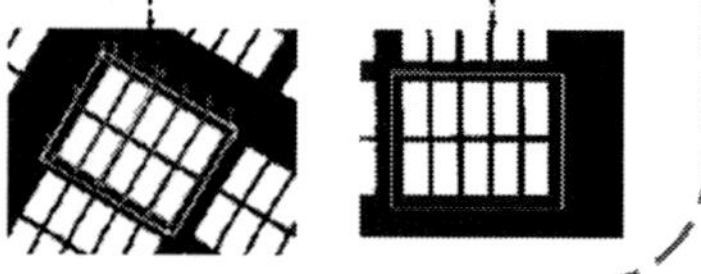

RESULTS AND DISCUSSION

The scenario of UAV capturing imageslight trapping ability

The original multiple regional images

The image stitching feature

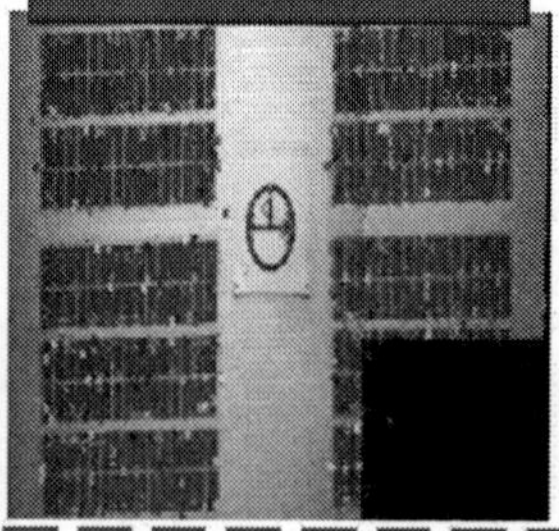

The panoramic reconstruction image

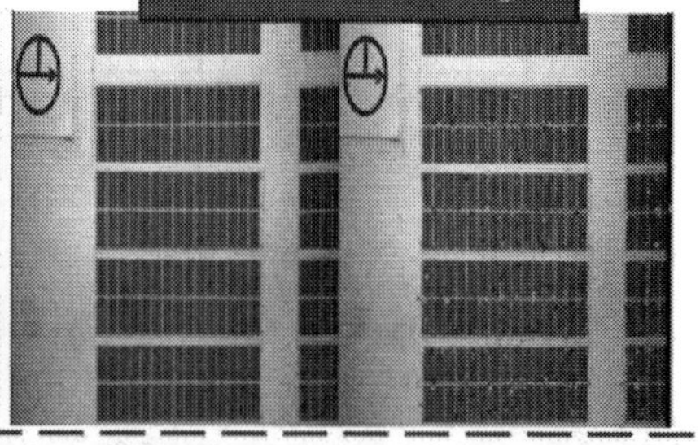

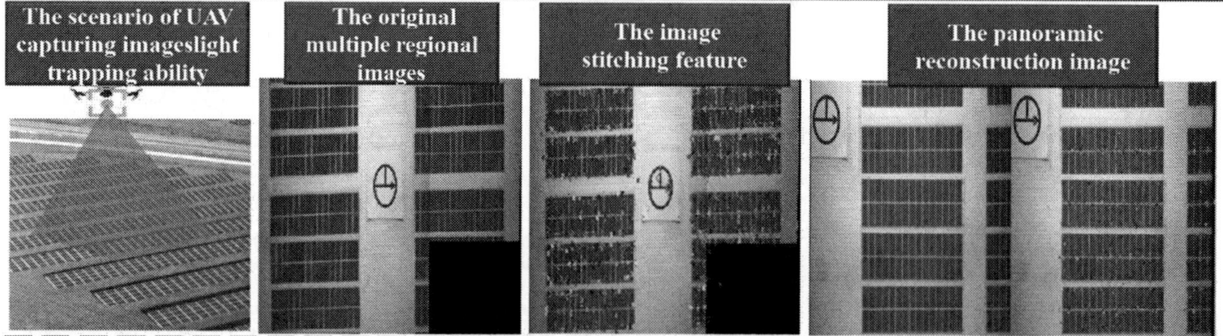

This study demonstrates the process of panoramic reconstruction for PV plant management by utilizing UAV-captured images. The original multiple regional images are obtained by a series of image processing techniques including binarization, erosion, semantic segmentation and edge detection to enhance the identification of PV module arrays.

RESULTS AND DISCUSSION

This demonstration shows panoramic reconstruction for PV plant management using UAV-captured images. Image processing techniques by the binarization, erosion, semantic segmentation, and edge detection enhance PV module identification. The result confirms the effectiveness of the proposed method for inspection and management. (Acknowledgement: The financial support provided by Energy Administration, Ministry of Economic Affairs, Taiwan, R.O.C. (Contract No: 114-S0102) is gratefully acknowledged.)

DETECTION AND CLUSTERING OF PHOTOVOLTAIC FAULTS

Anastasios Kladas, Bert Herteleer, Jan Cappelle
KU Leuven Research Group ELECTA Ghent, Gebroeders De Smetstraat 1, 9000 Ghent, Belgium
anastasios.kladas@kuleuven.be

ABSTRACT: Photovoltaic (PV) systems are susceptible to faults that diminish energy yield and efficiency. This paper presents a novel framework for detecting and clustering PV faults using accessible data: maximum power point voltage and current from the inverter's DC side, plus weather time series. Fault detection uses a degradation-adaptive model to estimate expected outputs, flagging anomalies via dynamic irradiance-based thresholds and performance filters. Fault impacts are quantified with current and voltage performance indices (CPI and VPI), serving as clustering features. Among tested algorithms (K-means, FCM, DBSCAN, HDBSCAN), HDBSCAN excels in robustness to noise on simulated data, grouping faults by system effects.
Keywords: PV fault diagnosis, Fault signatures, Fault Clustering

1 INTRODUCTION

PV system malfunctions reduce energy yield and revenue [1]. Rapid fault detection is essential, distinguishing unexpected issues (e.g., electrical faults, failures) from expected losses (e.g., degradation, soiling). Manual inspections are costly and error-prone, taking up to 8 h/MW for ground-mounted systems [2]–[5]. Automated monitoring with sensors and analytics enables real-time detection [2]. Methods include visual/thermal imaging, MPP monitoring, output comparisons, and machine learning [6], [7]. This work detects faults by comparing measured and estimated outputs.

Prior approaches like Chouder et al. [8] use fixed thresholds on one-diode model errors, but ignore degradation and variable errors. Yao et al. [9] employ ML thresholds from high/low-efficiency data, yet selecting periods is challenging and degradation may misclassify outputs. Kladas et al. [10] address this with degradation-adaptive modeling for accurate references.

Post-detection, diagnosis uses ML classification [11]–[13], rule-based assessment [8], [14], or IV curves [15]. However, labeled data scarcity, broad categories, and IV unavailability limit them.

Faults vary in impact by type/location [16]. Clustering groups similar effects without labels. Xu et al. [17] use MMD-enhanced FCM on IV/PV features for simulated faults, but predefine clusters and test small arrays. Lin et al. [18] apply CFSFDP with reference modules, impractical for many systems. Liu et al. [19] use GKFCM with references and labeled centers, limiting adaptability.

This work clusters faults using MPP voltage/current and weather data, integrable into O&M frameworks. It detects faults, quantifies impacts, clusters signatures with historical logs for efficient troubleshooting.

2 METHODOLOGY

Faults are detected by comparing measured and estimated power at DC measurement points (inverter or arrays). A Python-based degradation-adaptive model [10] estimates current, voltage, and power from plane-of-array irradiance (GPoA) and PV temperature (TPV).Data with malfunctions/downtime are filtered: daily R^2 (current vs. GPoA/GHI) <0.9 or energy performance index (EPI = measured/expected energy) <0.8/>1.1 discarded.Residuals (P_meas - P_est) yield dynamic thresholds: GPoA discretized in 25 W/m² steps; 99th/1st percentiles per bin form lookup table. Deviations >2 hours are faults.

Fault signatures: CPI* = I_meas / I_est, VPI* = V_meas / V_est (degradation-corrected). Clustering uses CPI*/VPI* per string; labels consolidated into composite (e.g., X1.X2... or "C" for clean).

The whole procedure is visualized in Figure 1.

3 DATA USED

Simulated data: MATLAB Simulink models 2×12 (441 V OC, 16 A SC) and 5×5 (184 V OC, 40 A SC) arrays (~5.3–5.5 kW STC) with De Soto model [20]. Faults: open-circuits, short-circuits (intra/cross-string, bypass-diode). Randomized daytime (>250 W/m²) using NIST weather (Jan–May 2015) [21].

4 RESULTS

Evaluation of Clustering Methods
The clustering performance is evaluated using simulated data from 2×12 and 5×5 PV array topologies, with fault signatures generated for scenarios including short circuits, open circuits, and partial shading, replicating ideal PV output estimations [23], [24], [25], [26], [27]. Four clustering algorithms are tested: K-means [23], [24], [25], Fuzzy C-Means (FCM) [26], DBSCAN [23], and HDBSCAN [27]. Parameters are automatically selected (e.g., elbow/silhouette for K-means, FPC for FCM). Performance is assessed using external metrics: completeness, homogeneity, V-measure [28], and Adjusted Rand Index (ARI) [29]. Clustering Results on

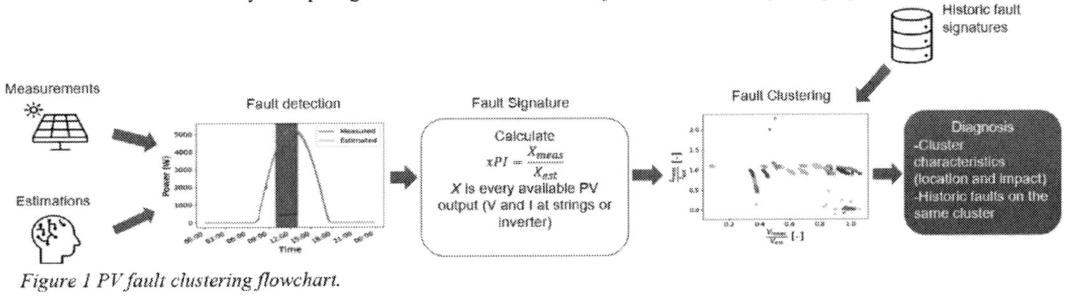

Figure 1 PV fault clustering flowchart.

10.4229/EUPVSEC2025/4CV.1.50

Noise-Free Simulated Data

Table 1 presents clustering metrics for the 2×12 topology. Density-based algorithms (DBSCAN, HDBSCAN) outperform centroid-based algorithms (K-means, FCM), with DBSCAN achieving the highest scores (e.g., V-measure: 0.8441, ARI: 0.5463). The underperformance of K-means and FCM is attributed to the curse of dimensionality affecting distance metrics.

Table 1 Clustering metrics (2×12 system).

METRIC	DBSCAN	FCM	HDBSCAN	KMEANS
COMPLETENESS	0.9741	0.9737	0.9725	0.9678
HOMOGENEITY	0.7448	0.6656	0.7441	0.6572
V-MEASURE	0.8441	0.7907	0.8431	0.7828
ARI	0.5463	0.4410	0.5415	0.4363

Analysis of Voltage Performance Index (VPI) and Current Performance Index (CPI) distributions reveals topology-specific fault patterns. As shown in Figure 2, the 2×12 topology, with more modules in series, forms clusters aligned with the VPI axis, indicative of short-circuit faults affecting voltage. The 5×5 topology, with more parallel strings, shows clusters along the CPI axis, characteristic of open-circuit faults impacting current. Topology influences feature space structure, with series-heavy configurations yielding diverse VPI clusters and parallel-heavy configurations producing varied CPI clusters.

5 DISCUSSION AND CONCLUSION

The proposed method leverages simulated maximum power point (MPP) voltage and current data, combined with weather time series, to cluster PV faults using HDBSCAN [27]. Unlike prior approaches requiring I-V curve parameters [15] or reference module data [18], [19], this method uses performance indices (CPI and VPI) to group faults by their impact on system performance. Integrated into an online operations and maintenance (O&M) framework, it enables rapid fault identification by comparing simulated fault patterns with historical logs.

HDBSCAN efficiently clusters fault signatures derived from simulated short circuits, open circuits, and partial shading, using CPI and VPI. Preprocessing, such as filtering samples with high variability, reduces computational demands, and supports near-real-time clustering. By grouping faults with similar performance impacts, the method simplifies diagnosis without requiring detailed fault-specific models, allowing technicians to cross-reference clusters with historical fault logs for faster resolution.

The method assumes accurate power estimation models in simulations. Inaccuracies, such as those from irradiance spectrum mismatches [31], may introduce noise, potentially masking fault signatures. The current focus is on DC-side faults (e.g., open/short circuits, bypass diode failures). Expanding to AC-side faults could enhance applicability by developing new AC-specific fault signatures. Excluding transient faults (e.g., from moving shadows) simplifies clustering but limits scope. Incorporating dynamic clustering, such as time-series analysis, could improve versatility.

Future work will validate the algorithm on real-world PV systems to assess its performance across diverse configurations and fault scenarios. Real data analysis will focus on integrating the clustering method into an active O&M platform, evaluating scalability, and testing robustness under operational conditions. Additionally, incorporating thermal imaging to establish baseline thermal profiles for PV panels could enhance diagnosis by identifying hotspots or temperature deviations not evident in electrical data [32], [33]. A large language model could further process cluster characteristics, thermal data, and external knowledge to identify root causes and perform cost-benefit analyses for repair decisions, optimizing maintenance strategies

8 REFERENCES

[1] I. Lillo-Bravo, P. González-Martínez, M. Larrañeta, and J. Guasumba-Codena, "Impact of Energy Losses Due to Failures on Photovoltaic Plant Energy Balance," Energies (Basel), vol. 11, no. 2, p. 363, Feb. 2018, doi: 10.3390/en11020363.

[2] S. Ansari, A. Ayob, M. S. Hossain Lipu, M. H. Md Saad, and A. Hussain, "A review of monitoring technologies for solar pv systems using data processing modules and transmission protocols: Progress, challenges and prospects," Sustainability (Switzerland), vol. 13, no. 15, 2021, doi: 10.3390/su13158120.

[3] A. Woyte, M. Richter, D. Moser, M. Green, S. Mau, and H. G. Beyer, Analytical Monitoring of Grid-connected Photovoltaic Systems, vol. 13, no. 2. 2014.

[4] K. Keisang, T. Bader, and R. Samikannu, "Review of Operation and Maintenance Methodologies for Solar Photovoltaic Microgrids," 2021. doi: 10.3389/fenrg.2021.730230.

[5] G. Di Lorenzo, R. Araneo, M. Mitolo, A. Niccolai, and F. Grimaccia, "Review of O&M Practices in PV Plants: Failures, Solutions, Remote Control, and Monitoring Tools," IEEE J Photovolt, vol. 10, no. 4, pp. 914–926, Jul. 2020, doi: 10.1109/JPHOTOV.2020.2994531.

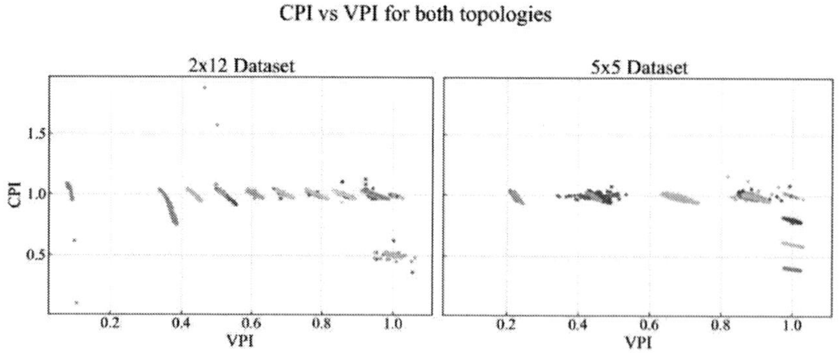

Figure 2 Comparison of VPI and CPI distributions for 2×12 and 5×5 PV array topologies. Each different colour indicates a different cluster.

[6] Y.-Y. Hong and R. A. Pula, "Methods of photovoltaic fault detection and classification: A review," Energy Reports, vol. 8, pp. 5898–5929, Nov. 2022, doi: 10.1016/j.egyr.2022.04.043.
[7] S. R. Madeti and S. N. Singh, "A comprehensive study on different types of faults and detection techniques for solar photovoltaic system," Solar Energy, vol. 158, pp. 161–185, Dec. 2017, doi: 10.1016/j.solener.2017.08.069.
[8] A. Chouder and S. Silvestre, "Automatic supervision and fault detection of PV systems based on power losses analysis," Energy Convers Manag, vol. 51, no. 10, pp. 1929–1937, Oct. 2010, doi: 10.1016/j.enconman.2010.02.025.
[9] S. Yao, Q. Kang, M. Zhou, A. Abusorrah, and Y. Al-Turki, "Intelligent and Data-Driven Fault Detection of Photovoltaic Plants," Processes, vol. 9, no. 10, p. 1711, Sep. 2021, doi: 10.3390/pr9101711.
[10] A. Kladas, B. Herteleer, and J. Cappelle, "A Degradation-Responsive Framework for Long-Term PV Power Estimation," Adv Theory Simul, Jul. 2025, doi: 10.1002/adts.202500631.
[11] K. H. Chao, S. H. Ho, and M. H. Wang, "Modeling and fault diagnosis of a photovoltaic system," Electric Power Systems Research, vol. 78, no. 1, pp. 97–105, Jan. 2008, doi: 10.1016/J.EPSR.2006.12.012.
[12] Z. Chen et al., "Random forest based intelligent fault diagnosis for PV arrays using array voltage and string currents," Energy Convers Manag, vol. 178, pp. 250–264, Dec. 2018, doi: 10.1016/J.ENCONMAN.2018.10.040.
[13] Z. Mustafa, A. S. A. Awad, M. Azzouz, and A. Azab, "Fault identification for photovoltaic systems using a multi-output deep learning approach," Expert Syst Appl, vol. 211, p. 118551, Jan. 2023, doi: 10.1016/j.eswa.2022.118551.
[14] L. Xu, Z. Pan, C. Liang, and M. Lu, "A Fault Diagnosis Method for PV Arrays Based on New Feature Extraction and Improved the Fuzzy C-Mean Clustering," IEEE J Photovolt, vol. 12, no. 3, pp. 833–843, May 2022, doi: 10.1109/JPHOTOV.2022.3151330.
[15] S. Fadhel et al., "PV shading fault detection and classification based on I-V curve using principal component analysis: Application to isolated PV system," Solar Energy, vol. 179, pp. 1–10, Feb. 2019, doi: 10.1016/j.solener.2018.12.048.
[16] K. I. Baradieh et al., "A Study on the Impact of Different PV Model Parameters and Various DC Faults on the Characteristics and Performance of the Photovoltaic Arrays," Inventions, vol. 9, no. 5, p. 93, Aug. 2024, doi: 10.3390/inventions9050093.
[17] L. Xu, Z. Pan, C. Liang, and M. Lu, "A Fault Diagnosis Method for PV Arrays Based on New Feature Extraction and Improved the Fuzzy C-Mean Clustering," IEEE J Photovolt, vol. 12, no. 3, pp. 833–843, 2022, doi: 10.1109/JPHOTOV.2022.3151330.
[18] P. Lin, Y. Lin, Z. Chen, L. Wu, L. Chen, and S. Cheng, "A Density Peak-Based Clustering Approach for Fault Diagnosis of Photovoltaic Arrays," International Journal of Photoenergy, vol. 2017, pp. 1–14, 2017, doi: 10.1155/2017/4903613.
[19] S. Liu, L. Dong, X. Liao, X. Cao, and X. Wang, "Photovoltaic Array Fault Diagnosis Based on Gaussian Kernel Fuzzy C-Means Clustering Algorithm," Sensors, vol. 19, no. 7, p. 1520, Mar. 2019, doi: 10.3390/s19071520.
[20] W. De Soto, S. A. Klein, and W. A. Beckman, "Improvement and validation of a model for photovoltaic array performance," Solar Energy, vol. 80, no. 1, pp. 78–88, Jan. 2006, doi: 10.1016/J.SOLENER.2005.06.010.
[21] Boyd M, Chen T, and Dougherty B, "NIST Campus Photovoltaic (PV) Arrays and Weather Station Data Sets. [Data set]." [Online]. Available: https://doi.org/10.18434/M3S67G
[22] M. Boyd, "Performance data from the NIST photovoltaic arrays and weather station," J Res Natl Inst Stand Technol, vol. 122, 2017, doi: 10.6028/JRES.122.040.
[23] F. Pedregosa et al., "Scikit-learn: Machine learning in Python," Journal of machine learning research, vol. 12, no. Oct, pp. 2825–2830, 2011.
[24] C. Ding, "K-means Clustering via Principal Component Analysis."
[25] F. Wang, H. H. Franco-Penya, J. D. Kelleher, J. Pugh, and R. Ross, "An analysis of the application of simplified silhouette to the evaluation of k-means clustering validity," in Lecture Notes in Computer Science (including subseries Lecture Notes in Artificial Intelligence and Lecture Notes in Bioinformatics), Springer Verlag, 2017, pp. 291–305. doi: 10.1007/978-3-319-62416-7_21.
[26] L. Madson and D. Dantas, "fuzzy-c-means: An implementation of Fuzzy C-means clustering algorithm," Zenodo. doi: 10.5281/zenodo.3066222.
[27] D. M. Bot, J. Peeters, J. Liesenborgs, and J. Aerts, "FLASC: a flare-sensitive clustering algorithm," PeerJ Comput Sci, vol. 11, p. e2792, Apr. 2025, doi: 10.7717/peerj-cs.2792.
[28] A. Rosenberg and J. Hirschberg, "V-Measure: A Conditional Entropy-Based External Cluster Evaluation Measure.," Apr. 2007, pp. 410–420.
[29] L. Hubert and P. Arabie, "Comparing partitions," J Classif, vol. 2, no. 1, pp. 193–218, Dec. 1985, doi: 10.1007/BF01908075.
[30] IEC 61724-1, Photovoltaic system performance – Part 1: Monitoring, " Edition 1.0. 2017.
[31] K. Paghasian and G. TamizhMani, "Photovoltaic module power rating per IEC 61853--1: A study under natural sunlight," in 2011 37th IEEE Photovoltaic Specialists Conference, IEEE, Jun. 2011, pp. 002322–002327. doi: 10.1109/PVSC.2011.6186418.
[32] J. A. Tsanakas, D. Chrysostomou, P. N. Botsaris, and A. Gasteratos, "Fault diagnosis of photovoltaic modules through image processing and Canny edge detection on field thermographic measurements," International Journal of Sustainable Energy, vol. 34, no. 6, pp. 351–372, Jul. 2015, doi: 10.1080/14786451.2013.826223.
[33] J. A. Tsanakas, L. Ha, and C. Buerhop, "Faults and infrared thermographic diagnosis in operating c-Si photovoltaic modules: A review of research and future challenges," Renewable and Sustainable Energy Reviews, vol. 62, pp. 695–709, Sep. 2016, doi: 10.1016/j.rser.2016.04.079.

KU LEUVEN GENT

Faculty of Technology Engineering

Detection and clustering of photovoltaic faults

WHY

Anastasios Kladas, Jarid Van Der Gucht, Bert Herteleer, Jan Cappelle
Research group ELECTA Ghent

Group faults with similar impact together → Faster troubleshooting

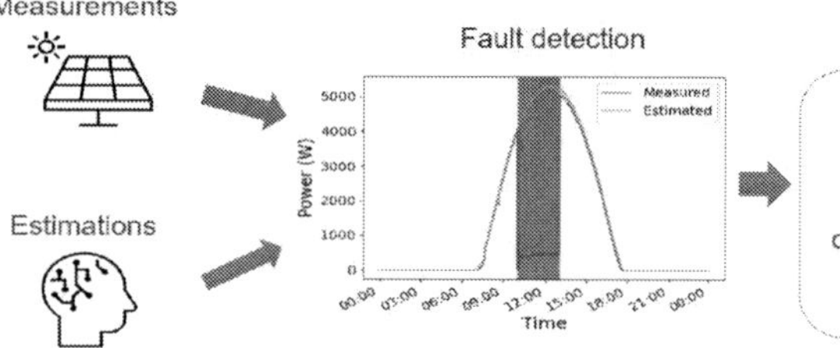

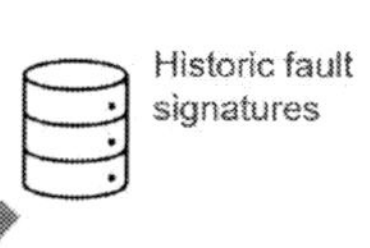

Process

Measurements

Estimations

Fault detection

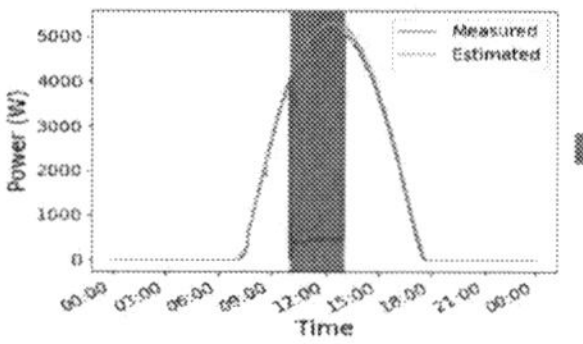

Fault Signature

Calculate

$$xPI = \frac{X_{meas}}{X_{est}}$$

X is every available PV output (V and I at strings or inverter)

A fault signature is the set of all *xPIs* for the examined fault

Historic fault signatures

Fault Clustering

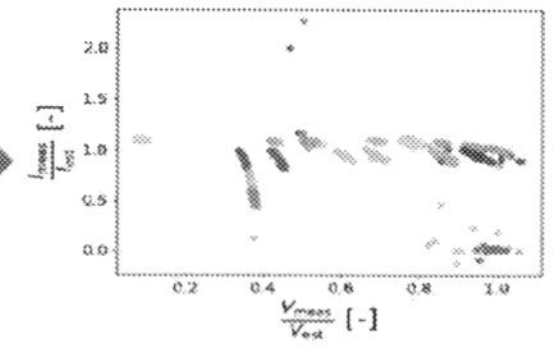

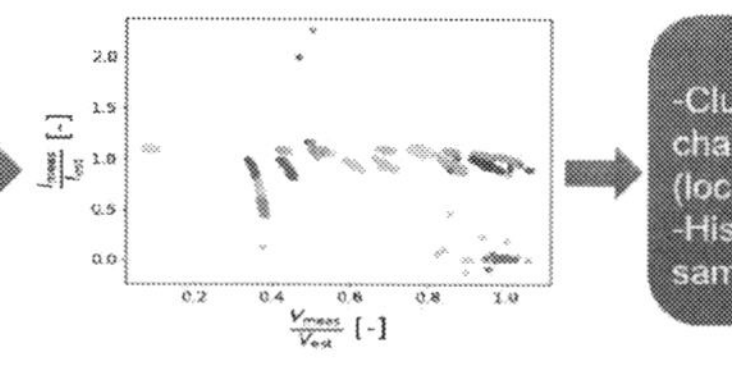

Diagnosis
-Cluster characteristics (location and impact)
-Historic faults on the same cluster

Best clustering algorithm (based on simulations)

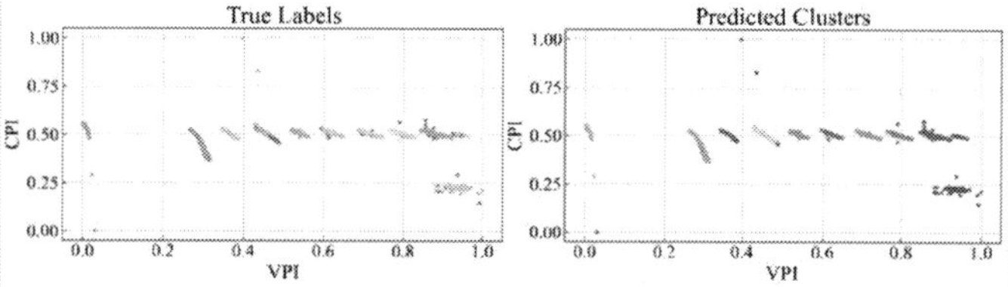

Metric	Without String Current Features				With String Current Features			
	DBSCAN	FCM	HDBSCAN	KMeans	DBSCAN	FCM	HDBSCAN	KMeans
Completeness	0.97	0.96	0.91	0.96	0.98	0.96	0.89	0.99
Homogeneity	0.24	0.43	0.61	0.43	0.22	0.46	0.65	0.33
V-measure	0.38	0.59	0.73	0.59	0.36	0.63	0.75	0.49
ARI	0.06	0.23	0.38	0.23	0.05	0.25	0.43	0.12

- **Simulated diverse faults** in a 2x12 PV setup using Simulink under varying environmental conditions
- **One-diode model [1]** applied for PV system simulation
- **Fault signatures** identified by comparing outputs to non-faulty condition estimates
- **Evaluated 4 clustering algorithms** using inverter or separate string measurements
- **Multi-string approach:** Clustering applied individually to each string's voltage and current performance, then combined for final fault labeling
- **HDBSCAN outperforms** other clustering algorithms
- **Better output estimations enhance** fault signature clarity, improving clustering accuracy

Real data example (Using real PV data from NIST ground system)

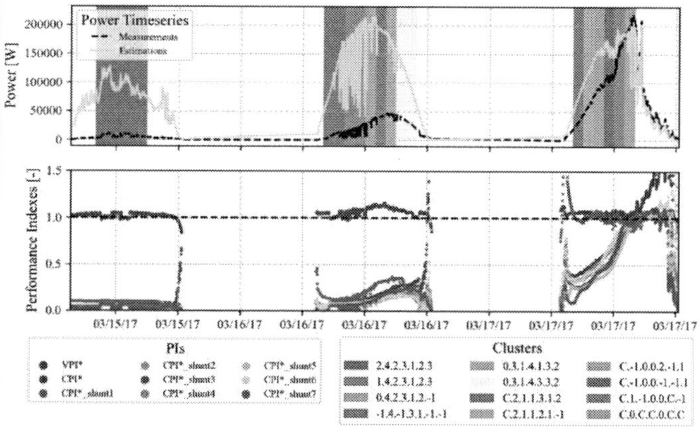

- **NIST ground system data** used for fault simulation and analysis [2]
- **Deep learning PV output model** trained according to [3] to generate output estimations
- **HDBSCAN clustering** applied to aggregated fault signatures (min. samples = 3, cluster selection epsilon = 0.04)
- **Cluster labels:** -1 for outliers, C for no-fault conditions
- **System downtime** occurred until the afternoon of March 16, 2017, followed by **gradual inverter reconnection**
    - Different clusters assigned to distinct reconnection stages
    - 2nd and 4th strings are the last to become functional

[1] De Soto, W., Klein, S. A., & Beckman, W. A. (2006). Improvement and validation of a model for photovoltaic array performance. Solar Energy, 80(1), 78–88. https://doi.org/10.1016/j.solener.2005.06.010
[2] Boyd, M. (2017). Performance data from the NIST photovoltaic arrays and weather station. Journal of Research of the National Institute of Standards and Technology, 122. https://doi.org/10.6028/JRES.122.040
[3] Kladas, A., Herteleer, B., & Cappelle, J. (2025). A Degradation-Responsive Framework for Long-Term PV Power Estimation. Advanced Theory and Simulations. https://doi.org/10.1002/adts.202500631

https://www.linkedin.com/in/anastasioskladas
AnastasiosKladas@kuleuven.be
+30 6975718485

PHOTOVOLTAIC MODULES SELF-TESTING BY JUNCTION BOX-EMBEDDED WIRELESS MONITORING SOLUTION

Eneko Ortega[1,2], Gerardo Aranguren[1], Julius Denafas[3], Paulius Laurikėnas[3], Ricardo Alonso[4] and Juan Carlos Jimeno[1]

[1] Technological Institute of Microelectronics, University of the Basque Country UPV/EHU, 48013, Bilbao, Spain
[2] Electricity and Electronics Department, University of the Basque Country UPV/EHU, 48940, Leioa, Spain
[3] Solitek, 08412, Vilnius, Lithuania
[4] TECNALIA, Basque Research and Technology Alliance (BRTA), 48160, Derio, Spain

eneko.ortegam@ehu.eus

ABSTRACT: Online monitoring of PV systems is essential to detect failures on the PV system, improve performance ratio and minimize degradation, extending module lifespan and increasing profitability by optimizing maintenance activities, reducing in-field inspections. PV system or string level monitoring approaches often fail to detect faults in individual modules, while module-level methods are more expensive. This work introduces a low-cost IoT device embedded in the junction box of the PV modules, which estimates the I-V characteristic near the operating point without disconnecting the PV module from the rest of the system, while also monitoring modules substrings and bypass diodes. The embedded circuit produces and measures small variations around the operating point to obtain, for the entire PV module and at substring level, the I-V characteristic around the operating point. From this information, for each PV module two numbers are obtained: degradation and misfit. In addition, the proposed solution would be able to estimate several PV module parameters as series and shunt resistances or saturation currents.

Keywords: photovoltaic systems, condition monitoring, performance ratio, fault detection

1 INTRODUCTION

Solar photovoltaic (PV) electricity generation is increasing at an exponential rate, with an expected installed PV capacity growth of more than 500 GW per year [1]. In this context, maximizing the performance and reliability of PV systems becomes essential. The performance of PV systems is typically measured in terms of the performance ratio (PR) [2] which ranges between 85% and 90% for different PV systems in function of the module technology, system architecture, the PV system location climate or in function of the degradation of the PV system [3].

This means that power losses can be up to 15%, even for modern PV systems, due to PV module technology, system architecture, inverter and wiring losses or failures in the PV modules itself [1]. Failures in PV modules, such as encapsulation failures, cell cracks, potential induced degradation or partial shadows, are behind a relevant part of PV systems power losses [4]. Extreme weather conditions such as hurricanes and hailstorms also have a severe impact on PV systems performance [5]. Furthermore, the failure of a single module can cause greater power loss, as photovoltaic modules are connected to each other.

Periodic monitoring is the only way to detect these failures and to minimize power losses, boosting PV systems profitability. In this context, several monitoring techniques have been proposed [6,7].

Some monitoring methods are PV system or string-level oriented whereas others are string or module-level oriented. However, it is unclear whether system or string-level methods are capable of detecting power losses affecting to a single PV module or to small groups of modules, as these faults can be difficult to detect within the entire system [8].

Module level monitoring methods can achieve higher resolution, but they tend to be expensive and difficult to automatize. Module level methods rely on different techniques, such as visual inspection of the PV module, thermal images analysis, electroluminescence testing or electrical measurement.

Monitoring methods based on electrical measurements usually measure the operating voltage or the output power of the PV module. However, with these methods it is not always possible to detect the fault or, even if the fault is detected, to identify which module is the defective one [6] since they are connected in series between them. Voltage-current (I-V) characteristic measurement provides more insight into the PV module's status and it is possible to identify the power losses origin.

However, this approach tends to be expensive and difficult to automatize, since to measure the full I-V characteristic power electronic components are required and, in addition, the PV module needs to be disconnected from the rest of the system, increasing non-productive periods.

In [9] and [10] the authors proposed a novel monitoring methodology, capable of performing, in a few milliseconds, partial measurements of individual PV modules I-V curve around its operating point and reconstructing their characteristics, using a low-cost electronic circuit based on two capacitors, in the range of tens of microfarads, without power electronics components and controlled by six switches.

This methodology, in combination with temperature and solar irradiation data which can be obtained by adding additional sensors to the PV system or can be estimated from publicly available meteorological data following different approaches [11], enables to estimate the PV modules status, without disconnecting it from the rest of the system and to estimate the module degradation.

In this work, a new version of the proposed methodology is introduced. The monitoring circuit will be integrated into Solitek's PV modules junction boxes, with access to the PV modules substrings and modules bypass diodes.

The electronic circuit includes Wi-Fi communications, which allow monitoring the PV system modules status remotely, reporting several parameters such as operating point, maximum power point (MPP), the I-V curve, the module temperature and the lighting or even the status of the bypass diodes. From this information, for each PV module two numbers are obtained: degradation and misfit. In addition, the proposed solution would be able to estimate several PV module parameters as series and shunt resistances or saturation currents.

2 PV MODULE MONITORING DEVICE

The PV modules monitoring circuit is a low-cost electronic circuit, that uses only low power components, and is capable of varying the operating point of the photovoltaic module by modifying its output current. This monitoring process, explained in detail in [9] is performed without disconnecting it from the rest of its string and without adding external wiring.

The monitoring circuit, as it can be seen in Fig. 1, is based on two capacitors in the order of tens of microfarads controlled by six switches. It has four operating modes: standby, T1, T2 and T3.

Most of the time, the monitoring circuit is in standby mode, and no current is drawn from the PV module. During T1, the first step in the monitoring sequence, the capacitors are charged slowly (50 ms) until they reach the module voltage, consuming little current from the module.

In T2, the first capacitor discharges into the photovoltaic module, increasing the module's output current with a stepped function limited to 0.3 A. In this way, the operating point shifts towards short circuit. This movement is performed outside the static I-V characteristics since, due to the intrinsic capacitance of the photovoltaic modules, the dynamic behavior cannot follow the I-V characteristics of the photovoltaic module. Once the capacitor is discharged, it returns to the initial operating point with values below the static I-V characteristics.

During T3, the operating point shifts to higher voltages, decreasing the output current by 0.3 A and moving it to open circuit with behavior similar to T2.

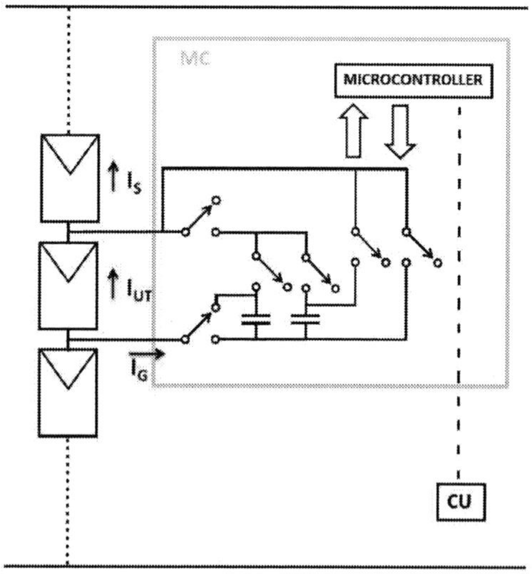

Figure 1: Simplified monitoring circuit, based on two capacitors and six switches.

Once the operating point reaches equilibrium again, the MC returns to standby mode. During T2 and T3, which are completed in a few milliseconds, the MC takes pairs of current and voltage values. In [10] a method to correct the dynamic effects on the I-V curve was presented, showing good results to estimate the static I-V characteristic around the operating point of the PV module.

Withing the SUPERNOVA project, the previously proposed and validated monitoring solution is being integrated into the PV module itself. For that, a new junction box is being designed integrating the developed monitoring device and all the necessary bypass diodes and connectors.

In addition to voltage and current measurements, the new circuits also includes a temperature sensor, front and rear illumination sensors, and a dirt sensor on the front of the PV module, enabling a complete diagnosis of the module. Fig. 2 shows a detailed electrical diagram of the testing circuit on a simplified circuit of a PV module with 3 bypass diodes.

The specific PV module where the monitoring solution is being integrated is a bifacial module manufactured by SOLITEK, composed of 108 half-cells arranged in six strings of 18 half-cells, each measuring 182 x 91 mm². The cell technology is n-type, bifacial TOPCon. The efficiency of the cells is 23.5%, and the efficiency of the module under STC conditions with front illumination is 21.51%. Under bifacial illumination, the expected maximum operating conditions of the PV module are:

$$P_{MAX} = 625\ W, V_{OC} = 38.24\ V\ and\ I_{SC} = 20\ A$$

The monitoring circuit integrated into the PV module is based on the circuit introduced in [9] and [10], designed for PV modules of 39 V, 9 A and 270 W but upgraded to the new expected operating conditions with voltage and current ranges of 50 V and 20 A. In addition, a new functionality, currently under evaluation, has been added to allow access to the negative voltage region of the PV module, enabling to assess the integrity of the bypass diodes.

As shown in Fig. 3, for each PV module and its

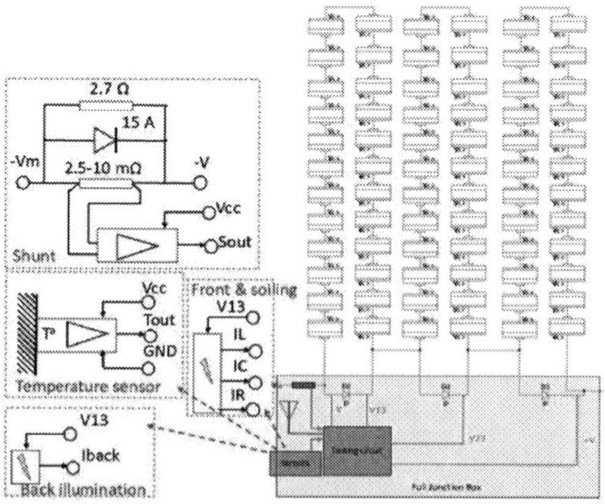

Figure 2: Detailed electrical diagram of the testing circuit on a simplified circuit of a PV module with 3 bypass diodes.

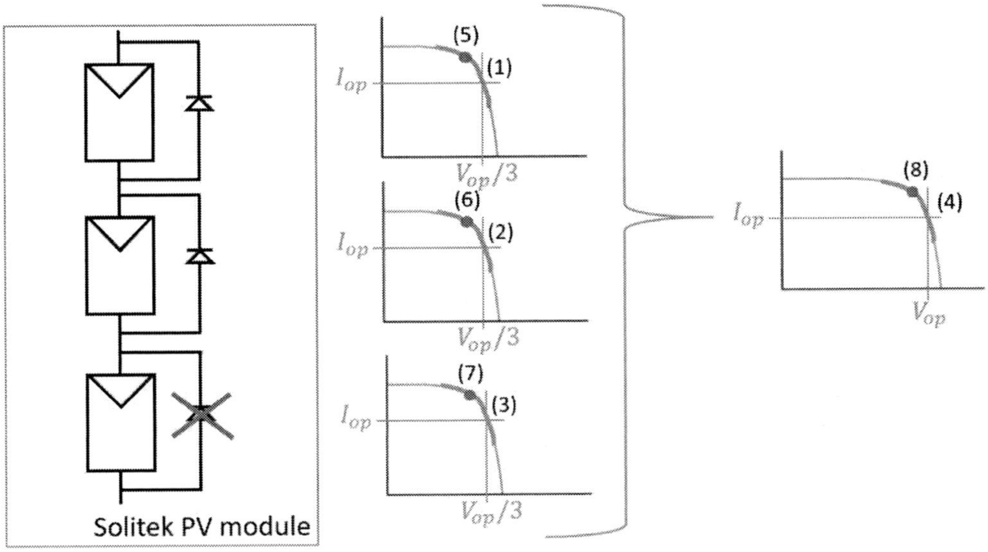

Figure 3: Implemented PV module substring level monitoring solution and parameters extraction: Module and module's substrings operating point (1-4), partial I-V characteristic (green line) and MPP (5-8). Access to bypass diodes enables to assess the integrity of the bypass diodes.

substrings, the following information can be obtained: operating point (1-4), partial I-V characteristic around the operating point (green line) and MPP (5-8).

For that, the monitoring circuit includes this circuit tripled, providing individual access to each of the module's substrings, and thus facilitating the evaluation of each string and its corresponding bypass diodes. The observation of its operating point also will reveal if any of the bypass diodes are short-circuited.

In addition, for each PV module two numbers can be obtained: mismatch and degradation. Mismatch is the ratio between the working point of the PV module (WP) and the MPP for the current operating conditions. It can be estimated from temperature and irradiation conditions and from PV module theoretical performance. Mismatch is associated with failures on the rest of the system.

Degradation is the ratio between the MPP and the expected power (EP) for the current operating conditions of the PV module and it is associated with failures on the PV module. Eq. 1 and 2 show the equations used to compute Mismatch and degradation parameters.

$$Mismatch = 1 - \frac{WP}{MPP} \qquad (1)$$

$$Degradation = 1 - \frac{MPP}{EP} \qquad (2)$$

Finally, from the partial I-V characteristic, several parameters associated with the PV module could be estimated, such as series or shunt resistance and saturation current, among others.

Fig. 4 shows the top and bottom views of the first prototype of the monitoring circuit to be integrated into the Solitek PV modules. Within the SUPERNOVA project, the proposed monitoring solution will be tested on a 50kW PV system.

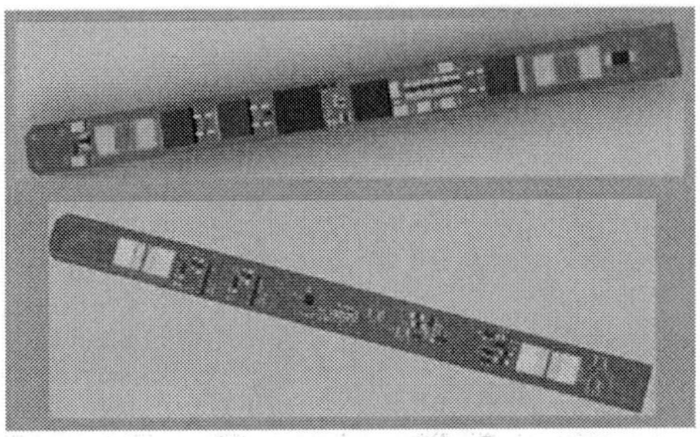

Figure 4: Top and bottom views of the first prototype to be integrated into the Solitek PV modules.

3 COMMUNICATION ARCHITECTURE

Each monitoring circuit integrated on the PV modules will operate as an Internet of Things (IoT) device. Each device will have an ESP32 microcontroller. The ESP32 is a low-cost dual-core 32-bit LX6 microprocessor with wireless (Wi-Fi) communication capabilities. The ESP32 operates at frequencies up to 240 MHz and it incorporates all the necessary functionalities to control the monitoring circuit and integrated sensors. It also executes the previously developed algorithms [10] to obtain the relevant parameters to determine the status of the PV module.

Each IoT device is provided with Wi-Fi communications. The proposed solution will enable remote monitoring of the PV system following the approach shown in Fig. 3.

Two different approaches can be observed. For small size PV systems, as domestic PV systems, each PV module IoT device will connect directly to an access point and send the monitoring data to an IoT cloud platform. For larger size PV systems, internet access will be granted by

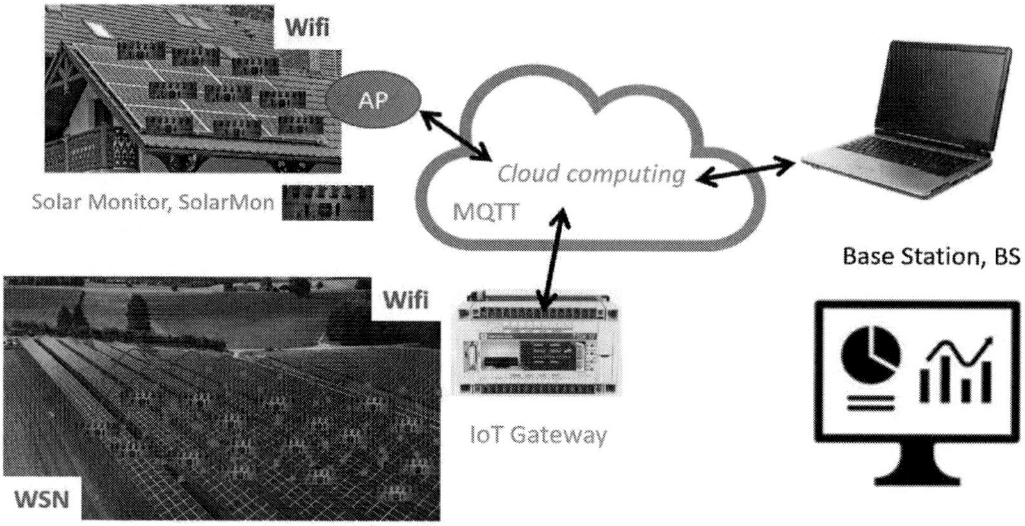

Figure 5. IoT solution architecture for module level PV systems monitoring. For small size PV system cloud access is granted through an access point. For larger PV systems cloud access is granted through an IoT Gateway. PV system owner access monitored data through a dashboard on a laptop or mobile device.

an IoT Gateway. Data will be stored on an IoT Cloud platform, and the PV system owner would be able to access remotely to modules status information.

One of the main challenges during the implementation of this communications architecture in the PV system is its reliability and stability. Wireless communications in low-power IoT devices with low-power antennas have limited range and intensity. They also present risks in terms of connection loss or data package losses. This problem can be even more significant in PV systems where the distance between each module and the access point is large, operating conditions are not stable, due to changes in atmospheric conditions, and the PV system itself can be a source of electromagnetic interferences [12], making wireless communications within the PV system more difficult.

Due to larger distances between PV modules and the IoT Gateway, direct connection will not be feasible for all IoT devices. Therefore, several connection levels will be generated to transmit information from every PV module to the access point. A mesh network is being deployed, where nodes are interconnected so that data can travel through multiple paths from a source to a destination. This allows to create a self-healing and fault-tolerant system where communication can still flow even if some nodes fail or connections drop.

Regarding the communication protocol, Message Queuing Telemetry Transport (MQTT) will be used in the context of this application. MQTT is a lightweight and efficient communication protocol, designed for message exchange between devices in networks with limited resources or unstable connections, such as the IoT. It works under a publish/subscribe model: clients publish messages to topics, and other clients subscribe to those topics to receive them, all managed by a broker that centralizes and distributes the information. Its low bandwidth consumption, simplicity, and support for real-time communication make it ideal for sensors, monitoring systems, and large-scale connected applications.

There will be two types of clients: the monitoring circuit integrated in each PV module (SolarMon) and the Base Station (BS) which would be the final user or device (computer, tablet, mobile phone) through which the system operator can observe the status of each individual PV module in the PV system.

The MQTT communication protocol in this system operates in two distinct modes: set-up and operation. In the set-up stage, each SolarMon device has no PV system assigned and connects first to a predefined Wi-Fi network and then to the MQTT broker. At this point, communication is handled through two temporary topics: one where devices publish their identifiers and availability, and another where the base station (BS) publishes assignments. This exchange allows the BS to detect unassigned devices and map them to their final PV system topics. Once a device has been successfully assigned, it confirms availability through its new status topic, signaling readiness to transition into normal operation.

In the operation stage, communication shifts to a set of PV system-specific topics structured around four main functions: configuration, status reporting, data requests, and data responses. Through the configuration topic, the BS can remotely update device parameters such as Wi-Fi credentials or measurement settings. The status topic provides real-time updates whenever devices boot, reconnect, or respond to configuration commands. Monitoring is supported by the request and data topics, where the BS issues measurement commands and devices return sensor and substring data. This structured use of topics ensures robust device management, fault tolerance, and scalability, allowing multiple PV systems to coexist within the same broker architecture while maintaining clear separation of control and data flows. Fig. 6 shows a

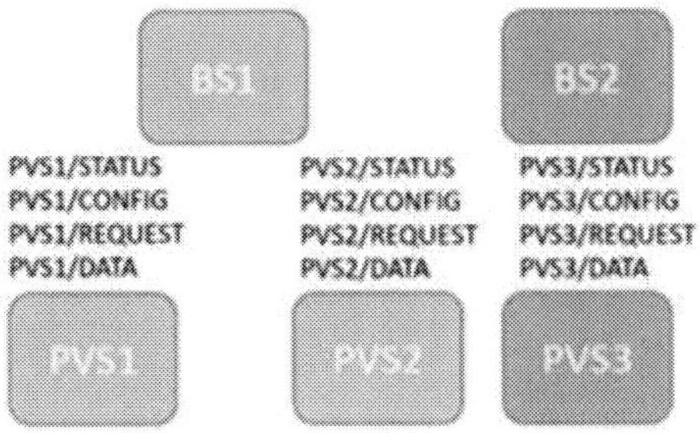

Figure 6. MQTT communication architecture where the same broker handles several PV systems and BS.

schematic diagram of the MQTT communication architecture, with several BS and PV systems in the same MQTT broker. However, each BS (PV system owner) can only access the PV systems to which it has been granted access.

4 CONCLUSIONS

This work presents the development of a low-cost solution for the online monitoring of PV systems, designed to be embedded directly into the PV module's junction box. Conceived as a self-testing system, the device addresses the limitations of traditional monitoring methods, which are often expensive or incapable of detecting failures at the individual module level. The proposed methodology allows for the estimation of the I-V characteristic around the PV module's operating point and its substrings without requiring disconnection from the system, with measurements completed in just a few milliseconds. This approach not only optimizes maintenance activities and reduces in-field inspections but also promises to improve the performance ratio and minimize degradation, thereby extending the lifespan of the modules.

The diagnostic capability of the device is comprehensive, providing detailed information on the status of each module. From the partial I-V curve, two key metrics are derived: degradation, which quantifies power losses associated with failures within the module itself, and misfit, which identifies performance issues caused by the rest of the system. Furthermore, the system can estimate electrical parameters such as series and shunt resistances and saturation currents. An additional feature is the ability to assess the integrity of the bypass diodes by individually accessing the module's substrings, enabling more precise fault detection.

The solution is implemented as an IoT device using an ESP32 microcontroller with Wi-Fi communications. To ensure reliability in large-scale installations, the communication architecture will be based on a mesh topology network. The MQTT protocol was selected for its efficiency in networks with limited resources as the one that is being developed on this work.

The proposed system, for which the first prototype is being manufactured, will be validated on a 50 kW PV system within the SUPERNOVA project, demonstrating its potential for remote, scalable, and robust monitoring of PV systems.

5 ACKNOWLEDGEMENTS

The European Union's Horizon Europe programme is acknowledged for financial support through the SUPERNOVA project (Grant Agreement No 101146883).

6 REFERENCES

[1] A. Jager-Waldau, Snapshot of photovoltaics - February 2024. EPJ Photovoltaics, vol. 15, p. 21, 2024.

[2] G. Blaesser, PV system measurements and monitoring the European experience. Solar Energy Materials, vol. 47, pp. 167-176, 1997.

[3] A. Louwen, S. Lindig, G. Chowdhury and D. Moser, Climate-and Technology-Dependent Performance Loss Rates in a Large Commercial Photovoltaic Monitoring Dataset. Solar RRL, vol. 8, p. 2300653, 2024.

[4] H. Al Mahdi, P.G. Leahy, M. Alghoul and A.P. Morrison, A Review of Photovoltaic Module Failure and Degradation Mechanisms: Causes and Detection Techniques. Solar, vol. 4, pp. 43-82, 2024.

[5] Jordan, D. C., Perry, K., White, R., and Deline, C. Extreme weather and PV performance. IEEE Journal of Photovoltaics, 13(6), 830-835. 2023

[6] E. Ortega, G. Aranguren, M.J. Saenz, R. Gutierrez and J.C. Jimeno, Study of Photovoltaic Systems Monitoring Methods, in 44th IEEE Photovoltaic Specialist Conference (IEEE PVSC), 2017.

[7] Aghaei, M., Kolahi, M., Nedaei, A., Venkatesh, N. S., Esmailifar, S. M., Moradi Sizkouhi, A. M., ... & Rüther, R. Autonomous Intelligent Monitoring of Photovoltaic Systems: An In-Depth Multidisciplinary Review. Progress in Photovoltaics: Research and Applications, 33(3), 381-409. 2025.

[8] Jones, C. B., Ellis, B. H., Stein, J. S., and Walters, J. Comparative review of high resolution monitoring versus standard inverter data acquisition for a single photovoltaic power plant. In 2018 IEEE 7th World Conference on Photovoltaic Energy Conversion. pp. 0715-0720. 2018.

[9] E. Ortega, G. Aranguren and J.C. Jimeno, New monitoring method to characterize individual modules in large photovoltaic systems. Solar Energy, vol. 193, pp. 906-914, 2019.

[10] E. Ortega, G. Aranguren and J.C. Jimeno, Photovoltaic modules transient response analysis and correction under a fast characterization system. Solar Energy, vol. 221, pp. 232-242, 2021.

[11] Rodriguez, S. M., Chicote, B., Ortega, E., Aranguren, G., and Jimeno, J. C. Software tool for weather parameters acquisition during photovoltaic systems monitoring. IEEE 53rd Photovoltaic Specialists Conference. pp. 0621-0626. 2025.

[12] Kane, M. M., Taylor, N., and Månsson, D. Electromagnetic interference from solar photovoltaic systems: A Review. Electronics, *14*(1), 31. 2024.

Photovoltaic modules self-testing by junction box-embedded wireless monitoring solution

Eneko Ortega[*,1,2], Gerardo Aranguren[2], Julius Denafas[3],
Paulius Laurikėnas[3], Ricardo Alonso[4] and Juan Carlos Jimeno[2]
*eneko.ortegam@ehu.eus
[1]Technological Institute of Microelectronics, UPV/EHU, 48013, Bilbao, Spain
[2]Electricity and Electronics Department, UPV/EHU, 48940, Leioa, Spain
[3]Solitek, 08412, Vilnius, Lithuania
[4]TECNALIA, Basque Research and Technology Alliance (BRTA), 48160, Derio, Spain

Introduction

- Exponential PV growth requires maximized performance and reliability.
- Power losses reach up to **15%** due to failures (cracks, shadows, etc.).
- System/string-level monitoring **fails to detect individual module faults.**
- Full I-V measurement is costly, hard to automate, and requires **disconnection.**

Aim

To introduce a low-cost self-testing IoT device embedded into the PV module's junction box with access to the PV modules substrings and modules bypass diodes and to determine PV module status.

Self-Testing Device

Circuit and Measurement:

- **Low-cost**, low-power electronic circuit .
- Based on two **capacitors** (tens of μF) and six switches .
- Method: Varies operating point by modifying output current (± 0.3 A).
- Partial I-V measurement completed in **milliseconds.**
- Estimates static I-V partial characteristic around the operating point.

Sensors and Functionality:

- Integrated sensors: Temperature, Illumination (front/rear), and **Dirt sensor.**
- Provides individual access to module **substrings.**
- New feature: Evaluates **bypass diode** integrity by accessing the negative voltage region.

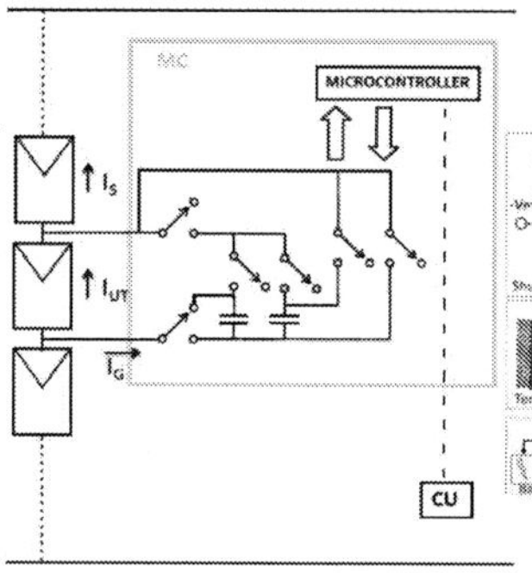

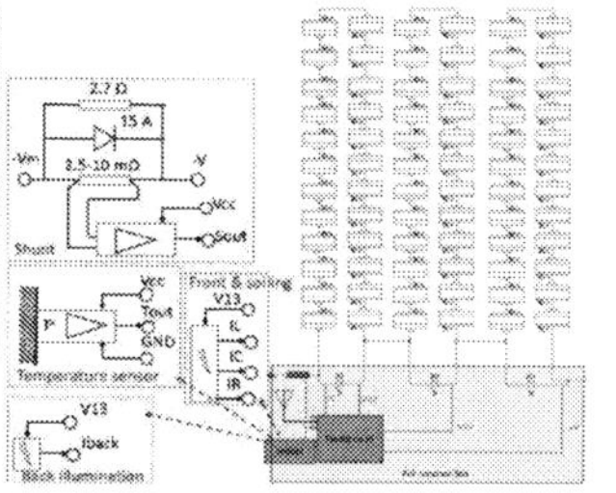

Diagnostics and Metrics

Two key numbers obtained for each PV module:

1. **DEGRADATION**
- Quantifies losses from **internal module failures.**
- $Degradation = 1 - \frac{MPP}{EP}$ (Maximum Power Point / Expected Power).

2. **MISFIT**
- Identifies performance issues caused by the **rest of the system.**
- $Mismatch = 1 - \frac{WP}{MPP}$ (Working Point / Maximum Power Point).

- Other estimated parameters: Series/shunt resistances and saturation currents.

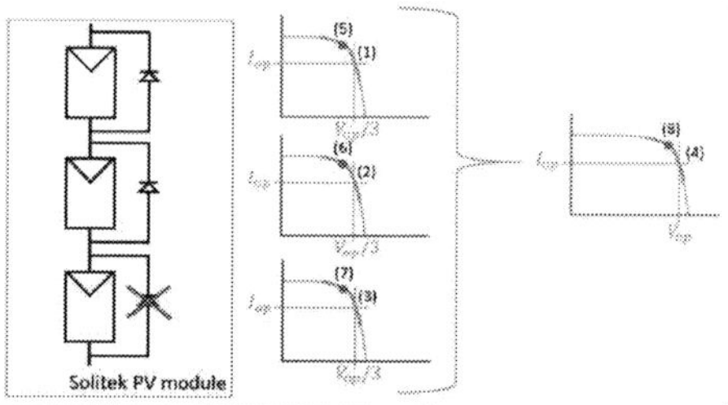

IoT Communication

1. **Hardware and Protocol**
- IoT device uses **ESP32 microcontroller** (low-cost, Wi-Fi).
- Protocol: **MQTT** (lightweight, efficient, Publish/Subscribe model).

2. **Network and Challenges**
- Challenges: Large distance, unstable conditions, **EMI** (Electromagnetic Interference).
- Topology: **Mesh Network** deployed for fault tolerance and self-healing in large systems.
- Flow: Base Station (BS) manages configuration, status reporting, and data Requests/Responses via structured topics.

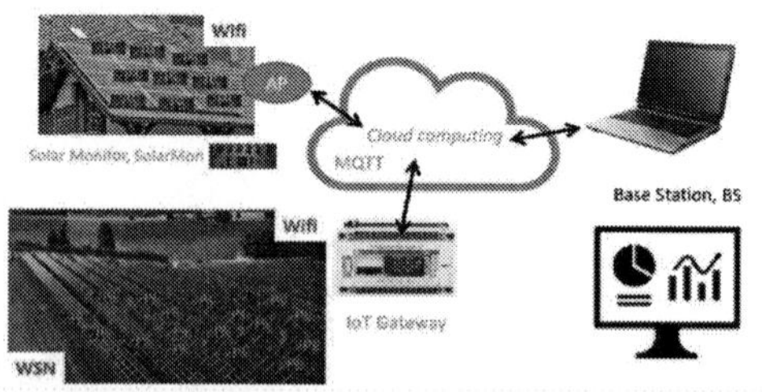

Acknowledgements

The European Union's Horizon Europe programme is acknowledged for financial support through the SUPERNOVA project (Grant Agreement No 101146883).

Conclusions

- **Low-cost, embedded online monitoring solution** developed, addressing traditional limitations.
- Fast I-V estimation and robust diagnostics (Degradation/Misfit) provided .
- IoT architecture (**Mesh/MQTT**) ensures reliability and scalability.
- Validation is underway on a **50 kW PV system.**

DATA-DRIVEN ASSESSMENT OF INVERTER EFFICIENCY LOSSES AND LOAD PROFILES IN PV SYSTEMS

David Daßler*,1, Stephanie Malik[1], Dharm Patel, Andreas Dietrich[2], Jan Spihola[2],
Kai Kaufmann[3], Carsten Hennig[4], Robert Klengel[1], Carola Klute[1], Ulrike Jahn[1], Matthias Ebert[1]

[1] Fraunhofer IMWS, Fraunhofer Institute for Microstructure of Materials and Systems IMWS, Walter-Hülse-Straße 1, 06120 Halle (Saale)
[2] DiSUN, Deutsche Solarservice GmbH, Mielestraße 2, 14542 Werder (Havel)
[3] DENKweit GmbH, Blücherstraße 26, 06120 Halle
[4] saferay holding GmbH, Rosenthaler Str. 34-35, 10178 Berlin
* = corresponding author: david.dassler@csp.fraunhofer.de

ABSTRACT: Maximizing energy yield in photovoltaic (PV) systems requires a precise understanding of losses and their root causes – they originate from either the inverter or the PV-generator side. Both parts experience multiple internal and external stresses, degradation mechanisms, and defects. A systematic distinction between these sources is essential for optimizing performance, reducing downtime, and implementing effective maintenance strategies. The approach presented in this study focuses on losses and operational stresses of inverters.
We present a data-driven approach that combines device-level stress comparisons with performance modeling using artificial neural networks to quantify long-term inverter efficiency losses. Based on 11 years of high-resolution monitoring data from a PV plant with nine identical central inverters, we investigate device-resolved differences in thermal loads, inverter clipping, and ventilation impacts. Even though the inverters are nominally identical and part of the same system, the results show pronounced thermal heterogeneities more than 5 °C on average per year, diverging ventilation profiles and increasing cooling effort over time, and strongly varying clipping exposure across devices. Long-term analysis indicates a systematic efficiency decline of approximately 2 percentage points over the operation lifetime, especially at moderate AC power levels. The combined method enables device-level stress profiling, trend detection from standard monitoring data and provides insights for predictive maintenance and lifecycle management.

Keywords: system monitoring, inverter, inverter efficiency, stress profile, machine learning

1 INTRODUCTION

Maximizing and stabilizing energy yield is essential to the technical and economic viability of photovoltaic (PV) systems worldwide. As PV assets grow, persistent efficiency losses translate into significant revenue impacts and undermine long-term energy forecasts, warranties, and financial assumptions. Ensuring high yield therefore requires not only periodic field inspections but also continuous performance assurance during operation.

Utility-scale PV plants are complex systems comprising thousands of interacting components – from cables, modules, and combiners to power electronics, transformers, monitoring, and control. Their interactions lead to the accumulation of multiple loss mechanisms along the generation chain. Typical contributors include, on the generator (DC side): soiling, shading, thermal ventilation, angle-dependency, ohmic losses, module quality variations, and long-term module degradation; and on the AC side: inverter or transformer conversion losses, cooling effects, clipping or grid-dependent curtailment (see [1], [2]) and injection. Because these effects vary with time, system layout, operating state, and weather, the resulting yield losses are highly dynamic and often difficult to attribute to a specific cause.

A closer look at losses is important for three reasons: (i) small systematic drifts accumulate over years, (ii) the correct attribution of component-driven losses is required, and (iii) device-specific actionable insights are needed to prevent localized overload and premature aging.

Conventional key performance-based monitoring (e.g., performance ratio, PR) is useful for reporting but provides limited causal resolution. Physics-based or empirical models (e.g., single- or two-diode models, module temperature models, see [3] and [4]) help, under controlled assumptions, to adjust estimations but struggle to capture proprietary control software, internal regulation, and the dynamic maximum power point tracking of inverters. Data-driven approaches, including machine learning, have shown potential for performance estimation and fault detection [5]. However, they often fail to capture device-level differences caused by site-specific and operational dependencies. Furthermore, long-term studies of module degradation (%/a) are well documented. Comparable studies on inverter stability are lacking.

The aim of this study was to develop a data-driven approach to systematically identify and quantify yield losses in PV systems. Understanding losses and their underlying mechanisms, whether caused by inverters or the PV generator, is crucial for enhancing system reliability, optimizing performance, and implementing effective maintenance strategies.

To achieve this, the study adopts two complementary perspectives. First, a comprehensive assessment of operational stress factors is conducted, considering thermal loads, inverter clipping, and ventilation effects. This enables a first characterization of how different stress factors and their frequencies affect system components over time.

Second, long-term inverter efficiency (P_{AC}/P_{DC}) trends are analyzed using historical operational data and machine-learning-based modeling. While physics-based models of inverter performance require detailed knowledge of internal system components, inverters are complex multicomponent devices influenced by both internal factors, operational and site-specific conditions. Moreover, inverter behavior is controlled by proprietary software algorithms that are not openly accessible and may introduce additional performance uncertainties or software-related anomalies. Artificial neural networks (ANN) enable a data-driven representation of real-world inverter behavior by capturing performance patterns when trained on data collected shortly after commissioning. This provides a robust method that accounts for site- and device-specific characteristics.

By comparing the expected performance with actual measured system performance, this approach enables a systematic evaluation of efficiency losses and helps identify potential loss patterns over time.

2 MATERIAL AND METHODS

2.1 Data source

This study draws on extensive, multi-year monitoring datasets from a utility-scale PV plant totaling 5.7 MWp. One-minute operational records of inverter performance provide a robust basis for analysis. As an initial step, a rigorous data quality assessment was performed using strict criteria to verify the plausibility, completeness, and internal consistency of the data.

The investigation focuses on nine subsystems, each equipped with a central inverter of the same type rated between 500 and 700 kWp, installed in Germany in a temperate climate, and monitored eleven years (2013–2023). The dataset comprises inverter measurements and status signals, as well as plane-of-array irradiance measured by a pyranometer and ambient temperature, all at one-minute resolution. The system is equipped with crystalline silicon PV modules.

2.2 Inverter efficiency modeling

For modeling inverter efficiency, an artificial neural network was used, trained on preprocessed operational and environmental data. The model was designed to predict the DC current, DC voltage, and DC power (P_{DC}), the AC power (P_{AC}), and inverter efficiency η_{Inv}.

Inverter efficiency was calculated as follows:

$$\eta_{Inv}\ [\%] = \frac{P_{AC}}{P_{DC}}\ 100$$

The training data comprised one year of data collected shortly after plant commissioning and was randomly split into training (70%) and test (30%) subsets to ensure an unbiased evaluation. Model inputs are plane-of-array irradiance, solar position (azimuth, elevation), and ambient temperature.

The ANN architecture used in this study, summarized in Table **I**, builds on prior work from other projects, which is described in detail in publications [6], [7]. Consequently, the following discussion focuses solely on the results of this investigation without detailing the modeling details.

The agreement between the model predictions and the actual measurements is illustrated in Figure 1 for a single inverter for both P_{AC} and η_{Inv}.

Table I: Dataset and parameters used for ANN modeling

Dataset	Hyperparameters
<u>input:</u> irradiance (POA) ambient temperature sun position (azimuth, elevation)	Batch size: 128 Activation function: ReLU Optimizer ADAM
<u>output:</u> DC current DC voltage DC power AC power Inverter efficiency	Loss function: Huber Epochs: 200
time frame: 1 year (1 min interval); 2014	

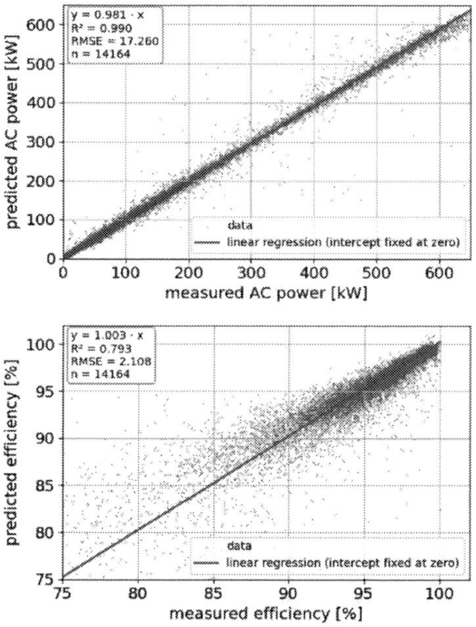

Figure 1: Comparison of measured and predicted values for one inverter. Top: P_{AC}, Bottom: η_{Inv}; Linear regression (red) with fit parameters is added for reference

To assess model quality, we used the Mean Absolute Percentage Error (MAPE), which computes the model error relative to the actual (measured) value (with $|x_{meas}(i)| > 0$ for all i):

$$MAPE\ [\%] = \frac{1}{N}\sum_{i=1}^{N}\left|\frac{x_{meas}(i) - x_{pred}(i)}{x_{meas}(i)}\right|\ 100$$

In this formula, x_{meas} denotes the measured (actual) values, x_{pred} the values predicted by the ANN, and N is the number of observations in the evaluation period. The advantage of MAPE over other error measures is that it evaluates error relative to the actual value. While high values (e.g., in summer) can lead to larger absolute errors, deviations at low values (e.g., in winter) are typically smaller. To enable comparability, the error is expressed relative to the actual value. A lower MAPE indicates higher model accuracy. The MAPE values for the model outputs are shown in Table II.

Table II: MAPE results for training period

	I_{DC}	V_{DC}	P_{DC}	P_{AC}	η_{Inv}
MAPE [%]	7.65	1.14	7.64	9.36	1.21

3 RESULTS

3.1 Operational stress factors

Matrix temperature is defined as the internal temperature of the power stage (power electronics matrix), measured at the heatsink or at the power module baseplate near the IGBT or MOSFET. The Figure 2 and Figure 3 show the Matrix Temperature distribution using kernel density estimation (KDE) for all inverters in two different years, based on 1-minute-resolution monitoring data. Two inverters are highlighted with bold lines (Inv 4 & Inv 7) to emphasize their differences with respect to matrix temperature.

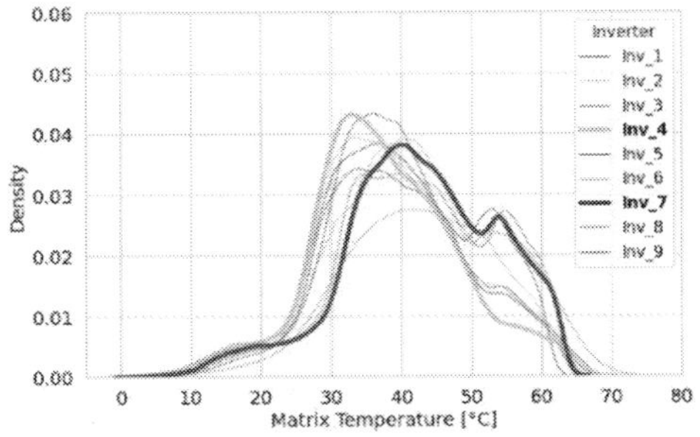

Figure 2: Matrix temperature distribution for year 2013 for all investigated inverters; Inv 4 and Inv 7 in bold for comparison

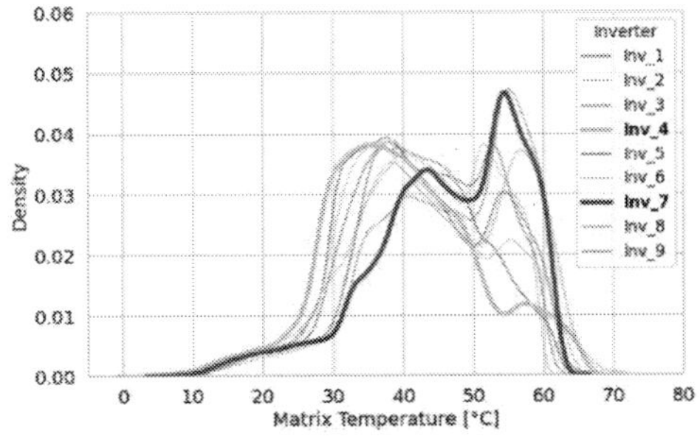

Figure 3: Matrix temperature distribution for year 2022 for all investigated inverters; Inv 4 and Inv 7 in bold for comparison

To further highlight the differences in matrix temperature between the two inverters (Inv 4 and Inv 7), an additional box plot was used, see Figure 4. This figure summarizes the distribution to compare central tendency, spread, and outliers across the inverters and years. Both the interquartile ranges and the medians of the two inverters differ markedly; their medians are at least 5 °C apart, from the very beginning.

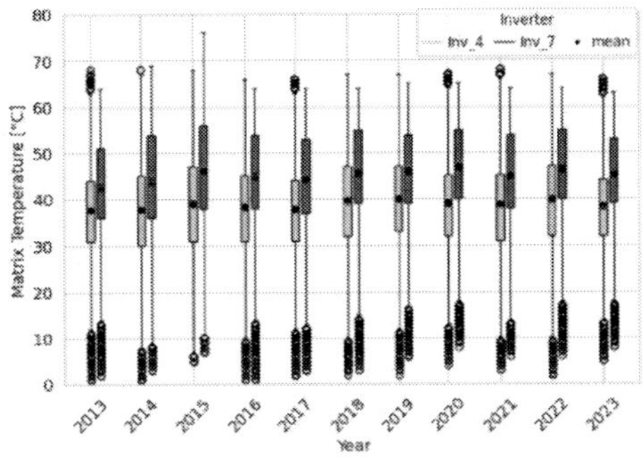

Figure 4: Annual Matrix Temperature for Inv 4 and Inv 7

Clipping in PV systems refers to the limitation of inverter output when the DC power available from the PV array exceeds the inverter's maximum capability. The inverter "clips" the power, producing a flat-topped AC power curve at or near its nameplate rating. The energy not converted is termed clipping loss. In this system, the DC/AC design ratio of all inverters is very moderate, at less than 1.2. Using the inverter status information, instances of clipping can be determined precisely. Figure 5 shows the number of minutes with clipping for each year and inverter. Inv 7 shows the highest number of clipping events.

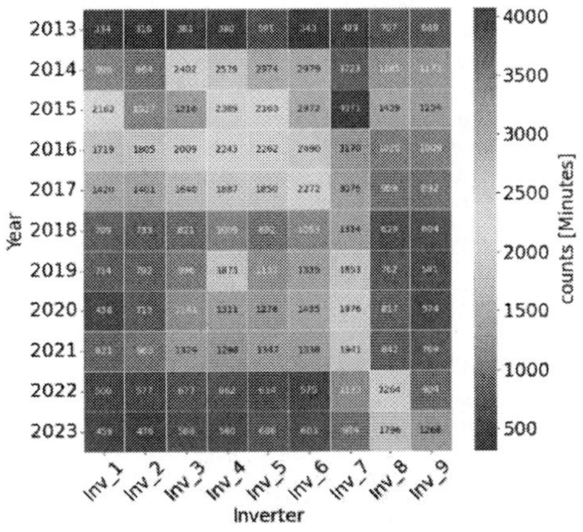

Figure 5: Minutes per year and inverter with clipping

In this context, the question arises whether clipping affects matrix temperature. To investigate this, 1-hours periods starting when clipping begins and ending one hour later were separated from the dataset for all clipping situations that occurred, and the median of the matrix temperature in these periods were calculated. These results are shown in Figure 6 for all inverters and years. Comparing Inv 4 and Inv 7 again, the median matrix temperatures differ by 5–12 °C. The figure illustrates significant differences in individual inverter behavior. While three inverters (Inv 1, Inv 4, and Inv 9) remain relatively cool, the matrix temperature of the most other inverters increases by approx. 10 °C.

10.4229/EUPVSEC2025/4CV.1.52

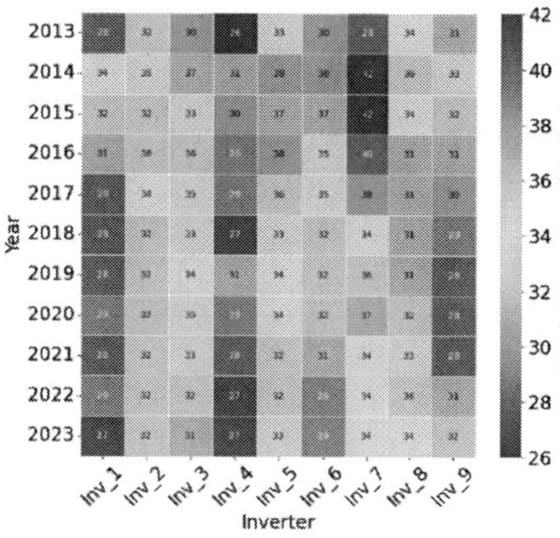

Figure 6: Median matrix temperature in °C during clipping events and one hour after

Another important factor affecting the performance of a PV inverter is ventilation. The fans are controlled by analog thermostats, and the only measured value is matrix temperature. The fans of the different inverters operate differently with respect to temperature thresholds and control cycles. A closer look at the matrix temperature throughout the day shows oscillations caused by ventilation switched on and off. At other times, when the inverter operates within its working range, the fan runs continuously, producing a smoother curve. This behavior is illustrated in Figure 7, for example, where the same devices (Inv 4 and Inv 7) are compared for a single day. The matrix temperature profiles are highly variable. In particular, the difference in cooling intensity is striking: while inverter 4 shows fewer but larger cooling ramps, inverter 7 exhibits many smaller and shorter cooling phases. These significant differences in high-frequency behavior will be examined further.

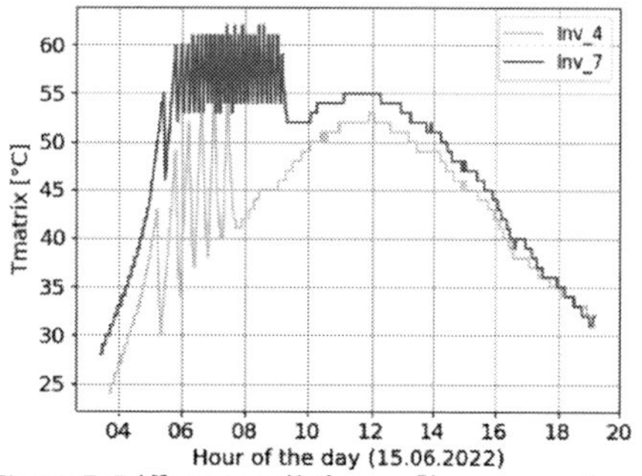

Figure 7: Different ventilation profiles, expressed as matrix temperature, for Inv 4 and Inv 7

To describe a possible decrease in ventilation intensity in high-frequency ranges, the local extreme points were determined. Subsequently, the difference between corresponding local minima and local maxima was calculated as Δ for each cooling process, removed by changes smaller 2 °C. The resulting frequency densities are shown in Figure 8 for five different years.

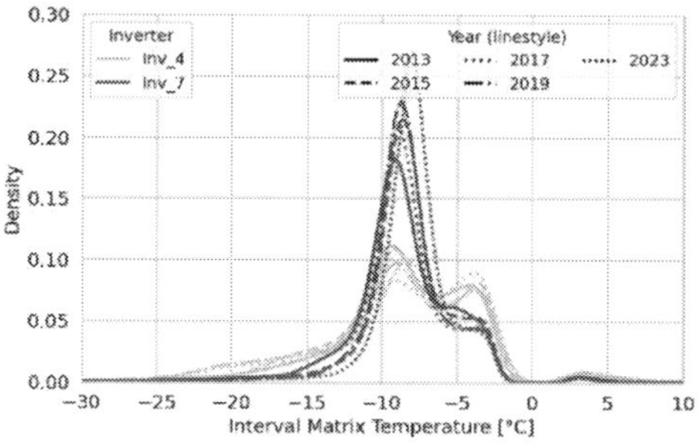

Figure 8: Difference of cooling impact Δ on matrix temperature for Inv 4 and Inv 7

It is apparent that cooling processes change slightly year to year. For example, the density curve for Inv 7 shifts to the right, indicating a change from higher to smaller absolute Δ temperatures (2013 to 2023).

3.2 Measured and predicted inverter efficiency

The measured–predicted comparison contrasts modeled and measured inverter efficiencies. The goal is to identify systematic deviations and possible causes.

Inverter efficiency is shown as a function of the inverter output power P_{AC} in Figure 9. Efficiency increases with increasing load. Inverters are optimized for specific load and voltage ranges in which they achieve their highest efficiency. At lower loads, they often operate outside their optimal range, so losses (e.g., switching and conversion losses, self-consumption by control electronics and cooling, and standby losses) carry greater weight in relative terms

This characteristic inverter efficiency curve is obtained by computing, over a given period, the median of efficiency values within separate power bins of several kilowatts each. The bin width depends on the inverter capacity; in this case, 10 kW (1.5% of rated capacity).

The curves shown in Figure 9 (measured and predicted) are based on an ANN model trained on inverter data shortly after commissioning and show close agreement. Figure 10 shows again the inverter efficiency as a function of the inverter's output power P_{AC} for the measured and predicted values but for 2023. Comparing efficiencies over the years of operation (2014 vs. 2023), increasing differences are evident. In the 40–50 kW range, efficiency differs by about 1.7 percentage points. Considering the model's accuracy in determining efficiency, a MAPE of 1.2% for the modeling year, this deviation exceeds the model error and should be regarded as relevant.

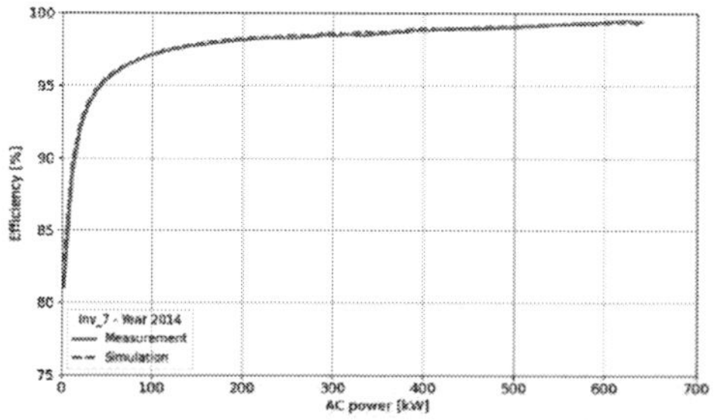

Figure 9: Inverter efficiency between measured (solid) and predicted (dashed) values for Inv 7, 2014

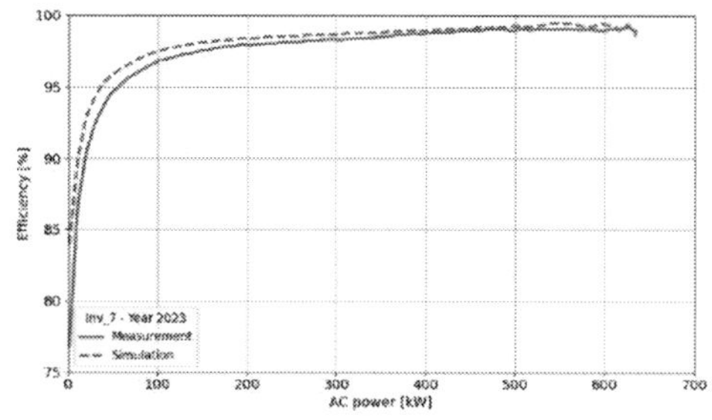

Figure 10: Inverter efficiency between measured (solid) and predicted (dashed) values for Inv 7, 2023

For comparison with Inv 7, Inv 4's efficiencies as a function of P_{AC} for 2014 (see Figure 11) and 2023 (see Figure 12) are also shown, respectively. In 2014 (the modeling year), measured and modeled efficiencies align almost perfectly, as they do for Inv 7. For 2023, Inv 4 shows smaller deviations than Inv 7; in the 40–50 kW range, the deviation is 0.8 percentage points.

In a previous publication [8], we examined in more detail whether the PV generator degraded in terms of its voltage level, which could have affected inverter operating by shifting it into less efficient regions. However, this was ruled out: the DC-side voltage level remained very stable over the period considered. We therefore conclude that a genuine change has occurred at the inverter level.

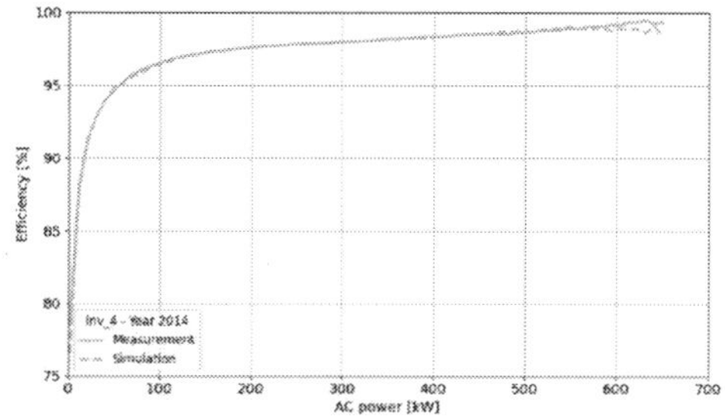

Figure 11: Comparison of inverter efficiency between measured (solid) and predicted (dashed) values, for Inv 4, 2014

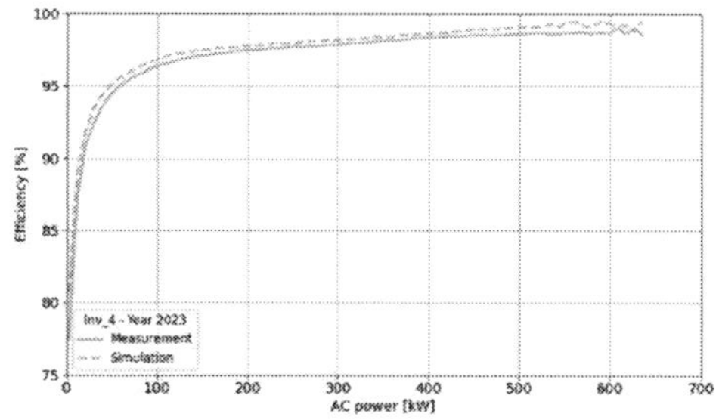

Figure 12: Comparison of inverter efficiency between measured (solid) and predicted (dashed) values, for Inv 4, 2023

4 DISCUSSION

The analysis reveal pronounced thermal heterogeneity (see Figure 2 & Figure 3). Despite being nominally identical and operating within the same plant, inverters exhibit markedly different matrix temperature distributions, with mean offset of up to 4 °C. These persistent differences translate into non-uniform thermal stress and aging, underscoring the need for device-level diagnostics rather than plant-level averages.

A second key observation is ventilation drift (see Figure 8). Cooling profiles vary significantly across devices, and the intensity of cooling ramps changes over time, indicating that fan behavior and thermal management changes gradually with age. This effect contributes to additional stress and explains part of the heterogeneity in temperature behavior.

Device-level stress also varies widely in frequency and intensity within the same plant. Factors such as clipping, shutdowns, and partial-load operation create distinct stress signatures, which can only be captured by constructing individual load and stress profiles for each inverter.

Over the long term, a systematic efficiency decline is evident. Across 11 years, efficiency decreased by approximately 1.7 percentage points (~0.2 %pt./a), with the strongest deviation occurring under partial-load conditions (around 10% P_{AC}, see Figure 10). This highlights the importance of monitoring low-P_{AC} regions, which are particularly sensitive to efficiency drift and often overlooked in conventional performance metrics. It is assumed that inverters are optimized for high power ranges in order to minimize conversion losses at high power levels. Small power ranges, as discussed, which are primarily used in the morning and evening hours, may be more susceptible to thermal loads.

Finally, these findings depend strongly on data quality. High-resolution monitoring data must be accompanied by rigorous plausibility checks, validation of sensor accuracy, and awareness of the inverter's operational state. Without such preprocessing, results risk being biased or misinterpreted.

5 CONCLUSION

The present study provides key insights into analyzing inverter efficiency losses in PV systems. By applying artificial neural networks (ANN), complex nonlinear relationships between operating parameters and environmental conditions were modeled with high precision. This enabled the identification and quantification of systematic efficiency losses that are highly relevant to PV plant operators.

The model accuracy depends strongly on the quality, completeness, and plausibility of operational data; faulty or incomplete data can impede the detection of efficiency losses. In this study, the trained ANN models achieved high predictive accuracy, with a mean absolute percentage error (MAPE) of 1.2% for inverter efficiency. This level of accuracy allows even small deviations between measured and modeled reference values to be detected reliably.

10.4229/EUPVSEC2025/4CV.1.52

Over time, we observed a systematic decrease in inverter efficiency of about 1.7 percentage points over ten years for a representative inverter, indicating long-term degradation mechanisms that are insufficiently monitored in current practice. In addition, a comprehensive assessment of operational stress factors, including clipping and ventilation, revealed their strong influence on inverter matrix temperature. There is pronounced thermal heterogeneity across apparently identical inverter, with temperature distributions differing by several degrees. These differences result in non-uniform thermal stress, accelerated aging, and diverging ventilation behaviors, with some inverters requiring progressively more cooling effort. Stress exposure also varies widely in frequency and intensity within the same plant, underscoring the need for device-specific stress and load profiles rather than plant-level averages.

These insights offer a valuable foundation for optimizing operation and maintenance strategies. Based on the identified efficiency losses and stress patterns, operators can implement targeted measures to extend inverter lifetimes, reduce unplanned downtime, and enhance overall PV system performance, by reducing or mitigating detected stresses and their potential causes. Early detection of deviations enables proactive responses and risk-based maintenance planning, ultimately supporting higher system reliability, improving profitability, and more accurate lifetime forecasting.

6 ACKNOWLEDGEMENT

Research was partially funded by the German Federal Bank Investitionsbank Sachsen-Anhalt, the German Federal State Saxony-Anhalt and the European Regional Development Fund (EFRE) in the project "KliMaTE" (ref.: 8377/1758) and „3D-Prove" (ref.: I 193) as well as by project "robStROM" (ref.: 03EE1163B) by the Federal Ministry for Economic Affairs and Climate Action in Germany.

7 REFERENCES

[1] S. Malik, D. Daßler, D. Patel, C. Klute, R. Klengel, A. Dietrich, K. Kaufmann, C. Hennig, D. Wehnert, M. Ebert. Analysis of Fault Detection and Defect Categorization in Photovoltaic Inverters for Enhanced Reliability and Efficiency in Large-Scale Solar Energy Systems. EPJ Photovoltaics 16, 25 (2025). Accepted 27.03.2025. Published 27.05.2025. DOI: https://doi.org/10.1051/epjpv/2025011

[2] S. Malik, D. Daßler, D. Patel, R. Klengel, C. Klute, M. Ebert. robStROM: Zuverlässiger Betrieb von PV-Wechselrichtern. PV Days – PV-Systeme: Optimierte Betriebsführung und Risikobewertung. 28. November 2024. Halle

[3] Gupta, P., & Singh, R. (2021). PV power forecasting based on data-driven models: a review. International, Journal of Sustainable Engineering, 14(6), 1733–1755. DOI: https://doi.org/10.1080/19397038.2021.1986590

[4] Martin János Mayer, Gyula Gróf. Extensive comparison of physical models for photovoltaic power forecasting. Applied Energy. Volume 283. 2021. DOI: https://doi.org/10.1016/j.apenergy.2020.116239.

[5] IEA-PVPS. Task 13 Report "The Use of Advanced Algorithms in PV Failure Monitoring". Report T13-19:2021. 2021. ISBN 978-3-907281-07-9

[6] D. Daßler, S. Malik, R. Gottschalg, M. Ebert. Effect of Availability and Quality of Data on the Detection of Defects Utilizing Artificial Neural Networks in PV System's Monitoring Data. 8th World Conference on Photovoltaic Energy Conversion. Milan. September 2022. DOI: https://10.4229/WCPEC-82022-4DO.1.5.

[7] D. Daßler, S.B. Kuppanna, S. Malik, R. Schmidt, M. Ebert. Training and Evaluation for Yield-Driven Detection of Losses in PV Systems Utilizing Artificial Neural Networks. IEEE 47th Photovoltaic Specialists Conference (PVSC). Virtual. 2020. DOI: https://10.1109/PVSC45281.2020.9300490

[8] D. Daßler, S. Malik, D. Patel, A. Dietrich, J. Spihola, K. Kaufmann, C. Hennig, R. Klengel, C. Klute, M. Ebert. Analyse der Effizienzverluste von Wechselrichtern in PV-Portfolios durch Auswertung von Betriebsdaten. 40. PV-Symposium. 2025.

42nd European Photovoltaic Solar Energy Conference and Exhibition

This presentation was selected by the Sc. Committee of the EU PVSEC 2025 for submission of a full paper to one of the EU PVSEC's collaborating peer-reviewed journals.

ENHANCING AUTONOMOUS AERIAL MONITORING OF LARGE-SCALE PHOTOVOLTAIC PLANTS USING A DEEP REINFORCEMENT LEARNING APPROACH FOR MULTI-AERIAL ROBOT SYSTEMS

A. Aghamohammadi [1], S.M. Esmaeilifar [1], M. Kolahi [2], A. Moradi Sizkouhi [3], and M. Aghaei[4,5*]

[1] Department of Aerospace Engineering, Amirkabir University of Technology, Tehran 15119-43943, Iran
[2] Department of Mechanical Engineering, Faculty of Engineering, University of Isfahan, 81746-73441, Isfahan, Iran
[3]Department of Electrical and Computer Engineering, Concordia University, Montreal, QC H3G 1M8, Canada
[4]Department of Ocean Operations and Civil Engineering, Norwegian University of Science and Technology (NTNU), 6009 Ålesund, Norway
[5]Department of Sustainable Systems Engineering (INATECH), University of Freiburg, 79110 Freiburg, Germany

*mohammadreza.aghaei@ntnu.no

ABSTRACT: Efficient inspection of large-scale photovoltaic (PV) power plants can be achieved using a multi-aerial robot system powered by Deep Reinforcement Learning (DRL). This study introduces an innovative algorithm for online coverage path planning to optimize the efficiency, scalability, and adaptability of multi-aerial robot systems. By dynamically adapting to real-time environmental changes, the algorithm ensures comprehensive inspection coverage while reducing computational overhead. Simulations conducted in both grid-based and realistic environments demonstrate the algorithm's robustness and its potential to revolutionize inspection tasks in dynamic and complex scenarios.

Keywords: Photovoltaic (PV) plants; Autonomous aerial monitoring (AAM), Artificial intelligence (AI), Deep Reinforcement Learning (DRL), Dueling Deep Q-network

1. INTRODUCTION

Large-scale photovoltaic (PV) power plants are anticipated to be a dominant renewable energy source by mid-century, playing a significant role in meeting the world's electricity needs. Ensuring their efficiency and reliability requires advanced monitoring strategies that can detect defects early, optimize energy yield, and reduce operational costs [1]. Aerial robots have emerged as an effective means of conducting inspections more quickly, accurately, and cost-effectively than conventional methods, significantly lowering monitoring expenses and labor requirements [2, 3]. This study presents a deep reinforcement learning (DRL)-based multi-aerial robot inspection framework that enables real-time coverage path planning, dynamic coordination, and collision avoidance for large-scale PV installations. The approach leverages Dueling Double Deep Q-Network (D3QN) architecture enhanced with Prioritized Experience Replay (PER), NoisyNets, and n-step returns, providing robust decision-making capabilities under high variability in environmental and operational conditions.

A Voronoi relaxation-based method is introduced to ensure balanced sub-area allocation, distributing inspection workloads evenly among multiple drones regardless of the solar field's irregular geometry. To maintain safe operation during multi-robot missions, a physics-based repulsive-force model dynamically adjusts flight paths to prevent collisions.

The system's RoboNN architecture integrates convolutional layers with batch normalization and fully connected layers, enabling stable and efficient learning while handling both abstract spatial representations and photorealistic visual inputs.

The framework supports online path planning, allowing aerial robots to adapt in real time to environmental changes such as variable lighting, wind effects, and unexpected obstacles. Furthermore, the scalable coordination mechanism allows efficient deployment of any number of drones to cover vast and irregularly shaped PV arrays without sacrificing inspection completeness or efficiency.

The proposed system is evaluated in both a simplified grid-world environment for algorithmic validation and a high-fidelity PV inspection simulation built on "Digital-PV" [4-7], modeling realistic aerodynamics, environmental disturbances, and camera-based defect detection scenarios. Experimental results demonstrate high coverage efficiency, low inspection redundancy, and real-time adaptability to dynamic conditions, verifying the system's suitability for operational deployment.

By integrating advanced DRL-based decision-making with scalable multi-robot coordination and intelligent collision avoidance, this study contributes to a flexible and high-performance solution that has the potential to reduce inspection time, lower operational costs, and ensure sustained energy yield reliability in the next generation of large-scale PV power plants.

2. SCIENTIFIC INNOVATION AND RELEVANCE

This study presents several innovations that address key challenges in multi-aerial robot systems:

- Dynamic Adaptability: Unlike conventional pre-planned paths, the proposed algorithm enables robots to adapt dynamically to environmental changes, such as obstacles or new area boundaries.
- Generalization: The algorithm generalizes to diverse environmental shapes and conditions, ensuring its applicability to a wide range of real-world scenarios.

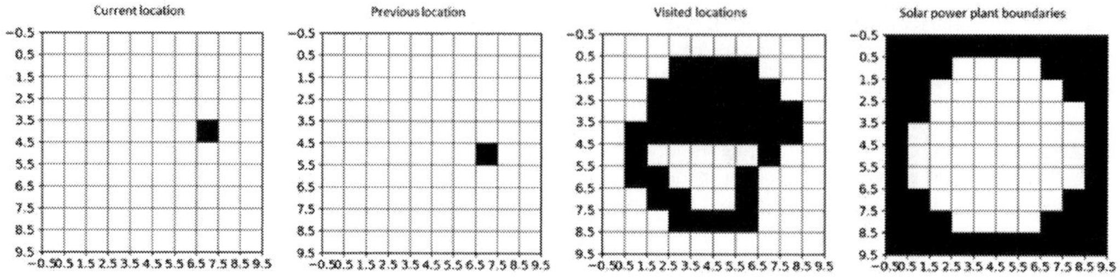

Figure 1 Space state description

- Collision Avoidance Mechanism: The repulsive force model integrates seamlessly into the system, ensuring safe and conflict-free navigation in multi-agent systems.
- Neural Network Advancements: The RoboNN architecture incorporates advanced DRL techniques, such as Dueling DQN and Prioritized Experience Replay, for better policy learning and decision-making efficiency.

The relevance of this work lies in its potential to improve the inspection of large-scale photovoltaic plants, reducing time, costs, and risks associated with manual methods. Its scalability and adaptability make it suitable for a variety of industrial applications.

3. DEEP REINFORCEMENT LEARNING

In the proposed framework, the environment is represented as a matrix that encodes four key elements: the distinction between visited and unvisited cells, the current and previous aerial robot position, and the location of obstacles as shown in Fig. 1. This spatial encoding ensures that the learning agent perceives both its operational context and the progress of its coverage task. The aerial robot operates within a discrete action space consisting of five possible maneuvers: moving forward, moving backward, rotating left, rotating right, or remaining stationary. The learning process is guided by a carefully designed reward function that combines positive incentives with penalties to encourage efficient and safe navigation. The aerial robot receives a positive reward when it successfully explores new cells and an additional terminal bonus when full coverage is achieved. Conversely, redundant revisits to already explored regions, unnecessary or excessive turning maneuvers, and collisions or near-miss events incur penalties, discouraging inefficient or unsafe behavior.

To approximate the optimal policy, a dueling deep Q-network (DQN) architecture is employed. The state matrix is processed by a convolutional neural network composed of four successive 3×3 convolutional layers, each followed by batch normalization to stabilize training. The resulting feature maps are flattened and concatenated with auxiliary information, forming a comprehensive feature vector. This vector is then split into two parallel streams: the value stream, which estimates the overall quality of a state, and the advantage stream, which evaluates the relative benefit of each action. Their outputs are recombined to produce the final Q-values, enabling more robust learning and faster convergence compared to traditional DQN formulations.

4. COORDINATION AND COLLISION AVOIDANCE

To ensure efficient multi-aerial robot operations, the environment is first partitioned into sub-areas using Voronoi diagrams constructed from the initial deployment positions of the agents. This geometric approach guarantees non-overlapping regions of responsibility while minimizing redundant coverage. Since differences in flight capacity may lead to workload imbalances, an iterative boundary relaxation procedure is applied to adjust dthe partitions dynamically. Through this process, the workload is redistributed according to the endurance and capabilities of each aerial robot, improving overall mission efficiency.

Collision avoidance is addressed through a decentralized strategy that combines local sensing and control. Each aerial robot continuously monitors the presence of neighboring agents within a predefined communication radius. When potential conflicts are detected, a smooth repulsive force function is applied to generate corrective avoidance maneuvers, thereby preventing abrupt or unstable deviations. This repulsive mechanism is integrated with a PID-based trajectory controller, which maintains adherence to the planned coverage path while ensuring safe separation between agents. The result is a coordinated system in which aerial robots achieve complete area coverage collaboratively while dynamically avoiding collisions.

5. SIMULATION AND EVALUATION

The proposed framework was first validated in a grid-world environment consisting of randomly generated 16×16 cell boundaries. Through training, the policy achieved a mean coverage rate of 99.6% with less than 9% redundancy, demonstrating both efficiency and completeness of area exploration. The learning process exhibited stable convergence, as reflected by a steadily decreasing loss curve over successive training episodes.

To further evaluate the system under realistic operating conditions, high-fidelity simulations were conducted using the "Digital-PV" environment. This platform accurately models environmental dynamics such as wind, gravity, and heterogeneous terrain, providing a physically grounded testbed for aerial robot coordination. Within this setting, the deep reinforcement learning policy was able to sustain real-time decision-making with an average action latency below 100 ms, ensuring responsiveness during flight. Across multiple cooperative aerial robot trials, the system consistently maintained safe separation, and no collision events were observed, confirming the robustness of the proposed coordination and collision avoidance strategies.

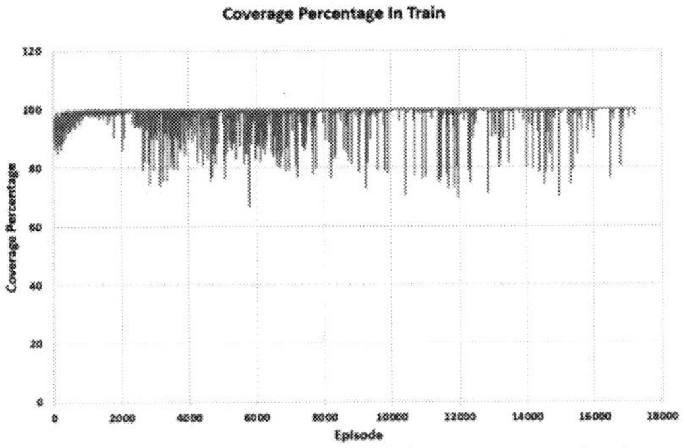

Figure 3: Coverage percentage of the agent over episodes.

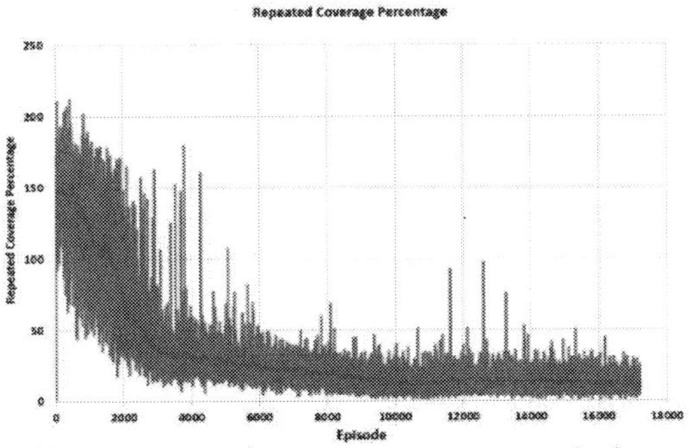

Figure 4: Repeated coverage percentage over episodes.

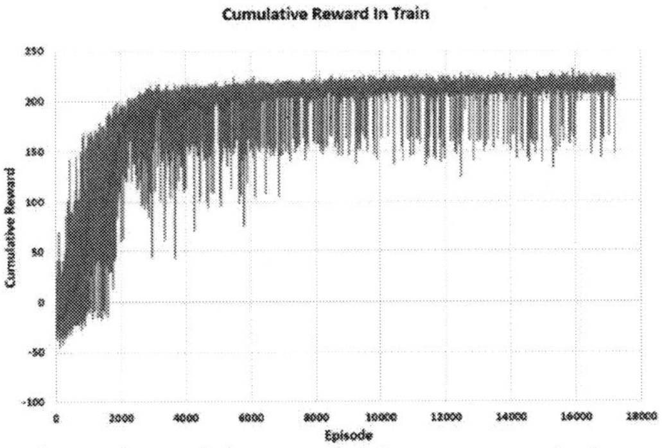

Figure 5: cumulative reward of the agent over episodes.

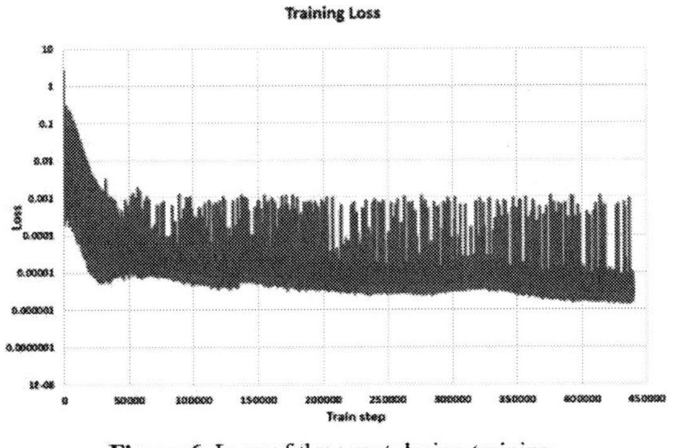

Figure 6: Loss of the agent during training.

6. RESULTS

The evaluation of the DRL-based coverage path planning algorithm was conducted through simulations in both grid-based and realistic environments, with the following key findings:

- Coverage Efficiency: The agent achieved a coverage rate of approximately 99.6% across randomly generated environments as shown in Fig. 2, showcasing its ability to handle diverse boundary shapes effectively.
- Repeated Coverage: The percentage of repeated coverage was minimized to 8.6%, demonstrating efficient navigation with minimal redundancy the results are shown in Fig. 3.

Figure 2: Simulated PV power plant in Digital-PV platform demonstrating algorithm adaptability in 3D environments.

- Total Reward: The cumulative rewards per episode stabilized, indicating the convergence of the agent's policy and consistent performance in achieving coverage objectives as shown in Fig. 4.
- Loss Reduction: Training loss decreased significantly over episodes, reflecting effective learning and optimization of the agent's policy (see Fig. 5).
- Realistic Simulation Performance: Integration with the Digital-PV platform revealed the algorithm's applicability to real-world scenarios, where it successfully adapted to 3D environmental constraints, such as wind and varied terrain, the simulation environment is shown in Fig. 6.

7. CONCLUSIONS

The proposed DRL-based approach demonstrates the following contribution:

1. Robustness in handling irregular area shapes and dynamic conditions.
2. Scalability, enabling coordination of multiple robots to efficiently cover large areas.
3. Safe operation through its integrated collision avoidance mechanism, ensuring conflict-free navigation.
4. Advanced learning efficiency via the RoboNN architecture, which provides stable and adaptable decision-making capabilities.

10.4229/EUPVSEC2025/4CV.1.54

These results highlight the potential of DRL to revolutionize inspection processes in PV power plants and other industrial settings. Future work will explore multi-modal sensing, environmental condition adaptations, and broader applications for autonomous inspection systems.

8. REFERENCES

1. M. Aghaei et al., "Autonomous Intelligent Monitoring of Photovoltaic Systems: An In-depth Multidisciplinary Review," Progress in Photovoltaics: Research and Applications, 2024.
2. P. Nooralishahi et al., "Drone-based non-destructive inspection of industrial sites: A review and case studies," Drones, vol. 5, no. 4, p. 106, 2021.
3. A. Moradi Sizkouhi, M. Aghaei, and S. M. Esmailifar, "A deep convolutional encoder-decoder architecture for autonomous fault detection of PV plants using multi-copters," Solar Energy, vol. 223, pp. 217–228, 2021.
4. M. Kolahi, S. M. Esmailifar, A. M. M. Sizkouhi, and M. Aghaei, "Digital PV: A digital twin-based platform for autonomous aerial monitoring of large-scale photovoltaic power plants," Energy Conversion and Management, vol. 321, p. 118963, 2024.
5. Sizkouhi, A.M.M., et al. Autonomous Path Planning by Unmanned Aerial Vehicle (UAV) for Precise Monitoring of Large-Scale PV plants. in 2019 IEEE 46th Photovoltaic Specialists Conference (PVSC). 2019.
6. Moradi Sizkouhi, A.M., et al., RoboPV: An integrated software package for autonomous aerial monitoring of large scale PV plants. Energy Conversion and Management, 2022. 254: p. 115217.
7. Sizkouhi, A.M.M., et al., Automatic Boundary Extraction of Large-Scale Photovoltaic Plants Using a Fully Convolutional Network on Aerial Imagery. IEEE Journal of Photovoltaics, 2020. 10(4): p. 1061-1067.

Preprocessing I-V curve data for enhanced CNN-based fault diagnosis in Photovoltaic strings

*Woo Gyun Shin[1], Young Chul JU[1], Hye Mi HWANG[1], Jin-Seok Lee[1], **Suk Whan Ko[1]

Korea Institute of Energy Research, Korea

presenting author (swghero@kier.re.kr)

Abstract

To respond to climate change and carbon neutrality, each country is actively investing in renewable energy sources. Among them, photovoltaic (PV) is a technology that converts light energy into electricity using solar cells, and is the fastest and most widely used. As of 2024, the cumulative PV installation worldwide is about 2TW, and it is expected to continue increasing. As PV installations increase, the PV plant maintenance and operation (O&M) market is also increasing. The solar O&M market size in 2024 is estimated to be approximately between $3.2 billion and $3.5 billion. PV O&M activity refers to a series of processes that ensure the stability of energy production goals of PV systems from efficient operation during their lifespan. Traditional PV O&M activities were PV module cleaning, vegetation management, and simple electrical inspection of PV modules and inverters. Such O&M activities make it difficult to diagnose power generation performance deterioration and failure. Recently, PV O&M companies and researchers are adopting digital technology in terms of asset management.

In this study, we propose a preprocessing method based on an I–V curve simulation model to improve the performance of convolutional neural network (CNN) trained with I–V curve data. The simulation is conducted using a single-diode model, which incorporates the number of series-connected modules within a PV string. By utilizing the irradiance and module temperature measured at the time of data acquisition, the model generates a simulated I–V curve representing the expected behavior of the PV string. The measured I–V curve is then preprocessed in two steps using the simulated curve, effectively minimizing discrepancies arising from variations in PV string capacity and measurement conditions. Comparative analysis shows that while the CNN trained on unprocessed I–V curve data tended to misclassify fault types, the model trained on preprocessed data accurately identified the actual faults, thereby demonstrating enhanced diagnostic accuracy.

Background

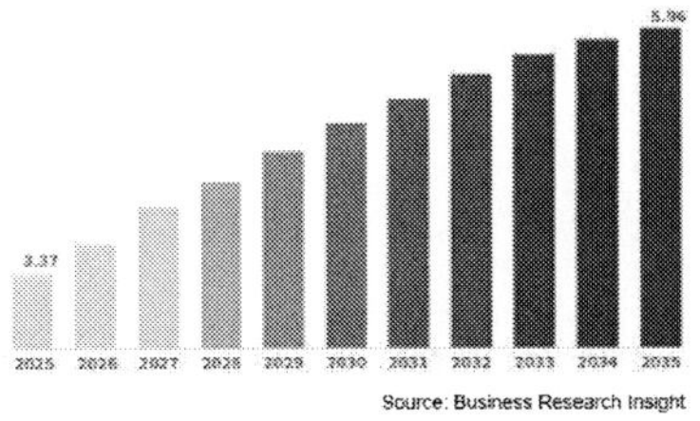

Increase in PV O&M Market

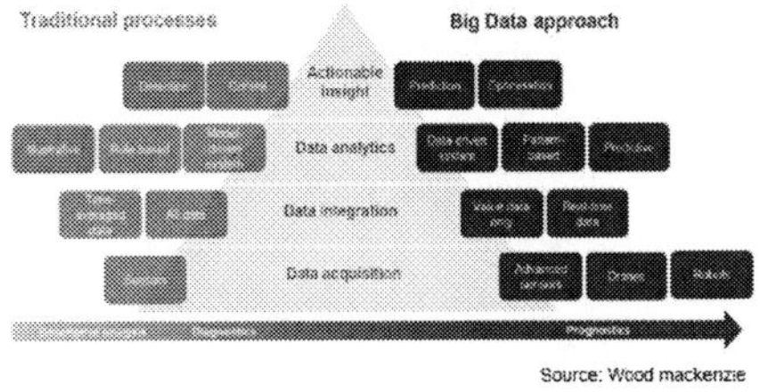

Evolution of PV O&M Technology: Past and Present

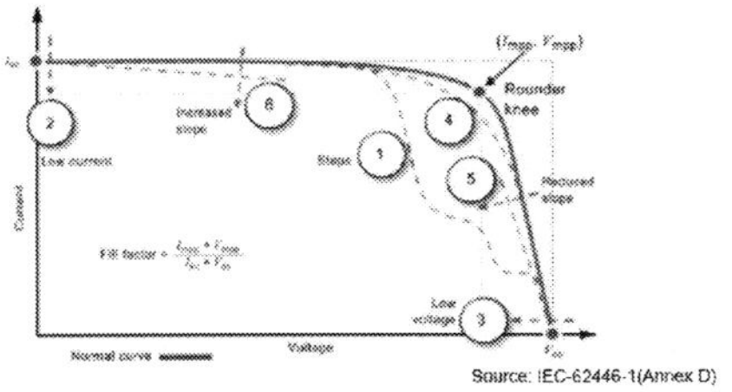

Electrical parameters derived from the I-V curve

Experiment and Result

◆ Necessity of Preprocessing I-V Curve Data for AI Training

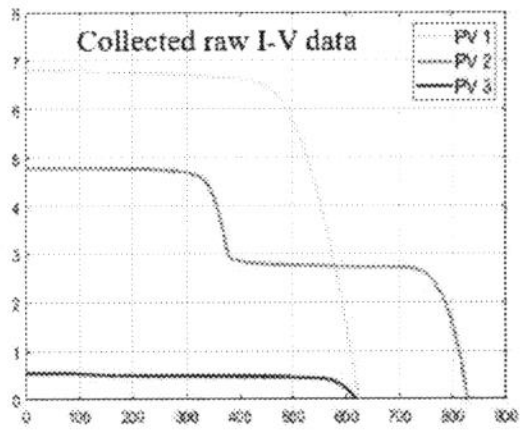

1. The rated capacity of PV strings differs among power plants due to variations in PV module types.
2. The I-V curves measured in the field do not correspond to those under Standard Test Conditions (STC).
3. It is not feasible to collect I-V curves under identical fault states, rated capacities, irradiance, and module temperature conditions.

Therefore, preprocessing is indispensable for fault diagnosis of I-V curves using artificial intelligence models.

◆ I-V Curve Data Before and After preprocessing

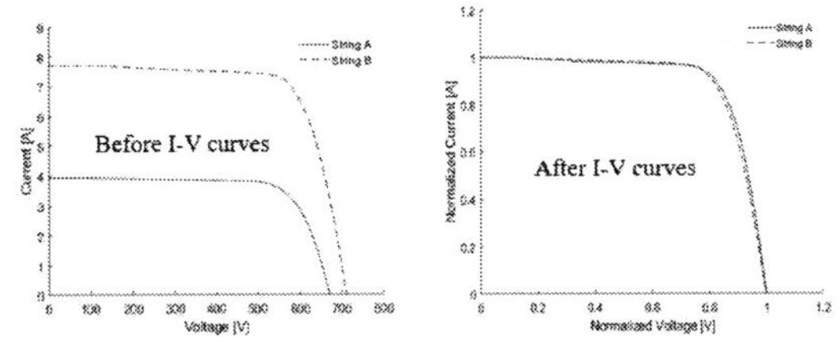

◆ Impact of Data Preprocessing on AI Model Training and Validation Results

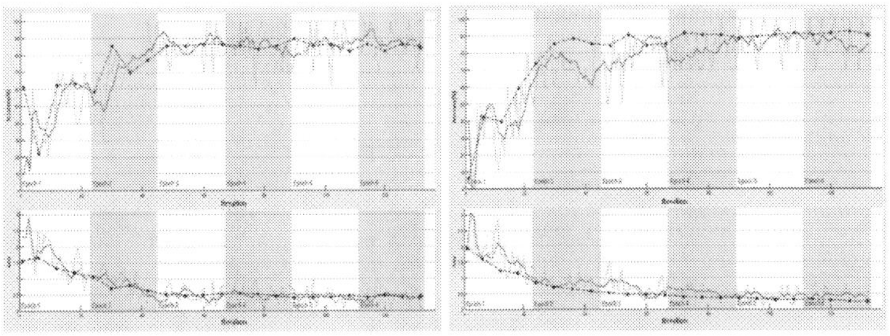

Training and Validation Results of I-V Curve Data (Left: Before Preprocessing, Right: After Preprocessing)

- The preprocessing of I-V curves consists of two steps. First, the I-V curve is normalized to the 0–1 range using the rated open-circuit voltage and short-circuit current of the PV string. Second, the measured I-V curve is adjusted based on the simulated I-V curve, which represents the normal condition under the given irradiance and temperature. This allows comparison of I-V curves under equivalent conditions despite differences in string capacity and measurement environment.
- The impact of data preprocessing on the accuracy of a CNN model was compared. The CNN model used for training was GoogLeNet, and transfer learning was performed with both preprocessed and non-preprocessed data. As shown in the figure above, the left side presents the training and validation results of GoogLeNet using non-preprocessed data, while the right side shows the results with preprocessed data. The validation accuracy of the model trained with non-preprocessed data was 84.38%, whereas that of the model trained with preprocessed data reached 90.63%. Thus, data preprocessing improved the accuracy by more than 6%.

Conclusion

- As the PV O&M market expands, new O&M technologies that combine data and artificial intelligence are being developed instead of traditional approaches.
- Among the various data collected from PV power plants, I-V curve data not only reflects the electrical performance of PV systems but also enables fault identification based on curve patterns.
- However, it is practically very difficult to collect faulty I-V curves while considering the rated capacity of PV strings and the environmental conditions at the time of measurement.
- In this study, a two-step preprocessing method was applied to measured I-V curves to minimize differences in rated capacity and environmental conditions of PV strings.
- It was verified that training with preprocessed data improved the accuracy of the CNN model by 6% compared with training on non-preprocessed data.
- Additionally, we plan to collect more data and train on a wider range of faulty I-V curve datasets to further validate our proposed approach.

This work was conducted under the framework of the research and development program of the Korea Institute of Energy Research(Project No: C5-2427).

SOLAR-ASP TOOL FOR EARLY FAULT DETECTION AND REMOTE DIAGNOSIS IN PHOTOVOLTAIC GENERATORS

Sandra Riaño[a] (sandra.riano@tecnalia.com), Ricardo Alonso[a], Jose Domingo Santos[a], Miguel Esteras[a], Ainhoa Pereda[a], Antonio Salvador[b], Jose Antonio Osuna[b], Javier Del Ser[c]

[a]TECNALIA, Basque Research & Technology Alliance (BRTA), 48160 Derio, Spain
[b] MAGTEL, P.E. Las Quemadas, Gabriel Ramos Bejarano, N.114, 14014 Córdoba
[c] University of the Basque Country (UPV/EHU), 48940 Leioa, Spain

ABSTRACT: This work presents results of SOLAR-ASP, a novel early Fault Detection ad Diagnosis (FDD) tool developed by TECNALIA and validated on a MAGTEL-operated photovoltaic (PV) plant. It combines data-driven analysis from SCADA measurements with domain-specific physical knowledge to assess PV asset health. This hybrid approach reduces reliance on labelled historical datasets (a common limitation observed in purely data-centric methods) while maintaining interpretability for PV experts. Field trials at a MAGTEL plant demonstrated its ability to estimate main characterization parameters, called Array State Parameters (ASPs), such as Maximum Power Point (MPP) current and voltage normalized to Standard Test Conditions (STC). SOLAR-ASP shows comparable performance to I-V curve measurements in the field, with errors lower than 3%. while enabling the earlier identification of performance degradation. This detection capability can inform proactive maintenance scheduling strategies, allowing for the reduction of in-field inspection campaigns and unnecessary preventative maintenance. This directly lowers OPEX costs while increasing performance by addressing issues before they increase.
Keywords: Photovoltaics, Operation and Maintenance, Hybrid Models, LCOE Reduction, Anomaly Detection

1 INTRODUCTION

The exponential rise of PV capacity installed in principal markets has recently surpassed the 2.2 TW threshold [1], while the Levelized Cost Of Energy (LCOE) of Solar PV utilities is kept on a sustained declining trend [2]. However, this rapid expansion has introduced significant operational challenges, particularly in the management of increasingly large and geographically dispersed PV systems. Modern solar farms now require monitoring vast component networks, while operators must adapt to the rapid deployment of evolving technologies in cells, modules, and system architectures [3]. These factors underscore the critical need for new approaches to support operational and maintenance (O&M) strategies, which represent 10–20% of the LCOE [7].

Traditional O&M practices used for this purpose, such as periodic I-V curve measurements, face limitations in scalability and cost-efficiency [5]. Alternatives like thermography delivered by drones or electroluminescence offer detailed diagnostics, but their high costs restrict their use to sporadic interventions [6]. This gap highlights the demand for real-time, automated monitoring solutions capable of detecting early degradations and faults.

In this regard, recent industry trends emphasize the growing adoption of Artificial Intelligence (AI) and Machine Learning (ML) to enable Condition-Based Maintenance (CBM) in PV systems [7]. By leveraging the Supervisory Control and Data Acquisition (SCADA) data and data-based models, AI-driven platforms can autonomously generate maintenance workflows, optimize resource allocation, and reduce reliance on reactive interventions [8]. Dynamic risk assessment frameworks further enhance this approach by combining historical failure data with real-time degradation indicators to prioritize critical assets [9]. Despite these advancements, the practical implementation of AI/ML tools in PV O&M is still emerging, with few operators achieving full integration of automated fault detection systems relying on this technology.

As the PV sector moves toward a 9% annual growth rate over the next three decades [10], the development of cost-effective, AI-powered CBM solutions will be decisive in O&M economic and technical sustainability. This paper aligns with this statement by presenting a hybrid framework for early fault detection and predictive maintenance. By integrating domain-specific physical models with data-driven machine learning, this hybrid framework enhances both accuracy and interpretability, ensuring that expert knowledge directly informs the patterns extracted from operational data. Our methodology leverages SCADA data and ML algorithms to bridge the gap between theoretical advancements and real-world implementation in large-scale PV systems.

The detection performance of SOLAR-ASP is validated over real-world data towards answering with empirical evidence 3 Research Questions (RQs):

- *RQ1: Can the MPP voltage (Vmp) and current (Imp) of PV arrays be accurately estimated using exclusively SCADA data?*
- *RQ2: What are the minimum data volume needed to achieve accurate and statistically stable estimates of Vmp and Imp?*
- *RQ3: Do the estimated Vmp and Imp values exhibit sufficient stability and low statistical dispersion to be comparable with the temperature-corrected Performance Ratio (PR)?*

The rest of the manuscript is organized as follows: Section 2 describes the diagnosis. The experimental setup is detailed in Section 3, whereas results are presented and discussed in Section 4. Finally, Section 5 summarizes the main conclusions and future research.

2 SOLAR-ASP TOOL

Whereas Section 2.1 provides a theoretical foundation for PV monitoring tool, Section 2.2 introduces SOLAR-ASP tool. Focusing on the practical implementation of the tool, Section 2.3 outlines the input data needed by

SOLAR-ASP, while Section 2.4 details the output data.

2.1 Categorization of monitoring tools for PV systems

PV system monitoring tools are broadly categorized into three groups based on their methodological foundations: physical models, data-driven models, and hybrid/digital twin models [11].

Physical models simulate the ideal behaviour of PV systems using optical, thermal, and electrical equations derived from technical specifications [12]. By comparing theoretical outputs with real-time data, the identified deviations are declared to be indicative of anomalies. However, physical models often fail to automate root-cause diagnostics due to mismatches with real-world system behaviour.

Data-driven models leverage statistical relationships without requiring theoretical assumptions [13]-[17]. Their core strength lies in modelling the normal performance of asset as reflected in its operational data, bypassing the need for explicit knowledge of the underlying physics. Nevertheless, effective implementation demands large, high-quality datasets, and their ability to identify fault origins depends on expert-labelled training data—though emerging explainable AI techniques are lately addressing this limitation [18].

Hybrid and digital-twin models combine physical principles with data-driven calibration to improve sensitivity and enable automated diagnostics [19]. They estimate energy losses associated with faults without requiring extensive historical records but demand precise operational measurements and may struggle with unforeseen failures. Digital twins not only integrate physical principles and data, but also extend this integration to simulate design or operational. This makes them a specific application of hybrid models.

2.2 SOLAR-ASP: overall design and features

Presented tool exemplifies a hybrid approach, integrating data-driven analysis and modelling with embedded physical knowledge of PV systems for early-stage fault detection.

As a result of its hybrid nature, the parameters estimated by SOLAR-ASP are specifically designed to be compared against design/operational benchmarks established during commissioning. This enables the early detection of performance deviations, such as gradual degradations in module efficiency or sudden faults in electrical components.

Moreover, the physics-informed nature of SOLAR-ASP models enables generalizability across diverse PV systems without requiring extensive historical datasets for training. Notably, a key advantage of this framework is that the tool can be calibrated and validated using only a few months (e.g. 1 or 3 months), contrasting with data-driven methods that often demand larger datasets for reliable performance.

2.3 Input data needed by SOLAR-ASP

Data sources needed by SOLAR-ASP could be categorized into two main groups: system design parameters and real-time operational data. These inputs are critical for ensuring the accuracy and adaptability of the SOLAR-ASP monitoring framework. On the one hand, key design parameters include:

- Geographical and environmental context: Latitude, longitude, and altitude.
- PV system design: main electrical and physical characteristics of PV system.
- Electrical configuration: arrangement of modules in series and parallel within each inverter input channel.

On the other hand, the continuous monitoring through SCADA systems provides dynamic operational data. The following variables are necessary inputs for SOLAR-ASP:

- Electrical measurements: operating voltage and current from inverter input channels.
- Environmental conditions: plane-of-array (POA) irradiance and module temperature.

2.4 Output data provided by SOLAR-ASP

The tool estimates ASPs, which perform as core indicators for fault detection and degradation analysis. ASPs can be compared to electrical parameters of PV system normalized at Standard Test Conditions (STC). Key ASPs include:

- MPP voltage at STC
- MPP current at STC

By isolating whether a performance loss is primarily voltage-driven or current-driven, SOLAR-ASP has the potential to guide more targeted O&M strategies.

3 EXPERIMENTAL SETUP

Real-world data from a large-scale PV plant in southern Spain is used to validate SOLAR-ASP.

3.1 PV system setup

The PV system is a commercial installation which includes six PV arrays, labelled as Inverter1 to Inverter6. This installation has been operational for over a decade with a total nominal capacity of approximately 626 kWp. Each array is configured with 32 strings connected in parallel per inverter channel, whereas each string consists of 20 monocrystalline PV modules. Notably, two PV arrays have modules with distinct power ratings compared to the remaining four. The key electrical specifications of the system components are summarized in Table I. The system is in a CSA area (hot-summer Mediterranean climate) as per the Köppen climate classification [20].

Table I: Electrical characteristics of PV system at STC, obtained through PV modules characteristics and the electrical connections.

Component	Imp [A]	Vmp [V]
Inverter1, Inverter2	147.84	692
Inverter3 to Inverter6	154.24	706

Data for the validation period spans from April to October 2024. The SCADA system of the plant provides irradiance and module temperature measurements at the inverter level, with a shared sensoring system covering all six PV arrays.

3.2 PV system IV curve characterization

IV curve tracing was conducted using an HT Instruments IV-400W tracer (Serial No. 11091591) at string level, in October 2024. The IV characterization includes for each of the 32 strings across the six PV arrays:

- Full IV curve operating points.
- Full IV curve points translated to STC.
- Instantaneous irradiance ranged from approximately 670 to 930 W/m².

- Instantaneous module temperature ranged from 35 to 50 °C.
- Measured and STC-translated values of open-circuit voltage (Voc), maximum power voltage (Vmp), short-circuit current (Isc), and maximum power current (Imp).

An aggregation process is implemented to align the string-level IV curve data with the SCADA-based SOLAR-ASP inputs, measured at inverter level. Firstly, individual string STC curves are aligned to a common array voltage via linear interpolation. The resolution of the array voltage-string is the one corresponding to 2000 points between minimum and maximum voltage at STC curves of each string. This ensures consistent voltage values across all strings. Secondly, the currents are aggregated at array-level. For parallel-connected strings, translated currents are summed at each voltage point. This methodology enabled direct comparison between the estimation values from SOLAR-ASP and empirical measurements.

4 RESULTS AND DISCUSSIONS

The empirical validation of SOLAR-ASP is structured around the presented RQ, each one addressing a distinct aspect of its hybrid modelling internals:

- Firstly, the accuracy of its estimation is evaluated by comparing them against the STC normalized values of measured IV curves. This assessment uses hybrid models trained on SCADA data from September 2024, a month preceding the measurement campaign, to address RQ1.
- Secondly, the influence of input data volume on estimation accuracy is investigated by applying different training windows to SCADA data. This analysis determines the minimum data requirements for achieving statistically stable and accurate estimates of Vmp and Imp, directly addressing RQ2.
- Finally, the seasonal variability of SOLAR-ASP estimations is evaluated by analysing its performance across multiple months. Hybrid models are trained using 30-day windows ending at the conclusion of each month. Nominal values normalized estimations are compared to the temperature-corrected PR, considering only Direct Current (DC) side. Temperature-corrected PR is a widely adopted standard metric [21][22] for assessing PV system efficiency. This comparison assesses whether the estimated Vmp and Imp values exhibit sufficient stability and low statistical dispersion to serve as reliable alternatives to PR for diagnostic purposes, addressing RQ3.

4.1 RQ1: SOLAR-ASP estimations against STC normalized IV curve measurements

The accuracy of the SOLAR-ASP tool is evaluated by comparing the estimations obtained from operational data collected in September 2024 with experimental IV curve measurements normalized to STC. 30-day training windows are used. Errors are gauged as relative percentage deviations, calculated as:

$$Error = 100\left(\frac{Estimation - Measurement}{Measurement}\right) \quad (1)$$

Figure 1 illustrates the estimation error across individual components, with current errors depicted in green and voltage errors in orange. Except from Inverter4, relative errors are ranging from -4 % to 1%. Across all six components, the error distribution could be represented by the mean and standard deviation (STD), −0.521%±2.984%, indicating a slight underestimation of magnitudes. However, the mean and STD may not fully capture the characteristics of distribution, particularly in the presence of outliers or skewness. Notably, Inverter4 exhibits a pronounced overestimation of Imp. To address this, the median error and interquartile range (IQR) are also computed. The IQR is defined as the difference between the 75th and 25th percentiles, complementing the median by quantifying the spread of the middle 50% of the data. In this case, the median of the errors is -0.893%, with a IQR of 3.11%. Therefore, the central tendency aligns with acceptable tolerances with industry benchmarks (±3%).

This analysis directly addresses RQ1: the ability of SOLAR-ASP to estimate voltage and current with accuracy comparable to I-V curve measurements, even when relying solely on SCADA data.

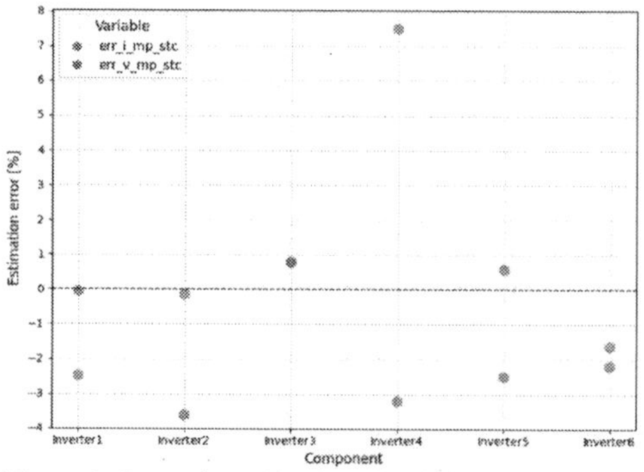

Figure 1: September 2024 SOLAR-ASP estimation error vs IV curve measurements normalized to STC.

4.2 RQ2: Impact of Training Window Duration on Estimation Accuracy

In response to this second RQ, windows of 15, 30, 45, 60 and 90 days, all ending in September 2024, are used to train hybrid models. The analysis is aimed to determine the minimum data volume required for accurate and reproducible prediction. Estimation errors are evaluated by comparing model outputs to STC-normalized I-V curves measurements. The results are summarized in Figures 2 and 3, and Tables II and III.

Intermediate windows (30-60 days) yield the lowest mean and median errors for both Imp and Vmp. Shorter and longer training windows exhibit greater variability. In case of Vmp estimation, training with 15 days causes the greatest errors: mean: −2.406%; median: −2.759%. In contrast, training with 90 days obtains the lowest errors: mean: −1.390%; median: −1.830%. Figure 2 shows that Inverter1 and Inverter3 deviates from this trend. However, their errors across all training-windows are under ±1%, which is comparable to the inherent measurement uncertainties in SCADA data. Regarding to Imp estimation, the 90-day window, while reducing median error (−3.405%), introduced higher mean error (−2.705%), suggesting that Imp is more sensitive to recent data.

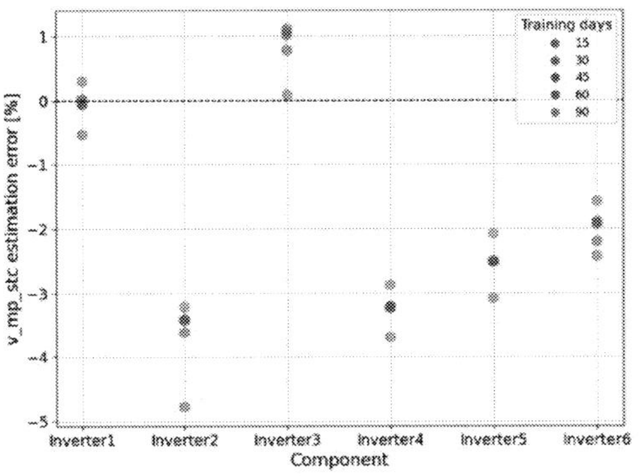

Figure 2: Comparison of Vmp estimation error vs IV curve measurements normalized to STC for varying training windows.

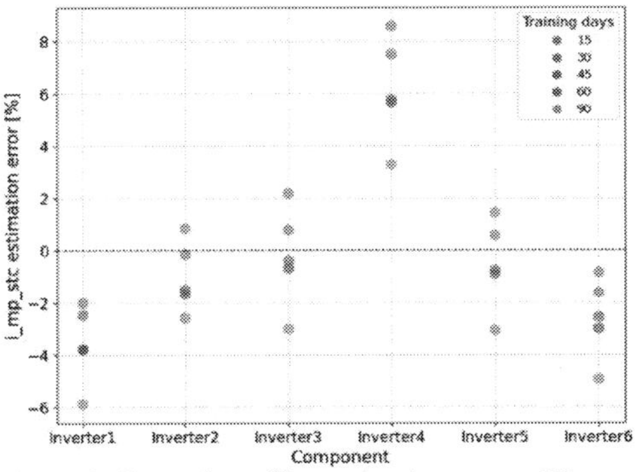

Figure 3: Comparison of Imp estimation error vs IV curve measurements normalized to STC for varying training windows.

Table II: Statistics of Imp estimation error.

Training days	MEAN	STD	MEDIAN	IQR
15	1.692	3.706	1.131	2.420
30	0.762	3.536	0.208	1.990
45	-0.540	3.333	-1.127	1.830
60	-0.739	3.335	-1.290	1.930
90	-2.705	3.198	-3.405	1.780

Table III: Statistics of Vmp estimation error.

Training days	MEAN	STD	MEDIAN	IQR
15	-2.406	1.873	-2.759	2.540
30	-1.804	1.770	-2.358	2.440
45	-1.664	1.831	-2.206	2.600
60	-1.686	1.795	-2.225	2.530
90	-1.390	1.743	-1.830	2.510

In response to RQ2, the obtained results identify 30-day window as the optimal compromise for estimation, balancing accuracy, data volume and operational feasibility. Although Vmp estimation benefits from longer windows, the 30-day window avoids excessive data smoothing and allows detecting short-term performance deviations.

4.3 RQ3: Long-Term Stability Analysis

The stability of SOLAR-ASP estimation for Imp and Vmp is evaluated by comparing their monthly variations to the temperature-corrected PR. The PR quantifies the ratio of actual energy production to the theoretical maximum achievable under given environmental conditions. Actual energy production is obtained as the product of measured current and voltage from available SCADA data. The theoretical production P_{ref} is derived using [21]:

$$P_{ref}(G,T) = \left(\frac{G}{1000}\right) P_{STC}\left(1 + \frac{\alpha_p(T-25)}{100}\right) \quad (2)$$

where G is the Global Tilted Irradiance (GTI) in W/m^2, T is the module temperature in °C, P_{STC} is the nominal power of PV array in W, and α_p is the power temperature coefficient in %/ °C. Data below a defined irradiance threshold ($G < 150\ W/m^2$) are excluded to mitigate the impact of low-irradiance noise on accuracy [23].

The estimations are normalized dividing them by design values from Table I, obtaining per unit (pu) magnitudes. The normalized estimations are compared to the PR across six available months of SCADA data to assess the reliability of SOLAR-ASP as a diagnosis framework. Table IV shows the Imp and Vmp estimations for each month. Table V reports the statistical variability of the estimated metrics and PR through STD, coefficient of variation (CV) and IQR. As can be seen in these tables, Vmp exhibits the lowest variability in all metrics, while Imp demonstrates slightly lower variability than PR.

Figure 4 illustrates the monthly evolution of normalized Imp and Vmp estimations and PR for Inverter6, as a graphical representation of one component of Table IV. Data in his figure reveal that while the PR decreases from 0.89 pu in April to 0.83 pu in September, this decline might be driven by a reduction in Imp (from 0.88pu to 0.85 pu) rather than Vmp, which remains almost stable around 0.97–0.99 pu. This fact suggests that current-limiting factors are the dominant contributors to performance loss in the analysed PV system.

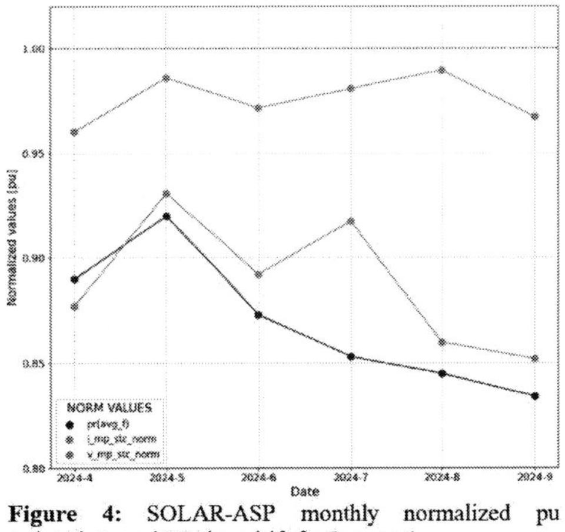

Figure 4: SOLAR-ASP monthly normalized pu estimations and PR time-drift for Inverter6.

The analysis directly answers RQ3 by demonstrating that estimations provided by SOLAR-ASP exhibit similar or lower variability than the temperature-corrected PR, validating their utility as stable and interpretable metrics for PV O&M. Moreover, SOLAR-ASP offers granular insights into the root causes of performance degradation, separating current and voltage instead of aggregating losses into a single metrics as PR. This distinction is critical for optimizing maintenance strategies, as it allows operators to prioritize interventions based on the specific nature of the fault

Table IV: Monthly normalized estimations and PR.

Date	Component	PR[pu]	Imp[pu]	Vmp[pu]
2024-4	Inverter1	0.877	0.859	0.988
	Inverter2	0.813	0.802	0.962
	Inverter3	0.828	0.825	0.957
	Inverter4	0.865	0.892	0.939
	Inverter5	0.872	0.887	0.959
	Inverter6	0.890	0.877	0.960
2024-5	Inverter1	0.904	0.912	1.017
	Inverter2	0.839	0.854	0.988
	Inverter3	0.853	0.880	0.979
	Inverter4	0.895	0.947	0.964
	Inverter5	0.913	0.957	0.986
	Inverter6	0.920	0.931	0.986
2024-6	Inverter1	0.780	0.878	0.996
	Inverter2	0.728	0.833	0.971
	Inverter3	0.810	0.851	0.970
	Inverter4	0.866	0.904	0.948
	Inverter5	0.858	0.915	0.970
	Inverter6	0.873	0.892	0.971
2024-7	Inverter1	0.842	0.894	1.018
	Inverter2	0.723	0.812	0.990
	Inverter3	0.793	0.869	0.977
	Inverter4	0.831	0.926	0.966
	Inverter5	0.853	0.936	0.989
	Inverter6	0.853	0.918	0.981
2024-8	Inverter1	0.834	0.860	1.022
	Inverter2	0.776	0.809	0.994
	Inverter3	0.784	0.844	0.972
	Inverter4	0.822	0.888	0.963
	Inverter5	0.845	0.890	0.993
	Inverter6	0.845	0.860	0.989
2024-9	Inverter1	0.826	0.841	1.001
	Inverter2	0.765	0.786	0.970
	Inverter3	0.778	0.813	0.974
	Inverter4	0.812	0.871	0.950
	Inverter5	0.832	0.876	0.971
	Inverter6	0.834	0.852	0.967

Table V: Statistics of estimated metrics and PR.

Variable	MEAN	STD	CV	IQR
PR	0.834	0.047	0.057	0.050
Imp	0.873	0.042	0.048	0.050
Vmp	0.978	0.019	0.020	0.020

5 CONCLUSIONS

The results of this study have demonstrated the effectiveness of SOLAR-ASP to assess the health of PV assets. SOLAR-ASP is a hybrid FDD tool that combines data-driven analytics from SCADA systems with domain-specific physical knowledge. SOLAR-ASP achieves estimation errors for operation current and voltage below 3%, which are comparable to those of traditional I-V curve measurements. This level of accuracy enables early identification of performance degradation, supporting proactive maintenance strategies in large-scale PV systems. Furthermore, its hybrid architecture ensures interpretable outputs for PV domain experts, eliminating the need for labelled historical datasets. Additionally, its minimal data requirements make it particularly suitable for newly commissioned systems or assets with limited historical operational data.

Our analysis of the results obtained over real data further revealed that SOLAR-ASP estimations exhibit lower variability than the temperature-corrected PR, while providing a granular diagnosis beyond the decline in performance. By separating current and voltage trends, SOLAR-ASP provides practical guidance for targeted maintenance, enhancing the cost-effectiveness of CBM strategies in large-scale PV plants.

In the future we will focus on quantifying the intrinsic uncertainty of hybrid models to establish robust thresholds that distinguish between estimation inaccuracies and real degradations. Moreover, we plan to evaluate the performance of SOLAR-ASP on diverse PV plants with varying configuration to assess its generalizability and scalability.

i

6 ACKNOWLEGMENTS

This work has been supported by SUNRISE-PV project (New Generation of Photovoltaic Technologies for energy cost reduction through circularity strategies), funded by The Centre for the Development of Industrial Technology (CDTI). "Science and Innovation Missions Program", of the State Program to Catalyze Innovation and Business Leadership of the State Plan for Scientific and Technical Research and Innovation 2021-2023 within the framework of the Recovery, Transformation and Resilience Plan. J. Del Ser also acknowledges funding support from the Basque Government through the consolidated research group MATHMODE (IT1456-22).

7 REFERENCES

[1] SolarPower Europe (2025): Global Market Outlook for Solar Power 2025-2029 https://www.solarpowereurope.org/insights/outlooks/global-market-outlook-for-solar-power-2025-2029/detail. Accessed August 2025.

[2] Lazard. (June 2024). LCOE+ (Levelized Cost of Energy)

[3] UNECE, "Carbon Neutrality in the UNECE Region: Integrated Life-cycle Assessment of Electricity Sources", 2022, Report.

[4] A. Walker et all, Model of Operation-and-Maintenance Costs for Photovoltaic Systems, National Renewable Energy Laboratory, 2020. https://docs.nrel.gov/docs/fy20osti/74840.pdf. Accessed August 2025.

[5] IEA-PVPS (2014): *Review of Failures of Photovoltaic Modules*, ISBN 978-3-906042-16-9.

[6] A. K. Vidal de Oliveira et al. (2019): *Automatic fault detection of photovoltaic array by convolutional neural networks during aerial infrared thermography*, European PV Solar Energy Conference.

[7] IEA\PVPS. Task 13. (2021) The use of advanced algorithms in PV failure monitoring. URL https://iea-pvps.org/key-topics/theuse-of-advanced-algorithms-in-pv-failure-monitoring/. Accessed August 2025.

[8] P.-C. Hwang et al. (2021). Detection of malfunctioning photovoltaic modules based on machine learning algorithms. 9:37210–37219. ISSN 2169-3536. doi: 10.1109/ACCESS. 2021.3063461.

URL https://ieeexplore.ieee.org/document/9367143
[9] Z. Zeng & E. Zio (2018): Dynamic Risk Assessment Based on Statistical Failure Data and Condition-Monitoring Degradation Data, IEEE Trans Reliab, 67(2):609–622.
[10] IRENA (2019): *Global Energy Transformation: A Roadmap to 2050*, ISBN 978-92-9260-122-8.
[11] A. Mellit, G. M. Tina, and S. A. Kalogirou, "Fault detection and diagnosis methods for photovoltaic systems: A review," Renewable and Sustainable Energy Reviews, vol. 91, pp. 1–17, 2018, doi: 10.1016/j.rser.2018.03.062.
[12] M. J. Mayer and G. Grof, "Extensive comparison of physical models for photovoltaic power forecasting," Applied Energy, vol. 283, p. 116239, 2021.
[13] K. S. Garud, S. Jayaraj, and M.-Y. Lee, "A review on modeling of solar photovoltaic systems using artificial neural networks, fuzzy logic, genetic algorithm and hybrid models," Int J Energy Res., 2020.
[14] C.-C. H. et al., "Real-time fault detection in massive multi-array PV plants based on machine learning techniques," 36th European Photovoltaic Solar Energy Conference and Exhibition, 2019.
[15] H. A. M. et al., "Real Time Fault Detection in Photovoltaic Systems," Energy Procedia, vol. 111, pp. 914–923, 2017.
[16] Å. Skomedal et al., "General, Robust and Scalable Methods for String Level Monitoring in Utility Scale PV Systems," 36th European Photovoltaic Solar Energy Conference and Exhibition, 2019.
[17] M. Carpentieri and S. Vergura, "Statistics to Detect Low-Intensity Anomalies in PV Systems," Energies, vol. 11, no. 30, pp. 1–12, 2018.
[18] C. Utama et al., "Explainable artificial intelligence for photovoltaic fault detection: A comparison of instruments," Solar Energy, vol. 249, pp. 139–151, 2023, doi: 10.1016/j.solener.2022.11.018.
[19] A. Jain, "How might data analytics help advance solar PV research?" DURAMAT consortium Webinar, 2020.
[20] Kottek M, Grieser J, Beck C, Rudolf B, Rubel F. World Map of the Köppen-Geiger climate classification updated. Meteorologische Zeitschrift. 2006 Jul;15(3):259–263. Available from: https://www.schweizerbart.de/papers/metz/detail/15/55034/World_Map_of_the_Koppen_Geiger_climate_classificat?af=crossref. Accessed August 2025.
[21] IEC 61724-1:2021, Photovoltaic system performance – Part 1: Monitoring, International Electrotechnical Commission, Geneva, Switzerland, 2021.
[22] B. Marion et al., "Performance parameters for grid-connected PV systems," Conference Record of the Thirty-first IEEE Photovoltaic Specialists Conference, 2005., Lake Buena Vista, FL, USA, 2005, pp. 1601-1606, doi: 10.1109/PVSC.2005.1488451.
[23] IEA-PVPS Task 13-22: Assessment of Performance Loss Rate of PV Power Systems. 2021. https://iea-pvps.org/wp-content/uploads/2021/04/IEA-PVPS-T13-22_2021-Assessment-of-Performance-Loss-Rate-of-PV-Power-Systems-report.pdf. Accessed July 2025.

FIRE PERFORMANCE OF POWER OPTIMIZERS IN PHOTOVOLTAIC SYSTEMS

Lasse Halle[1], David Joss[1], Christof Bucher[1]
[1] Bern University of Applied Sciences (BFH), School of Engineering and Computer Science (TI), Institute for Energy and Mobility Research (IEM), Laboratory for Photovoltaic Systems (PV-Lab)
[1]lasse.halle@bfh.ch, [1]christof.bucher@bfh.ch

ABSTRACT: This study investigates the behaviour of photovoltaic (PV) systems with power optimizers under externally induced fire exposure, with a particular focus on facade-mounted installations. The objective is to determine whether power optimizers increase fire risk due to energy absorption at various abnormal operating temperatures and how the system behaviour of a PV installation with power optimizers responds to elevated external temperatures. Experimental investigations were conducted on grid-connected PV systems consisting of inverters, power optimizers, and PV module simulation sources. Devices from three manufacturers were analysed: Huawei, SolarEdge, and Tigo. Two types of experiments were performed: (I) non-destructive heating up to 140 °C, and (II) destructive flame exposure at temperatures of at least 800 °C. In both cases, one optimizer within the PV system was exposed to abnormal temperature. The results show that power optimizers detect overtemperature, stop energy conversion, and switch to bypass mode on the string side while opening the module side. After cooling, devices resume operation even with visible damage. Under destructive flame tests, burning droplets, enlarged flames, smoke, and moving burning parts were observed due to melting brackets. No Rapid Shutdown of system voltage occurred, although string current was interrupted by the inverter. Overall, PV systems with power optimizers exhibit similar behaviour to systems without optimizers during fire, but additional material increases the fire load.
Keywords: PV Fire Performance, Rapid Shutdown, Fire Safety, Facade-mounted PV, Power Optimizers

1 INTRODUCTION

Photovoltaic (PV) facade systems are gaining increasing importance in Europe and worldwide. In addition to the energetic utilisation of building surfaces, the integration of PV modules into the building envelope also offers architectural advantages [1]. At the same time, the installation of PV systems on facades is subject to stringent requirements for preventive fire protection. In Switzerland, the fire safety requirements for facades are subject to regulations, as these building elements usually extend across the entire building height and can significantly contribute to fire spread. PV facade systems therefore lie at the intersection of ambitious energy policy objectives for the expansion of renewable energies and strict building and fire safety regulations. At the European level, test procedures and standards exist, for example within the framework of EN standards on the fire performance of construction products, but their national implementation differs significantly [2].

While the fire behaviour of PV modules and their mounting structures has been the subject of extensive research, the behaviour of PV systems with power optimizers under fire conditions has so far hardly been investigated [3]. For these power electronic components, there are currently no specific standards or testing procedures in the context of fire testing. This results in a regulatory gap that creates uncertainty for designers, manufacturers, and fire safety authorities. In particular, it remains unclear whether power optimizers increase the fire load due to their additional material content or whether their protective functions, such as overtemperature detection, may contribute positively to safety in the event of fire.

The objective of this study is therefore to systematically analyse the fire behaviour of PV systems with power optimizers. The central research question is whether power optimizers increase the fire risk due to energy absorption at abnormal operating temperatures and how the system behaviour responds to externally induced temperature increases. For this purpose, representative market products from major manufacturers – Huawei, SolarEdge, and Tigo – were selected, in order to provide results with high practical relevance and applicability.

2 METHODOLOGY

The experimental investigations were conducted at the Photovoltaics Laboratory (PV-Lab) of the Bern University of Applied Sciences (BFH). The systems consisted of 16 simulated PV modules connected to one Maximum Power Point Tracker (MPPT) of a grid-connected inverter. As module sources, programmable PV simulators of the type Delta Elektronika SM330-AR-22 were used, each configured to a nominal power of 330 W (≈ 33 V, 10 A) with STC (1000 W/m^2, 25 °C). The electrical parameters of the simulated modules were $V_{oc} \approx 40$ V and $I_{sc} \approx 11$ A, resulting in a total installed DC capacity of ≈ 5.28 kWp. The current-voltage characteristics were software-controlled to ensure reproducible and comparable operating conditions across all test series.

The investigated power optimizers were operated in combination with the corresponding manufacturer-specific inverters. Devices from Huawei, SolarEdge, and Tigo were tested, each together with a compatible inverter. In each test series, a single optimizer was subjected to targeted thermal stress, while the rest of the system remained in regular operation.

Table I: Tested device configurations:

Power Optimizers with	Inverter
Huawei: SUN2000-450W-P2	Huawei SUN2000-10KTL-M1
SolarEdge: S440	SolarEdge: SE10K
Tigo: TS4-A-O	Fronius: SYMO 6.0-3-M

2.1 Test Procedure

The investigations were divided into two main series. In the first experimental series (I), non-destructive heating tests were carried out in a climate chamber. The aim was

10.4229/EUPVSEC2025/4CV.1.61

to determine the temperature thresholds at which the optimizers detect overheating and to characterize their switching behaviour under controlled conditions. For each manufacturer, three independent test runs were performed. Each run followed a stepwise heating protocol with four plateaus at 80 °C, 100 °C, 120 °C, and 140 °C. Each plateau was maintained for 30 minutes to ensure a steady thermal state. After each heating step, the device was cooled down to 25 °C and held for an additional 30 minutes to guarantee complete thermal recovery before the next heating sequence. The subsequent plateau was then reached by a controlled ramp starting from 25 °C. This cycle of heating and cooling was repeated four times within each run, thereby provoking multiple overtemperature detections per device. To further increase the stress on the tested optimizer, the irradiance applied to its simulated PV module was pulsed between 1000 W/m² for two minutes and 300 W/m² for six minutes. This pulsed irradiance profile was applied only to the stressed optimizer, while all remaining simulated modules were operated at constant irradiance. Functional control sequences were performed before and after each full heating cycle to confirm correct system operation and to document any changes in device behaviour.

The second experimental series (II) consisted of destructive flame tests in which a single optimizer was exposed to an open flame generated by a burner. The objective was to reproduce a realistic fire scenario within the ventilated cavity of a PV facade system, with local surface temperatures reaching at least 800 °C. The test stand was designed to represent typical mounting conditions of a ventilated facade, enabling observation of both electrical and mechanical effects under external fire exposure [4]. In contrast to series (I), the irradiance profile was simplified for these tests: after an initial control sequence, a constant irradiance of 1000 W/m² was applied throughout the entire experiment to reduce complexity and to facilitate the analysis of the electrical response under dynamic fire conditions.

For this series, three flame tests were planned per manufacturer. For Huawei and Tigo, all three runs were successfully completed and documented. In the case of SolarEdge, however, only two experiments could be carried out, as the third planned test had to be cancelled due to a defect in the inverter.

2.2 Measurement and Monitoring

Across both experimental series, the system response was recorded with regard to string current, voltage, and power absorption, while the switching behaviour of the optimizers was monitored, including overtemperature detection, transition of the PV input side to open circuit, transition of the string output side to bypass, and possible reactivation after cooling. During the flame tests, visual observations were made systematically, including flame propagation, smoke emission, formation of burning droplets, and movement or detachment of components. Error and warning messages in the manufacturer monitoring portals were logged according to the firmware versions installed on the devices at the time of testing (November 2024 to January 2025), ensuring that the analysis reflects the actual operational states of the products.

3 RESULTS

The results are presented in two parts, corresponding to the experimental design: (I) controlled temperature increases in a climate chamber and (II) destructive flame tests representing external fire exposure in ventilated facade systems. In both series, the electrical response of the PV system, the switching behaviour of the optimizers, and the observed fire phenomena were evaluated. Manufacturer-specific monitoring data were additionally analysed with respect to fault detection and reporting.

3.1 Non-destructive temperature increase (Series I)

In the controlled heating experiments in the climate chamber, the PV-string voltage and current remained stable throughout the runs. The only electrical deviation was the interruption of power absorption by the thermally stressed optimizer once its overtemperature threshold was reached. Upon detection of excessive temperature, the optimizer disconnected its PV input side to open circuit and simultaneously placed the string output in bypass. This ensured that the overall PV system remained operational and that total power output was reduced only by the contribution of the affected device.

After cooling to normal operating conditions, the optimizers reactivated automatically and resumed normal operation, even when visible deformation of the housings was present. The switching response consistently exhibited a hysteresis effect: the restart temperature was lower than the shutdown temperature, preventing oscillatory switching behaviour while allowing the devices to return to operation after cooling.

Across all Series I experiments, the manufacturers' monitoring systems consistently issued fault or warning messages corresponding to the detected overtemperature condition. These messages were automatically cleared once the devices cooled down, leaving no persistent entries in the portals.

The applied irradiance pulsing sequence, consisting of short-term alternations between 1000 W/m² for two minutes and 300 W/m² for six minutes, did not trigger additional switching events. However, it confirmed that the optimizers maintained stable functionality under combined thermal and electrical stress, with no additional deviations observed in the string performance.

Figure 1 presents a representative measurement from Series I, showing the temperature trajectory and the corresponding switching response of one device, with shutdown and restart thresholds marked to highlight the hysteretic behaviour. Figure 2 summarizes the shutdown and restart temperatures for all test runs by optimizer type.

10.4229/EUPVSEC2025/4CV.1.61

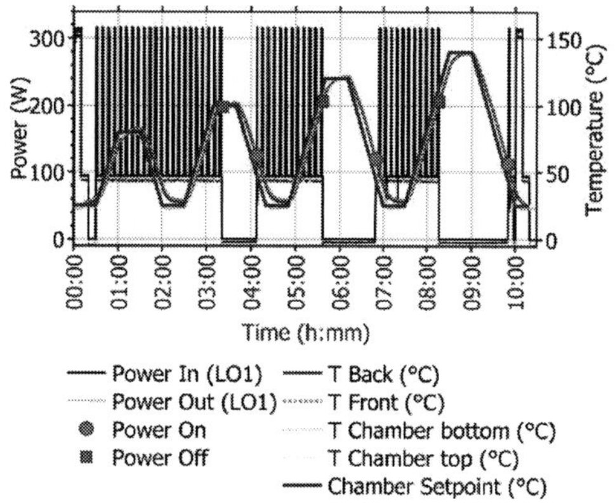

Figure 1: Electrical and thermal response of a representative optimizer under thermal stress in the climate chamber (Series I). Left axis: power; right axis: temperatures. Green and red markers indicate optimizer switching events (on/off).

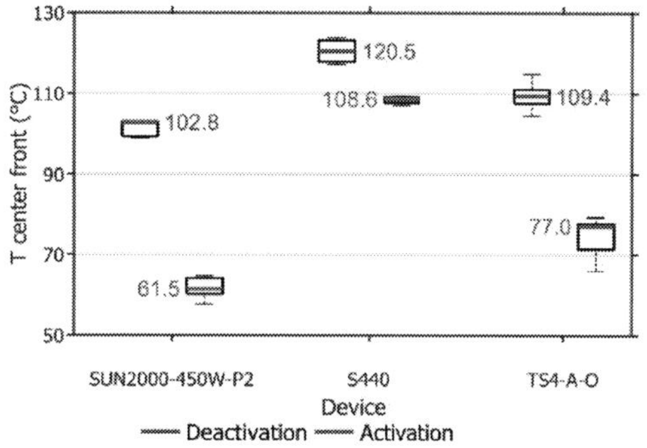

Figure 2: Boxplot of shutdown and restart temperatures for all tested optimizers (Series I) with median values.

3.2 Destructive flame tests (Series II)

In the flame exposure experiments, the thermal and mechanical behaviour of the optimizers under extreme external heating was markedly different from the controlled climate chamber tests. Local surface temperatures of at least 800 °C were reached, and in several cases, peak temperatures exceeded 1000 °C.

The electrical response of the systems varied depending on manufacturer and test conditions. In multiple experiments, the inverters disconnected the string within a few minutes of ignition, typically as a result of residual current device (RCD) tripping. In other cases, however, no system shutdown occurred and the PV string continued operating despite the burning optimizer. In none of the tested devices did the fire trigger a Rapid Shutdown or a complete reduction of system voltage. Instead, the optimizers exhibited either open-circuit or short-circuit behaviour on the PV input side, depending on the mode of failure.

The mechanical consequences of flame exposure were significant. In nearly all cases, the mounting structures of the optimizers melted, resulting in detachment of the devices from the test stand and, in some instances, swinging or falling components still partially connected by cables. Burning droplets were frequently observed, sometimes combined with molten metal residues.

The visual fire behaviour was characterized by strong flame formation and dense black smoke in most tests, with noticeable variability between devices. A representative frontal view of flame growth is shown in Figure 3, highlighting the rapid development of tall flames above the optimizer. To capture the side perspective, Figures 4 document the same experiment before and after the optimizer detached from its mounting.

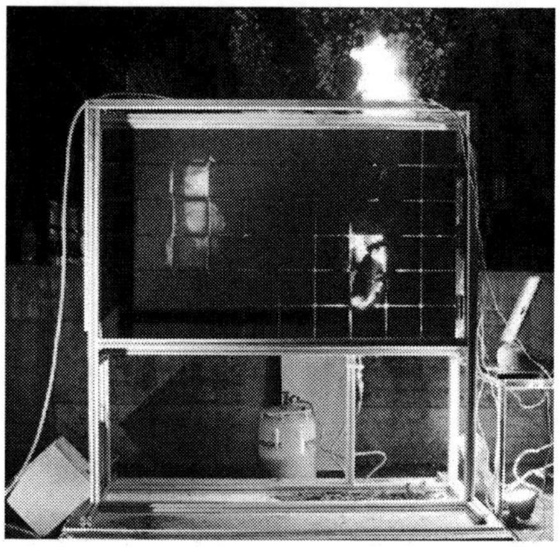

Figure 3: Frontal view of flame formation during Series II test.

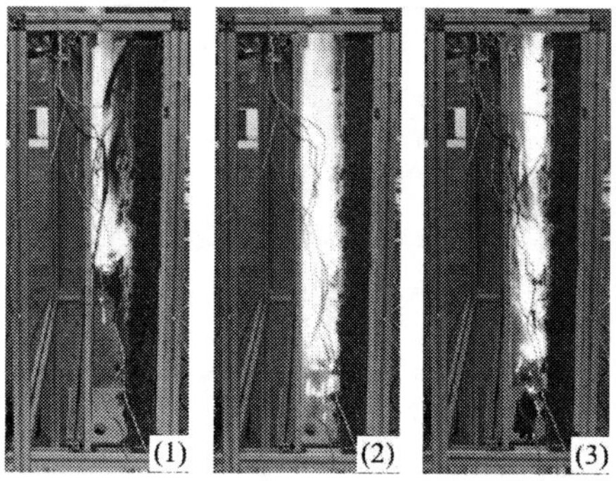

Figure 4: Side view of flame formation during Series II test with (1) optimizer still attached, (2) optimizer partially detaching, and (3) optimizer fully detached.

The chaotic burning behaviour made systematic comparisons difficult, as the fire dynamics differed strongly even between repeated runs of the same optimizer type. In total, error or warning messages were issued only in two out of six flame exposure tests, although an overtemperature-related switching response was observed in three of the six runs. In contrast, during Series I experiments consistently produced corresponding fault messages in the monitoring systems depending on optimizer typ.

While the electrical contribution of the burning optimizers was eliminated in all cases, the added fire load of the optimizer materials contributed significantly to flame growth, smoke production, and the spread of burning droplets. The chaotic behaviour observed under fire exposure limits the possibility of systematic evaluation, but the overall trend indicates that the presence of power optimizers increases the fire load in facade systems without providing a corresponding benefit in terms of system shutdown or voltage reduction.

10.4229/EUPVSEC2025/4CV.1.61

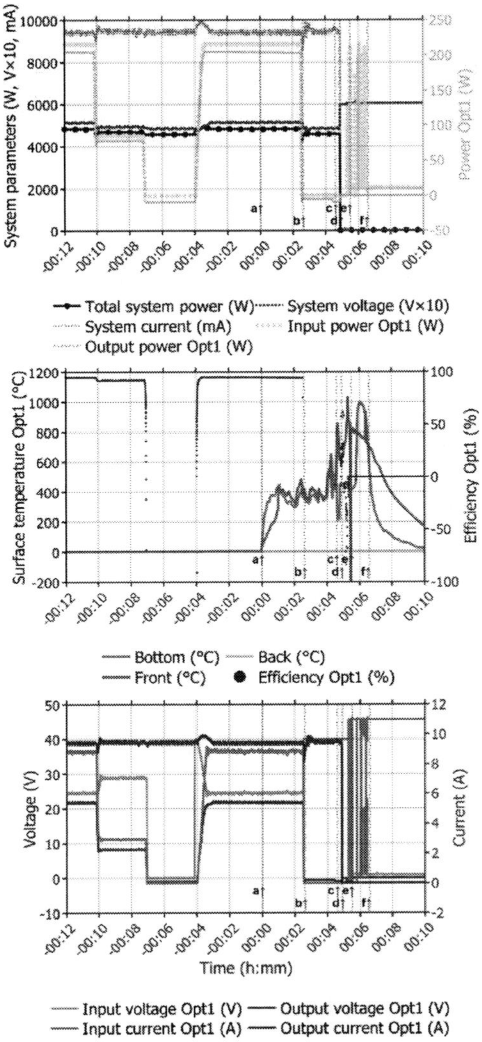

Figure 5: Exemplary evaluation chart with electrical and thermal response of a representative optimizer under thermal stress during a flame test in the ventilated facade cavity (Series II). Top: system power/voltage/current (left) and Optimizer-1 input/output power (right). Middle: module surface temperatures (left) and Optimizer-1 efficiency (right). Bottom: Optimizer-1 voltages (left) and currents (right). Letters a–f mark key events.

Table II: Event summary for the flame test in the ventilated facade cavity (Series II). Listed are lettered events a–f (as in Fig. 5) with synchronized electrical values at the event time: System current/voltage, Optimizer-1 Output current/voltage, Optimizer-1 Input current/voltage, and a brief Remark.

Event	Parameter	Measured value
a↑	System current (A)	9.2921
	System voltage (V)	516.2000
	Output current Opt1 (A)	9.2884
	Output voltage Opt1 (V)	22.0065
	Input current Opt1 (A)	8.8260
	Input voltage Opt1 (V)	24.4532
	Remark: Ignition	
b↑	System current (A)	8.5631
	System voltage (V)	506.7600
	Output current Opt1 (A)	8.5582
	Output voltage Opt1 (V)	-0.4368
	Input current Opt1 (A)	0.0114
	Input voltage Opt1 (V)	39.9679
	Remark: Overtemperature detection Opt1	
c↑	System current (A)	9.4476
	System voltage (V)	483.6700
	Output current Opt1 (A)	9.4430
	Output voltage Opt1 (V)	-0.9398
	Input current Opt1 (A)	-0.0017
	Input voltage Opt1 (V)	39.9818
	Remark: Detachment Opt1	
d↑	System current (A)	0.0225
	System voltage (V)	598.2700
	Output current Opt1 (A)	0.0160
	Output voltage Opt1 (V)	-0.1431
	Input current Opt1 (A)	-0.0002
	Input voltage Opt1 (V)	39.9802
	Remark: String disconnection inverter	
e↑	System current (A)	0.0289
	System voltage (V)	604.7400
	Output current Opt1 (A)	0.0222
	Output voltage Opt1 (V)	0.0835
	Input current Opt1 (A)	10.9662
	Input voltage Opt1 (V)	1.2567
	Remark: Chaotic input behaviour Opt1	
f↑	System current (A)	0.0284
	System voltage (V)	604.4800
	Output current Opt1 (A)	0.0217
	Output voltage Opt1 (V)	0.0330
	Input current Opt1 (A)	10.9667
	Input voltage Opt1 (V)	0.8262
	Remark: Input short circuit Opt1, burner off	

4 CONCLUSION

The experimental results provide a differentiated picture of the fire-related behaviour of PV systems with power optimizers. In the non-destructive heating tests (Series I), all tested devices reliably detected overtemperature and switched into a defined state, thereby ensuring that the affected optimizer stopped power absorption without interrupting the current flow of the string. The switching thresholds and hysteresis behaviour were reproducible, and the reactivation after cooling was consistently observed across all manufacturers. Even in cases where visible damage to the housings occurred, the optimizers resumed operation after cooling. System warnings and error messages, when generated, were automatically archived once the temperature returned to normal, leaving no persistent indication in the portals.

In the destructive flame exposure tests (Series II), the behaviour was markedly less systematic. The devices contributed to increased fire load through additional material, leading to intensified flame formation, smoke development, burning droplets, and in some cases detachment of components. The system reaction under these conditions varied considerably, with chaotic and non-reproducible patterns that limited systematic evaluation. In several cases, the PV system continued to operate until interrupted by inverter protection mechanisms, typically triggered by residual current device (RCD) tripping. Importantly, the electrical response of the PV systems with optimizers did not differ significantly from systems without optimizers, as shutdowns were initiated mainly by the inverter rather than by the optimizers themselves.

A central finding of this study is that, despite reliable overtemperature detection in controlled conditions, no full system shutdown with reduction of string voltage was observed in either test series. This contradicts the expectation that abnormal temperature events would trigger rapid-shutdown-like behaviour, a feature often assumed to enhance safety in facade-integrated PV systems. Instead, the results show that optimizers provide only local protection by halting energy absorption, while at the same time adding combustible material that increases the fire load. Nevertheless, catastrophic malfunctioning such as continued power absorption at high temperature, bursting, or explosive failure was not observed in any of the experiments.

The results highlight a regulatory gap, as no standards currently exist that address the fire behaviour of power optimizers in PV facade applications [2] [3]. For safety-critical building integration, this underscores the need for further research and potential adaptation of testing protocols to account for both the electrical and fire-related contributions of these devices. At the same time, the findings must be interpreted with caution, as the number of test runs was limited and the experimental conditions cannot fully reproduce the complexity of real facade fire scenarios. A structured overview of the identified advantages and disadvantages is provided in Table III.

Table III: Summary of advantages (+) and disadvantages (–) of power optimizers regarding electrical and fire-related behaviour.

Category	Behaviour
Electrical	(+) Detection of overtemperature
	(+) No electrical power absorption
	(–) No reduction of system voltage
	(–) Poor / missing alarm functionality
Fire	(–) Additional fire load
	(–) Detachment of burning parts
	(–) Burning droplet formation

5 OUTLOOK

The conducted investigations provide a first systematic insight into the thermal and fire-related behaviour of PV power optimizers. However, the limited number of tested devices and the simplified laboratory conditions restrict the general validity of the findings. Future work should therefore include large-scale facade fire tests under more realistic boundary conditions, as well as long-term cycling experiments to assess the effects of repeated overtemperature exposure on the reliability and safety of optimizers. In addition, further research is needed to evaluate the interaction of optimizers with defective PV modules and to define standardized procedures for testing and classifying their fire behaviour. Regulatory developments should particularly address requirements for fault reporting and system-level shutdown functionality in building-integrated PV applications.

6 ACKNOWLEDGMENT

The authors acknowledge the financial support of the Building Insurance of the Canton of Bern (GVB). Experimental work was conducted at the Photovoltaics Laboratory (PV-Lab) of the Bern University of Applied Sciences (BFH).

7 REFERENCES

[1] C. Bucher, (2025). Photovoltaic Systems: Planning, Installation, Operation (2nd rev. ed.). Zürich: Faktor Verlag.

[2] F. Fjaerestad, et al., Fire performance of building-integrated photovoltaics: A review, Fire Safety Journal 113 (2020) 102978.

[3] J. Benick, et al., Fire safety testing of PV modules: Current status and future needs, Proceedings of the 36th European Photovoltaic Solar Energy Conference (EU PVSEC), (2019) 1741–1746.

[4] L. Klintberg, et al., Experimental studies on fire safety of PV modules in façades, Solar Energy Materials and Solar Cells 220 (2021) 110851.

42nd European Photovoltaic Solar Energy Conference and Exhibition

Fire Behaviour of PV Power Optimizers

EU PVSEC 2025, 22.-26. September 2025 Bilbao (Spain)
Lasse Halle[1], David Joss[1], Christof Bucher[1]
[1]Bern University of Applied Sciences (BFH), School of Engineering and Computer Science (TI), Institute for Energy and Mobility Research (IEM), Laboratory for Photovoltaic Systems (PV-Lab), Burgdorf (Switzerland)
christof.bucher@bfh.ch

This project investigates the fire performance of facade-integrated photovoltaic (PV) systems with power optimizers. Experiments show that optimizers detect overtemperature and switch into bypass mode, ensuring continued system operation without module power absorption. After cooling, optimizers resumed operation even when visible damage was present. During flame tests, however, optimizers contributed to additional fire load, burning droplets, and smoke. The electrical behaviour of PV systems with optimizers was similar to systems without optimizers: no shutdown or system voltage reduction was triggered. The results allow for a critical assessment of the overall system behaviour.

Methodology

The behaviour of optimizers was examined experimentally using simulated PV modules (16 × 330 Wp ≈ 5.28 kWp). Two test series were carried out to investigate both controlled overtemperature behaviour and fire exposure:

- **Series I:** Controlled heating in a climate chamber up to 140 ° C.
- **Series II:** Flame exposure in a ventilated façade setup with burner temperatures > **800** ° C.

Devices from three manufacturers were tested with their compatible inverters:

- **Huawei:** SUN2000-450W-P2 with SUN2000-10KTL-M1 inverter
- **SolarEdge:** S440 with SE10K inverter
- **Tigo:** TS4-A-O with Fronius SYMO 6.0-3-M inverter

Figure 1: Test setup in PV-Lab with climate chamber heating.

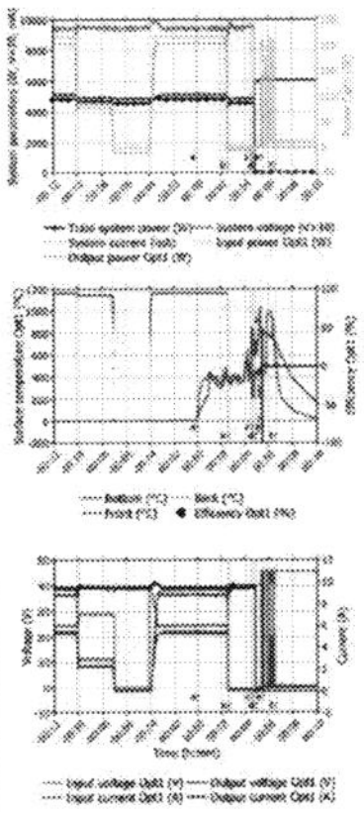

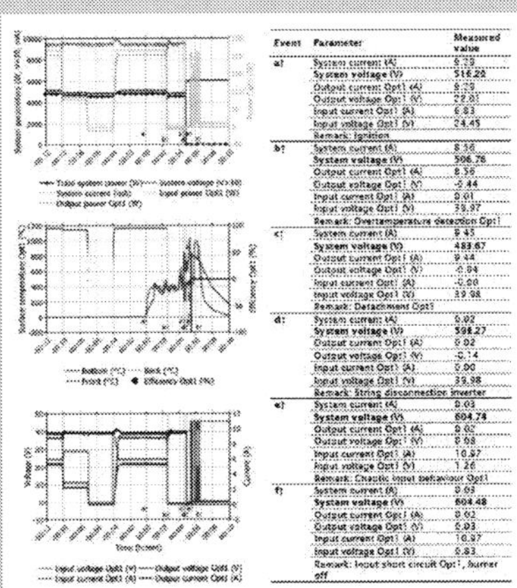

Event	Parameter	Measured value
a)	System current (A)	9.29
	System voltage (V)	**516.22**
	Output current Opt1 (A)	9.29
	Output voltage Opt1 (V)	22.01
	Input current Opt1 (A)	6.83
	Input voltage Opt1 (V)	24.45
	Remark: Ignition	
b)	System current (A)	8.36
	System voltage (V)	**506.76**
	Output current Opt1 (A)	8.36
	Output voltage Opt1 (V)	-0.44
	Input current Opt1 (A)	0.01
	Input voltage Opt1 (V)	39.97
	Remark: Overtemperature detection Opt1	
c)	System current (A)	9.45
	System voltage (V)	**483.67**
	Output current Opt1 (A)	9.44
	Output voltage Opt1 (V)	-0.04
	Input current Opt1 (A)	-0.00
	Input voltage Opt1 (V)	39.98
	Remark: Detachment Opt1	
d)	System current (A)	0.02
	System voltage (V)	**598.27**
	Output current Opt1 (A)	0.02
	Output voltage Opt1 (V)	-0.14
	Input current Opt1 (A)	0.00
	Input voltage Opt1 (V)	39.98
	Remark: String disconnection inverter	
e)	System current (A)	0.03
	System voltage (V)	**604.74**
	Output current Opt1 (A)	0.02
	Output voltage Opt1 (V)	0.08
	Input current Opt1 (A)	10.37
	Input voltage Opt1 (V)	1.26
	Remark: Chaotic input behaviour Opt1	
f)	System current (A)	0.03
	System voltage (V)	**604.48**
	Output current Opt1 (A)	0.02
	Output voltage Opt1 (V)	0.03
	Input current Opt1 (A)	10.37
	Input voltage Opt1 (V)	0.83
	Remark: Input short circuit Opt1, burner off	

Figure 2 and Table I: Exemplary evaluation of Series II flame test with system behaviour and event summary (a-f).

Behaviour with Overtemperature

Optimizers reliably detected overtemperature and switched to bypass, removing only their own contribution while the string continued operation. After cooling, they reactivated automatically even when visibly deformed. Switching thresholds showed consistent hysteresis, and monitoring warnings were only temporary.

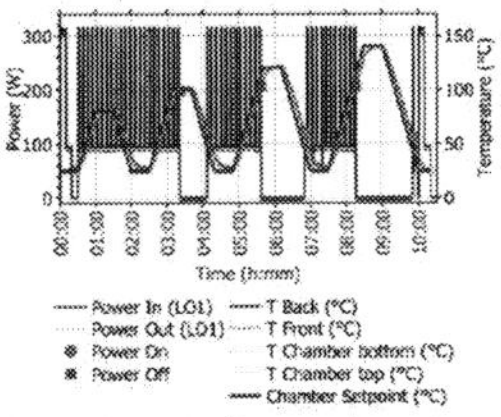

Figure 3: Exemplary switching behaviour of a thermally stressed optimizer (Series I)

Monitoring portals differed: Huawei gave position warnings, SolarEdge general errors, Tigo none. After cooling, all messages were archived, leaving no active faults or records, even when visible device damage was present.

A boxplot (Fig. 4) summarizes shutdown and restart temperatures by optimizer type.

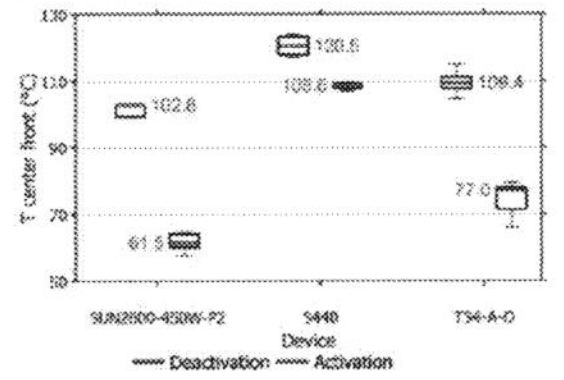

Figure 4: Shutdown and restart temperatures of optimizers (Series I) with hysteresis.

Behaviour under Fire Conditions

Evaluation was based on visual and electrical analysis (example in Fig. 2 and Tab. I). The flame process was highly chaotic, leading to non-reproducible system behaviour between runs.

In most cases, the inverter interrupted the string current within minutes, typically due to RCD tripping, while system voltage remained unaffected. In other tests, no shutdown occurred and the string kept operating despite the burning optimizer. Rapid Shutdown was never triggered due to the Fire Conditions.

Mechanically, brackets melted, causing optimizers to detach or swing while connected by cables. Burning droplets, strong flames, and dense smoke were frequently observed, showing that optimizers increase the fire load.

Figure 4 & 5: Flame tests in facade setup (front, side)

Conclusions and Outlook

In this research project it was observed that optimizers can detect overtemperature, but they do not trigger a complete system shutdown. From the flame test observations, the following fire safety–relevant behaviours can be derived:

Table II: Assessment of electrical (+) and fire-related (-) behaviour of PV systems with optimizers.

Category	(+) Pro	(-) Contra
Electrical behaviour	Detection of overtemperature	No reduction of system voltage
	No electrical power absorption	Poor / missing alarm functionality
Fire behaviour		Additional fire load
		Detachment of burning parts
		Burning droplet formation

The impact on fire safety should be discussed. The findings are shared openly, and the results should be critically questioned.

In further research projects, possible fire spread caused by optimizers should be investigated.

Acknowledgment

This research project was supported by the Building Insurance of the Canton of Bern (GVB).

GVB

References

[1] C. Bucher, (2025). *Photovoltaic Systems: Planning, Installation, Operation* (2nd rev. ed.). Zürich: Faktor Verlag.
[2] F. Fjaerestad et al., *Fire performance of building-integrated photovoltaics: A review*, Fire Safety Journal 113 (2020) 102978.

Berner Fachhochschule
Haute école spécialisée bernoise
Bern University of Applied Sciences

› Department of Engineering and Computer Science (TI)
› Institute for Energy and Mobility Research (IEM)

Laboratory for Photovoltaic Systems
3400 Burgdorf | Jlcoweg 1
www.bfh.ch/pvlab | christof.bucher@bfh.ch

020360-001

Applied Photovoltaic Research
Swiss Solar Competence

ONLINE CHARACTERIZATION OF PV STRINGS BY SMART INVERTERS USING A SELF REFERENCING ALGORITHM

Maximilian Schönau[1,2], Darwin Daume[3], Sasikumar Krishnan[1], Marius Weiß[1], Alexander Kusch[1], Christian Knausdorf[1], Sahereh Obeidavi[1], Achim Schulze[3,4], Dieter Landes[1], Bernd Hüttl[1]
[1]Coburg University of Applied Sciences, Dept. of Electrical Engineering and Computer Sciences, Coburg, Germany,
[2]smartblue AG, Kistlerhofstraße 75, Munich, Germany
[3]pvnode UG, Gabelsbergerstr. 9, 83022 Rosenheim
[4]Rosenheim Technical University of Applied Sciences, Germany,
Maximilian.Schoenau@smartblue.de, darwin@pvnode.com

ABSTRACT: We present a remote diagnostic method that uses the IV measurement function of smart inverters and a so called self-referencing procedure to represent the performance of the PV generator vs. operating conditions irradiance and temperature (G and T). We have recorded 200 IV-curves of a PV string within a period of six months using a smart inverter. A deep autoencoder detected disturbed or IV measurements so that these were not included in the evaluation. The effective irradiance G_{eff} at the PV string was determined, which was included in the evaluation instead of the measured irradiance. In addition, the cell temperature of the PV generator T_{eff} was determined using physical models for the evaluation. As a result, we create smooth power-surfaces over G_{eff} and T_{eff} conditions in the range of 100–1100 W/m² and 15–90 °C. For validation, the performance data of the PV string were compared by indoor measurements with a calibrated flasher at standard test conditions. The approach offers a remote and real-time diagnostic by smart inverters. It is well suited for accurate power monitoring of PV generators or degradation or soiling tracking without the need for additional sensor capabilities.
Keywords: Smart inverter IV tracing, IEC 61853-1, G–T performance matrix, Degradation monitoring, Soiling

1 INTRODUCTION

It is desirable for operators of PV systems to have continuous remote diagnostic performance monitoring for PV generators to detect degradation effects or soiling at an early stage. Performance determinations are possible by measuring current-voltage characteristics (IV-curves). The applicable standards IEC 60904, IEC 61829 and IEC 61853-1 define the procedures for measuring the IV-curves under controlled conditions of irradiance G and temperature T in order to create a performance matrix for G-T conditions [1].

However, very accurate performance determination of PV modules is only possible in measurement laboratories by means of calibrated solar simulators. Outdoor performance determinations on site often do not meet these accurate requirements and are also very costly. As a result, plant operators often lack a reliable, continuous overview of the performance of PV generators.

Smart inverters feature IV measurement capabilities that enable IV-curves of PV strings to be tracked directly without significantly interrupting the energy supply at the maximum power point (MPP). This function has opened promising possibilities for remote performance diagnostics of PV generators. Several studies have investigated the measurement uncertainties of IV measurements by inverters and their suitability for condition monitoring [2], [3]. In addition, self-referencing algorithms (SRA) have recently been developed that reduce the uncertainty of outdoor power ratings [4], [5].

In this article, we present a fully remote-controlled diagnostic measurement method for determining the power of PV generators based on the recording of IV-curves with smart inverters and on SRA.

To test and validate the measurement method, approximately 200 IV measurements were performed over a period of 6 months. The measurements were performed within a wide range of measurement conditions, G and T. IV measurements recorded under unsuitable measurement conditions are sorted out by means a deep autoencoder operating as a filter [6].

The result of the outdoor analysis was compared and verified with laboratory measurements under standard test conditions (STC) on PV modules of the string using a calibrated solar simulator.

2 SETUP

We used a smart inverter of SMA (Sunny Boy Smart Energy 5.0 inverter, type SBSE5.0-50) for energy harvesting and outdoor measuring the IV-curves of the connected string. By means of a well oriented pyranometer of Kipp & Zonen (SMP 10-A) and a temperature sensor, the global tilted irradiation (G_{mod}) and ambient temperature (T_{amb}) was measured.

In addition to that, we used satellite weather data of pvnode, to acquire the ambient temperature and the global tilted irradiation [7], to evaluate the need of accurate but costly on site sensors. In the future, it will also be possible to determine the measurement conditions by using machine learning based on data of satellites and of reference PV systems [8].

In total, we collected 200 IV-curves of a PV string consisting of six modules from supplier IBC: MonoSol 320 VL5-HC. These modules have a rated output of $P_{\text{MPP, STC}} = 320\,\text{W}$. To eliminate IV measurements recorded under unsuitable measurement conditions (e.g., with shadowing scenarios or with non-constant irradiance), a deep autoencoder was used as a filter [6]. The autoencoder was trained using "good" or "usable" IV curves so that IV curves from unsuitable conditions could be easily identified and sorted out.

The weather conditions of G_{mod} and T_{mod} varied over a wide range of measurement conditions. The SRA or referencing methodology developed in earlier work for on-site characterizations [4, 5] replaces the measured conditions G_{mod} and T_{mod} by the conditions G_{eff} and T_{eff}, which effectively affect the PV generator [4]. For realizing the remote concept, the SRA was modified regarding the determination of the temperature T_{eff} to reduce the number of electrical measurements required. We used the thermal

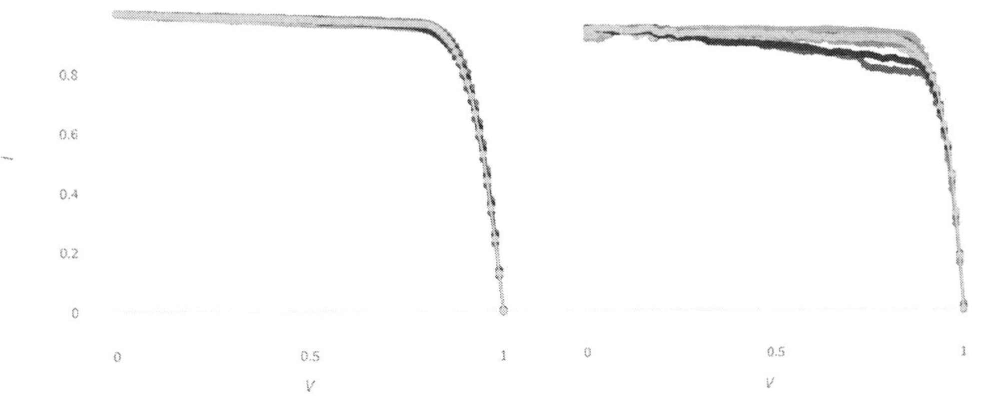

Figure 1: Examples of normalized deformed and undeformed IV-curves of our measurement campaign

model auf Sandia [9], [10] developed for physical modelling of cell temperature, using the ambient temperature T_{amb}, G_{eff} and some well-chosen parameters.

The power of PV string ($P_{mpp,\,string}$) is presented by our software concept as a surface versus the measurement conditions G_{eff} and T_{eff} to specify the nominal power ratings in accordance with the power matrix of the IEC 61853-1 standard [1].

For final validation of our remote performance determination concept, the outdoor P_{mpp} of the PV string at STC was compared with results of STC measurements on PV modules of the string by calibrated solar simulator cetisPV-XF-M of the company h.a.l.m.

3 ONLINE CHARACTERIZATIONS OF PV STRINGS USING SMART INVERTERS

Our remote measurement concept, which was described in the previous chapter, is mapped in our software and it is processed in three steps: (1): IV-curve filtering, (2): determination of the effective measurement conditions, and (3) adjusting the power surface by parameter fitting

3.1 IV-Curve Filtering

Typically, outdoor IV measurements suffer considerably from uncertainty regarding regular test conditions. For example, complete or partial shading or fluctuations in irradiance during the measurement lead to distorted IV curves, which are unusable for performance determinations [5].

To ensure that only undeformed IV-curves are used in performance analysis, we use a deep autoencoder as a monitoring filter: An autoencoder is an unsupervised neural network that learns a compact, nonlinear embedding of high-dimensional inputs by being trained to reproduce its own inputs at the output. In our implementation, each measured IV-curve was first normalized by it short-circuit current and open-circuit voltage and then passed through an encoder E that encodes the curve $I_V$into a seven-dimensional latent code,

$$E: I_V \to \mathbb{R}^7 \qquad (1)$$

as well as a decoder D that reconstructs the complete curve [6]:

$$D: \mathbb{R}^7 \to I_V' \qquad (2)$$

We trained the autoencoder network exclusively with "good" (undeformed), labeled in previous work [6]. After that, the model was used to decode and encode all IV curves,

$$I_V' = (D \circ E)(I_V) \qquad (3)$$

which were then compared with the original:

$$\mathrm{RMSE} = \sqrt{\frac{1}{n_V} \cdot \sum_{V}^{n_V} (I_V - I_V')^2} \qquad (44)$$

Deformed IV-curves show significant reconstruction deviations as a result. Since the autoencoder has never seen a deformed IV curve in the training process, these curves have significantly different encodings when given to the model due to their deformation. Reconstruction deviations can be quantified by the RMSE between reconstructed and ideally undeformed IV-curves. With the help of a sensibly defined threshold value, IV-curves with unacceptable deformations can be sorted out.

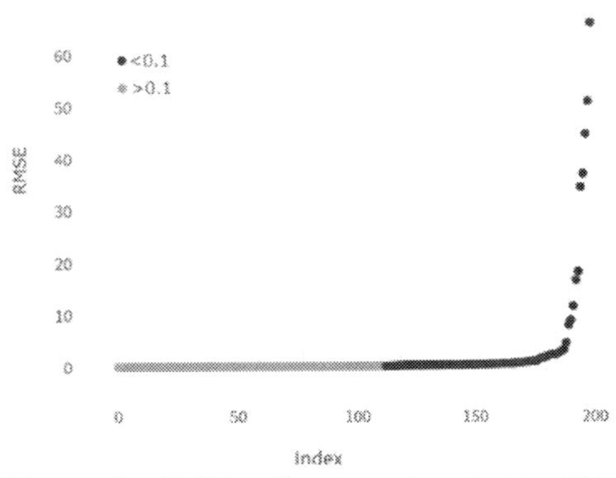

Figure 2: RMSE of autoencoder reconstruction uncertainty of measured IV-curves

Figure 2 shows the RMSE of the reconstruction deviations of all measured IV curves. We set a threshold value of 10 % for the RMSE of the reconstruction deviation, so that 90 IV-curves were sorted out from further analysis.

Figure 1 shows normalized usable and undistorted and distorted IV curves from our measurement campaign, that were filtered using the reconstruction error of the autoencoder.

3.2 Determination of the Effective Measurement Conditions

Using the measured IV-curves, the effective irradiance and the effective temperature are calculated from the module irradiance G_{mod} and the ambient temperature T_{amb}. The effective cell temperature T_{eff} is calculated using the thermal model of PV lib [10]:

$$T_{\mathrm{mod}} = G_{\mathrm{mod}} \cdot e^{a} \cdot \frac{\mathrm{m}^2 \cdot {}^\circ\mathrm{C}}{\mathrm{W}} + T_{\mathrm{amb}} \tag{5}$$

$$T_{\mathrm{eff}} = T_{\mathrm{mod}} + \frac{G_{\mathrm{mod}}}{G_{\mathrm{STC}}} \cdot \Delta T \tag{6}$$

With a and ΔT being empirical parameters, and G_{STC} being $1000\ \frac{\mathrm{W}}{\mathrm{m}^2}$. Windspeed correction was not applied. For the glass/polymer open-rack PV modules the fit parameters were -3.56 and 3 °C for a and ΔT, respectively.

Moreover, the effective irradiation G_{eff} is calculated by means the short current at STC $I_{\mathrm{SC,STC}}$ taken from the datasheet and the measured short circuit $I_{\mathrm{SC,\,mod}}$ according to [4]:

$$G_{\mathrm{eff}} = \frac{G_{\mathrm{STC}}}{I_{\mathrm{sc,\,STC}}} \cdot \frac{I_{\mathrm{sc,\,mod}}}{1 + \alpha_{I_{sc}} \cdot (T_{\mathrm{cell}} - 25\ {}^\circ\mathrm{C})} \tag{7}$$

The temperature coefficient α_{Isc} was taken from datasheet too. Note, G_{eff} is the irradiance reaching the photovoltaic cell in the module and considering any AOI losses and losses of soiling or shadowing by degradation.

For our modelling we calculate theoretical power P_{model} and short circuit current $I_{\mathrm{SC,model}}$ of the PV string for given irradiance G_{eff} and temperatures T_{eff} according with:

$$P_{\mathrm{model}} = n_{\mathrm{mod}} \cdot P_{\mathrm{mpp,STC}} \cdot \frac{G_{\mathrm{eff}}}{G_{\mathrm{STC}}} \left(1 + \gamma_{P_{\mathrm{mpp}}} \cdot (T_{eff} - 25\ {}^\circ\mathrm{C})\right) \tag{8}$$

In equation (8) $\gamma_{P_{\mathrm{mpp}}}$ is the temperature coefficient of power and n_{mod}, is the quantity of modules of the string. The accuracy of our methodology will be further improved in the future by considering illumination-dependent modeling of the temperature coefficient [11].

3.3 Adjusting the Power Surface by Parameter Fitting

Using data of i IV-curves ($P_{\mathrm{mpp,\,string},i}$, $I_{\mathrm{sc,\,mod},\,i}$) vs. effective conditions $G_{\mathrm{eff},i}$ and $T_{\mathrm{eff},i}$ we can calculate $P_{\mathrm{mpp,STC}}$ and $\gamma_{P_{\mathrm{mpp}}}$ of equation (8) by minimizing the summed quadratic deviation of P_{model} and $P_{\mathrm{mpp,\,string}}$ for all i measurements:

$$\left(P_{\mathrm{mpp,STC}}, \gamma_{P_{\mathrm{mpp}}}\right) = \arg\min_{x} \sum_{i} \left(P_{\mathrm{model},i}(x) - P_{\mathrm{mpp,\,string},i}\right)^2 \tag{9}$$

with $\boldsymbol{x}$ being the fit parameter set:

$$\boldsymbol{x} = \left(P_{\mathrm{mpp,STC}}, \gamma_{P_{\mathrm{mpp}}}\right) \tag{10}$$

By using the derived parameters $P_{\mathrm{mpp,STC}}$ and $\gamma_{P_{\mathrm{mpp}}}$ and equation (8) the power matrix vs. test conditions according to standard IEC 61853-1 can be calculated as shown in table 1.

4 RESULTS

Our measurement method was fed with data from a period of six months, during all 200 IV curves were measured. According to chapter 3 and figure 2, 115 measurements were chosen to be useful and were considered for analysis. Figure 4 shows the presentation of string power $P_{\mathrm{mpp,\,string}}$ vs. effective measurement conditions, closely based on the performance matrix in accordance with the IEC 61853-1 standard. Please note that the effective conditions in use are based on our on-site measurements of G_{mod} and T_{mod}.

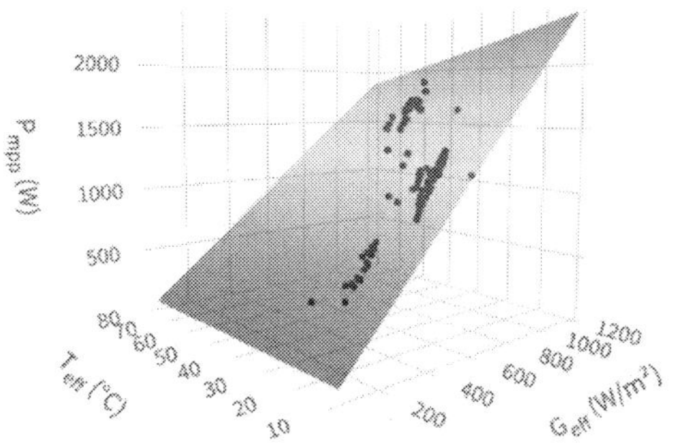

Figure 3: String power $P_{\mathrm{mpp,\,string}}$ vs. effective irradiance G_{eff} and effective cell temperature T_{eff}, based on experimental data of smart inverter.

Table 1 was calculated by using equation (8), like the performance matrix of the IEC 61853-1 standard.

Table 1: String power $P_{\mathrm{mpp,\,string}}$ vs. effective module temperature T_{eff} and irradiance G_{eff} derived from electrical measurements with smart inverter and based on on-site data T_{amb} and G_{mod}.

P_{mpp} in W	15 °C	25 °C	45 °C	50 °C	75 °C
100 W/m²	196	190	178	175	159
200 W/m²	393	380	355	349	318
400 W/m²	785	760	711	698	636
500 W/m²	981	950	888	873	795
600 W/m²	1178	1140	1066	1047	954
800 W/m²	1570	1521	1421	1396	1272
1000 W/m²	1963	**1901**	1777	1745	1590
1100 W/m²	2159	2091	1954	1920	1749

For comparison with calibrated solar simulator, we have determined the STC power of all modules of the string. The six modules of the string were performing $P_{\mathrm{mpp,\,module,\,STC}} = 312\ \mathrm{W} \pm 2\ \mathrm{W}$ resulting in a string power of $P_{\mathrm{mpp,\,string,\,STC}} = 1872\ \mathrm{W}$, representing a loss of 1.39 % from the nominal 6-module rating of 1920 W. The outdoor performance rating using on-site data shows for STC a $P_{\mathrm{mpp,\,string}}$ which is approximately 29 W or 1.5% higher than that of the indoor reference measurement.

Finally, we have used the complete remote concept for outdoor power rating, using satellite data of pvnode for determination of the temperature T_{amb} and irradiation G_{mod}. The results of the remote concept are very similar to the data of on-site measurements, as shown in table 2. Table 2 represents the measurement deviation of the two concepts. For all operating conditions, the string power $P_{mpp,\ string}$ based on remote data are typically lower by around 2 % in comparison to on-site data. For STC $P_{mpp,\ string,\ remote}$ is 1855 W, close to the reference level of calibrated indoor measurement.

Table 2: Deviation of the two analysis concepts using measured on-site and remote satellite data with: $\Delta P_{mpp} = P_{mpp,\ string,on\text{-}site} - P_{mpp,\ string,\ remote}$

ΔP_{mpp} in W	15 °C	25 °C	45 °C	50 °C	75 °C
100 W/m²	4	5	6	7	9
200 W/m²	8	10	12	13	17
400 W/m²	16	19	24	26	33
500 W/m²	20	23	30	32	41
600 W/m²	23	28	36	38	49
800 W/m²	31	37	48	51	65
1000 W/m²	39	46	60	64	81
1100 W/m²	43	50	66	70	90

5 CONCLUSIONS

We have demonstrated that modern smart inverters in combination with an intelligent evaluation concept, based on self-referencing and machine learning methods, are well suited to determine the performance behavior of PV strings across a wide range of measurement conditions in accordance with the performance matrix of the IEC 61853-1 standard.

The methodology can be set up entirely for remote diagnostics if reliable satellite data are available to determine the measurement conditions. The method is suitable for real-time diagnostics and degradation analysis.

Future work may continue with the validation and determination of uncertainty of the methodology. In addition to that, the methodology may be utilized for the detection of degradation and soiling.

ACKNOWLEDGEMENTS

The authors gratefully acknowledge the Bavarian Research Foundation for their financial support of the project Kick-PV: "AI-based characterization and classification of PV-plants for predictive maintenance" under reference number AZ-1564-22.

Portions of the manuscript text were drafted or edited with assistance from large language models. The authors reviewed, revised, and took full responsibility for the content.

LITERATURE

[1] *IEC 60904-1:2020, Photovoltaic devices. Part 1, Measurement of photovoltaic current-voltage characteristics*, Edition 3.0. Geneva, Switzerland: International Electrotechnical Commission, 2020.

[2] Alexander Kusch *et al.*, "Validierung von Smart-Wechselrichtern für die Leistungsferndiagnose von PV-Strängen," presented at the RET.Con, Nordhausen, Feb. 2025.

[3] M. Bartholomäus, L. Morino, P. B. Poulsen, and S. V. Spataru, "Evaluating the Accuracy of Inverter Based String IV Measurements," *40th European Photovoltaic Solar Energy Conference and Exhibition*, pp. 020370-001-020370–005, 2023, doi: 10.4229/EUPVSEC2023/4CV.1.4.

[4] B. Hüttl, L. Gottschalk, S. Schneider, D. Pflaum, and A. Schulze, "Accurate performance rating of photovoltaic modules under outdoor test conditions," *Solar Energy*, vol. 177, pp. 737–745, Jan. 2019, doi: 10.1016/j.solener.2018.12.002.

[5] M. Scheler *et al.*, "Precise On-Site Power Analysis of Photovoltaic Arrays by Self-Reference Algorithm," *8th World Conference on Photovoltaic Energy Conversion; 1070-1073*, p. 4 pages, 28190 kb, 2022, doi: 10.4229/WCPEC-82022-4DO.1.4.

[6] M. Schönau, D. Daume, B. Hüttl, and D. Landes, "Improving IV Curve Classification by Machine Learning Methods Using Deep Autoencoders," *40th European Photovoltaic Solar Energy Conference and Exhibition*, pp. 020410-001-020410–004, 2023, doi: 10.4229/EUPVSEC2023/4CV.1.53.

[7] "pvnode: Your partner for the new generation of precise PV data." Accessed: Feb. 18, 2025. [Online]. Available: https://www.pvnode.com/

[8] M. Schönau *et al.*, "Hindcasting Solar Irradiance by Machine Learning using Photovoltaic Data," *41st European Photovoltaic Solar Energy Conference and Exhibition*, pp. 020400-001-020400–005, 2024, doi: 10.4229/EUPVSEC2024/4CV.1.4.

[9] K. S. Anderson, C. W. Hansen, W. F. Holmgren, A. R. Jensen, M. A. Mikofski, and A. Driesse, "pvlib python: 2023 project update," *JOSS*, vol. 8, no. 92, p. 5994, Dec. 2023, doi: 10.21105/joss.05994.

[10] J. Kratochvil, W. Boyson, and D. King, "Photovoltaic array performance model.," SAND2004-3535, 919131, Aug. 2004. doi: 10.2172/919131.

[11] S. M. F. Zhang *et al.*, "Illumination-dependent temperature coefficients of the electrical parameters of modern silicon solar cell architectures," *Nano Energy*, vol. 98, p. 107221, Jul. 2022, doi: 10.1016/j.nanoen.2022.107221.

42nd European Photovoltaic Solar Energy Conference and Exhibition

Online Characterization of PV Strings by Smart Inverters Using a Self Referencing Algorithm

Maximilian Schönau, Darwin Daume, Sasikumar Krishnan, Marius Weiß, Alexander Kusch, Christian Knausdorf, Sahereh Obeidavi, Achim Schulze, Dieter Landes, Bernd Hüttl

Introduction

- **Challenge:** Creation of a remote performance diagnosis system for PV strings for early detection of performance degradation or soiling
- **Approach:** Application of the IV-measurement function of smart inverters for determination of a string-power matrix vs. operating conditions irradiance (*G*) and temperature (*T*).
- **Data Processing:** Improvement of measurement accuracy by using a self-referencing algorithm (SRA) and a deep autoencoder for sorting out distorted I-V curves.

Experimental Setup

- **Device under Test:** PV string of 6 monocrystalline PV modules with STC power of 320 W
- **IV-Tracer:** Sunny Boy Smart Energy 5.0 inverter
- **Operating Conditions:** G and T were measured on-site or were acquired by data service providers using satellite weather data
- **Measurement Campaign:** approximately 200 IV curves were collected within 6 months for varying operating conditions

IV Curve Evaluation by Autoencoder

- Shading or fluctuating irradiances during IV measurements result in deformed IV curves which are not useful for power rating
- Machine Learning by training of autoencoders can be used to recognize deformed IV curves
- Autoencoder was used to filter or non-deformed IV-curves (right hand side figure) and measurements with useless deformed IV curves (left hand side figure)

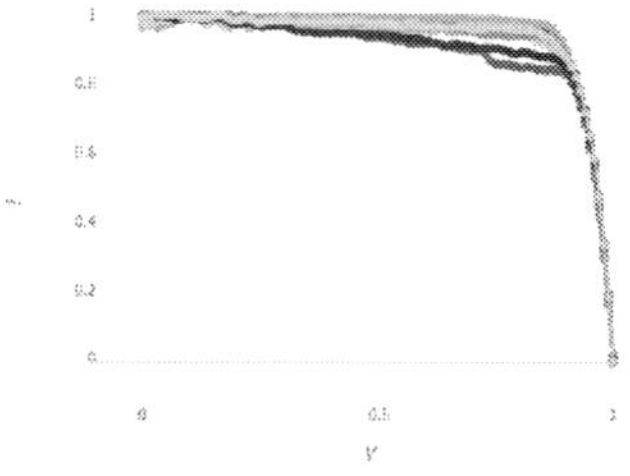

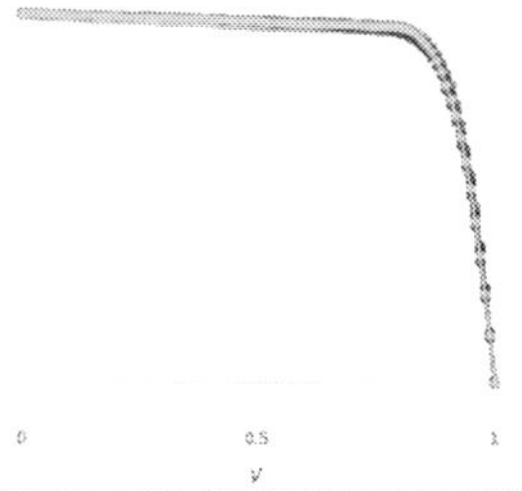

Determination of the Effective Measurement Conditions

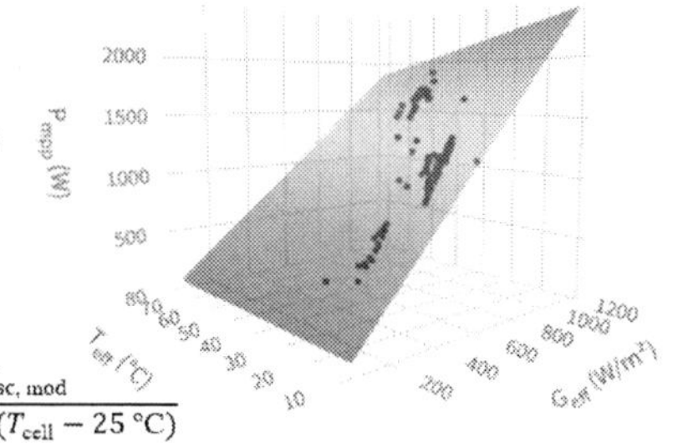

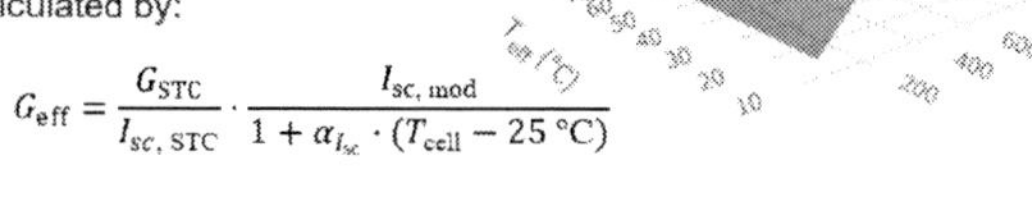

- The module temperature is modeled from the ambient temperature using pvlib
- The effective irradiance is calculated by:

$$G_{\text{eff}} = \frac{G_{\text{STC}}}{I_{sc,\,\text{STC}}} \cdot \frac{I_{\text{sc, mod}}}{1 + \alpha_{I_{sc}} \cdot (T_{\text{cell}} - 25\,°\text{C})}$$

- For all operating conditions, the power can be modeled with:

$$P_{\text{model}} = n_{\text{mod}} \cdot P_{\text{mpp,STC}} \cdot \frac{G_{\text{eff}}}{G_{\text{STC}}} \left(1 + \gamma_{P_{\text{mpp}}} \cdot (T_{\text{eff}} - 25\,°\text{C})\right)$$

- P_{mpp} is fitted as a surface over the temperature and irradiance over all measurements

By fitting all IV-curves at once to the performance matrix, the accuracy of the characterization is drastically increased.

Results

- A performance matrix similar to the IEC 61853-1 standard can be calculated
- At STC, the measurement deviation between the outdoor campaign and an indoor reference measurement is only 1.5 %
- Using satellite data instead of on-site sensors lead to the same results
  → Deviations in inaccurate satellite data are corrected by the fitting process

String Power over Module Temperature and Irradiance

P_{mpp} in W	15 °C	25 °C	45 °C	50 °C	75 °C
100 W/m²	196	190	178	175	159
200 W/m²	393	380	355	349	318
400 W/m²	785	760	711	698	636
500 W/m²	981	950	888	873	795
600 W/m²	1178	1140	1066	1047	954
800 W/m²	1570	1521	1421	1396	1272
1000 W/m²	1963	1901	1777	1745	1590
1100 W/m²	2159	2091	1954	1920	1749

Modern smart inverters in combination with an intelligent evaluation concept, are well suited to determine the performance behavior of PV strings in accordance with the performance matrix of the IEC 61853-1 standard

Download

EU PVSEC Bilbao
22nd to 26th September 2025

Full Paper

smartblue
smartblue AG, Kaiserhofstraße 75, Munich, Germany

COBURG UNIVERSITY of applied sciences and arts
Coburg University of Applied Sciences, Dept. of Electrical Engineering and Computer Sciences, Coburg, Germany

pvnode
pvnode UG, Gabelsbergerstr. 9, 83022 Rosenheim

Technische Hochschule Rosenheim
Rosenheim Technical University of Applied Sciences, Germany

Bayerische Forschungsstiftung

42nd European Photovoltaic Solar Energy Conference and Exhibition

This presentation was selected by the Sc. Committee of the EU PVSEC 2025 for submission of a full paper to one of the EU PVSEC's collaborating peer-reviewed journals.

BRIDGING THE GAP: INSIGHTS INTO BACKTRACKING-ANGLE RELATED DISCREPANCIES BETWEEN ESTIMATES AND ACTUAL PERFORMANCE IN LARGE-SCALE PHOTOVOLTAIC PLANTS

Juan Santamaría-Sancho, Javier Martín-Rueda, Eduardo Lorenzo Pigueiras, Javier R. Ledesma
Instituto de Energía Solar, Universidad Politécnica de Madrid
C/ Nikola Tesla, s/n
juan.santamariasan@upm.es, javier.martin@upm.es, antonio.lorenzo@upm.es, javier.ledesma@upm.es

ABSTRACT: Energy yield overestimation in large-scale photovoltaic (PV) simulations is a recurring issue that affects the accuracy of performance predictions. Analysis of SCADA data from four single-axis PV plants in different regions revealed systematic deviations between simulated and measured tracker angles during backtracking periods, prompting an investigation into the role of the estimated tracking irradiation gain (TIG) in these discrepancies. These deviations seemed to be linked to empirical corrections implemented to mitigate shading caused by terrain unevenness, which introduces elevation differences between tracker rows. While these adjustments reduce shading losses, they also modify the trackers' optimal tilt, lowering incident irradiance and ultimately reducing energy yield. A reverse-engineering approach was used to derive an equivalent correction model, based on a theoretical reduction in the effective inter-row spacing. When implemented in simulation tools, this correction produced TIG values 7–10% lower than those predicted under ideal flat-terrain conditions, leading to annual energy yield overestimations of around 3%. The results underscore the importance of accounting for realistic tracking behavior in energy yield simulations to improve both technical accuracy and the financial predictability of PV projects.
Keywords: energy yield overestimation, tracking irradiation gain, backtracking, terrain unevenness effects, PV simulation.

1 INTRODUCTION

In recent years, the growth of installed PV capacity and the increasing relevance of solar energy have drawn attention to the persistent overestimation of expected energy yields in large-scale PV plants [1] [2]. Within these discrepancies between actual and simulated results, the tracking irradiation gain (TIG) emerges as a key performance indicator (KPI), as it directly influences the energy yield.

Reports and consultations received at the Instituto de Energía Solar (IES) of the Universidad Politécnica de Madrid (UPM) frequently indicate that the TIG observed in large commercial single-axis tracking PV plants is systematically lower than the values predicted by simulations performed during the project design phase for bankability purposes. TIG, defined as the relative increase in irradiation collected by single-axis tracking systems compared to horizontal (zero-tilt) configurations, plays a central role in energy yield modelling and is given by

$$\mathrm{TIG}_T(\omega) = \frac{G_T(\omega) - G_T(0)}{G_T(0)}, \qquad (1)$$

where $G_T(\omega)$ and $G_T(0)$ represent the solar irradiation accumulated during a period T on a plane tilted at angle ω and on a horizontal plane, respectively. It must be noted that a reduction in TIG does not affect the performance ratio (PR) or the availability indicators of the PV plants. For this reason, despite its relevance, this phenomenon has so far received little attention in the open literature.

This work investigates the causes of the lower-than-expected TIG through the analysis of four PV plants equipped with different tracker models installed on horizontal terrain. The study shows that terrain irregularities, often ignored in simulation models, produce small but systematic deviations in tracker alignment. These deviations require corrective adjustments in tracking operation to mitigate shading and the appearance of hot spots, but such adjustments come at the cost of reducing the amount of captured irradiance.

By focusing on TIG itself, this study aims to improve the understanding of the gap between simulated and actual values of this KPI and to emphasize the need to incorporate these effects into future energy yield assessments, leading to more accurate and financially reliable PV project evaluations.

2 MODELLING THE TRACKING ANGLES

This work focuses on quantifying the impact of tracker positioning during backtracking periods on the TIG in utility-scale PV plants equipped with horizontal single-axis trackers. This configuration is projected to represent nearly 40% of the market share in utility solar PV installations by 2030 [3]. To that end, the geometric framework underlying the computation of tracker rotation angles is introduced, as implemented in SISIFO, a simulation software developed by IES-UPM. SISIFO was developed within the European projects PVCROPS [4], MASLOWATEN [5] and PVOP [6] . It supports the simulation of grid-connected and pumping PV systems, including features such as mutual shading modeling [7] [8], multiple tracking strategies [9], and bifacial operation on sloped terrain [10]. The models for irradiance distribution, decomposition, transposition, and spectral correction are detailed in [11] [12] [13].

The physical domain is modeled as a three-dimensional affine space $\mathcal{A}_0 \equiv (\mathbb{R}^3, \mathbb{R}^3, \phi)$, where $\phi\colon \mathcal{A}_0 \times \mathcal{A}_0 \to \mathbb{R}^3$ denotes the vector difference, and the associated vector space $(\mathbb{R}^3, \|\cdot\|)$ is equipped with the standard Euclidean norm derived from the usual scalar product. The natural Euclidean distance $d_0\colon \mathcal{A}_0 \times \mathcal{A}_0 \to \mathbb{R}$ is used to compute physical distances in this space.

A right-handed Cartesian coordinate system-(x, y, z) is introduced, with origin $O \in \mathcal{A}_0$ located on the rotation axis of a reference tracker, at a height H_0 above ground level. The x-axis points East–West, the y-axis points North–South, and the z-axis is aligned with the zenith direction.

Trackers are assumed to be arranged in equidistant,

parallel rows indexed by $n \in \mathbb{Z}$, where $n = 0$ corresponds to the reference tracker. Rows to the right (respectively, left) are indexed by consecutive positive (respectively, negative) integers.

The solar position is calculated using the standard solar position equations [11] and is characterized by two standard angles: the solar azimuth γ_S, defined as the angle between the projection of the Sun onto the horizontal plane and the geographic North (positive eastwards), and the solar zenith angle θ_S, defined as the angle between the Sun and the vertical direction.

Tracker rotation is described by its tilt angle ω, measured with respect to the horizontal plane, and its azimuth angle, corresponding to the orientation of the rotation axis. In typical utility-scale configurations, including the ones considered in this work, trackers are aligned along the North–South direction, corresponding to azimuth $\alpha = 0$.

To simplify the analysis, SISIFO adopts a two-dimensional geometric representation in which the working domain is defined as the vertical plane orthogonal to the tracker rotation axis. For North–South-aligned trackers, this plane is orthogonal to the local meridian and is modeled as an affine plane $\mathcal{A} \subset \mathcal{A}_0$, endowed with the Euclidean distance $d: \mathcal{A} \times \mathcal{A} \to \mathbb{R}$ induced from d_0. An affine frame $\mathcal{R} = \{O; \mathcal{B}\}$ is fixed in $\mathcal{A}$, where $\mathcal{B}$ is the standard orthonormal basis of $\mathbb{R}^2$. Coordinates in this plane are denoted by (x, z). Within this working plane, the projection of the Sun's position is represented by the point $P_S \equiv (x_S, z_S)$, where $x_S = \cos\gamma_S \sin\theta_S$ and $z_S = \sin\theta_S$.

For subsequent analysis, the Euclidean distance in $\mathcal{A}$ is normalized so that the projected width of a tracker cross-section equals one unit. Specifically, if the projected endpoints of the n-th tracker cross-section in $\mathcal{A}$ are denoted by $E_{1,n}$ and $E_{2,n}$, for every $n \in \mathbb{Z}$ it is imposed the following condition,

$$d(E_{1,n}, E_{2,n}) = 1. \quad (2)$$

As a result, trackers are assumed to be evenly spaced by a normalized distance L_{EW} (East–West spacing) between consecutive rotation axes.

Figure 1 shows an schematic of the model implemented where blue segments represent the cross-sections of the trackers on the working domain. The baseline corresponds to the intersection between the working plane and the ground, assumed to be a perfectly horizontal plane. Yellow segments indicate illuminated ground areas, and black segments correspond to shaded ground regions. The trace of the Sun's ray is shown as a dashed black line. These colour conventions will be maintained in all subsequent figures, unless explicitly stated otherwise.

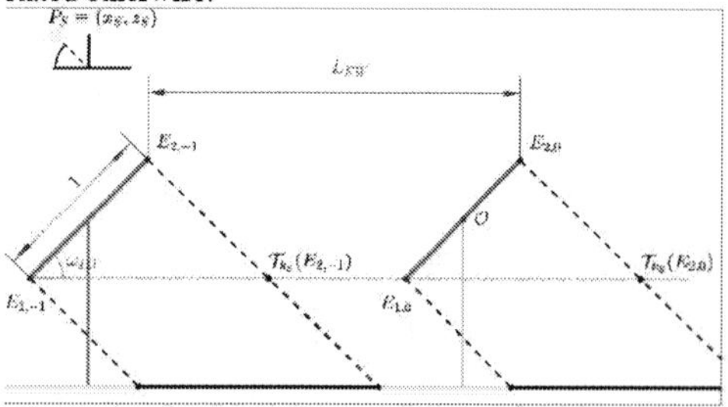

Figure 1: Simplified layout of the model. Trackers are shown in blue, and the ground is a horizontal line at height $-H$, with sunlit (yellow) and shaded (black) regions. The sun path appears as a dashed black line. The colour code employed for the notation corresponds to the colour of the respective elements it denotes.

2.1 Backtracking angles

In configurations with horizontal single-axis trackers, the rotation angle of each tracker is dynamically adjusted according to the position of the Sun. The ideal tracking condition corresponds to orienting the active surface of each generator such that the projection of the incident solar rays onto the working plane is orthogonal to the generator's cross-section. Equivalently, the normal vector to the tilted surface becomes collinear with the projection of the solar rays within this plane, thereby maximizing the irradiance collected by the active surface.

From simple trigonometric considerations, the corresponding ideal tracking angle ω_{ID} with respect to the horizontal is given by

$$\omega_{ID} = atan\frac{x_S}{z_S}. \quad (3)$$

However, this ideal configuration is not always feasible. At low solar altitudes, insufficient inter-row spacing may lead to one tracker row casting a shadow over the adjacent one, as schematically illustrated in **Figure 2**.

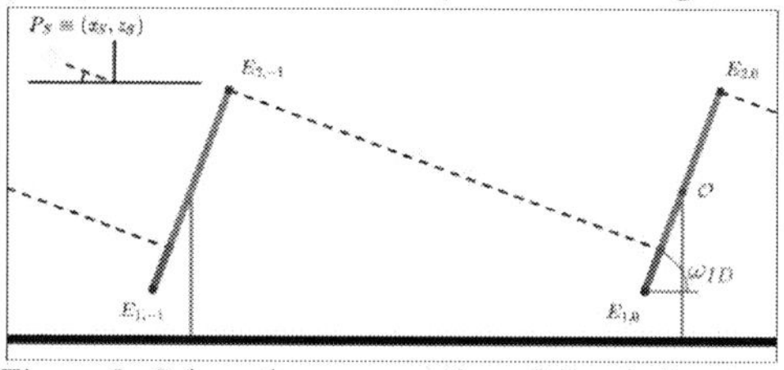

Figure 2: Schematic representation of the shadow cast between adjacent tracker rows at low solar altitudes, represented as red segments. The notation uses the same colour as the element it represents.

To avoid mutual shading between rows under these conditions, trackers are intentionally rotated away from the ideal direction, this strategy is known as backtracking.

To formalize the backtracking condition, the direction of sunlight projected onto the working domain $\mathcal{A} \subset \mathbb{R}^3$ is considered. Let

$$k_S = \frac{(x_S, z_S)}{\sqrt{x_S^2 + z_S^2}}, \quad (4)$$

denote the unit vector indicating the solar ray direction in the working plane, and $\pi_z: \mathbb{R}^3 \to \mathbb{R}$ the projection onto the vertical axis, that is, for any point $(x, y, z) \in \mathbb{R}^3$, $\pi_z(x, y, z) = z$. Based on the vector in Equation (4), an oblique projection operator $\mathcal{T}_{k_S}: \mathcal{A} \to \mathcal{G}$ is defined, mapping each point $P \in \mathcal{A}$ to the intersection of the ray emitted from P in the direction of k_S with the horizontal line $\mathcal{G} = \{(x, -H) \in \mathcal{A} | x \in \mathbb{R}\}$, where $H = \left(H_0 + min\left(\pi_z(E_{1,n}), \pi_z(E_{2,n})\right)\right) / d_0(E_{1,n}, E_{2,n})$ for any $n \in \mathbb{Z}$. That is,

$$\mathcal{T}_{k_S}(P) = (P + \lambda \cdot k_S) \cap \mathcal{G}, \quad (5)$$

for some $\lambda \in \mathbb{R}$. Formally, backtracking is triggered when the distance between the points $\mathcal{T}_{k_S}(E_{2,n})$ and $E_{1,n}$ or between the points $\mathcal{T}_{k_S}(E_{1,n})$ and $E_{2,n}$ exceeds the normalized inter-row spacing L_{EW}, for any $n \in \mathbb{Z}$. During the morning backtracking period, simple geometric analysis yields

$$d\left(E_{1,n}, \mathcal{T}_{k_S}(E_{2,n})\right) = sec(\omega_{ID}). \quad (6)$$

It should be noted that this equation is well-defined, since during backtracking it always holds that $\omega_{ID} \neq 0$.
Hence, the condition for activating backtracking becomes

$$sec(\omega_{ID}) \geq L_{EW} \Leftrightarrow L_{EW}cos(\omega_{ID}) \leq 1. \qquad (7)$$

An analogous condition applies symmetrically during the afternoon backtracking period.

To avoid shading, the tracker angle is corrected from the ideal value ω_{ID} by applying a backtracking correction angle ω_C^{BT} such that [14]

$$cos(\omega_C^{BT}) = L_{EW}cos(\omega_{ID}). \qquad (8)$$

Accordingly, the resulting angle ω_{IDC} of the generator with respect to the horizontal during backtracking is given by

$$\omega_{IDC} = \omega_{ID} - \omega_C^{BT}. \qquad (9)$$

This correction is the minimum required to prevent shading while minimizing energy losses due to deviation from the optimal angle. Therefore, the trackers are not rotated further than necessary, and under ideal conditions, the ground between rows remains completely shaded during backtracking periods, as illustrated in **Figure 3**.

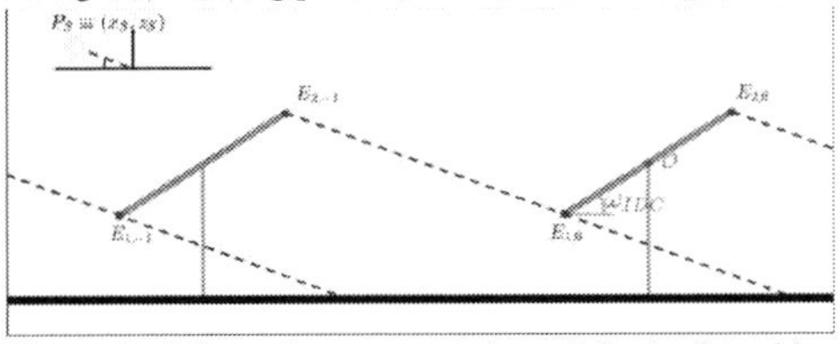

Figure 3: Schematic representation of the backtracking configuration. Colours in the notation match the corresponding elements they refer to.

2.2 Unevenness effect on backtracking

An essential assumption in the geometric model introduced above is the flatness of the terrain, whereby all tracker axes are assumed to lie on the same horizontal plane. While this simplification facilitates simulation and analytical treatment, it does not accurately reflect the conditions of real-world utility-scale PV plants. In practice, field inspections conducted during backtracking periods consistently revealed the presence of illuminated strips of ground between adjacent tracker rows, as illustrated in **Figure 4**. This empirical observation contradicts the theoretical prediction of complete ground shading during backtracking, indicating that additional factors must be influencing the actual behavior.

Figure 4: Field observation during backtracking showing systematic presence of light strips between adjacent tracker rows.

One of the contributors to this discrepancy is terrain unevenness, which introduces small but significant elevation differences between tracker rows. These vertical misalignments give rise to two possible shading scenarios. Focusing on the morning backtracking period, though the same reasoning applies in the afternoon, if a given tracker row $n \in \mathbb{Z}$ is situated at a slightly higher elevation than its preceding row $n-1$, its shadow fails to reach the adjacent row, resulting in a light strip on the ground. Conversely, if row n is at a lower elevation than row $n-1$, the shadow extends beyond the intended spacing, causing inter-row shading losses, the very outcome that backtracking algorithms are designed to avoid. These effects are illustrated schematically in **Figure 5**.

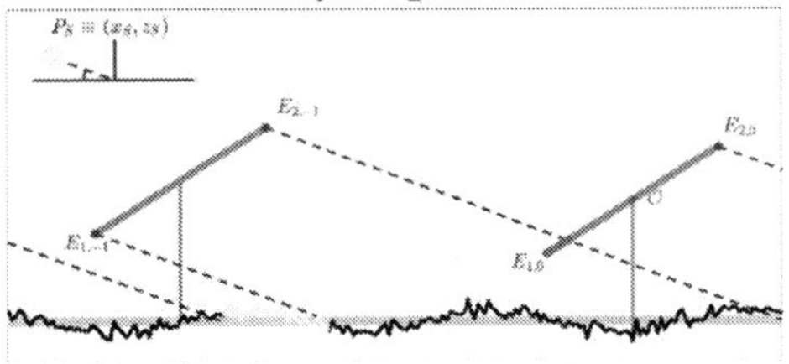

Figure 5: Schematic representation of the effects of terrain-induced elevation differences between tracker rows. The first generator row illustrates the appearance of light strips on the ground when the preceding row lies at a lower elevation. The second row depicts unintended shading (represented as a red segment) caused by a higher preceding row. The notation of each element is directly associated with its representative colour.

Interestingly, in actual PV plants, only the first of these scenarios, i.e. light strips between rows, was commonly observed. A plausible explanation is that shading between rows is undesirable not only due to its impact on energy yield but also because it generates hotspots that must be addressed during maintenance, and it is visually conspicuous. Consequently, it is hypothesized that the theoretical tracker positioning is deliberately adjusted in practice to prioritize the elimination of inter-row shading, even at the cost of reduced irradiance capture. This adjustment explains the systematic presence of ground illumination during backtracking periods, even on seemingly flat terrains.

3 APPROACH AND RESULTS

To validate the hypothesis proposed at the end of the previous section, SCADA data from the four PV plants under consideration were analyzed. These datasets included the angular position of each tracker, recorded as the empiric inclination angle ω_E with respect to the horizontal. To assess whether the angular position differs significantly across trackers within each PV plant, a pre-selection of trackers was performed based on data availability and quality. After this filtering, it was observed that the angular behavior of the selected trackers within each plant remained largely consistent over time. This observation supports the assumption that a single representative tracker per PV plant can reliably characterize the overall tracking behavior. Accordingly, the subsequent analysis focuses on one tracker per PV plant.

Table I summarizes the main characteristics of the analyzed PV plants, including their geographical location and the normalized inter-row spacing L_{EW} of each configuration. The second Mexican plant corresponds to a separate parcel within the same facility as the first and is therefore labeled 1.2, while the original is labeled 1.1 for clarity.

Table I: Some relevant technical specifications of the studied PV plants.

PV Plant	Location	L_{EW}/ []
1.1	Mexico	3.00
1.2	Mexico	3.00
2	Chile	2.26
3	Chile	2.56
4	Spain	2.74

Figure 6 illustrates, for PV plant 1.1 located in Mexico, the evolution of the generator's inclination angle throughout a full day, specifically on the spring equinox. The orange curve corresponds to the simulated tracker angle ω_{IDC}, while blue dots represent the experimental SCADA data ω_E. The difference between both values, shown as a dashed purple line (referenced to the right axis), reveals a sharp increase during backtracking intervals, highlighted with a white background. This confirms the deviation of real tracker behavior from the theoretical prediction specifically during those periods.

It should also be noted that the purple curve experiences a sudden change in trend at the end of the first daily backtracking period and at the beginning of the second. This behavior can be explained by the trackers reaching their mechanical saturation position, typically fixed around 55°. In the orange curve of **Figure 6**, this saturation is clearly visible as a flat region, reflecting the fact that, beyond this limit, the trackers can no longer follow the theoretical trajectory.

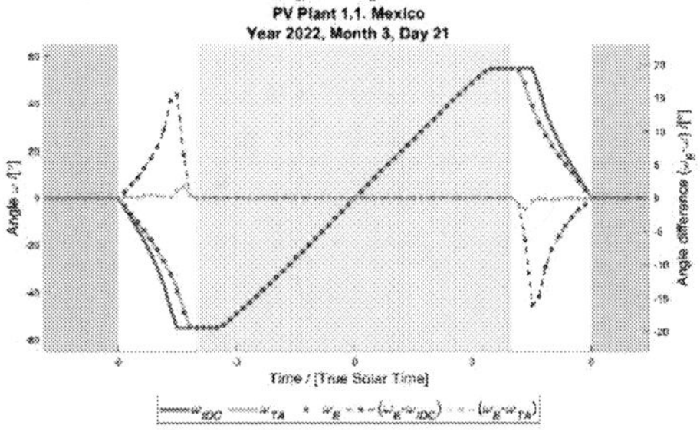

Figure 6: Comparison between simulated and measured tracker angles throughout the spring equinox day for PV plant 1.1, located in Mexico. The orange curve represents the theoretical inclination angle ω_{IDC} obtained from the ideal backtracking model, while the dark blue dots correspond to the experimental SCADA data ω_E. The dashed purple line, referenced to the right axis, quantifies the deviation between both values, which becomes particularly pronounced during backtracking intervals, highlighted with a white background. To account for this effect, a corrected simulation ω_{TA} was performed by introducing a reduced effective row-to-row distance $\tilde{L}_{EW}$. This correction, shown in dark yellow, results in a noticeable improvement, as reflected in the reduced discrepancy displayed in light blue, also , referenced to the right axis.

Figure 7 presents analogous results for the remaining PV plants located in Spain, Chile, and the second parcel in Mexico (PV plant 1.2), focusing exclusively on the first backtracking interval of the same day. Owing to the symmetry of the tracker motion with respect to solar noon, the analysis of this initial interval is sufficient, since the behavior observed during the second backtracking period mirrors that of the first.

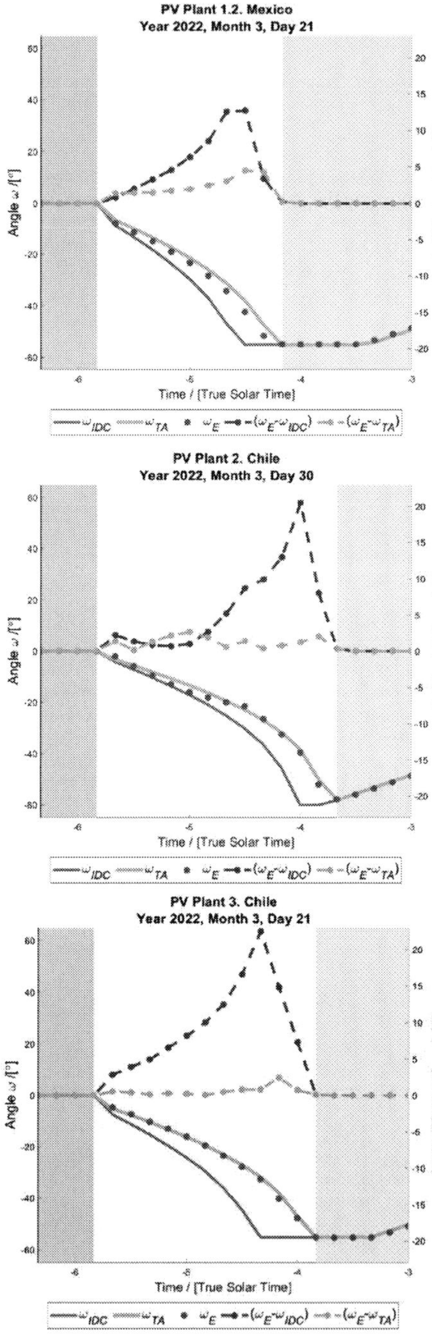

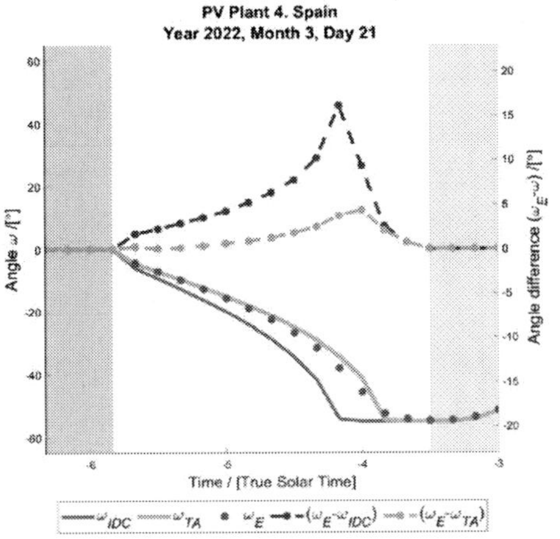

Figure 7: Simulated and measured tracking angles during the morning backtracking interval on the spring equinox for four PV plants. Each plot shows the original simulation ω_{IDC} (orange curve), the measured SCADA data ω_E (blue dots), and the initial discrepancy between them (dashed purple line, referenced to the right axis). The corrected simulated ω_{TA} using a reduced normalized spacing $\tilde{L}_{EW}$ is shown in dark yellow, while the resulting new discrepancy with ω_E is plotted in light blue (also referenced to the right axis). The backtracking interval is highlighted with a white background, where angular deviations are more pronounced and the correction significantly improves agreement.

In response to these observations, the angular configuration of the trackers at the PV plants was not modified. Instead, a correction was introduced within the simulation algorithm to replicate the observed deviations. This correction consists of recalculating the backtracking angle ω_{IDC} by assuming a reduced normalized inter-row spacing $\tilde{L}_{EW}$ in Equation (8), while preserving the actual physical configuration. In other words, a lower L_{EW} is used as an input to the backtracking algorithm, which forces a slightly smaller tracking angle, thereby generating light strips on the ground in the idealized model that mimic those observed in the field.

Focusing on the morning backtracking period, this correction accounts for terrain unevenness: if a row is slightly lower than its predecessor, the margin introduced by the modified angle allows it to remain illuminated, provided the elevation difference remains within acceptable bounds. Conversely, if the row is slightly higher than the preceeding one, the light strip widens, leading to reduced irradiance capture, but without introducing shading and, thus, maintaining one of the fundamental objectives of backtracking.

It is also worth noting that outside the backtracking periods, the tracker angle is independent of L_{EW}, making this correction easily implementable in practice by simulating the tracking angles for an entire day with a modified L_{EW}. However, as shown in Equation (7), the limits of the backtracking period do depend on L_{EW}. In practice, this effect is not observed in the analyzed plants, since the saturation angle of the trackers is reached before the theoretical backtracking periods end (or begin, in the case of the afternoon backtracking intervals).

The same figures discussed in this section also include, in dark yellow, the results of the simulation with the corrected angle ω_{TA}, obtained using $\tilde{L}_{EW}$. The light blue curve (again referenced to the right axis) represents the new discrepancy with respect to the measured values ω_E, which is now reduced by several orders of magnitude compared to the original simulation.

Finally, the relative annual variation $\Delta(\mathrm{TIG}_A)$ in tracking irradiation gain (TIG) between the ideal and corrected configurations is computed as

$$\Delta(\mathrm{TIG}_A) = \frac{\mathrm{TIG}_A(\omega_{IDC}) - \mathrm{TIG}_A(\omega_{TA})}{\mathrm{TIG}_A(\omega_{IDC})} \cdot 100, \qquad (10)$$

where the explicit dependence of TIG on the tracking angle used in the simulation has been indicated in brackets. Moreover, to reflect the annual nature of the analysis, the temporal subscript T previously used is replaced by A. It should be noted that the simulation results obtained with SISIFO are computed using a Typical Meteorological Year (TMY) as input. Furthermore, the applied correction is conceptually analogous to introducing an artificial East–West slope on the terrain, thereby modifying the effective geometry of the PV plant [10]. This scenario can be easily simulated in SISIFO, which natively supports simulations on sloped terrain, representing a major improvement over most existing PV simulation tools. The resulting values of $\Delta(\mathrm{TIG}_A)$ for each PV plant are summarized in **Table II**, together with the corresponding normalized spacing $\tilde{L}_{EW}$ used in the corrected simulations.

Table II: Normalized inter-row spacing $\tilde{L}_{EW}$ and relative annual tracking irradiation gain variation $\Delta(TIG_A)$ for the analyzed PV plants.

PV Plant	$\tilde{L}_{EW}$/ []	$\Delta(\mathrm{TIG}_A)$/ [%]
1.1	2.50	7.3
1.2	2.50	7.3
2	1.96	9.4
3	2.24	9.2
4	2.16	7.8

4 CONCLUSIONS

The widespread overestimation of energy production in PV simulations can be partly attributed to an overvaluation of the tracking irradiation gain. Experimental data from four PV plants across different countries show that systematic angle corrections are applied in the field to prevent mutual shading caused by terrain unevenness. A reverse-engineering approach, based on considering a reduced inter-row spacing, reveals that these corrections lead to TIG values 7–10% lower than theoretical estimates. This results in an average annual energy yield overestimation of about 3%, roughly half of the typical discrepancy between simulated and actual performance [10].

5 ACKNOWLEDGEMNETS

The authors express their sincere appreciation for the financial support provided through the project PVOP, funded by the European Union. Views and opinions expressed are however those of the authors only and do not necessarily reflect those of the European Union or CINEA. Neither the European Union nor the granting authority can be held responsible for them.

The authors are also grateful to EU PVSEC for the opportunity to present their work at the 2025 edition held in Bilbao, Spain. Special thanks go to the research staff at the Instituto de Energía Solar of the Universidad Politécnica de Madrid for their valuable contributions.

REFERENCES

[1] kWh Analytics, "Solar Risk Assessment 2024," 2024. Accessed: Sep. 17, 2025. [Online]. Available: https://kwhanalytics.com/wp-content/uploads/2025/02/2023-Solar-Risk-Assessment.pdf

[2] Solar Power World, "Solar projects are underperforming by 6.3%, new report suggests better assessment standards." Accessed: Sep. 17, 2025. [Online]. Available: https://www.solarpowerworldonline.com/2020/10/solar-projects-are-underperforming-by-6-3-new-report-suggests-better-assessment-standards/

[3] D. Keiner, L. Walter, M. ElSayed, and C. Breyer, "Impact of backtracking strategies on techno-economics of horizontal single-axis tracking solar photovoltaic power plants," *Solar Energy*, vol. 267, p. 112228, Jan. 2024, doi: 10.1016/j.solener.2023.112228.

[4] European Commission, "PhotoVoltaic Cost reduction, Reliability, Operational performance, Prediction and Simulation," 2015. Accessed: Sep. 17, 2025. [Online]. Available: https://cordis.europa.eu/project/id/308468

[5] European Commission, "MArket uptake of an innovative irrigation Solution based on LOW WATer-ENergy consumption," Sep. 01, 2015. doi: 10.3030/640771.

[6] European Commission, "Digitalising the PV sector for the era of Terawatts." Accessed: Sep. 17, 2025. [Online]. Available: https://cordis.europa.eu/project/id/101147000

[7] F. Martínez-Moreno, J. Muñoz, and E. Lorenzo, "Experimental model to estimate shading losses on PV arrays," *Solar Energy Materials and Solar Cells*, vol. 94, no. 12, pp. 2298–2303, Dec. 2010, doi: 10.1016/j.solmat.2010.07.029.

[8] L. Narvarte and E. Lorenzo, "Tracking and ground cover ratio," *Progress in Photovoltaics: Research and Applications*, vol. 16, no. 8, pp. 703–714, Dec. 2008, doi: 10.1002/pip.847.

[9] E. Lorenzo, L. Narvarte, and J. Muñoz, "Tracking and back-tracking," *Progress in Photovoltaics: Research and Applications*, vol. 19, no. 6, pp. 747–753, Sep. 2011, doi: 10.1002/pip.1085.

[10] J. R. Ledesma, E. Lorenzo, and L. Narvarte, "Single-Axis Tracking and Bifacial Gain on Sloping Terrain," *Progress in Photovoltaics: Research and Applications*, vol. 33, no. 2, pp. 309–325, Feb. 2025, doi: 10.1002/pip.3847.

[11] E. Lorenzo, "Energy Collected and Delivered by PV Modules," in *Handbook of Photovoltaic Science and Engineering*, Wiley, 2003, pp. 905–970. doi: 10.1002/0470014008.ch20.

[12] N. Martín and J. M. Ruiz, "A new method for the spectral characterisation of PV modules," *Progress in Photovoltaics: Research and Applications*, vol. 7, no. 4, pp. 299–310, Jul. 1999, doi: 10.1002/(SICI)1099-159X(199907/08)7:4<299::AID-PIP260>3.0.CO;2-0.

[13] J. Muñoz; N. Tyutyundzhiev; L. Marroyo; M. Collares-Pereira; M. Conlon; B. Wilkin, *AN OPEN-SOURCE SIMULATION TOOL OF GRID-CONNECTED PV SYSTEMS*. Paris, 2013. Accessed: Sep. 17, 2025. [Online]. Available: https://www.researchgate.net/publication/338047197_AN_OPEN-SOURCE_SIMULATION_TOOL_OF_GRID-CONNECTED_PV_SYSTEMS

[14] E. Lorenzo and M. H. Macagnan, "Considerations in the design of a one-axis tracking photovoltaic system," *Progress in Photovoltaics: Research and Applications*, vol. 2, no. 1, pp. 45–55, Jan. 1994, doi: 10.1002/pip.4670020107.

Bridging the Gap:

Insights into Backtracking-Angle Related Discrepancies Between Estimates and Actual Performance in Large-Scale Photovoltaic Plants

Juan Santamaría Sancho
Fco. Javier Ramírez Ledesma, Javier Martín Rueda, Eduardo Lorenzo Pigueiras

Instituto de Energía Solar
Universidad Politécnica de Madrid

Problem:

Overestimation of energy yield in utility-scale PV simulations.

Approach:

Assess how tracker positioning during backtracking contributes to the overestimation of Tracker Irradiation Gain (TIG),

$$\mathrm{TIG}_A(\omega) = \frac{G_A(\omega) - G_A(0)}{G_A(0)},$$

where $G_A(\omega)$ and $G_A(0)$ are the annual irradiation per square meter on a plane tilted at an angle ω and on a horizontal plane, respectively.

Model features

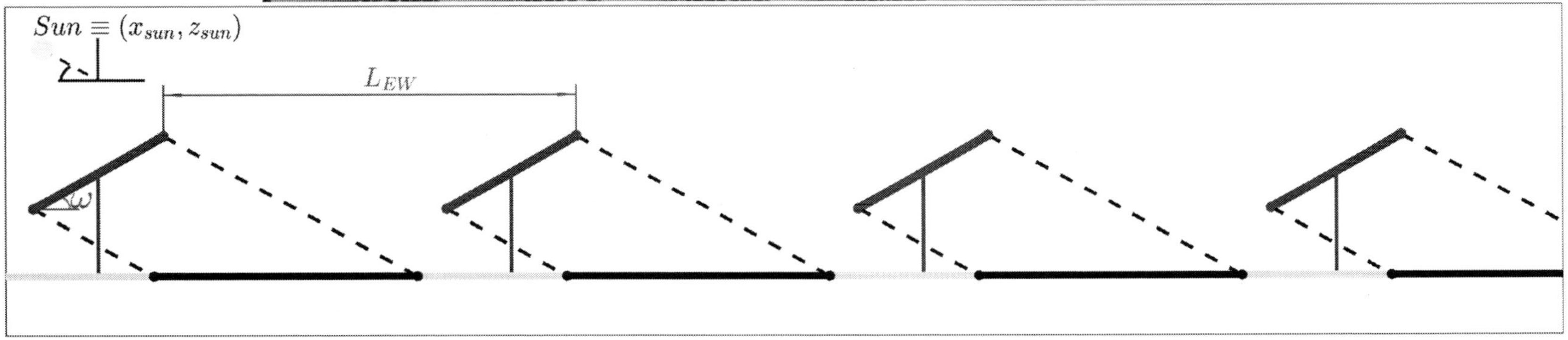

Non-backtracking behaviour

$$\omega_{ID} = \text{atan}\frac{x_{sun}}{z_{sun}}$$

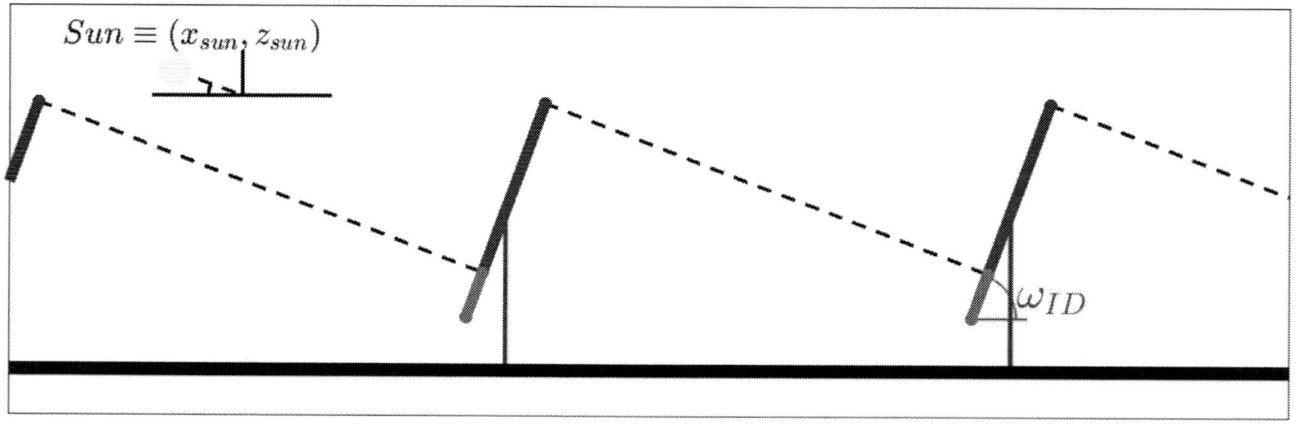

Backtracking behaviour for flat terrains

$$\omega_{IDC} = \omega_{ID} - \mathrm{acos}\left[L_{EW}\cos(\omega_{ID})\right]$$

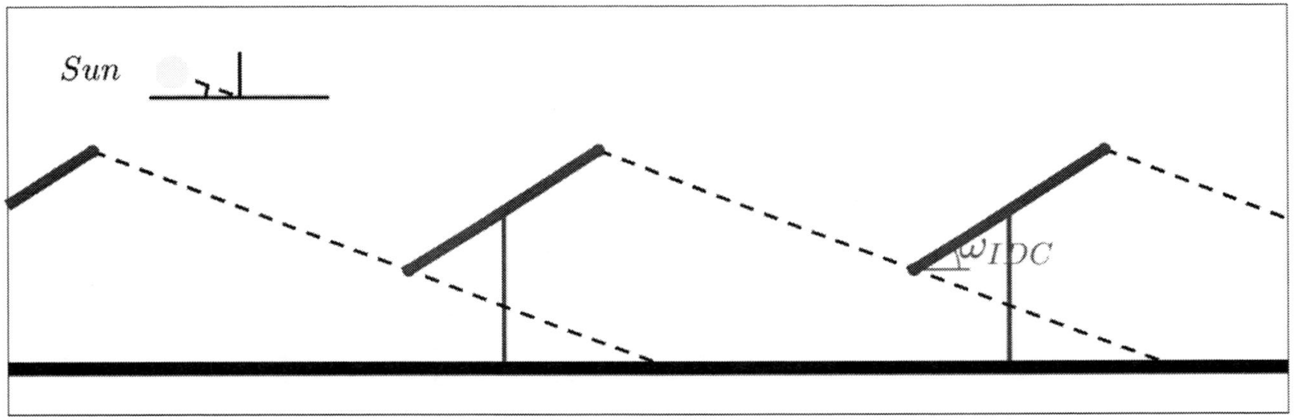

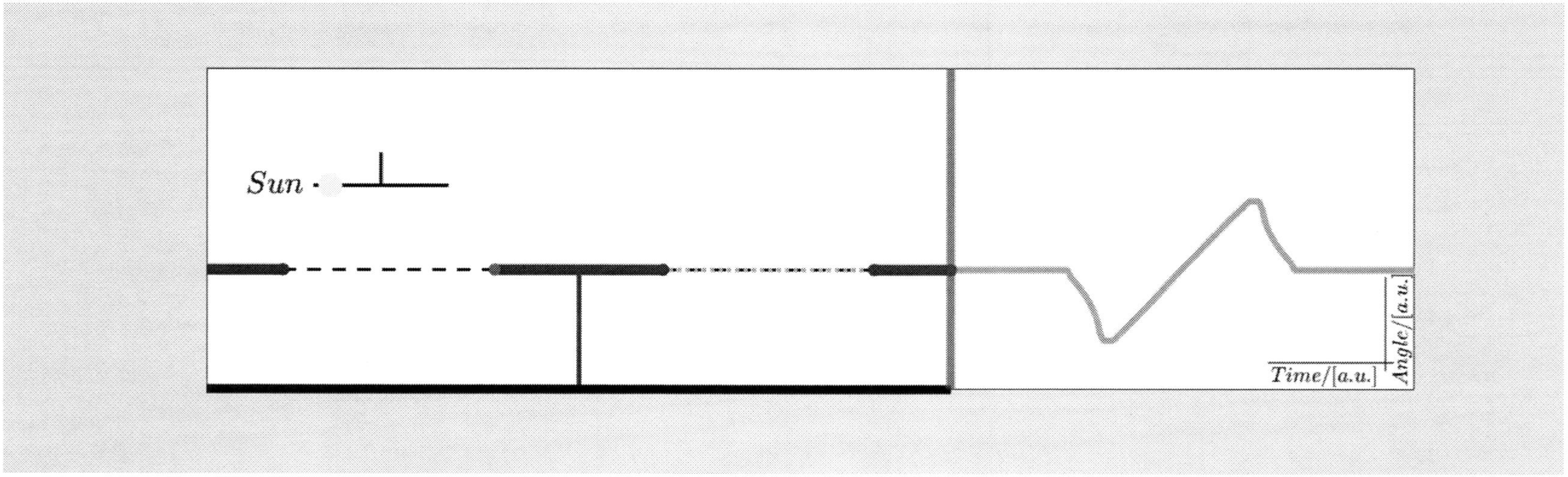
Sun
Time/[a.u.]
Angle/[a.u.]

PV plants during the backtracking period

Effect of terrain unevenness

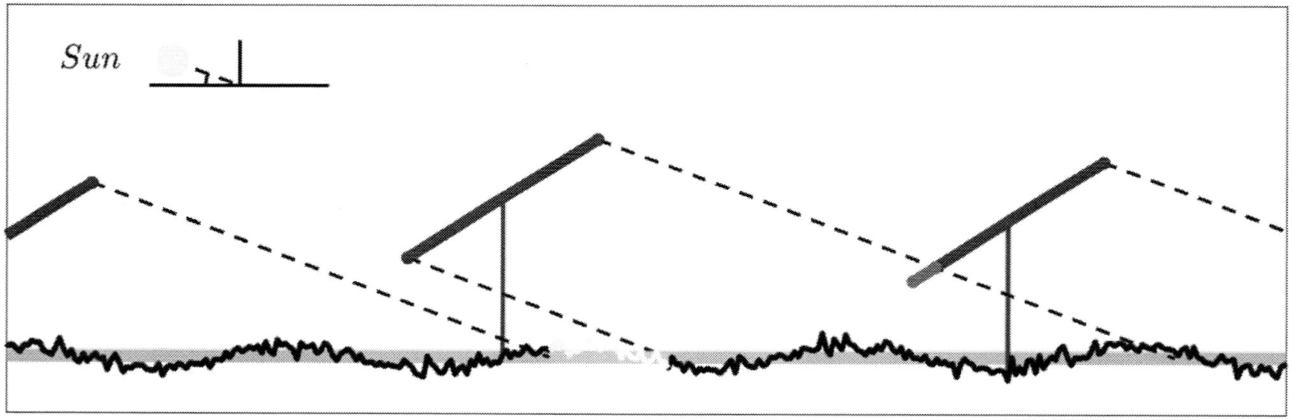

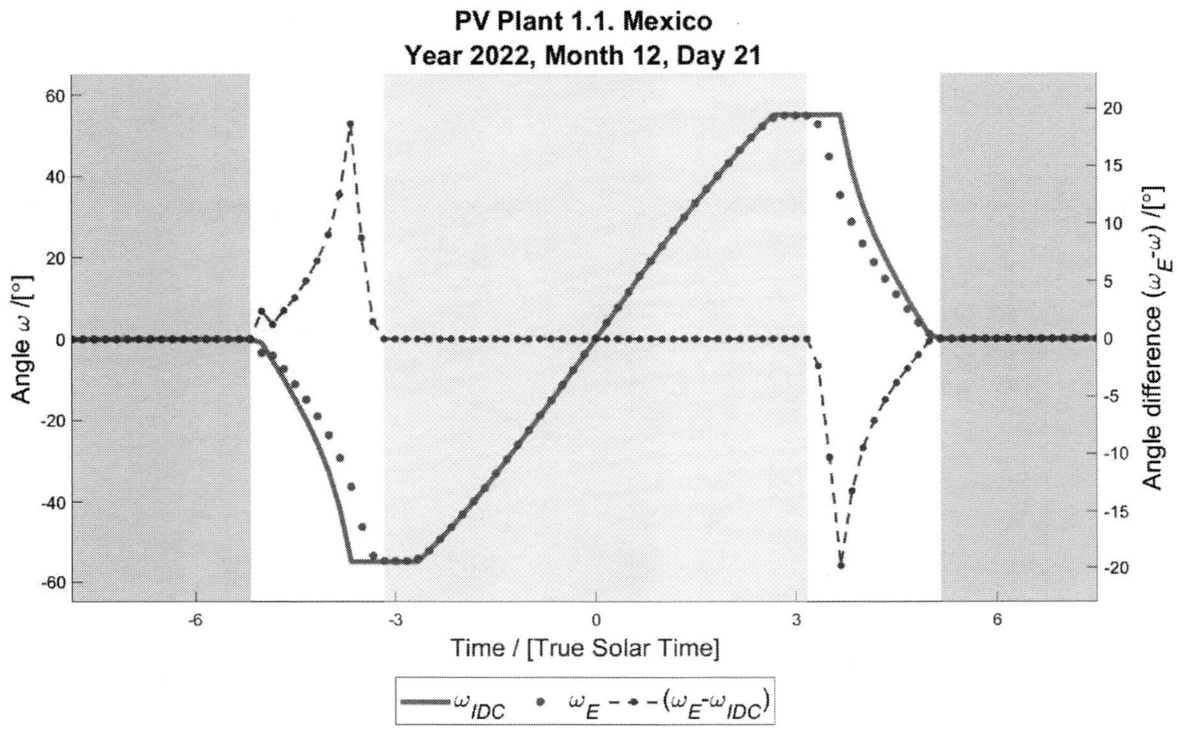
PV Plant 1.1. Mexico
Year 2022, Month 12, Day 21
Angle ω /[°]
60
40
20
0
-20
-40
-60
Angle difference (ω_E-ω) /[°]
20
15
10
5
0
-5
-10
-15
-20
-6
-3
0
3
6
Time / [True Solar Time]
ω_IDC
ω_E
(ω_E-ω_IDC)

- Compute the backtracking angles using a row spacing $\tilde{L}_{EW}$ different from L_{EW}.

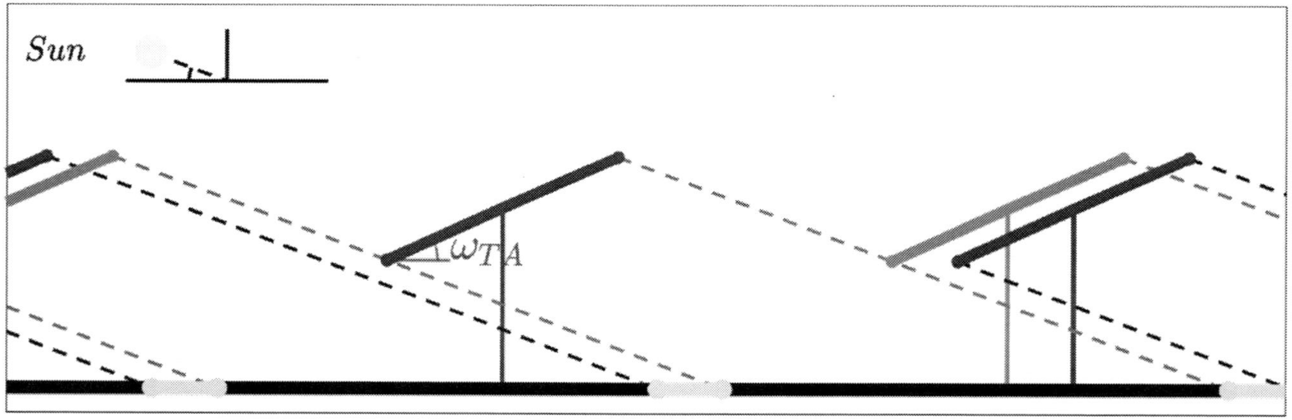

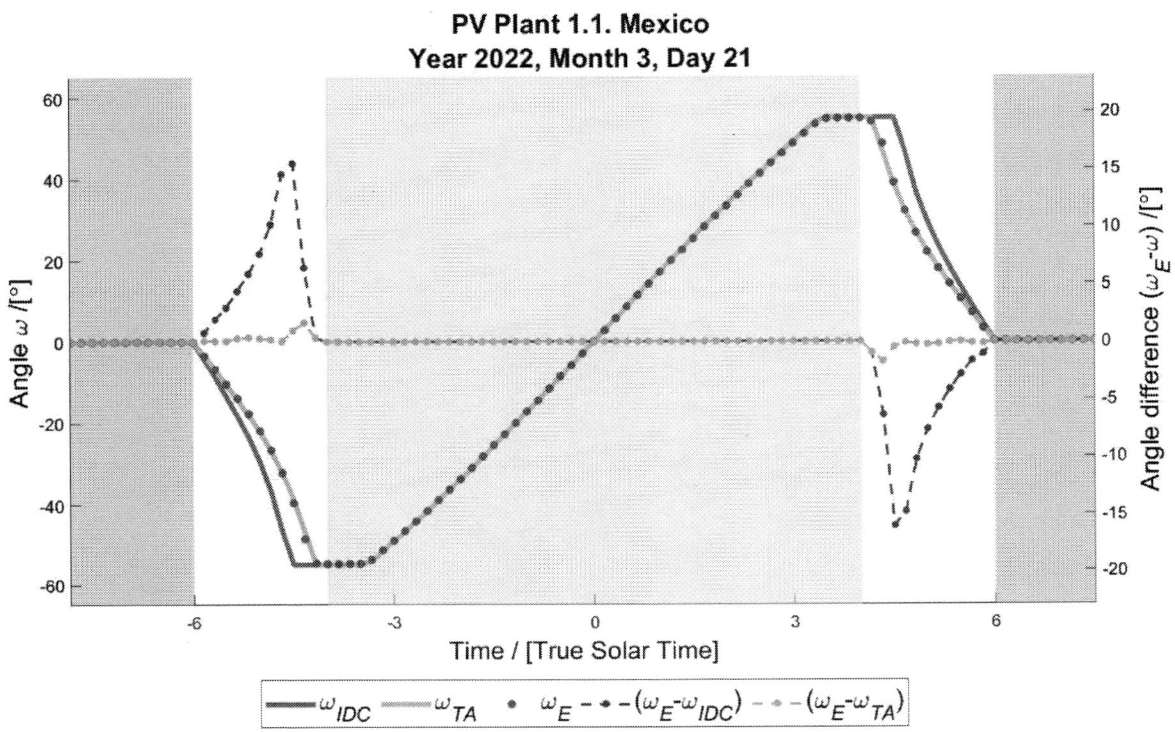
PV Plant 1.1. Mexico
Year 2022, Month 3, Day 21
Angle ω /[°]
60
40
20
0
-20
-40
-60
Angle difference (ω_E-ω) /[°]
20
15
10
5
0
-5
-10
-15
-20
-6
-3
0
3
6
Time / [True Solar Time]
ω_IDC
ω_TA
ω_E
(ω_E-ω_IDC)
(ω_E-ω_TA)

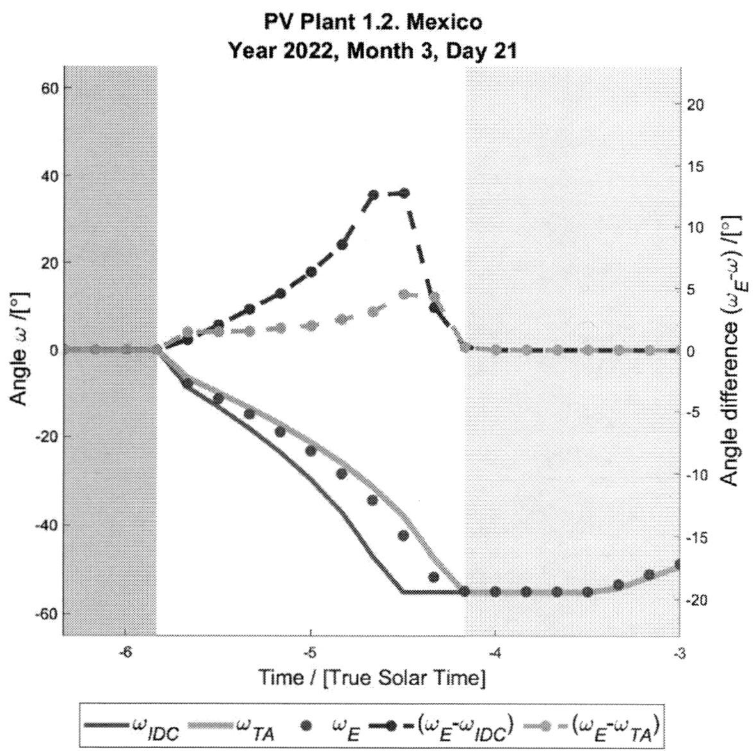
PV Plant 1.2. Mexico
Year 2022, Month 3, Day 21
Angle ω /[°]
Angle difference (ω_E-ω) /[°]
Time / [True Solar Time]
ω_IDC
ω_TA
ω_E
(ω_E-ω_IDC)
(ω_E-ω_TA)

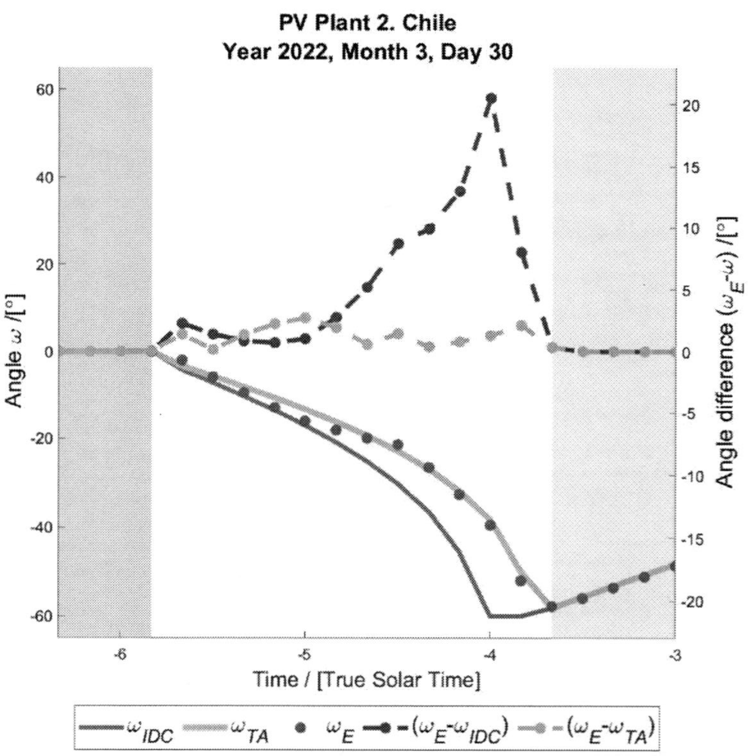
PV Plant 2. Chile
Year 2022, Month 3, Day 30
Angle ω /[°]
Angle difference (ω_E-ω) /[°]
Time / [True Solar Time]
ω_IDC
ω_TA
ω_E
(ω_E-ω_IDC)
(ω_E-ω_TA)

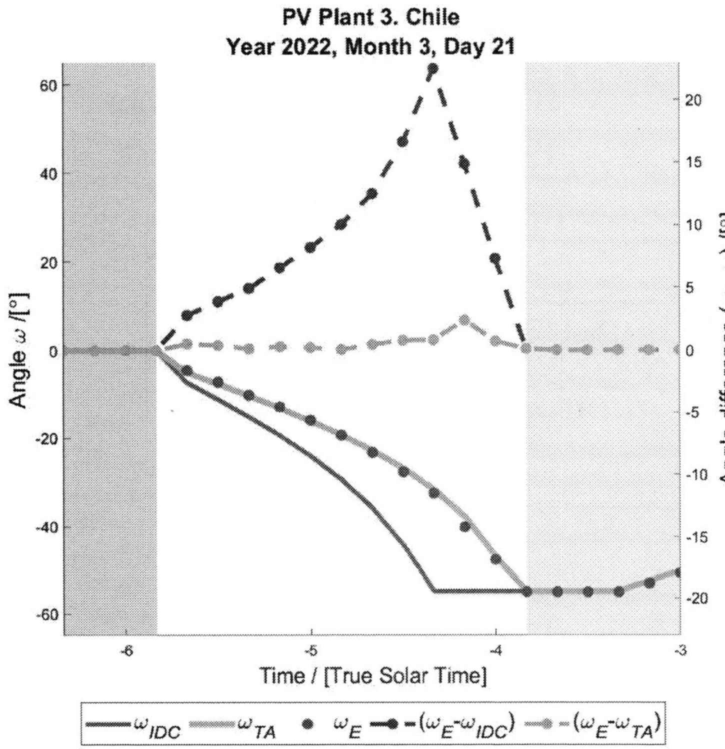
PV Plant 3. Chile
Year 2022, Month 3, Day 21
Angle ω /[°]
Angle difference (ω_E-ω) /[°]
Time / [True Solar Time]
60
40
20
0
-20
-40
-60
20
15
10
5
0
-5
-10
-15
-20
-6
-5
-4
-3
ω_IDC
ω_TA
ω_E
(ω_E-ω_IDC)
(ω_E-ω_TA)

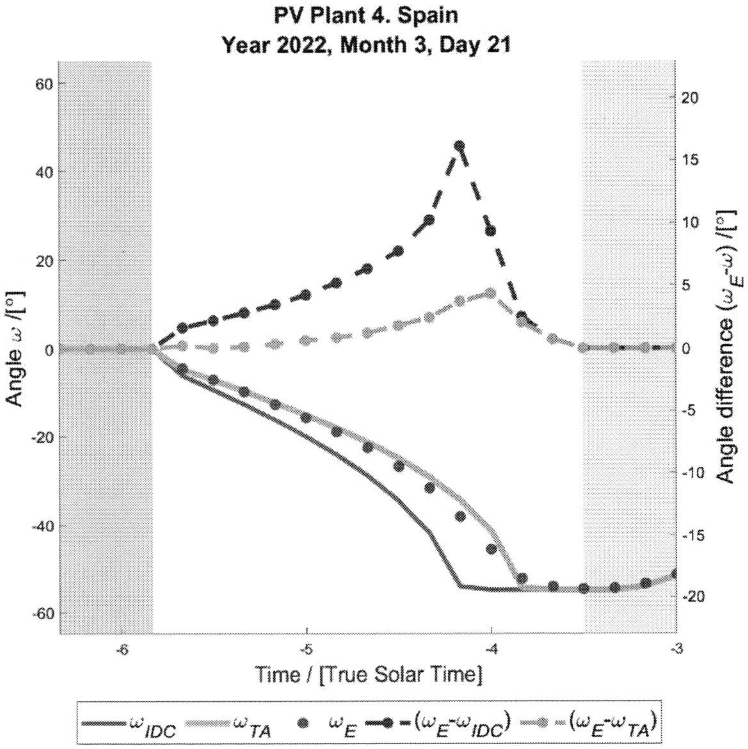
PV Plant 4. Spain
Year 2022, Month 3, Day 21
Angle ω /[°]
Angle difference (ω_E-ω) /[°]
Time / [True Solar Time]
60
40
20
0
-20
-40
-60
20
15
10
5
0
-5
-10
-15
-20
-6
-5
-4
-3
ω_IDC
ω_TA
ω_E
(ω_E-ω_IDC)
(ω_E-ω_TA)

TIG overestimation analysis

$$\Delta(\mathrm{TIG}_A) = \frac{\mathrm{TIG}_A(\omega_{IDC}) - \mathrm{TIG}_A(\omega_{TA})}{\mathrm{TIG}_A(\omega_{IDC})} \cdot 100$$

PV Plant	**Location**	L_{EW} / []	$\widetilde{L}_{EW}$ / []	$\Delta(\mathrm{TIG}_A)$ / [%]
1.1	Mexico	3.00	2.50	7.3
1.2	Mexico	3.00	2.50	7.3
2	Chile	2.26	1.96	9.4
3	Chile	2.56	2.24	9.2
4	Spain	2.74	2.16	7.8

Tracking irradiation losses between 7-10%

↓

Losses in energy production of approximately 3%

Thank you for your time!

https://www.sisifo.info

CONTACT ME: juan.santamariasan@upm.es

The authors express their sincere appreciation for the financial support provided through the project PVOP, funded by the European Union. Views and opinions expressed are however those of the authors only and do not necessarily reflect those of the European Union or CINEA. Neither the European Union nor the granting authority can be held responsible for them.

Funded by the European Union

PVOP

EUPVSEC 2025 – Bilbao

42nd EUROPEAN PHOTOVOLTAIC SOLAR ENERGY CONFERENCE AND EXHIBITION

EXPERIMENTAL VALIDATION OF HORIZONTAL SINGLE-AXIS SOLAR TRACKER ALGORITHMS IN TERMS OF ENERGY PRODUCTION AND OPERATIONAL PERFORMANCE

Ildefonso Muñoz, Gregorio Olivares, Sara Díaz, Aritz Legarrea, Ana Gracia

Solar Energy Technologies & Storage Dept. - CENER

CENER | CENTRO NACIONAL DE ENERGÍAS RENOVABLES

Ciemat

Gobierno de Navarra
Nafarroako Gobernua

INTRODUCTION & MOTIVATION

CURRENT STATUS

- **Horizontal single axis:** the most widely used solar tracker system in large utility-scale PV plants
- **Astronomical algorithm:** the most used solar tracking strategy, based on minimizing the angle of the normal vector of the POA and the solar vector

CHALLENGERS & OPPORTUNITIES

- Astronomical algorithm, **is not always the optimal** tracking algorithm
- Electronic control system of solar tracker **allows an easy implementation of new solar tracking algorithms**

4DO.1.3 - EXPERIMENTAL VALIDATION OF HORIZONTAL SINGLE-AXIS SOLAR TRACKER ALGORITHMS IN TERMS OF ENERGY PRODUCTION AND OPERATIONAL PERFORMANCE

CENER | CENTRO NACIONAL DE ENERGÍAS RENOVABLES

Gobierno de Navarra Nafarroako Gobernua

BACKGROUND (1)

Simulation study presented in 40th EUPVSEC (Lisbon) and paper published in SolarRRL: "***Evaluation of Horizontal Single-Axis Solar Tracker Algorithms in Terms of Energy Production and Operational Performance***" (DOI: 10.1002/solr.202300507) based on:

- **In–depth comparative and evaluation** in terms of energy production and operational performance of solar tracking algorithms for a horizontal single axis solar tracker with monofacial PV modules
- Comparison of performance with Astronomical algorithm **based on high temporal resolution data (1 minute)** taking into account:
  - Atmospheric conditions (radiation and temperature)
  - Mechanical constrains of horizontal solar tracker (non-continuous movement)
  - Disposition of PV modules on the solar tracker
- Solar tracking algorithms proposed for this study:
  - **DIFFUSE RADIATION ALGORITHMS**
  - **ANALYTICAL ALGORITHM** (new development by CENER)

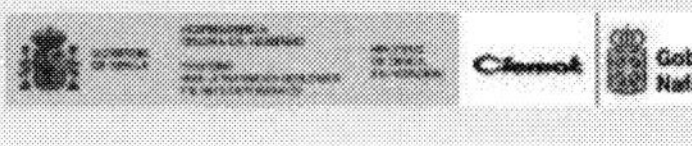

BACKGROUND (2)

DIFFUSE RADIATION ALGORITHM

- On cloudy day, diffuse component of radiation can be higher than beam component
- Diffuse Radiation Algorithm criteria:
  - *GHI > G_{POA} → Horizontal Position*
  - *GHI ≤ G_{POA} → Astronomical Tracking*

ANALYTICAL ALGORITHM (Developed by CENER)

- Diffuse Radiation algorithm only consider as optimal position the one according to Astronomical algorithm or the horizontal position.
- In multiple situations and locations, beam and diffuse radiation components may not be so different → **Optimal angle could be an intermediate position between horizontal and Astronomical**.

$$\frac{\partial G_{POA}}{\partial \beta} = \frac{\partial G_B}{\partial \beta} + \frac{\partial G_D}{\partial \beta} + \frac{\partial G_G}{\partial \beta} = 0$$

Max. Irradiance condition, as function of β

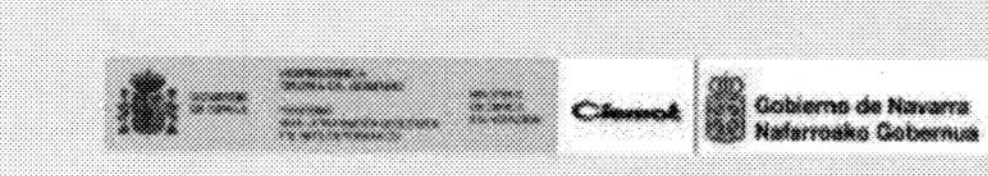

DIFFUSE RADIATION ALG.

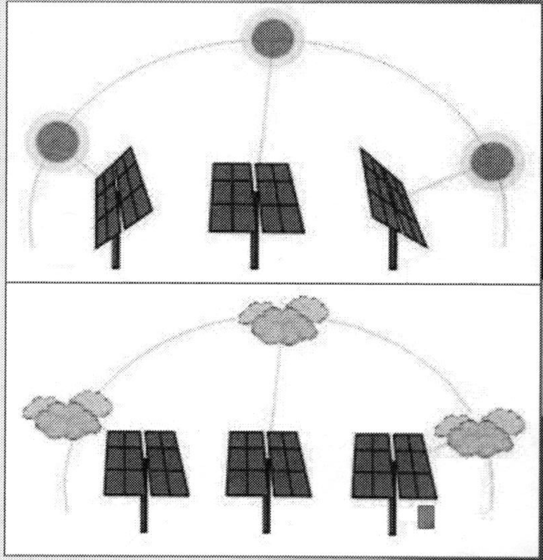

ANALYTICAL ALG.

PREVIOUS WORK SUMMARY AND OBJECTIVES

PREVIOUS WORK: Simulation study carried out for six locations with different climates and GHI/DHI ratios (diffuse radiation fraction)

PREVIOUS RESULTS:

- In all cases, studied algorithms present a gain compared with the Astronomical algorithm
- The higher diffuse fraction, the higher gain
- Astronomical & Analytical algorithms present highest values of number of movements per year
- Diffuse Radiation Algorithm presents the highest value of accumulated angular displacement and risk of oscillating positions on days with cloudy intervals

OBJECTIVES FOR THE PRESENT WORK:

- ***Validation of previous simulation results by applying algorithms to real solar trackers***

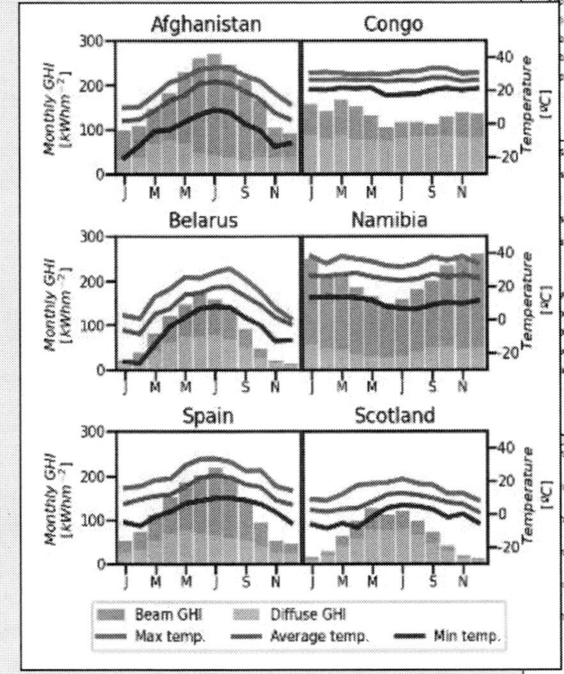

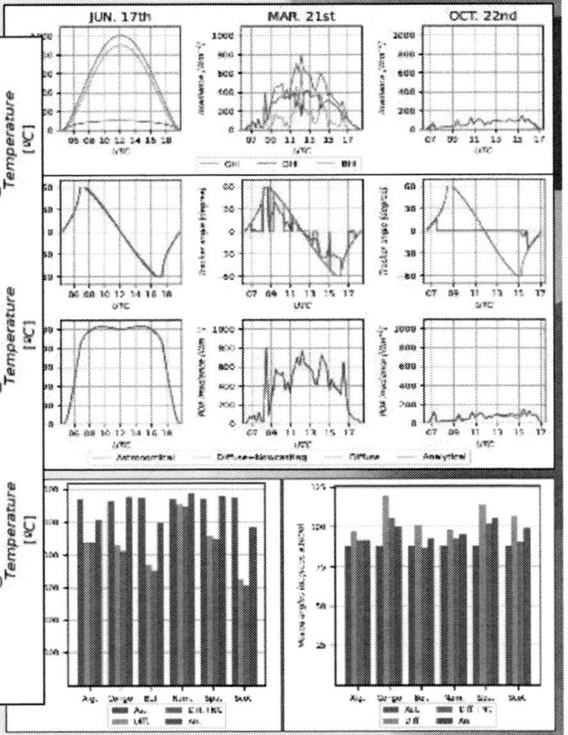

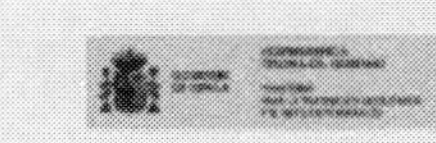

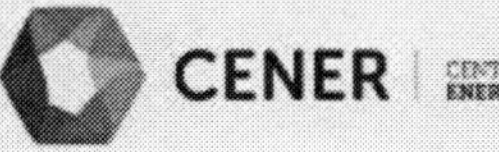

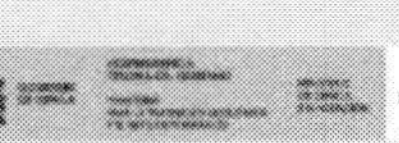

4DO.1.3 - EXPERIMENTAL VALIDATION OF HORIZONTAL SINGLE-AXIS SOLAR TRACKER ALGORITHMS IN TERMS OF ENERGY PRODUCTION AND OPERATIONAL PERFORMANCE

CENER | CENTRO NACIONAL DE ENERGÍAS RENOVABLES

Gobierno de Navarra
Nafarroako Gobernua

ANALYTICAL ALGORITHMS – NEW DEVELOPMENTS

SOLAR RADIATION TRASPOSITION MODELS

ISOTROPIC (LIU-JORDAN)
HAY-DAVIES
PEREZ

$$\frac{\partial G_{POA}}{\partial \beta} = \frac{\partial G_B}{\partial \beta} + \frac{\partial G_D}{\partial \beta} + \frac{\partial G_G}{\partial \beta} = 0$$

Max. Irradiance condition, as function of β

$$\beta_{opt} = arctan\left(\frac{DNI \cdot sin\,\theta_s \cdot cos(\gamma_s - \gamma)}{\frac{DHI - GHI \cdot a}{2} + DNI \cdot cos\,\theta_s}\right)$$

Isotropic

$$\beta_{opt} = arctan\left(\frac{DNI \cdot sin\,\theta_s \cdot cos(\gamma_s - \gamma)}{\frac{DHI - GHI \cdot a}{2} + DNI \cdot cos\,\theta_s}\right)$$

Hay-Davies

$$\beta_{opt} = arctan\left(\frac{sin\,\theta_Z \cdot cos(\gamma_s - \gamma) \cdot \left[DNI + DHI \cdot \frac{F_1}{f_b}\right] + DHI \cdot \frac{F_1 \cdot F_2}{f_b}}{DNI \cdot cos\,\theta_Z + DHI\left[\left(\frac{F_1 - 1}{2}\right) \cdot \frac{F_1}{f_b} \cdot cos\,\theta_Z\right] - \frac{1}{2} \cdot GHI \cdot a}\right)$$

Perez

EXPERIMENTAL SET-UP

Test carried out in Experimental PV installation of CENER (CENIFER)

Main Set-Up equipment:
- Solar Trackers and electronic controllers (EC)
  - Solar Tracker 1, with EC Prototype 1
  - Solar Tracker 2, with EC Prototype 2
  - Solar Tracker Control, with commercial EC
- Meteo station (GHI, albedo, Tamb & Wind)
- G_{POA} sensors on each solar tracker

4DO.1.3 - EXPERIMENTAL VALIDATION OF HORIZONTAL SINGLE-AXIS SOLAR TRACKER ALGORITHMS IN TERMS OF ENERGY PRODUCTION AND OPERATIONAL PERFORMANCE

CENER | CENTRO NACIONAL DE ENERGÍAS RENOVABLES

Gobierno de Navarra Nafarroako Gobernua

ELECTRONIC CONTROLLER PROTOTYPE

CENER hardware developments

In-house hardware for implementing tracking algorithms, based on:

- Raspberry Pi 5 8Gb
- Inclinometer ifm EC2045
- A-D Converter ADS1115 16 bits (8 inputs)

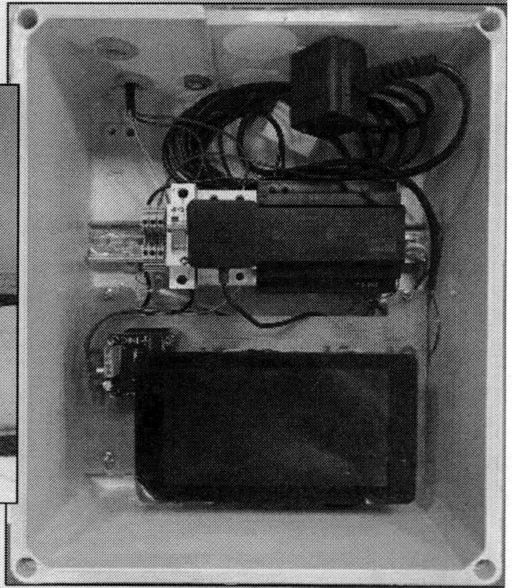

python

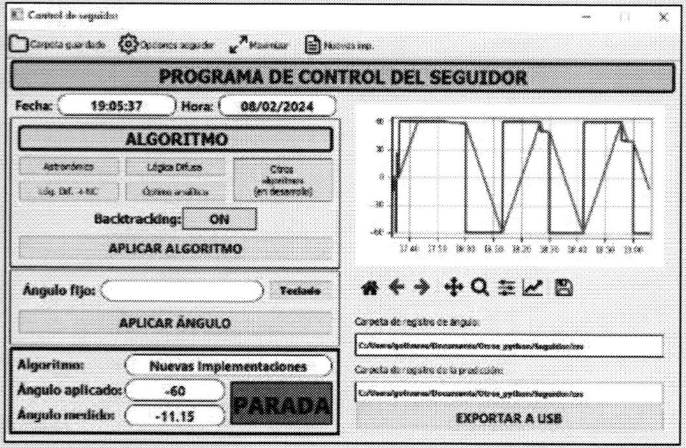

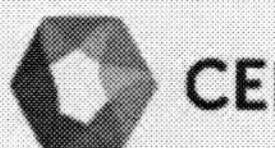

CENER software developments

- Tracking algorithms designed and programmed in open source code (Python)
- User-friendly communication and GUI systems to select tracking algorithm and download measured data

4DO.1.3 - EXPERIMENTAL VALIDATION OF HORIZONTAL SINGLE-AXIS SOLAR TRACKER ALGORITHMS IN TERMS OF ENERGY PRODUCTION AND OPERATIONAL PERFORMANCE

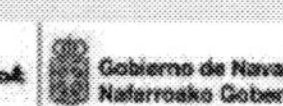

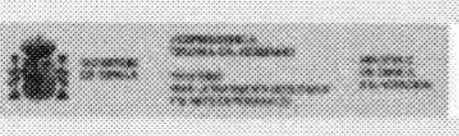

CENER | CENTRO NACIONAL DE ENERGÍAS RENOVABLES

Gobierno de Navarra Nafarroako Gobernua

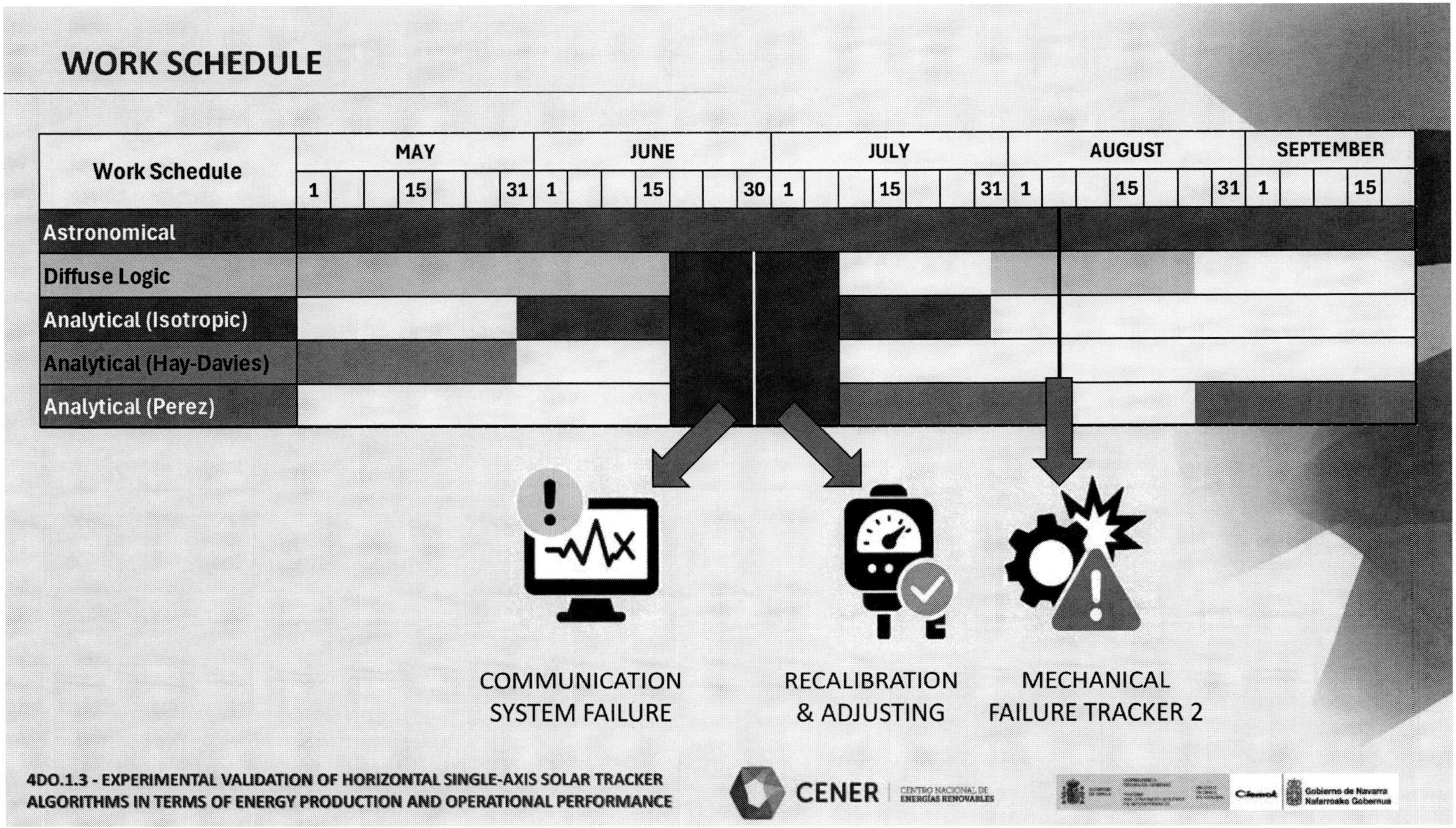
WORK SCHEDULE
Work Schedule
MAY
JUNE
JULY
AUGUST
SEPTEMBER
1 15 31 1 15 30 1 15 31 1 15 31 1 15
Astronomical
Diffuse Logic
Analytical (Isotropic)
Analytical (Hay-Davies)
Analytical (Perez)
COMMUNICATION SYSTEM FAILURE
RECALIBRATION & ADJUSTING
MECHANICAL FAILURE TRACKER 2
4DO.1.3 - EXPERIMENTAL VALIDATION OF HORIZONTAL SINGLE-AXIS SOLAR TRACKER ALGORITHMS IN TERMS OF ENERGY PRODUCTION AND OPERATIONAL PERFORMANCE
CENER
CENTRO NACIONAL DE ENERGÍAS RENOVABLES
Gobierno de Navarra
Nafarroako Gobernua

RESULTS (1) – ASTRONOMICAL, DIFFUSE & ANALYTICAL (HAY-DAVIES)

Cloudy Day Condition	ASTR.	DIFFUSE	ANALYTICAL (HAY-D)
G_{POA} (W/m^2/day)	186.9	209.1	209.9
# Movements	108	92	84
Angular displacement (°)	252	609	454

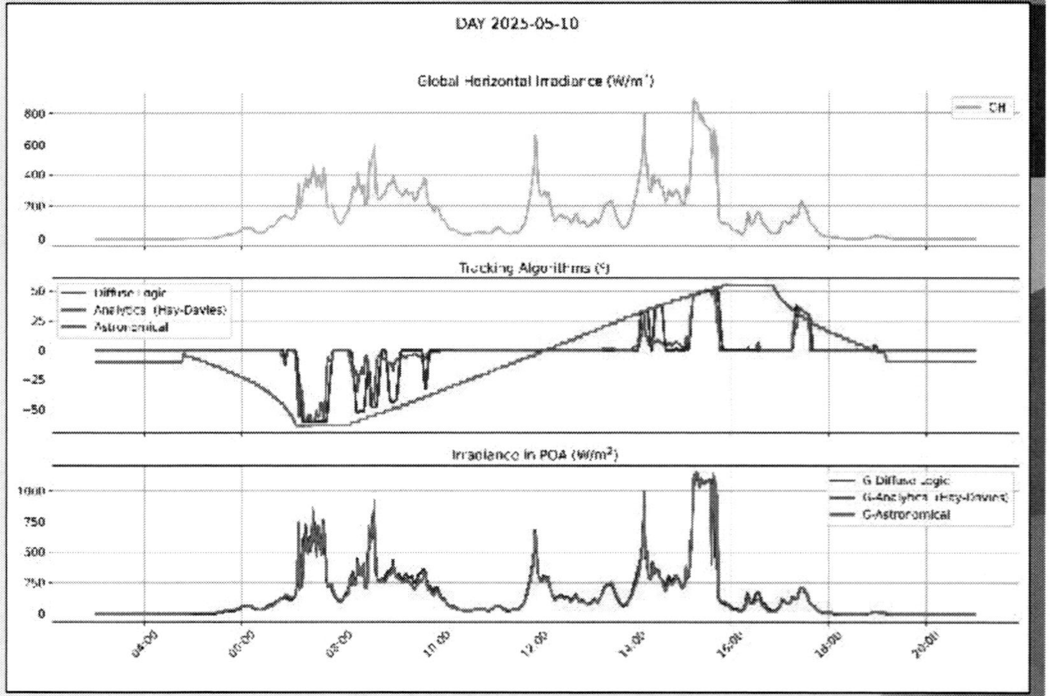

4DO.1.3 - EXPERIMENTAL VALIDATION OF HORIZONTAL SINGLE-AXIS SOLAR TRACKER ALGORITHMS IN TERMS OF ENERGY PRODUCTION AND OPERATIONAL PERFORMANCE

CENER | CENTRO NACIONAL DE ENERGÍAS RENOVABLES

Gobierno de Navarra Nafarroako Gobernua

RESULTS (2) – ASTRONOMICAL, DIFFUSE & ANALYTICAL (ISOTROPIC)

Sunny-Cloudy Day Condition	ASTR.	DIFFUSE	ANALYTICAL (ISOTROPIC)
G_{POA} (W/m²/day)	408.9	447.8	460.3
# Movements	106	120	133
Angular displacement (°)	251	274	689

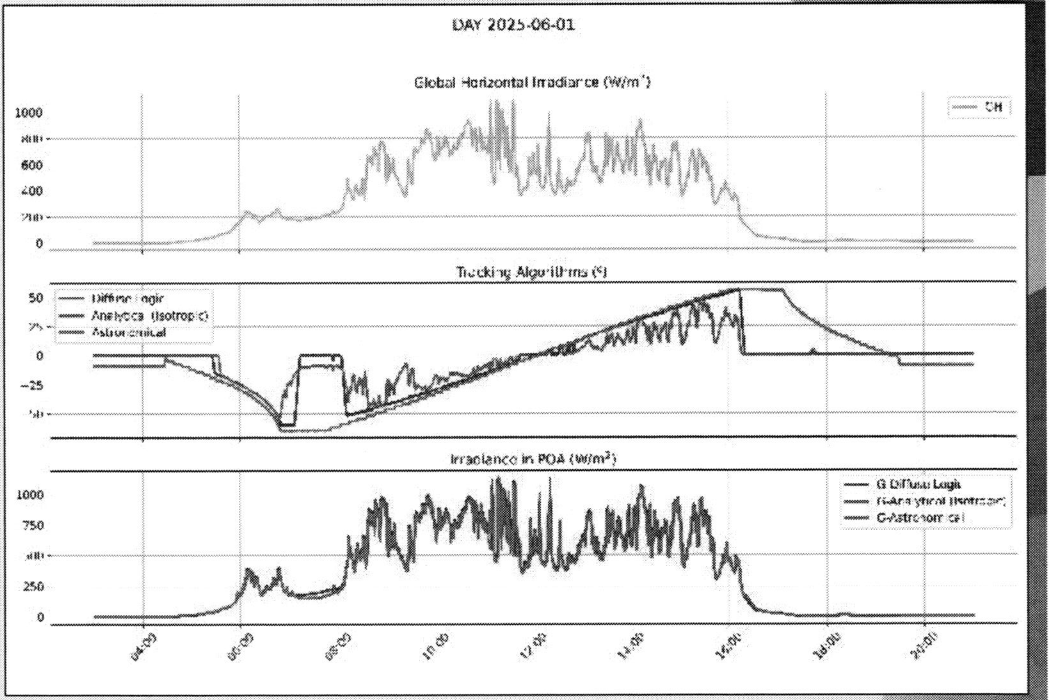

4DO.1.3 - EXPERIMENTAL VALIDATION OF HORIZONTAL SINGLE-AXIS SOLAR TRACKER ALGORITHMS IN TERMS OF ENERGY PRODUCTION AND OPERATIONAL PERFORMANCE

CENER | CENTRO NACIONAL DE ENERGÍAS RENOVABLES

Gobierno de Navarra
Nafarroako Gobernua

RESULTS (3) – ASTRONOMICAL, A.(ISOTROPIC) & A.(PEREZ)

Sunny-Cloudy Day Condition	ASTR.	ANALYTICAL (ISOTROPIC)	ANALYTICAL (PEREZ)
G_{POA} (W/m²/day)	295.7	309.5	319.4
# Movements	106	135	123
Angular displacement (°)	251	274	398

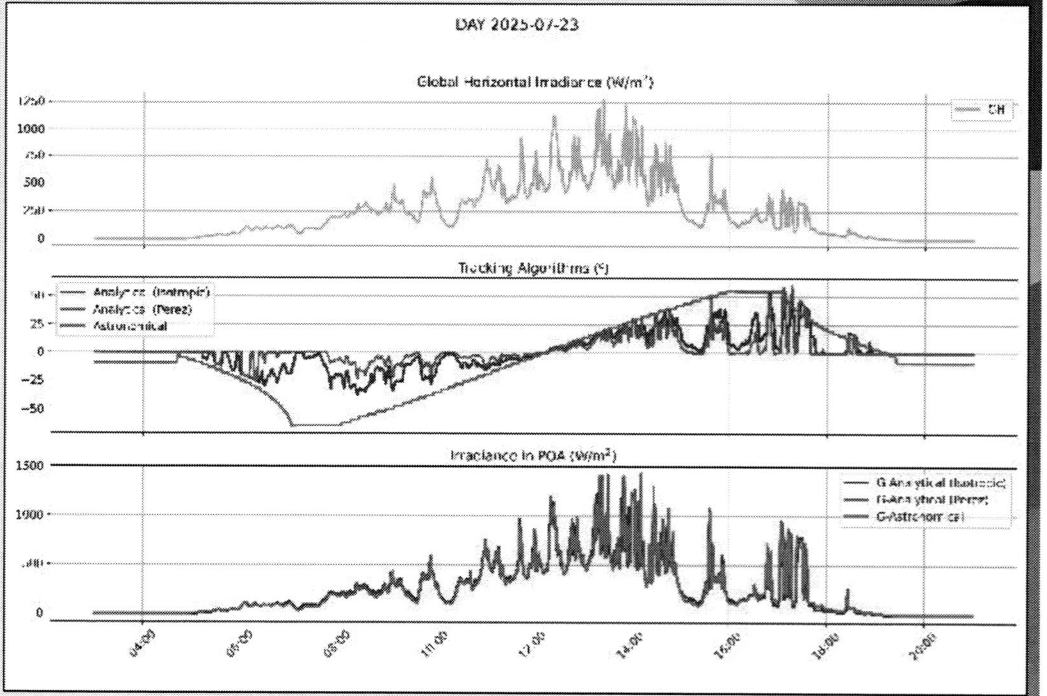

4DO.1.3 - EXPERIMENTAL VALIDATION OF HORIZONTAL SINGLE-AXIS SOLAR TRACKER ALGORITHMS IN TERMS OF ENERGY PRODUCTION AND OPERATIONAL PERFORMANCE

CENER | CENTRO NACIONAL DE ENERGÍAS RENOVABLES

Gobierno de Navarra Nafarroako Gobernua

RESULTS (4) – ASTRONOMICAL, DIFFUSE & ANALYTICAL (PEREZ)

Sunny-Cloudy Day Condition	ASTR.	DIFFUSE	ANALYTICAL (PEREZ)
G_{POA} (W/m²/day)	597.7	621.2	638.1
# Movements	106	144	151
Angular displacement (°)	251	518	623

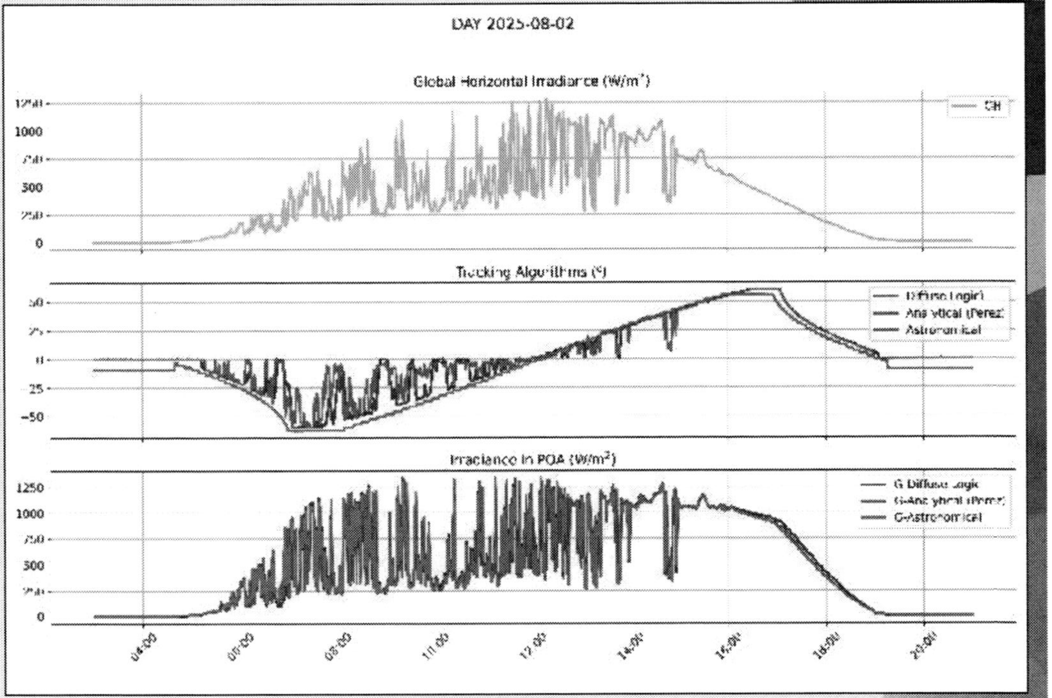

4DO.1.3 - EXPERIMENTAL VALIDATION OF HORIZONTAL SINGLE-AXIS SOLAR TRACKER ALGORITHMS IN TERMS OF ENERGY PRODUCTION AND OPERATIONAL PERFORMANCE

CENER CENTRO NACIONAL DE ENERGÍAS RENOVABLES

Gobierno de Navarra Nafarroako Gobernua

RESULTS (5) – BEHAVIOUR IN SUNNY-CLOUDY DAYS

- Sunny and cloudy days: most days recorded
- Effect of not setting the angle demanded by the algorithm in the event of rapid cloud movement → Oscillating positions (as expected in previous work)
- Effect registered in all new tracking algorithms, but especially in Diffuse Radiation Algorithm
- No application of Hysteresis or delays techniques for checking this effect in experimental results

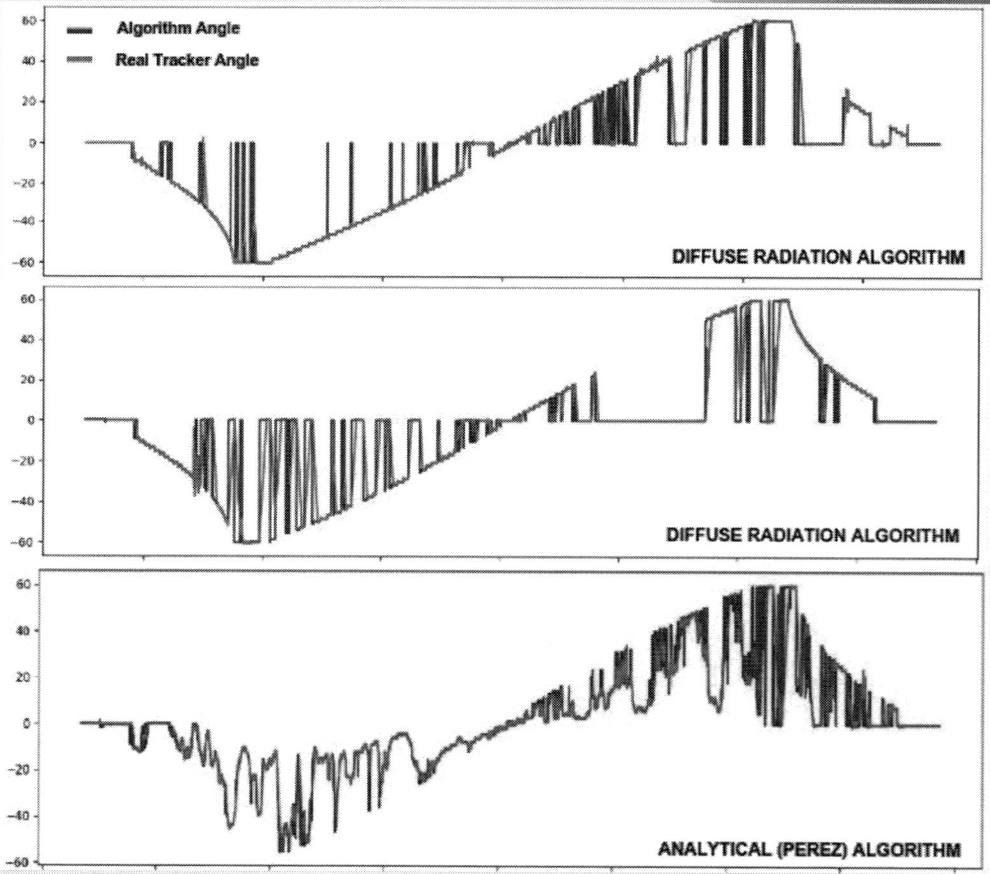

4DO.1.3 - EXPERIMENTAL VALIDATION OF HORIZONTAL SINGLE-AXIS SOLAR TRACKER ALGORITHMS IN TERMS OF ENERGY PRODUCTION AND OPERATIONAL PERFORMANCE

CENER | CENTRO NACIONAL DE ENERGÍAS RENOVABLES

Gobierno de Navarra Nafarroako Gobernua

SUMMARY & CONCLUSIONS

- CENER has developed new tracking algorithms and their application in open-source software (Python).
- CENER has created a prototype of electronic controller (two units) and the appropriate software to run any solar tracker algorithm. It has been applied with real solar trackers.
- Main results of the previous work have been confirmed in real tests:
  - Increase of G_{POA} of new algorithms compared to Astronomical algorithm
  - The higher diffuse fraction, the higher gain (lack of enough measurement days with high diffuse fraction)
  - Increase of number of movements and angle displacement (consideration of reliability and energy consumption aspects)
  - Effect of sunny-cloudy days confirmed (oscillating positions)
- CENER's ability to test any tracking algorithm (whether its own or that of an external developer) has been confirmed and is available to future clients.

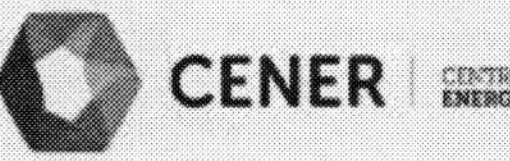

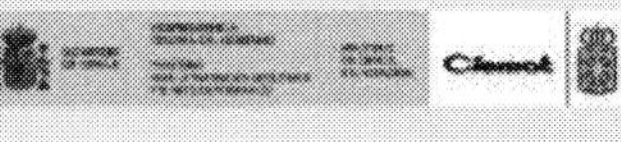

ONGOING & FUTURE WORKS

- Complete the study for all cases of day types and algorithms developed (tests conducted between spring and summer).
- Study of algorithm modification in situations of rapid cloud movement (hysteresis techniques), evaluation, and real-test validation.
- Consideration of bifacial PV modules for the modification or design of new solar tracker algorithms → **Non-homogeneous condition** of the radiation on the back side of PV modules
- Evaluation of new solar tracker algorithms, designing and adapted for specific systems (e.g. agriPV)

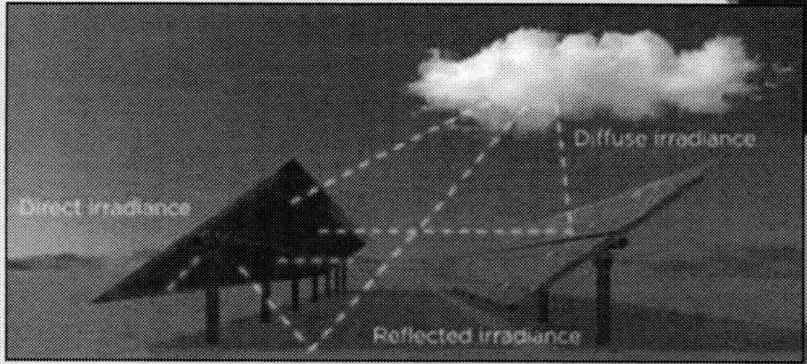

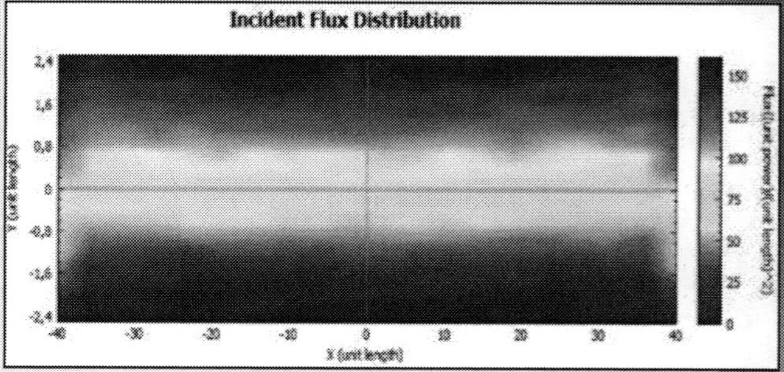

4DO.1.3 - EXPERIMENTAL VALIDATION OF HORIZONTAL SINGLE-AXIS SOLAR TRACKER ALGORITHMS IN TERMS OF ENERGY PRODUCTION AND OPERATIONAL PERFORMANCE

CENER | CENTRO NACIONAL DE ENERGÍAS RENOVABLES

Gobierno de Navarra Nafarroako Gobernua

Thank you for your attention!
CENER
Solar Energy Technologies & Storage Department
imunoz@cener.com
Ciudad de la Innovación, 7
31621 Sarriguren, Spain
+34 669 18 83 03
+34 902 25 28 00
CENER | NATIONAL RENEWABLE ENERGY CENTRE

2025 EU PVSEC
22-26 September 2025
Bilbao (Spain)

4DO.1.4: DEVELOPMENT AND EVALUATION OF NEW BACKTRACKING STRATEGIES (N-BT AND IRR-BT) FOR HORIZONTAL SINGLE-AXIS SOLAR TRACKERS

Gregorio Olivares, Ildefonso Muñoz, Sara Díaz, Ana Gracia
Solar Energy Technologies & Storage Dept. – CENER

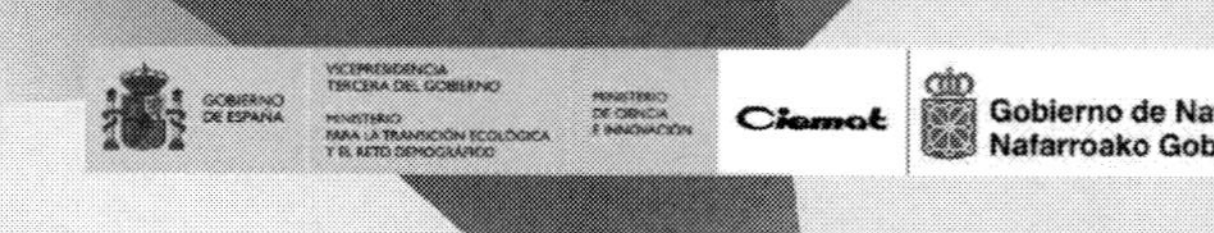

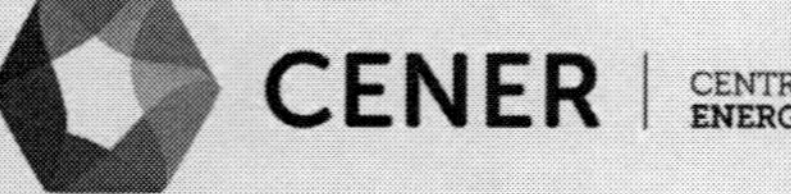

CENER | CENTRO NACIONAL DE ENERGÍAS RENOVABLES

Gobierno de Navarra
Nafarroako Gobernua

INTRODUCTION & MOTIVATION (1)

CURRENT STATUS

- **Horizontal single axis** → most widely used solar tracker system.
- **Astronomical algorithm with Backtracking strategy** is the most basic and usual algorithm in single axis trackers.

CHALLENGERS & OPPORTUNITIES

- Classic backtracking strategy is calculated **using ground coverage ratio** (GCR) as input[1].
- These strategies **could use other inputs** in order to increase production during sunrise and sunset time.

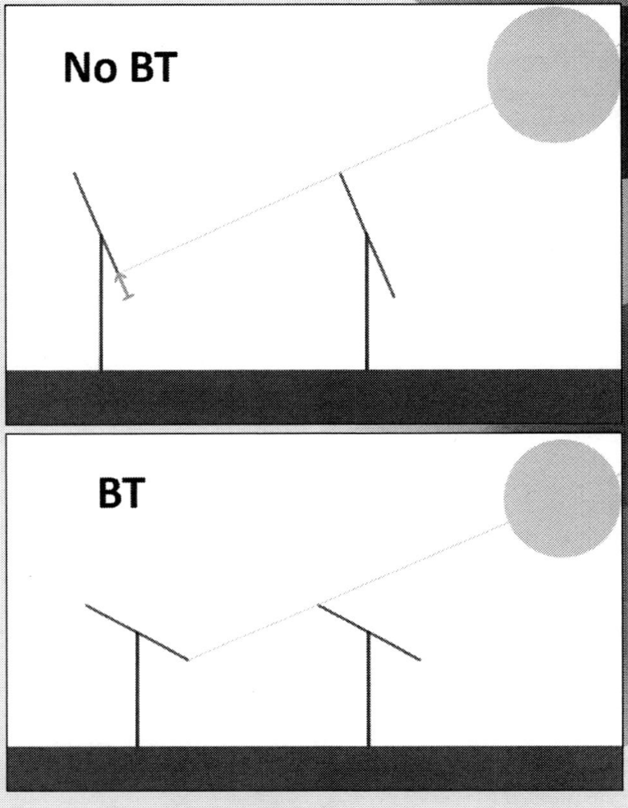

[1] K. Anderson, M. Mikofski. *Slope-Aware Backtracking for Single-Axis Trackers*. NREL, Jul. 2020.

CENER | CENTRO NACIONAL DE ENERGÍAS RENOVABLES

Gobierno de Navarra
Nafarroako Gobernua

INTRODUCTION & MOTIVATION (2)

- Study presented: **Evaluation** in terms of energy production of three different backtracking strategies
- Solar backtracking strategies proposed for this study:
  - **Classical/Standard backtracking (BT)**
  - **Layout-adapted backtracking (N-BT)**
  - **Terrain-adapted backtracking (Irr-BT)**
- Comparison based on **high temporal resolution TMY (1 minute)** considering:
  - **Disposition of PV modules** on the solar tracker
  - **Terrain complexity** and height difference between trackers

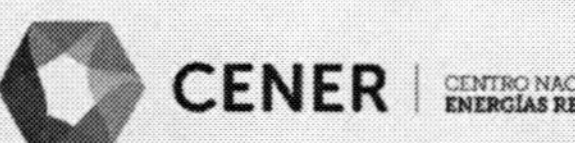

CENER | CENTRO NACIONAL DE ENERGÍAS RENOVABLES

Gobierno de Navarra Nafarroako Gobernua

METHODOLOGY – SOLAR BACKTRACKING STRATEGIES (1)

Standard BT strategy

- Avoid shading in the entire structure
- Only GCR as input

N - Backtracking

- **Adapt shading** to structure layout
- Repeat backtracking N times to apply shading to **module subdivisions**
- A **modification of the standard BT** eq. is used

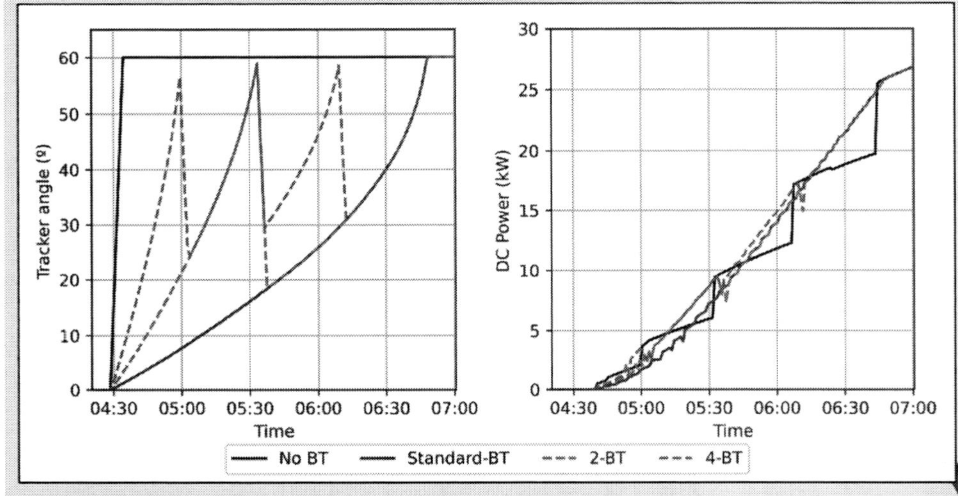

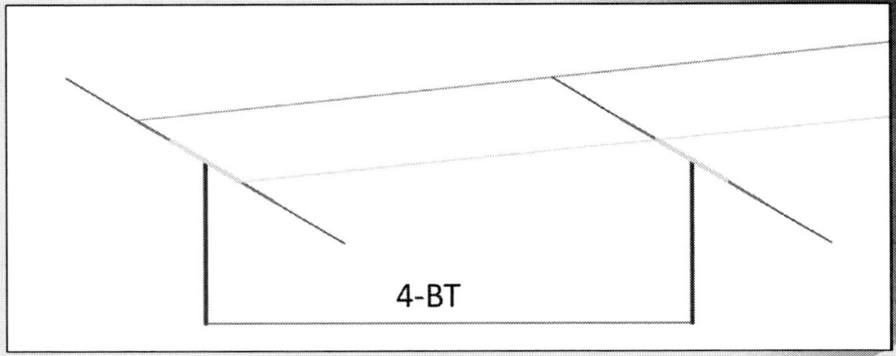

CENER | CENTRO NACIONAL DE ENERGÍAS RENOVABLES

Gobierno de Navarra
Nafarroako Gobernua

METHODOLOGY – SOLAR BACKTRACKING STRATEGIES (2)

Irr - Backtracking

- Adapt tracker angle in order to **avoid inter-row shadings on complex terrains**
- Each tracker angle are **individually-calculated**.
- Tracking angle is adapted based **only on the tracker at the front** (2D considered)
    - If no angle can avoid shading, the front tracker angle is modified

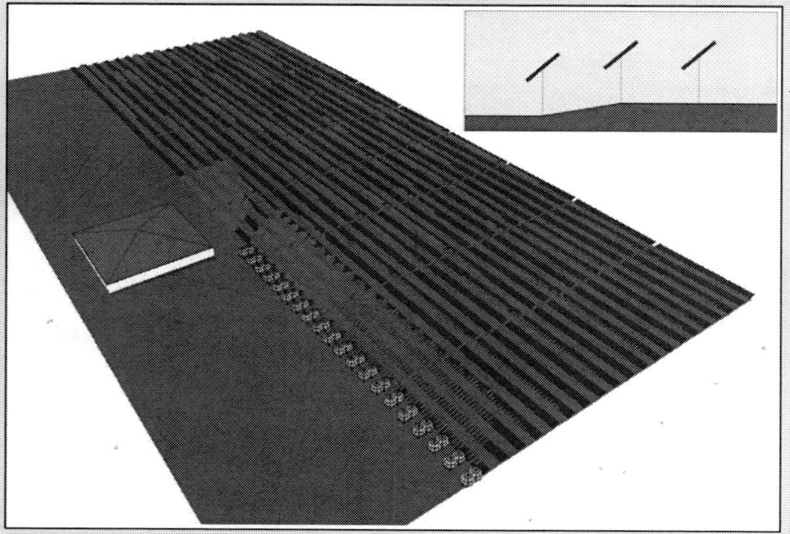

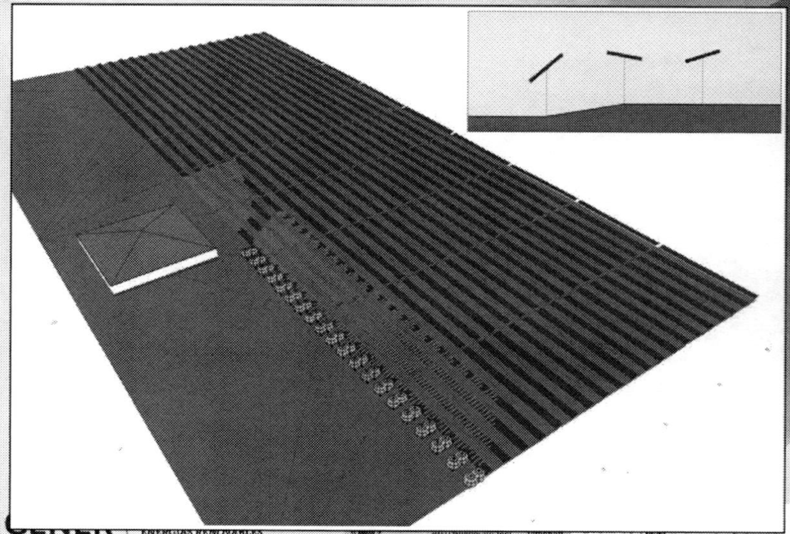

METHODOLOGY – SOLAR BACKTRACKING STRATEGIES (3)

- Backtracking strategies are **independent of the tracking algorithm** applied.
- While the algorithm keep avoiding inter-row shading, **it can override the strategy**.
- **Astronomical algorithm will be applied** on all strategies of this study to avoid false gains.

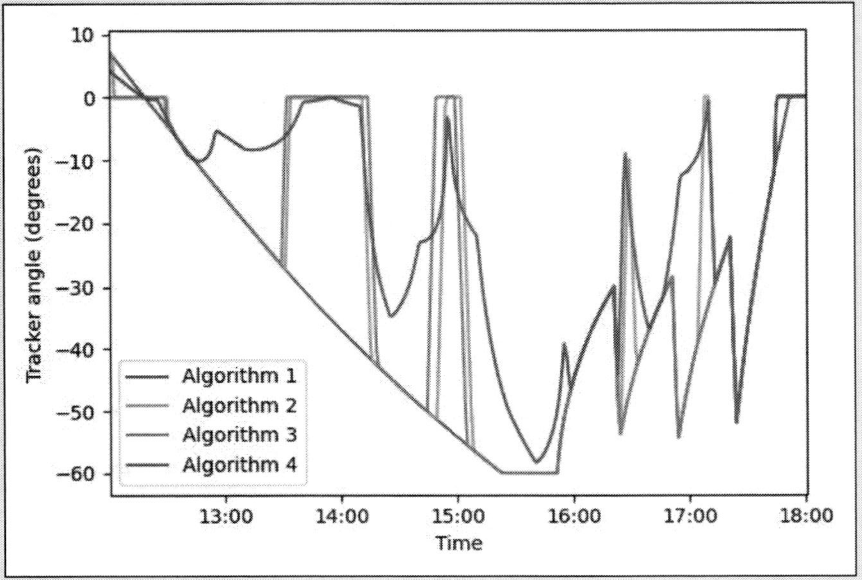

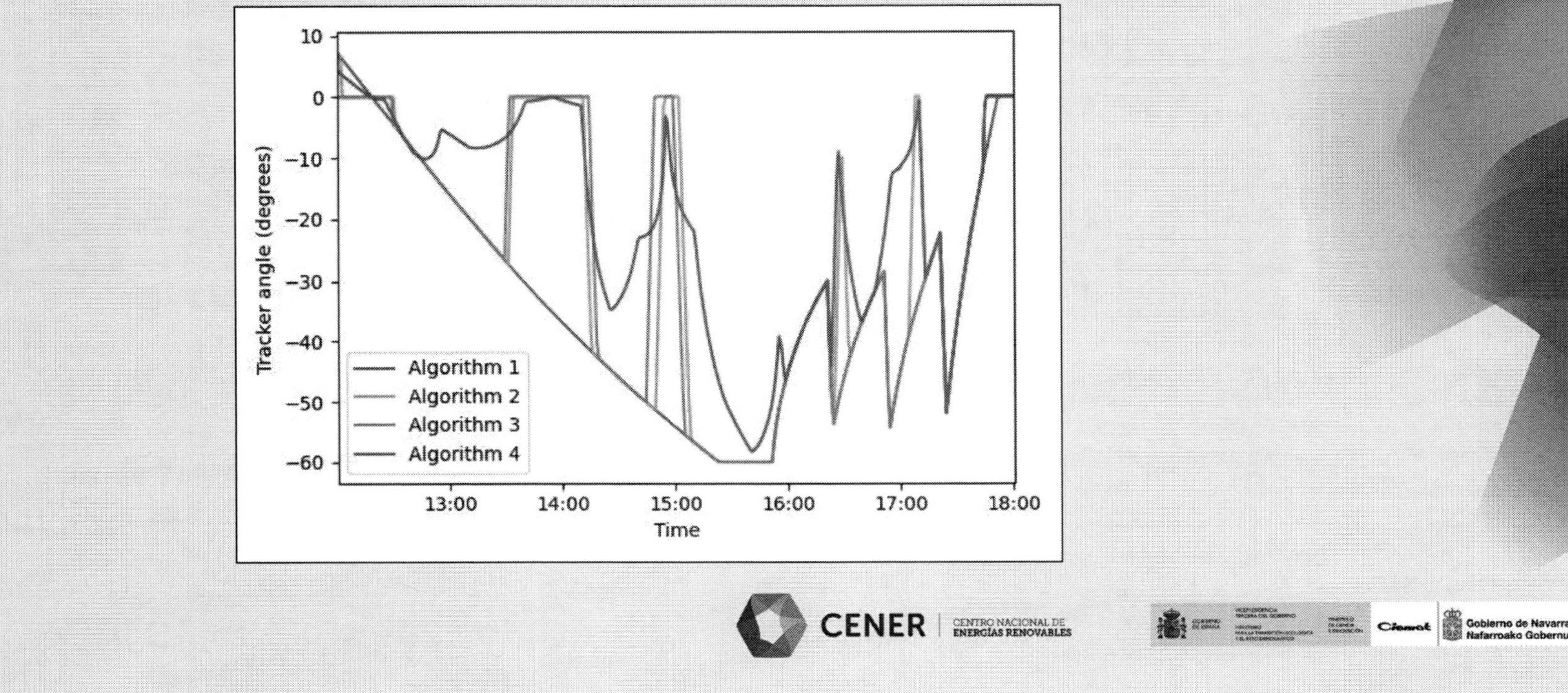

CENER | CENTRO NACIONAL DE ENERGÍAS RENOVABLES

Ciemat | Gobierno de Navarra Nafarroako Gobernua

METHODOLOGY – STUDY SCENARIOS

N - Backtracking

- Simulations in Pamplona, Sevilla (Spain) and Libya
- **1P and 2P** (portrait) module disposition.

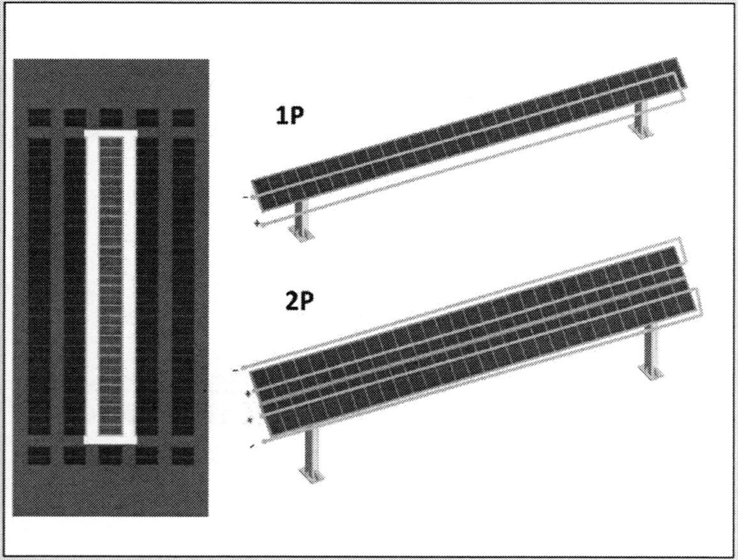

Irr - Backtracking

- Simulation of terrain close to Zamora (Spain)
- Up to 10% slope between trackers

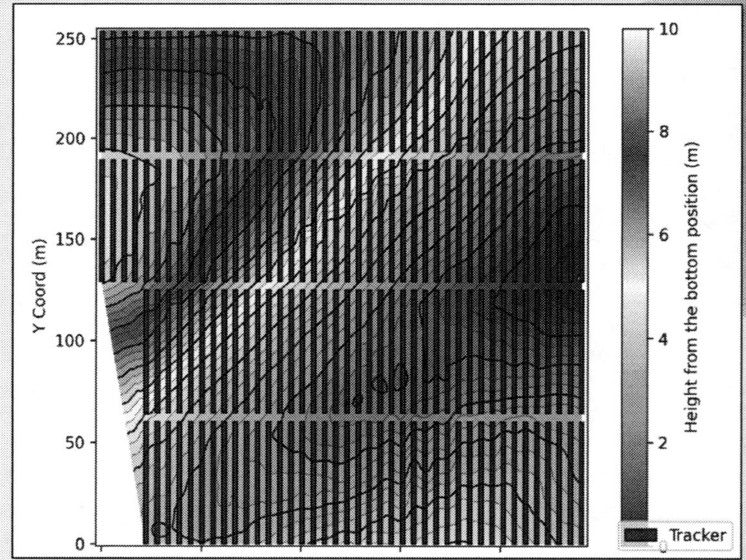

CENER | CENTRO NACIONAL DE ENERGÍAS RENOVABLES

Gobierno de Navarra
Nafarroako Gobernua

METHODOLOGY – SOLAR RADIATION & METEOROLOGICAL DATA

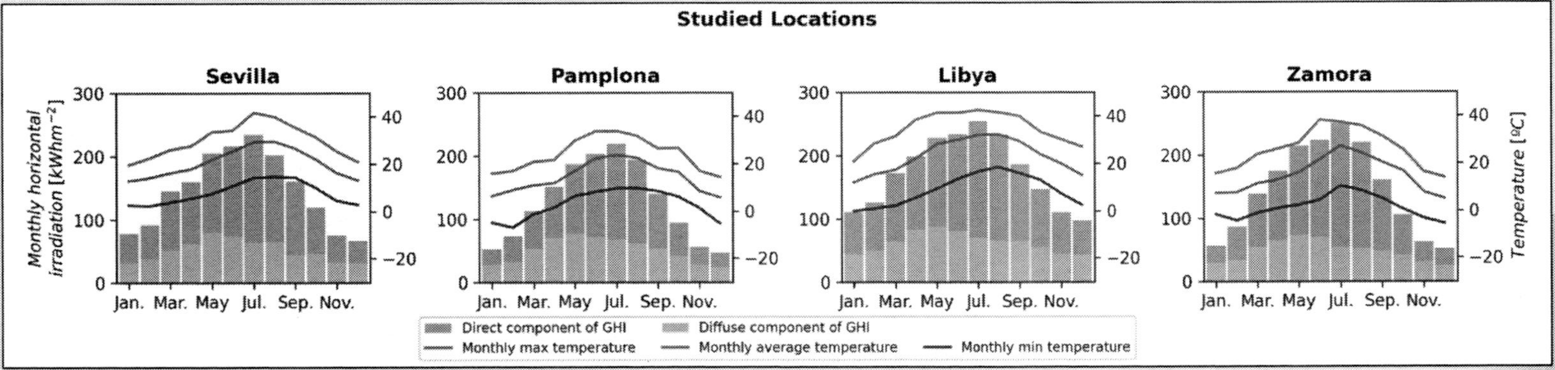

Strategy	Location	LAT. [º]	LON. [º]	H_{GHI} [kWh·m^{-2}]	H_{DHI} [kWh·m^{-2}]
N-BT	Spain 1 (Pamplona)	42.80	-1.60	1527	600
	Spain 2 (Sevilla)	37.38	-5.98	1755	609
	Libya	31.31	13.4	2100	746
Irr-BT	Spain 3 (Zamora)	41.5	-5.75	2072	572

- Generation of **one-minute resolution TMY** based on:
  - CAMS & MERRA-2 one-minute resolution data (SoDa platform): 19 years of data (Feb 2004 – Jan 2023)
  - Generation of TMY according to CENER methodology [2] implemented in UNE 206013:2017 standard [3]

[2] C.M. Fernández-Peruchena, et al. *Renewable Sustainable Energy Rev.* 2018, 91, 802.
[3] UNE 206013:2017. *Solar thermal electric plants. Procedure for the generation of solar radiation percentiles years.* UNE:Normalización Española, 2017.

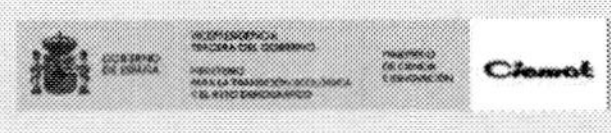

CENER | CENTRO NACIONAL DE ENERGÍAS RENOVABLES

Gobierno de Navarra Nafarroako Gobernua

METHODOLOGY – ESTIMATION OF ENERGY PRODUCTION (1)

Evaluation demands a software tool that enables:

- **High resolution** data (1 minute)
- Programming **any solar backtracking strategy**
- Calculating **derate factors** on each tracker individually

SIMPV: PV plant simulation software developed by CENER with the ability of simulate behaviour and production of a complete photovoltaic installation.

SI.MP.V

pvlib python

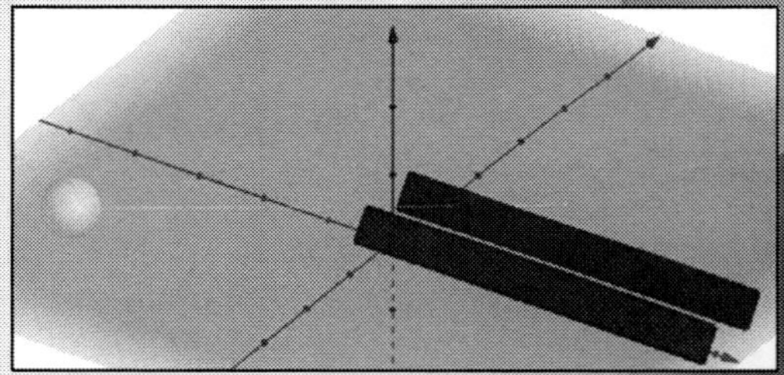

Some of the considered effects:

- **Real solar tracker movement** (non-continuous movement) .
- **Inter-row shadings** (self-shading) by trigonometrical relations between PV modules*.
- **Transient effects** considered.
- **Full I-V curve** at the MPPT input.
- **Electrical effect of shadings** applied on I-V curve.

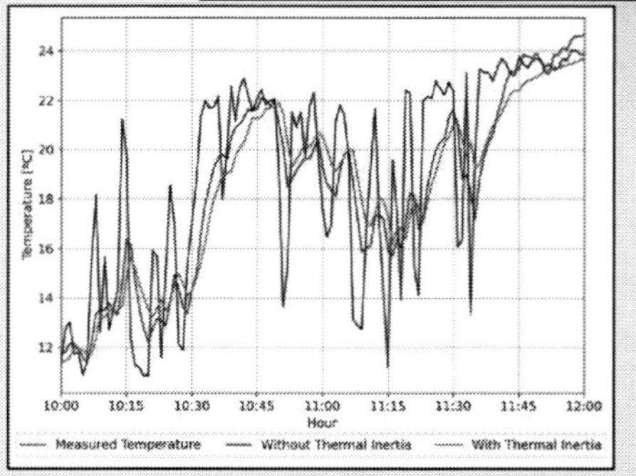

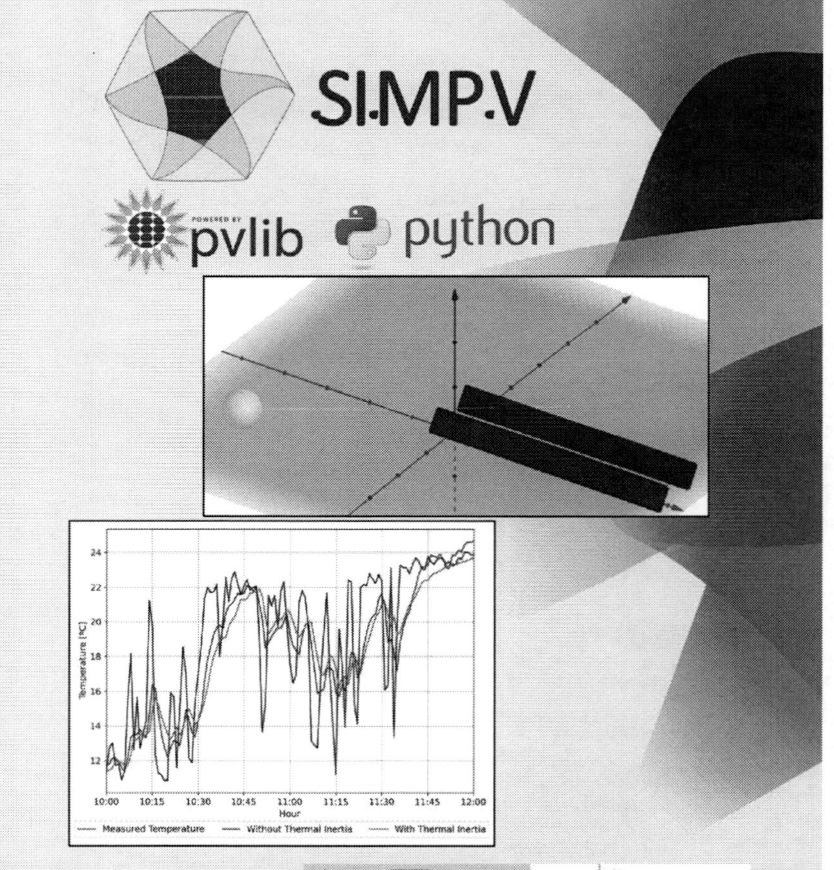

CENER | CENTRO NACIONAL DE ENERGÍAS RENOVABLES

Gobierno de Navarra Nafarroako Gobernua

METHODOLOGY – ESTIMATION OF SHADING POSITION

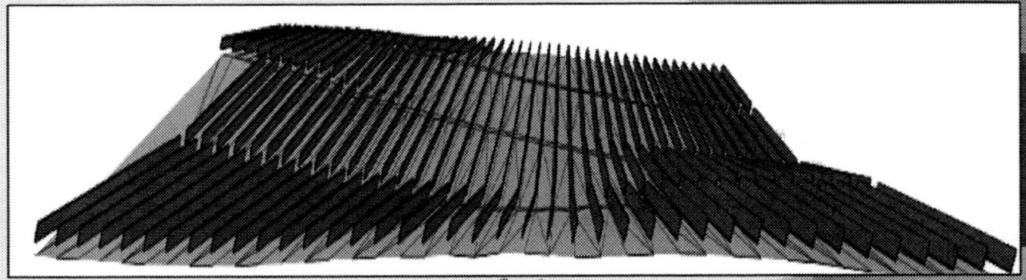

Complex terrains difficult use of trigonometrical relations for shading estimation

- Also applied to near shadings (buildings, trees…)
- This method is **not suitable** for shading estimations in complex terrains or roof installations.

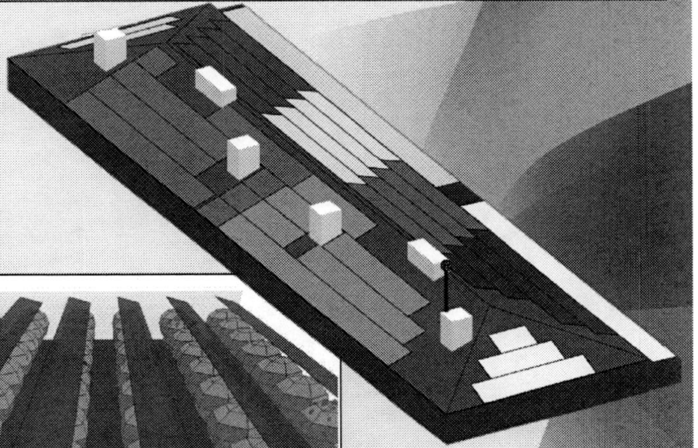

SIMPV Shading Tool: Shading simulation tool developed by CENER to estimate the shading position on photovoltaic structures, obtaining a **high-precision shading profile**.

The program evaluates if an element is shaded by the surrounding elements, with the precision defined by the user.

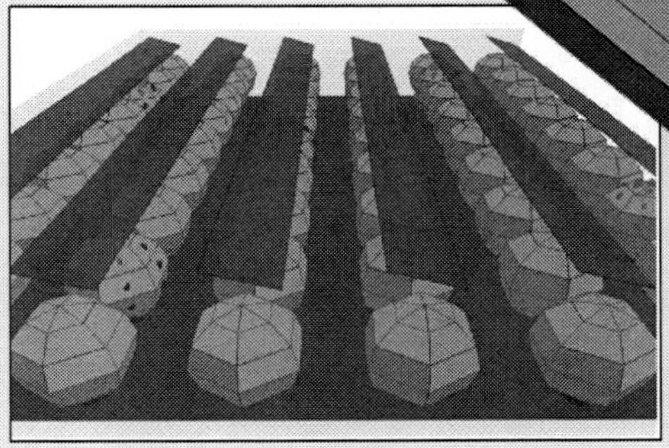

The tool can be used for calculate shading position in trees, making suitable its use as an agrivoltaic tool:

- ***4DO.5.4***: *Development and Evaluation of an Agrivoltaic System in Olive Groves based on a Novel Smart Tracking Algorithm.*
  <u>*Thursday 25th, 17:00, Room 1B.*</u>

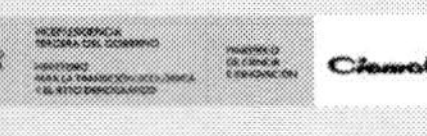

CENER | CENTRO NACIONAL DE ENERGÍAS RENOVABLES

Gobierno de Navarra Nafarroako Gobernua

RESULTS – N-BACKTRACKING STRATEGY (N-BT)

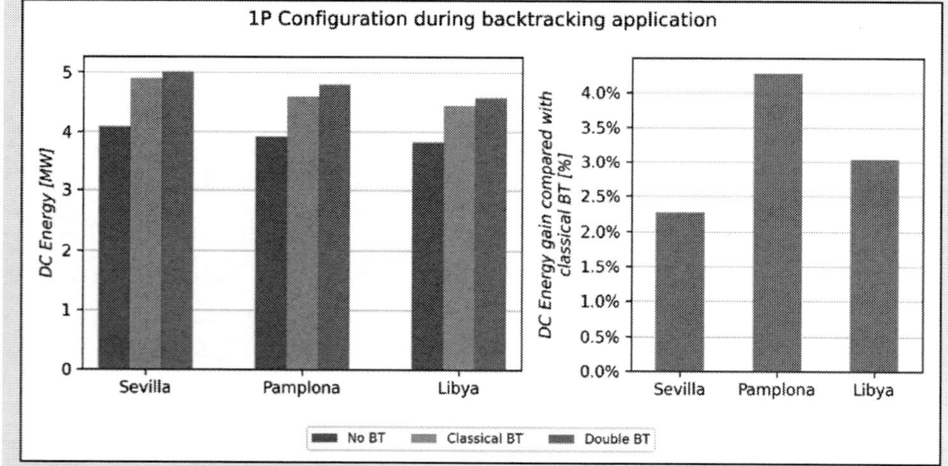

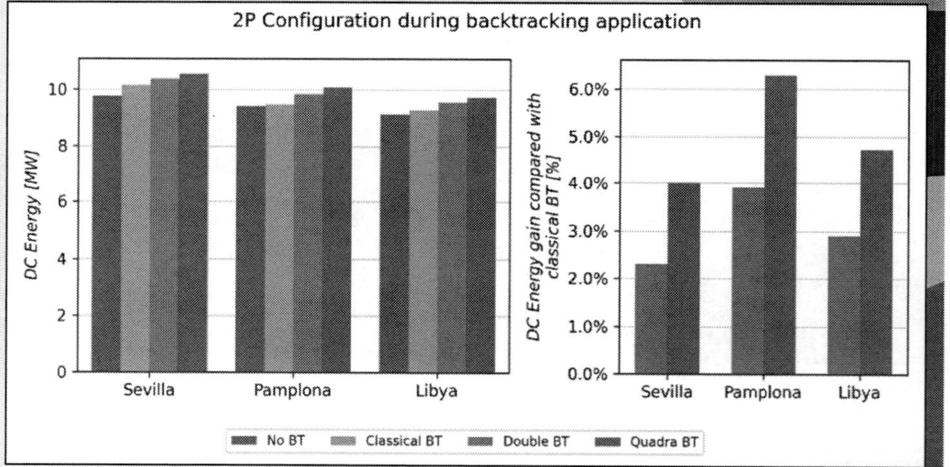

- N-Backtracking strategy **increase the energy generated** compared with classical BT:
  - **1P**: 0.32% - 0.67% with Double-BT
  - **2P**: 0.34% - 0.62% with Double-BT, 0.56%-1% with Quadra-BT
- During backtracking application, gain could reach **up to 4% in 1P** configuration and **6% in 2P** configuration.
- **All N-BT strategies override classical BT.**

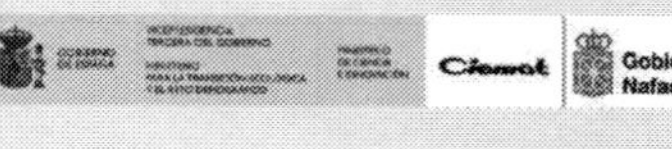

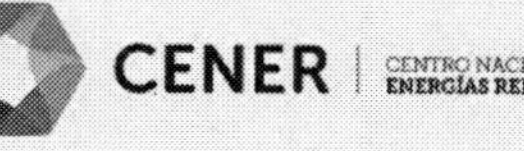

CENER | CENTRO NACIONAL DE ENERGÍAS RENOVABLES

Gobierno de Navarra
Nafarroako Gobernua

RESULTS – IRR-BACKTRACKING STRATEGY (Irr-BT) (1)

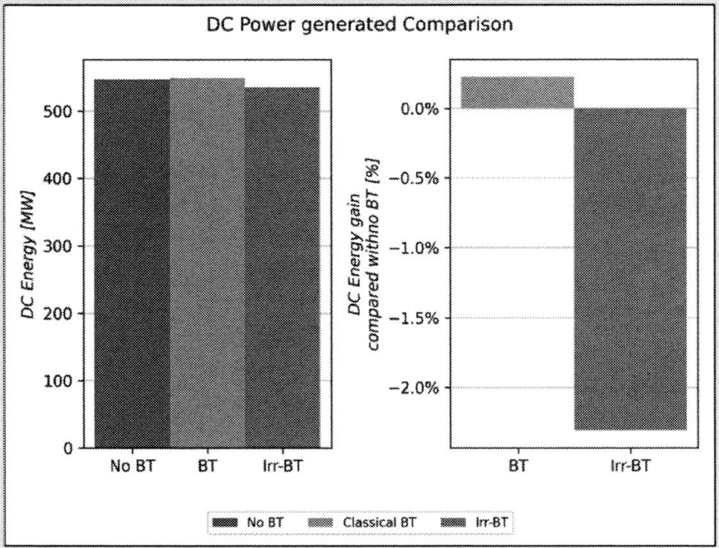

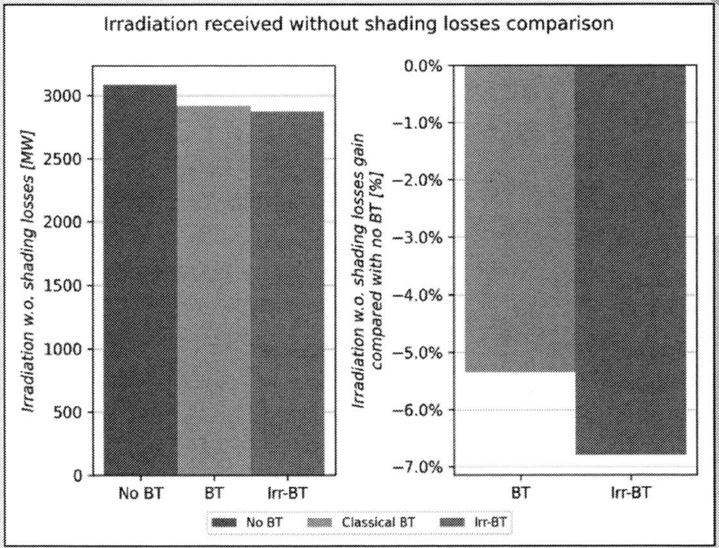

- Application of Irr-BT strategy **does not imply a gain** in DC energy production.
- **Two** main reasons:
  - Loss due to misalignment of modules during backtracking (even if not shading is applied) **is higher than gain** by avoiding shading.
  - **Undesired shadings** are applied by other surrounding trackers.

CENER | CENTRO NACIONAL DE ENERGÍAS RENOVABLES

Gobierno de Navarra
Nafarroako Gobernua

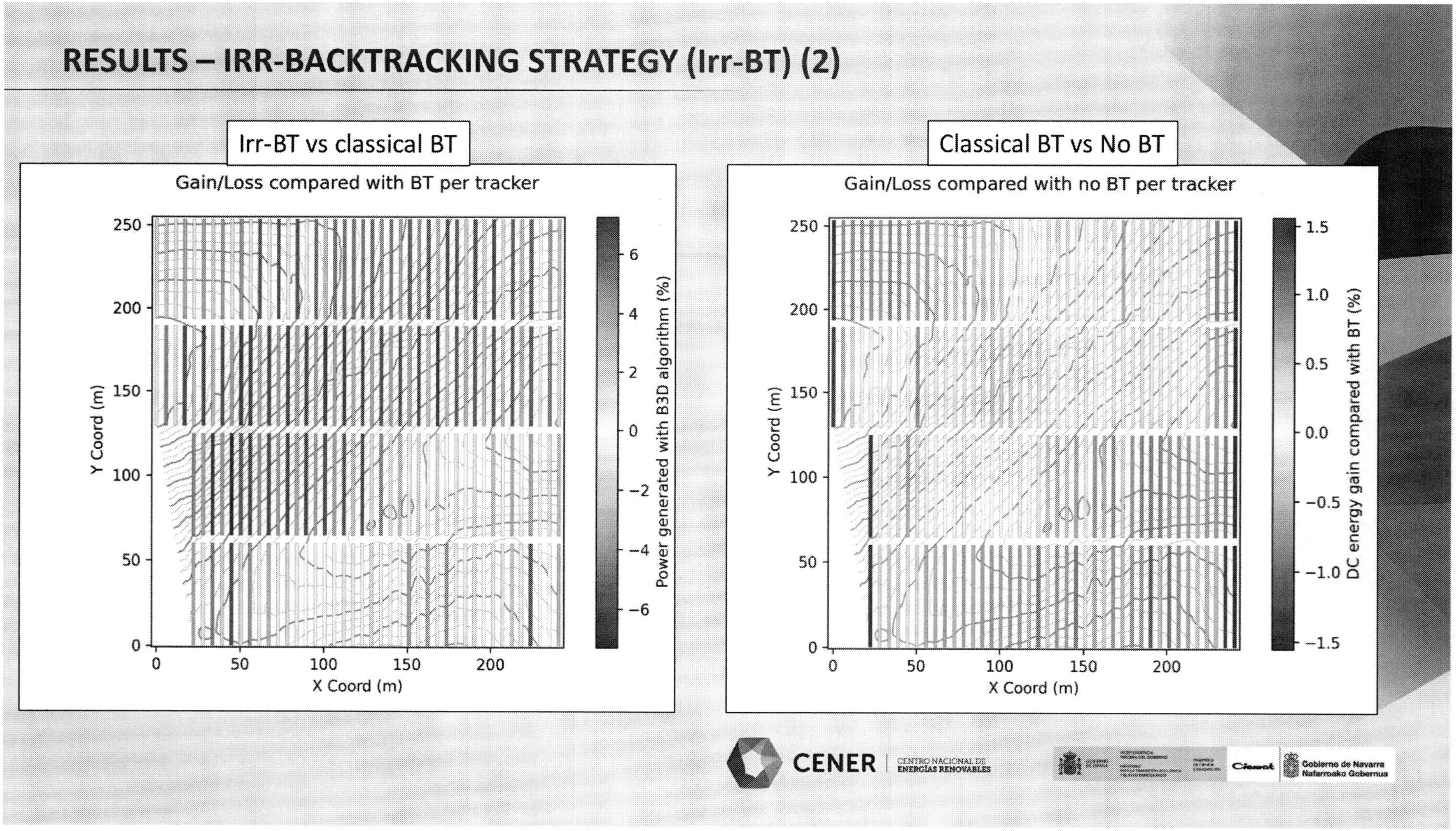
RESULTS – IRR-BACKTRACKING STRATEGY (Irr-BT) (2)
Irr-BT vs classical BT
Gain/Loss compared with BT per tracker
Y Coord (m)
X Coord (m)
Power generated with B3D algorithm (%)
Classical BT vs No BT
Gain/Loss compared with no BT per tracker
DC energy gain compared with BT (%)
CENER
CENTRO NACIONAL DE ENERGÍAS RENOVABLES
Ciemat
Gobierno de Navarra
Nafarroako Gobernua

SUMMARY & CONCLUSIONS

SUMMARY

- In-depth & **high-resolution study** performed for **three different backtracking strategies**
- Proposed **two new backtracking strategies called N-BT and Irr-BT**.

CONCLUSIONS

- **Backtracking strategies are necessary** on all solar tracking algorithms.
- **Higher backtracking adaptation to** installation could improve performance.
- **N-BT strategy:**
  - Adapt backtracking repetitions to structure layout could reach up to 6% gain during BT application time compared with classical backtracking.
- **Irr-BT strategy:**
  - Terrain-dependent backtracking strategy has not increased PV generation compared with classical backtracking.
  - A full study of surrounding trackers could be considered in high-slope zones

CENER | CENTRO NACIONAL DE ENERGÍAS RENOVABLES

Gobierno de Navarra
Nafarroako Gobernua

ONGOING & FUTURE WORKS

- Both strategies could be complementary: **Merge of N-BT and Irr-BT.**
- Study of backtracking strategies with **other module cell technologies** (bifacial, back contact...)
- **Clearing works** (cuttings and embankments) could be considered to bring the tracking angle closer to the astronomical angle.
- Validation of strategies on a real PV installation.

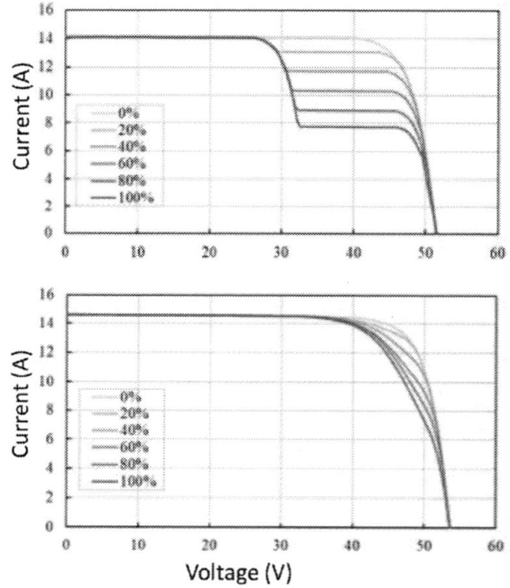

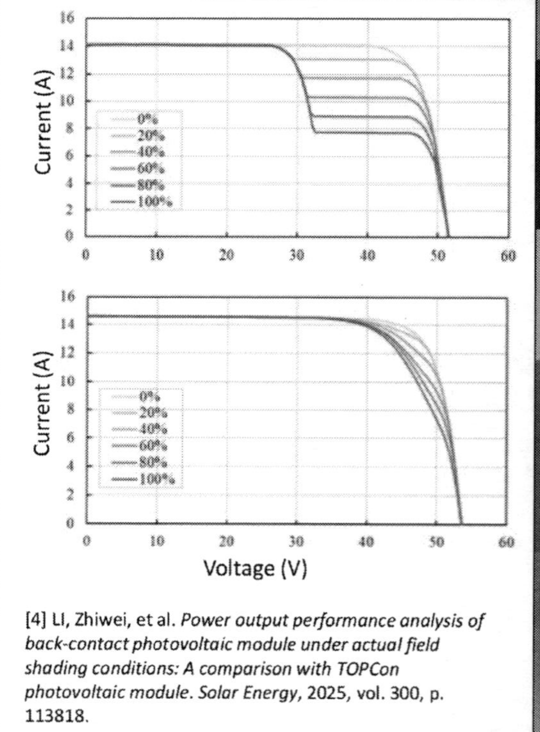

[4] LI, Zhiwei, et al. *Power output performance analysis of back-contact photovoltaic module under actual field shading conditions: A comparison with TOPCon photovoltaic module. Solar Energy*, 2025, vol. 300, p. 113818.

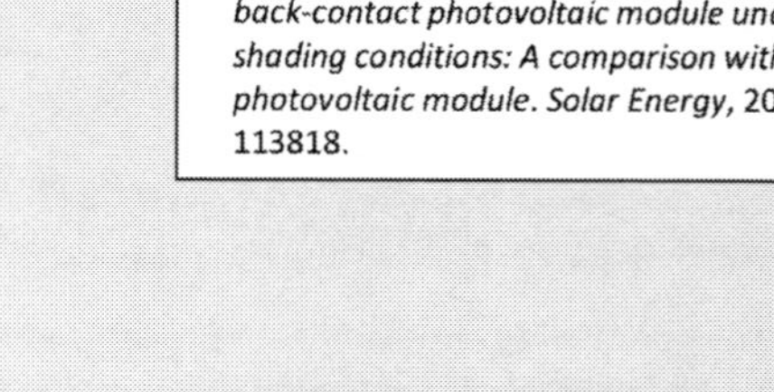

CENER | CENTRO NACIONAL DE ENERGÍAS RENOVABLES

Ciemat Gobierno de Navarra Nafarroako Gobernua

CENER
Solar Energy Technologies &
Storage Department
golivares@cener.com
Ciudad de la Innovación, 7
31621 Sarriguren, Spain
+34 669 18 83 03
+34 902 25 28 00
Thank you for your attention!
CENER
NATIONAL RENEWABLE ENERGY CENTRE

42nd European Photovoltaic Solar Energy Conference and Exhibition

This presentation was selected by the Sc. Committee of the EU PVSEC 2025 for submission of a full paper to one of the EU PVSEC's collaborating peer-reviewed journals.

Terrain-Following Single-Axis Tracking PV Systems: Civil Work Reduction, Performance Impact, and Lifetime Financial Analysis

Abhinav Ratnagiri[1], Shrey Bhatnagar[1], Angel Velasco[1], Viktor Kapetanovic[1], Claire Puttock[1], Amir Asgharzadeh Shishavan[1]

[1] Nextracker, Inc. Fremont, CA, USA 94555

*Corresponding Author – email: aratnagiri@nextracker.com – phone number: +1(302) 660–1105
Address:
Nextracker, Inc.
ATTN: Abhinav Ratnagiri
6200 Paseo Padre Pkwy
Fremont, CA 94555
USA

Keywords: Terrain-Following Trackers, Performance Impact, Lifetime Financial Analysis

Abstract: Single-axis tracking (SAT) systems have quickly become the most deployed photovoltaic systems at the utility-scale. Conventional SAT systems were designed originally for flat and semi-flat terrain, utilize a straight torque tube around which the modules rotate. However, availability of as flat and semi-flat terrain continues to dwindle, PV system developers are looking to utilize increase undulating land for development. In undulating conditions, conventional SAT systems require either additional grading to level the terrain or a variably adjusted pile height along the tracker to maintain a straight torque tube. However, both approaches incur high costs—either from increased civil work or the additional steel required for piers. As an alternative, terrain-following trackers have been introduced, allowing the tracker to adapt to the natural terrain while maintaining consistent pier heights. While this can induce significant cost savings, the nominal concern with terrain-following systems is the potential for increased electrical mismatch due to variations in the angle of incidence (AOI) across a string, as well as the risk of higher shading losses. Any performance loss will lead to decreased lifetime revenue, a contrasting financial force to the civil work savings incurred in a terrain-following system. While this performance loss has previously been studied in synthetic conditions, we are extending this analysis to a real selection of SAT sites in this work. We have paired this performance analysis with an evaluation of the reduction in civil work at the same set of sites. Using a real-site case study structure, a variety of site conditions were analyzed, seeking to quantify the financial impacts of both the reduction in civil work and the potential performance loss due to terrain-following trackers. Across this selection of sites, the use of terrain-following trackers reduced the need for civil work by an average of over 80%, constituting a significant benefit to the developer of the PV system. In contrast, even the most significant performance loss was just 0.65%, contributing to a minimal impact on lifetime revenue. As a result, across all sites in the selection, the use of terrain-following tracking systems had a positive financial impact, reducing the levelized cost of energy (LCOE) by up to 1.51$/MWh.

1. Introduction

Increasing the financial viability of photovoltaic (PV) systems has been a driving force for innovation across the industry, with particular focus on adapting technology to a growing variety of environmental conditions. As part of this innovation, single-axis tracking (SAT) systems have become the preferred choice for utility-scale PV deployment [1]. The earliest SAT systems—referred to as conventional SAT systems—were designed with a single tube around which the modules rotated, mounted on piles of uniform height. While effective on flat ground, these systems lack the adaptability needed for all site conditions. As flat land becomes increasingly saturated with PV projects and access to such terrain declines, developers are turning to more undulating topographies. To adapt conventional SAT systems to uneven terrain, extensive earthwork or variable pile heights are required. Both solutions, however, come at significant cost and can hinder project development. To address this challenge, terrain-following systems have been introduced. These systems allow the torque tube—the axis of module rotation—to conform to the ground, thereby reducing the need for grading. This approach can dramatically decrease civil work requirements, but it has also raised concerns about system performance. Unlike conventional SAT systems, terrain-following trackers can introduce varying angles of incidence (AOI) across a single row of modules, leading to greater electrical mismatch. Additionally, these systems may create complex shading patterns that standard tracking algorithms are not designed to manage. Consequently, performance losses remain a concern with terrain-following designs. Previous research has examined these potential losses under synthetic conditions; the present work extends that analysis to a real-site case study. Any performance loss in a PV system directly translates into reduced revenue for the asset owner, a financial risk that could prevent project development. Therefore, a holistic financial evaluation of terrain-following systems must weigh both the savings from reduced grading requirements and the potential revenue loss from decreased energy production.

2. Civil Work Approach

The potential savings from installing terrain-following systems stem directly from the reduced need for civil work. Leveling existing ground requires two opposing processes, cut (removing earth material) and fill (inserting earth material). Terrain-following trackers greatly reduce the need for both processes due to their ability to adapt to the existing topography.

Given an existing site topography, the grading necessary to implement both tracking systems were analyzed using the earthwork tool TerrainPro from Terabase Energy [3]. In performing this analysis, both the original ground topography and the mechanical characteristics of the tracker configuration, either conventional SAT or terrain-following, were considered. In the terrain-following case, the maximum deflection angle between bays of a tracker is a key consideration, while in both cases the allowable variation in pier reveal height is a necessary input to determine the total amount of grading necessary. In this analysis, real sites with two different terrain-following systems were used – using a maximum deflection angle of 0.75 or 1.5 degrees between each bay. The variation in pier reveal height constitutes the maximum allowable range in distance from the ground to the tracker. Varying this distance allows the tracker to remain closer to flat on undulating terrain, once again affecting the amount of change necessary to the original topography. For the sake of our tracker configurations, both conventional SAT and terrain-following systems, the maximum pier reveal height was assumed to be 18 inches, consistent with current tracking system standards. To quantify the necessary civil work for a given site, the metric Balanced Earthwork (BE) was used, defined as twice the larger of the necessary cut and necessary fill in cubic yards, representing the total volume of earth altered. This metric was used because it allows for a reasonable cost model to be applied by determining a price per cubic meter of earth moved. By analyzing the difference in the required BE between conventional and terrain-following tracker systems, a quantitative measure of the civil work avoided with the terrain-following system was determined. Figure 1 shows the areas of a site where grading was necessary, with Fig. 1a showing the numerous locations throughout the site where earthwork was necessary, with sharper colors indicating larger amounts of work. In Fig. 1b, many of these colored patches disappear, clearing demonstrating that the need for earthwork has reduced significantly because of a terrain-following system.

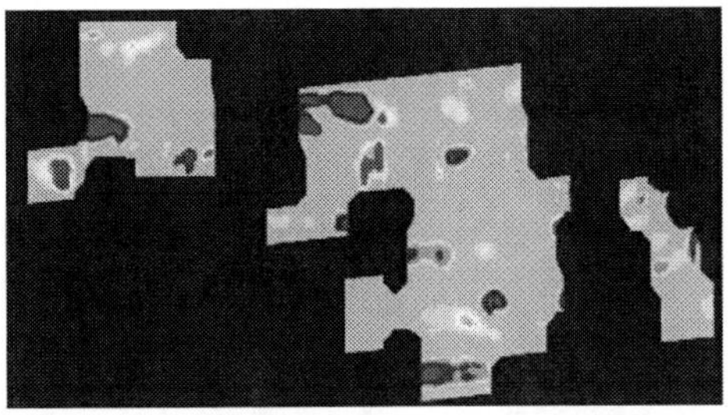

a) Cut/Fill Map with Conventional Trackers

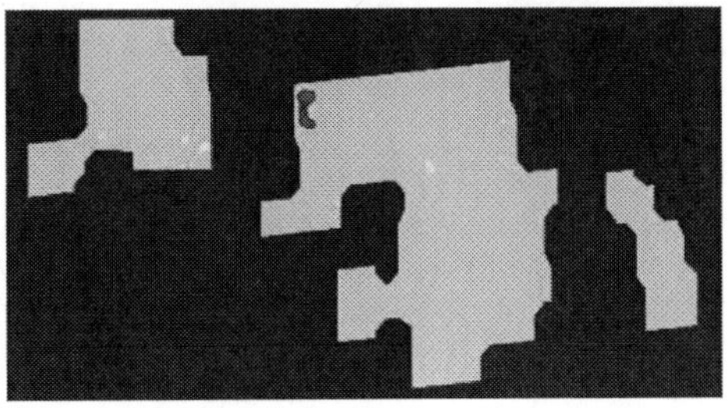

b) Cut/Fill Map with Terrain-Following Trackers

Cut/Fill Legend		
Range (feet)		Color
Maximum Cut	-2.00	
-2.00	-1.50	
-1.50	-1.00	
-1.00	-0.50	
-0.50	-0.10	
0.10	0.50	
0.50	1.00	
1.00	1.50	
1.50	2.00	
2.00	Maximum Fill	

Figure 1: Reduction in Cut/Fill Requirements with use of Terrain-Following Trackers (b) as opposed to Conventional Trackers (a)

3. Energy Performance Modeling

To accurately quantify the differences in energy performance between a conventional SAT system and a terrain-following one, Nextracker's performance modeling engine, TrueSim [4], was used. This model is built on foundations from open-source PV performance modeling tools including pvlib [5], System Advisor Model (SAM) [6], and PVMismatch [7]. Using the physical configuration of a PV project, TrueSim performs cell-level irradiance and shade calculations given a set of tracking angles for the SAT system. Cell-level calculations are essential to accurately account for the potential additional mismatch and shading loss in terrain-following systems. TrueSim's 3D shading model calculates shade polygons for each module along a tracker. In conjunction, plane-of-array (POA) irradiance is computed for both front and back sides of the module using the infinite-sheds model [8], which itself considers both ground and diffuse shading. Due to the 3D nature of the TrueSim shading model, the same methodology was applicable for all tracker configuration solutions. Using the shading pattern and the calculated POA, the resulting total effective irradiance is computed for each module cell. Cell IV curves are then calculated based on the single-diode model [9], using both effective irradiance and cell temperature as inputs. These cell-level IV curves are aggregated to module-level IV curves while considering the module's bypass diodes. Similarly, module IV curves are aggregated to produce string-level and system-level IV curves from which the maximum power point is used to determine the total DC output of the site as whole. For the purposes of this study, DC power output calculations were performed according to this process over the course of a typical meteorological year (TMY), interpolated to 15-minute intervals. To derive an AC power output better suited for downstream revenue calculations, an assumed AC conversion factor of 98% was used.

4. Economic Analysis

The civil work reduction and the performance impact of utilizing a terrain-following system often fall on opposing sides of a cost-benefit analysis. To perform this contrasting analysis, cost and revenue models were necessary to convert the BE and AC energy output metrics into a dollar value that was relevant over the lifetime of the project.

The earthwork cost savings model was derived from historical cost data collected across Nextracker's fleet. The cost per cubic meter of earthwork required was calculated as shown in Equation (1):

$$\text{Unit Cost (\$/cu.m.)} = (43.7 \times \text{BE})^{-0.185} \qquad (1)$$

to account for the diminishing marginal costs of additional cut and fill. This was used to determine the cost per cubic yard of BE, which was used to calculate the total gross savings due to terrain-following trackers. For the purposes of this analysis, further cost differences between tracker types were ignored to isolate the impact of civil work reduction. With this being an upfront capital expenditure (CAPEX), no discount was necessary to account for the potential future implications on total cashflow.

However, estimating the present value of revenue loss due to the performance impact required a more complex model. To quantify the annual financial impact over the lifetime of the project, degradation, inflation, and price per MWh were necessary assumptions. Degradation because of standard site conditions was assumed to be 1% year-to-year, whereas inflation was assumed to be 3% to best account for the value of future revenue. Regarding the price per MWh, this can vary significantly from project to project, heavily dependent on the region where the project is located. Across the selection of sites chosen for analysis, the power purchase agreement (PPA) price varied from \$40-80/MWh. In regions such as Texas and the southern US, lower PPA prices were considered, whereas European sites and northern US sites often had higher PPA prices [10]. Once the annual revenue was calculated for each year in the project lifetime, a discount rate of 7% was applied to calculate the net present value (NPV) of the lifetime project revenue. An established financial modeling concept, NPV was calculated using the following formula:

$$NPV = \sum_{t=0}^{30} \frac{R_t}{(1+0.07)^t} \qquad (2)$$

where t is the year and R_t is the revenue for that year over the full, 30-year lifetime of the project. This NPV allowed for a reasonable comparison with the upfront, CAPEX savings from earthwork reduction. Calculating the difference between these values resulted in the lifetime financial impact (LFI) and dividing this value by the total discounted lifetime production in MWh resulted in the impact on the levelized cost of energy in terms of \$/MWh.

5. Case Study Structure

Fourteen real sites were chosen to best analyze the trade-off between performance loss and civil work reduction in a variety of conditions. It was important to vary each facet of analysis, both related to civil work reduction as well as performance analysis. The varied tracker technologies combined with a range of site land areas and topographies caused differences across the selection in civil work reduction. In terms of performance analysis, choosing sites with different capacities, different regions, and different layouts was essential. As a result, different electrical configurations, weather conditions, and shading patterns were modeled. Varying these important factors, allowed for conclusions that could be applicable to a wide range of site conditions.

6. Results and Discussion

Comparative analysis demonstrates that terrain-following tracker systems consistently deliver substantial reductions in civil work requirements while maintaining nearly identical energy performance relative to conventional designs. Figure 2 shows that, across the portfolio of case studies, earthwork volumes reduce by 65–92%, with most projects clustered above 80% reduction. This large decrease in cut/fill activity represents a significant practical benefit to the developer of the PV plant.

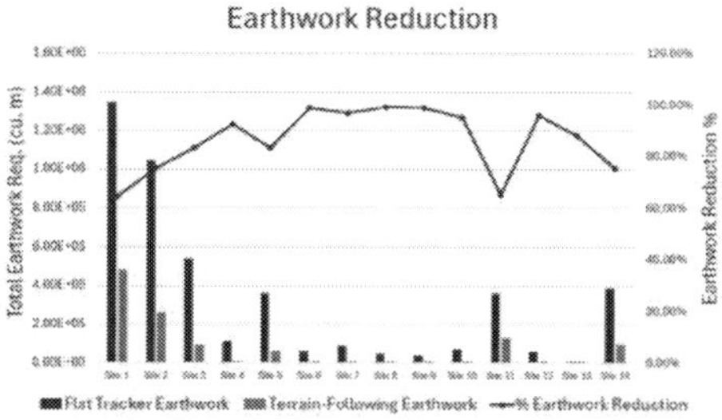

Figure 2: Balanced Earthwork reduction with terrain-following trackers at a selection of real PV sites.

In contrast, energy production differences between flat and terrain-following configurations were found to be negligible. As shown in Fig. 3, performance loss was at an average of 0.34%, with even the most severe case having a loss of just 0.65% per year. These results confirm that concerns about mismatch or shading penalties associated with terrain-following systems are minimal.

10.4229/EUPVSEC2025/4DO.1.5

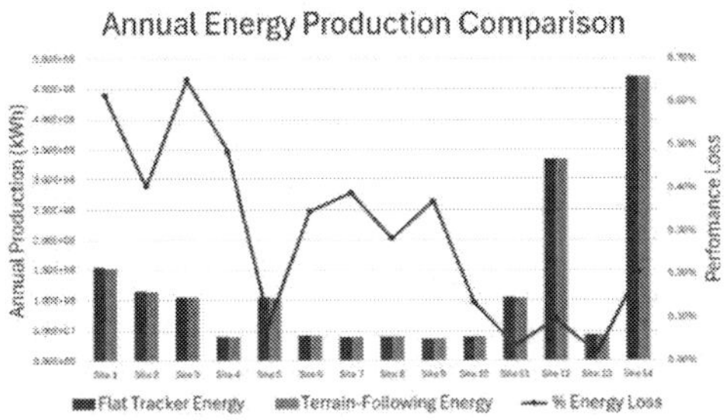

Figure 3: Energy production comparison between terrain-following systems and their conventional SAT counterparts.

Analyzed as financial forces, the avoided earthwork expenditures outweighs the minor revenue losses from reduced performance in every case evaluated, as shown in Figure 4. Net cost effects are uniformly positive, reaching hundreds of thousands to several million dollars, while even smaller projects demonstrate clear gains. This translates into consistent improvements in the LCOE, with savings between $0.03/MWh and $1.51/MWh with a mean value of $0.50/MWh across the selection. Considering the scale of production over the full lifetime of a project, these savings are significant.

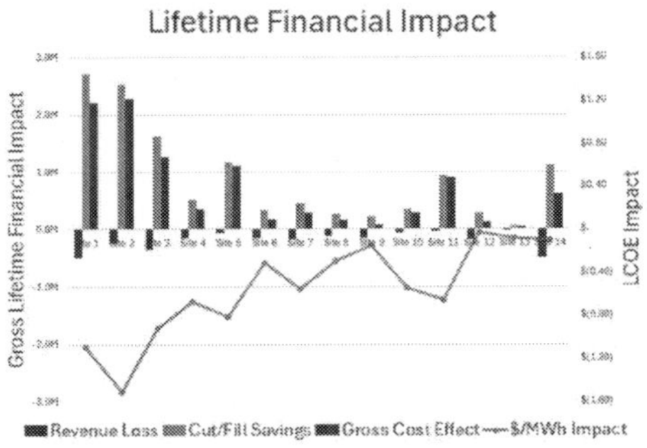

Figure 4: Lifetime financial analysis for terrain-following and conventional SAT systems.

7. Conclusions

Terrain-following trackers have an overall positive impact on the financial viability of a PV project over its lifetime across a variety of given site conditions. Across the selection of sites chosen, terrain-following systems led to an 80% reduction in civil work. When this reduction was contrasted with a maximum terrain loss of 0.65% the result was a significant reduction in LCOE and lifetime financial impact, up to $1.51/MWh at utility-scale production. Beyond the direct cost savings, these improvements have practical real-world implications. By minimizing grading requirements, terrain-following trackers expand the pool of viable project sites, shorten construction timelines, and reduce environmental disruption. Together, these benefits strengthen the economic case for adopting terrain-following designs, representing a scalable strategy to improve the competitiveness and feasibility of PV deployment across diverse landscapes.

7. REFERENCES

[1] J. [Lawrence B. N. L. (LBNL) Seel Berkeley CA (United States)] et al., "Utility-Scale Solar, 2024 Edition: Empirical Trends in Deployment, Technology, Cost, Performance, PPA Pricing, and Value in the United States [Slides]."

[2] A. A. Shishavan, V. R. Abbaraju, A. Dobos, and F. Borrelli, "Terrain-Following Single-Axis Tracking PV Systems: Advantages and Performance Analysis," 38th European Photovoltaic Solar Energy Conference and Exhibition; 1060-1064, 2021, doi: 10.4229/EUPVSEC20212021-5DO.3.3.

[3] Terabase Energy, "Terrain Pro," https://plantpredict.com/.

[4] Nextracker, Inc., "TrueSim Version 4.2.4."

[5] K. S. Anderson, C. W. Hansen, W. F. Holmgren, A. R. Jensen, M. A. Mikofski, and A. Driesse, "pvlib python: 2023 project update," J Open Source Soft, vol. 8, no. 92, p. 5994, 2023, doi: 10.21105/joss.05994.

[6] National Renewable Energy Laboratory, "System Advisor Model (SAM) Version 2023.12.17."

[7] M. Mikofski, B. Meyers, and C. Chaudhari, "PVMismatch Project: https://github.com/SunPower/PVMismatch," 2018, SunPower Corporation, Richmond, CA.

[8] Mikofski, M., Darawali, R., Hamer, M., Neubert, A., and Newmiller, J. "Bifacial Performance Modeling in Large Arrays". 2019 IEEE 46th Photovoltaic Specialists Conference (PVSC), 2019, pp. 1282-1287.

[9] W. De Soto et al., "Improvement and validation of a model for photovoltaic array performance", Solar Energy, vol 80, pp. 78-88, 2006

[10] LevelTen Energy, *PPA Price Index Report: North America Q1 2024*, LevelTen Energy, 2024

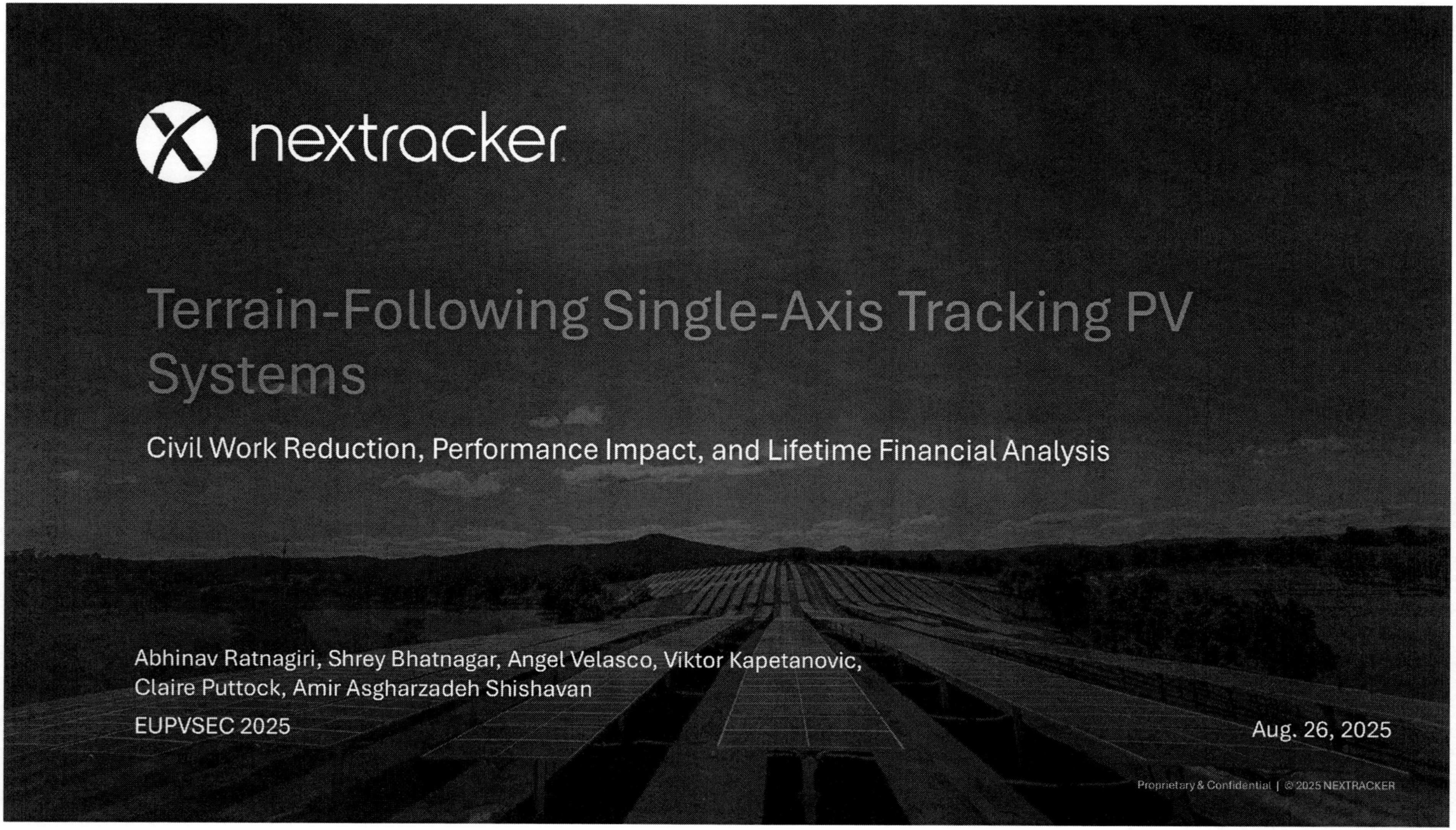
nextracker
Terrain-Following Single-Axis Tracking PV Systems
Civil Work Reduction, Performance Impact, and Lifetime Financial Analysis
Abhinav Ratnagiri, Shrey Bhatnagar, Angel Velasco, Viktor Kapetanovic,
Claire Puttock, Amir Asgharzadeh Shishavan
EUPVSEC 2025
Aug. 26, 2025
Proprietary & Confidential | © 2025 NEXTRACKER

Terrain-Following PV Systems: Background

Flat Tracker System

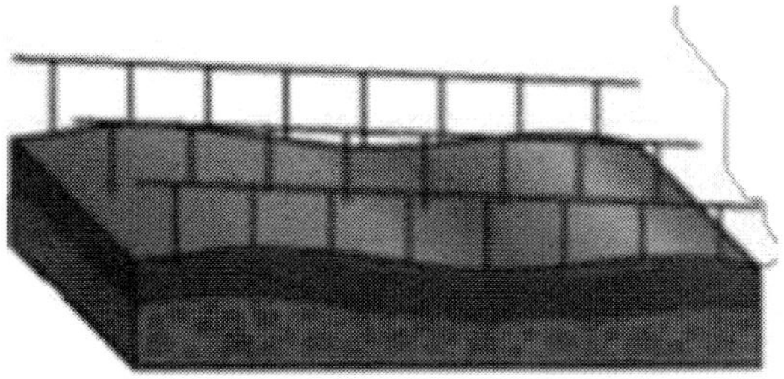

Terrain-Following System

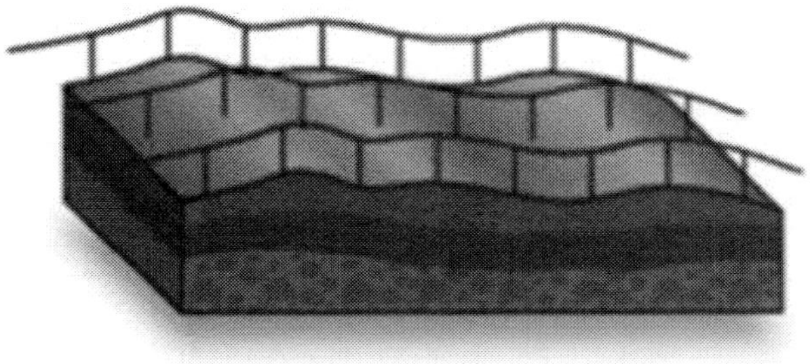

nextracker

Terrain-Following PV Systems: Implementation

Motivations

- Can be installed on undulating terrain
- Significantly less earthwork required

Concerns

- Increased irradiance mismatch across single tracker
- Operation at a lower MPP
- Complex shading patterns
- Potential resultant performance loss

Do the savings due to earthwork reduction outweigh the potential performance loss when considering terrain-following systems?

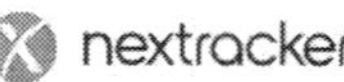

nextracker

Methodology

Provide Quantitative Financial Analysis of Terrain-Following System

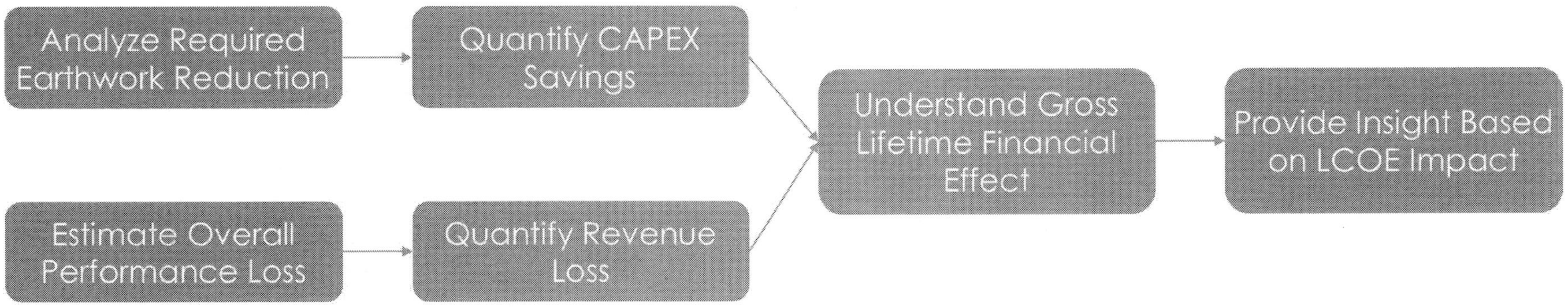

nextracker

Earthwork Analysis

Quantify Earthwork Reduction due to Terrain-Following Systems

- Comparison between Flat Trackers & Terrain Following
- Grading analysis performed by Terabase Terrain Pro
  - Required Cut/Fill based on original topography
  - Mechanical assumptions based on **NX Horizon** and **NX XTR 0.75, NX XTR 1.5**
  - Proposed Final Grading Metric:

$$\boldsymbol{BE = 2 \times \max(C, F)}$$

BE -- Balanced Earthwork
C -- Required Cut (cu. m)
F -- Required Fill (cu. m)

nextracker

Terrain Pro Grading Maps

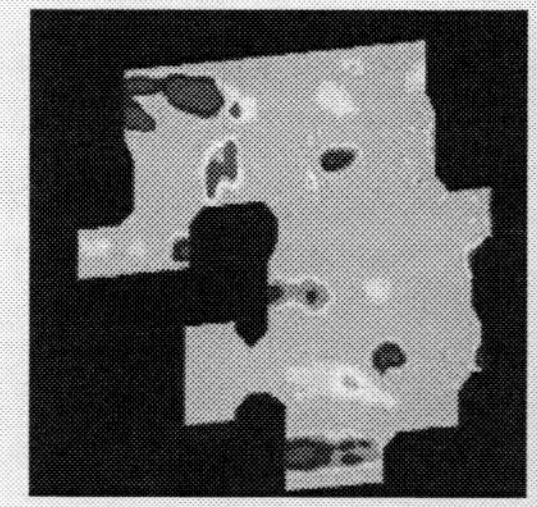

Flat Tracker Grading Map

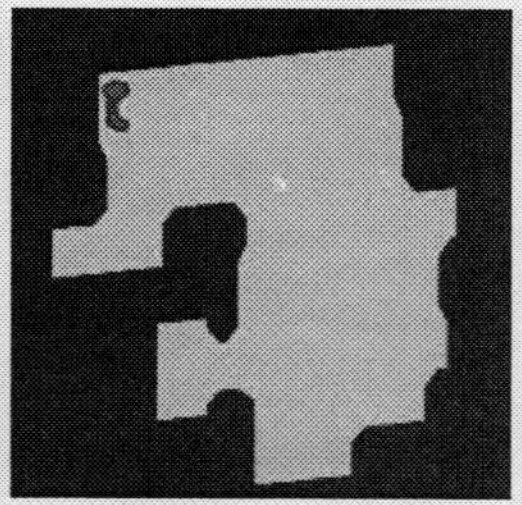

Terrain-Following Grading Map

Cut/Fill Legend		
Range (feet)		Color
Maximum Cut	-2.00	
-2.00	-1.50	
-1.50	-1.00	
-1.00	-0.50	
-0.50	-0.10	
0.10	0.50	
0.50	1.00	
1.00	1.50	
1.50	2.00	
2.00	Maximum Fill	

 5

Energy Yield Analysis

Estimate Performance Differences due to Irradiance Mismatch

- TrueSim Performance Modeling Engine
  - High-Fidelity tool to model Terrain-Following Systems
  - 3D shade model to determine cell-level shading losses
  - Infinite-Sheds, Single Diode models determine cell-level irradiance, IV curves
  - PVLIB based DC mismatch calculations for string level IV curve, MPPT estimation
  - Performed with 15-min time resolution with typical meteorological year (TMY) data for increased accuracy
  - Fixed AC Conversion factor of 98% for financial comparison
- Total Energy Loss (kWh), Energy Loss Percentage Calculated

nextracker

TrueSim 3D Shade Model

Terrain-Following Solution

Flat Tracker Solution

 6

Financial Impact Analysis

Understand Lifetime Financial Impact of Terrain-Following System

- Quantify CAPEX savings
  - Exponential formula based on empirical data applied to account for diminishing marginal cost

$$\mathrm{BEC} = (43.7 \times \mathrm{BE})^{-0.185} \times \mathrm{BE}$$

BEC -- Balanced Earthwork Cost ($)
BE -- Balanced Earthwork (cu. m)

- Quantify performance-related revenue loss
  - Net Present Value (NPV) of cashflow calculated
    - Region Specific PPA price applied ($/kWh)
    - Inflation rate: **3%**, Discount rate: **7%**
- Lifetime Financial Impact Measured:
  - $\mathrm{LFI} = \mathrm{Cost\ Savings} - \mathrm{NPV\ Revenue\ Loss}$
- LCOE Impact Calculated:
  - $\mathrm{LCOE\ Impact} = \mathrm{LFI} / \mathrm{Discounted\ Energy\ Production}$

nextracker

Real Site Case Study

14 total sites analyzed across North America and Europe

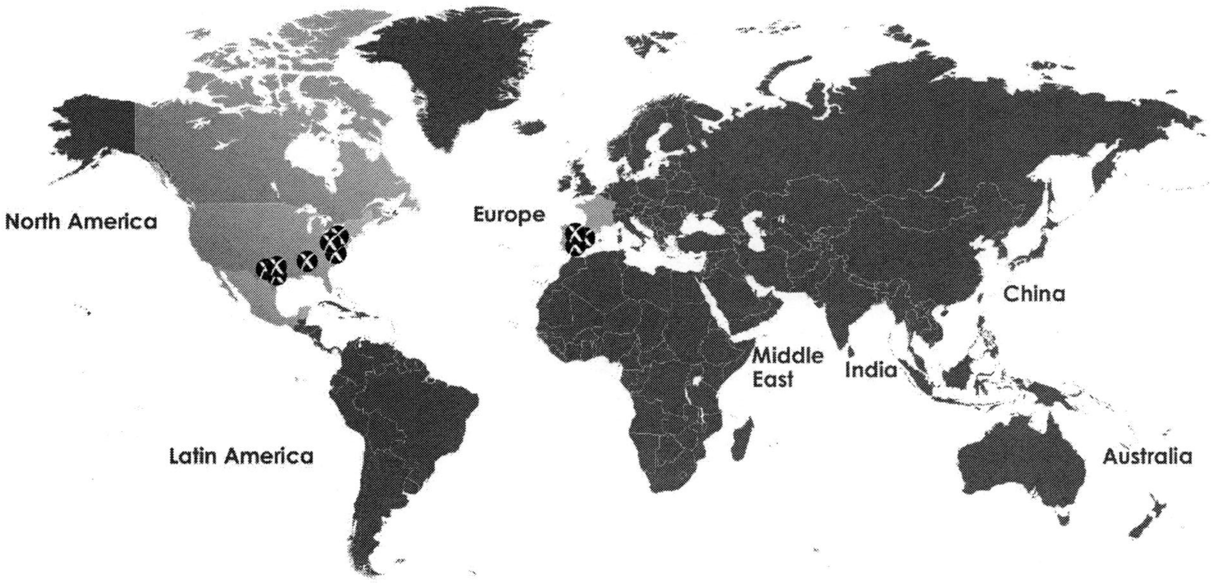

Locations of Case Study Sites

nextracker

Varied Site Capacity

Up to 200 MW

Varied Terrain-Following Systems

Multiple Tracker Configurations

Varied Energy Markets

PPA prices: \$40 – \$80 / kWh

Earthwork Analysis Results

Significant Reduction in Necessary Grading Across All Sites

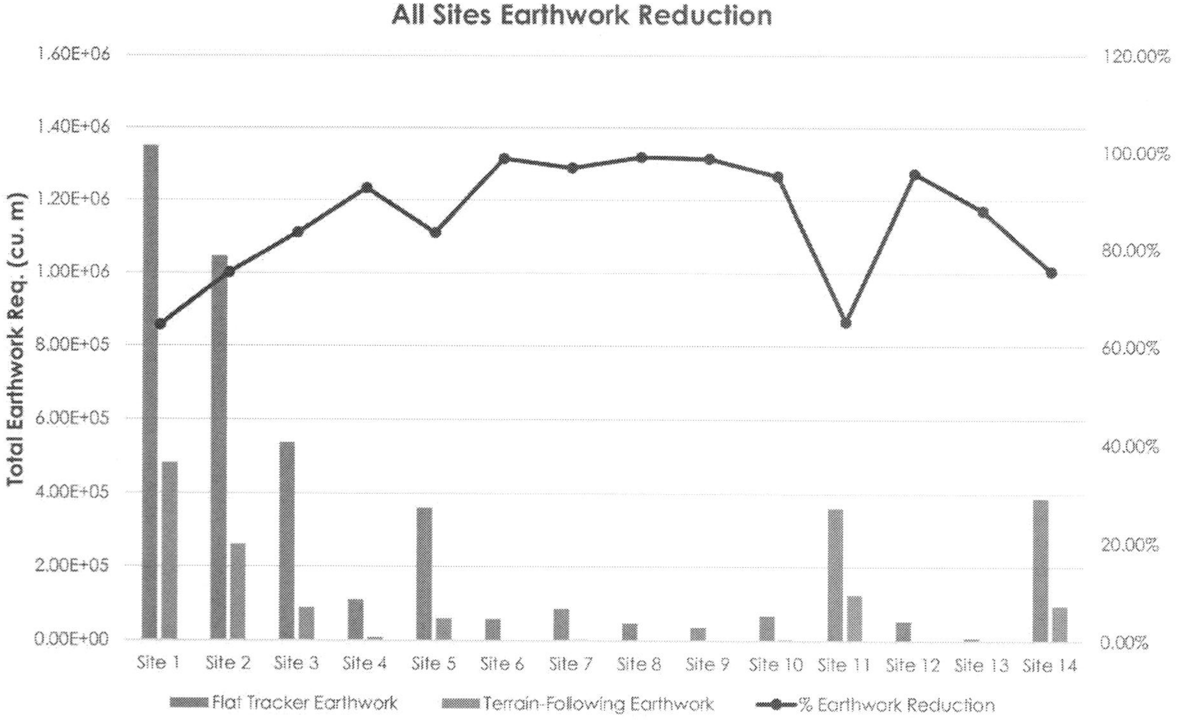

nextracker

303,260 cu. m

Average Flat Tracker BE required

75,633 cu. m

Average Terrain-Following BE required

87.28%

Average Earthwork Reduction

Performance Analysis Results

Minimal Performance loss due to Terrain-Following Systems

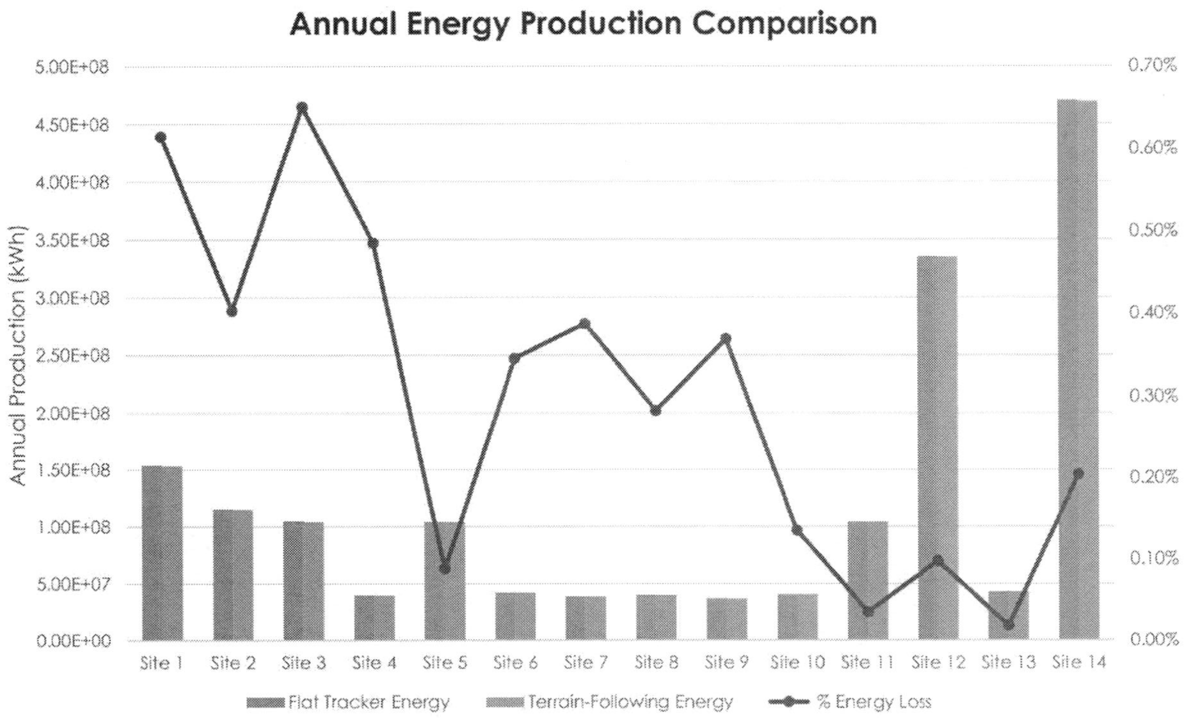

0.65%
Maximum Annual Performance Loss

0.02%
Minimum Annual Performance Loss

0.34%
Average Annual Performance Loss

nextracker

Lifetime Financial Impact

Cost savings, LCOE decrease observed due to Terrain-Following Systems

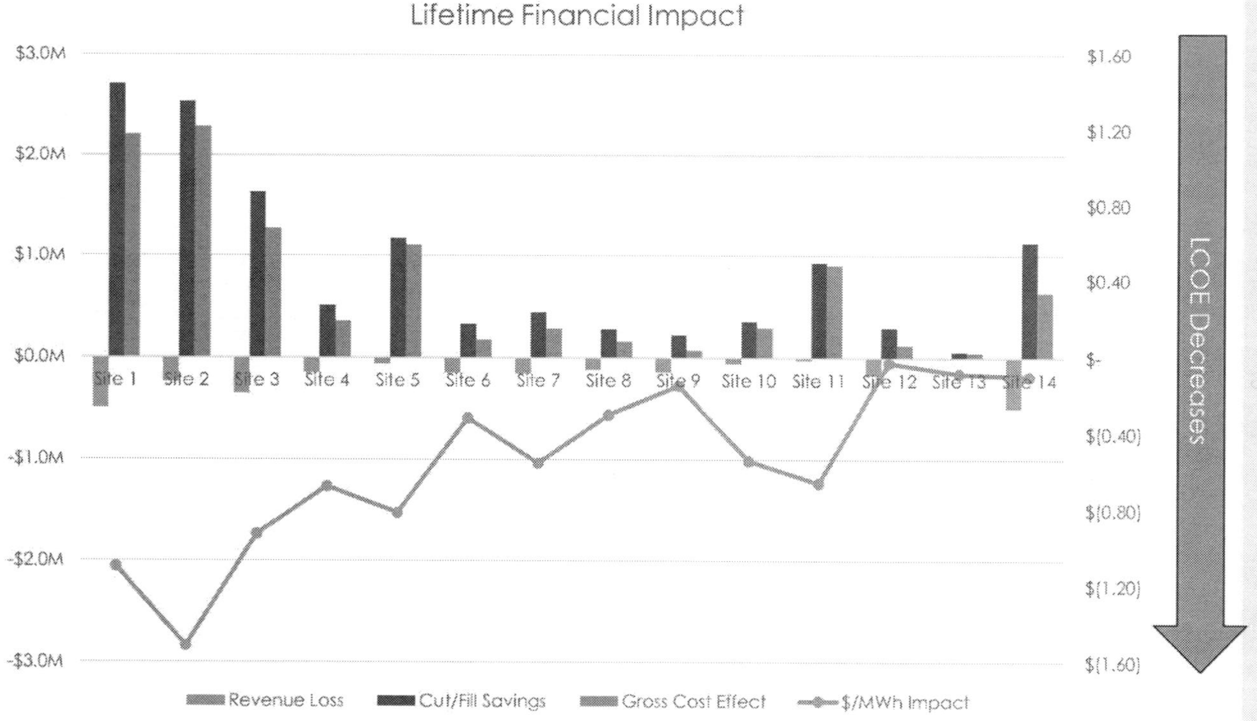

$200,732
Average Discounted Revenue Loss

$853,470
Average Cost (CAPEX) Savings

$652,737
Average Overall Cost Impact

($0.50)
Average LCOE Reduction per MWh

nextracker

Conclusions & Outlook

Terrain-Following Trackers have a POSITIVE Financial Impact Across a Variety of Site Conditions

Future Studies

- Increased range of regions/sites in case study
- Comparison of different Terrain-Following Solutions
- Analysis of OPEX/O&M costs, Installation times
- Inclusion of dynamic pricing for increasingly accurate revenue calculations

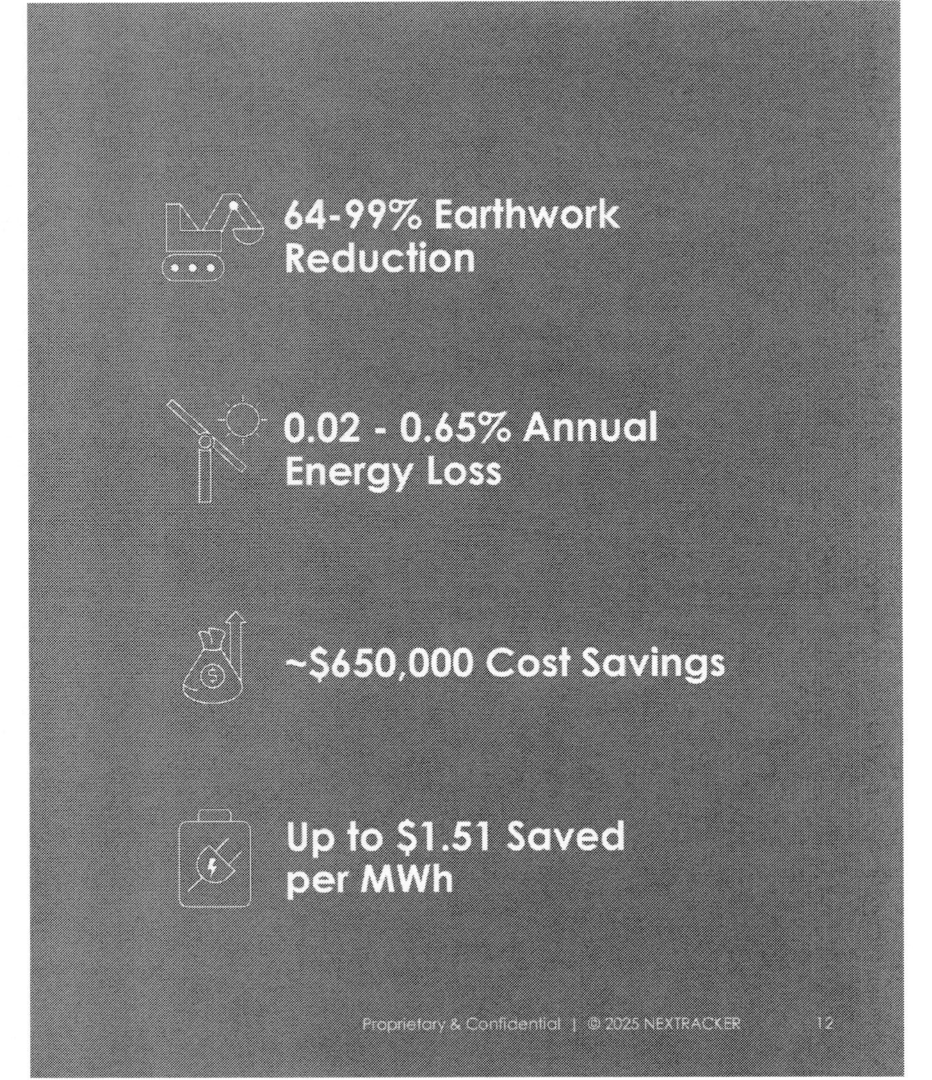

nextracker

64-99% Earthwork Reduction

0.02 - 0.65% Annual Energy Loss

~$650,000 Cost Savings

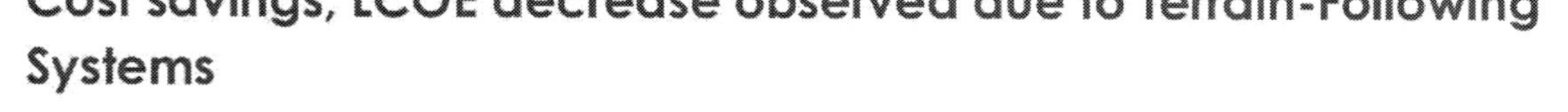

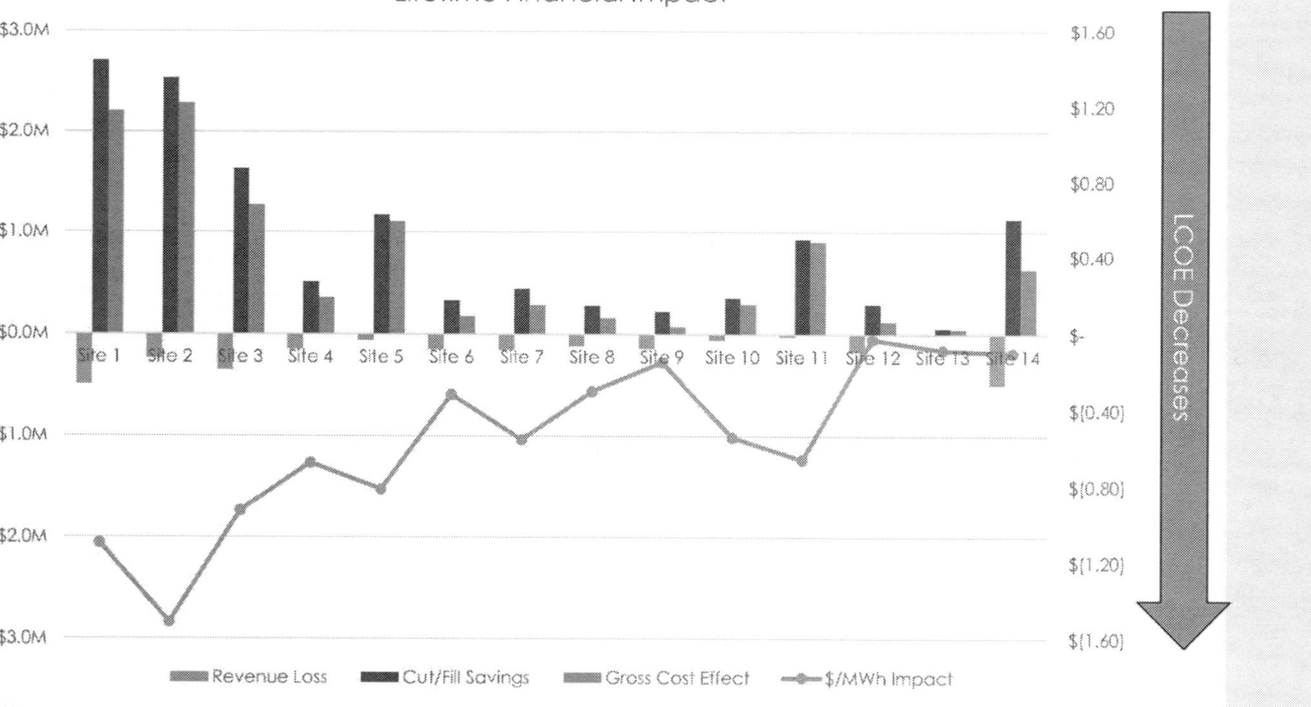

Up to $1.51 Saved per MWh

Thank you

aratnagiri@nextracker.com

nextracker

References

- J. [Lawrence B. N. L. (LBNL) Seel Berkeley CA (United States)] et al., "Utility-Scale Solar, 2024 Edition: Empirical Trends in Deployment, Technology, Cost, Performance, PPA Pricing, and Value in the United States [Slides]."
- A. A. Shishavan, V. R. Abbaraju, A. Dobos, and F. Borrelli, "Terrain-Following Single-Axis Tracking PV Systems: Advantages and Performance Analysis," 38th European Photovoltaic Solar Energy Conference and Exhibition; 1060-1064, 2021, doi: 10.4229/EUPVSEC20212021-5DO.3.3.
- Terabase Energy, "Terrain Pro," *https://plantpredict.com/*.
- Nextracker, Inc., "TrueSim Version 4.2.4."
- K. S. Anderson, C. W. Hansen, W. F. Holmgren, A. R. Jensen, M. A. Mikofski, and A. Driesse, "pvlib python: 2023 project update," J Open Source Soft, vol. 8, no. 92, p. 5994, 2023, doi: 10.21105/joss.05994.
- National Renewable Energy Laboratory, "System Advisor Model (SAM) Version 2023.12.17."
- M. Mikofski, B. Meyers, and C. Chaudhari, "PVMismatch Project: https://github.com/SunPower/PVMismatch," 2018, SunPower Corporation, Richmond, CA.
- W. De Soto et al., "Improvement and validation of a model for photovoltaic array performance", Solar Energy, vol 80, pp. 78-88, 2006

42nd European Photovoltaic Solar Energy Conference and Exhibition

This presentation was selected by the Sc. Committee of the EU PVSEC 2025 for submission of a full paper to one of the EU PVSEC's collaborating peer-reviewed journals.

STANDARDIZED ASSESSMENT OF PV ARRAY SIMULATORS

Theo Zwahlen[1], David Joss[1], Christian Messner[2], Christof Bucher[1], Luciano Borgna[1], Michael Gafert[2], Steffen Eyhorn[3] and Roland Bründlinger[2]

[1] Laboratory for Photovoltaic Systems (PV-Lab) - Bern University of Applied Sciences (BFH), Jlcoweg 1, 3400 Burgdorf, Switzerland

[2]AIT – Austrian Institute of Technology GmbH, Giefinggasse 2, 1210 Vienna, Austria

[3] Fraunhofer Institute for Solar Energy Systems ISE, Heidenhofstr. 2, 79110 Freiburg, Germany

[1]christof.bucher@bfh.ch

ABSTRACT: PV array simulators are used for testing PV and PV battery inverters. A test procedure has been developed to evaluate these simulators, ensuring realistic PV module and array behavior. It provides laboratories with uniform test conditions and helps developers optimise their devices. The proposed procedure includes three phenomenological tests with random PV inverters and three potentially standardisable tests examining properties like accuracy and frequency response.

Keywords: PV array simulator assessment / solar array simulator evaluation / photovoltaic inverter testing / I–V curve emulation / SAS quality

1 INTRODUCTION

Correct functionality of photovoltaic inverters is vital for renewable energy expansion, requiring extensive testing. Standards such as EN50530 [1], the BVES/BSW Efficiency Guideline [2], and various grid codes define inverter testing. Beyond grid-connection standards [3–5], precise characterisation of grid-support functions will become increasingly important [6].

Testing laboratories need AC grid simulators and PV array simulators, which must accurately mimic grid behaviour and PV module strings, including inverter-induced DC ripple [7,8]. A review in [9] outlines PV array simulator architectures and their I-V reproduction characteristics. While IEC provides a specification for DC source performance [10], no guideline exists for testing the simulators themselves, and current requirements remain vague. Literature shows only one prior publication on PV array simulator assessment [11], proposing tests for steady-state and dynamic performance under load changes and irradiance fluctuations.

Recent tests at AIT revealed that some advanced simulators produce excessive DC ripple or oscillations. These oscillations led to MPPT efficiency values above 100%. To address such issues, BFH and AIT developed a dedicated test procedure for PV array simulator evaluation, later joined by Fraunhofer ISE for additional expertise. The full work presents the procedure and anonymised results from completed assessments.

2 TEST METHOD AND BACKGROUND

Most modern PV array simulators emulate I-V curves using digital switching power supplies without linear output stages. Their small-signal behaviour depends on power electronics and control software. Compared to real PV modules, the tested simulators show slower dynamics, especially with inverters: current output lags voltage changes, delaying PV dynamics and impairing MPPT accuracy. This often causes oscillations between simulator and inverter.

Existing criteria are necessary but insufficient for realistic inverter operation, particularly in grid-support mode. Individual tests are required to determine simulator–inverter compatibility. The authors propose two categories Each category includes three tests, summarised in Table I (Phenomenological Tests) and Table II (Standard Tests).

2.1 Phenomenological tests

The tests offer limited repeatability but can quickly reveal issues when simulators are used with PV inverters. However, the results depend strongly on the chosen inverter, and since no pass–fail criteria are defined, standardisation remains difficult.

Table I. Phenomenological Tests

Category	Cat. 1: Phenomenological Tests		
Test No	Phen 1	Phen 2	Phen 3
Test Name	I-V Curve Stability	Current Ripple	MPPT Efficiency Difference
Short description	Slow I-V curve tracing. Plotting the I-V curve.	Connected to a PV inverter. Measurement of current ripple.	Comparison of array simulator internal measurement with external measurement.
Pass-Fail criterion (remarks)	n. a. (no oscillations should be seen)	n. a. (current ripple should be small)	n. a. (difference should be small)

2.2 Standard tests

In these tests, the array simulator is operated under defined conditions and without a PV inverter. Pass-fail criteria are defined for these tests.

10.4229/EUPVSEC2025/4DO.1.6
020369-001

Table II. Standard Tests

Category	**Cat. 2: Standard Tests**		
Test No	Std 1	Std 2	Std 3
Test Name	MPP Accuracy and Drift	Frequency Response	Irradiance Variation
Short description	Manual MPP tracing after startup and after 10 minutes. Power measurement.	Superimpose an AC signal at a given DC operating point. Measure phase shift.	Measure difference between setpoint (ramp) and actual value (step function).
Pass-Fail criterion (remarks)	MPP accuracy be below 1 %	Frequency shift shall be below 30° from 0 Hz to 150 Hz	RMSE shall be below 1 %

3 TEST SETUP

Four setups were used, with largely identical measurement equipment. For accuracy-focused tests (Phen 3, Std 3), a high-precision power analyser records voltage, current, and power. If it provides raw data >50 kHz, these values can support further analysis. Otherwise, an oscilloscope with appropriate probes must be added.

3.1 Setup 1:

The PV array simulator is loaded with a DC power supply able to sink power across the full operating range and perform simple functions (e.g., ramps) (***Figure 1***).

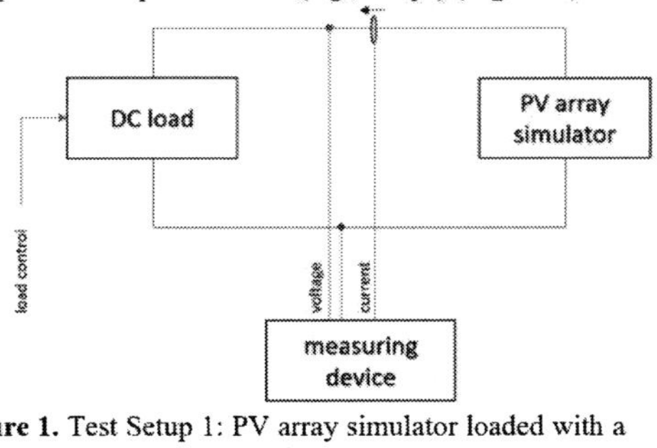

Figure 1. Test Setup 1: PV array simulator loaded with a bidirectional DC power supply.

3.2 Setup 2:

The simulator is tested with at least two different PV inverters. Using the same reference inverters across assessments ensures comparability (***Figure 2***).

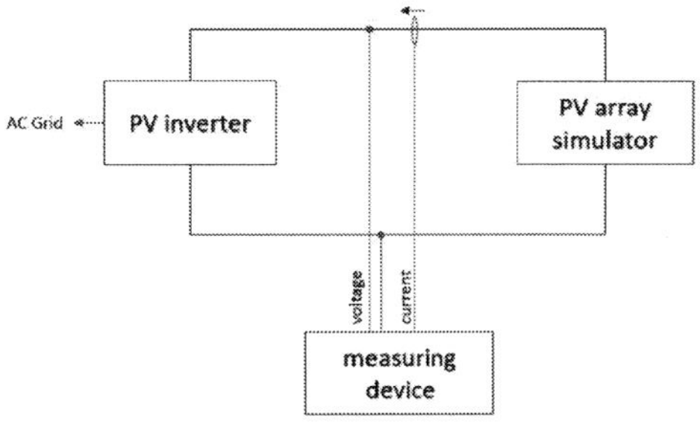

Figure 2. Test Setup 2: PV array simulator loaded with a common PV inverter.

3.3 Setup 3:

As in Setup 1, but with an added AC power supply to apply dynamic signals. A single device may provide both DC load and AC modulation if capable (***Figure 3***).

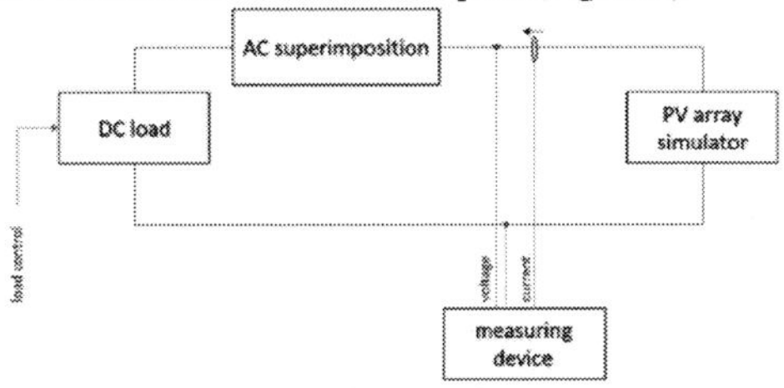

Figure 3. Test Setup 3: PV array simulator loaded with a bidirectional DC power supply and an additional AC source to superimpose an alternating voltage.

3.4 Setup 4:

Simplest configuration, with the simulator short-circuited to observe irradiance variation effects via short-circuit current. Voltage measurement is unnecessary (***Figure 4***).

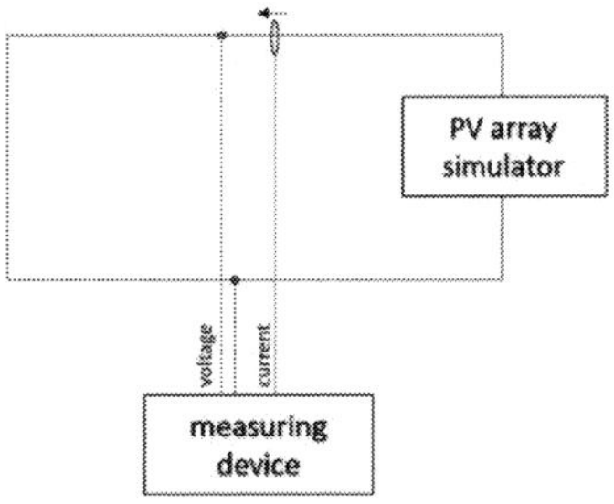

Figure 4. Fig. 4. Test Setup 4: PV array simulator with short-circuited output

4 OPERATING POINTS

For tests with a static I-V curve, the PV array simulator is parametrised as described here. Characterisation follows EN50530 with crystalline silicon (cSi) cells [1]. Four operating points (OP) are defined (Table III) for simulators up to 1500 V output. OP1 represents a single PV module, while OP2–OP4 cover a broader output range.

Table III. Operating point parameters for tests with static I-V curve

Operating point (OP)	V_{MPP} [V]	I_{MPP} [A]
1	40	15
2	100	25
3	500	20
4	1000	15

To adapt for simulators with different ratings, OP1 remains fixed, while OP2–OP4 use V_{MPP} values scaled relative to the simulator's maximum output voltage $V_{PVAS,MAXV}$. Operating currents can either follow the absolute values in Table III or be scaled from relative power as in Table IV.

Table IV. Operating point parameters for tests with static I-V curve, relative to the output specifications of the PV array simulator under test

Operating point (OP)	VMPP	PMPP
2	7 % of $V_{PVAS,MAX}$	10 % of $P_{PVAS,MAX}$
3	33 % of $V_{PVAS,MAX}$	40 % of $P_{PVAS,MAX}$
4	66 % of $V_{PVAS,MAX}$	60 % of $P_{PVAS,MAX}$

4.1 PV inverters used in Setup 2

In Setup 2, at least two PV inverters serve as reference devices. Table V lists those used in the Results and Discussion. Since the aim is not to evaluate inverter quality, the devices are not anonymised.

Table V. PV inverter used in Test Setup 2

Designation	Manufacturer	Model name
SMA	SMA Solar Technology AG	STP6.0-3AV-40
Huawei	Huawei Digital Power Technologies Co., Ltd.	SUN2000-10KTL-M1

5 DEVICE UNDER TEST (DUT)

The proposed test procedure was developed alongside PV array simulator evaluations. Most devices were tested at BFH, with some at AIT.

A distinction is made between bidirectional and unidirectional simulators. Unless noted, both types use nonlinear switched-mode power supplies.

In some tests, a real PV system was also used as reference.

At this stage PV array simulators are referred anonymously to protect manufacturer interests. The results aim to support overall progress, not critique specific devices.

6 PHENOMENOLOGICAL TESTS

Test laboratories often encounter unexpected phenomena, which may arise from the DUT or its interaction with lab infrastructure. For PV array simulators, some phenomena can be induced with simple tests. These tests have no strict pass-fail criteria but help verify the accuracy of subsequent evaluations.

6.1 Phen 1: I-V Curve Instability

PV array simulators can exhibit instabilities at certain I-V curve operating points, dependent on the load. The proposed test uses Setup 1: the simulator operates at each operating point, while the load is swept from 0 V to U_{OC} in 5 seconds, then back to 0 V in 5 seconds. This slow, semi-static sweep avoids intentionally triggering oscillations or secondary distortions. ***Figure 5*** shows expected data without instabilities, calculated in MATLAB from the EN50530 I-V model for OP3 settings.

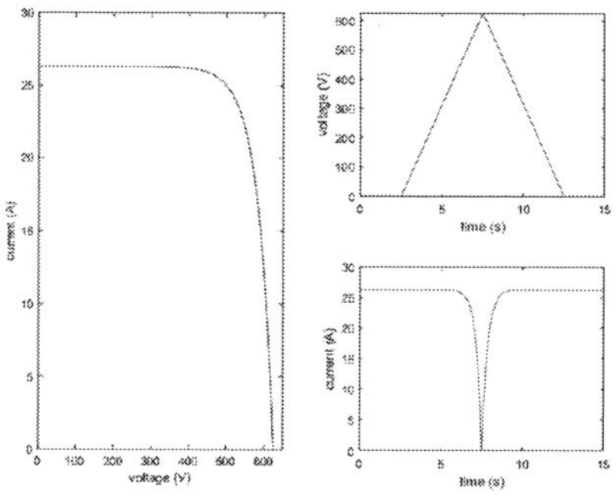

Figure 5. Theoretical simulation result of an I-V curve instability test without any instabilities. Left: X-Y plot corresponding to the I-V curve. Right: time series of voltage (top in blue) and current (bottom in orange). The calculation follows an I-V model according to EN50530.

6.2 Phen 2: Current Ripple

Some PV array simulators generate high current ripple, which can affect inverter MPPT and efficiency measurements. Ripple magnitude depends on load and varies between inverters. ***Figure 6*** shows measured current during an EN50530 MPP tracking test: the red trace is raw current (100 kHz), the green trace is a 10 ms moving average.

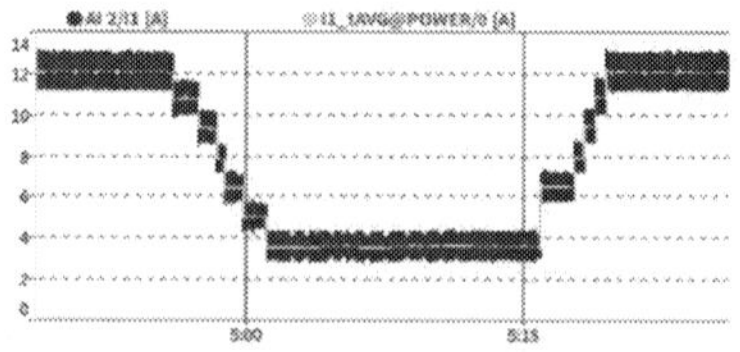

Figure 6. Part of an MPP tracking efficiency measurement with raw current values (red) and averaged current values (green). Screenshot is taken from Dewetron power analyser.

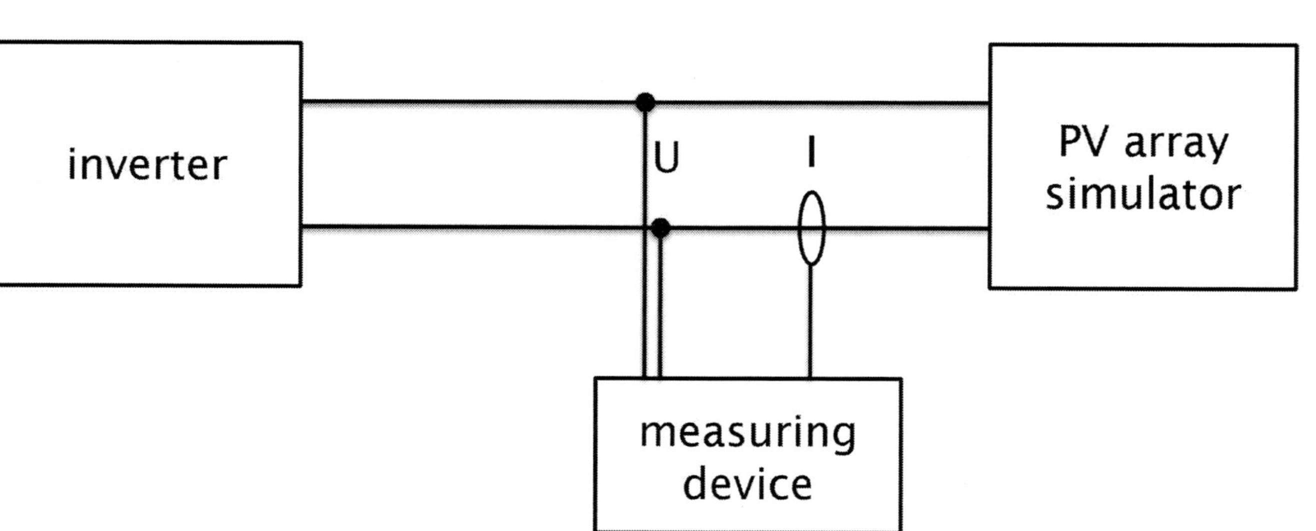

Ripple can be reduced with a series inductance, though this affects other behaviours, such as dynamics.

Phen 2 compares current ripple across simulators using a partly dynamic MPP tracking test with at least two inverters. The test follows the last line of Table B.3 in EN50530 [1] with parameters in

Table ***VI***. High-frequency ripple (>20 kHz) from inverter switching is filtered using a 10 kHz, fourth-order

n [Number]	10
Slope [W/m2/s]	1000
Ramp UP [s] t1	7
Dwell time[s] t2	10
Ramp DN [s] t3	7
Dwell time [s] t4	10
Duration [s]	640

low-pass filter.

Table VI. Parameters of the irradiance sequence part according to EN50530 [1]

n [Number]	10
Slope [W/m²/s]	1000
Ramp UP [s] t_1	7
Dwell time[s] t_2	10
Ramp DN [s] t_3	7
Dwell time [s] t_4	10
Duration [s]	640

Ripple is quantified by peak-to-peak values over 200 ms of the filtered signal, for both high and low static current levels (3.8 A and 12 A, ***Figure*** *7*), expressed relative to the current setpoint.

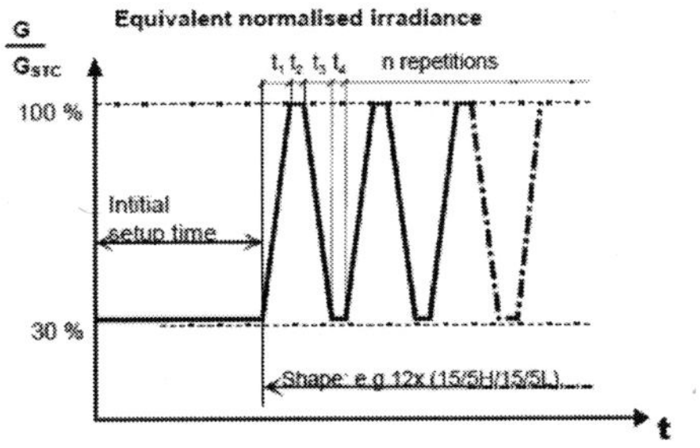

Figure 7. Test sequence with a 30 % - 100 % ramp according to EN50530 [1]

6.3 Phen 3: MPPT Efficiency Difference

This test evaluates whether measured MPPT efficiency of an inverter varies with different PV array simulators.

The evaluation is not discussed further in this short report.

7 STANDARD TESTS

While phenomenological tests provide a general overview, standard tests offer detailed, reproducible assessment of PV array simulators. They highlight deviations from real PV module behaviour and suitability for inverter testing. Tests can be used with pass/fail criteria or to compare simulators.

7.1 Std 1: MPP Accuracy and Drift

The accuracy drift provides information on the operational accuracy of the source and the extent to which it varies due to heating during operation. A detailed discussion of the measurement or the results is not included in this short report.

7.2 Std 2: Frequency Response

PV inverters can impose oscillations or rapidly changing loads on PV array simulators, e.g., 100 Hz ripple from single-phase inverters [1,3] or minor fluctuations from three-phase inverters [10].

To evaluate simulator response, Test Setup 3 is used at all operating points. The simulator is loaded at MPP with a DC load, while an AC signal (±2% V_{MPP}) is superimposed. The AC frequency is swept 0–1000 Hz, and the phase shift between voltage and current is measured. Ideally, voltage increases cause current decreases, giving a 180° phase shift.

Figure 8 shows a theoretical current response (amplitude ±3% for clarity). The pass criterion is 180° ± 30° phase shift up to at least 150 Hz. This accounts for typical inverter-induced loading and allows some lab measurements despite minor deviations. Many commercial PV array simulators fail this conservative requirement.

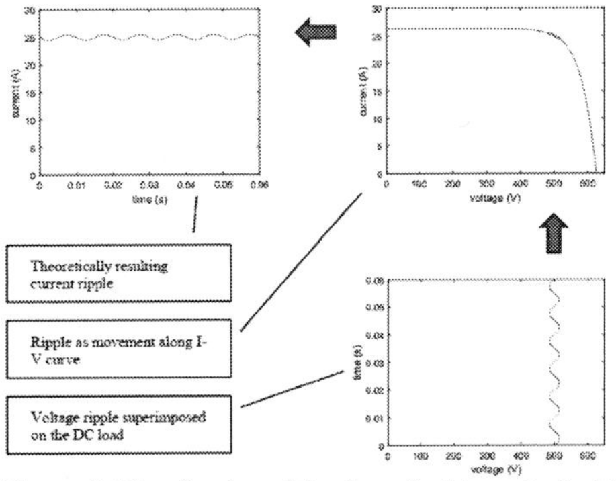

Figure 8. Visualization of the theoretical impact of a 100 Hz voltage ripple on the current, generated by simulation.

7.3 Std 3: Irradiance Variation

PV array simulators are often required to follow irradiance ramps, e.g., for dynamic MPP tracking tests (EN50530). Most simulators adjust power in discrete steps rather than continuously. A basic evaluation measures the minimum step interval, while a detailed assessment calculates the RMSE between the expected continuous ramp and the simulator's step response.

Since irradiance changes directly affect short-circuit current, the simulator is tested with the output short-circuited (Setup 4), and performance is assessed from the measured current.

8 RESULTS AND DISCUSSION

This chapter presents results from an exemplary test series with several PV array simulators. The first part highlights phenomenological test outcomes, showing varying simulator behaviour and unexpected responses. The second part covers standardized tests, illustrating performance ranges.

10.4229/EUPVSEC2025/4DO.1.6

8.1 Phen 1: I-V Curve Stability

Several simulators showed unstable I-V behaviour. ***Figure 9*** displays I-V curves of four devices across all operating points. Three devices are classified as unstable; PVAS2 shows minor oscillations only at the lowest voltage. Oscillation magnitude and occurrence vary between simulators and tend to increase at lower voltages. For OP4, a second series load ensured full voltage coverage, which may affect stability.

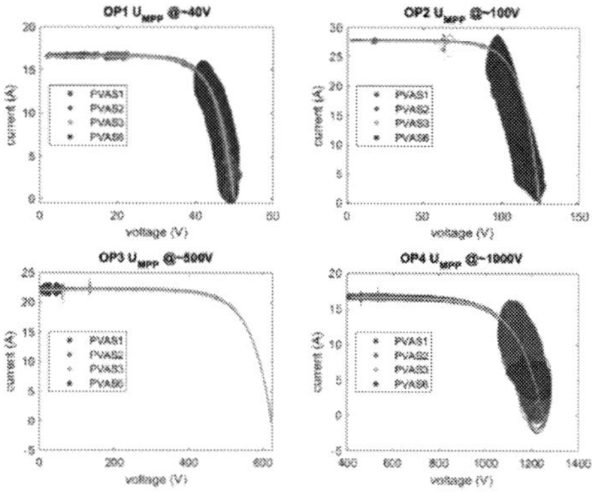

Figure 9. Measured I-V curves of four PV array simulators at all four operating points

Figure 10 illustrates the impact on a real inverter: PV current of an SMA inverter (Table V) supplied by PVAS1 shows clear oscillations at ~13 s and ~23 s during startup.

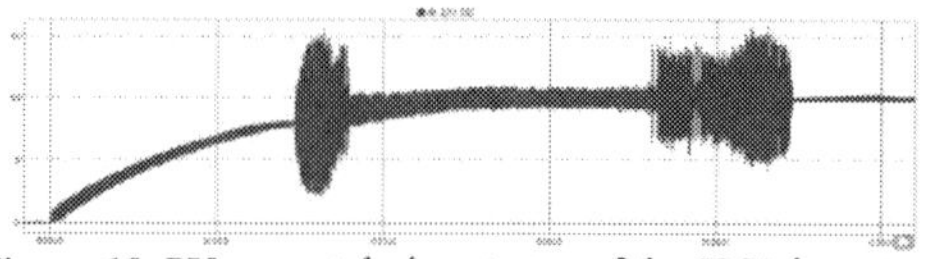

Figure 10. PV current during startup of the SMA inverter supplied by PVAS1 (Dewetron screenshot).

8.2 Phen 2: Current Ripple

Current ripple was assessed for PVAS1–PVAS3. **Figure *11*** shows a segment of measured and filtered currents, with peak-to-peak values and a 4-second moving average as a reference during steady irradiance.

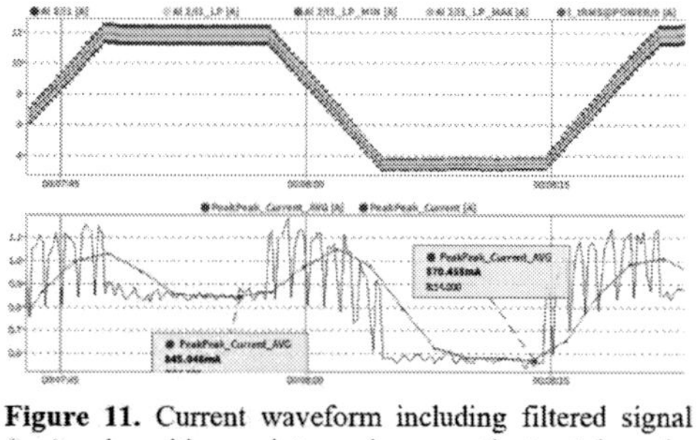

Figure 11. Current waveform including filtered signal (top) and resulting peak-to-peak current (bottom) from the ripple test. (Dewetron screenshot)

Figure *12* presents ripple normalized to average current. Results show the connected inverter strongly influences ripple: all simulators exhibit higher ripple with the SMA inverter. The method is consistent, as lower ripple with one inverter correlates with lower ripple on another.

Even at 3.5 A, ripple above 20% is excessive; the best simulator reached ~16% at worst. Ripple remains significant at other operating points or with the second inverter, though under higher power conditions, two simulators achieved <5% ripple.

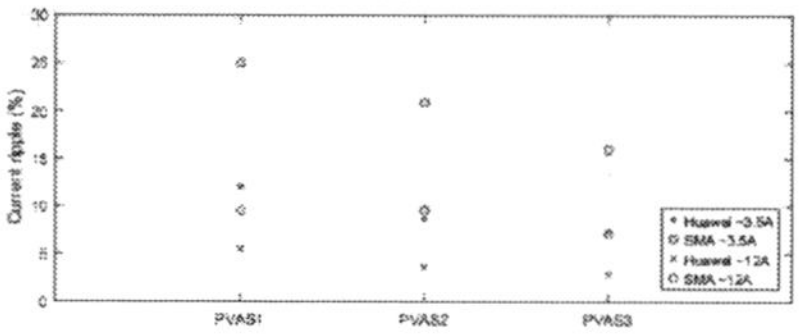

Figure 12. Comparison of current ripple normalized to the average current at the respective power level.

8.3 Std 2: Frequency Response

Frequency response was tested for multiple PV array simulators. Some could be tested at all operating points (OP1–OP4), while others were limited, e.g., PVAS7 and PVAS8 lack OP4 data, and PVAS4 was tested at 800 V instead of 1000 VMPP due to its voltage limit.

Figure *13* shows measured phase shifts for all devices, compared with real PV modules (RealPV) at OP1–OP3. Phase response varies significantly. Many simulators show considerable phase shift at low frequencies, especially at higher voltages (OP3–OP4).

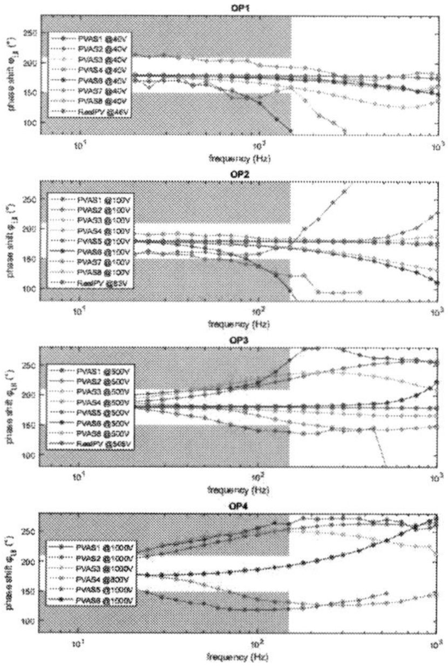

Figure 13. Phase shift across frequency for all measured PV array simulators

8.4 Std 3: Irradiance Variation

The following plot shows the dynamics of each DUT (***Figure 14***).

10.4229/EUPVSEC2025/4DO.1.6

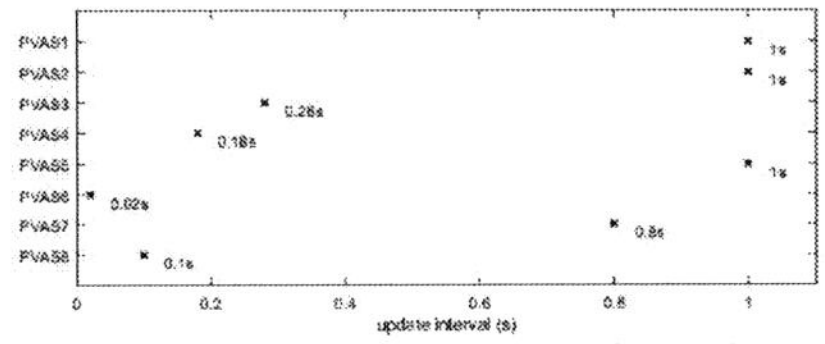

Figure 14. Minimum I-V curve update interval measured for PVAS1 to PVAS8

Instead of the intended ramp, a 100–500 W/m² MPPT efficiency profile (5 s ramp, 100 W/m²/s) was used, with current normalized to account for differing I-V characteristics. ***Figure 15*** shows measured currents, with the red trace as the reference ramp.

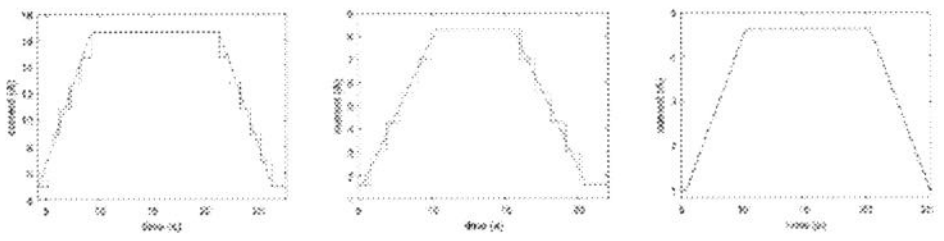

Figure 15. Current profiles of PVAS1 (left), PVAS2 (middle), PVAS8 (right) with reference ramp (red).

Figure *16* presents current errors and RMSE over each ramp. Upward ramps show decreasing error, downward ramps increasing error, indicating deviations from the intended slope.

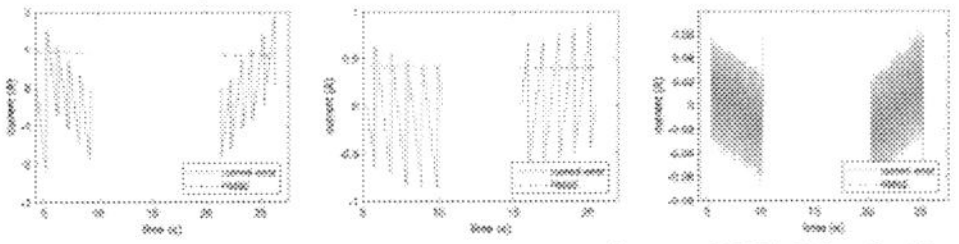

Figure 16. Current error measured on PVAS1 (left), PVAS2 (middle), and PVAS8 (right), including the respective calculated RMSE value.

Table VII reports normalized RMSE for ramp-up and ramp down. PVAS1 and PVAS2 have similar errors (1 s transition), while PVAS8 has lower RMSE due to a 100 ms transition set by external SCPI commands.

Table VII. Relative RMSE (as a percentage of the current at maximum irradiance) for three simulators during ramp-up and ramp-down.

	PVAS1	**PVAS2**	**PVAS8**
Relative RMSE during ramp-up	5.55 %	4.96 %	0.51%
Relative RMSE during ramp-down	5.11 %	4.81 %	0.54%

9 CONCLUSION

The full work presents a test procedure for evaluating PV array simulators, with results from varying numbers of devices from different manufacturers. Not all tests include every simulator, limiting generalisability.

The results reveal substantial differences in output characteristics, affecting inverter tests. For example, MPPT efficiency (Phen 3) varies between simulators, questioning its reliability as a comparative metric. I-V curve instabilities are particularly critical, especially under power curtailment where voltage exceeds MPP, a region prone to oscillations, potentially invalidating tests.

The proposed tests provide a comprehensive assessment framework, but some behaviours remain unaddressed, such as synchronised control of multiple simulator outputs. Many simulators offer limited multi-channel support, with observable time delays. Future updates could include a dedicated multi-channel synchronisation test.

ACKNOWLEDGMENTS

Many of the measurement data originate from PV array simulators that were provided by distributors or manufacturers for testing purposes. Thank goes out to them for their cooperation.

FUNDING

This research received no external funding.

CONFLICTS OF INTEREST

BFH has a paid consulting agreement with a manufacturer aimed at improving their PV array simulator. However, the data used in this study was collected prior to this collaboration and is therefore not considered a conflict of interest. The other authors have nothing to disclose

DATA AVAILABILITY STATEMENT

For reasons of manufacturer confidentiality, the data associated with this article cannot be shared.

AUTHOR CONTRIBUTION STATEMENT

Conceptualization, Theo Zwahlen, Luciano Borgna, David Joss and Christof Bucher.; Methodology, Theo Zwahlen, Luciano Borgna, David Joss and Christof Bucher.; Validation, Christian Messner, Steffen Eyhorn and Michael Gafert.; Data Curation, Theo Zwahlen and Michael Gafert.; Writing – Original Draft Preparation, Theo Zwahlen.; Writing – Review & Editing, Theo Zwahlen, David Joss, Christof Bucher, Christian Messner, Michael Gafert and Steffen Eyhorn.; Visualization, Theo Zwahlen, David Joss.; Supervision, Christof Bucher and Roland Bründlinger.; Project Administration, Theo Zwahlen and David Joss

REFERENCES

[1] EN 50530:2010, Overall efficiency of grid connected photovoltaic inverters, (2010).

[2] BVES Bundesverband Energiespeicher Systeme, BSW-solar Bundesverband Solarwirtschaft, Efficiency guideline for PV storage systems, (n.d.). https://solar.htw-berlin.de/wp-content/uploads/Efficiency-guideline-for-PV-storage-systems-2.0.pdf (accessed June 30, 2025).

[3] SN EN 50549-1:2019(E) - DV-31964/1 - Electrosuisse, (n.d.). https://shop.electrosuisse.ch/de/SN-EN-50549-1_2019_E_-48355.html (accessed July 16, 2025).

[4] SN EN 50549-2:2019+AC:2019(D) - DV-34426/1 - Electrosuisse, (n.d.). https://shop.electrosuisse.ch/de/SNEN-50549-

2_2019_AC_2019_D_-54247.html (accessed July 16, 2025).

[5] SN EN 50549-10:2022(E) - DV-45035/1 - Electrosuisse, (n.d.). https://shop.electrosuisse.ch/de/SN-EN-50549-10_2022_E_-397612.html (accessed July 16, 2025).

[6] TC 82, Project: IEC 63409-6 ED1, IEC (International Electrotechnical Commission) (n.d.). https://www.iec.ch/dyn/www/f?p=103:38:601780107873093::::FSP_ORG_ID,FSP_APEX_PAGE,FSP_PROJECT_ID:1276,23,105972 (accessed July 16, 2025).

[7] R. Ayop, C.W. Tan, A comprehensive review on photovoltaic emulator, Renewable and Sustainable Energy Reviews 80 (2017) 430–452. https://doi.org/10.1016/j.rser.2017.05.217.

[8] Spitzenberger & Spies, Necessity for high speed PV Simulators, n.d. www.spitzenberger.de/weblink/1005 (accessed January 24, 2025).

[9] J.P. Ram, H. Manghani, D.S. Pillai, T.S. Babu, M. Miyatake, N. Rajasekar, Analysis on solar PV emulators: A review, Renewable and Sustainable Energy Reviews 81 (2018) 149–160. https://doi.org/10.1016/j.rser.2017.07.039.

[10] IEC TS 63106-2, Simulators used for testing of photovoltaic power conversion equipment - Recommendations - Part 2: DC power simulators, (2022).

[11] V.M. Cavalcante Junior, R.C. Neto, E.J. Barbosa, F. Bradaschia, M.C. Cavalcanti, G.M. de S. Azevedo, Evaluation of the Effectiveness of Solar Array Simulators in Reproducing the Characteristics of Photovoltaic Modules, Sustainability 16 (2024) 6932. https://doi.org/10.3390/su16166932.

10.4229/EUPVSEC2025/4DO.1.6

Berner Fachhochschule
Haute école spécialisée bernoise
Bern University of Applied Sciences

Standardised Assessment of PV Array Simulators

EUPVSEC, 22.-26. September 2025, Bilbao

- Organisationseinheit oder Leistungsbereich

Background

- Maximum power point trackers (MPPT) are tested using solar array simulators (SAS).
- Other inverter functions (e.g. grid connection functions) can also be tested using SAS.
- Two types of simulators
  - Switching power supply
  - Linear power supply
- Advances in power electronics: linear power supplies are no longer necessary (at least according to manufacturers' claims)

But…

- … then why do we see such behaviour?

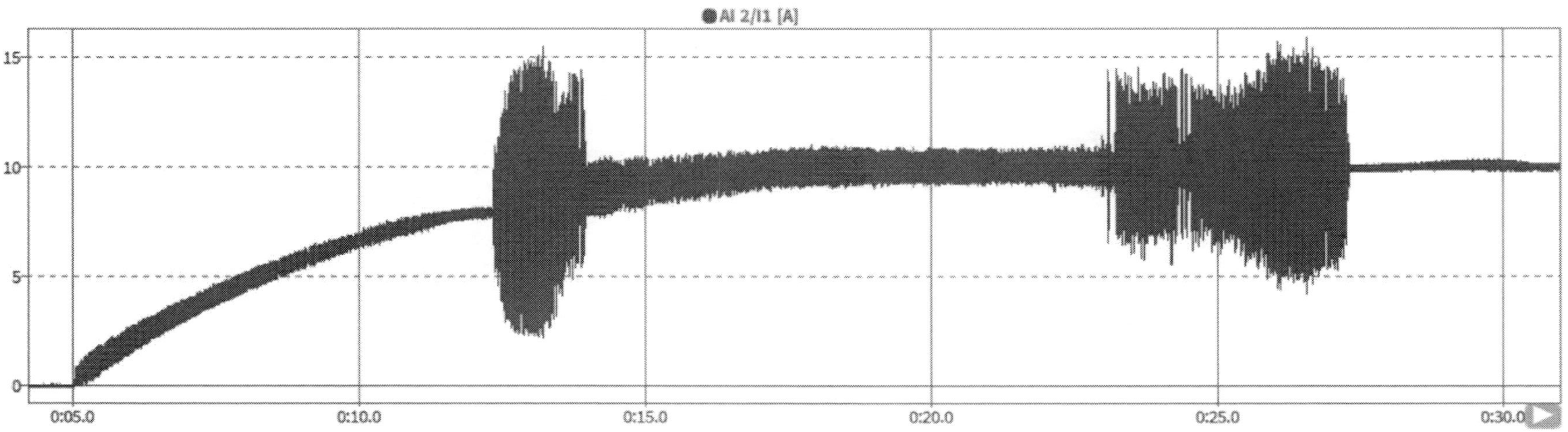

Array simulator DC current during inverter startup

But…

- … then why do we see such behaviour?

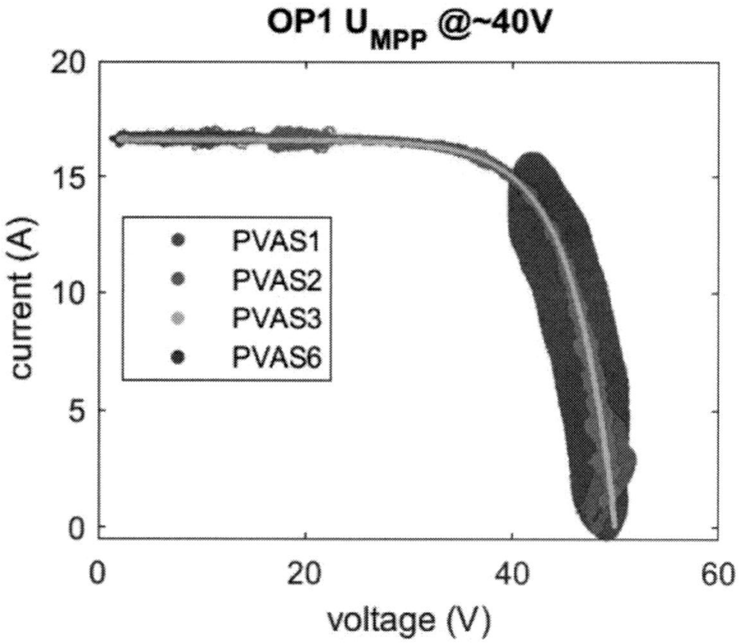

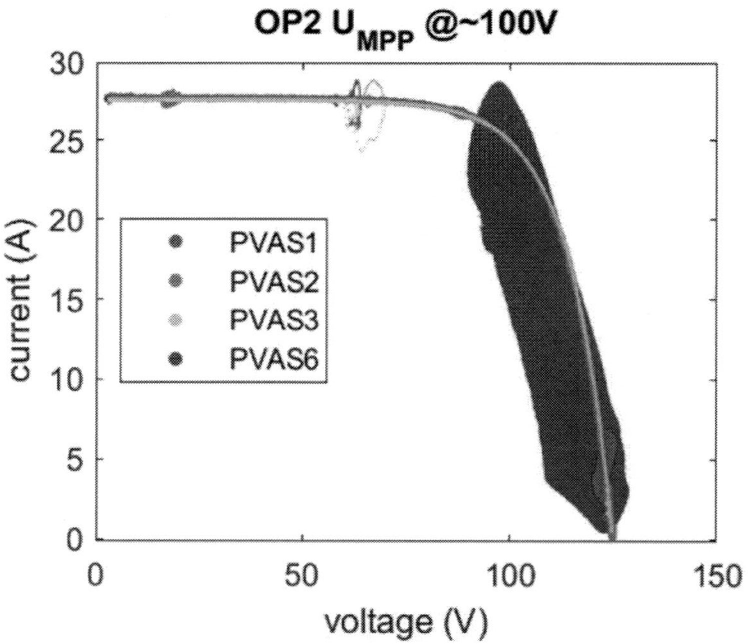

...and this?

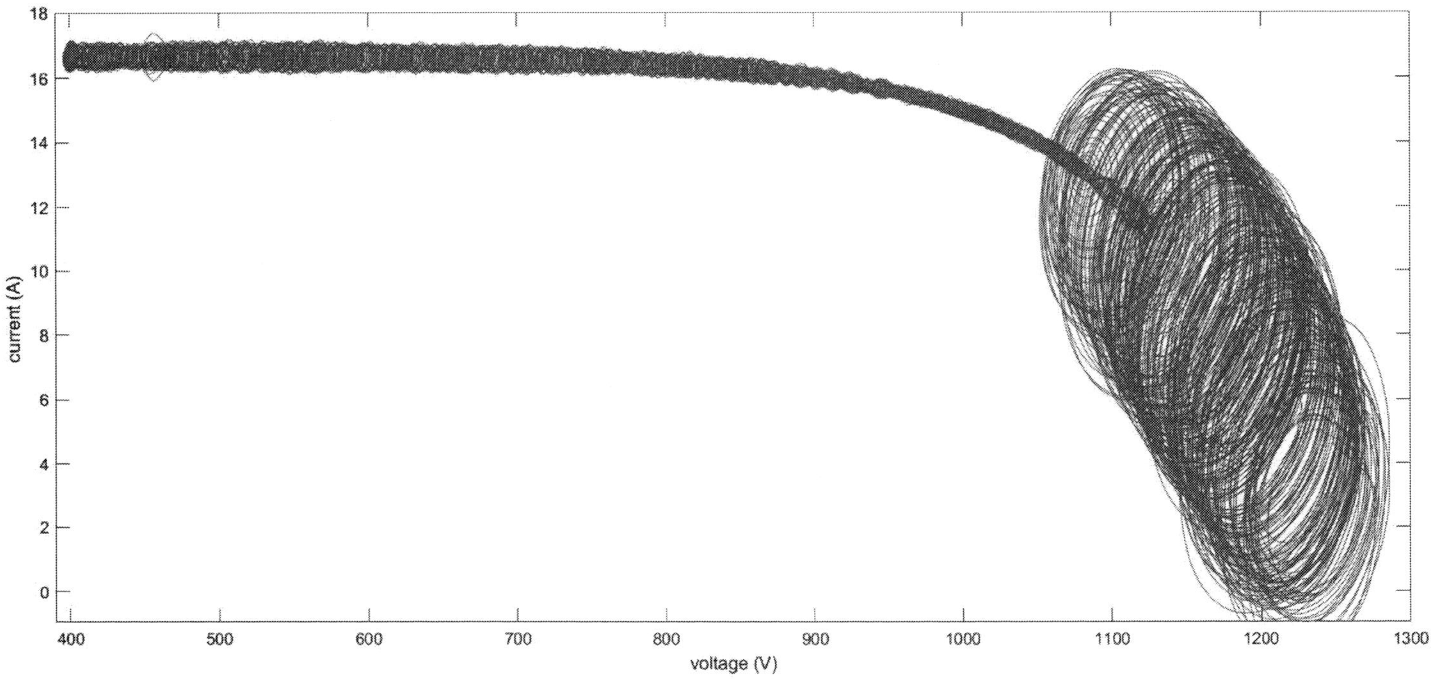

Berner Fachhochschule | Haute école spécialisée bernoise | Bern University of Applied Sciences

Initial situation PV laboratory

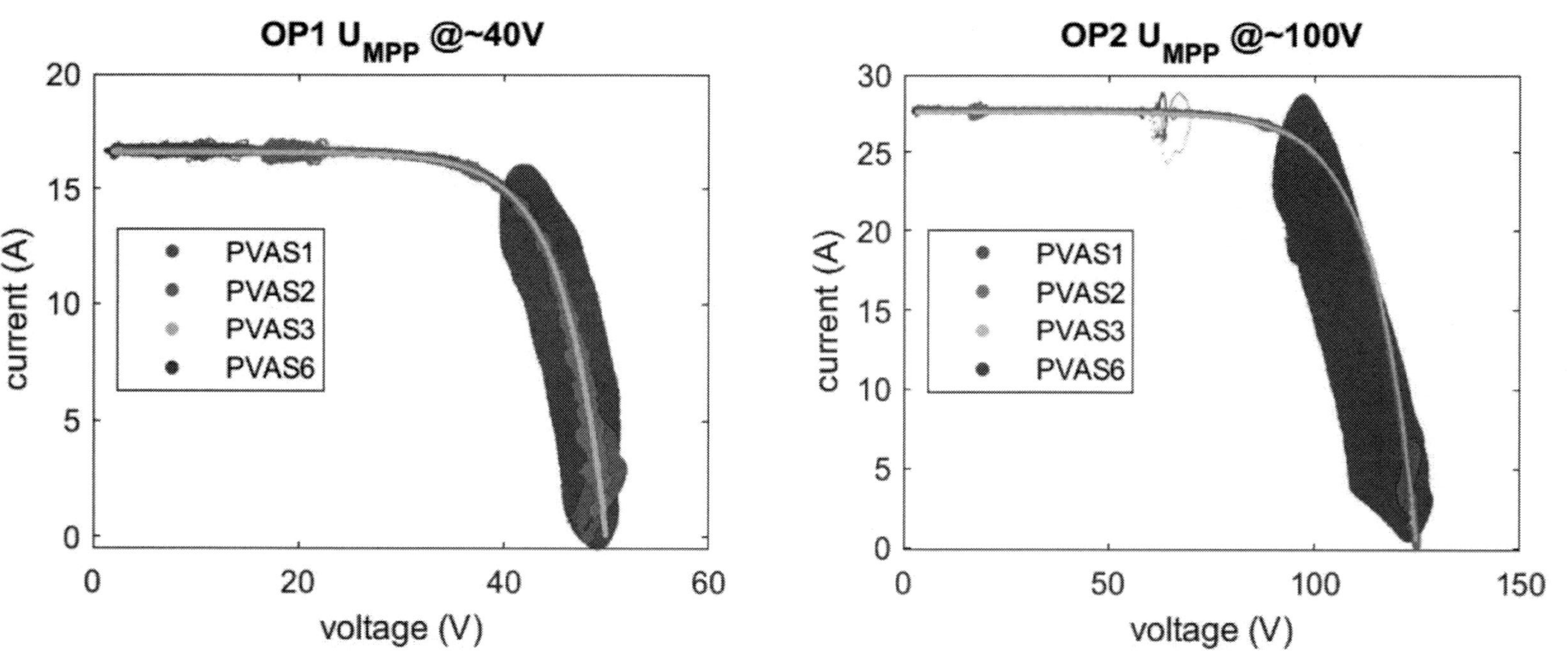

- Budget for procurement of approx. 150 kW DC array simulators
- 8 devices from 6 manufacturers delivered and tested
- Stability problems
  - Too slow (does not follow the IV curve during MPPT)
  - Unstable, especially at U > Umpp
- Consultation with manufacturers leads to minor improvements
- Contact with AIT and Fraunhofer ISE
- Joint development of test routines
- Procurement cancelled, in-house development of an array simulator with linear output stage

Development of 6 tests

Cat 1: Phenomenological tests

- Phen 1: I-V curve stability → "manual, visual curve inspection"
- Phen 2: Current ripple → connected to an inverter
- Phen 3: MPPT eff. difference → internal vs. external measurement

Cat 2: Standard tests

- Std 1: MPP accuracy and drift → MPPT after 10 minutes
- Std 2: Frequency response → DC with AC superposition
- Std 3: Irradiance variation → step functions

Berner Fachhochschule | Haute école spécialisée bernoise | Bern University of Applied Sciences

Test Setup Std 2: Frequency response

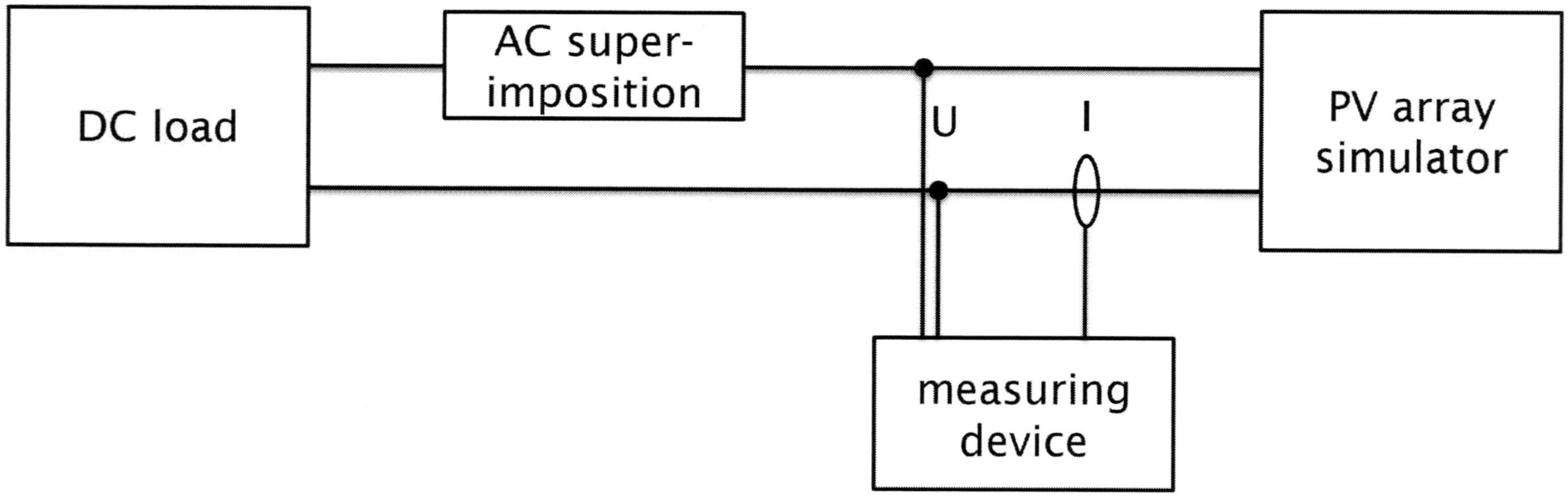

Std 2: Frequency Response

Expected behaviour

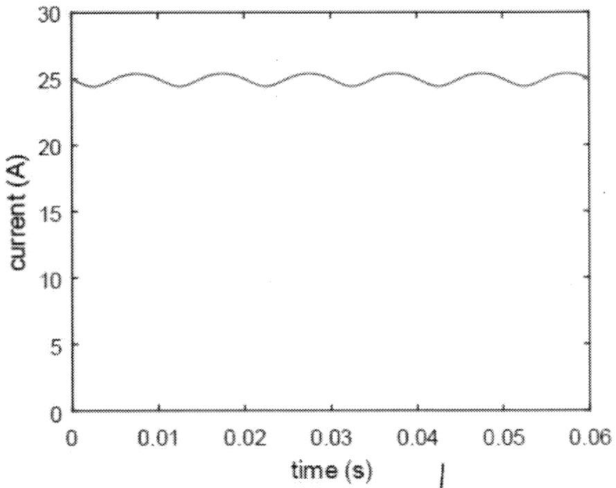

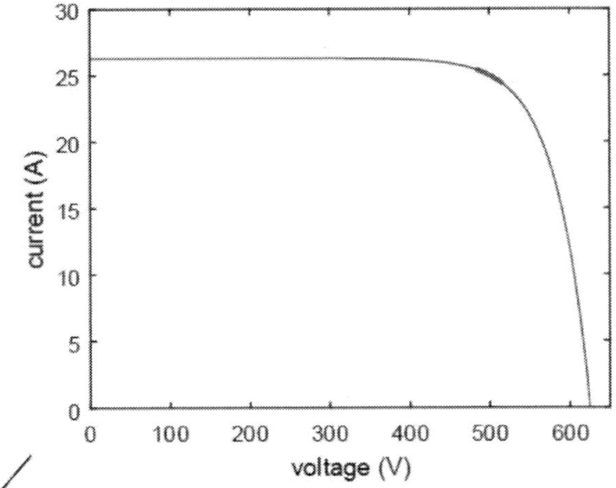

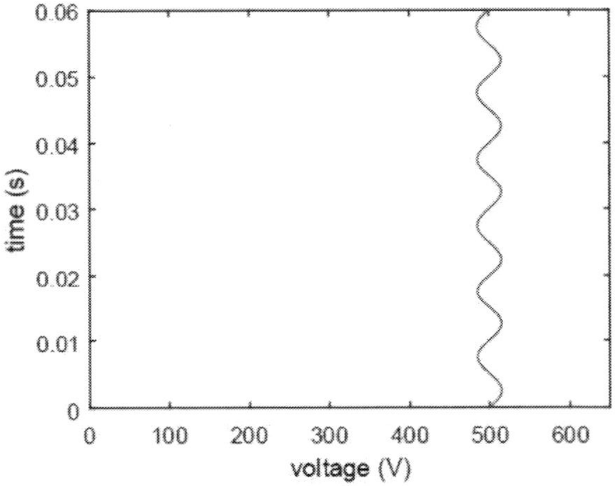

Theoretically resulting current ripple

Ripple as movement along I-V curve

Voltage ripple superimposed on the DC load

Berner Fachhochschule | Haute écol

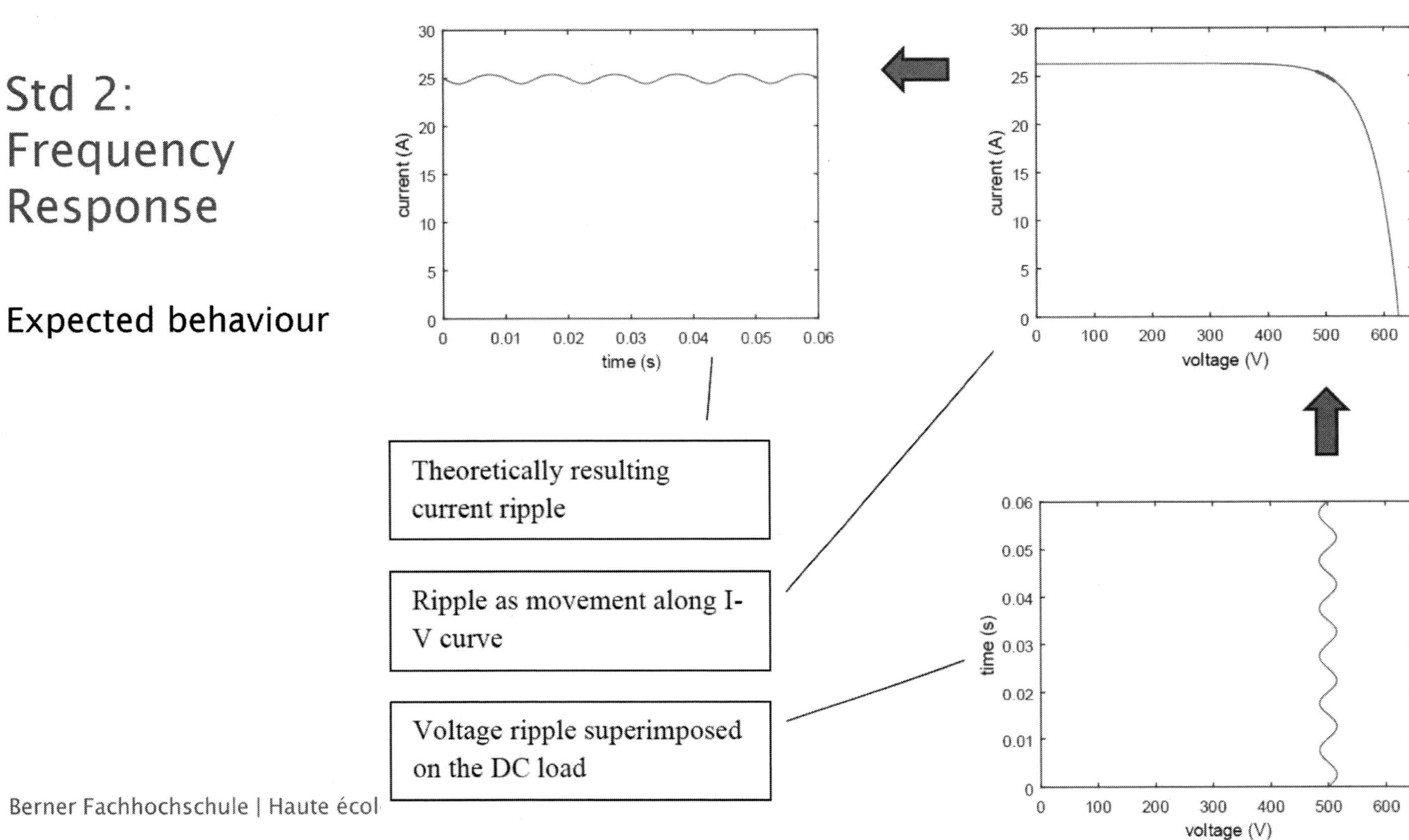

But instead of this…

Expe

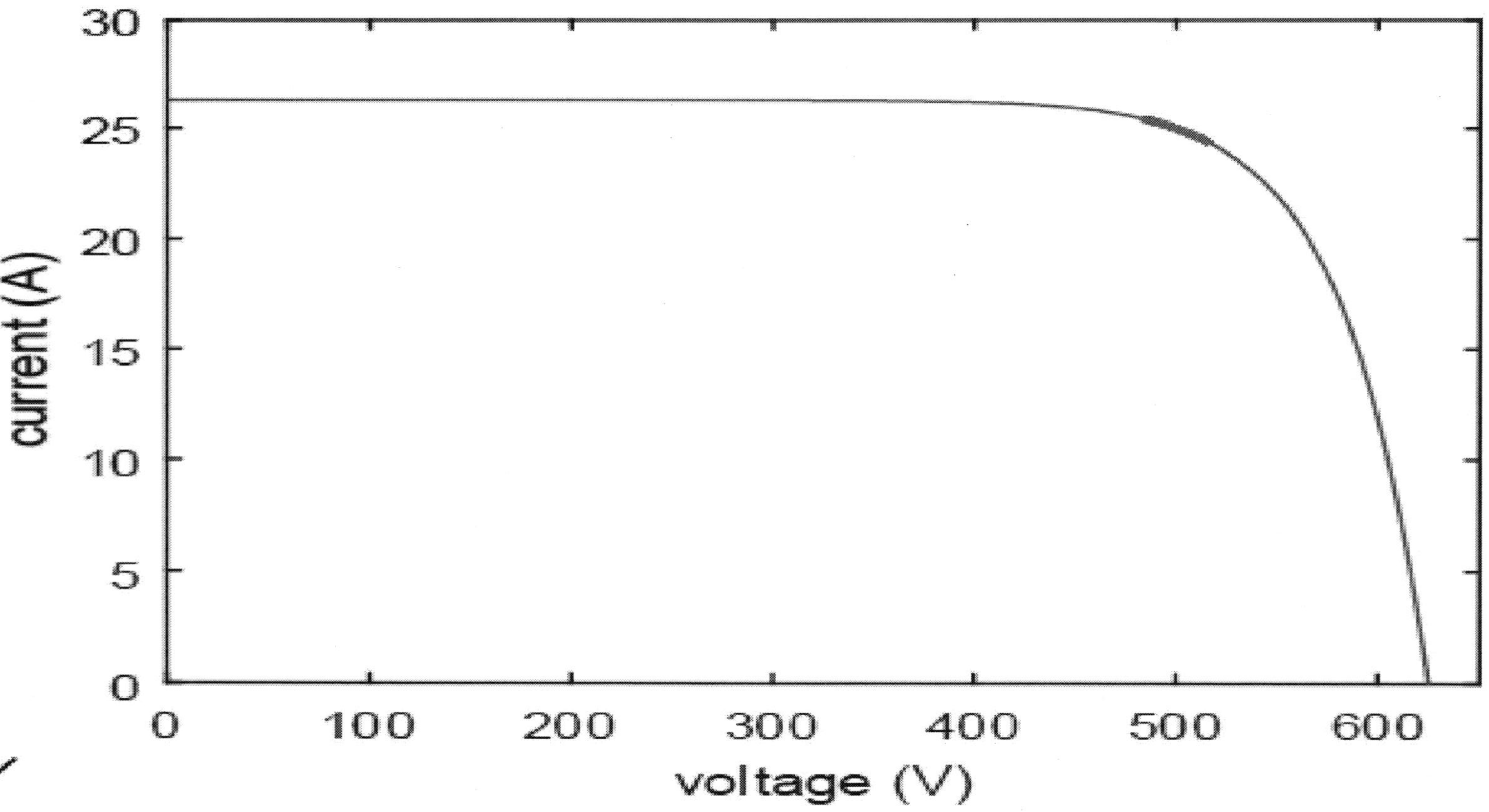

Berner

…we get this. (100 Hz AC ripple on MPP voltage)

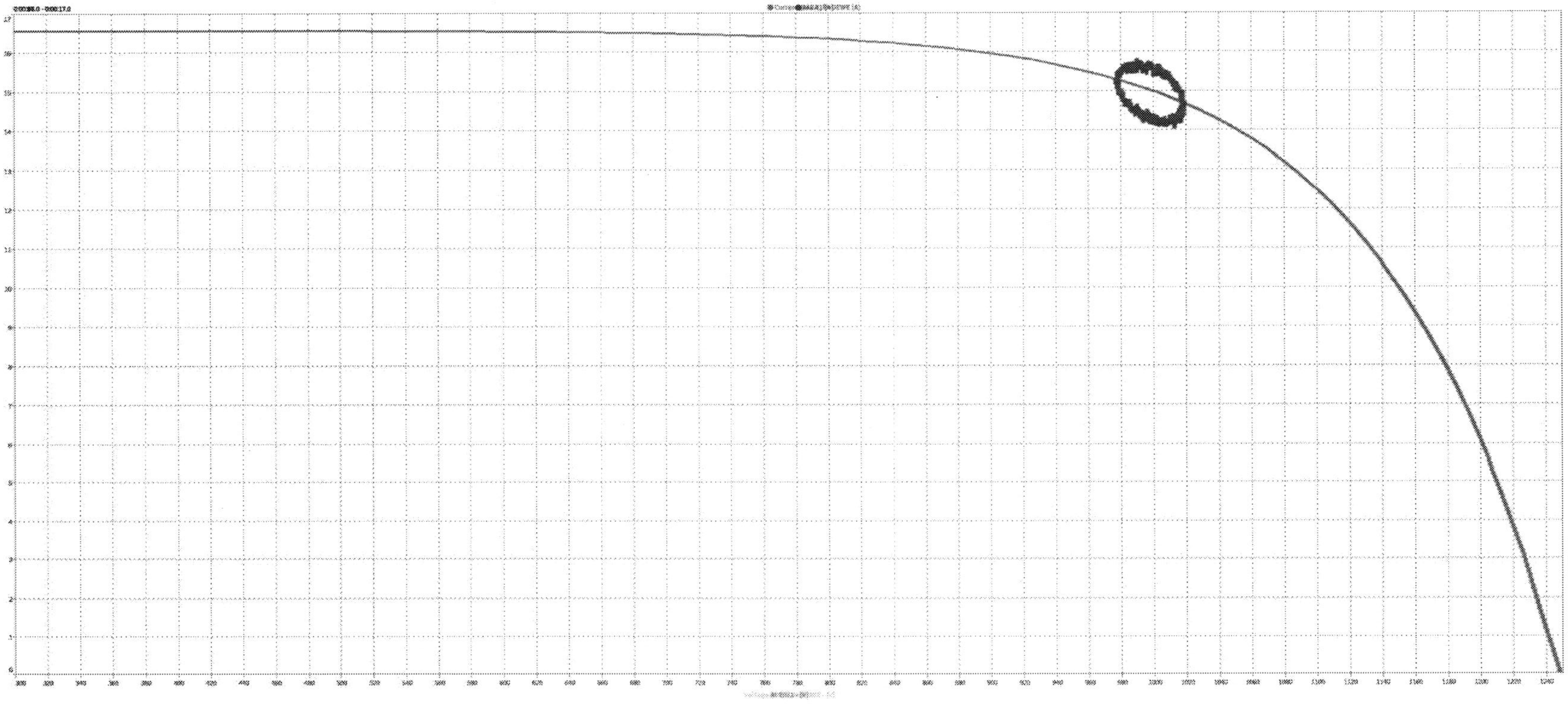

Berner Fachhochschule | Haute école spécialisée bernoise | Bern University of Applied Sciences

Proposed pass / fail criteria

Max. 30° phase shift

- At MPP
- Between 0 Hz and 150 Hz ripple
- Given an amplitude of 2%

All AS

Operating
Point 1: 40 V

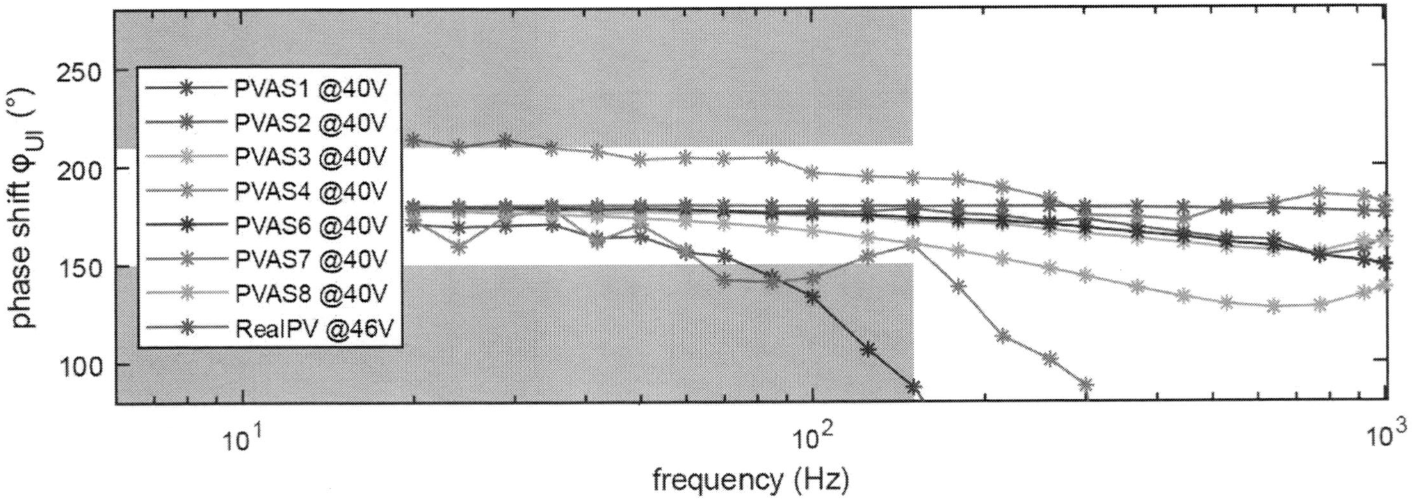

Operating
Point 1: 1000 V

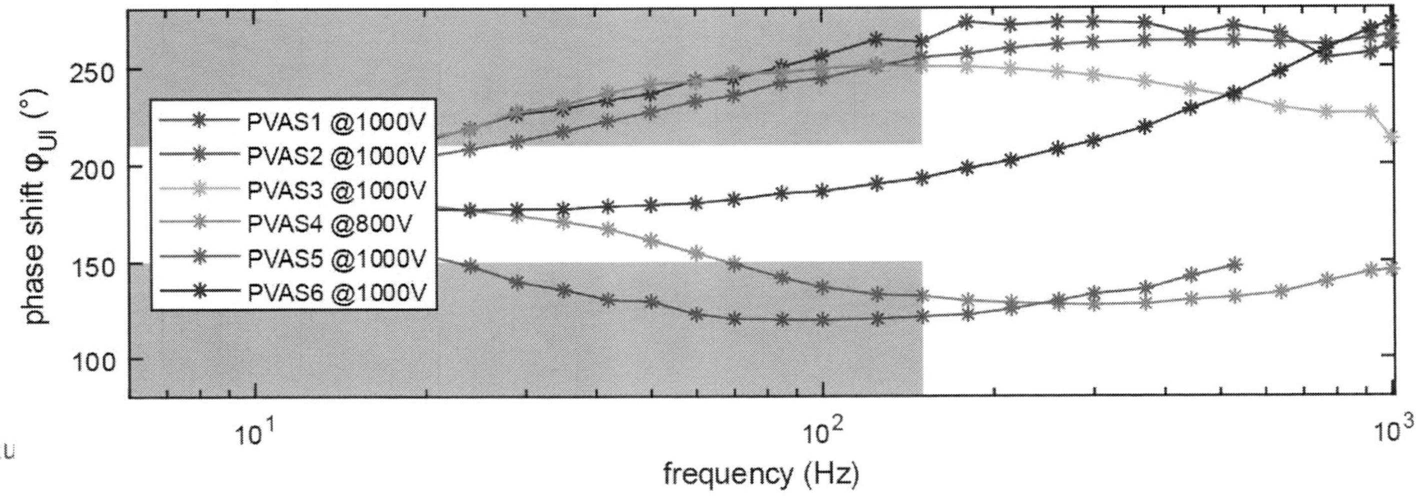

Berner Fachhochschule | Hau

Best AS

Operating Point 1: 40 V

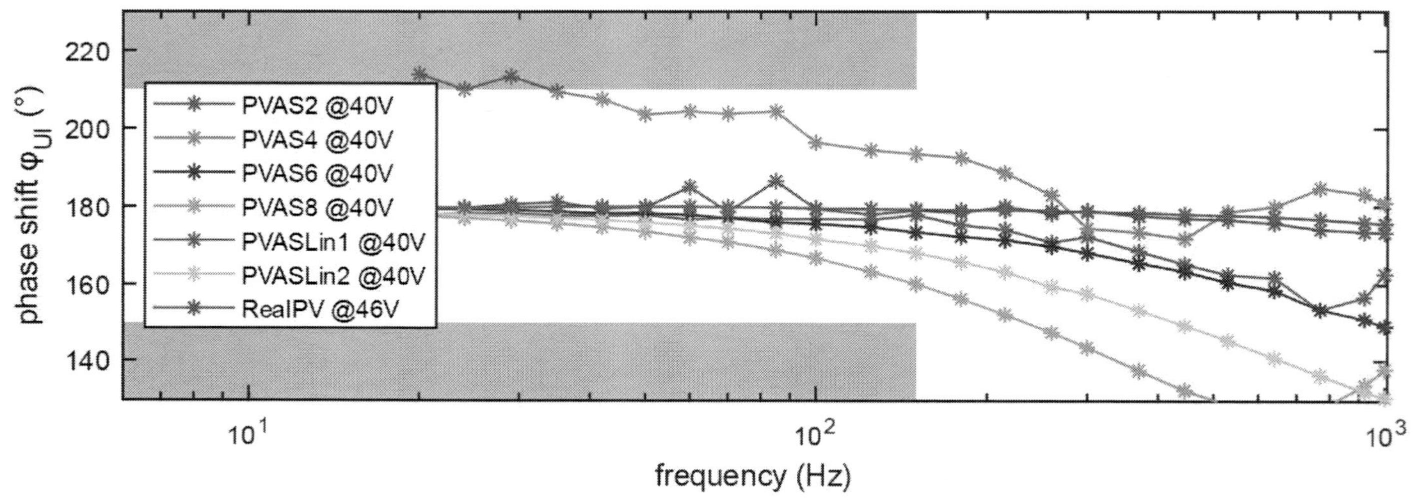

Operating Point 1: 1000 V

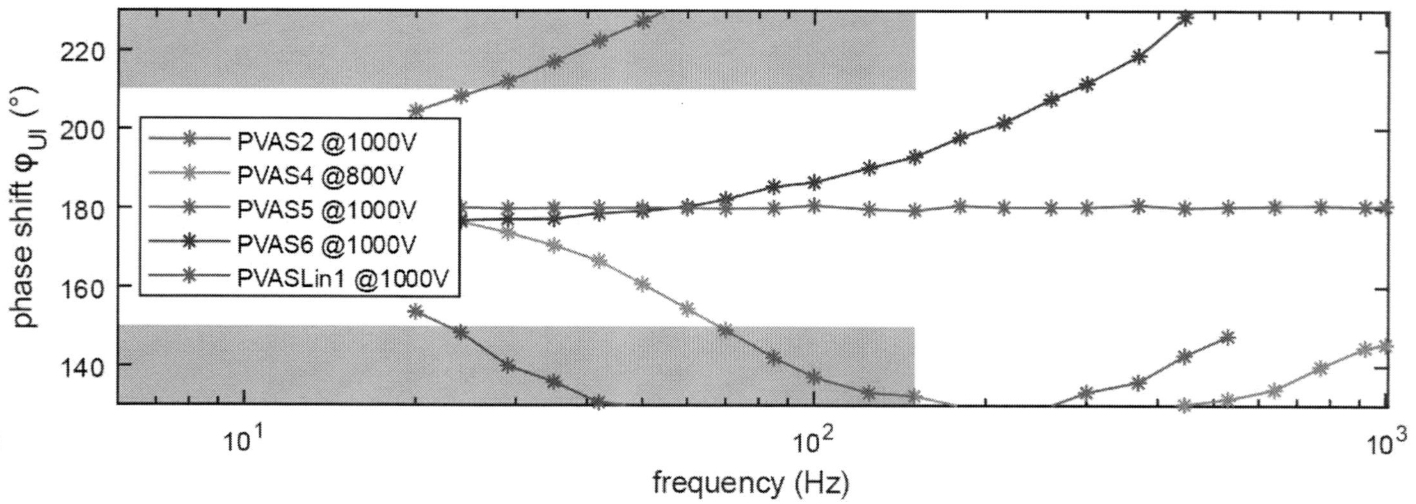

Berner Fachhochschule | Haute

Conclusion

- It is difficult to equip laboratories with bidirectional, high quality DC sources.
- We have not found any array simulator on the market that meet all our criteria out of the box. Adjustments and trial and error setup are often needed.
- Manufacturers of DC sources to be used in Solar Array Simulator (SAS) application seem not to be aware of the challenges present in this field of application.
- Linear power amplifiers have almost completely disappeared from the mass market although their SAS simulation is still more promising.
- Thus, we think it is important to have a new set of standardized test sequences to compare SAS on an international level.

Prototype of Linear Solar Module Simulator of BFH

Berner Fachhochschule | Haute école spécialisée bernoise | Bern University of Applied Sciences

Berner Fachhochschule
Haute école spécialisée bernoise
Bern University of Applied Sciences

Thank you for your attention!

christof.bucher@bfh.ch

Table 1. Overview of the proposed tests for evaluating array simulators.

Category	**Cat. 1: Phenomenological Tests**			**Cat. 2: Standard Tests**		
Test No	Phen 1	Phen 2	Phen 3	Std 1	Std 2	Std 3
Test Name	I-V Curve Stability	Current Ripple	MPPT Efficiency Difference	MPP Accuracy and Drift	Frequency Response	Irradiance Variation
Short description	Slow I-V curve tracing. Plotting the I-V curve.	Connected to a PV inverter. Measurement of current ripple.	Comparison of array simulator internal measurement with external measurement.	Manual MPP tracing after startup and after 10 minutes. Power measurement.	Superimpose an AC signal at a given DC operating point. Measure phase shift.	Measure difference between setpoint (ramp) and actual value (step function).
Pass-Fail criterion (remarks)	n. a. (no oscillations should be seen)	n. a. (current ripple should be small)	n. a. (difference should be small)	MPP accuracy be below 1 %	Frequency shift shall be below 30° from 0 Hz to 150 Hz	RMSE shall be below 1 %

Table 2. Operating point parameters for tests with static I-V curve

Operating point (OP)	**V_{MPP} [V]**	**I_{MPP} [A]**
1	40	15
2	100	25
3	500	20
4	1000	15

Table 4. PV inverter used in Test Setup 2

Designation	Manufacturer	Model name
SMA	SMA Solar Technology AG	STP6.0-3AV-40
Huawei	Huawei Digital Power Technologies Co., Ltd.	SUN2000-10KTL-M1

Table 5. PV array simulators included in any of the tests.

No	Manufacturer	Model name	Device type	Tested by
α	Chroma	62180D	Bidirectional	BFH
β	Elektro-Automation (EA)	PSB11500	Bidirectional	BFH
γ	ET System	N35500	Bidirectional	BFH
δ	Itech	IT6018C	Bidirectional	BFH
ε	Itech	IT6642C	Bidirectional	BFH
ζ	Keysight	PV8922A	Unidirectional	AIT
η	Keysight	RP7982A	Bidirectional	BFH
θ	Regatron	G5.UNV	Bidirectional	BFH
ι	AIT	PVS	Linear Unidir.	AIT
κ	BFH	MSS	Linear Unidir.	BFH
λ	Siemens	SM55	Real PV Modules	BFH

Test Setup Phen 1: I-V curve stability

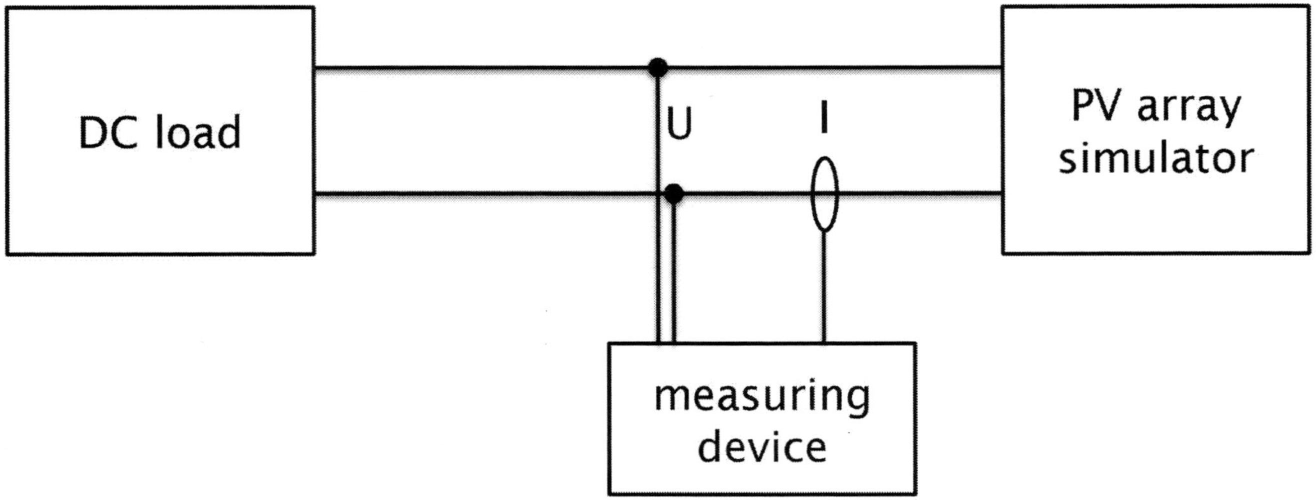

Berner Fachhochschule | Haute école spécialisée bernoise | Bern University of Applied Sciences

Test Setup Phen 2: Current ripple

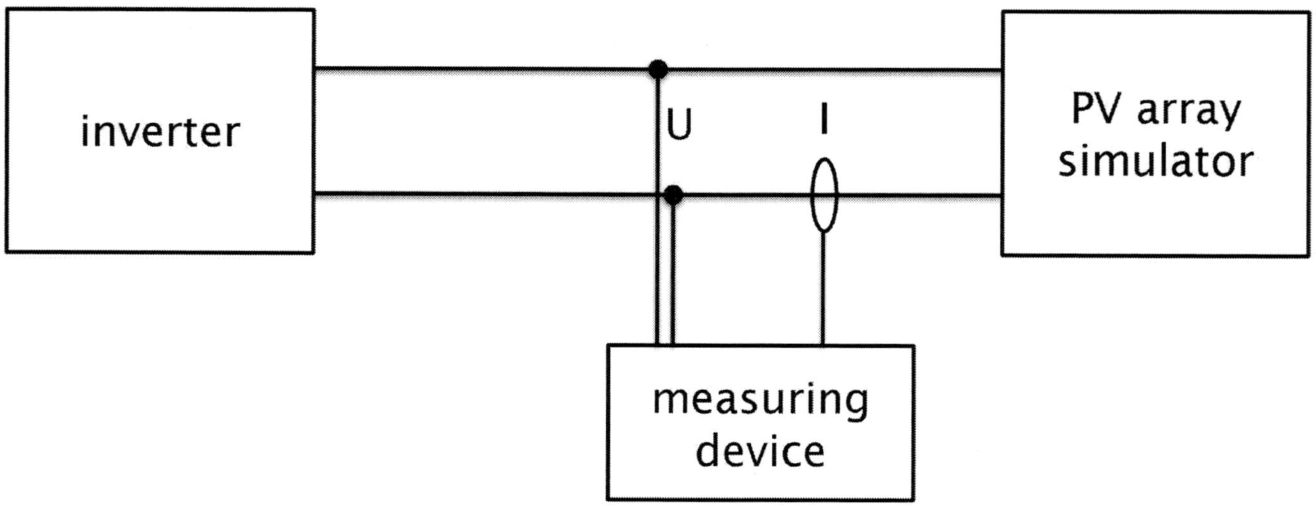

Berner Fachhochschule | Haute école spécialisée bernoise | Bern University of Applied Sciences

42nd European Photovoltaic Solar Energy Conference and Exhibition

This presentation was selected by the Sc. Committee of the EU PVSEC 2025 for submission of a full paper to one of the EU PVSEC's collaborating peer-reviewed journals.

DEVELOPING A NOVEL SENSOR HEALTH KPI FOR EVALUATING IRRADIANCE SENSOR PERFORMANCE

Sascha Lindig, Spyros Theocharides, Julián Ascencio-Vásquez
Univers SAS
1 Passerelle des Reflets, 92400 Courbevoie, France
sascha.lindig@univers.com

ABSTRACT: Reliable irradiance measurements are essential for accurate performance analysis in PV systems, influencing everything from system health diagnostics to financial forecasting and energy modeling. However, irradiance sensors such as pyranometers or reference cells can be impacted by a range of issues including miscalibration, soiling, misalignment, and data corruption. To address this challenge, we introduce the **Sensor-Health KPI**—a data-driven metric designed to evaluate and rank the data quality and reliability of each irradiance sensor in a PV system daily. The proposed KPI incorporates six evaluation parameters encompassing general data quality metrics and irradiance related performance attributes. Each parameter is individually scored, weighted, and aggregated to yield a normalized KPI score ranging from 0 to 100. This framework is integrated into the photovoltaic analytics software Solar -AI Analytics Univers. The method fills a gap in current PV monitoring standards such as IEC 61724-1:2021 by providing a structured methodology for sensor selection in performance assessments. Ultimately, the Sensor-Health KPI enables more robust downstream calculations, leading to improved performance evaluation and operational decision-making in PV systems.
Keywords: photovoltaic performance, weather station, data quality, operation and maintenance

1 INTRODUCTION

Accurate and reliable irradiance measurements are a cornerstone of photovoltaic (PV) system performance evaluation. From expected power estimation and performance ratio calculations to loss estimations, irradiance data are a critical input. Despite its importance, ensuring the quality and reliability of irradiance measurements over the operational life of a PV plant remains a considerable challenge, both from a technical and a computational point of view.

Irradiance sensors such as pyranometers and reference cells can be affected by multiple sources of error, including calibration drift, dirt accumulation, physical misalignment, and data communication issues. These problems can distort downstream performance indicators, potentially leading to inaccurate diagnostics, misinformed decisions, or even financial losses. Notably, current PV monitoring guidelines, such as IEC 61724 [1, 2, 3], cover basic data quality practices but fall short in providing a methodology for disregarding irradiance sensors or selecting among different irradiance sources.

To address this gap, we present a novel metric—the **Sensor-Health Key Performance Indicator (SH-KPI)**—developed to assess and rank irradiance sensors based on data quality and data accuracy. The SH-KPI evaluates several aspects of sensor behavior, including compliance with existing data boundaries, and correlation with other sources. It combines the individual aspects with a single score, ranging from 0 to 100, thereby enabling an automated sensor selection on a daily. This is combined with a strict prioritization scheme of irradiance sources including plane-of-array (POA) and global horizontal (GHI) sensors as well as satellite data.

In this paper, we describe the structure and scoring logic of the SH-KPI and provide examples of its application to real-world PV data. We demonstrate how the SH-KPI can improve operational performance assessments by dynamically selecting the most trustworthy irradiance data source, especially in systems with multiple sensors or varying data quality. To the best of our knowledge, there are no directly comparable approaches in the literature; most related work focuses on weather-corrected performance ratios or insolation-based adjustments. This highlights the novelty of our method and its potential to complement existing performance assessment techniques.

2 HIGH LEVEL ARCHITECTURE

The sensor-health KPI is a newly established key performance indicator which is used to evaluate and compare individual irradiance sensors with one another. The aim is to decide which sensor is the most reliable for each day. The SH-KPI rates each individual sensor based on individual factors to make an informed decision which of the available sensors is most suited to be used for all downstream calculations.

The KPI ranges from 0 to 100 with higher values indicating high-quality sensor readings. An SH-KPI of -99 represents a disregarded sensor which did not pass one or several of the data reliability tests. The SH-KPI is an aggregate across several data quality and reliability related parameters:

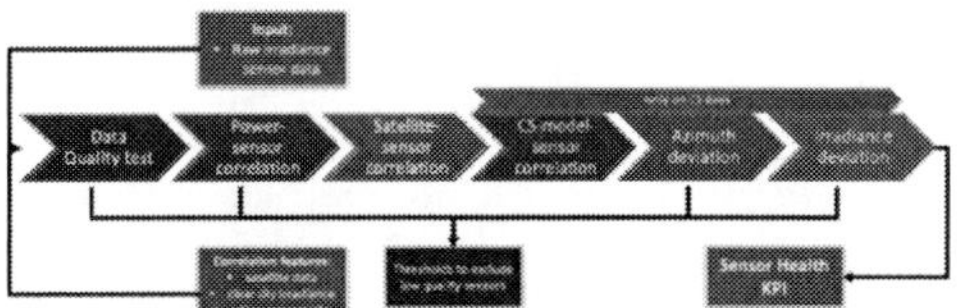

Figure 1: Sensor-health KPI structure with individual rating parameters

The individual rating parameters are discussed in chapter 3. The sensor health KPI is calculated daily for every ground-based irradiance sensor to select the best suited sensor per inverter for downstream calculations.

10.4229/EUPVSEC2025/4DO.10.1
020371-001

3 SENSOR HEALTH KPI - DETAILS

As introduced in **Figure 1**, the SH-KPI is constructed based on several parameters. In this section, the individual parameters will be introduced and described in detail. All correlation steps use the Pearson correlation parameter [4]. The KPI is constructed daily. The data are evaluated in five-minute resolution but practically it can be applied to all resolutions up to 15 minutes.

3.1 Data quality

The first set of parameters are data quality (DQ) parameters. Thereby, the following DQ parameters are being considered:

- **Missing data**: NaN values
- **Corrupt data**: corrupt values are commonly one of the following:
  [-99, -999, -9999, -99999, -999999, -9999999]
- **Stuck data**: Stuck or unchanging values are identified by checking whether data points vary as expected over time
- **Outlier data**: outlier data are defined as values out of pre-defined bounds

The definitions of stuck values as well as outlier bounds are in line with standard IEC 61724-3:2016 [3].

Every datapoint during daytime is subject to data quality tests. If the daily amount of datapoints affected by DQ issues amounts to more than 20%, that day is flagged and the sensor will be excluded. Data quality data are aligned based on the Univers Solar-AI data quality page:

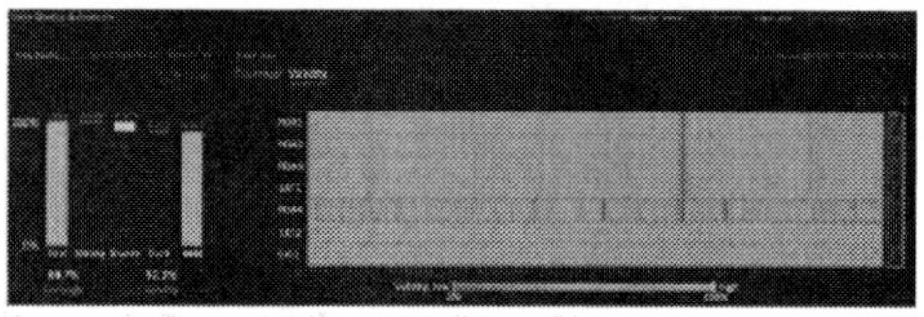

Figure 2: Data quality overview of irradiance sensors

3.2 Power-sensor correlation parameter

Under normal operating conditions, PV power output shows a string, approximately linear correlation with irradiance. That is why this correlation parameter was introduced and has a high weight in the determination of the SH-KPI. The difficulty is to select a suitable power parameter which is used for the power-irradiance correlation. Given the position of the SH-KPI algorithm within the processing pipeline (following data ingestion and basic quality control, but preceding KPI calculation and loss categorization), the power readings available were only subject to basic quality checks but not yet to extended quality testing regarding reliability and IEC states. The objective is to select the most reliable DC string reading per irradiance orientation, if available. It is important to select one string per orientation so that the POA orientation (tilt & azimuth) of the DC string is aligned to the orientation of the irradiance sensor.

The parameter is prepared in three steps:

a. Inverter string selector: Select the highest-yielding DC string per inverter after filtering out strings with data quality issues, curtailment, or anomalous daily patterns.

b. Racking string selector: From the pre-selected strings, group by onboarded orientation and choose the highest daily energy yield string.

c. Inverter racking string builder: Combine the selected strings from step b to create the final dataset for power-irradiance correlation calculation.

3.3 Satellite-sensor correlation parameter

For satellite correlation, transposed global horizontal irradiance (GHI) satellite data are used. Before calculating the satellite correlation, the satellite data are tested against the reference irradiance. To compute the reference irradiance, the median value of all POA sensors with the same specified orientation is calculated. In the next step, the Pearson correlation of the selected satellite irradiance and the reference irradiance is computed. If the correlation value exceeds 0.75, the satellite data are included in the SH-KPI calculation. If it is below, the satellite correlation is not being executed. The reason for this is to avoid using "poor" satellite data.

An example can be seen in **Figure 3**. This site experienced a day of extremely low irradiation. Especially under such conditions, it is not unusual for satellite data to divert from the irradiance/power profile on site. The reference irradiance parameter is the median value across the POA sensors 1 to 5, and the correlation between the selected satellite data sat_poa_1 and the reference irradiance is 0.56. So, the parameter did not meet the quality threshold and is excluded for this particular day.

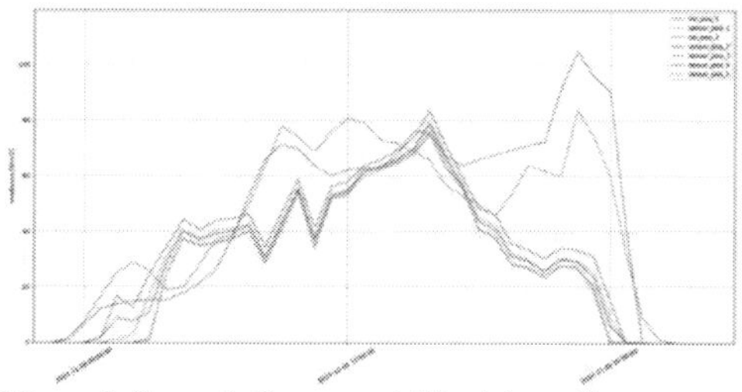

Figure 3: Example for poor satellite data quality

3.4 Transposed clear-sky model-sensor correlation parameter

The clear-sky (CS) model is modelled based on the Ineichen and Perez clear sky model [5, 6] available in the Python package pvlib [7]. To transform the global horizontal clear-sky model into clear-sky POA [8, 9, 10]. The parameter is only being used on clear-sky days. A clear-sky day is defined as a day in which at least 80% of the datapoints are clear-sky instances.

3.5 Azimuth deviation

The azimuth alignment check is performed only on fixed tilt systems with a tilt greater than (or equal to) 10° and only on clear-sky days. Azimuth analysis for lower tilt systems is not sufficiently reliable.

First, the true sensor azimuth is determined from the time series data. This is done using an azimuth fitting subroutine. The objective is to find the azimuth parameter for the clear-sky POA model that minimizes the root-mean-square-error (RMSE) between the magnitude-scaled clear-sky POA and measured POA. The minimization is implemented via the scipy.optimize.minimize method [11, 12]. The azimuth value that minimizes RMSE is the "observed" azimuth. If the POA sensor's observed azimuth is more than 12° different from the specified sensor azimuth in the site configuration, the sensor is flagged as “misaligned” and is eliminated from use in further analysis.

3.6 Irradiance deviation

Irradiance deviation is based on the reference irradiance introduced in section 3.3. The irradiance deviation parameter is only used on clear sky days. At each timestamp, the median value of all POA sensors with the same specified orientation is calculated. Then, for each sensor, the percentage error between the total daily irradiance measured and the medium value is determined:

$$poa_{error} = \frac{\sum poa_{meas} - \sum irr_{ref}}{\sum irr_{ref}}$$

The aggregation step is daily. Here, poa_{meas} are the sensor readings and irr_{ref} is the reference irradiance. If poa_{error} is greater than 12% for a sensor, the sensor is flagged and excluded from further use.

3.7 Sensor-health KPI calculation

The SH-KPI is an aggregated KPI based on the results from the quality test parameters described above.

The parameters 1) data quality, 2) power–irradiance correlation, 5) azimuth deviation, and 6) irradiance deviation have fail-thresholds. If one of them is surpassed, the SH-KPI is set to −99 and the sensor excluded from the sensor selection for that day. These fail-thresholds are intentionally defined as conservative cut-off values: they serve to eliminate sensors whose data is very likely unreliable rather than to capture subtle deviations. This approach ensures that severely erroneous or inconsistent measurements do not bias the subsequent scoring and selection process, while less critical deviations are still reflected through the gradual scoring scale.

Each parameter has score levels between 1 and 5. The SH-KPI is calculated according to:

$$SH - KPI\ [\%] = \frac{\sum score * 100}{\sum score_{max}}$$

Here, $score_{max}$ is the maximum reachable sum if all parameters under consideration are returning the highest possible score. $score$ is the sum of all individual scores of the parameters considered.

The final SH-KPIs across a PV site and for each day can be seen exemplarily in **Figure 4**. It is visible that also GHI sensors are being evaluated, but without considering power-irradiance correlation as well as azimuth deviation. If any of the parameters seen in **Figure 1** are not available, the SH-KPI is computed excluding this specific parameter (for instance CS-irradiance correlation, irradiance deviation and azimuth deviation on clear-sky days).

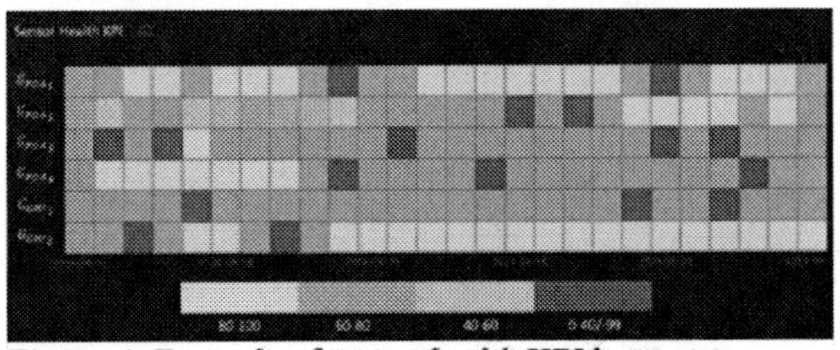

Figure 4: Example of sensor-health KPI heatmap

4 IRRADIANCE SENSOR SELECTION

The final step is to pass the SH-KPI information to the irradiance source selection. Here, the best-performing irradiance source (sensor or satellite) is selected for each day and for each inverter. The selection follows a strict prioritization scheme (see Table 1) which can be adjusted by the user if required. The process consists of three steps:

Figure 5: Sensor selection decision making

After, calculating the SH-KPI for each individual sensor, the user-defined sensor prioritization scheme is loaded, anf the irradiance source selected based on these inputs. Based on the prioritization and the SH-KPI values, one irradiance source is chosen for downstream calculations. Assigned and backup sensors are specifically assigned sensors for individual inverters (set by the user). Such manual assignment may be required in cases where a particular sensor must be used to meet contractual obligations, for regulatory reporting, or to align with existing operational procedures, even if other sensors might show better data quality.

In addition to directly assigned sensors, two further strategies are available. The average sensor combines data from all reliable irradiance sensors with the same orientation, while the highest-rated sensor is the sensor with the highest SH-KPI within a given racking group/orientation. The prioritization gives preference to POA sensors, followed by GHI sensors transposed to POA.

For quality control, sensors are first considered only if their SH-KPI exceeds 90. If no sensor passes this threshold, a second selection round includes sensors above a lower threshold. If none of the ground-mounted sensors achieve at least 60, the system falls back on satellite data, since it must be assumed that all sensors are either corrupt or of insufficient quality.

Table 1: Default sensor prioritization

Priority	**Irradiance Source**	**Description**
1	Assigned POA sensor	**User-defined** preferred choice
2	Backup POA sensor	**User-defined** 2nd preferred choice
3	Average POA	Mean across all well-functioning POA sensors
4	Highest rated POA sensor	POA sensor with highest sensor health KPI
5	Transposed assigned GHI sensor	**User-defined** preferred GHI choice
6	Transposed average GHI	Transposed irradiance of mean across all well-functioning GHI sensors
7	Transposed highest rated GHI sensor	Transposed GHI sensor with highest sensor health KPI
8	Satellite POA	Irradiance from onboarded satellite POA source
9	Transposed satellite GHI	Transposed irradiance from onboarded satellite GHI source

5 CONCLUSIONS

This work presents the Sensor-Health Key Performance Indicator (SH-KPI), a comprehensive data-driven metric designed to evaluate and rank irradiance sensor reliability in photovoltaic systems. The SH-KPI addresses a critical gap in current PV monitoring standards by providing an automated methodology for daily sensor selection and quality assessment, thereby building upon the IEC 61724 framework. The proposed SH-KPI not only standardizes sensor evaluation but also directly improves the reliability of downstream PV analytics, by supporting more accurate performance assessments and operational decisions.

The SH-KPI incorporates six evaluation parameters that encompass both general data quality metrics and irradiance-specific performance attributes: 1) data quality, 2) string-power correlation, 3) satellite-sensor correlation, 4) clear-sky model-sensor correlation, 5) azimuth deviation, and 6) irradiance deviation.

The methodology successfully addresses common irradiance measurement challenges including calibration drift, soiling effects, physical misalignment, and data corruption. The normalized scoring system (0-100) with fail-safe thresholds ensures consistent evaluation across diverse PV installations and varying environmental conditions. The hierarchical sensor selection process, ranging from assigned POA sensors to satellite fallback options, provides resilience against sensor failures while maintaining data continuity for critical performance assessments.

In the future, we want to explore several opportunities for enhancement and validation of the methodology. First, the current framework requires extension to accommodate tracking systems, where sensor orientation dynamics and tracking accuracy significantly impact irradiance measurements. Future iterations will incorporate tracking error detection algorithms and develop specialized correlation metrics that account for the temporal alignment challenges inherent in tracking systems. Second, comprehensive bias analysis is essential to identify potential blind spots in the SH-KPI evaluation framework. Additionally, machine learning approaches could enhance the methodology by enabling adaptive weighting of the six evaluation parameters based on site-specific characteristics and seasonal variations. Finally, expanding the framework to incorporate emerging sensor technologies, such as silicon photodiodes and low-cost pyranometers, will ensure the methodology remains relevant as PV monitoring technology evolves. Long-term field validation studies across diverse geographical locations and plant configurations will be crucial for establishing the robustness and universal applicability of the SH-KPI methodology.

6 REFERENCES

[1] International Electrotechnical Commission, "IEC 61724-1:2021 Photovoltaic system performance, Part 1: Monitoring Standard," Geneva, 2021.

[2] International Electrotechnical Commission, "IEC 61724-2:2016: Photovoltaic system performance - Part 2: Capacity evaluation method," Geneva, 2016.

[3] International Electrotechnical Commission, "IEC 61724-3:2016: Photovoltaic system performance, Part 3: Energy evaluation method," Geneva, 2016.

[4] I. Cohen, Y. Huang, J. Chen and J. Benesty, Noise Reduction in Speech Processing, Springer, 2009.

[5] R. Perez and P. Ineichen, "A new airmass independent formulation for the Linke turbidity coefficient," *Solar Energy,* vol. 73, pp. 151-157, 2002.

[6] R. Perez et al., "A new operational model for satellite-derived irradiances: description and validation," *Solar Energy,* vol. 73, pp. 307-317, 2002.

[7] W. F. Holmgren, C. W. Hansen and M. A. Mikofski, "pvlib python: a python package for modeling solar energy systems," *Journal of Open Source Software,* vol. 3, no. 29, 2018.

[8] R. Perez, P. Ineichen, E. Maxwell, R. Seals and A. Zelenka, "Dynamic Global-to-Direct Irradiance Conversion Models," *ASHRAE Transactions-Research Series,* pp. 354-369, 1992.

[9] R. Perez, R. Seals, P. Ineichen, R. Stewart and D. Menicucci, "A new simplified version of the perez diffuse irradiance model for tilted surfaces," *Solar Energy,* vol. 39, no. 3, pp. 221-232, 1987.

[10] M. Mikofski and K. Anderson, "Slope-Aware Backtracking for Single-Axis Trackers," NREL, 2020.

[11] R. H. Byrd, P. Lu, J. Nocedal and C. Zhu, "A Limited Memory Algorithm for Bound Constrained Optimization," *SIAM Journal on Scientific and Statistical Computing,* vol. 16, no. 5, pp. 1190-1208, 1995.

[12] C. Zhu, R. H. Byrd and J. Nocedal, "L-BFGS-B: Algorithm 778: L-BFGS-B, FORTRAN routines for large scale bound constrained optimization," *ACM Transactions on Mathematical Software,* vol. 23, no. 4, pp. 550-560, 1997.

10.4229/EUPVSEC2025/4DO.10.1

univers Proprietary and Confidential

A novel Sensor Health KPI for evaluating irradiance sensor performance

Dr. Sascha Lindig

Senior Solar Performance Engineer

EUPVSEC, Bilbao, 25.09.2025

univers Proprietary and Confidential

Univers AS (former Bazefield)

- Global software company within renewables. Roots back to 1991 as an industrial IT company
- OEM independent offering within renewable since 2010
- Market leading Bazefield® Operations Management System. Based on the same foundation that has shown its scalability, performance, reliability and robustness for many clients over many years in different industries
- Offer off-the-shelf support for solar, wind, battery storage, hydro, biomass and other renewable technology sources
- Univers AS operates fully independent regarding governance, data confidentiality, cybersecurity etc.

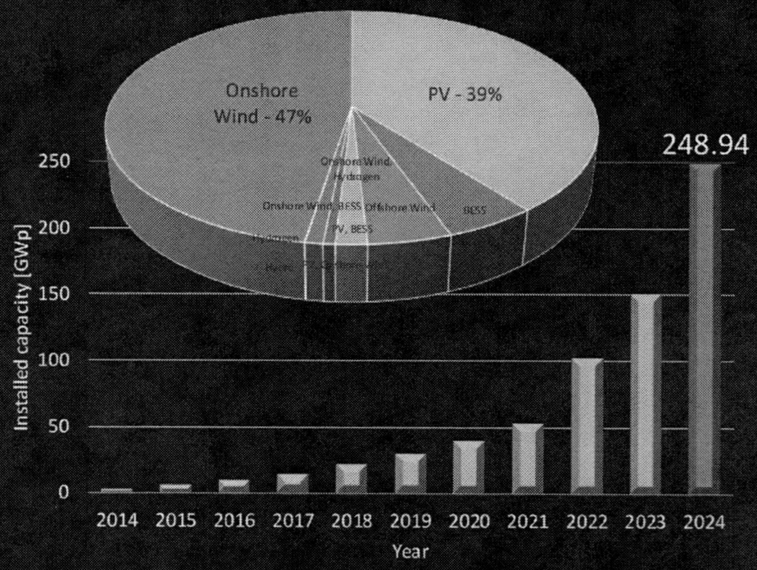

Kingfield Solar Portfolio (Excelsior Energy, Minnesota , US)

Fallago Rig (Natural Power, UK)

Hornsdale Power Reserve (Australia)

Sheringham Shoal (Equinor, UK)

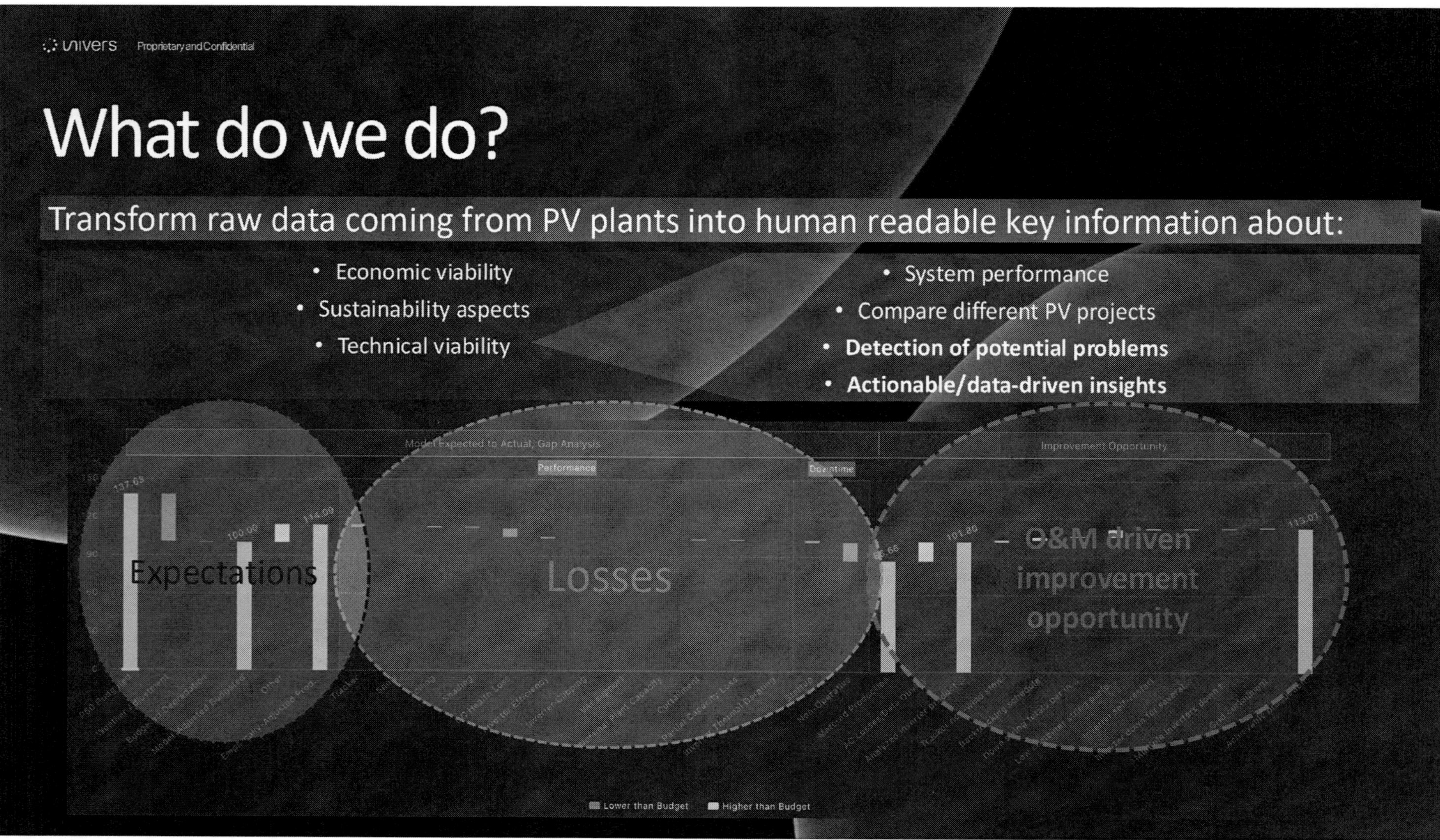

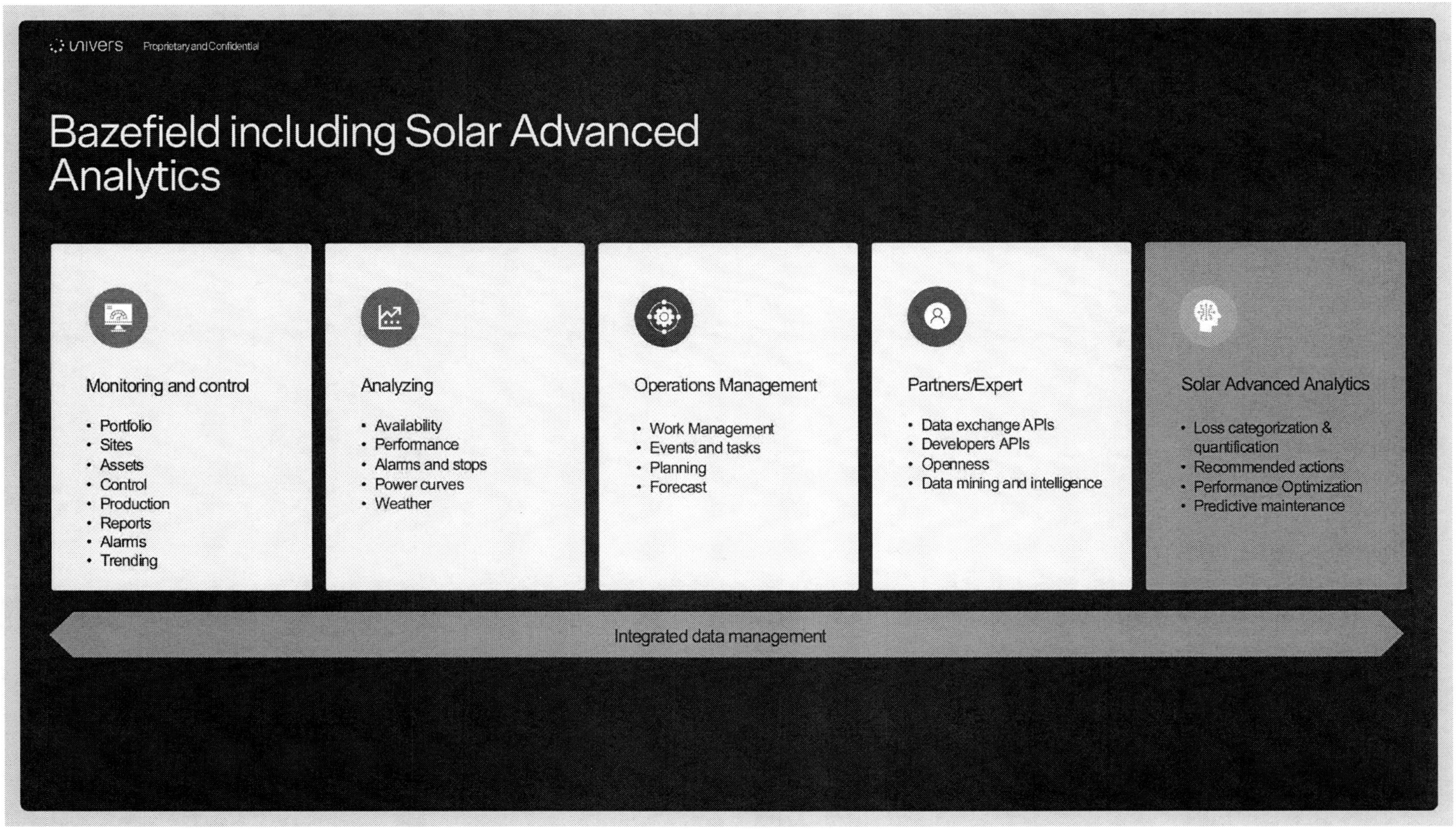
univers Proprietary and Confidential
Bazefield including Solar Advanced Analytics
Monitoring and control
• Portfolio
• Sites
• Assets
• Control
• Production
• Reports
• Alarms
• Trending
Analyzing
• Availability
• Performance
• Alarms and stops
• Power curves
• Weather
Operations Management
• Work Management
• Events and tasks
• Planning
• Forecast
Partners/Expert
• Data exchange APIs
• Developers APIs
• Openness
• Data mining and intelligence
Solar Advanced Analytics
• Loss categorization & quantification
• Recommended actions
• Performance Optimization
• Predictive maintenance
Integrated data management

univers Proprietary and Confidential

What do we do?

Transform raw data coming from PV plants into human readable key information about:

- Economic viability
- Sustainability aspects
- Technical viability

- System performance
- Compare different PV projects
- **Detection of potential problems**
- **Actionable/data-driven insights**

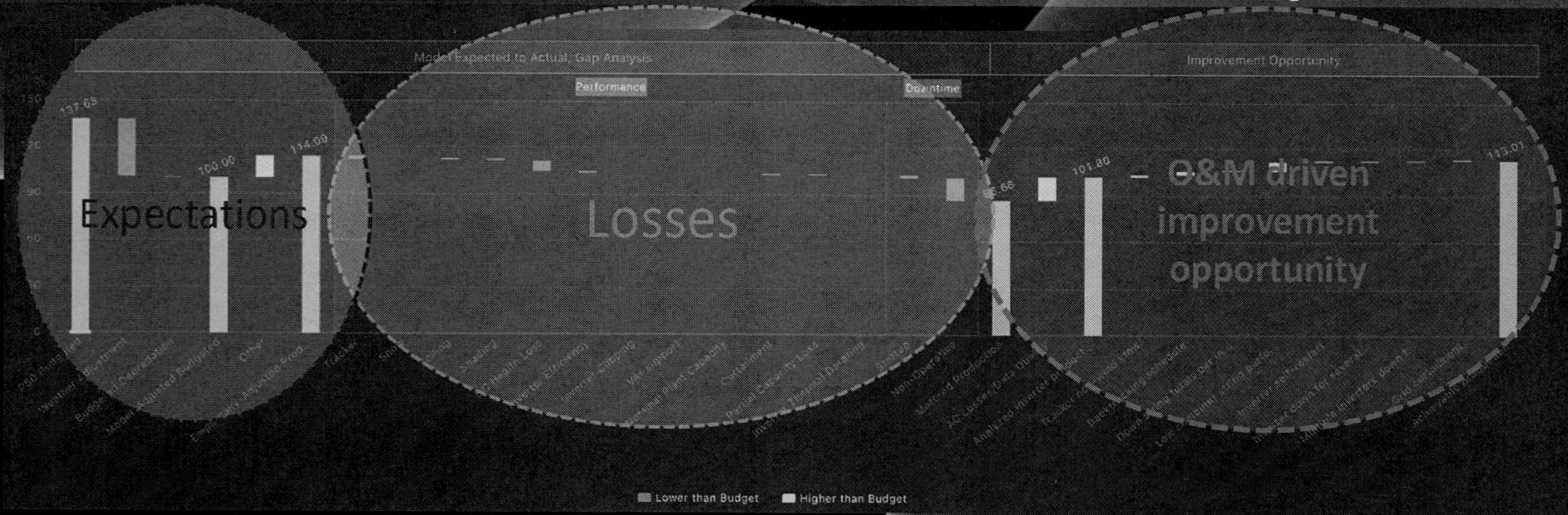

univers Proprietary and Confidential

Data usage, calculations

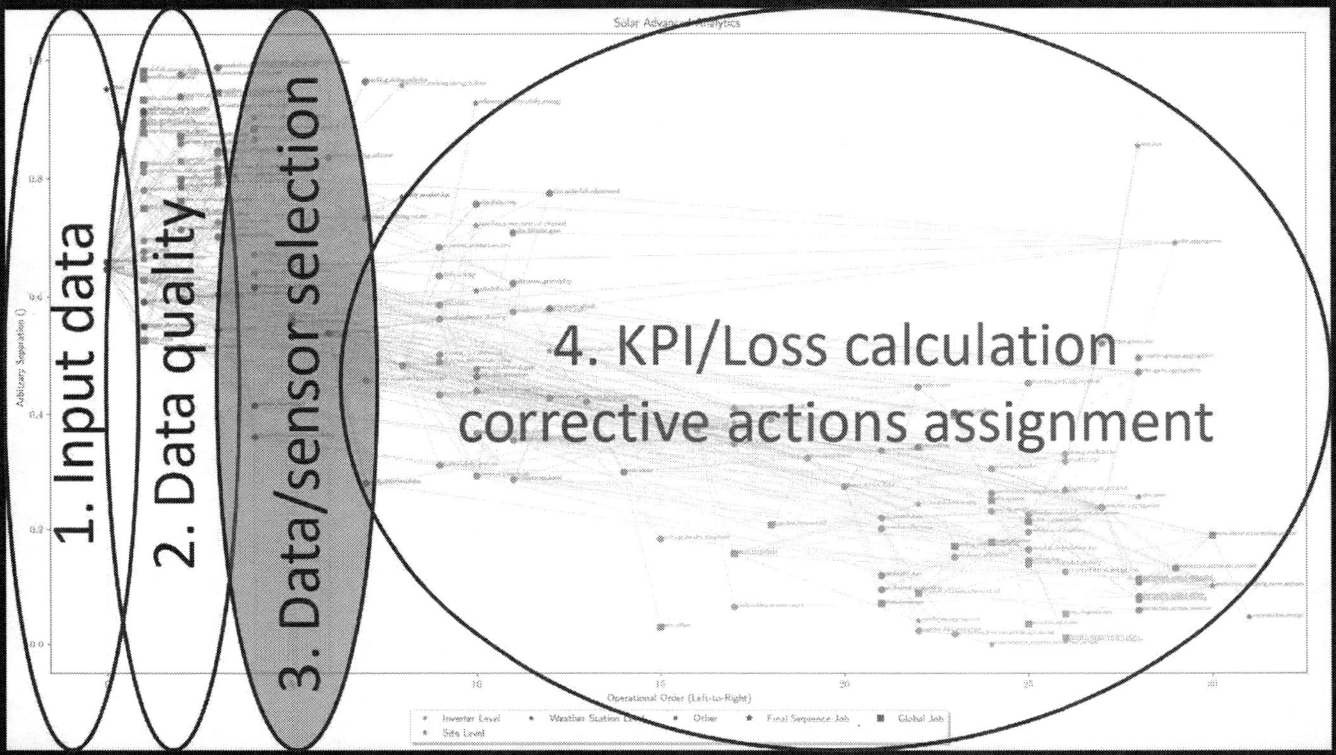

Categorization

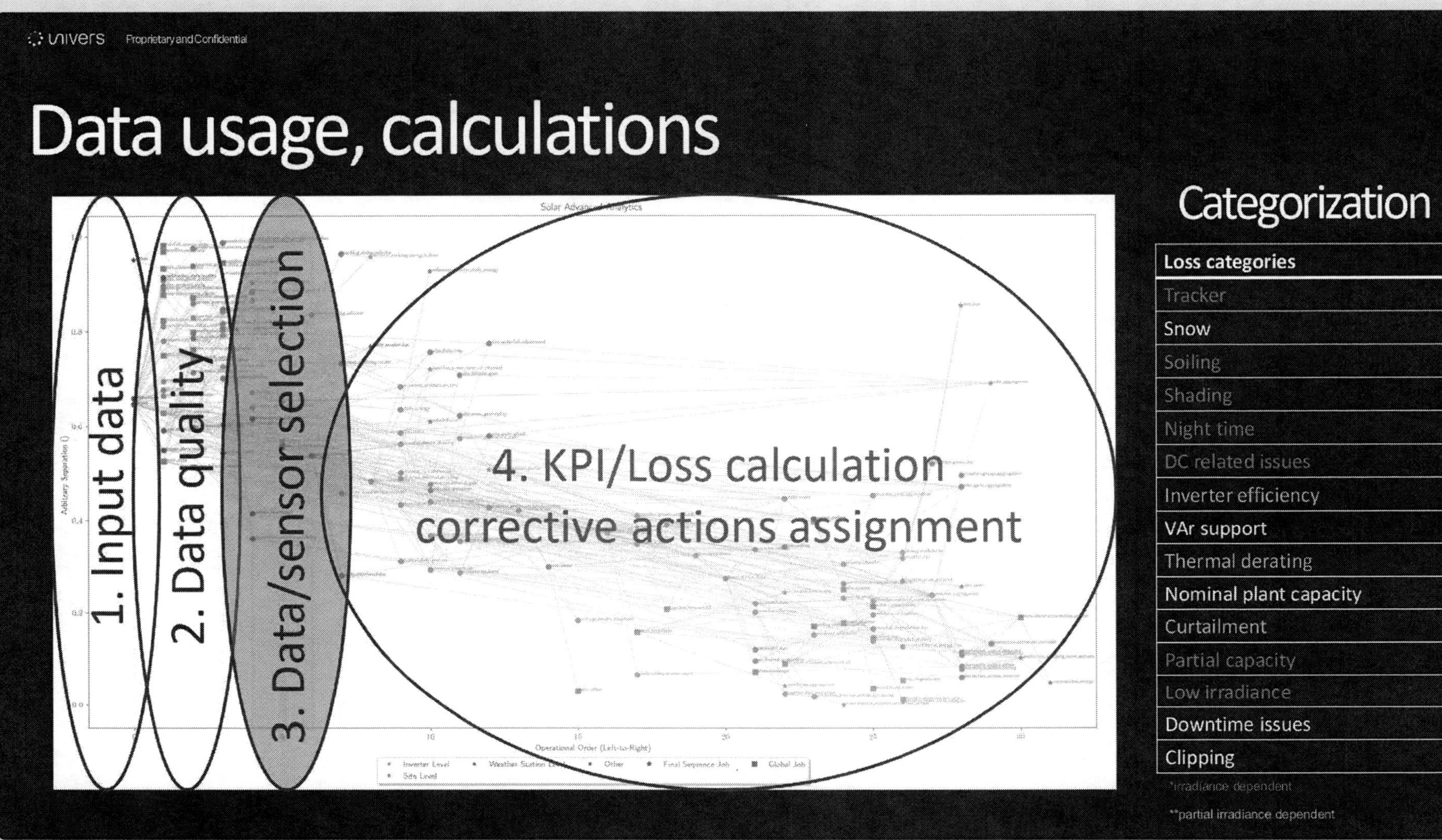

Loss categories
Tracker
Snow
Soiling
Shading
Night time
DC related issues
Inverter efficiency
VAr support
Thermal derating
Nominal plant capacity
Curtailment
Partial capacity
Low irradiance
Downtime issues
Clipping

*irradiance dependent

**partial irradiance dependent

Which irradiance sensor to choose?

- plane-of-array sensors
- global horizontal sensors
- satellite

IEC 61724-1:2021[1]

- requires class A pyranometers
- provides # of sensors per plant
- location shall be selected representative
- sensor shading shall be avoided
- GHI sensors leveled within 0.5°
- POA sensors leveled within 0.5° tilt and 1° azimuth

[1] International Electrotechnical Commission, "IEC 61724-1:2021 Photovoltaic system performance - Part 1: Monitoring, Standard", Geneva, CH 2021.

univers Proprietary and Confidential

Which irradiance sensor to choose?

- Data quality
- Data logging, communication
- Orientation
- Correlation with power
- Correlation vs other available sensors/satellite
- Affected by soiling?
- long-term stability & calibration drift
- ....

EURAC Research – ABD Plant

Daily job – select irradiance source → Across 1000+ sites → For each inverter → Input to more than 90% of downstream jobs

Trade-off: Accuracy vs Computational performance

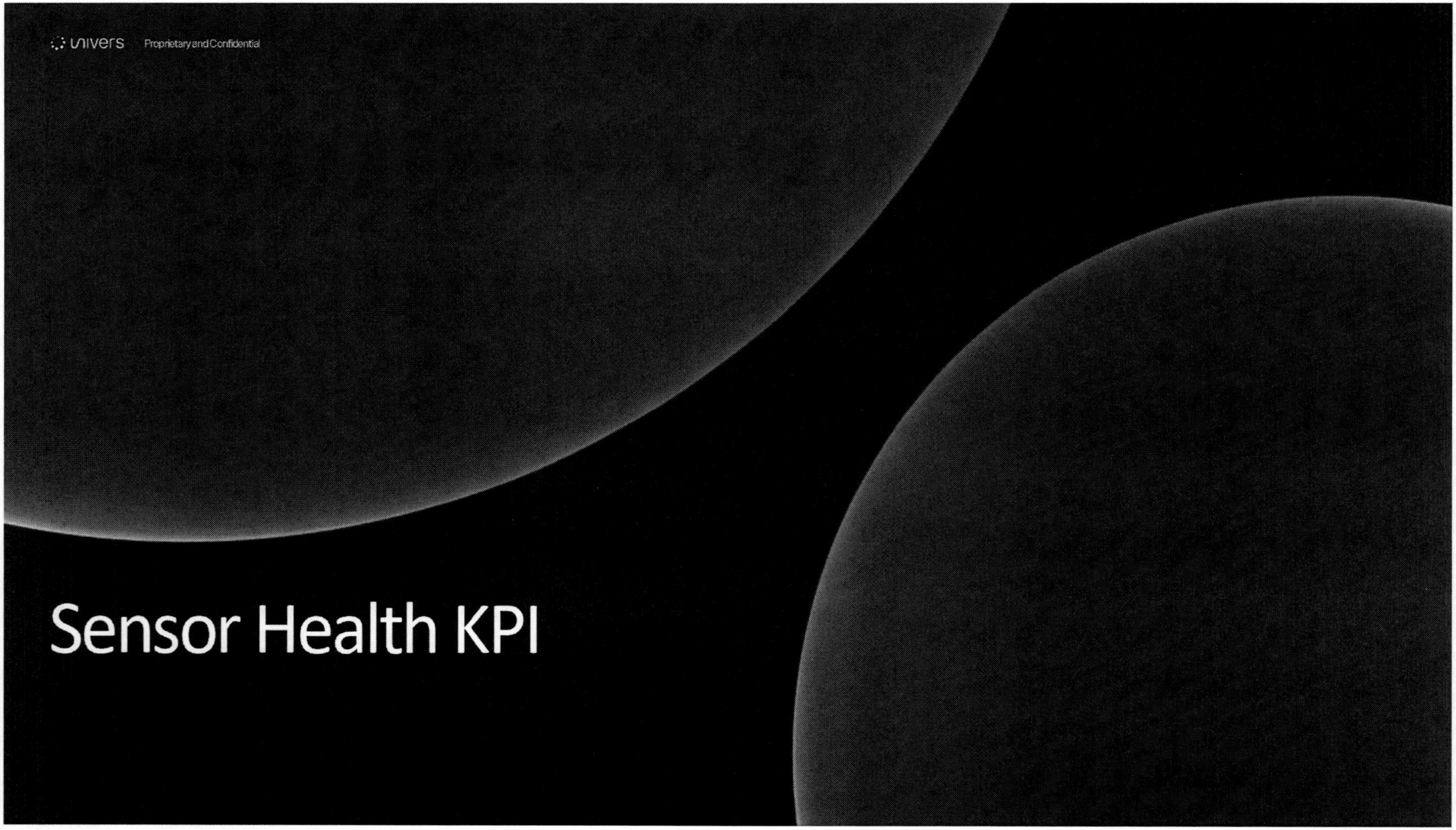
univers
Proprietary and Confidential
Sensor Health KPI

univers Proprietary and Confidential

Definition

- in-house developed daily KPI (0–100) that rates the data quality and reliability of individual irradiance sensors
- used to select the most reliable sensor per inverter for downstream calculations

• 90 – 100	Very good	The sensor is perfoming optimally, with high data quality, validity, and accuracy.
• 80 – 90	Good	The sensor is functioning well, though there may be minor issues.
• 60 – 80	Average	The sensor’s peformance is adequate, but closer attention is needed.
• Below 60 / -99	Failing	The sensor’s performance is subpar and requires attention.

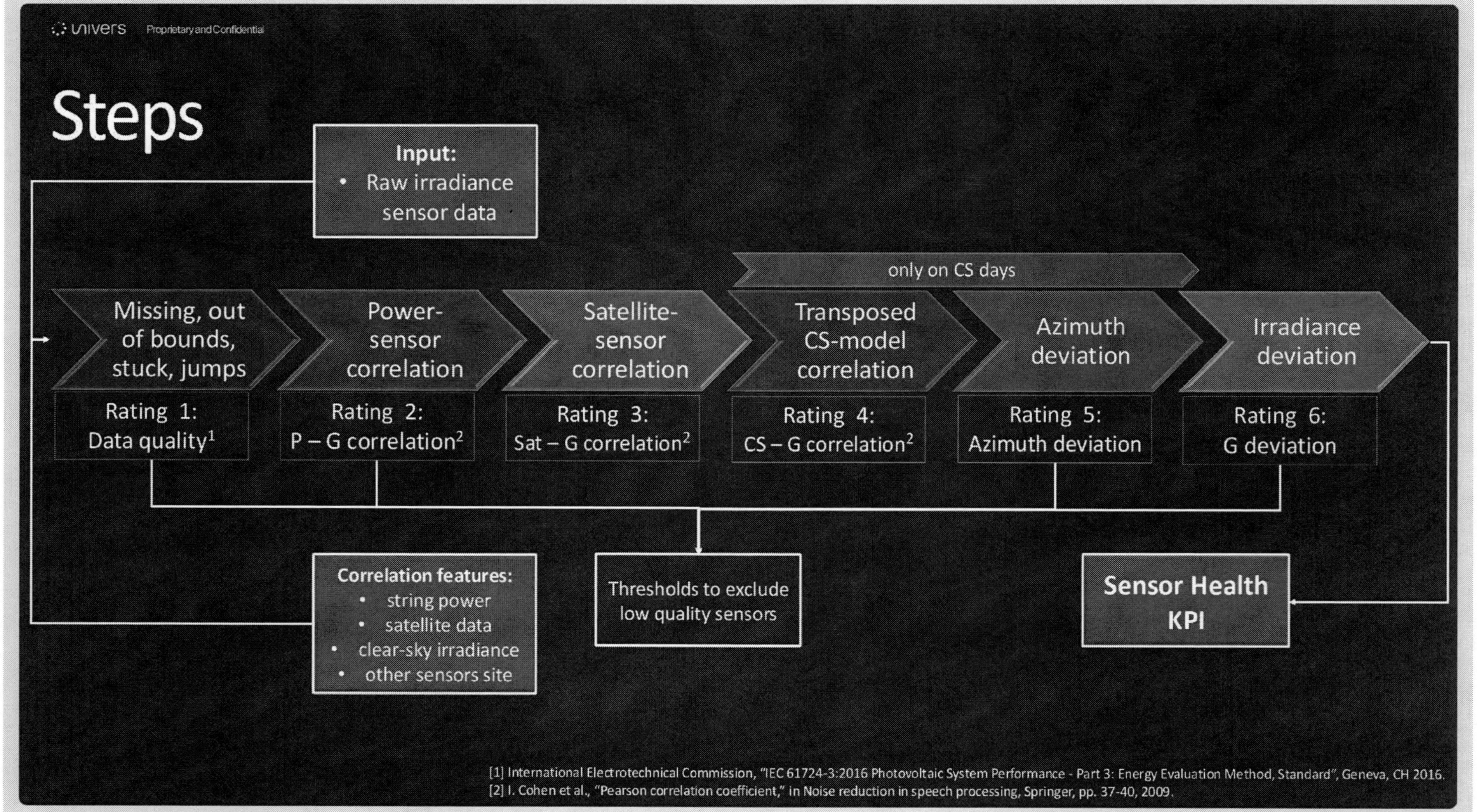
univers Proprietary and Confidential
Steps
Input:
• Raw irradiance sensor data
only on CS days
Missing, out of bounds, stuck, jumps
Power-sensor correlation
Satellite-sensor correlation
Transposed CS-model correlation
Azimuth deviation
Irradiance deviation
Rating 1: Data quality[1]
Rating 2: P – G correlation[2]
Rating 3: Sat – G correlation[2]
Rating 4: CS – G correlation[2]
Rating 5: Azimuth deviation
Rating 6: G deviation
Correlation features:
• string power
• satellite data
• clear-sky irradiance
• other sensors site
Thresholds to exclude low quality sensors
Sensor Health KPI
[1] International Electrotechnical Commission, "IEC 61724-3:2016 Photovoltaic System Performance - Part 3: Energy Evaluation Method, Standard", Geneva, CH 2016.
[2] I. Cohen et al., "Pearson correlation coefficient," in Noise reduction in speech processing, Springer, pp. 37-40, 2009.

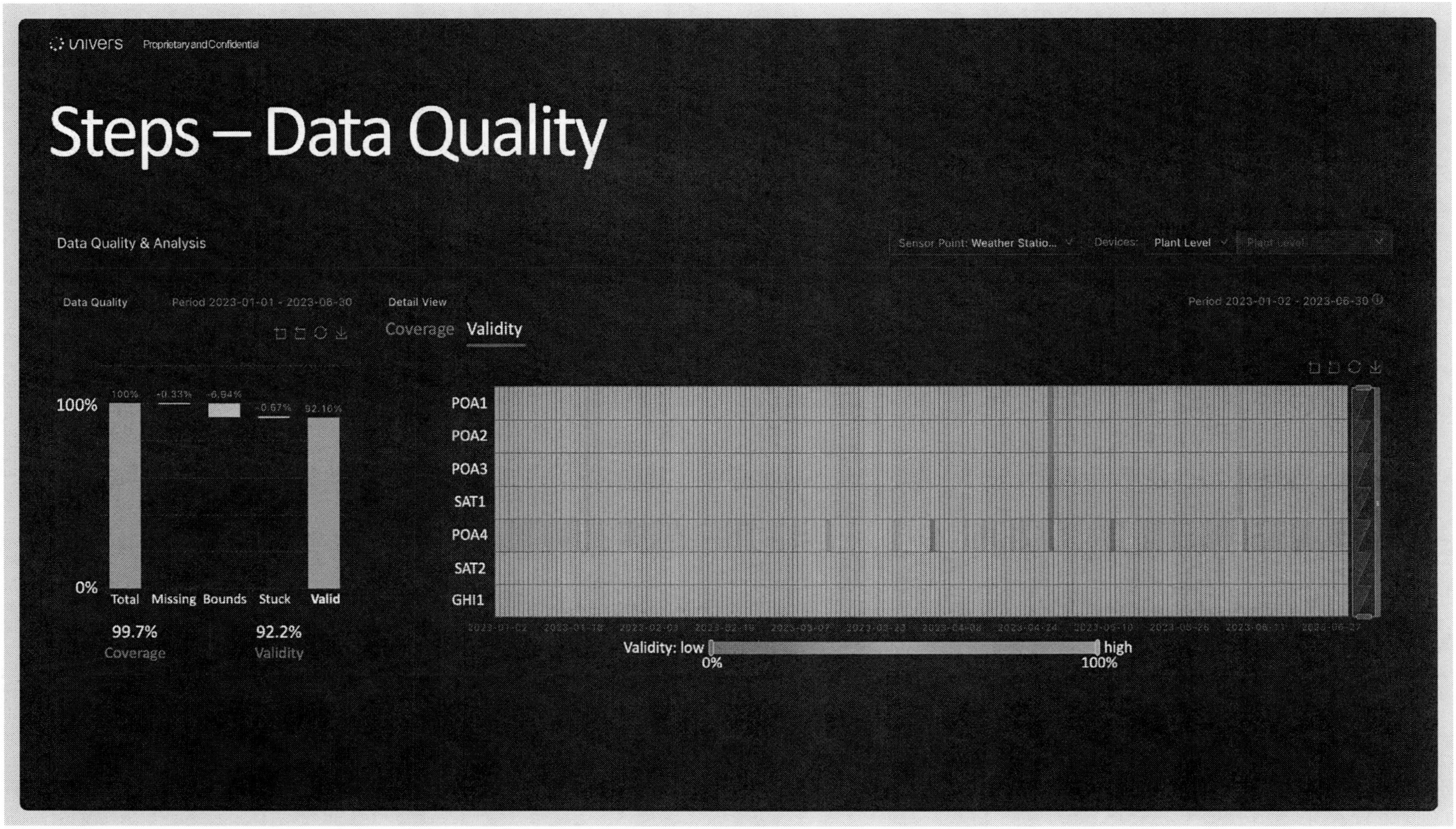
univers
Proprietary and Confidential
Steps – Data Quality
Data Quality & Analysis
Sensor Point: Weather Statio...
Devices: Plant Level
Data Quality
Period 2023-01-01 - 2023-08-30
Detail View
Coverage
Validity
Period 2023-01-02 - 2023-06-30
100%
0%
100%
-0.33%
-6.94%
-0.67%
92.16%
Total
Missing
Bounds
Stuck
Valid
99.7%
Coverage
92.2%
Validity
POA1
POA2
POA3
SAT1
POA4
SAT2
GHI1
Validity: low
high
0%
100%

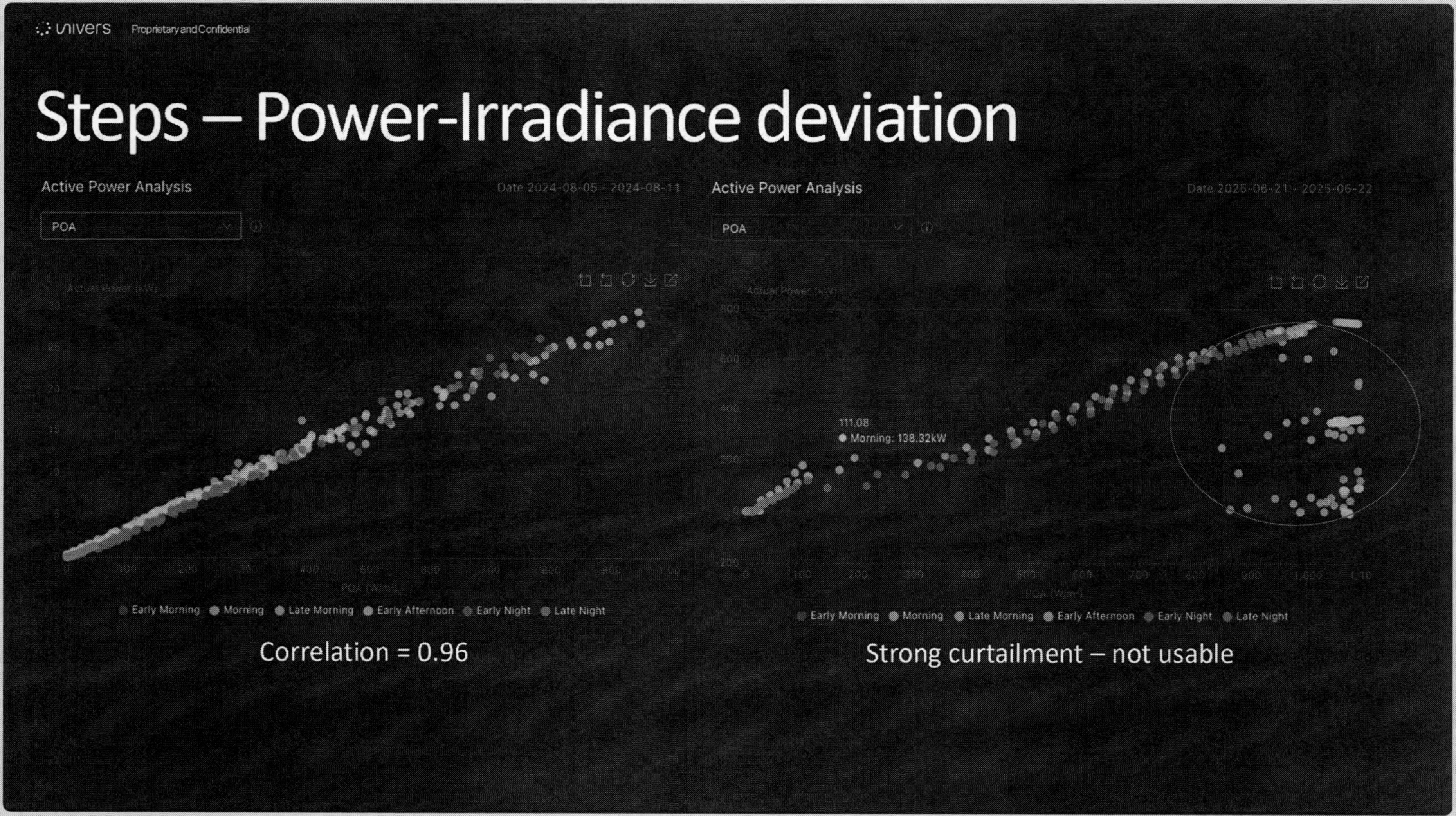
univers
Proprietary and Confidential
Steps – Power-Irradiance deviation
Active Power Analysis
Date 2024-08-05 - 2024-08-11
POA
Early Morning
Morning
Late Morning
Early Afternoon
Early Night
Late Night
Correlation = 0.96
Active Power Analysis
Date 2025-06-21 - 2025-06-22
POA
111.08
Morning: 138.32kW
Early Morning
Morning
Late Morning
Early Afternoon
Early Night
Late Night
Strong curtailment – not usable

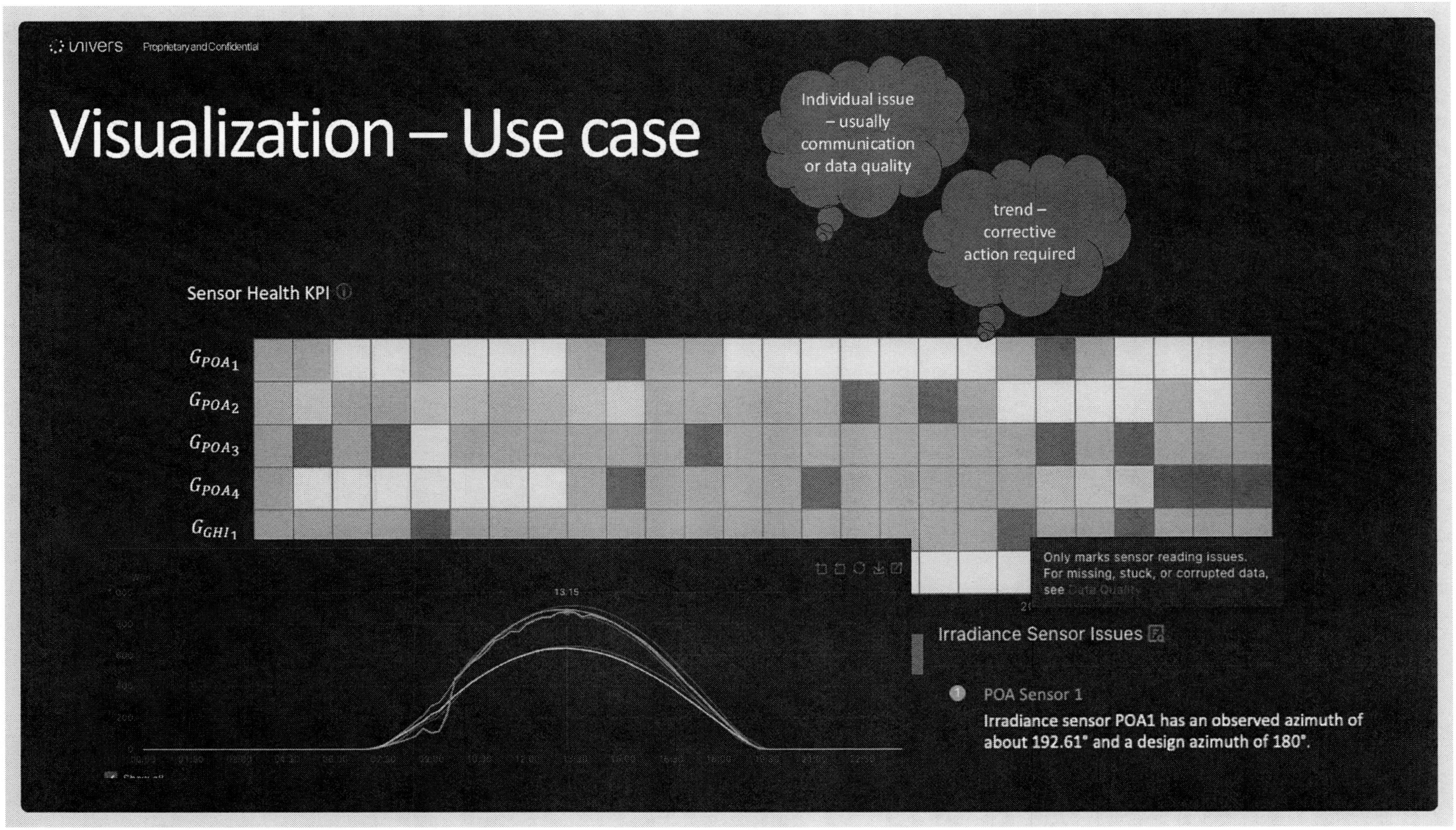
univers
Proprietary and Confidential
Visualization – Use case
Individual issue – usually communication or data quality
trend – corrective action required
Sensor Health KPI
G_{POA_1}
G_{POA_2}
G_{POA_3}
G_{POA_4}
G_{GHI_1}
13:15
Only marks sensor reading issues.
For missing, stuck, or corrupted data,
Irradiance Sensor Issues
POA Sensor 1
Irradiance sensor POA1 has an observed azimuth of about 192.61° and a design azimuth of 180°.

univers Proprietary and Confidential

Sensor Selection

Priority	Irradiance Source	Description
1	Assigned POA sensor	**User-defined** preferred choice
2	Backup POA sensor	**User-defined** 2nd preferred choice
3	Average POA	Mean across all well functioning POA sensors
4	Highest rated POA sensor	POA sensor with highest sensor health KPI
5	Transposed assigned GHI sensor	**User-defined** preferred GHI choice
6	Transposed average GHI	Transposed irradiance of mean across all well functioning GHI sensors
7	Transposed highest rated GHI sensor	Transposed GHI sensor with highest sensor health KPI
8	Satellite POA	Irradiance from onboarded satellite POA source
9	Transposed satellite GHI	Transposed irradiance from onboarded satellite GHI source

univers Proprietary and Confidential

Wrong assignment

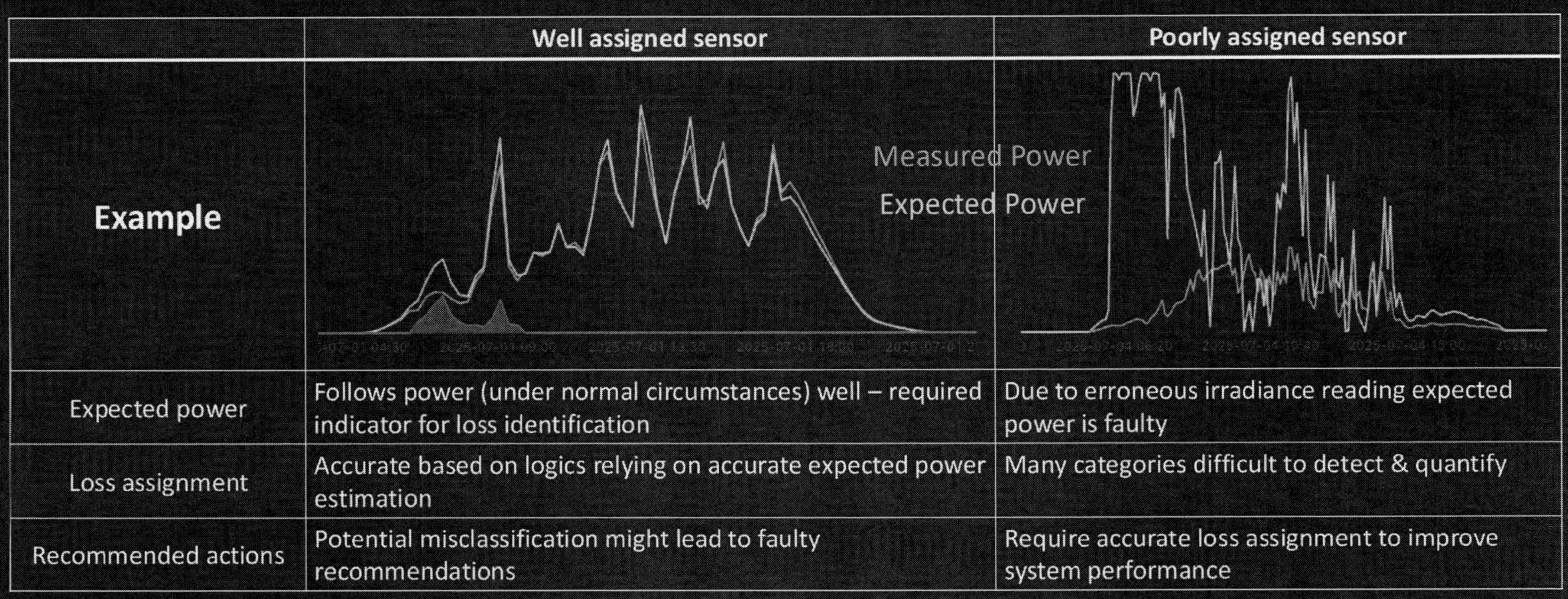

	Well assigned sensor	Poorly assigned sensor
Example	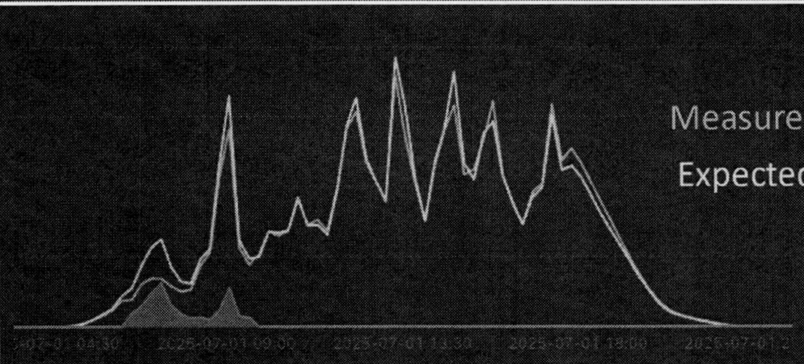	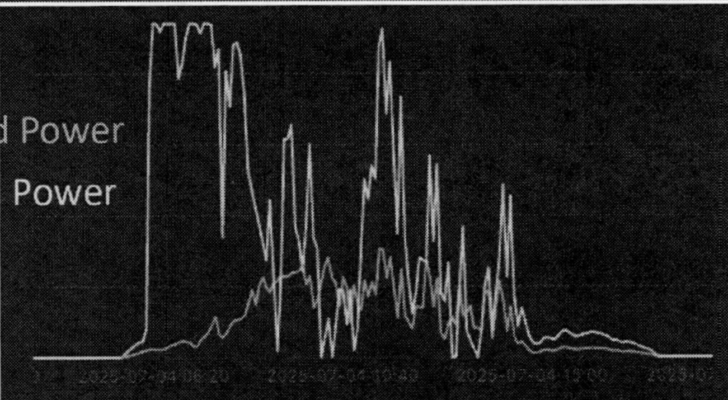
Expected power	Follows power (under normal circumstances) well – required indicator for loss identification	Due to erroneous irradiance reading expected power is faulty
Loss assignment	Accurate based on logics relying on accurate expected power estimation	Many categories difficult to detect & quantify
Recommended actions	Potential misclassification might lead to faulty recommendations	Require accurate loss assignment to improve system performance

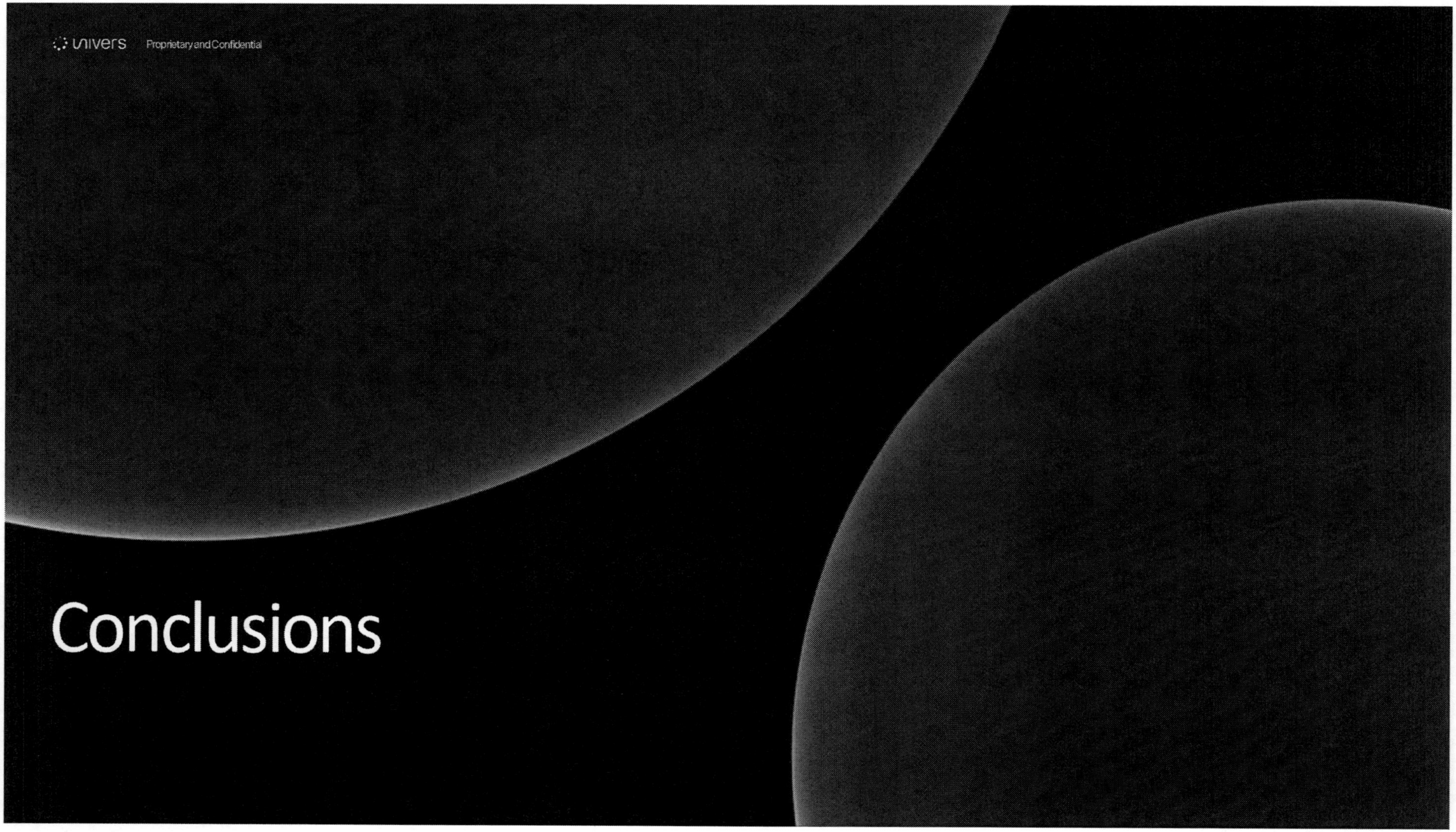
univers
Proprietary and Confidential
Conclusions

univers Proprietary and Confidential

Conclusions

- development of a new KPI to rate irradiance sensor data
  - ➢ accuracy-efficiency trade-off to find best possible source
  - ➢ On-site sensor care will go a long way!!!
- Why not employing “more sophisticated” AI methodologies?
  - ➢ computational speed
  - ➢ universal applicable – edge cases
  - ➢ transparency -> reporting to stakeholder
    - ➢ justification of why specific sensors are selected

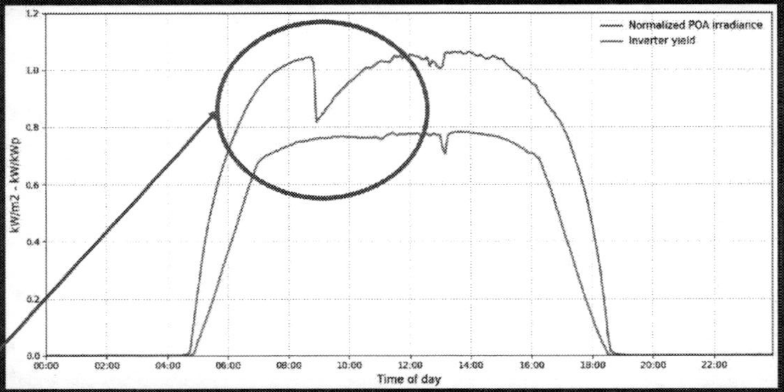

- Future improvements
  - ➢ account for tracking issues in SAT sites
  - ➢ ensure SH-KPI has no bias or blind spots
  - ➢ additional fail-safe logic for small & strongly curtailed sites with low amount of sensors

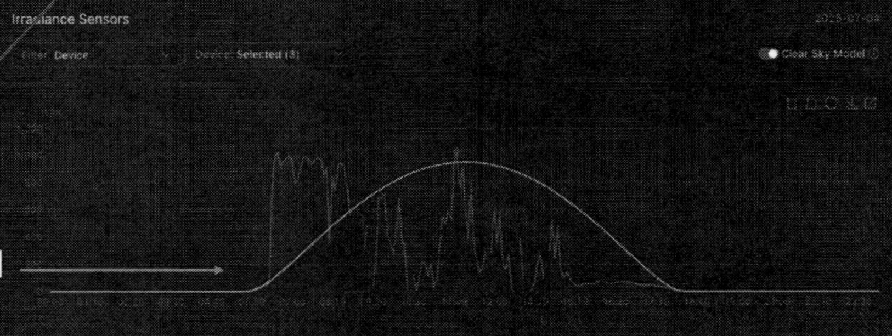

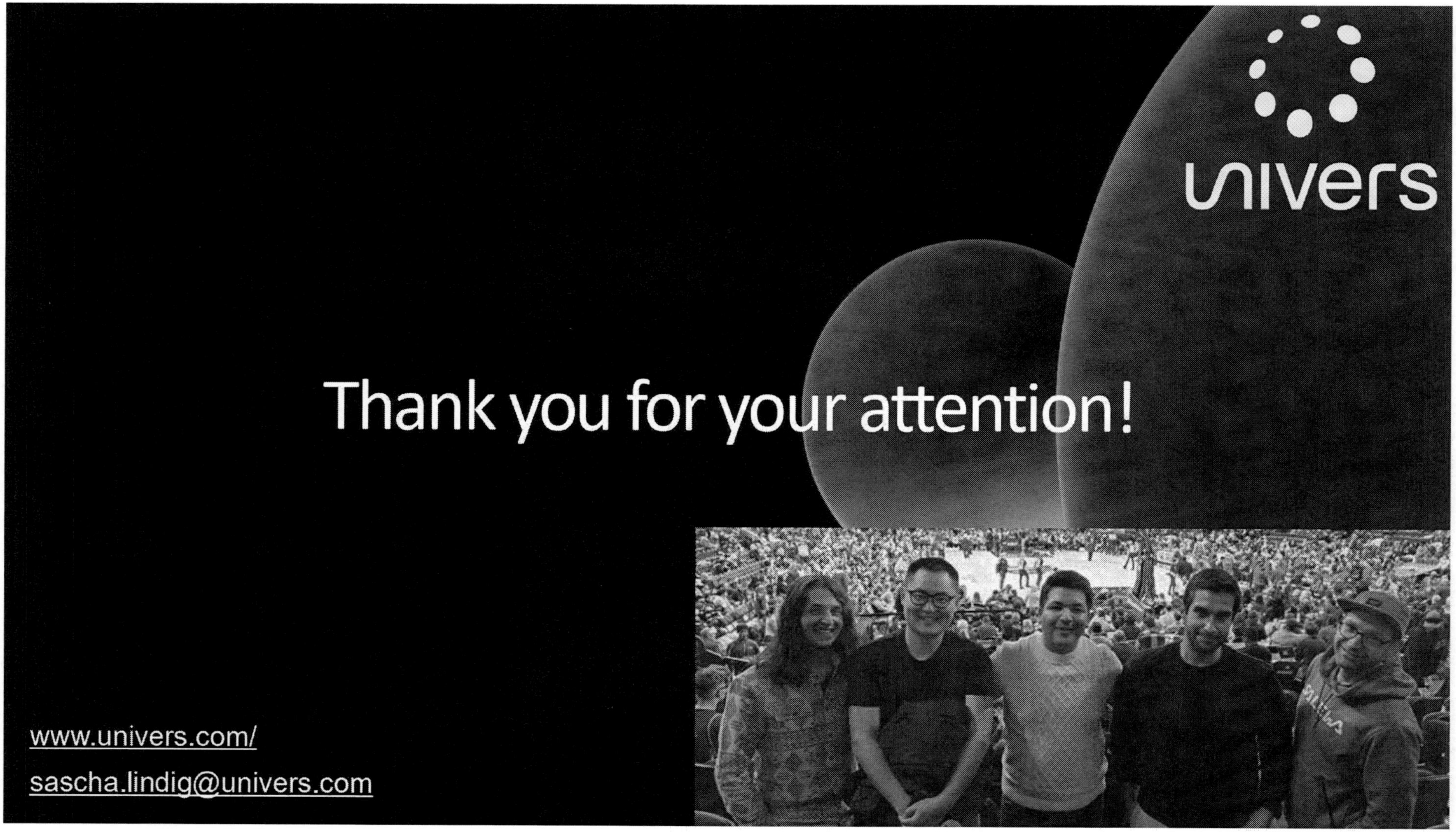
univers
Thank you for your attention!
www.univers.com/
sascha.lindig@univers.com

EU PVSEC 2025

INES INSTITUT NATIONAL DE L'ENERGIE SOLAIRE

cythelia ENERGY

trace software

Measurement and Analysis of Bifacial Gain for Commercial & Industrial PV Systems: Impact of Building Structure and Environmental Factors

-

Pierre Besson[1], Jean-Francois Lelièvre[1], Antoine Dizier[1], Ismael Lokhat[2], Benoit Lelong[3]
[1] INES Training and Expertise Department; [2] Trace Software; [3] Cythelia Energy

Jean-François LELIEVRE – jf.lelievre@ines-solaire.org

25/09/2025

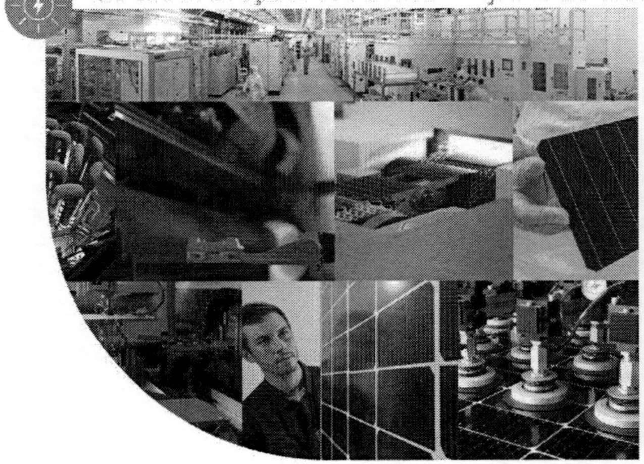

PLATEFORME FORMATION & ÉVALUATION

Bifacial Gain for Commercial & Industrial PV Systems

INSTITUT NATIONAL DE L'ENERGIE SOLAIRE

cythelia ENERGY

PLATEFORM

3

The Promise vs. Reality

INES INSTITUT NATIONAL DE L'ENERGIE SOLAIRE

- Simulations & lab tests: 5 to 25% energy gain (!)
- Theoretical benefits well known
  but local conditions can reduce or cancel them
  → Real installations face shadows, non uniform albedo, **rear irradiance and temperature inhomogeneities**
- Simulation tools oversimplify albedo & rear irradiance
  → *Field data is key to refine models*
- Lack of detailed field data for C&I systems
  → Help for **better design** and **improve energy yield**

A Real-World Laboratory

INES INSTITUT NATIONAL DE L'ENERGIE SOLAIRE

- **70 kW_p bifacial PV system**
- 214 Soluxtec bifacial PV modules (330 W_p)
- Enphase IQ7+ Micro-inverters on each module
- 10 front & rear irradiance sensors + 3 thermocouples + meteorologial station
- 10-min resolution, **2-year period monitoring**

A Real-World Laboratory

- 2 representative C&I PV sub-systems
- **<u>Flat Rooftop:</u> 28 kW$_p$**
  3 PV modules converted to monofacial

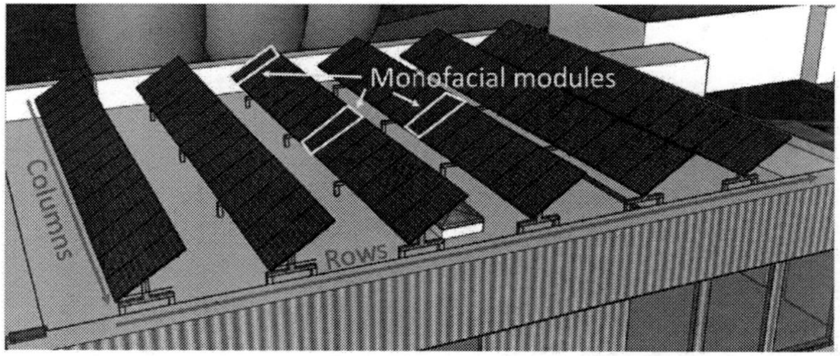

- **<u>Carport:</u> 43 kW$_p$**
  Impact of the carport structure and building

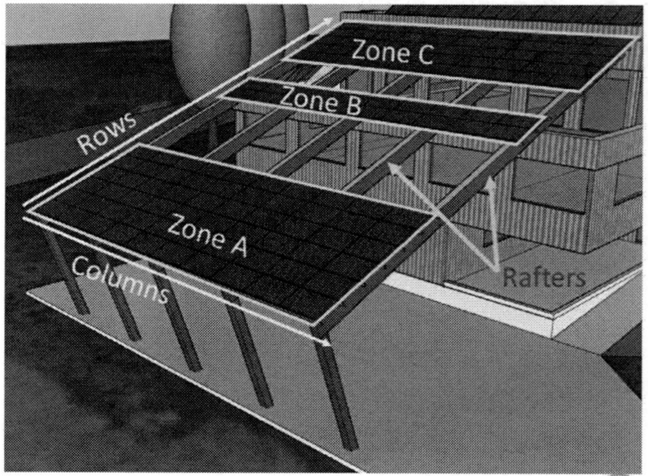

- *Nearby shading due to vegetation and neighbouring buildings has been modelled and the data filtered accordingly*

Flat rooftop – 28 kW_p : the simple case

- 1.5m height – 20° Tilted – Albedo= 30%
- Soluxtec 330W_p bifacial modules
  PERC+ solar cells – BiFi=70%
- *3 PV modules converted to monofacial*
  → **Real bifacial gain**

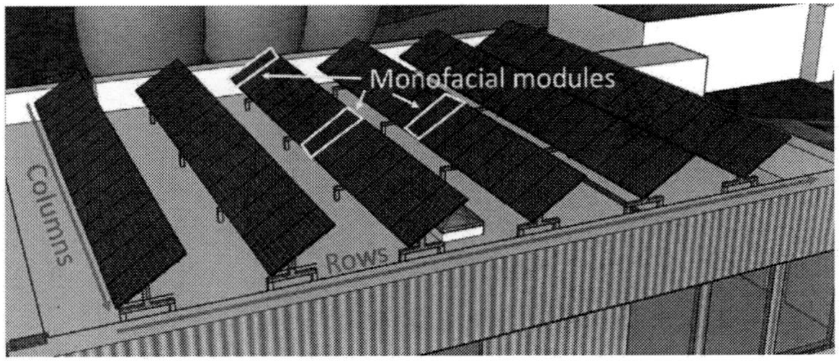

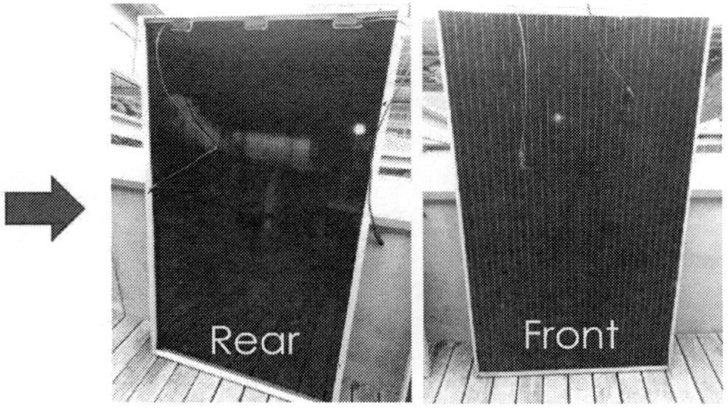

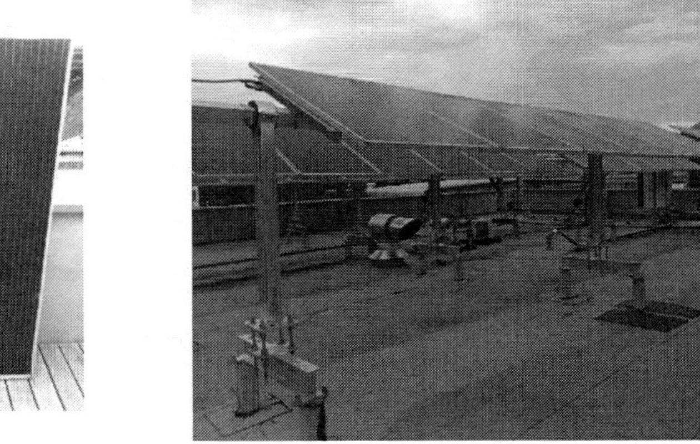

Rear-side irradiance & irradiation

Hourly irradiance – Front & Rear

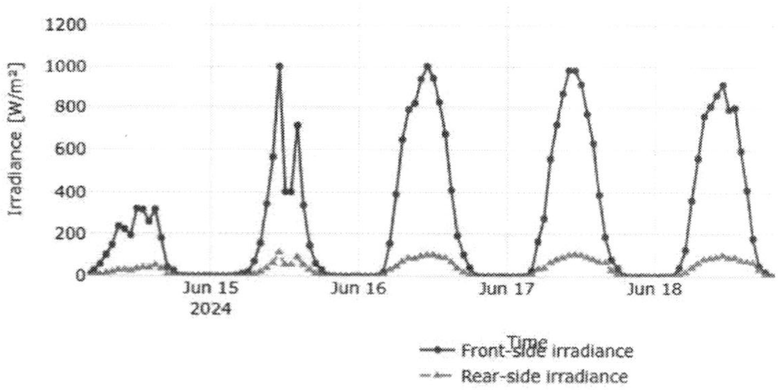

Irradiation and Rear/Front ratio

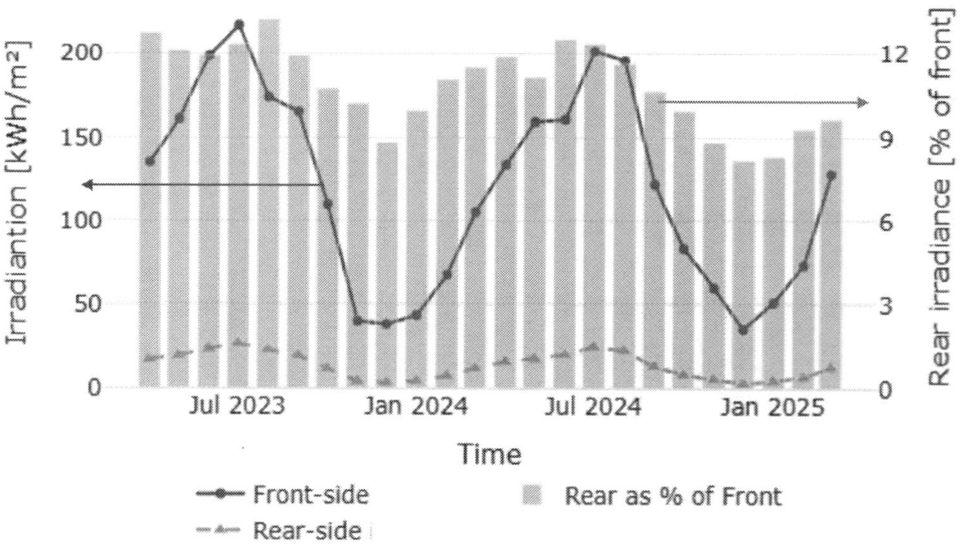

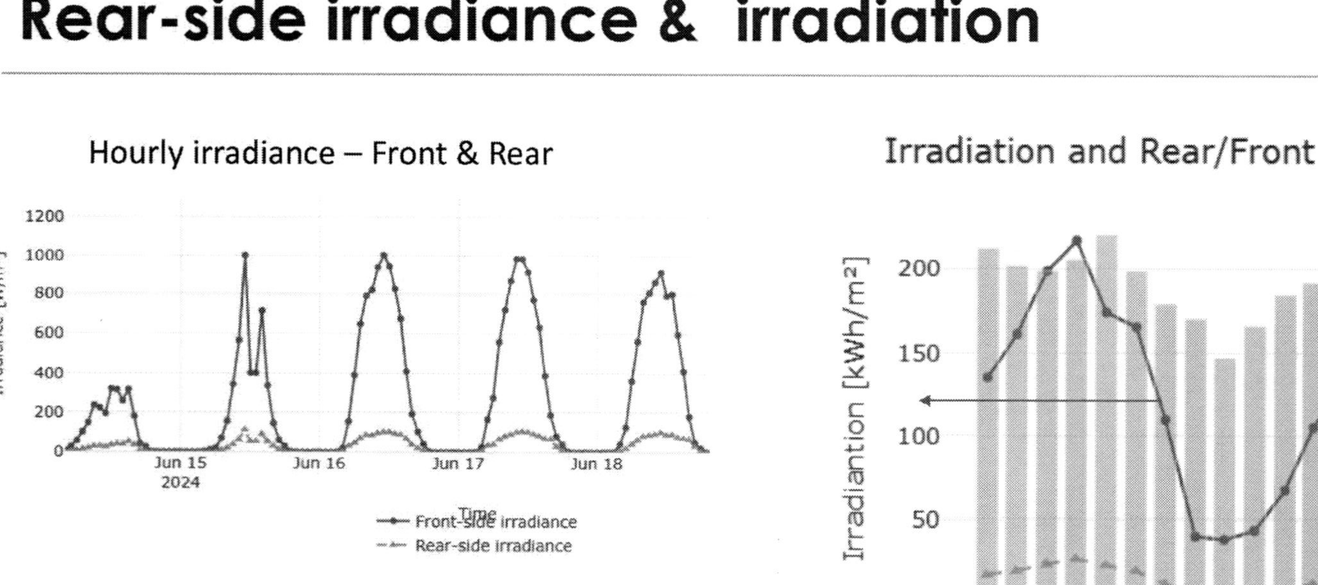

- 8-12% rear irradiation gain
  → *Favourable albedo and height*
- Seasonal effects

Energy distribution & Bifacial gain

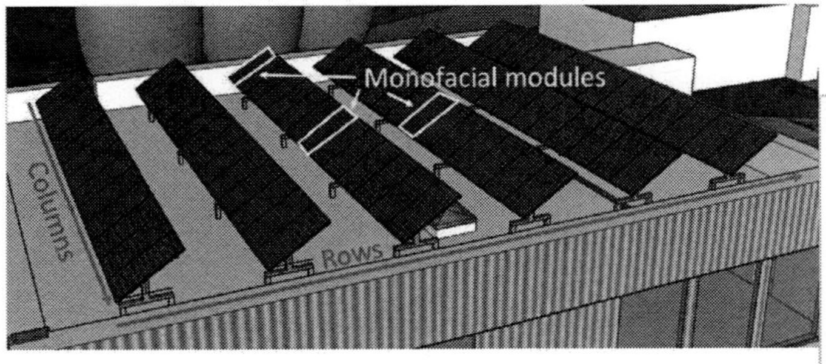

- *Homogeneous installation conditions*
- **Significant but not fully uniform bifacial energy gain**
- Higher relative gain at PV system edges (S & E)

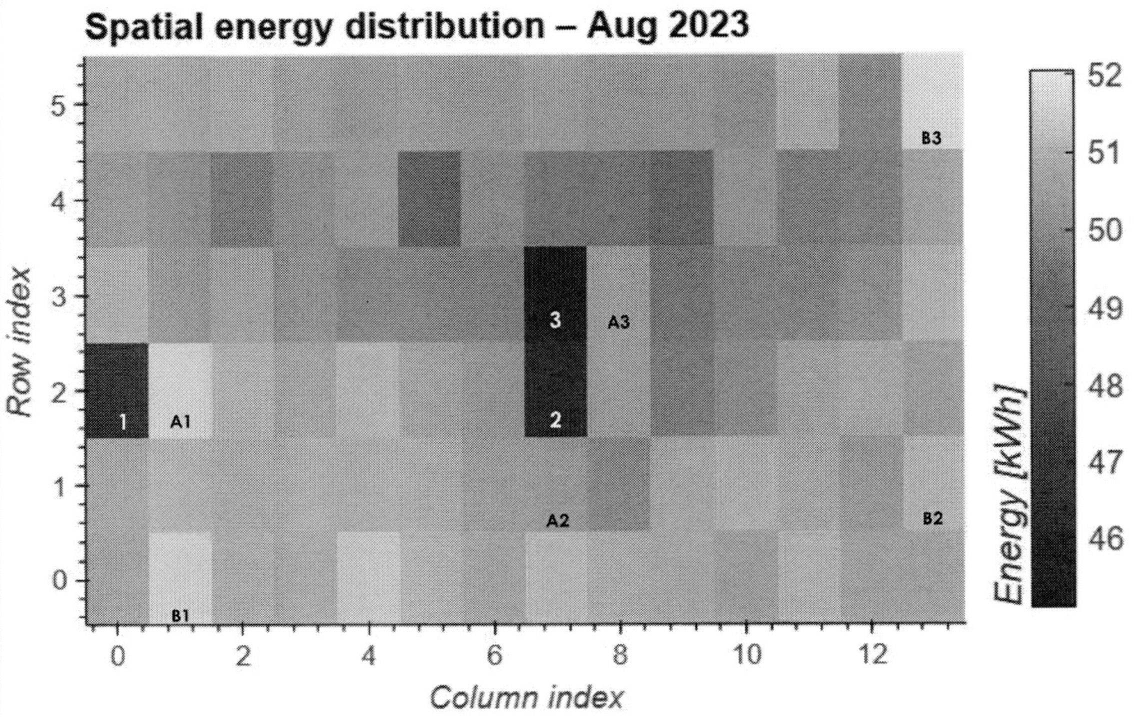

Energy distribution & Bifacial gain

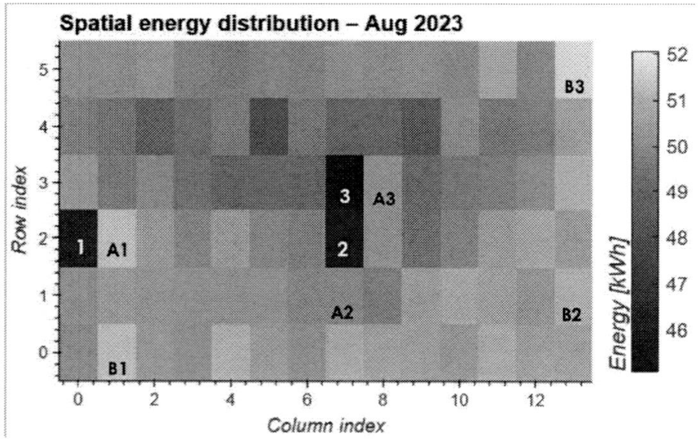

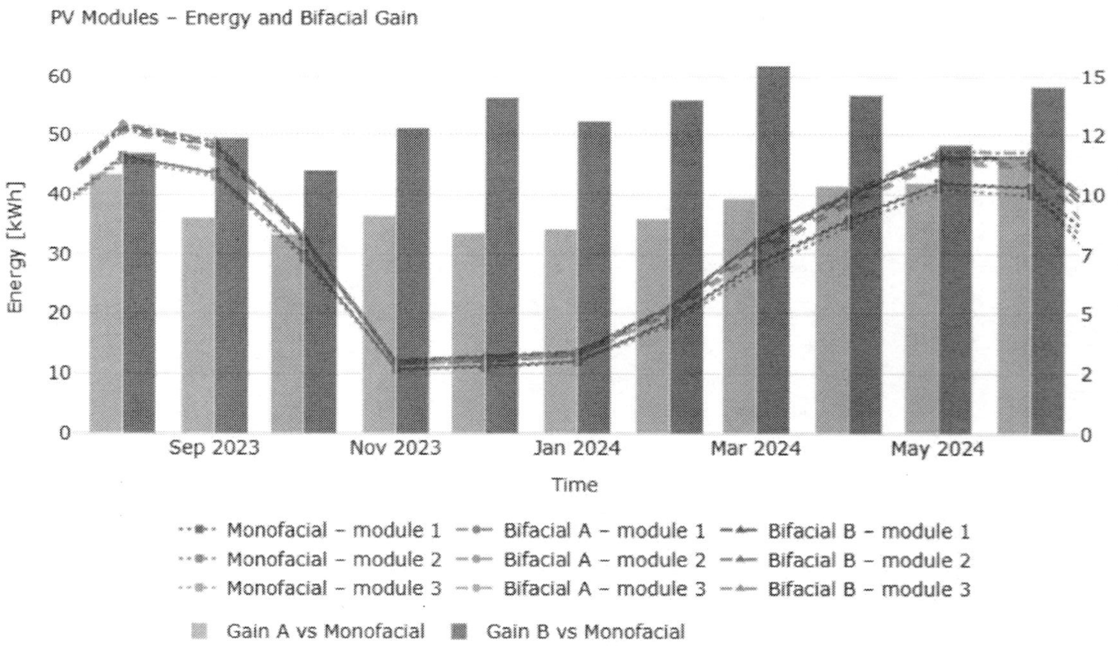

- **8 to 11% real absolute bifacial gain**
- Higher relative gain at PV system edges
- Small but non negligeable **3% current mismatch** in such homogeneous installation conditions → *cabling*

PLATEFORME FORMATION & ÉVALUATION

P. Besson et al. – EUPVSEC 2025

10

Carport – 43 kW_p : Rear Side Heterogeneity

INES – INSTITUT NATIONAL DE L'ENERGIE SOLAIRE

- Design phase vs. Reality

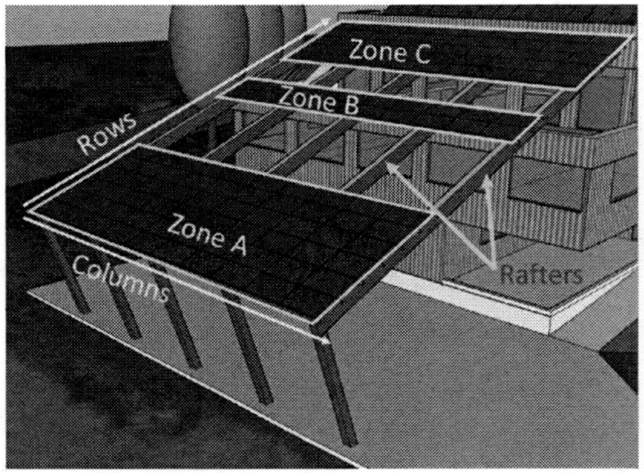

Carport – 43 kW_p : Rear Side Heterogeneity

INES INSTITUT NATIONAL DE L'ENERGIE SOLAIRE

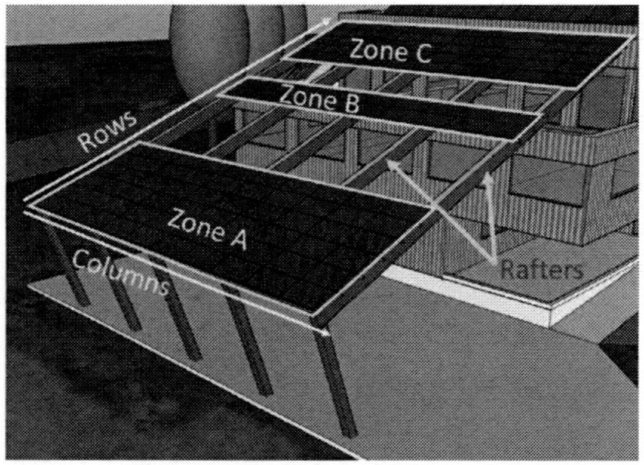

Carport – 43 kW_p : Rear Side Heterogeneity

INSTITUT NATIONAL DE L'ENERGIE SOLAIRE

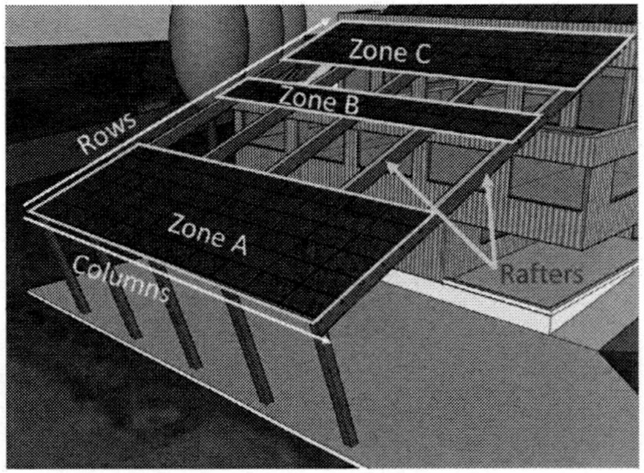

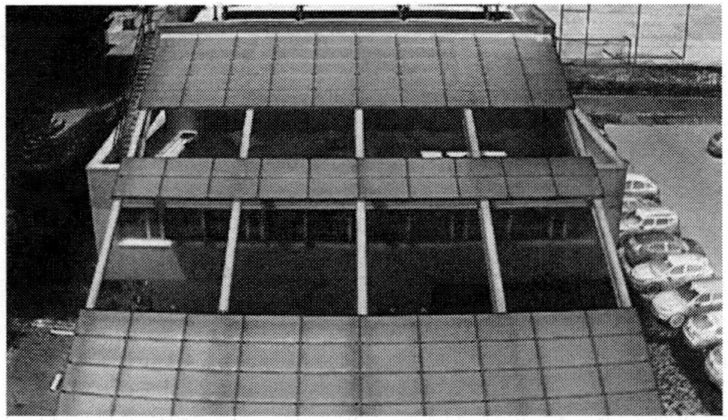

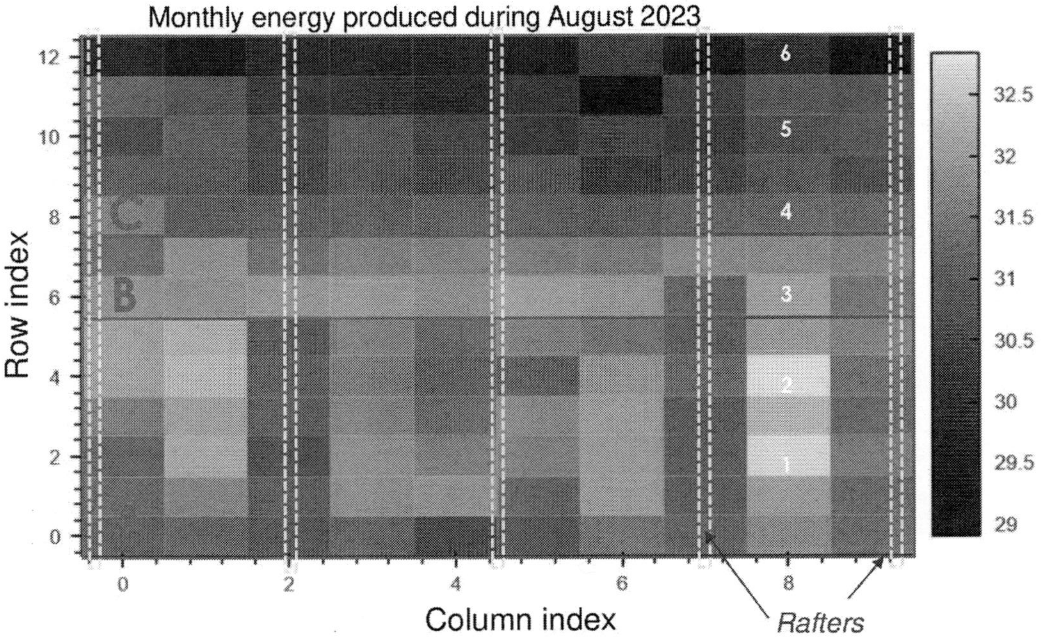

- **Impact of the carport/shading structure**
  → *up to 5% current mismatch along a row*
- Combined effect of **reduced rear side irradiance** and **higher temperature** near building

Carport – 43 kW_p : Rear Side Heterogeneity

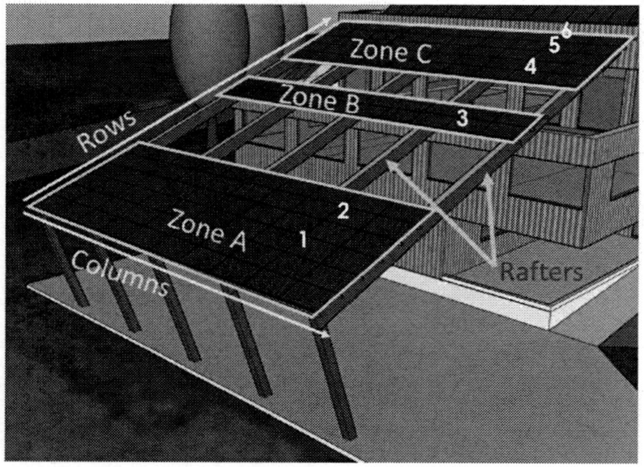

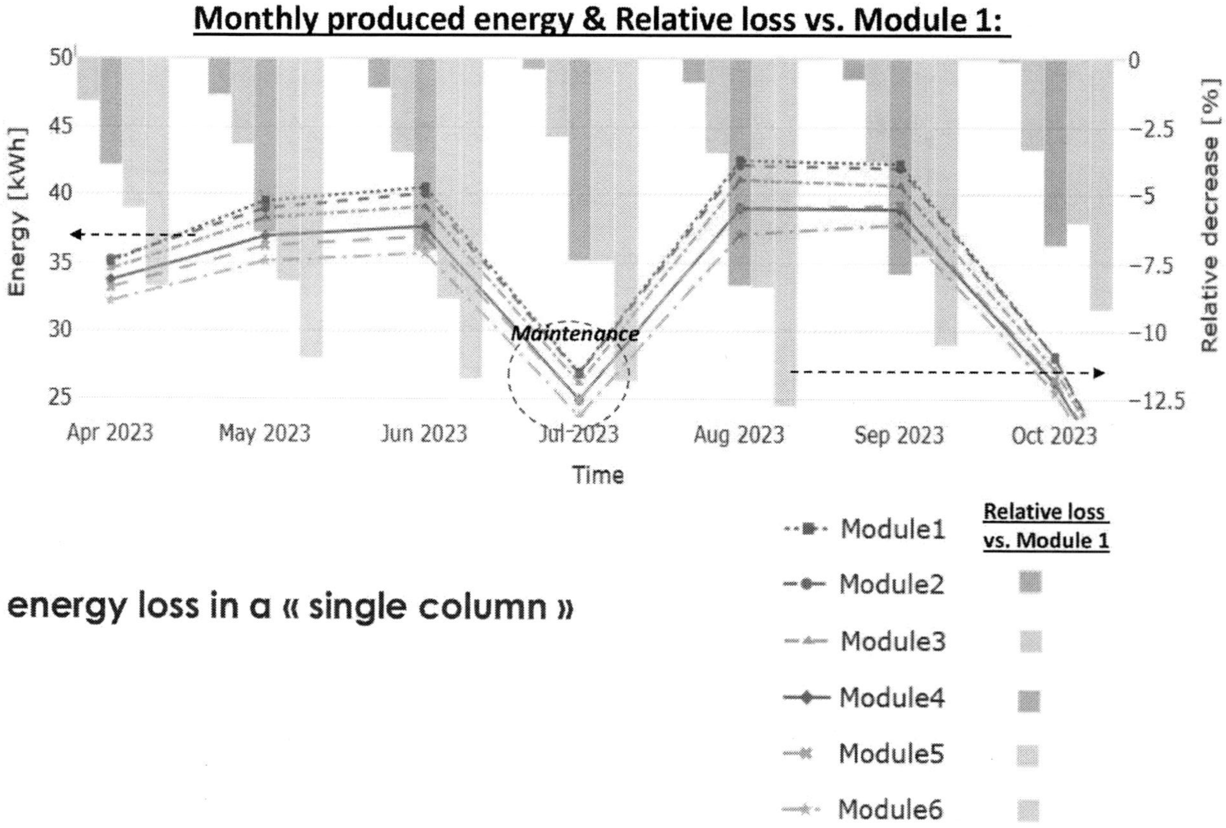

- Up to -12.5% relative monthly energy loss in a « single column »

When Temperature Cancels the Gain

Modules – Current over time

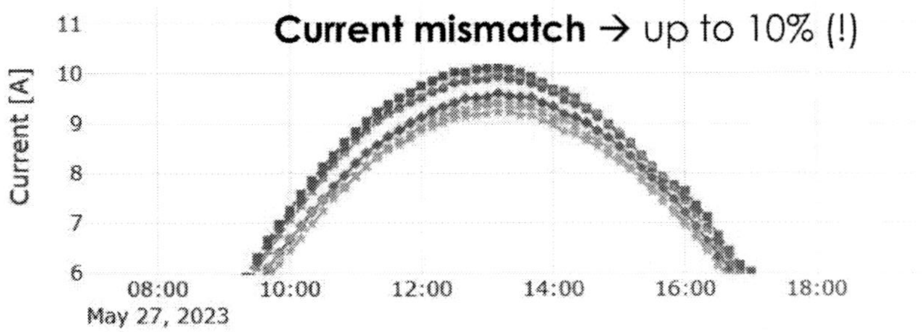

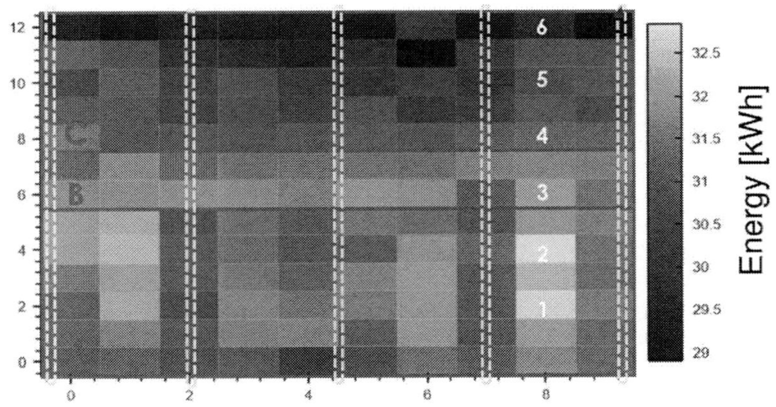

Modules – Voltage over time

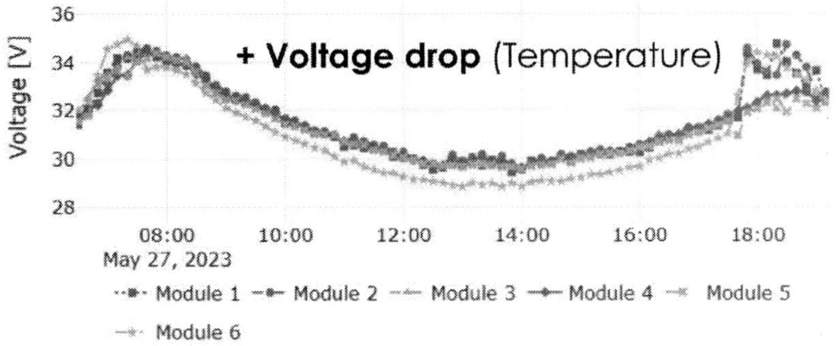

Module temperature (estimated from V & I)

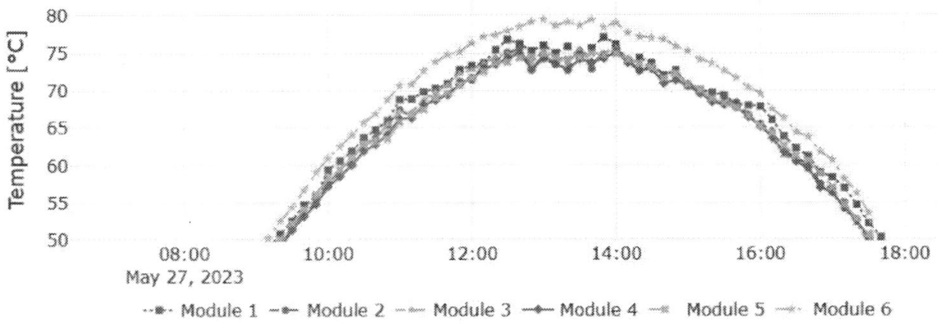

Conclusion

INSTITUT NATIONAL DE L'ENERGIE SOLAIRE

- Flat Rooftop: reliable bifacial gain (8 to 11%)
  → Edge effect lead to additional 3% relative bifacial gain (and current mismatch)

- Carport: rear side irradiance heterogeneity + temperature increase near building
  → Up to 10% relative **current mismatch**
  → Difficult to simulate overall bifacial gain

- Non-uniform PV module degradation (T) may increase current mismatch

- *Points to watch out for when designing PV systems for C&I buildings:*
  → **Cabling** according to specific configurations (string inverters)
  → Micro-inverters and power-optimizers may be beneficial

- Simulation tools (PVlib, PVsyst, Archelios PRO)
  must handle **heterogeneity** *and rear-side shading losses*
  → Bridge the gap between models & reality

EU PVSEC 2025

INSTITUT NATIONAL DE L'ENERGIE SOLAIRE

Thanks for your attention

Jean-François LELIEVRE | jf.lelievre@ines-solaire.org

www.ines-solaire.org

PV Training Catalogue

INES
INSTITUT NATIONAL DE L'ENERGIE SOLAIRE

- Consulting, sizing, design, installation, operation and maintenance
  - **35 PV training courses in the catalogue** (face-to-face, 100% online or hybrid)
  - **1 900 m² technical and teaching facilities**
  - **Short, long, certifying and tailor-made trainings**

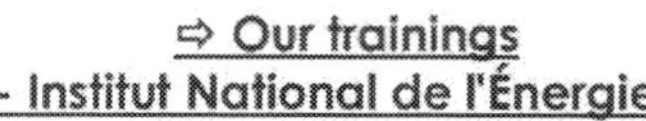

Qualiopi processus certifié
RÉPUBLIQUE FRANÇAISE
La certification qualité a été délivrée au titre de la catégorie d'action suivante :
- Actions de formation

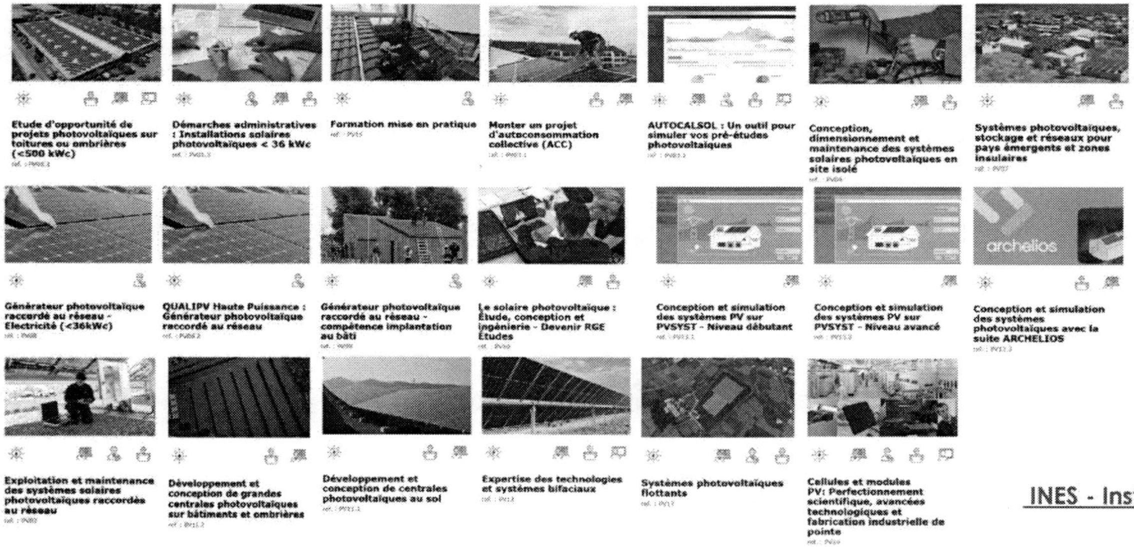

Qualit'EnR

QUALIFELEC

RGE OPQIBI
L'INGÉNIERIE QUALIFIÉE
Efficacité énergétique ENR

⇨ Our trainings
INES - Institut National de l'Énergie Solaire

Photovoltaic Expertise services

ines
INSTITUT NATIONAL DE L'ENERGIE SOLAIRE

Consulting & Audits for professionals

- Review of technical documentation
- Study of innovative markets (technologies, economic models, etc.)
- Analysis on design or production (due diligence)
- Data analysis, specific R&D work

Installators | Design office | Developers | Energy unions | Chamber of Agriculture

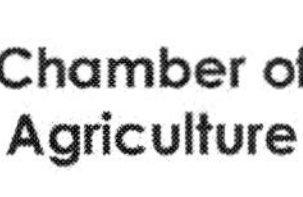

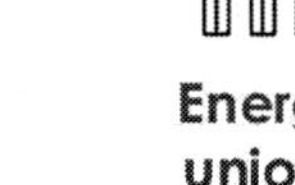

Contracting authority support

- Solarization strategies, advice on regulatory requirements
- Global feasibility study
- Support for consulting with companies, critical review of bids
- Field performance audits for operating facilities

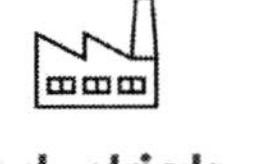

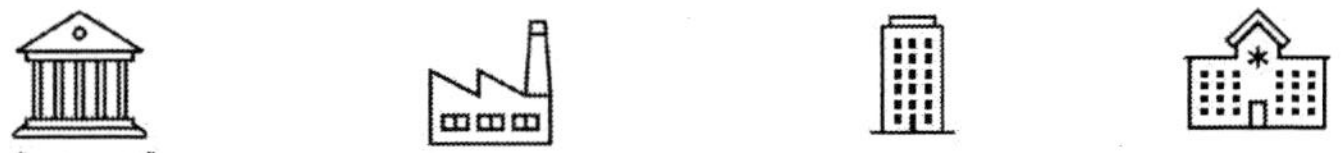

Local authorities | Industrials | Lenders | C&I

MODEL OPTIMIZATION FOR MULTI-CLASS REAL TIME UAV THERMAL ANOMALY DETECTION IN SOLAR PV SYSTEMS

G. Taghipour Kani [1], S.M. Esmailifar [1], A. Ghahremani[1], and M. Aghaei[2,3*]

[1] Department of Aerospace Engineering, Amirkabir University of Technology, Tehran 15119-43943, Iran
[2]Department of Ocean Operations and Civil Engineering, Norwegian University of Science and Technology (NTNU), 6009 Ålesund, Norway
[3]Department of Sustainable Systems Engineering (INATECH), University of Freiburg, 79110 Freiburg, Germany

* mohammadreza.aghaei@ntnu.no

ABSTRACT: This study investigates an intelligent UAV-based thermal inspection framework for photovoltaic (PV) modules, aiming to improve fault detection accuracy while ensuring suitability for real-time aerial deployment. Utilizing deep learning techniques, the system evaluates and compares multiple Convolutional Neural Network (CNN) architectures and YOLO classifiers for multi-class thermal anomaly detection. A comprehensive dataset of 20,000 aerial infrared images, categorized into nine distinct fault classes, was used to assess each model's classification performance and computational efficiency. CNNs such as EfficientNet and ResNet50 achieved strong classification results, with EfficientNet reaching an accuracy of 84%. However, their high inference latency and large model sizes pose challenges for onboard processing in UAV-based systems, particularly under power and memory constraints. Alternatively, the YOLO family of models demonstrated a compelling balance of speed, compactness, and accuracy. Among them, YOLOv8n offered exceptional runtime performance with an inference time of just 8 ms and a model size of 2.94 MB, making it ideal for lightweight deployment. At the same time, YOLOv8l achieved a Top-1 accuracy of 83.02% after hyperparameter tuning. The study highlights how YOLO classifiers can outperform traditional CNNs in practical UAV deployment scenarios, maintaining high accuracy while significantly reducing computational costs. The findings underscore YOLO's viability as a scalable and efficient solution for real-time PV anomaly detection, supporting the main goal of autonomous and cost-effective solar farm maintenance.

Keywords: UAV-based monitoring; thermal anomaly detection; photovoltaic modules; convolutional neural networks (CNNs); YOLO classifiers; real-time inspection; PV fault detection

1 INTRODUCTION AND MOTIVATION

The growing demand for renewable energy has led to a rapid expansion of photovoltaic (PV) installations globally. As solar farms scale up, maintaining their performance and detecting faults in a timely manner becomes increasingly critical. Undetected anomalies such as hot spots, diode failures, or module cracking can significantly reduce energy output, impacting the overall system efficiency and lifespan. Traditional inspection methods including manual walk-throughs, infrared thermography using handheld devices, and electroluminescence imaging, are labor-intensive, time-consuming, and often impractical for large-scale solar farms. These approaches fail to provide the responsiveness required for real-time maintenance, particularly when instant anomaly detection is essential to minimize operational downtime [1-5].

The convergence of UAV (Unmanned Aerial Vehicle) technology, infrared imaging systems, and machine learning has introduced promising alternatives for automated PV monitoring. UAVs equipped with thermal cameras can perform rapid, non-contact inspections across vast areas, also, machine learning models can process thermal imagery to identify and classify a wide range of PV anomalies [6-8].

One notable system, RoboPV, developed by Moradi Sizkouhi et al. [9], exemplifies this integration by combining autonomous UAV navigation with fault detection capabilities. However, despite its strengths in visual inspection and automation, existing solutions often fall short in terms of real-time responsiveness when deployed onboard UAVs. Specifically, the challenge lies in selecting a model that balances classification accuracy with computational efficiency, ensuring deployment feasibility within the hardware constraints of UAVs.

To address this challenge, the present study proposes a comprehensive framework for model optimization tailored to UAV-based thermal anomaly detection in PV farms. We conduct a comparative evaluation of Convolutional Neural Networks (CNNs) and YOLO (You Only Look Once) classifiers using a dataset of 20,000 aerial infrared images spanning nine PV fault categories. While CNNs like EfficientNet offer high classification accuracy, their deployment is hindered by inference latency and model size. In contrast, YOLO models demonstrate substantial promises for real-time onboard deployment due to their lightweight architecture and high-speed inference. The key contributions of this work are as follows:

- A multi-class thermal image dataset comprising diverse PV anomalies is curated and preprocessed for model training.
- A comparative study is conducted across several CNN architectures and YOLO classifiers, considering both classification and computational metrics.
- A hyperparameter tuning process is employed to improve model efficiency and accuracy, especially for real-time UAV operations.
- The best-performing models are analyzed for practical integration into UAV-based inspection workflows, highlighting the trade-offs and deployment strategies.

By optimizing both detection performance and operational efficiency, this study provides actionable insights for developing intelligent UAV-based inspection platforms in large-scale solar energy systems.

1.2 Dataset Description

The dataset used in this study comprises 20,000 aerial infrared images, each labeled into one of nine distinct classes representing various PV module conditions. Eight of these classes correspond to common anomalies found in operational solar farms, such as diode failures, vegetation obstruction, or surface cracking, while one class represents normal, defect-free modules. This diverse composition ensures that the dataset closely reflects real-world scenarios encountered during solar PV farm inspection [10, 11]. All images were captured using UAVs equipped with high-resolution mid-wave and long-wave infrared sensors, covering wavelengths between 3 and 13.5 µm. Depending on the sensor and altitude, the ground sampling distance (GSD) varied between 3.0 and 15.0 cm per pixel, ensuring adequate thermal granularity for detecting subtle anomalies.

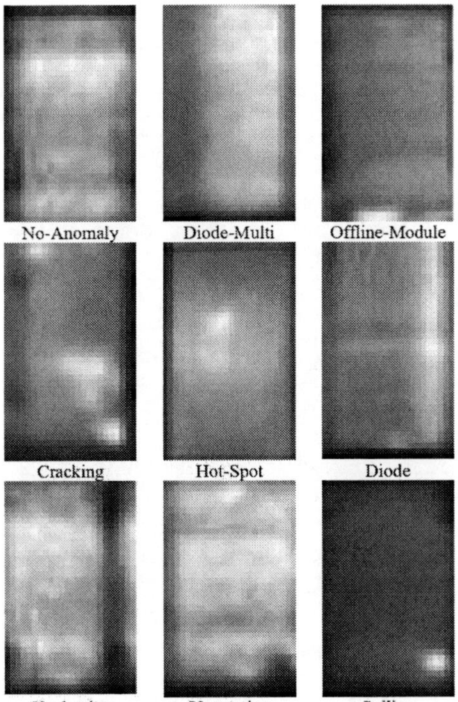

Figure 1. Representative sample images from each of the nine classes in the dataset, showcasing the variety of thermal anomalies and the no-anomaly condition in PV modules.

Class distribution was intentionally imbalanced to reflect operational conditions in large PV farms, where most modules function nominally. The "No-Anomaly" class, comprising half of the dataset (10,000 images), helps the model generalize effectively by exposing it to a wide range of normal patterns. The remaining 10,000 images are distributed among the eight anomaly classes, each representing critical conditions that may lead to performance degradation.

Representative sample images for each class are shown in Figure 1, illustrating the diversity of thermal features across the dataset. For better visual clarity, thermal colormaps were applied to the originally grayscale infrared images, allowing more intuitive observation of temperature differences and localized heat signatures.

Table 1. Dataset Description

Class Name	Number of Images	Description
Hot-Spot	3,663	High-temperature regions indicating faults.
Cracking	941	Surface cracks visible through thermal imaging.
Shadowing	1,056	Obstructions caused by vegetation or structures.
Diode	1,499	Activation of bypass diodes, reducing module efficiency.
Diode-Multi	175	Multiple activated bypass diodes.
Vegetation	1,639	Panels blocked by vegetation.
Soiling	205	Dirt or debris affecting energy generation.
Offline-Module	828	Entire modules disconnected from the circuit.
No-Anomaly	10,000	Defect-free modules.

2. IMPLEMENTING ANOMALY MODELS

2.1 CNN Models

This study evaluated a variety of convolutional neural network (CNN) architectures to identify thermal anomalies in PV modules using aerial infrared imagery. The models were selected based on their popularity in image classification tasks and their diversity in depth, complexity, and computational requirements. Evaluation focused not only on classification performance measured by metrics such as test accuracy and F1 score but also on computational aspects like inference time and model size, which are critical for UAV deployment.

All CNNs were implemented using the TensorFlow framework, chosen for its extensive support for deep learning development and its compatibility with both GPU and embedded hardware environments. To ensure a fair comparison, all models were trained under consistent conditions. The dataset was split into training, validation, and test sets, using an 80–10–10 ratio, and standardized image input sizes of 96×96 pixels were applied across all networks.

Training was performed for up to 600 epochs with a batch size of 32, utilizing the early stopping technique with a patience threshold of 100 epochs to prevent overfitting. This allowed training to stop once validation performance stopped improving, saving computation time and preserving generalizability. Furthermore, data augmentation techniques such as random rotations, horizontal and vertical flips, brightness variation, and zooming, were employed to simulate real-world variations in UAV flight conditions and environmental factors, thus enhancing model robustness.

10.4229/EUPVSEC2025/4DO.17.2

The evaluated CNN architecture ranged from lightweight custom-designed models to well-established deep networks, including:

- Simple CNN: A baseline model with minimal convolutional and dense layers.
- Deep CNN: A deeper variant of the baseline with increased layers and complexity.
- VGG16: A widely used deep model characterized by a fixed set of 3×3 convolution filters and large parameter count.
- DenseNet: An architecture utilizing dense connectivity for improved feature propagation.
- EfficientNet: A compound-scaled network that balances accuracy and efficiency.
- InceptionV3: A multi-scale processing architecture for diverse feature extraction.
- MobileNet: A lightweight model utilizing depthwise separable convolutions, well-suited for resource-limited applications.
- ResNet50: A residual learning network that enables deep model training by mitigating gradient vanishing.

Each of these models offers distinct trade-offs in terms of depth, parameter count, and memory footprint, allowing a comprehensive evaluation of their feasibility for deployment in UAV-based PV inspection platforms. The following section details the performance of each model and their implications for real-time anomaly detection.

2.2 YOLO Classification Models

YOLO (You Only Look Once) classifiers are modern deep learning models engineered for high-speed computer vision tasks such as object detection, classification, and segmentation. Unlike traditional multi-stage pipelines, YOLO performs all tasks in a single forward pass, making it exceptionally fast and suitable for real-time applications such as UAV-based thermal monitoring of solar farms.

In this study, we utilized YOLO models for pure classification purposes by employing classification-specific versions of YOLOv8 and YOLO11. These variants are designed to handle multi-class classification efficiently. This architectural modification reduces computational load while retaining the core benefits of YOLO's backbone and feature extraction layers.

The YOLO models were implemented using the Ultralytics framework, which offers a high-level, modular interface for training and deployment. This framework supports rapid prototyping, GPU acceleration, and straightforward conversion for edge inference, aligning well with the constraints of UAV onboard processing.

A total of 14 YOLO models including .pt-based pre-trained models and .yaml-based custom configurations were trained and evaluated. Consistent training parameters were used across all models:

- Input resolution: 96×96 pixels (to match CNN training)
- Training epochs: Up to 600
- Batch size: 32
- Early stopping: Patience of 100 epochs

Data augmentation was also applied during YOLO training using random horizontal flips, scaling, HSV augmentation, and mosaic augmentation. These augmentations help improve model generalization, especially under variable UAV altitudes, lighting conditions, and vegetation interference.

YOLO classifiers were evaluated based on classification performance (Top-1 and Top-5 accuracy), as well as computational efficiency (inference time and model size). Given that UAV platforms often rely on embedded hardware or edge AI accelerators with limited memory and processing power, inference latency and memory footprint were critical metrics in our selection process.

The results, discussed in later sections, demonstrate that YOLO architectures, particularly YOLOv8n and YOLOv8l, offer a promising balance between high classification accuracy and minimal computational demand. This makes them strong candidates for real-time, onboard fault detection in UAV-based PV inspection systems.

3. TRAINING RESULTS AND MODEL OPTIMIZATION

3.1 CNN Models Results

As summarized in Table 2, the performance of CNN architectures varied significantly in terms of both classification accuracy and computational efficiency. Among the evaluated models, EfficientNet achieved the highest test accuracy (84%) and F1 score (0.837), making it the top-performing CNN for identifying PV module anomalies. Its compound-scaling strategy, which simultaneously balances depth, width, and input resolution, allows it to extract highly discriminative features, contributing to its superior classification performance.

Table 2. Performance Report of CNN Models

CNN Model	Test Accuracy	F1 Score	Inference Time (ms)	Model Size (MB)
Simple CNN	0.751	0.736	76	23.4
Deep CNN	0.620	0.598	144	126.7
VGG16	0.500	0.333	410	186.4
DenseNet	0.791	0.789	2121	110.7
EfficientNet	0.840	0.837	2522	82.4
InceptionV3	0.779	0.770	1200	262.2
MobileNet	0.807	0.808	886	61.3
ResNet50	0.822	0.816	1012	331.9

However, this accuracy came at a computational cost: EfficientNet's inference time was measured at 2522 ms, and its model size reached 82.4 MB. These figures indicate significant processing and memory requirements, making EfficientNet less suitable for real-time deployment on UAV platforms where latency and power efficiency are critical.

ResNet50, another high-performing architecture, attained a test accuracy of 82.2% and an F1 score of 0.816. Its residual learning framework facilitates deeper networks by avoiding vanishing gradients, enabling robust learning even with complex data like thermal anomalies. While ResNet50 demonstrated faster inference compared to EfficientNet (1012 ms), its model size of 331.9 MB poses a significant limitation for embedded deployment.

In contrast, MobileNet emerged as the most balanced CNN for real-time applications. With a test accuracy of 80.7%, an F1 score of 0.808, and an inference time of 886 ms, MobileNet offers reasonable classification performance while maintaining a compact model size of 61.3 MB. Its use of depthwise separable convolutions significantly reduces computational complexity, making it well-suited for lightweight deployment on UAVs.

Other models such as DenseNet, InceptionV3, and VGG16 demonstrated moderate to low classification performance or suffered from high computational costs. Notably, DenseNet achieved a decent accuracy of 79.1%, but required 2121 ms for inference and 110.7 MB of memory. The VGG16 model, while historically impactful, performed poorly in this study, highlighting the limitations of older architectures in real-time aerial thermal classification tasks.

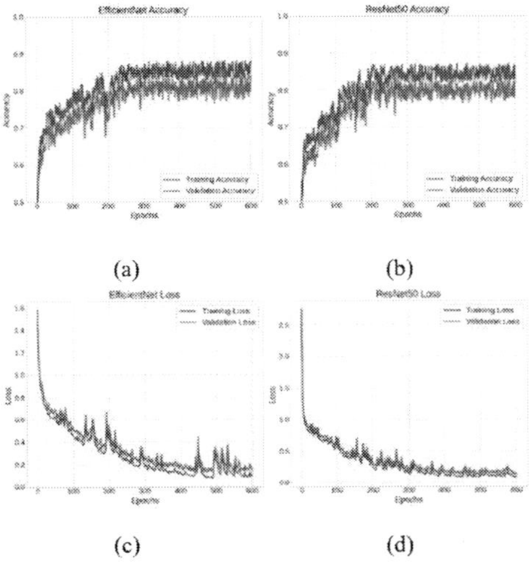

Figure 2. Loss and accuracy curves for two best-performing CNN models: a) EfficientNet accuracy curve, b) ResNet50 accuracy curve, c) EfficientNet loss curve and d) ResNet50 loss curve.

Training and validation learning curves for EfficientNet and ResNet50 (shown in Figure 2) further confirm the robustness of these models. Both displayed steady convergence during training. EfficientNet exhibited consistently higher validation accuracy and lower validation loss across epochs, indicating stronger generalization.

Overall, while CNNs excel at anomaly classification when computational resources are not a constraint, their use in real-time UAV-based monitoring is limited unless compressed or accelerated variants are deployed. In such scenarios, MobileNet offers a feasible trade-off, enabling on-board inference with acceptable accuracy and latency.

3.2 YOLO Classifiers Results

The YOLO classification models were assessed based on their Top-1 and Top-5 classification accuracy, inference time, and model size. These metrics are critical when evaluating model suitability for real-time UAV-based deployment, where processing speed and memory usage must be tightly controlled without sacrificing detection precision.

Table 3. YOLO Model Performance

YOLO Classifier	Top-1 Accuracy	Top-5 Accuracy	Inference Time (ms)	Model Size (Mb)
yolov8l-cls.pt	0.815	0.991	11.0	70.92
yolov8l-cls.yaml	0.817	0.990	12.07	70.93
yolov8m-cls.pt	0.808	0.992	10.0	30.97
yolov8m-cls.yaml	0.807	0.993	10.0	30.98
yolov8n-cls.pt	0.807	0.992	8.0	2.94
yolov8n-cls.yaml	0.804	0.991	14.0	2.95
yolov8s-cls.pt	0.809	0.990	8.95	10.06
yolov8s-cls.yaml	0.808	0.992	8.0	10.05
yolov8x-cls.pt	0.814	0.993	21.0	109.88
yolov8x-cls.yaml	0.811	0.993	12.0	109.89
yolo11l-cls.pt	0.806	0.991	17.06	25.37
yolo11m-cls.pt	0.802	0.989	14.96	20.44
yolo11n-cls.pt	0.792	0.991	10.0	3.15
yolo11s-cls.pt	0.800	0.990	11.00	10.81
yolo11x-cls.pt	0.810	0.992	16.04	55.71

As shown in Table 3, YOLOv8n-cls.pt stood out for its exceptional computational efficiency. With an inference time of 8 ms and a compact model size of 2.94 MB, it offers ultra-fast processing and minimal memory footprint, ideal characteristics for embedded systems on UAVs. Despite its compact size, it maintained strong classification accuracy with Top-1: 0.807 and Top-5: 0.992, highlighting its robustness even in lightweight configurations.

Meanwhile, YOLOv8l-cls.pt emerged as the most accurate classifier among the tested YOLO variants, achieving a Top-1 accuracy of 0.815 and Top-5 accuracy of 0.991. Its inference time of 11 ms and moderate model size of 70.92 MB place it comfortably within the operational limits of many UAV hardware setups, especially those equipped with edge AI accelerators. Its balance of accuracy and efficiency makes it particularly suitable for large-scale PV farm monitoring where real-time decision-making is essential.

The larger model YOLOv8x-cls.pt also delivered competitive results, with a Top-1 accuracy of 0.814 and Top-5 of 0.993. However, its inference time of 21 ms and model size of 109.88 MB limit its applicability to higher-end platforms, where computational capacity is more abundant.

The performance of YOLO11 models was slightly lower across the board, although YOLO11l-cls.pt provided the best trade-off in this group with 0.806 Top-1 accuracy and 17.06 ms inference time. These models still demonstrated reliable performance but did not surpass their YOLOv8 counterparts in either speed or accuracy.

10.4229/EUPVSEC2025/4DO.17.2
020374-004

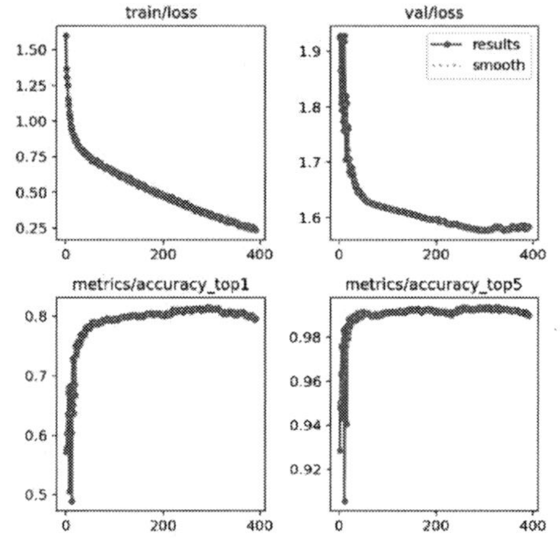

(a)

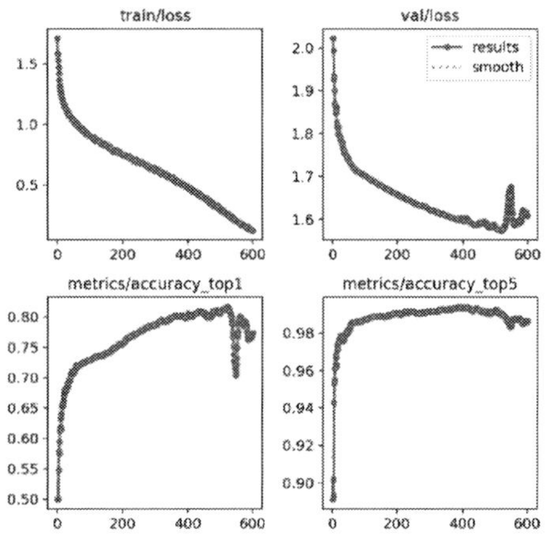

(b)

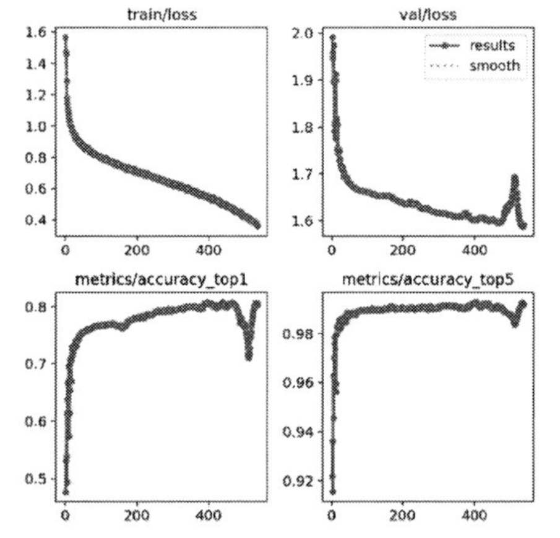

(c)

Figure 3. Loss and accuracy curves for best-performing YOLO classifiers: a) yolov8x-cls.pt training process, b) yolov8l-cls.yaml and c) yolov8n-cls.pt during the training process.

The training and validation curves shown in Figure 3 (for YOLOv8x, YOLOv8l, and YOLOv8n) illustrate consistent convergence patterns and highlight the impact of the built-in early stopping mechanism in the Ultralytics framework. This strategy effectively prevented overfitting by stopping the training once validation metrics stopped improving, thereby saving computational resources and promoting generalization.
Key insights from this evaluation are as follows:

- Performance Trade-offs: YOLOv8l offers the best overall accuracy, while YOLOv8n achieves the lowest inference latency and model size, making each suitable for different UAV deployment scenarios.
- High Top-5 Accuracy: All models consistently exceeded 99% Top-5 accuracy, indicating that even when misclassifications occurred, the correct class remained among the top candidates.
- Real-Time Feasibility: The combination of fast inference times and compact model footprints confirms the YOLOv8 series' viability for real-time thermal anomaly detection on UAVs.

In summary, the YOLO models, particularly those from the v8 series, demonstrate strong classification performance and superior computational efficiency compared to traditional CNN architectures. These traits make them well-suited for deployment in UAV-based PV inspection systems where speed, reliability, and hardware constraints are critical factors.

3.3 Performance Optimization and Model Tuning

To enhance the real-time applicability of YOLO models for UAV-based thermal anomaly detection, a comprehensive hyperparameter tuning was conducted. The aim was to boost classification performance, particularly Top-1 accuracy, while preserving computational efficiency for large-scale solar monitoring. Three models (YOLOv8n, YOLOv8l, and YOLOv8x) were selected due to their strong pre-tuning accuracy and manageable footprints. A grid search explored 30 hyperparameter combinations per model, including learning rates (lr0, lrf), momentum, weight decay, warmup epochs, and augmentation factors (HSV range, scale, mosaic probability). The objective was to improve the fitness score, a composite of accuracy and loss convergence, without increasing inference time or size.
Post-tuning results (Tables 4 and 5) showed clear gains:

- **YOLOv8x:** Fitness 0.902, Top-1 82.13%, Top-5 99.37%. Validation loss decreased with smoother convergence, enhancing generalization. Though still computationally heavy, it is better suited for precision-critical use.
- **YOLOv8n:** Fitness 0.90238, Top-1 82.25%, Top-5 99.23%. Maintained 8 ms inference and 2.94 MB size, reinforcing its role as the best trade-off for resource-limited UAVs.
- **YOLOv8l:** Highest fitness 0.9055, Top-1 83.02%, Top-5 99.17%. Its larger capacity improved detection of subtle anomalies, making it ideal where accuracy and real-time performance must both be met.

Table 4. Tuned Hyperparameter Configurations

Model	lr0	lrf	Momentum	Weight Decay	Warmup Epochs	HSV-H	Scale	Mosaic
YOLOv8x	0.01	0.01	0.937	0.0005	3.0	0.015	0.5	1.0
YOLOv8n	0.0101	0.01112	0.91359	0.00047	2.78907	0.015	0.6	0.99306
YOLOv8l	0.00939	0.01112	0.92606	0.00044	3.01336	0.014	0.488	0.977

Table 5. Tuning Results

Model	Pre-Tuning Accuracy	Post-Tuning Accuracy	Inference Time (ms)	Model Size (MB)
YOLOv8n	0.807	0.822	8.0	2.94
YOLOv8l	0.817	0.830	12.07	70.92
YOLOv8x	0.814	0.821	21.0	109.88

The tuned hyperparameter configurations (Table 4) and resulting performance metrics (Table 5) clearly illustrate the impact of tuning on model effectiveness. Visualizations of normalized confusion matrices (Figure 4) further confirm that class-level misclassifications were reduced post-tuning, especially in minority classes such as "Soiling" and "Diode-Multi," which are often difficult to distinguish in thermal images.

By optimizing these YOLO models, the framework not only achieved better predictive accuracy but also ensured that deployment feasibility on UAV platforms remained intact. This tuning process plays a vital role in closing the gap between high-performance classification and the practical requirements of real-world aerial inspection systems.

(a)

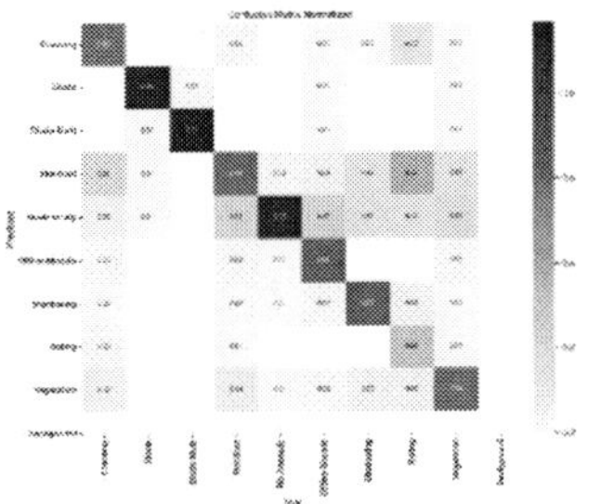

(b)

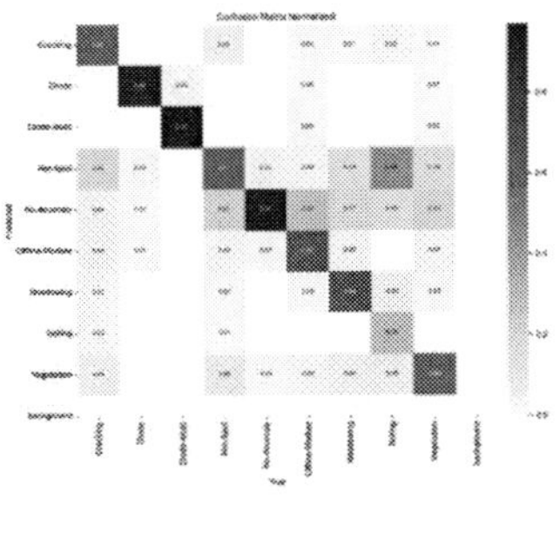

(c)

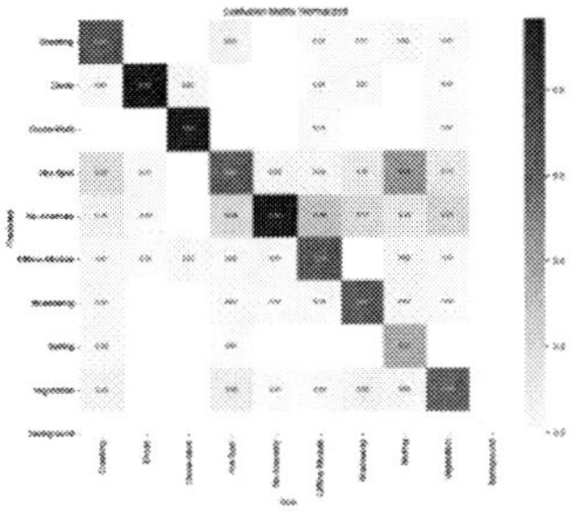

Figure 4. Normalized confusion matrices for tunned YOLO models: a) YOLOv8x, b) YOLOv8n, and c) YOLOv8l.

4 CONCLUSIONS

This study compared CNN and YOLO architectures for UAV-based thermal anomaly detection in PV systems, highlighting the trade-off between accuracy and computational efficiency. CNNs like EfficientNet and ResNet50 achieved strong Top-1 accuracies (84% and 82.2%) but suffered from high inference times (2522 ms and 1012 ms) and large sizes (82.4 MB and 331.9 MB), limiting real-time UAV deployment.

YOLO models proved far more practical. YOLOv8n achieved 82.25% Top-1 accuracy (post-tuning) with just 8 ms inference and a 2.94 MB size, ideal for UAV hardware constraints. YOLOv8l offered the best balance, with 83.02% Top-1 accuracy and 11 ms inference, suitable for missions requiring both precision and speed. All YOLO variants maintained Top-5 accuracies above 99%, confirming robustness in complex solar environments.

Hyperparameter tuning further improved detection, especially for minority classes, without raising computational costs. Overall, YOLO-based classifiers, particularly lightweight and tuned variants, represent a scalable solution for autonomous real-time PV inspection. Their efficiency and adaptability enable intelligent fault detection at scale, reducing downtime, streamlining maintenance, and supporting renewable energy optimization.

5 REFERENCES

1. Sriraman, D. and R. Ramaprabha. *Application of Machine Learning and Convolutional Neural Networks for the Fault Detection and Classification Monitoring System in PV Plants*. in *2023 9th International Conference on Electrical Energy Systems (ICEES)*. 2023.
2. Deitsch, S., et al., *Automatic classification of defective photovoltaic module cells in electroluminescence images*. Solar Energy, 2019. **185**: p. 455-468.
3. Fonseca Alves, R.H., et al., *Automatic fault classification in photovoltaic modules using Convolutional Neural Networks*. Renewable Energy, 2021. **179**: p. 502-516.
4. Nie, J., T. Luo, and H. Li, *Automatic hotspots detection based on UAV infrared images for large-scale PV plant*. Electronics Letters, 2020. **56**(19): p. 993-995.
5. Sinap, V. and A. Kumtepe, *CNN-based automatic detection of photovoltaic solar module*

anomalies in infrared images: a comparative study. Neural Computing and Applications, 2024.

6. Aghaei, M., A. Esksndari, and A. Reinders, *Autonomous Monitoring and Analysis of PV Systems by Unmanned Aerial Vehicles, Internet of Things and Big Data Analytics*. 2020.
7. Eskandari, A., et al., *Autonomous Monitoring of Line-to-Line Faults in Photovoltaic Systems by Feature Selection and Parameter Optimization of Support Vector Machine Using Genetic Algorithms.* Applied Sciences, 2020. **10**(16): p. 5527.
8. Moradi Sizkouhi, A., M. Aghaei, and S.M. Esmailifar, *A deep convolutional encoder-decoder architecture for autonomous fault detection of PV plants using multi-copters.* Solar Energy, 2021. **223**: p. 217-228.
9. Moradi Sizkouhi, A.M., et al., *RoboPV: An integrated software package for autonomous aerial monitoring of large scale PV plants.* Energy Conversion and Management, 2022. **254**: p. 115217.
10. Millendorf, M., E. Obropta, and N. Vadhavkar. *Infrared solar module dataset for anomaly detection.*
11. M. Aghaei, et al, *Autonomous Intelligent Monitoring of Photovoltaic Systems: An In-Depth Multidisciplinary Review,* Progress in Photovoltaics: Research and Applications, 2024, https://doi.org/10.1002/pip.3859.

OPTIMIZING AUTONOMOUS AERIAL MONITORING OF PHOTOVOLTAIC POWER PLANTS VIA AN INTEGRATED SOFTWARE PACKAGE AND A DIGITAL TWIN BASED SIMULATION ENVIRONMENT

M. Kolahi[1], S.M. Esmaeilifar[2], A. Moradi Sizkouhi[3], and M. Aghaei[4,5*]

[1] Department of Mechanical Engineering, Faculty of Engineering, University of Isfahan, 81746-73441, Isfahan, Iran
[2] Department of Aerospace Engineering, Amirkabir University of Technology, Tehran 15119-43943, Iran
[3]Department of Electrical and Computer Engineering, Concordia University, Montreal, QC H3G 1M8, Canada
[4]Department of Ocean Operations and Civil Engineering, Norwegian University of Science and Technology (NTNU), 6009 Ålesund, Norway
[5]Department of Sustainable Systems Engineering (INATECH), University of Freiburg, 79110 Freiburg, Germany

*mohammadreza.aghaei@ntnu.no

ABSTRACT: This paper presents an advanced embedded software package tailored for the autonomous aerial monitoring (AAM) of photovoltaic (PV) plants. It employs an encoder-decoder deep learning model to accurately pinpoint the boundary points of the PV plants. Additionally, a unique path-planning algorithm guarantees comprehensive coverage of the monitoring area. A highly precise neural network is also utilized to analyze images in real time, enabling automatic fault detection. To improve performance during inspections, custom decision-making, and maneuvering algorithms are designed to adapt to various flight conditions. To showcase and optimize the software's performance and test autonomous PV monitoring flights and missions, a virtual environment is also presented. This innovative platform allows for the examination of different scenarios and configurations of PV power plants, assessing their impact on the AAM process. It features tools for generating data that enable the development of intelligent monitoring and inspection models. The creation of this platform involved building a digital twin of a PV plant using Unreal Engine, simulating drone flight with AirSim, and expanding the application programming interfaces (APIs) to adapt to various scenarios for evaluating smart monitoring models and collecting datasets. Additionally, a dataset of aerial images was compiled from this platform to train a segmentation model aimed at identifying bird droppings on PV panels.

Keywords: Photovoltaic (PV) plants; Autonomous aerial monitoring (AAM), Artificial intelligence (AI); Digital twin (DT); Fault detection.

1 AIM AND APPROACH

The rapid growth of large-scale photovoltaic (PV) power plants is projected to supply over one-third of global electricity by 2050 [1]. To ensure energy performance and reliability, efficient monitoring strategies are essential as the number and size of PV plants continue to grow [2]. The use of AI and drones for inspections has transformed traditional monitoring methods, offering faster, more accurate assessments while reducing costs [3]. In this regard, we present an advanced embedded software package tailored for the autonomous aerial monitoring (AAM) of PV plants.

This software package is designed to revolutionize PV plant monitoring and inspection by providing an autonomous, efficient, and intelligent aerial inspection solution. It uses advanced deep learning and drones to facilitate real-time analysis during aerial inspections. It aims to improve the reliability and speed of detecting faults in large-scale PV plants, overcoming the limitations of traditional human-operated methods and significantly reducing inspection time.

When utilizing AI techniques for monitoring PV plants, one of the main challenges is the difficulty in obtaining a substantial set of annotated data [4]. Public datasets are often limited [3], [5], and conducting field flights to gather data or testing autonomous flights with intelligent models can be both costly and risky, as errors might lead to damage to either the drone or the PV panels. To address these challenges, this paper also introduces a digital twin (DT)-based environment designed for developing, simulating, and evaluating different smart monitoring models in the context of AAM of PV plants. This virtual testing environment is essential for evaluating our autonomous flight missions, incorporating aspects such as boundary detection, path planning, and fault detection, thus offering an important understanding of their abilities and possible efficiency in practical situations. Additionally, this framework enables efficient augmentation of our dataset with labeled images, which is useful for training a robust intelligent fault detection model.

Our approach for developing this environment involved first creating a virtual model of a utility-scale PV plant using the Unreal Engine. Subsequently, we conducted drone flight simulations with AirSim, expanding its Python APIs to test various monitoring models in defined scenarios. Through these contributions, our work aims to advance monitoring applications for PV systems, with a focus on optimizing the AAM of large-scale PV plant monitoring.

2 SCIENTIFIC INNOVATION AND RELEVANCE

2.1 Integrated Software Package

The proposed software automates inspections, path planning, image acquisition, fault detection, and decision-making. As Figure 1 provides, the software consists of four key units: i) A boundary detection module that Uses an encoder-decoder network to define the PV plant's boundaries before inspection. ii) A path planning module that generates an optimal flight path, ensuring full coverage of the PV area, is tailored to the drone's capabilities, such as endurance and maneuverability. iii) A dynamic processing unit that monitors flight data, allowing for real-time decision-making and remedial actions during inspections. Additionally, it allows the drone to maneuver closer to detected faults for detailed

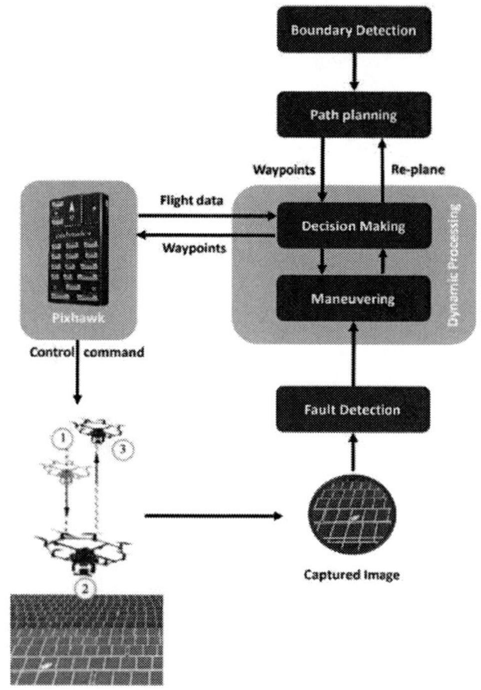

Figure 1: An overview of the proposed software package in AAM of a PV plant.

analysis and adjusts the flight plan based on battery levels, ensuring efficient operation. iv) A fault detection module that Processes video streams from PV modules to identify defects and locate their positions accurately [6].

Boundary Detection: Boundary detection is achieved using a modified encoder-decoder network built on a Fully Convolutional Network (FCN) backbone, which can identify the pixel-level boundaries of PV plants. The architecture of the proposed network can be seen in Figure 2.

To develop a robust image segmentation model, a comprehensive dataset of aerial images of large-scale photovoltaic plants, was utilized [7]. This dataset comprises a total of 3,584 aerial images of PV plants sourced from twelve different countries. For the purpose of training and validation, 80% of the dataset was randomly allocated for training, while the remaining 20% was set aside for validation.

Path Planning: The proposed software features an autonomous path-planning method designed to create the shortest, most efficient "lawn mower" path for monitoring PV plants. It uses data like camera field of view (FoV) and imaging height to calculate waypoints, ensuring full coverage of the plant. Waypoints are determined by intersecting the plant boundary with guidelines based on plant width, flight altitude, and camera FoV. This optimal path ensures drone effectively covers all areas, including corners.

Dynamic Processing: A dynamic algorithm that adjusts the route to capture closer images of identified anomalies enhances the proposed path planning method. An in-built control block establishes waypoints based on flight conditions. In Home Mode, the drone is at the home position and should take off and fly to the first waypoint. During Flight Mode, it follows a predetermined path, constantly updating its target waypoint as it approaches the current one. In Maneuver Mode which would be activated if a fault is detected, the drone descends to a height of 5 meters and hovers for 60 seconds to assess the situation. After this monitoring period, it will determine whether to continue on its current path or alter its trajectory based on the remaining battery life.

Fault Detection: This study proposes an encoder-decoder-based architecture for automatic fault detection in PV panels. A dataset of 2,400 synthetic aerial images was collected from the virtual PV plant in the DT-based simulation environment, to train an end-to-end segmentation model. This model is designed to detect bird droppings on PV panels without the need to separately extract individual modules from aerial images that feature multiple PV installations. The encoder, a modified VGG16, downsamples the input image and extracts feature maps, with the first 14 layers initialized using pre-trained ImageNet weights to improve training accuracy. The decoder upsamples the features via deconvolution, mapping low-resolution features to full-resolution images for pixel-level segmentation

2.2 DT-Based Simulation Environment

Our DT-based simulation environment comprises a dashboard that features a visualization interface, a flight simulation module, and a back-end system involving intelligent decision-making models and Python APIs designed for monitoring scenarios [8]. For the visualization interface, we have utilized Unreal Engine to build a highly realistic virtual PV plant, employing advanced graphics and physics simulations to closely replicate real-world conditions. The development process included modeling a 4-square-kilometer terrain and

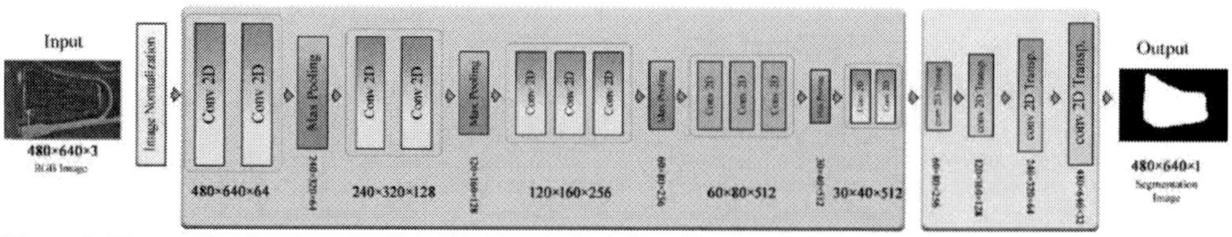

Figure 2: The encoder-decoder network architecture for boundary detection.

10.4229/EUPVSEC2025/4DO.17.3
020375-002

integrating various 3D assets such as vegetation, environmental features, and PV panels, all optimized for enhanced performance and realism.

Additionally, we crafted custom meshes to simulate faults on the PV panels. To simulate drone dynamics in the virtual PV plant environment, we use AirSim, which includes a quadrotor model, a physics engine for drag and collisions, and an environment model with magnetic fields, gravity, and air pressure. It also features sensors like barometers, gyroscopes, accelerometers, GPS, and RGB and depth cameras [9]. The camera settings were configured to a resolution of 480×640 with a 90-degree view, motion blur was disabled, and auto exposure speed was increased to 100 for improved image quality. Finally, to interact with the drone during simulations, the Airsim Python APIs were expanded to perform different tasks like tracking the generated flight path for monitoring, capturing images of PV arrays along the path, and executing maneuvers for detailed inspections when faults or anomalies are detected.

3 PERFORMANCE EVALUATION AND SIMULATION RESULTS

The performance of the proposed software package can be evaluated using two approaches: qualitative and quantitative assessments. Qualitative evaluations are performed in the computer simulation environment, while quantitative analyses are conducted using AI metrics like precision, F1-score, recall, accuracy, the Dice coefficient, and Intersection over Union (IoU), to measure the monitoring model's performance.

To quantitatively assess the performance of fault detection and boundary detection models, pixel accuracy is utilized. The boundary detection model achieved a training accuracy of 97.61% and a testing accuracy of 96.99%. Also, the fault detection model attained a training accuracy of 98.31% and a testing accuracy of 95.20%. Additionally, the fault detection model achieved a precision rate of 76.44% and a recall rate of 84.89%.

To qualitatively demonstrate the accuracy of the developed software package in performing AAM of a PV plant, it is essential to simulate the entire aerial monitoring process in real-world conditions.

For this purpose, All functions of the software package are simulated in real time within the developed DT-based simulation environment. A predefined scenario will be followed in the simulation environment which begins by extracting the boundaries of the virtual PV plant using a trained deep neural network. As illustrated in Figure 3, after the boundary of the PV plant is identified, a convex curve is drawn around it.

Figure 4: The designed trajectory for a PV plant (up) and trace line of the drone after passing the given waypoints (down).

The curve is input into the path planning algorithm, which creates the waypoints for aerial monitoring. The drone then proceeds to the first waypoint to begin its monitoring mission. During monitoring, the drone aims for the next waypoint in its path. It switches to the following waypoint when it gets close to the current one, and it continues this procedure until it successfully reaches the last waypoint (see Figure 4).

The drone flies along the planned path and takes pictures of the panels' surfaces with its camera. The fault detection model analyzes these images as shown in Figure 5, to find faults and sends a "fault flag" to a decision-making unit. Images also are tagged with locations, allowing the drone to investigate detected issues off its path. If the drone finds a faulty panel, it lowers itself to the problem's location for a closer look, taking detailed images of its modules and analyzing them (see Figure 6). After the investigation, the fault flag is reset, and the drone returns to its original height to continue its mission. Upon reaching the final waypoint, the drone is instructed to return home and lands back at the take-off location to complete the simulation.

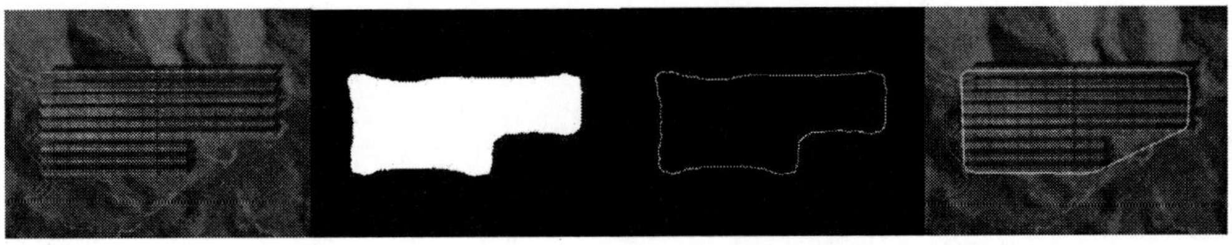

Figure 3: Boundary detection and convex closure drawing steps, employing the proposed model.

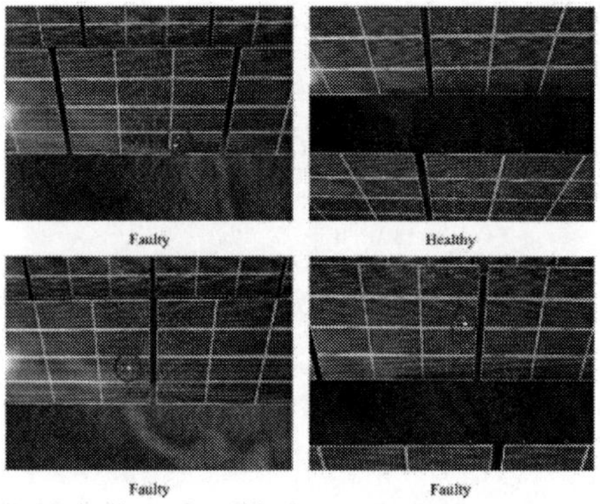

Figure 5: Examples of the images from monitoring with their predicted labels.

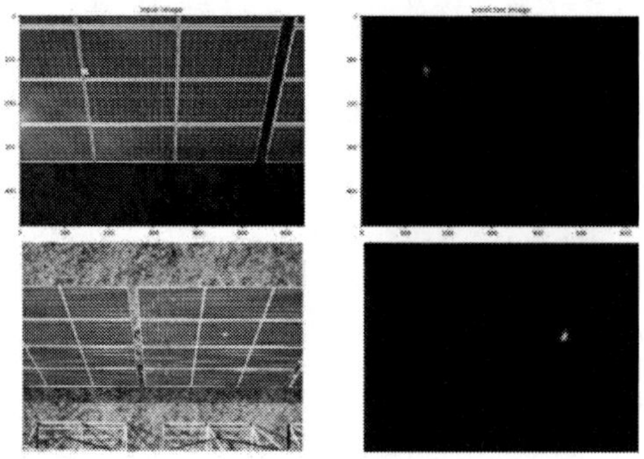

Figure 6: Examples of the images of the affected modules and their predicted masks.

4 CONCLUSIONS

This study proposed an embedded software package designed for managing drones in large-scale AAM of PV plants. Both qualitative and quantitative assessments have validated the software's performance. Additionally, functionalities such as path planning and dynamic processing are simulated in real time using a DT-based realistic simulation environment. The results indicate that the software achieves a high level of accuracy in conducting autonomous aerial inspections. Furthermore, this study demonstrates how innovative technologies, such as AI and DT integration, can enhance the accuracy of PV monitoring.

5 REFERENCES

[1] IRENA, "Future of Solar Photovoltaic: Deployment, investment, technology, grid integration and socio-economic aspects (A Global Energy Transformation: paper)," Abu Dhabi, 2019. doi: 978-92-9260-156-0.

[2] M. Aghaei *et al.*, "A Holistic Study on Failures and Diagnosis Techniques in Photovoltaic Modules, Components and Systems," in *2023 International Conference on Future Energy Solutions (FES)*, IEEE, 2023, pp. 1–6.

[3] M. Aghaei *et al.*, "Autonomous Intelligent Monitoring of Photovoltaic Systems: An In-depth Multidisciplinary Review," *Progress in Photovoltaics: Research and Applications*, 2024.

[4] A. K. V. de Oliveira, M. Aghaei, and R. Rüther, "Automatic Inspection of Photovoltaic Power Plants Using Aerial Infrared Thermography: A Review," *Energies*, vol. 15, no. 6, p. 2055, 2022.

[5] B. Li, C. Delpha, D. Diallo, and A. Migan-Dubois, "Application of Artificial Neural Networks to photovoltaic fault detection and diagnosis: A review," *Renewable and Sustainable Energy Reviews*, vol. 138, p. 110512, 2021.

[6] A. M. Moradi Sizkouhi *et al.*, "RoboPV: An integrated software package for autonomous aerial monitoring of large scale PV plants," *Energy Conversion and Management*, vol. 254, p. 115217, 2022, doi: https://doi.org/10.1016/j.enconman.2022.115217.

[7] A. M. M. Sizkouhi, M. Aghaei, S. M. Esmailifar, M. R. Mohammadi, and F. Grimaccia, "Automatic boundary extraction of large-scale photovoltaic plants using a fully convolutional network on aerial imagery," *IEEE Journal of Photovoltaics*, vol. 10, no. 4, pp. 1061–1067, 2020.

[8] M. Kolahi, S. M. Esmailifar, A. M. M. Sizkouhi, and M. Aghaei, "Digital-PV: A digital twin-based platform for autonomous aerial monitoring of large-scale photovoltaic power plants," *Energy Conversion and Management*, vol. 321, p. 118963, 2024.

[9] S. Shah, D. Dey, C. Lovett, and A. Kapoor, "Airsim: High-fidelity visual and physical simulation for autonomous vehicles," in *Field and Service Robotics: Results of the 11th International Conference*, Springer, 2018, pp. 621–635.

42nd European Photovoltaic Solar Energy Conference and Exhibition

This presentation was selected by the Sc. Committee of the EU PVSEC 2025 for submission of a full paper to one of the EU PVSEC's collaborating peer-reviewed journals.

INFLUENCE OF IRRADIANCE AND DRONE ALTITUDE IN INFRARED THERMOGRAPHY INSPECTIONS OF PHOTOVOLTAIC PLANTS

Rodrigo del Prado Santamaría, Gisele A. dos Reis Benatto, Mahmoud Dhimish, Timurhan Koc, Rizal Friansyah, Thøger Kari, Aysha Mahmood, Peter B. Poulsen and Sergiu V. Spataru
Technical University of Denmark, Department of Electrical and Photonics Engineering
Frederiksborgvej 399, 4000 Roskilde, Denmark

ABSTRACT: This study evaluates the effectiveness of drone-based infrared thermography (IRT) for detecting photovoltaic (PV) module defects under varying drone altitudes and irradiance levels. Several PV modules were artificially degraded to induce common faults, including cell cracks, cell interconnect disconnections and short-circuited bypass diodes. IRT images were acquired under irradiances ranging from 200 W/m^2 to 1000 W/m^2 and at four different drone altitudes (8 m, 10 m, 14 m, and 20 m). A detailed temperature pattern analysis at both the module and cell level was performed to characterize the thermal signatures of each fault type under the different imaging conditions. Results show that modules with cell cracks are difficult to distinguish from healthy modules while disconnected interconnects display distinct elongated thermal patterns that remain detectable at a minimum irradiance of 600 W/m^2 and are robust to detect even at higher imaging altitudes. Modules with short-circuited bypass diodes caused prominent hotspots of around 80°C which remained clearly detectable even at low irradiance levels (200 W/m^2) and elevated drone altitudes. To support further research, the complete IRT image dataset generated in this study will be made publicly available.
Keywords: Infrared Thermography, Photovoltaics, Defects, Drone Inspections

1 INTRODUCTION

Regular and efficient operation and maintenance (O&M) procedures are critical for ensuring the longevity and efficiency of PV plants. Among the available diagnostic tools, infrared thermography (IRT) is widely employed due to its non-contact, non-destructive nature. IRT enables the rapid detection of hotspots in PV modules and strings, which may indicate underlying degradation [1, 2, 3]. These thermal anomalies can be caused by various fault types, including cell cracks, potential-induced degradation (PID), defective bypass diodes, cell interconnect faults, and external stressors such as soiling—each exhibiting a characteristic thermal signature [4, 5].

IRT has gained popularity in utility-scale PV plants because it offers a fast and cost-effective inspection solution, particularly when deployed via drone-mounted thermal cameras. However, the accuracy of IRT-based fault detection is highly dependent on environmental conditions. Optimal performance typically requires a plane-of-array (POA) irradiance above 600 W/m^2, wind speeds below 28 km/h, and minimal cloud cover or soiling according to current inspection practices, as described in the IEC TS 62446-3 [6]. Such conditions are not consistently present in all regions; for example, in Nordic countries, where IRT inspections are often restricted to summer months.

In addition to weather conditions, the relative position of the thermal camera significantly influences the accuracy of temperature measurements and defect visibility. Previous research has shown that non-optimal imaging angles, particularly in drone-based inspections, can lead to temperature errors of up to 10°C [7]. Several studies have addressed the challenges of IRT under non-ideal scenarios, such as partial shading [8, 9], and have proposed best practices for the inspection setup and procedure.

This work aims to provide a comprehensive evaluation of IRT images under varying irradiance levels and drone altitudes. We analyzed the thermal behavior of PV modules subjected to different types of degradation, namely, cell cracks, cell interconnect degradation and short-circuited bypass diodes. The experiments were conducted across irradiance levels ranging from 200 to 1000 W/m^2 and drone altitudes from 8 m to 20 m. The influence of windspeed was not evaluated in this work due to constraints for drone flying safety.

The key contribution of this study is to identify the conditions under which IRT remains a reliable diagnostic tool beyond the standard recommendations and to outline its limitations for specific fault types. These findings have practical implications for improving inspection protocols, optimizing drone-based inspection strategies, enhancing the robustness of automated defect detection algorithms, and estimating which failures are happening in the plants, knowing their temperature ranges and signatures.

All the data acquired in this study is released as an open dataset containing IRT images of the studied modules at all irradiances and drone altitudes, EL images and I-V curves.

2 MATERIAL AND METHODS

2.1 Background

PV modules in the field can be subject to different types of degradation mechanisms that can affect their performance and potentially cause reliability issues and safety risks.

Cell cracks can appear in PV modules as a result of mechanical stress, for example during transport and installation, due to extreme weather conditions or through extended thermal cycling and field exposure [10]. These cracks can develop at any point in the module's lifetime; although often considered an early-life failure, they may propagate over time, leading to significant power losses and the formation of hotspots. When hotspots appear, cell cracks pose a safety risk to the installation. Moreover, cracks are not visually detectable, making characterization techniques such as EL or IRT essential for their identification. Cell cracks have been extensively studied in literature. They increase the module's series resistance, which, under illumination and operation at the maximum power point, causes additional losses to dissipate as heat. This thermal behavior forms the basis for using IRT imaging to characterize and detect this defect [11-15].

Cell interconnect disconnections or degradations refer to a physical or electrical break of the tab ribbons between cells in the PV modules. This defect can appear due to thermo-mechanical stress or during manufacturing as a problem with the soldering process. This degradation causes an

increase in series resistance of the cells, because of a current mismatch between the cells [16]. As shown in Table I, this defect can affect up to 15% of the module power production based on the severity of the disconnections, and if severe enough, it could trigger the bypass diodes leading to a larger power loss contribution.
Modules with short-circuited bypass diodes pose a significant problem in PV plants. Defective bypass diodes are often reported after a few years of field exposure; however, they have a large impact on power generation, as a short circuit in a PV module bypass diode can lead to power losses ranging from 33% to the full module being bypassed if all diodes fail. This is one of the most common targets of IRT inspections due to their characteristic thermal signal, which is a complete or partial PV module substrings heating with very high temperatures [5].

2.2 Experimental Setup and Methodology

Table I summarizes the types of defects, number of affected modules and estimated power loss ranges. The study includes both monofacial and bifacial Passivated Emitter Rear Cell (PERC) modules with nominal powers of 295 W and 305 W.

Table I. Summary of defective modules in this study.

Defect Type	Module #	Power Loss	Details
Cell cracks	8	4 - 5%	Cells cracked by mechanical stress test. Total of 69 cells affected.
Cell interconnections	8	3-14%	Cell ribbon interconnection cut from the back sheet. Total of 98 cells affected.
Short-circuited bypass diode	7	33-66%	4 modules with 1 Shorted diode and 3 with 2 Shorted diodes

All these defect types have been induced through accelerated stress testing or replicating common failures that modules experience in the field. Thereafter, the modules were installed in different PV strings at DTU's PV plant in Risø.
Every stress-tested module was characterized before and after degradation by I-V flashing at Standard Test Conditions (STC) (1000 W/m^2, 25°C, and AM 1.5) using a class AAA solar simulator; EL images were recorded at 100 and 10% I_{sc} bias with a NIKON D3500 CMOS camera. After installing the stress-tested modules in the plant, IRT inspections were carried out. A DJI Mavic M3T drone with a thermal camera of 640x480 px and a sensitivity <40 mK was used. The inspections were conducted under four irradiance conditions, monitored by an in-plane reference cell: 200 W/m^2, 600 W/m^2, 800 W/m^2 and >800 W/m^2. For each irradiance, the drone acquired images at four flight altitudes: 8 m, 10 m, 14 m and 20 m.
Image processing consisted of module corner detection and perspective correction. For each of the modules, statistical parameters such as the average and maximum module temperature have been calculated.

3 RESULTS

3.1 Cell cracks
Fig. 1 shows a selected module with cell cracks EL image and its corresponding IRT images. The module presents several cracked cells with different degrees of severity. At 200 W/m^2 the temperature difference within the module between cracked and healthy cells is very small, between 0.2 and 0.3°C, however, as the temperature increases the cells on the left start heating up, indicating the cracks location. Under high irradiance, where the temperature differences are more significant, the temperature difference between a cracked cell and the healthy one is between 1 and 2°C.

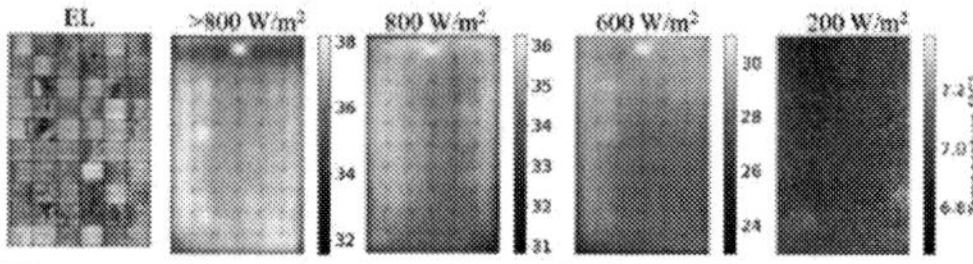

Figure 1. Example of a cell cracked module IRT images at different irradiances. EL image as a reference.

3.2 Cell interconnect degradation
Fig. 2 shows an example of a module with cell interconnection failures EL image and the resulting IRT images under different irradiances. This defect shows significantly under high irradiances with temperature differences in affected cells of up to 4°C; furthermore, imaging at irradiances of 600 W/m^2 can effectively distinguish this degradation mode, whose thermal characteristic resembles the pattern of the EL image.

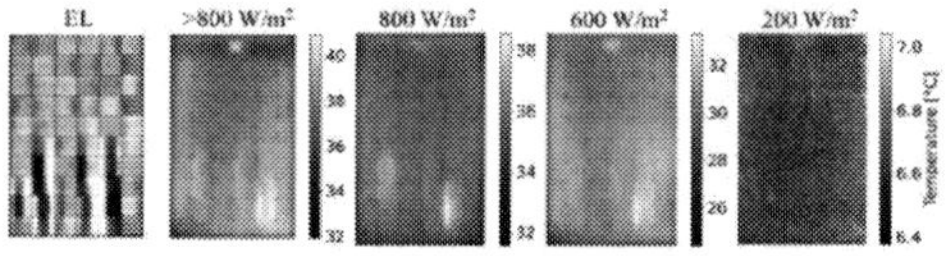

Figure 2. Example of a module with damaged cell interconnects where the IRT images were taken at different irradiances. EL image as a reference.

3.3 Shot-circuited bypass diodes

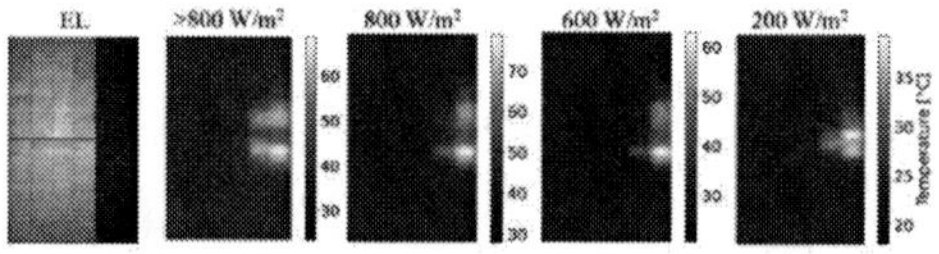

Figure 3. Example of a module with one short-circuited bypass diode where the IRT images were taken at different irradiances. EL image as a reference.

In this study, PV modules were artificially degraded by short-circuiting either one or two bypass diodes per module. Fig. 3 shows an example of a module with one shorted bypass diode and the evolution of the thermal patterns as the irradiance increases. Notably, the cells surrounding the middle section of the module, where the defective diode is located, are where the hot spots appear, with temperature differences of up to 20 °C. The maximum temperature difference is reduced as irradiance goes down; however, the patterns are still visible even at 200 W/m^2. These defective modules were always identifiable under all conditions and, certainly, low

irradiance imaging is possible for this defect, as the observed average module temperature difference at low irradiance was 10 °C or larger.
Modules with short-circuited bypass diodes were also shown to be detectable under high drone altitudes.

4 DISCUSSION

Drone altitude is a critical parameter in IRT inspections, as it significantly influences image quality and diagnostic accuracy. As drone altitude increases, the spatial resolution of thermal images decreases; each pixel covers a larger surface area of the PV module, resulting in a lower pixel density per cell. This reduction in resolution compromises the detectability of small or localized defects, potentially hindering reliable fault detection.
Fig. 4 illustrates this effect by comparing thermal images of a module with cell cracks and another with cell interconnect failure, captured at 8 m and 20 m drone altitude. A substantial degradation in image detail is observed with increasing altitude, particularly at the cell level. The camera used in this study has a resolution of 640x512 pixels with a focal length of 40 mm. As a result, the detectability of small-area defects such as cell cracks is significantly impaired. While interconnect failures remained partially detectable at higher altitudes in severe cases, their characteristic elongated thermal patterns became indistinct at 20 m. This loss of pattern fidelity complicates root-cause analysis, as the defect-specific thermal signature is no longer discernible.
However, not all fault types are equally sensitive to reduced spatial resolution. Large-area defects such as short-circuited bypass continued to produce prominent and easily identifiable thermal anomalies at high altitudes.
Consequently, for the reliable detection of small, localized faults, lower drone altitudes—preferably between 8 m and 10 m—are recommended. In contrast, for large-area defects, inspections can still be effectively conducted at higher altitudes without substantial loss of diagnostic capability.

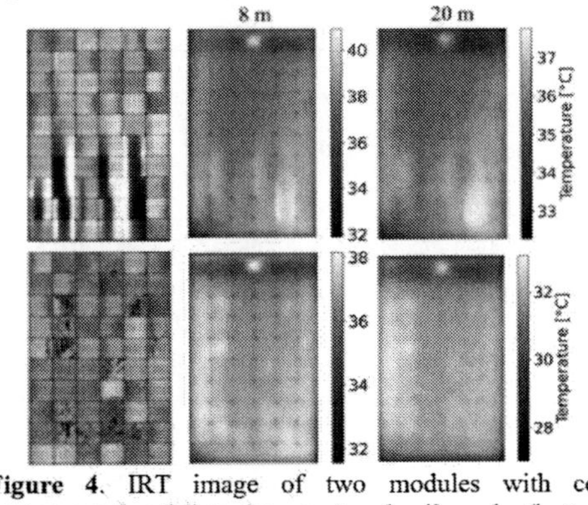

Figure 4. IRT image of two modules with cell interconnection failure (top row) and cell cracks (bottom row) imaged at 8 m and 20 m drone altitude at >800 W/m^2. EL image of each module is displayed as a reference.

In addition to drone altitude, solar irradiance is one of the most influential parameters affecting IRT reliability. At higher irradiance levels, modules operating at maximum power dissipate more heat at defect sites, enhancing thermal contrasts and improving defect visibility. As recommended by current technical specifications, irradiance levels above 600 W/m^2 are optimal for accurate IRT inspections. The results from this study confirm that most defect types exhibited increased thermal contrast under high irradiance compared to healthy modules. Conversely, under low irradiance, thermal gradients were minimal, and most defects were difficult or impossible to detect. Notably, short-circuited bypass diodes remained detectable even at low irradiance levels (e.g., 200 W/m^2), further confirming their robust thermal signature.

Table II. Maximum temperature difference of each defect severity vs the average healthy cell or module. Data taken from the inspections at 8 m altitude and over 800 W/m^2 irradiance.

Module Type	Max. cell T [°C]
Healthy	38
Cell cracks	38.7
Defective cell interconnects	44.17
Shorted bypass diodes	84.37

These qualitative trends are supported by the quantitative results presented in Table II. Under optimal imaging conditions (8 m drone altitude and >800 W/m^2 irradiance), modules with cell cracks exhibited temperature differences of less than 1°C compared to healthy modules. In contrast, defective cell interconnects exhibited higher thermal anomalies, with hotspot temperatures reaching 44.2°C depending on degradation severity. This corresponds to a 6.2°C increase over the healthy module baseline.
The largest thermal anomalies were observed for shorted bypass diodes with hotspot temperatures exceeding 40°C relative to healthy modules. This defect generates large-area heating that remains visible even under suboptimal irradiance and at high drone altitudes, demonstrating IRT's robustness for detecting such failures.
Taken together, these results emphasize that IRT detectability is strongly dependent on both the size and severity of the defect, as well as inspection conditions. While IRT is effective for large or severe faults, it has notable limitations in identifying small-scale or subtle defects, especially when inspections are conducted at high altitudes or under low irradiance.

5 CONCLUSIONS

Drone-based infrared thermography is widely employed to assess the operational state of PV power plants. It enables the identification of hotspots in PV modules and strings, which may result from defects, shading, or soiling. While IRT is a valuable diagnostic tool for plant operators, its limitations under non-optimal weather conditions are often overlooked. Current IRT standards recommend that IRT inspections be conducted under irradiance levels above 600 W/m^2, low wind speeds, and minimal cloud cover. However, these ideal conditions are not always achievable all year round in many regions, particularly in northern climates.
Although the thermal signatures of common PV module defects have been previously studied under standard conditions, the behavior of these signatures under sub-

optimal weather conditions remains poorly understood. This study investigated the influence of irradiance and drone altitude on the visibility and characteristics of thermal anomalies in IRT images, aiming to assess whether typical PV failures remain detectable under varying inspection scenarios.

A comprehensive thermal analysis was performed on defective PV modules under controlled field conditions, with irradiance levels ranging from 200 W/m^2 to 1000 W/m^2 and drone altitudes between 8 m and 20 m. The modules exhibited various defect types, including cell cracks, defective cell interconnects and short-circuited bypass diodes. Defects were introduced via stress testing, and modules were operated under realistic conditions in a PV farm environment.

Our findings show that drone altitude significantly affects image resolution and, consequently, diagnostic accuracy. At low altitudes (8 to 10 m), spatial resolution is sufficient to capture cell-level temperature inhomogeneities, enabling the identification of small or localized defects. However, at higher altitudes, spatial resolution degrades, obscuring subtle thermal patterns such as those caused by interconnect failures or cell cracks. In contrast, large-area defects like shorted bypass diodes remain clearly detectable even at higher altitudes due to their broad and intense thermal signatures.

Solar irradiance was also found to be a critical parameter for reliable fault detection. While current standards recommend irradiance levels above 600 W/m^2, our results show that certain large-area faults can still be detected at 200 W/m^2.

Cell cracks, which showed temperature differences below 1°C, were largely undetectable even under optimal imaging conditions. Interconnect failures exceeded this threshold in severe cases, while shorted bypass diodes and soiling produced the most pronounced hotspots.

These results have direct practical implications. For accurate fault localization, especially in diagnostic or warranty contexts, drone flights should be conducted at low altitudes during periods of high irradiance. For general condition monitoring or the detection of severe, high-impact faults, higher-altitude inspections may suffice, making such strategies more viable in regions with limited solar availability or access constraints.

To further support future efforts in developing and benchmarking automated defect detection algorithms, the IRT image dataset produced in this work has been made publicly available.

REFERENCES

[1] G. Schirripa Spagnolo, P. Del Vecchio, G. Makary, D. Papalillo, and A. Martocchia, "A review of IR thermography applied to PV systems," in 2012 11th International Conference on Environment and Electrical Engineering, IEEE, May 2012, pp. 879–884. doi: 10.1109/EEEIC.2012.6221500.

[2] A. K. V. de Oliveira, M. Aghaei, and R. Rüther, "Automatic Inspection of Photovoltaic Power Plants Using Aerial Infrared Thermography: A Review," Energies (Basel), vol. 15, no. 6, p. 2055, Mar. 2022, doi: 10.3390/en15062055.

[3] A. W. Kandeal et al., "Infrared thermography-based condition monitoring of solar photovoltaic systems: A mini review of recent advances," Solar Energy, vol. 223, pp. 33–43, Jul. 2021, doi: 10.1016/j.solener.2021.05.032.

[4] M. Köntges et al., "Review of Failures of Photovoltaic Modules," International Energy Agency (IEA) PVPS Task 13, Subtask 3.2, 978-3-906042-16–9, Mar. 2014.

[5] U. Jahn et al., "Review on Infrared and Electroluminescence Imaging for PV Field Applications," International Energy Agency (IEA) PVPS Task 13, Subtask 3.3, 978-3-906042-53–4, Mar. 2018.

[6] "IEC Technical Specification 62446-3. Photovoltaic (PV) systems - Requirements for testing, documentation and maintenance - Part 3: Photovoltaic modules and plants - Outdoor infrared thermography," 2017.

[7] S. Vergura, "Criticalities of the Outdoor Infrared Inspection of Photovoltaic Modules by Means of Drones," Energies (Basel), vol. 15, no. 14, p. 5086, Jul. 2022, doi: 10.3390/en15145086.

[8] O. E. Ikejiofor, Y. E. Asuamah, H. O. Njoku, and S. O. Enibe, "Detection of Hotspots and Performance Deteriotations in PV Modules under Partial Shading Conditions Using Infrared Thermography," in 7th International Electronic Conference on Sensors and Applications, Basel Switzerland: MDPI, Nov. 2020, p. 71. doi: 10.3390/ecsa-7-08201.

[9] G. Álvarez-Tey, J. A. Clavijo-Blanco, Á. Gil-García, R. Jiménez-Castañeda, and C. García-López, "Electrical and Thermal Behaviour of Crystalline Photovoltaic Solar Modules in Shading Conditions," Applied Sciences, vol. 9, no. 15, p. 3038, Jul. 2019, doi: 10.3390/app9153038.

[10] M. Köntges, I. Kunze, S. Kajari-Schröder, X. Breitenmoser, and B. Bjørneklett, "The risk of power loss in crystalline silicon based photovoltaic modules due to micro-cracks," Solar Energy Materials and Solar Cells, vol. 95, no. 4, pp. 1131–1137, Apr. 2011, doi: 10.1016/j.solmat.2010.10.034.

[11] M. Dhimish, V. d'Alessandro, and S. Daliento, "Investigating the Impact of Cracks on Solar Cells Performance: Analysis Based on Nonuniform and Uniform Crack Distributions," IEEE Trans Industr Inform, vol. 18, no. 3, pp. 1684–1693, Mar. 2022, doi: 10.1109/TII.2021.3088721.

[12] A. Morlier, F. Haase, and M. Kontges, "Impact of Cracks in Multicrystalline Silicon Solar Cells on PV Module Power—A Simulation Study Based on Field Data," IEEE J Photovolt, vol. 5, no. 6, pp. 1735–1741, Nov. 2015, doi: 10.1109/JPHOTOV.2015.2471076.

[13] J. I. van Mölken et al., "Impact of Micro-Cracks on the Degradation of Solar Cell Performance Based On Two-Diode Model Parameters," Energy Procedia, vol. 27, pp. 167–172, 2012, doi: 10.1016/j.egypro.2012.07.046.

[14] M. Dhimish, V. Holmes, B. Mehrdadi, and M. Dales, "The impact of cracks on photovoltaic power performance," Journal of Science: Advanced Materials and Devices, vol. 2, no. 2, pp. 199–209, Jun. 2017, doi: 10.1016/j.jsamd.2017.05.005.

[15] M. Dhimish and P. I. Lazaridis, "An empirical investigation on the correlation between solar cell cracks and hotspots," Sci Rep, vol. 11, no. 1, p. 23961, Dec. 2021, doi: 10.1038/s41598-021-03498-z.

[16] R. Asadpour, D. B. Sulas-Kern, S. Johnston, J. Meydbray, and M. A. Alam, "Dark Lock-in Thermography Identifies Solder Bond Failure as the Root Cause of Series Resistance Increase in Fielded Solar Modules," IEEE J Photovolt, vol. 10, no. 5, pp. 1409–1416, Sep. 2020, doi: 10.1109/JPHOTOV.2020.3003781.

STRATEGY FOR SIMPLE, ON-SITE FAILURE ANALYSIS: INVESTIGATING BUBBLES AND BURN MARKS IN BACKSHEETS OF PV MODULES

C. Buerhop[1], A. Kirsten Vidal de Oliveira[2], O. Mashkov[1], L. Nascimento[2], R. Rüther[2], M. I. Peters[1]
[1] Forschungszentrum Jülich GmbH, Helmholtz-Institute Erlangen-Nürnberg, HI ERN, 91058 Erlangen, Germany
[2] Solar Energy Research Laboratory Fotovoltaica/ UFSC, Florianópolis, Brazil

ABSTRACT: This study investigates localized degradation in PV modules, focusing on bubbles and burn/scorch marks on the backsheet. These defects were discovered in 3.4% of 714 inspected modules at a multi-MWp PV plant in Brazil after three years of operation on a single-axis tracker system. High-throughput methods—visual inspection, serial number scanning, UV fluorescence imaging, and selective methods like current-voltage measurements, near-infrared spectroscopy, and electroluminescence imaging —were applied. The defects were concentrated at specific areas, occurring predominantly at the edges of the top and bottom cell rows, particularly at the contact points and corners. IV measurements and insulation measurements showed no impact on electrical properties. The study concludes that the localized degradation is likely caused by partial shading from adjacent tracker rows, inducing reverse bias, localized heating, and polymer breakdown. Additionally, the proposed method for on-site fault detection proved to be an effective, high-throughput approach for identifying degradation patterns in operational PV plants, offering a practical strategy for early fault detection and proactive maintenance.
Keywords: Field measurements, defect detection, backsheet degradation

1 INTRODUCTION

Photovoltaic (PV) power plants are subject to various degradation mechanisms that can compromise long-term performance and safety. While electrical testing is commonly used to assess system health, many defects first manifest as anomalies in module materials. These anomalies can serve both as indicators of malfunction and as root causes of accelerated degradation, making their early detection critical for reliable operation.

In this study, we investigate bubbles (blisters) and burn marks found on the backsheets of PV modules that were reported by operators. To analyze their origin and potential risks, we applied a structured inspection approach combining high-throughput on-site methods with more targeted techniques. This integrated methodology provides insight into both the material-level degradation and its correlation with electrical performance. It also establishes a practical framework for large-scale failure inspection in operational PV plants, enabling early fault detection and proactive maintenance.

2 AIM AND APPROACH

The aim of this paper is to propose a strategy for failure inspection in PV power stations, utilizing straightforward methods for on-site testing. It recognizes that observed anomalies can serve both as root causes of system weaknesses and as indicators of malfunction or poor component interaction. Using the example of modules with bubbles (blisters) and burn marks observed on their rear side by the operators, whose cause is unknown (see **Fehler! Verweisquelle konnte nicht gefunden werden.**), we present our measurement strategy. This degradation phenomenon was studied in multi-MWp PV power plant in the northeast region of Brazil, installed on a single-axis tracking system operating for four years. A total of 714 PV modules were analyzed using simple, high-throughput on-site methods on site, including visual inspection (VIS), serial number (SN) scanning to build a comprehensive database, and UV fluorescence imaging (UVF) with a UV lamp and camera during nighttime to detect polymer degradation. More targeted methods, requiring additional effort, were applied to a subset of modules. These included current-voltage (IV) measurements for electrical properties, near-infrared spectroscopy (NIRA) for polymer identification in the encapsulant and backsheet, and electroluminescence (EL) imaging to detect cell defects.

3 RESULTS AND DISCUSSION

Our inspection revealed that 3.4% of the inspected modules exhibit bubbles (blisters) and burn marks on the backsheet. Typical characteristics of these defects are illustrated in **Figure 1**. It is striking, that these anomalies occur in very specific locations, rather than randomly across the module, and are confined to either the bottom or top row of cells along the module's edge (**Figure 2**). The faults consistently appear at critical points such as cell

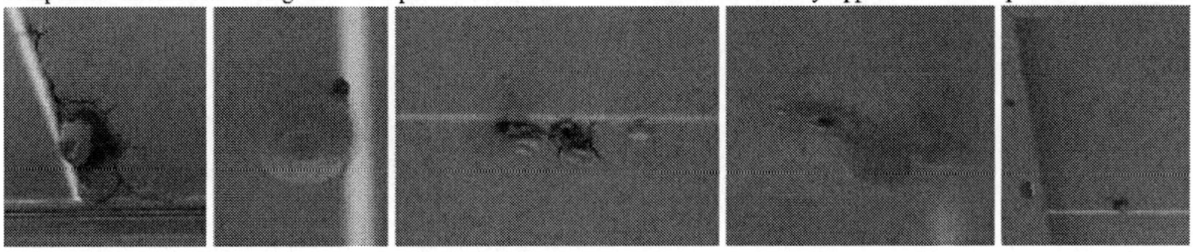

Figure 1: Failure of polymeric backsheets showing formation of bubbles and burn marks.

10.4229/EUPVSEC2025/4DO.17.6
020377-001

edges, corners, contact points, or between the contact points.

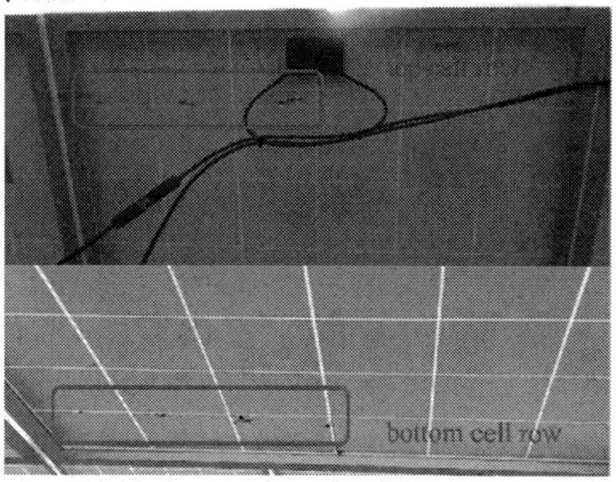

Figure 2: Typical positions of bubbles and burn marks: top cell row on junction box side and bottom cell row opposite junction box side.

To document/map the findings, we scanned the serial numbers of the modules. The SN were categorized into eight distinct groups (A-H). Modules with blisters and burn marks were exclusively found in SN group D, which accounted for approx. 34% of the inspected modules. Within this group, 9.8% of the modules exhibited these anomalies. The distribution of the SN groups and the positions of the anomalies are visualized in the map in **Figure 3**.

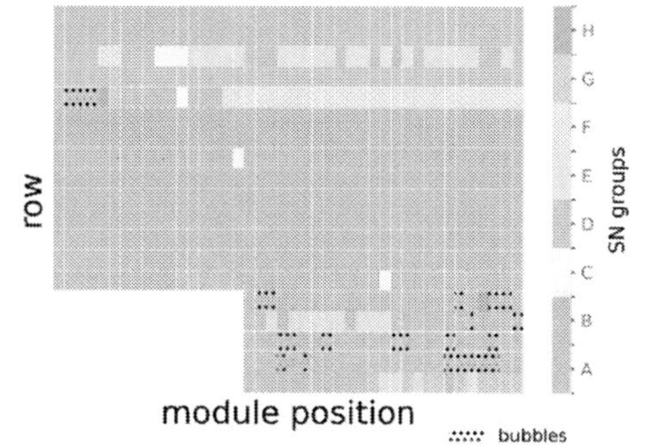

Figure 3: Typical positions of bubbles and burn marks: mapping of batches and marking modules with bubbles.

From the front, the defects were relatively inconspicuous. However, with prior knowledge of the rear side anomalies, the anomalies became identifiable from the front as well, see **Figure 4**. Close-up images reveal clear signs of delamination, corrosion, and scorch marks.

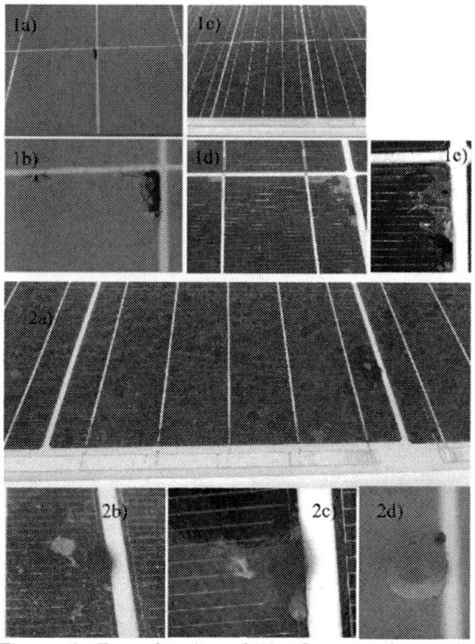

Figure 4: Examples (1 and 2) of two modules with bubbles and burn marks including close-ups (1c-1e, 2b-2-d), rear side (images vertically flipped).

Additionally, EL images of the affected modules showed electrically inactive cell areas. In **Figure 5**, the edges of the peripheral cells appear dark, indicating deactivated regions. This phenomenon is absent in the central cells, as confirmed by EL images of two sample modules. These defects are highly concentrated in specific areas.

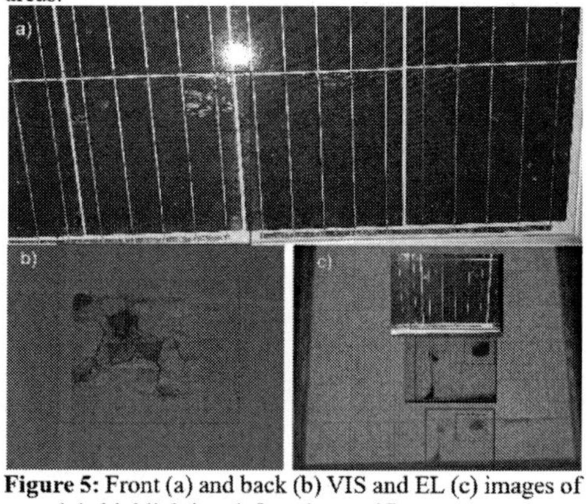

Figure 5: Front (a) and back (b) VIS and EL (c) images of a module highlighting defects in specific areas.

UVF images highlight signs of polymer ageing. For instance, the module in **Figure 6** displays typical square-shaped ring patterns in the lower row of cells. Irregularities with intense UVF intensity are visible at the upper cell edge. These patterns are typically caused by high temperatures degrading polymers [1]. These positions align with the dark areas in EL images and the bubbles and burn marks observed in VIS inspection.

10.4229/EUPVSEC2025/4DO.17.6

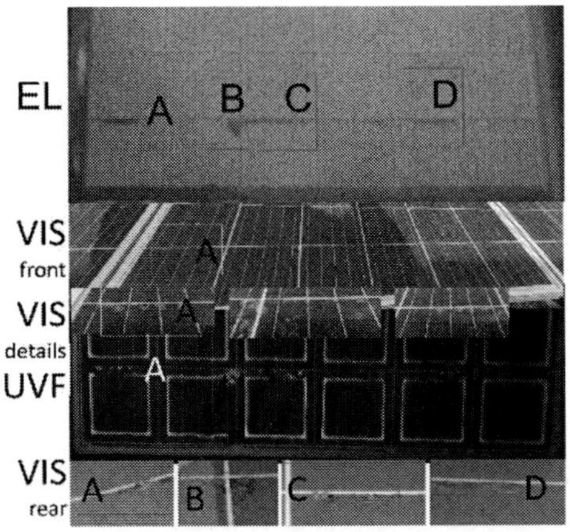

Figure 6: Module with bubbles and burn marks: VIS (front and rear), EL, and UVF. Aeras marked A-D guide the eye to the same spots in different image.

The polymer materials identified through NIRA measurements include EVA as the encapsulation material and a symmetric double-fluoropolymer backsheet, namely PVDF-PET-PVDF [2]. This backsheet comprises polyvinylidene fluoride (PVDF) and polyethylene terephthalate (PET), both of which were consistently identified in the inspected modules. A literature review was carried out to investigate the decomposition behavior of the polymers. PVDF is thermally stable up to approx. 150°C, with a melting temperature of 170°C. PET remains stable up to 80°C, although its melting temperature is higher at 260°C. The decomposition of these polymers produces gases such as carbon monoxide CO and carbon dioxide CO_2 [3]. The decomposition characteristics of EVA for thermal degradation are according to Norrish I process, which begins at 150- 200°C, with the formation of methane CH_4, CO, CO_2, and acetaldehyde [4,5]. - The IV measurements show no significant impact on the electrical parameters.

Statistical analysis highlights that the formation of bubbles and scorch marks is a highly concentrated phenomenon. These defects occur exclusively at the top or bottom cell rows and appear to be caused by temperature-induced damage. We hypothesize that adjacent tracker rows create partial shading of these cells, either early in the morning or late in the afternoon. Partial shading induces reverse bias in the affected cells, concentrating current density at the weakest points, such as cell edges and soldering points. This leads to localized temperature increases, forming hot spots that damage the solar cells. The heat accelerates the deterioration and decomposition of the polymers, resulting in gas formation, bubbles, embrittlement (cracking), burn marks on the polymer, and delamination. Additionally, burn marks on the front side and a loss of adhesion may occur. While the immediate implications for module performance are negligible, cracks and open bubbles create pathways for moisture ingress, potentially leading to electrical hazards and safety concerns [6]. In conclusion, the issue of bubbles and burn marks arises from a superposition of system design factors and variations in module batch quality. The risk of bubbles and burn marks is estimated to affect between 2% and 4.7% of the modules across the entire PV power station.

4 SUMMARY

Localized defects, including bubbles and scorch marks, were found in 3.4% of the inspected PV modules, primarily in the top and bottom cell rows at contact points, edges, and corners. Statistical analysis revealed that 9.8% of modules in one SN group exhibited these anomalies. Partial shading from adjacent tracker rows, occurring early morning or late afternoon, is believed to cause reverse bias, creating hot spots that locally degrade polymers.

Key findings include: 1) EL images showed electrically inactive areas at the edges of affected cells, 2) UV fluorescence imaging revealed polymer degradation, with strong UVF signals correlating with visible defects, and 3) NIRA analysis identified EVA encapsulants and PVDF-PET-PVDF backsheets as the degraded polymers.

Although IV measurements show no immediate performance impact, these defects pose a potential risk of accelerated degradation. Key concerns include vulnerabilities to moisture ingress, which could significantly increase the likelihood of electrical hazards.

The proposed method of high-throughput, on-site inspection using visual inspection, UV fluorescence, EL imaging, and NIRA analysis has proven effective in identifying degradation patterns early, providing a practical and efficient approach for fault detection in operational PV plants. This method facilitates proactive maintenance, allowing operators to identify weak points and mitigate potential risks before they impact system performance.

5 ACKNOWLEDGEMENTS

We gratefully thank the Alexander von Humboldt Stiftung for funding the collaboration between UFSC and HI ERN. HI ERN thanks for the support of the ZIM Project RobInspec FKN: 16KN083044, dig4morE," FKZ: 03EE1090B, "REMBup" FKZ: 03WR021F by the Federal Ministry for Economic Affairs and Climate Action on the basis of a decision by the German Bundestag, and the Helmholtz Association in the framework of the innovation platform "Solar TAP" (No. 714-62150-3/1 (2023)).

6 REFERENCES

[1]D. J. Colvin, et al.; IEEE Journal of Photovoltaics (2025).
[2]O. Stroyuk, et al.; Progress in Photovoltaics: Research and Applications (2022).
[3]S. Uličná, et al.; Scientific Reports 12 (2022) 14399.
[4]M. Oliveira, et al.; Renewable and Sustainable Energy Reviews (2017).
[5]S. Jiang, et al.; Macromolecular Reaction Engineering (2015).
[6]O. K. Segbefia, et al.; Solar Energy (2021).

42nd European Photovoltaic Solar Energy Conference and Exhibition

This presentation was selected by the Sc. Committee of the EU PVSEC 2025 for submission of a full paper to one of the EU PVSEC's collaborating peer-reviewed journals.

DESIGN AND TESTING OF AN INNOVATIVE CLOSED AGRIVOLTAIC SYSTEM: "ALGAEVOLTAICS™"

Alessandra Scognamiglio*[1], Aniello Borriello[1], Carmine Cancro[1], Mariam De Blasi[2], Maria Genovese[2], Marcello Diano[3], Stefano Mazzoleni[4], Fabrizio Carteni[4], Paola Delli Veneri[1]
[1]ENEA - Energy Technologies and Renewable Sources Department, Portici Research Center
[2]Enel Green Power (EGP), Environment and Impacts Mitigation Unit
[3]M2M Engineering
[4]Dept. of Agricultural Sciences, University of Naples Federico II
***Corresponding author: alessandra.scognamiglio@enea.it**

ABSTRACT: Agrivoltaics (agri-PV) is acknowledged an optimal way to combine energy generation from photovoltaics (PV) and crop production on the same land unit. In general, the economic value of the crops generated is significantly lower than the economic value of energy, and therefore the energy component of the system design and performance is better evaluated than the plants (agri) one. Nevertheless, the seek for optimal light transmission conditions through or underneath the PV modules, suitable for the plants growth, leads to spatial designs that can lower the energy production from PV as the density of power is lower than in a standard PV layout (e.g. increased distance between the modules stripes). This project experiments with an optimized energy and economic combination between a standard PV layout and a crop characterized by a high photosynthesis efficiency and a high market value. The result is an innovative integrated design that combines PV and micro algae generation, with several advantages with respect to current PV designs and crop selections for agrivoltaics. The name of this system is Algaevoltaics™.
The paper presents and discusses preliminary data (energy and micro algae) from the monitoring of the pilot realized at the ENEA facilities in Portici, in October 2023. This is made of two 3.4kW$_p$ PV systems, integrating two identical circuits of tubular photobioreactors. These two units differ because of the use of mono facial (glass-tedlar technology) or bifacial (glass-glass technology) PV modules.
Keywords: agrivoltaics: microalgae; photobioreactors; innovative agrivoltaics.

1 "LAND FOR ENERGY OR LAND FOR FOOD?"

As it is well known, the scarcity of land compared to our ecological footprint is nowadays an urgent issue, especially in high densely inhabited areas, or with limited agricultural land. Therefore, the use of land, i.e. agricultural land, for installing renewable energy generation systems, such as Photovoltaics (PV), is often a concern, especially for local communities. This low acceptance generates limitations to the use of PV on ground. For example, in some countries there is a ban to the implementation of PV in agricultural area.

Given this framework, agrivoltaics (APV), that is the combined use of land for agriculture and for energy is becoming increasingly common. The combined efficiency of such systems is still under investigation; as the reduction of daylight (due to PV) affects the growth rate of crops, through changes in air, ground and crop temperature with respect to traditional crop systems. Studies are ongoing on the selection of the most suitable crops for such uses, and on optimal arrangements of PV modules to meet the best lighting conditions. In several countries guidelines exist on the design of agrivoltaics to meet the national definitions.

Despite being agrivoltaics still a field for innovation and research, a rich literature already acknowledges the many advantages of this approach, besides the combined use of land, such as the beneficial effects of the shadow from the PV modules on the crops, especially in terms of water requirements, the mechanical protection of the crops.

This paper reports about the design and experimentation of an innovative agrivoltaic systems, whose design is aimed to maximise the energy and economic efficiency of both PV and crops. This is made by combining a traditional layout of on-ground PV (energy density maximisation for the lowest energy cost) and a high photosynthetic efficient, and high market value crop, which benefits from the shadow of the PV modules.

The proposed innovative agrivoltaic system is a combination of PV and microalgae (Chlorella) integrated into a unique design, which maximizes the energy generation per single land unit, by combining the electricity production and the biomass production into one integrated, engineered PV system. The typical dilemma "land for energy or land for food" is here overcome by an optimised design which merges the two approaches.

2 INTRODUCTION

Current approaches integrate the energy production and the food production in the so called "agrivoltaic concept", where PV modules and crops are placed in the same land unit. In this case, to find a good balance between the PV and the crop needs, the light transmission is a key element of the design: the crop yield can be in fact decreased because of the shading effect of PV.

In general, the standard layout of on ground mounted PV (which is corresponding to the optimal energy and economic performance for PV) requires some spatial adjustments in order to ensure the optimal light transmission balance to allow a satisfying crop production, i.e. the distance in between the stripes of modules is increased, the height of the modules from the ground is higher compared to standard on ground PV (Figure 1).

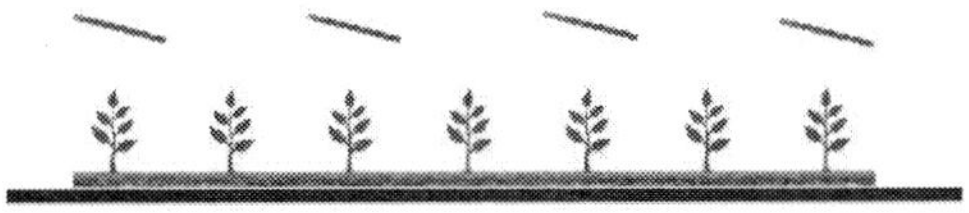

Figure 1: To ensure an optimal light transmission, allowing for a satisfying crop yield, in a typical agrivoltaic layout the height of the modules from the ground is bigger than the standard height to be considered for the standard on ground photovoltaic pattern, with an increased cost related to the materials of the supporting structure. Image from the Italian guidelines for agrivoltaic plants, June 2022, Ministry of Ecological Transition.

Consequently, APV systems are in general less energy effective and more expensive than standard PV systems.

A possible alternative approach is limiting the area for crops to the area in between the photovoltaic modules, which is interested only by a dynamic shading from the PV modules (Figure 2). Nevertheless, in this case, the area underneath the modules surface is not useful for crops because of the insufficient height. This is known as "intercropped agrivovoltaics".

Figure 2: The typical agrivoltaic layout that use the standard patterns of on ground photovoltaics allow the crop production only in between the stripes of photovoltaic modules. The area corresponding to the projection of the photovoltaics modules on ground remains unused. Image from the Italian guidelines for agrivoltaic plants, June 2022, Ministry of Ecological Transition.

In this project the starting point is the willingness to experiment with standard PV layout (orientation of the modules, distance between the stripes of the modules, and height of the modules from the ground) with the purpose of finding solutions for using the unused area of the PV field in the best possible way from an energy and economical point of view.

3 GENERAL OBJECTIVES

The specific objectives that have driven the design of the algaevoltaic system are: a) keeping the standard layout of on ground PV; 2) maximizing the PV power generation (on a land unit); 3) improving the yield of the biomass by means of an appropriate design.

Specific key performance parameters for such objectives are: a) the market value of the produced biomass; b) the PV energy yield (KWh/kWp/year); c) the biomass yield (t/year)

To maximize the performance related to the specific biomass related design objectives, microalgae (Chlorella) have been selected because of their low light requirements (highest photosynthesis efficient among vegetable species) and because of their high economic market value.

More in detail, microalgae present several advantages, if compared with other crops or algae: they need low levels of solar radiation; their market value is high as they are used as food and as integrators (e.g. Chlorella market value ranges from 100 to 200€ per kg); do have low water requirements.

Microalgae cultivation techniques are essentially based on the use of open and closed systems.

Open systems use large tanks, ponds, canals, low-water circulation units in the form of panels or circuits consisting of polycarbonate pipes with forced circulation as the culture environment.

Closed systems, on the other hand, use large polyethylene systems or cylindrical, helical, annular or panel photobioreactors as the culture environment, which are supplied with semi-continuous radiant energy in order to maximise algal growth. Among closed systems, photobioreactors stand out, with tubular and plate reactors being the most widely used.

This equipment can achieve high cell density and facilitate the maintenance of monocultures of algal species, thanks to its closed structure and relatively controllable environment with consequent better contamination control.

Figure 3: Example of vertical tubular photobioreactors. The tubes are typically oriented horizontally or vertically and are supplied from a central unit with pump, sensors, nutrients and CO_2.

Among the different forms of photobioreactors the use of tubular, vertical photobioreactors was chosen (Figure 3). This allows for a complete engineered design, including a closed system, with an optimal control of the growth features of the microalgae.

Photobioreactors are closed systems in which a single species is inoculated to keep a clean colture operation.

Since the tubes behave as solar collectors, overheating is detrimental; in this sense, the shading offered by the PV modules can advantage the efficiency of the system. Furthermore, the engineering of photobioreactors offers a good opportunity for experiencing with the integration of the PV system and the photobioreactor, if an appropriate engineering design is performed.

The photobioreactors are made of closed circuits including a circulation pump, a system for releasing oxygen into the atmosphere (degasser) and a centrifuge, which is used to collect the algae. The advantages of this approach concern: a) the possibility of creating a dynamic culture in continuous recirculation and with a single control point; b) low water consumption; c) the complete automation of the plant.

4 THE PILOT @ENEA RESEARCH CENTER FACILITY IN PORTICI

4.1 The system design

The algaevoltaic pilot plant @ENEA Portici is the result of an accurate design and simulation work conducted by a multi-disciplinary team. Combining since the very early design both the competences in several fields of PV and in microalge allowed for a design able to optimize the integrated energy performance. In this sense, the final design of the project into a unique, integrated system the results of simulations made both for PV and for the microalgae.

Figure 4: The pilot algaevoltaic plant @ENEA Research Center in Portici (IT).

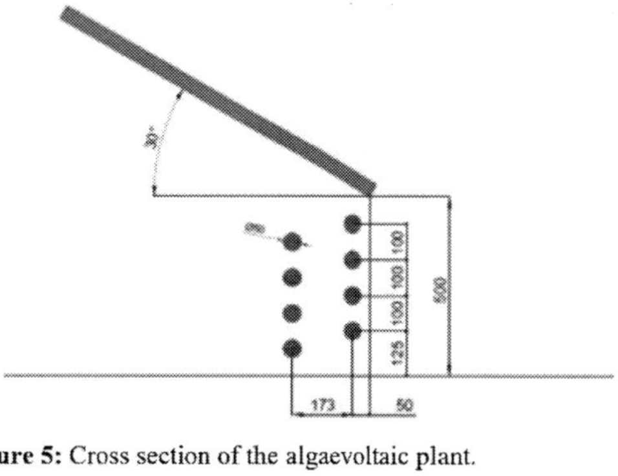

Figure 5: Cross section of the algaevoltaic plant.

The light transmission optimisation (finding the optimal balance between the shade from PV and the microalgae growth) oriented the geometry of the system and therefore the mounting position of the tubular photobioreactors with respect to the PV array; i.e. identifying a geometric configuration that determines partial shading of the photobioreactors when the sun is particularly high on the horizon, but which still allows sufficient irradiation for the growth of the microalgal culture.

Several combinations of PV and microalgae photobioreactors have been considered for meeting all the above-mentioned requirements. Several simulations have been run by using PVSyst for different integrated solutions in order to: 1) calculate the solar radiation on the surfaces of the PV tubes (which is not immediate due to the circular section of the tubes), and evaluating the corresponding biomass yield; 2) calculate the solar radiation on the photovoltaic modules surface (Figure 6), and evaluating the corresponding energy yield.

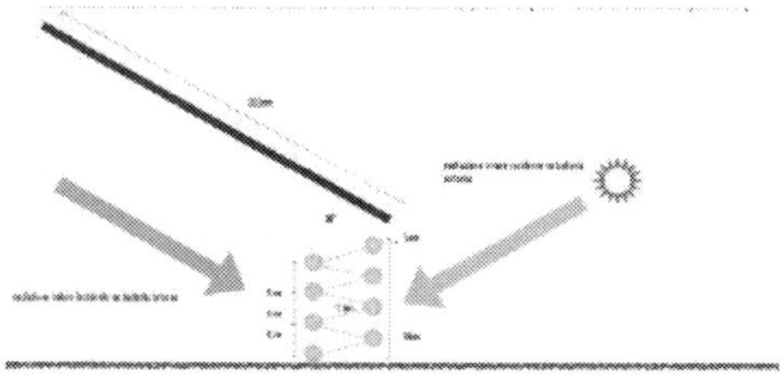

Figure 6: The incident radiation on both internal and external tubes has been evaluated along with the diffuse radiation from the North and the beam radiation from the South.

The final configuration corresponds to a typical on ground PV layout, being the modules organized in stripes East-West oriented and facing the South with a tilt angle of 30° (optimised on the site latitude), which allow also for the use of bifacial PV modules. The positioning of the photobioreactors has been chosen to ensure an optimal irradiation value on the tubes' surface (Figure 5 and Figure 6).

Figure 7: General view of the algaevoltaic plant @ENEA. The two sub-field are made with monofacial and bifacial PV modules, respectively.

The algaevoltaic field is divided into two sub-fields, that are exactly the same but built one with standard photovoltaic modules (glass-tedlar), and the other one with bifacial PV modules (glass-glass). These systems are equipped with two perfectly equal circuits of photobioreactors each with a capacity about of 450l, connected to a centrifuge used for the separation of microalgae from the culture water.

Figure 8: The degasser.

Figure 9: Samples of Chlorella, collected @the algaevoltaic pilot in Portici.

4.2 The monitoring system

Both the electrical production data and the microalgae parameters, such as temperature, pH, oxygen concentration, are continuously monitored. From these data it is possible to control the grope of microalgae and to regulate parameters affecting the growth such as CO_2 rate (automatically injected by the degasses). The microalgae solution is periodically analysed using a spectrophotometer to measure the light absorption @720nm: when this parameter becomes particularly high, the algae harvesting proceeds, connecting the circuit to the centrifuge.

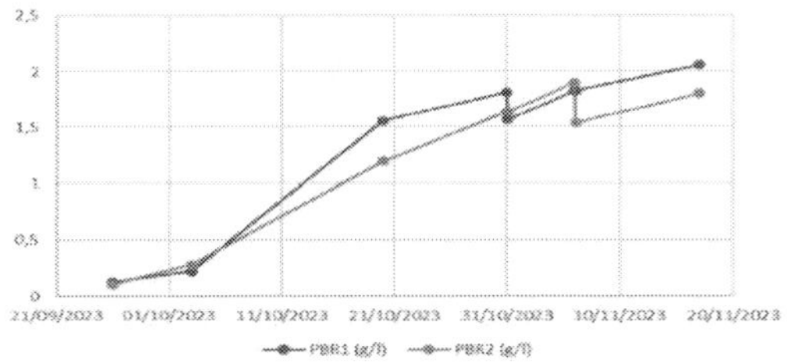

Figure 10: Growth curves of the microalgal cultivation: in blue double-sided PV plant, in orange single-sided PV plant (the steps observed in the curves are in correspondence with the algae harvesting).

4.3 Microalgae growth optimisation

Regarding the microalage growth optimisation, once the geometrical configuration of the system has been defined, the work involved the development of a mathematical model for the growth of microalgae in photobioreactors.

In particular, the optimization of irradiance utilization by microalgae grown in photobioreactors is a topic of great interest, and its mathematical modelling can be crucial for the commercial exploitation of microalgae. The microalgal photosynthesis model studied for this work is a modular model, in which various phenomena regulating algal growth are reproduced. The modules can be activated or deactivated depending on the simulation to be performed and possibly combined. The modules integrated into the microalgae growth model concern the various photoadaptation responses to excess light, which, if channelled into the photosynthetic process, could damage the cells through oxidative.

The phenomena at play include the reduction of pigments involved in photo-capture and the damage and repair of the D1 protein in photosystem II, known as "photoinhibition" both of which result in a reduction in photosynthetic efficiency in cells grown under high light.

A third module, based on previous work on plants reproduces two more relevant processes, i.e. the activation of the Rubisco enzyme after exposure to light (night-day cycle), and the dissipation of excess energy in the form of heat through the process called Non-Photochemical Quenching (NPQ).

The parameters of the developed simulation model, composed of a set of Ordinary Differential Equations (ODE), has been calibrated using data from the pilot algal bioreactor. Specifically, data of O2 concentration (expressed in ppm) in the growth solution has been used to calibrate the simulated photosynthetic flow at daily scale

The potential of this approach if of high importance. In fact, once the model is validate (through experimental data), this can be applied to a system in any location. For this reasons, in order to make the model easily applicable to different locations, the main inputs of the model are solar radiation measured as global horizontal irradiance (GHI expressed in W m-2) and air temperature (oC).

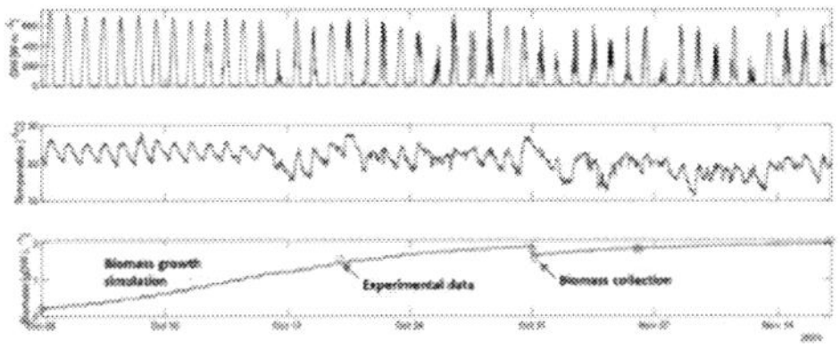

Figure 11: Comparison between simulated growth curves and experimental data.

4.4 Field experimental data

Starting from October 2023 to June 2024, the plant was continuously monitored, obtaining the first experimental results.

Regarding the PV section, there are no significant differences in electricity production between the system with monofacial PV modules and the one with bifacial modules: both have a Performance Ratio about of 84%.

Several microalgae collections were performed, growth curves were obtained (Figure 10), and growth rates were calculated for both plants. The data shows that the system with bifacial modules has growth rate that is approximately 20% higher than those of the single-facial system. This is probably due both to the partial transparency of the bifacial modules and to the better reflection of the incident light on the back-sheet of the module, the latter being made of glass, while that of the standard module is made of Tedlar. These effects produce better irradiation of the photobioreactors placed under the bifacial modules, compared to those placed under the monofacial ones.

The microalgae growth model was used to simulate their production using the real horizontal incident global radiation and ambient temperature as input data. The experimental data show a very good correspondence between the simulated and the experimental data (Figure 11).

5 PRELIMINARY NUTSHELL CONCLUSIONS

In terms of implementation possibility, the potential of the proposed approach is very high, as the study considered can be applied in several cases such as revamping and repowering of standard PV layouts, or, also, improvements of existing power PV plants, though increased energy production and economic efficiency.

It is worth notice that the cultivation of microalgae is carried out through an almost completely automatic process which requires much less manpower than conventional open agrivoltaic systems. Lastly, the market value of microalgae is very high, and this could significantly reduce the break-even point of the investment.

10.4229/EUPVSEC2025/4DO.2.1
020378-005

EXPERIMENTAL INVESTIGATION OF AN AGRIVOLTAIC COLLECTOR WITH PLANAR SPECTRAL BEAM SPLITTING

Inga Krasilnikov[1,3], Abraham Kribus[1]*, Gur Mittelman[2], Liad Reshef[3], Shay Ozer[3], Lavi Rosenfeld[3], Helena Vitoshkin[3]

[1]School of Mechanical Engineering, Faculty of Engineering, Tel Aviv University, Tel Aviv, Israel
[2]Afeka Tel-Aviv Academic College of Engineering, Tel Aviv, Israel
[3]Institute of Agricultural Engineering, Agricultural Research Organization, Rishon LeZion, Israel
* Corresponding author: kribus@tauex.tau.ac.il

ABSTRACT: Spectrum splitting agrivoltaic collectors allow photosynthetic radiation to pass through the collectors in contrast to conventional collectors that produce full shading. The rest of the solar spectrum is redirected for electricity generation. The current study presents experimental results for the optical and electrical performance of a laboratory-scale prototype of a spectrum splitting collector, aimed at validating the theoretical performance predictions. Commercially available architectural Low-E window glass panes were used as spectral splitters. An off-the-shelf bifacial PV module was illuminated equally on both sides with modified sunlight reflected from the splitters, containing a reduced share of visible light. Measurements included incident fluxes on the PV module from both sides, module temperature, and electrical output as well as the radiation flux reaching the ground. The experimental results were compared against theoretical predictions and demonstrated good agreement for both the radiation fluxes and electrical output. The results confirm the potential of collectors with spectrum splitting to significantly increase the ground-level PAR flux compared to full shading, thus reducing the impact of agrivoltaics on shade-sensitive crops, while maintaining a high level of electricity production.
Keywords: Agrivoltaics, Spectrum splitting, Hot mirror, Bifacial module

1 INTRODUCTION

Agrivoltaics (or agri-photovoltaics, APV), with photovoltaic (PV) modules installed over cropland, can open vast agricultural land resources for renewable electricity generation. However, conventional PV modules are opaque and create significant shading, which can reduce photosynthesis and the crop yield [1]. Some crops are insensitive or even benefit from partial shading, but most of the agricultural area globally (about 70% according to FAO database) is allocated to crops that are sensitive to shading. Therefore, solutions that minimize the damage to crop yield are essential.

Spectrum splitting of sunlight is one such solution: APV collectors that transmit the photosynthetic part of sunlight to the crop, while using the rest of the solar spectrum for electricity generation [2], [3]. Dichroic mirrors that transmit either the entire visible light range (hot mirror), or the red and blue parts only (dual bandpass mirror), while reflecting the rest of the spectrum, can be used as splitters. While some published concepts use curved surfaces and concentration, a simpler design was proposed with flat splitter mirrors and a bifacial solar module receiving equal illumination from both sides as shown in Figure 1 [3], [4]. The photosynthetically active radiation (PAR, 400 nm – 700 nm) part of incident sunlight is transmitted through the splitters towards the crop. The rest of the sunlight spectrum containing near infrared (NIR, 700 nm – 1100 nm), and possibly also green light (500 nm – 570 nm) in the case of a dual bandpass mirror, is reflected to the PV module to generate electricity. The bifacial module is illuminated equally on both sides, in contrast to conventional use where the back side receives only a small amount of reflected radiation. The spaces among collector rows allow full sunlight to reach the crop. During east-west daily tracking the regions of full and filtered sunlight move across the crop field, minimizing the variations in illumination during the day and promoting uniform crop growth.

Our previous work focused on modeling the performance of this collector [4] and showed that the loss of PAR on the crop can be reduced from about 20% in a conventional APV field that uses opaque modules, to approximately 10%. At the same time, electricity generation per unit land area can be about the same or even higher. However, these results are based on a theoretical model of the spectrum splitting and of the module performance, which needs experimental validation. In particular, the illumination of the bifacial PV module with a modified spectrum of sunlight, and under equal flux on both sides, is an unusual set of conditions that needs validation. The current study provides the needed experimental demonstration with a comparison to the theoretical predictions.

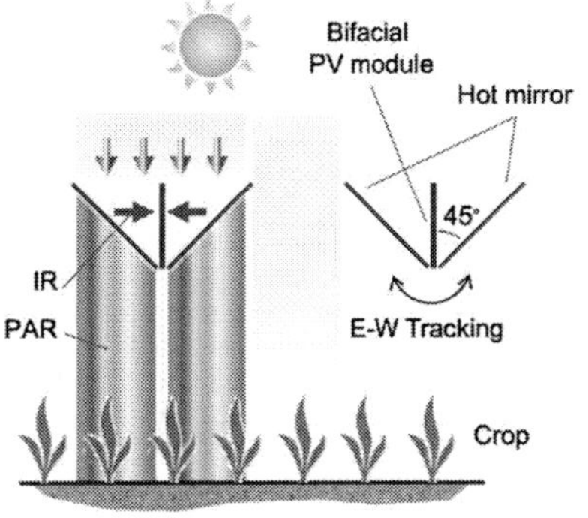

Figure 1: The concept of spectral beam splitting with planar splitters: PAR is transmitted to the crops, and the rest of the spectrum is reflected to both sides of a bifacial PV module.

2 EXPERIMENTAL METHODS

Figure 2 shows the experimental setup located at the Institute of Agricultural Engineering in Beit-Bagan, Israel.

Commercially available hot mirror spectral splitters were used (Low-E glass SN-75 by Guardian Glass). These were selected for their availability at reasonable cost, even though their spectral selectivity is only moderate and their absorptance is too high as shown in Figure 3. The splitters are at 45° angle to a bifacial PV module (LR5-72HBD, LONGi, China). An additional identical module was installed facing the direction of the sun as reference. A single axis tracking mechanism rotates the collector from east to west following the daily apparent motion of the sun, guided by a sun sensor.

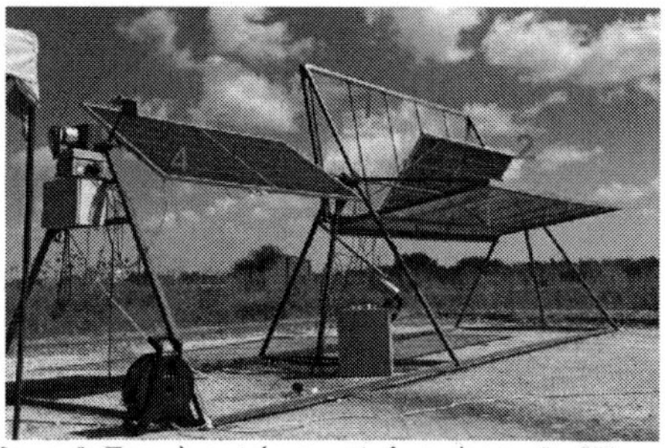

Figure 2: Experimental setup: 1- hot mirrors, 2 - PV module, 3 - single axis tracking mechanism and sun sensor, 4 – reference PV module.

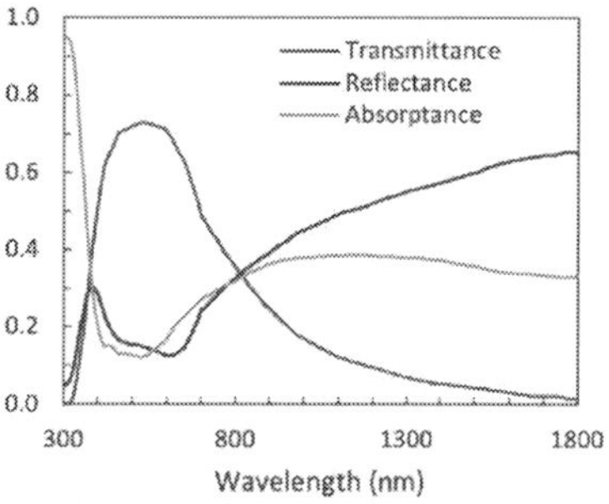

Figure 3: SN-75 hot mirror optical properties.

The setup was equipped with global irradiation pyranometers (Apogee Instruments, USA) installed on both sides of the module, and global and PAR sensors (LI-COR Biosciences, USA) on the ground in the filtered radiation area below the test setup. The module temperature was monitored using T-type thermocouples (XF-1166-FAR Labfactory) attached to the back side of each module using thermally conductive foil. Ambient conditions were obtained by the local meteorological station (METOS by Pessl, Austria). The data was logged in a Campbell Scientific Inc datalogger (model 21X Micrologger) with a 1-minute sampling interval. The electrical power output was recorded every 10 minutes by a EKO MP-11 Solar Module Analyzer.

3 RESULTS

3.1 Incident radiation on module

Figure 4(a) shows the radiation flux measurements taken during several hours on August 30. The global horizontal insolation (GHI) data taken from a nearby meteorological station indicates clear day behavior. The tracking pyranometer installed near the reference module shows almost constant incident flux of about 980 W/m^2. The fluxes reflected by the splitters and incident on both sides of the PV module are similar and are lower due to the transmission of part of the light towards the ground. The sum of radiation fluxes incident on the module from both sides is also nearly constant at about 1070 W/m^2.

The radiation flux reaching the module contains contributions of direct radiation reflected from the splitters, diffuse radiation from the sky, and radiation reflected from the ground which mostly passes through the splitters on its way up. These contributions were calculated assuming standard reference spectra (ASTM G173 standard) for each solar radiation component, the measured values of direct and diffuse radiation fluxes, the optical properties of the splitters, and the reflectance of the ground surface (0.4, measured separately).

Figure 4(b) shows the calculated spectrum reaching the module, accounting for both sides. The large deficit in the visible range compared to the spectrum of GHI is due to the selective reflectance of the splitters, where much of the visible light is transmitted. In the NIR, there is a smaller reduction compared to GHI due to higher reflectance of the splitters in this range. The total incident flux (integral over the spectrum) on the two sides of the module according to the theoretical prediction is 977 W/m^2, about 6% lower than the actual measurement. This is a good match considering the measurement uncertainty and the modeling inaccuracy.

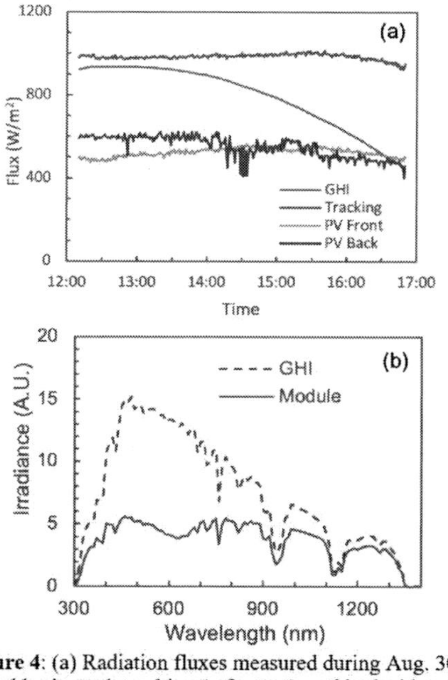

Figure 4: (a) Radiation fluxes measured during Aug. 30: global horizontal, tracking (reference), and both sides of the PV module. (b) Calculated spectrum of radiation incident on the module at 12:50, in comparison to the spectrum of GHI.

3.2 Module temperature

Figure 5 shows the measured temperature of the PV module in comparison to that of the reference module which received full sunlight while tracking. There is a small difference until about 14:00 and then the two

10.4229/EUPVSEC2025/4DO.2.2

modules have approximately the same temperature (46°C ±1.5°C). This qualitative change can be understood by considering the wind: its speed was generally constant during the day, but around 14:00 the wind direction changed from west to north-west. The western wind was largely blocked by the splitters which are aligned in the north-south direction, leading to higher module temperature compared to the reference module. The later appearance of a north wind component increased the airflow and the convection heat transfer in the space enclosed by the splitters, leading to module temperature comparable to the conventional tracking reference module.

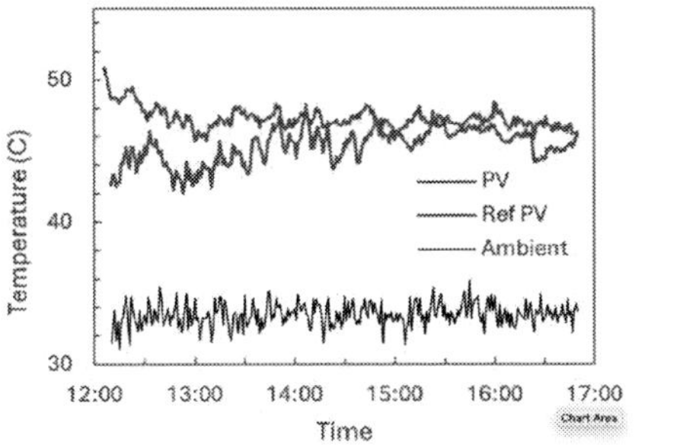

Figure 5: Module temperature in comparison to reference module.

3.3 Electrical output

Figure 6 shows the power output of the module compared to the reference module during the test day. There is a large difference even though the two modules are subject to similar total incident flux and are at similar temperatures. However, the spectra of incident radiation on the two modules are different, and therefore a more detailed analysis is needed to understand the different performance.

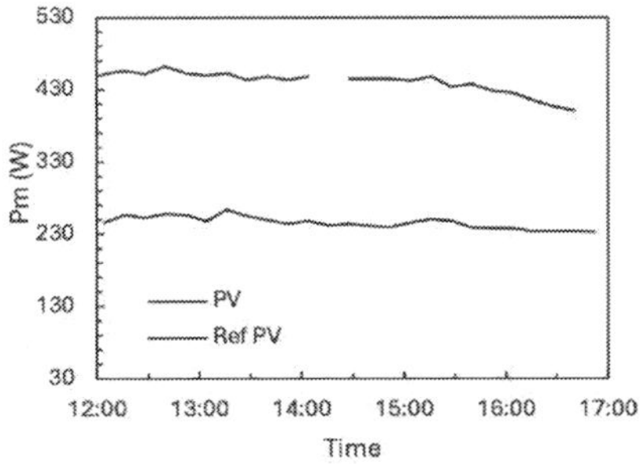

Figure 6: Power output of the two modules.

The electrical performance of the module was modeled using the CEC six-parameter single-diode equivalent circuit model [5] that provides the relation of current and voltage:

$$I(V) = 2A_c J_L - I_o\left[exp\left(\frac{V + IR_s}{a}\right) - 1\right] - \frac{V + IR_s}{R_{sh}} \quad (1)$$

A_c is the area of a half-cell, multiplied by 2 to represent two parallel strings of half-cells in the module. I_o, a, R_s and R_{sh} are the module parameters that are derived from the manufacturer's data of the module and corrected to the temperature measured in the experiment [4]. The photogeneration (light) current density J_L is determined by the modified spectrum incident on the module and is calculated using the spectral response SR of a typical silicon cell [6]:

$$J_L = (1 + BF) \cdot \int_{300}^{2500} q_{in}(\lambda)\, \tau_m\, SR(\lambda)\, d\lambda \quad (2)$$

q_{in} is the spectral flux incident on one side of the module as shown in Figure 4(b). τ_m is the transmittance of the module glass, and BF is the module bifaciality factor.

Figure 7 shows the measured and predicted current-voltage and power-voltage at solar Noon. The measured value of the short-circuit current is lower than the prediction by 4.3%, and the open-circuit voltage matches to within 1.1%. However, the measured curve shows a drop in current as the voltage increases, which can represent a current mismatch behavior attributed to flux non-uniformity. This leads to a large difference of 23% between the predicted and measured maximum power. Some cells were indeed partially shaded on the back side by the module frame due to imperfect tracking, and by the tracking mechanism shaft. These effects can be eliminated by changes in the mechanical design.

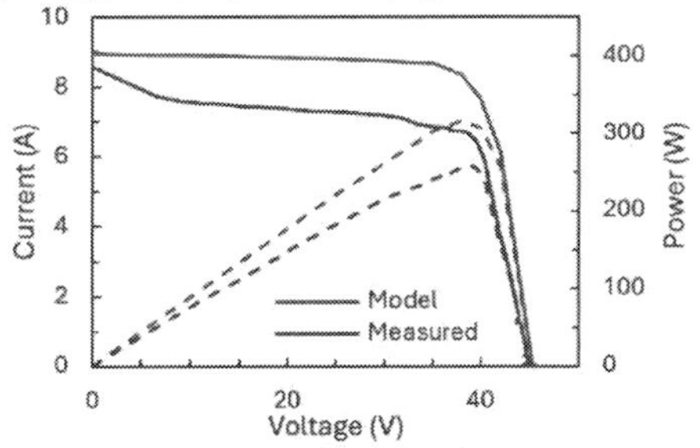

Figure 7: Current-voltage (solid lines) and power-voltage (dashed lines) model predictions vs. measured values.

3.4 Incident radiation of the ground

Figure 8(a) shows incident total flux and PAR flux of filtered radiation incident on the ground during the experiment, measured locally in the shaded area. Also shown are the corresponding fluxes for full shade, i.e., diffuse radiation only, representing the situation in the shaded area under conventional PV collectors. The amount of PAR reaching the ground under the collector is about 3.3 times higher than the amount that would reach the ground under the full shade. The short time intervals of low flux in Figure 8(a) correspond to times when the sensor is shaded by a structural element. The PAR fraction in the filtered light is 65% - 70%, much higher than about 45% in normal sunlight.

The calculated spectrum of filtered radiation on the ground corresponding to the experimental conditions at 12:50 is shown in Figure 8(b). The visible or PAR section is high while the NIR part is much lower as can be seen by comparison the GHI spectrum. This is due the preferential transmission of visible light and reflection of NIR by the splitters. Comparison the spectrum of diffuse radiation representing full shade shows the much higher PAR content of the filtered light. The integrals of the calculated spectra over wavelength result in total flux and PAR flux of 393 W/m^2 and 276 W/m^2, both about 12% higher

10.4229/EUPVSEC2025/4DO.2.2

than the measured values. This reasonable difference can be partly attributed to measurement uncertainty and the rest to simulation inaccuracy.

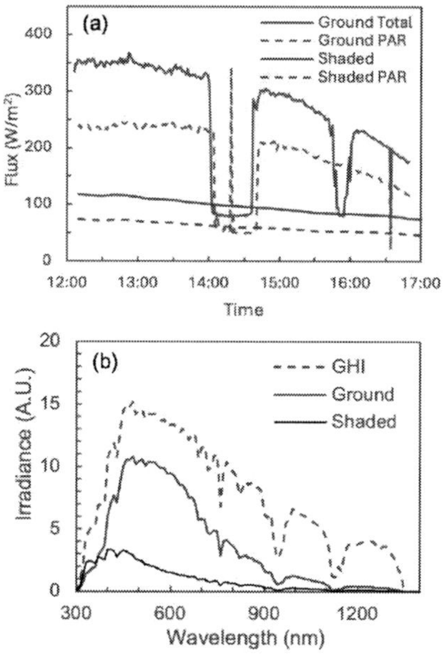

Figure 8: (a) Total and PAR fluxes of filtered radiation incident on the ground compared to full shade, (b) calculated spectrum of radiation incident on the ground, in comparison to GHI and to full shade.

3.4 Prediction for an improved splitter

The splitter used in this work is not optimized for agrivoltaics and its spectral selectivity is quite low. It is possible to produce much better dichroic mirrors using thin-film technologies such as vapor deposition and polymer film co-extrusion [7] having the potential to achieve very low cost when mass-produced. To consider the potential of such splitters and their impact on performance, we define a high-quality splitter specifically designed for the agrivoltaic application. The following optical properties (which can be achieved with dichroic mirrors) are used: transmittance 0.9 for red (600 nm – 700 nm) and blue (400 nm – 500 nm) wavelengths, reflectance 0.9 for the rest of the spectrum, and negligible absorptance. The expected performance of our test setup was recalculated for this splitter using the same test conditions.

Figure 9(a) shows the calculated spectra of radiation incident on the module and on ground in the presence of the improved splitter. Clearly, both the radiation reaching the module (including most of the green light), and the red and blue photosynthetic radiation reaching the ground, are higher compared to the low-performance splitter as shown in Figure 4 and Figure 8. Figure 9(b) shows the predicted current-voltage curve for the improved splitter, with much higher current due to the increase of incident radiation on the module.

Table I shows a comparison of module performance as measured, as calculated by our model for the experiment conditions (eliminating the effect of flux non-uniformity), and as calculated for the improved splitter. The current and the power output with the improved splitter are significantly higher due to the improved reflectance of the splitter at the relevant wavelengths, and the additional reflection of green light to the module. The maximum power is close to the nominal rating of the module adjusted for temperature: 483 W. The loss of red and blue light reaching the ground is only 12% with the improved splitter compared to 35% with the low-grade splitter that was used in the experiment. Considering that each location on the ground receives alternately filtered light and full sunlight, the average loss of photosynthetic light should be significantly less than 10%.

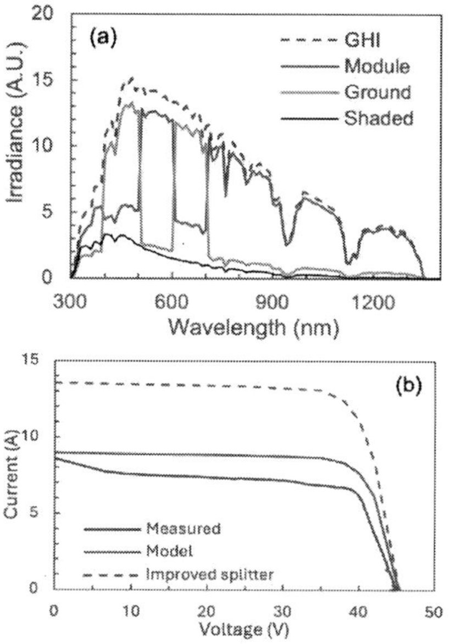

Figure 9: (a) Calculated spectra of radiation incident on the module and on the ground with the improved splitter, compared to GHI and full shade. (b) modeled current-voltage curve of the module with the improved splitter, compared to the actual experimental measurement and corresponding model.

Table I: Open circuit voltage, short circuit current, maximum power, and flux of red and blue (RB) radiation on the ground, for the experiment, the model of the experiment, and model with an improved splitter

	V_{OC} (V)	I_{SC} (A)	P_m (W)	RB (W/m²)
Experiment	44.80	8.58	257.1	
Model	45.30	8.95	316.6	175.9
Improved splitter	45.37	13.56	470.1	237.1

4 CONCLUSIONS

A bifacial PV module was tested under the unusual conditions of spectrum-splitting collector, including a modified spectrum and equal illumination of both sides of the module. The measured optical and electrical performance was in reasonable agreement with the prediction based on the properties of the splitter and a standard single-diode equivalent circuit model. A deviation of the measured maximum power from the prediction was observed, and this is due to the non-uniformity of the incident flux which can be improved with better mechanical design. Measurements of the photosynthetic radiation incident on the ground showed a significant advantage over conventional collectors that create full shade.

A comparison of the experimental results vs. a theoretical prediction of performance with improved high-quality splitters showed a potential for significant improvements in both the module electrical performance and the photosynthetic radiation reaching the ground. This should be therefore a major avenue for future development and optimization.

The current experimental results allow the model validation and refining required to predict the performance of large-scale APV fields based on the proposed concept of spectrum splitting collectors.

ACKNOWLEDGMENTS

Funding for this work was provided by the Israel Ministry of Energy and Infrastructure, grant 219-11-125, and by the US-Israel binational agricultural research and development fund (BARD), grant US-5236-20.

REFERENCES

[1] Z. Tahir and N. Z. Butt, "Implications of spatial-temporal shading in agrivoltaics under fixed tilt & tracking bifacial photovoltaic panels," *Renew Energy*, vol. 190, pp. 167–176, 2022, doi: 10.1016/j.renene.2022.03.078.

[2] W. Huang *et al.*, "A dish-type high-concentration photovoltaic system with spectral beam-splitting for crop growth," *Journal of Renewable and Sustainable Energy*, vol. 9, no. 6, 2017, doi: 10.1063/1.5009319.

[3] G. Mittelman, H. Vitoshkin, B. Lew, H. Mamane, and A. Kribus, "Innovative Solar Spectral Beam Splitting Concepts: Cogeneration and Photochemistry," in *35th European Photovoltaic Solar Energy Conference and Exhibition*, Brussels, 2018, pp. 203–207. doi: 10.4229/35thEUPVSEC20182018-1CV.4.75.

[4] B. A. Shalom, G. Mittelman, A. Kribus, and H. Vitoshkin, "Optical and electrical performance of an agrivoltaic field with spectral beam splitting," *Renew Energy*, vol. 219, Dec. 2023, doi: 10.1016/j.renene.2023.119438.

[5] A. P. Dobos, "An improved coefficient calculator for the california energy commission 6 parameter photovoltaic module model," *Journal of Solar Energy Engineering, Transactions of the ASME*, vol. 134, no. 2, pp. 1–6, 2012, doi: 10.1115/1.4005759.

[6] M. A. Green, K. Emery, Y. Hishikawa, W. Warta, and E. D. Dunlop, "Solar cell efficiency tables (version 48)," *Progress in Photovoltaics: Research and Applications*, vol. 24, no. 7, pp. 905–913, Jul. 2016, doi: 10.1002/pip.2788.

[7] W. Liu *et al.*, "A novel agricultural photovoltaic system based on solar spectrum separation," *Solar Energy*, vol. 162, no. June 2017, pp. 84–94, 2018, doi: 10.1016/j.solener.2017.12.053.

Agri-PV Potential in Northern Climates An Experimental Study on Panel Transparency, and Leafy Vegetable Productivity

M. Rudzikas[1], G. Samuolienė[2], J. Raginskis[3], P. Dubravskij[4], A. Baležentis[1], S. Baležentienė[1]

[1] The Applied Research Institute for Prospective Technologies, Vismaliukų str. 34, Vilnius LT-10243, Lithuania;

[2] The Lithuanian Research Centre for Agriculture and Forestry, Instituto av. 1, LT-58344 Kėdainiai distr., Lithuania

[3] Kaunas University of Technology, K. Donelaicio st. 73, 44249 Kaunas, Lithuania

[4] JSC "Modern E-Technologies", Vismaliukų str. 34, Vilnius LT-10243, Lithuania;

matas.rudzikas@protechnology.lt

EU PVSEC 2025, Bilbao

Outline

- About PROTECH;
- Motivation;
- Methodology;
- Results;
- Conclusions;

2

protech

About PROTECH

PROTECH - The Applied Research Institute for Prospective Technologies is an Industrial Research Institute of renewable energy technologies research in Lithuania since 2005. In-depth research, patent and infrastructure the following topics for industrial applications in:

- Photovoltaic technologies;
- Thermal and energy storage technologies;
- Measurement technologies and devices;
- Digital solutions;

Motivation

- Agrivoltaic systems combine solar energy production with agriculture, more sustainable solution, reduction of CO_2 footprint.
- A barrier to renewable energy adoption in Agriculture - fear of potential yield losses.
- Widely studied in temperate/arid regions (for example Italy, Greece, Almeria, Agadir).
- This study addresses the gap of northern climates by evaluating the potential of agrivoltaics in Lithuania (northern climates), focusing on the impact of different PV panel transparencies on the growth of leafy vegetables.

Mothodology – PV modules and shading

- 4 sites without and with PV panels with transparencies: 76%, 56%, 43%;
- PV module power: 77.7 W, 56.9 W, 29W;
- Each site of 3x4 = 12 of PV modules with area of: 2.77 x 3.27 m;
- Lightweight PV panels made with PERC bifacial solar cells, PET backsheets, EVA encapsulation, aluminum frame.frontsheets and

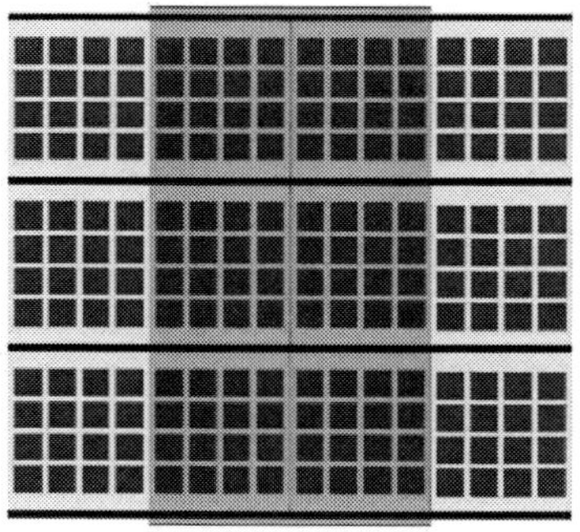

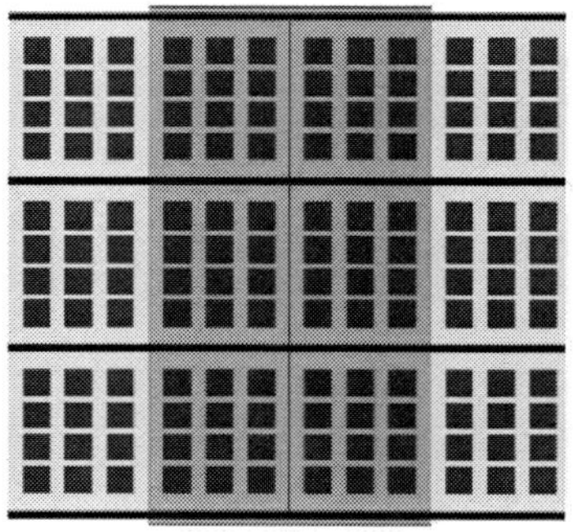

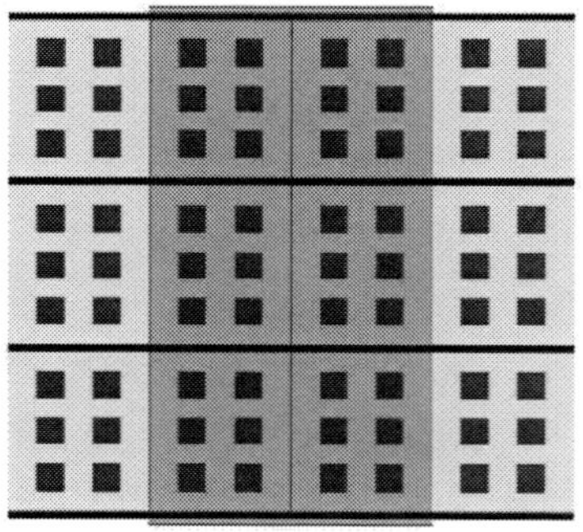

Methodology – plant characterization and growth cycles

- Four different vegetables: lettuce (*Lactuca sativa*), spinach (*Spinacia oleracea*), mustard (*Brassica juncea*), and purslane (*Portulaca oleracea*);
- The plants were cultivated for around 3 weeks before analysis;
- First trial: September 12 – October 2 (no additional lightning);
- Second trial: October 9 – October 30 (additional lightning using high-pressure sodium lamps daily from 6AM to 8AM and from 4PM to 6PM). Included in sensor loggings;
- Fructose and glucose measured using UPLC (Shimdazu) ELSD-LTII detector with NUCLEOSIL Carbohydrate chromatography column (250 x 4mm);
- Leaf area measured using leaf area measurement device: AT Delta –T Devices.

6

Methodology – Greenhouse and Irradiance measurement

- Venlo type greenhouse made from glass;
- Irradiance sensors placed in each of 4 zones: Si-V-1.5TC;
- Measured irradiance in AM1.5g solar spectrum;
- DLI – daily light integral;
- PAR - Photosynthetically Active Radiation from 400 to 700 nm;
- Conversion from AM1.5g to Photosynthetically Active Radiation (PAR) was done by coefficient of 0.48 [1];

[1] J. Schallenberg-Rodriguez et al., Energy Reports. 9 (2023) 5420–5431.

Results – Measured DLI of PAR per Zone

- Balanced DLI for Spinach: ≈ 10 mol/day·m^2;
- Balanced DLI for Mustard: ≈ 12 mol/day·m^2;
- Balanced DLI for Salad and Portulaka: ≈17 mol/day·m^2;

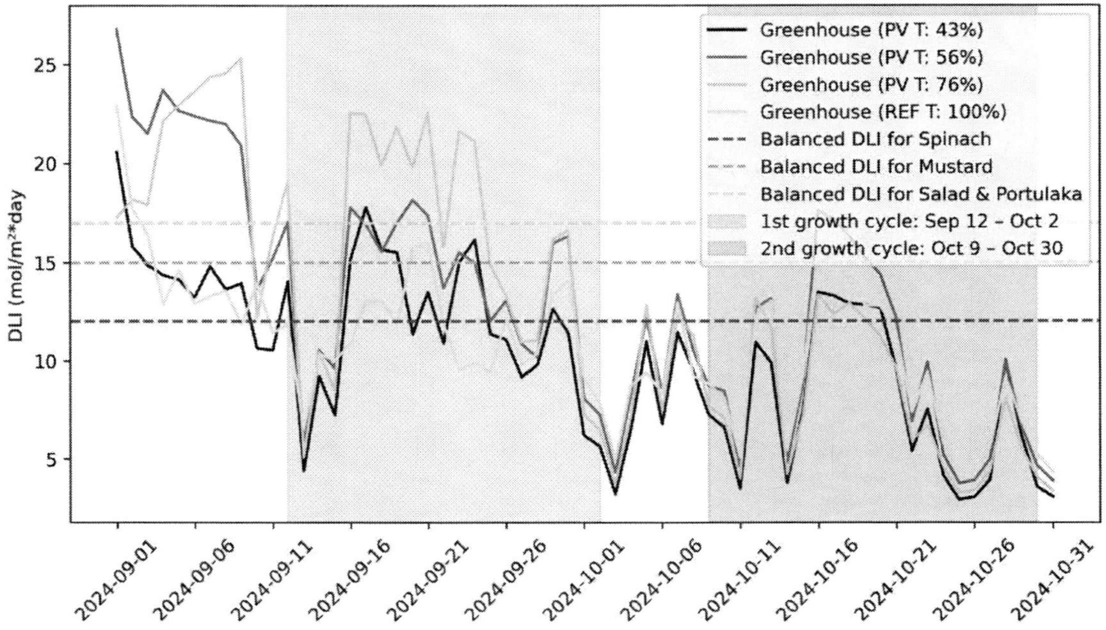

Results – Measured DLI of PAR per Zone for growth cycle 1

- Balanced DLI for Spinach: ≈ 10 mol/day·m^2;
- Balanced DLI for Mustard: ≈ 12 mol/day·m^2;
- Balanced DLI for Salad and Portulaka: ≈17 mol/day·m^2;

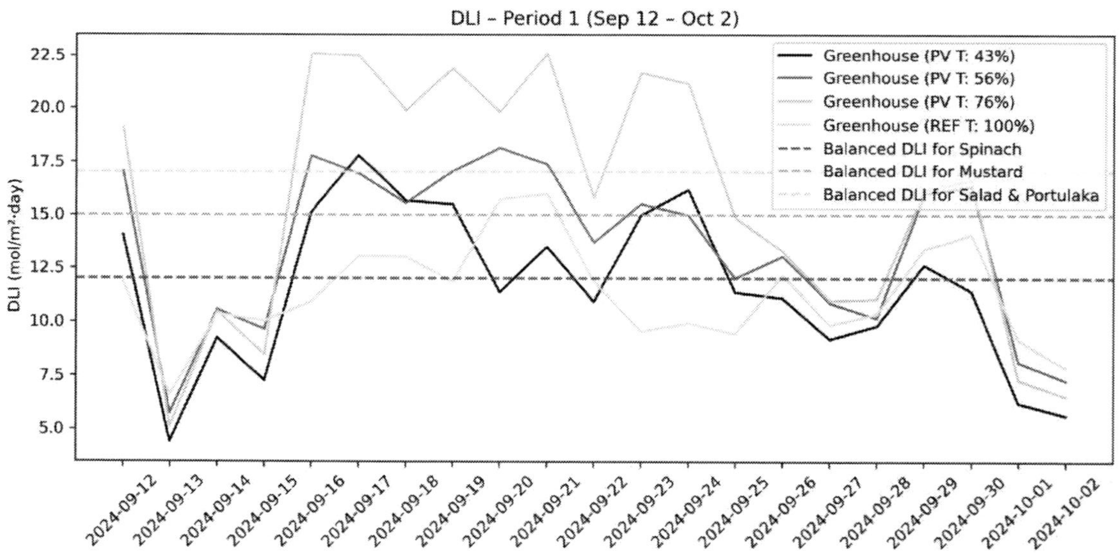

Results – Measured DLI of PAR per Zone for growth cycle 2

- Balanced DLI for Spinach: ≈ 10 mol/day·m^2;
- Balanced DLI for Mustard: ≈ 12 mol/day·m^2;
- Balanced DLI for Salad and Portulaka: ≈17 mol/day·m^2;

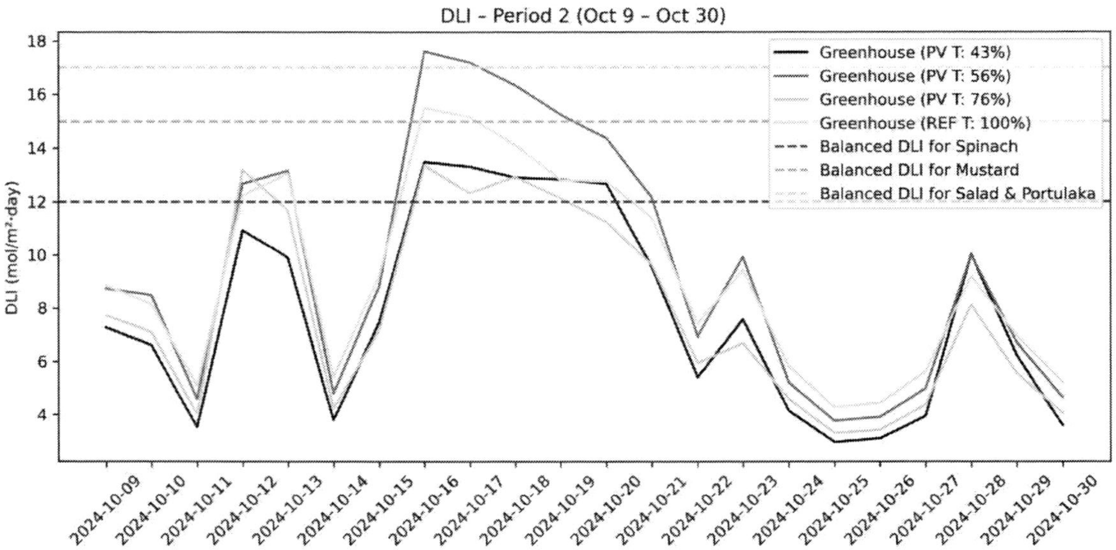

Results – monthly average DLI PAR values per Zone

Period:	Greenhouse (PV T: 43%)	Greenhouse (PV T: 56%)	Greenhouse (PV T: 76%)	Greenhouse (REF T: 100%)
1st growth cycle: Sep 12 – Oct 2	11.59	13.51	15.60	11.28
2nd growth cycle: Oct 9 – Oct 30	7.78	9.56	7.86	9.19

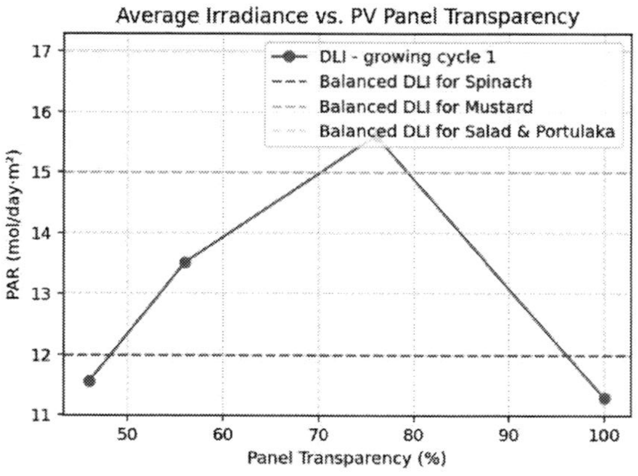

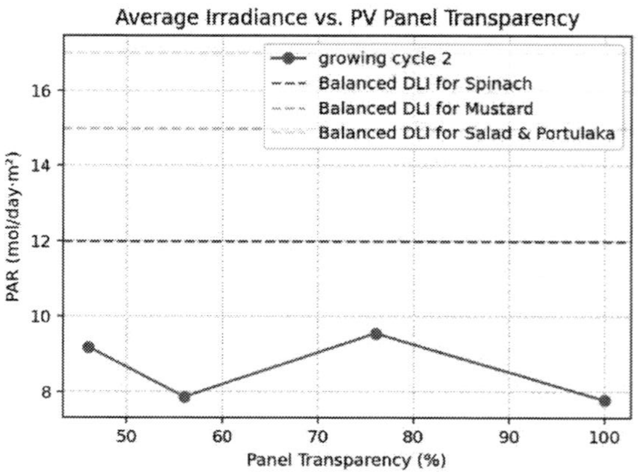

11

Results – monthly average DLI PAR values per Zone

- Figure of merit for the analysis: actual DLI / required DLI.

Period:	Greenhouse (PV T: 43%)	Greenhouse (PV T: 56%)	Greenhouse (PV T: 76%)	Greenhouse (REF T: 100%)
1st growth cycle: Sep 12 – Oct 2	11.59	13.51	15.60	11.28
2nd growth cycle: Oct 9 – Oct 30	7.78	9.56	7.86	9.19

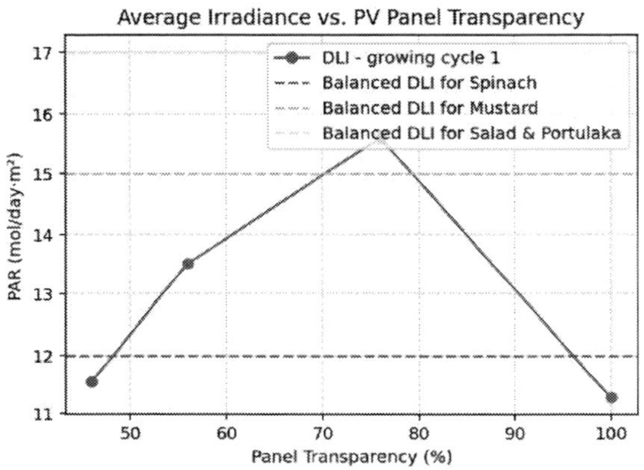

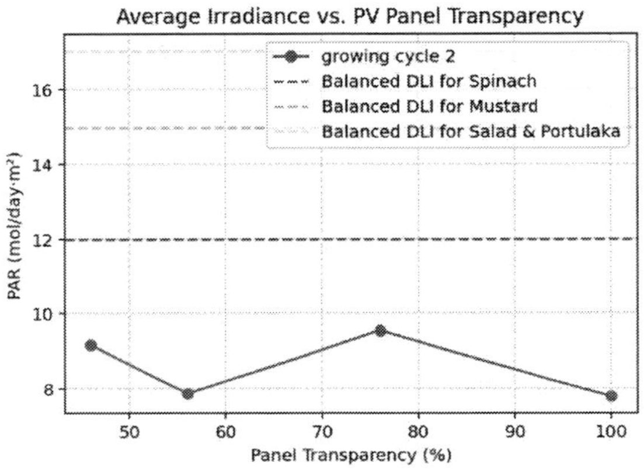

Results – Fructose and Glucose content

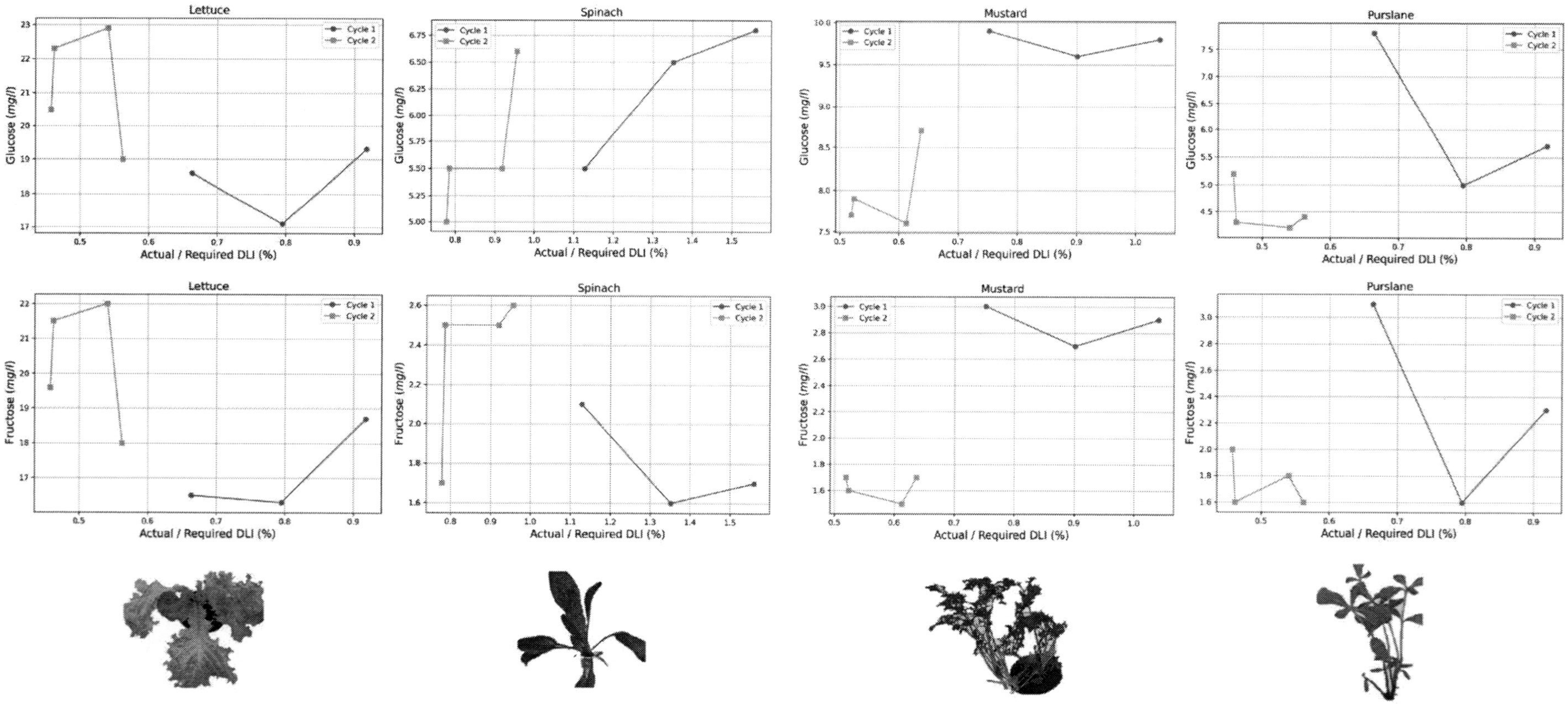

13

Results – Fructose and Glucose content

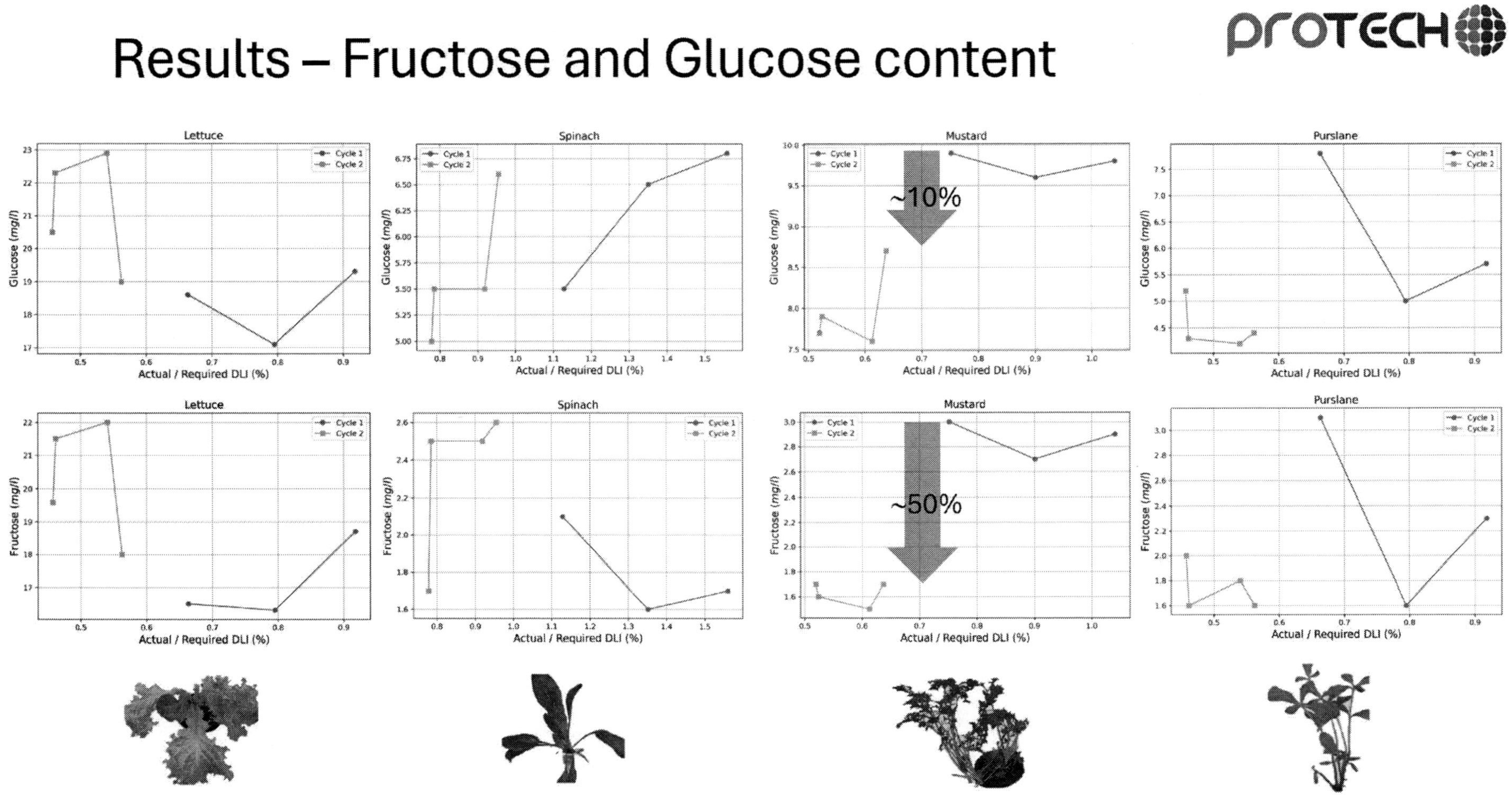

Results – leaf size and green mass

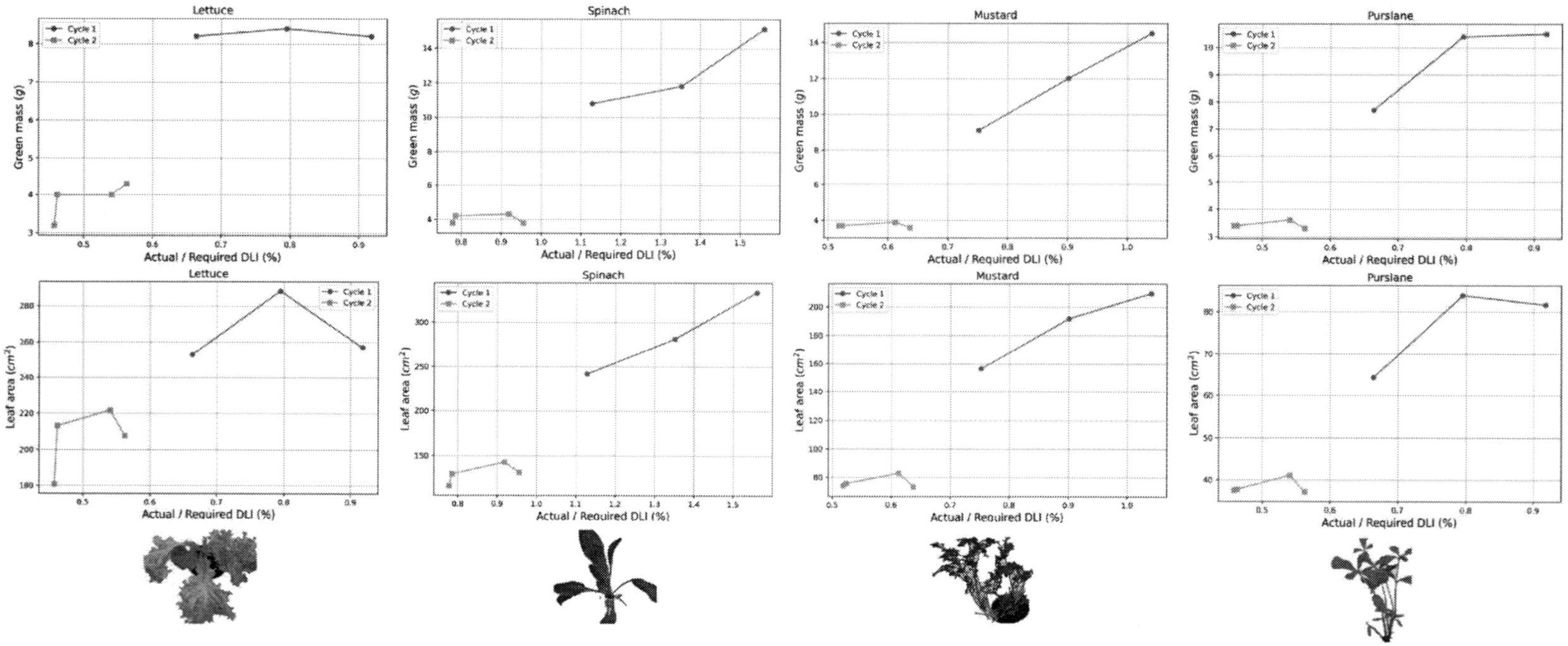

- Green mass declined 50–65% or more for all plant species at DLI ratios below 0.6–0.65, except spinach, which showed similar reductions only below 1;
- Leaf area reduced for 15-50% below 0.6-0.65 except for, where spinach reduction observed below 1.

Results – leaf size and green mass

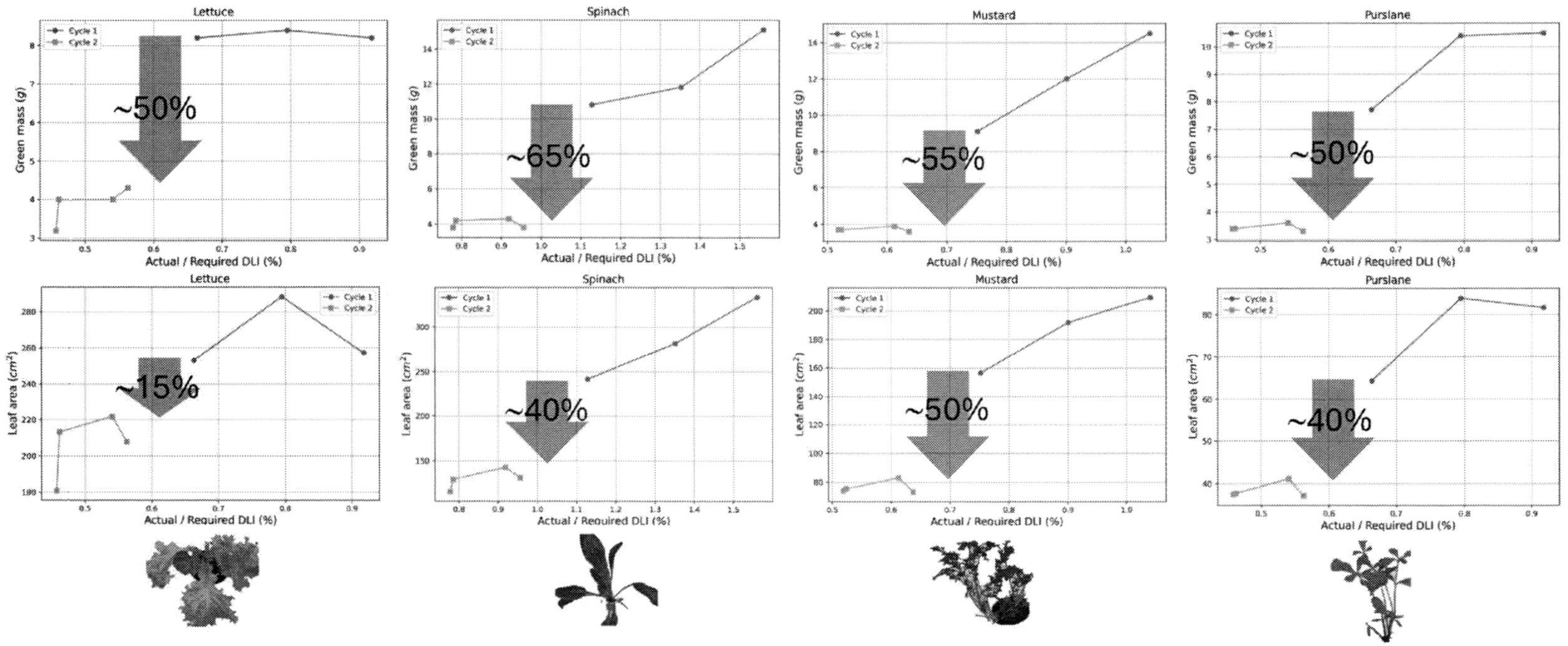

- Green mass declined 50–65% or more for all plant species at DLI ratios below 0.6–0.65, except spinach, which showed similar reductions only below 1;
- Leaf area reduced for 15-50% below 0.6-0.65 except for, where spinach reduction observed below 1.

Results – leaf size and green mass

protech

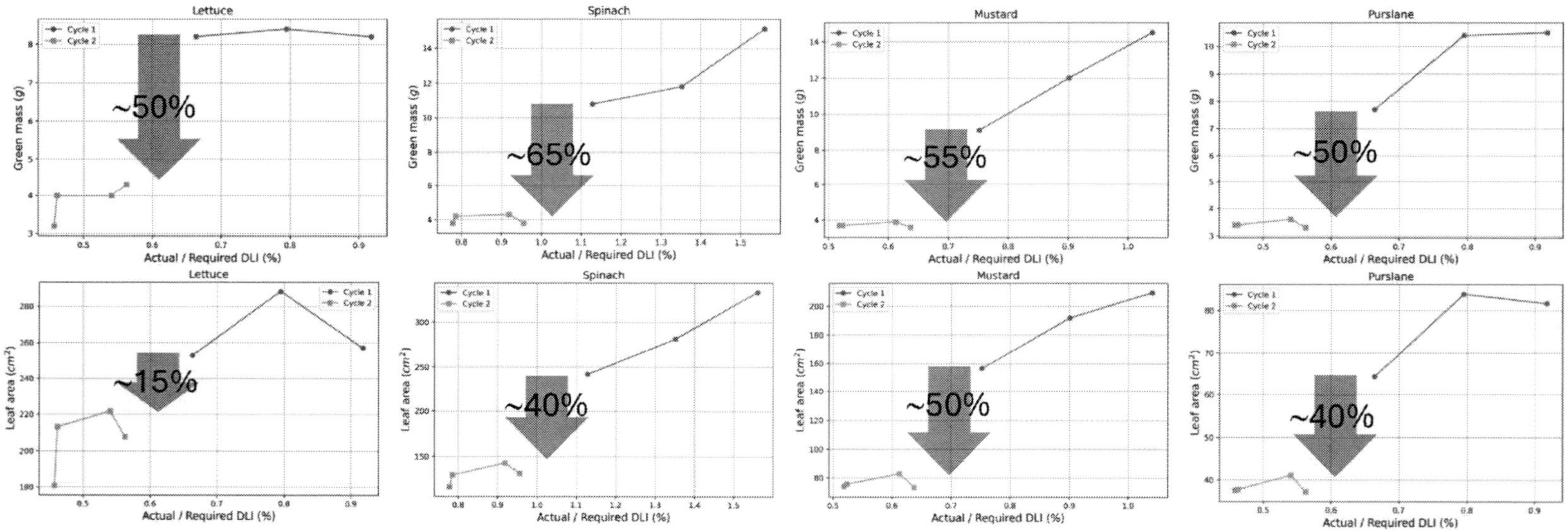

Cycle 1:

Cycle 2:

protech

Conclusions

- **Experimental design:** The plot size (2.77 × 3.27 m) was too small, and daily/ regional solar variability (and possibly greenhouse construction elements) made direct comparisons of PV shading effects unreliable. Analysis was therefore based on actual irradiance relative to required DLI.
- **Sugar content:** Glucose and fructose showed no clear pattern across species, except in mustard, where glucose decreased 10–20% and fructose nearly 50% when actual/required DLI fell below 0.6–0.65.
- **Biomass:** Green mass declined 50–65% or more for all plant species at DLI ratios below 0.6–0.65, except spinach, which showed similar reductions only below 1. Leaf area reduced for 15-60% below 0.6-0.65 except for, where spinach reduction observed below 1.
- **Supplemental lighting:** Four extra hours of high-pressure sodium lighting (Oct 9–30) still left irradiance 35–55% below required DLI for most species, and 5–22% for spinach.

Thank you for your attention!

met. PROTECH ktu 1922 LAMMC

19

Coloured Semi-Transparent CdTe PV Module in Agrivoltaics:
A 2-Year Study on Broccoli Growth and System Potential

Silvia Ma Lu[1], Xiaolin Wang[1], Arash Khosravi[1] and Pietro Elia Campana[1]
[1]Mälardalen University, Västerås, Sweden

25 September 2025 – Session 4DO.2: Agrivoltaic Technologies
The 42nd European Photovoltaic Solar Energy Conference and Exhibition
22 – 26 September 2025, Bilbao, Spain

EUPVSEC European Photovoltaic Solar Energy Conference and Exhibition

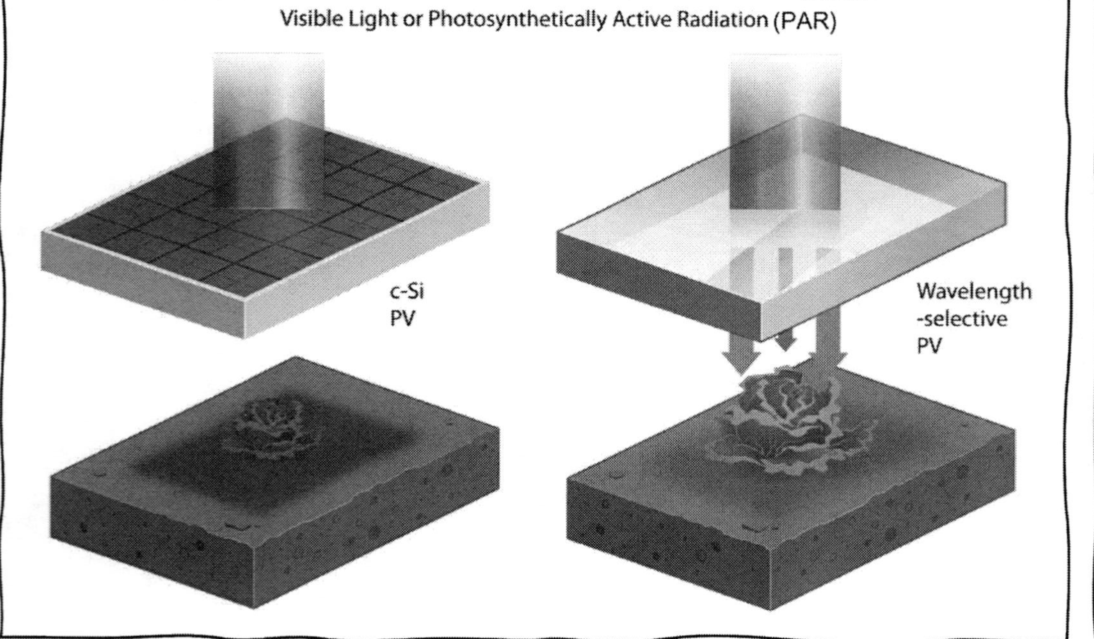

Mälardalen University

Background

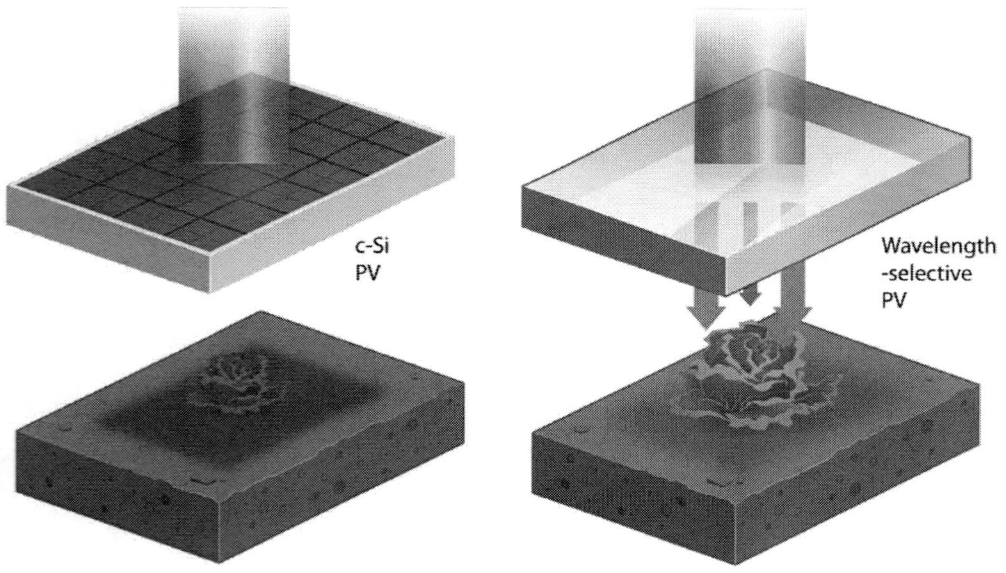

- Plants require a specific spectrum of solar irradiance to perform photosynthesis and grow: photosynthetically active radiation (PAR).
- Excessive high light intensity can harm plant growth by causing photo-inhibition.
- Severe shading is generally detrimental to plant growth.

S. Zhen, M. van Iersel and B. Bugbee. (2021) Why Far-Red Photons Should Be Included in the Definition of Photosynthetic Photons and the Measurement of Horticultural Fixture Efficacy. Front. Plant Sci. 12:693445.
N. R. Baker. (1996). "Photoinhibition of Photosynthesis," in Light as an Energy Source and Information Carrier in Plant Physiology, eds R. C. Jennings, G. Zucchelli, F. Ghetti, and G. Colombetti (New York, NY: Plenum Press), 89–97.
S. Touil, A. Richa, M. Fizir et al. (2021). Shading effect of photovoltaic panels on horticulture crops production: a mini review. Rev Environ Sci Biotechnol 20, 281–296.
Illustrations: S. Ma Lu, S. Amaducci, S. Gorjian et al. (2024). Wavelength-selective solar photovoltaic systems to enhance the spectral sharing of sunlight in agrivoltaics. Joule, 8, 2483–2522.

Background

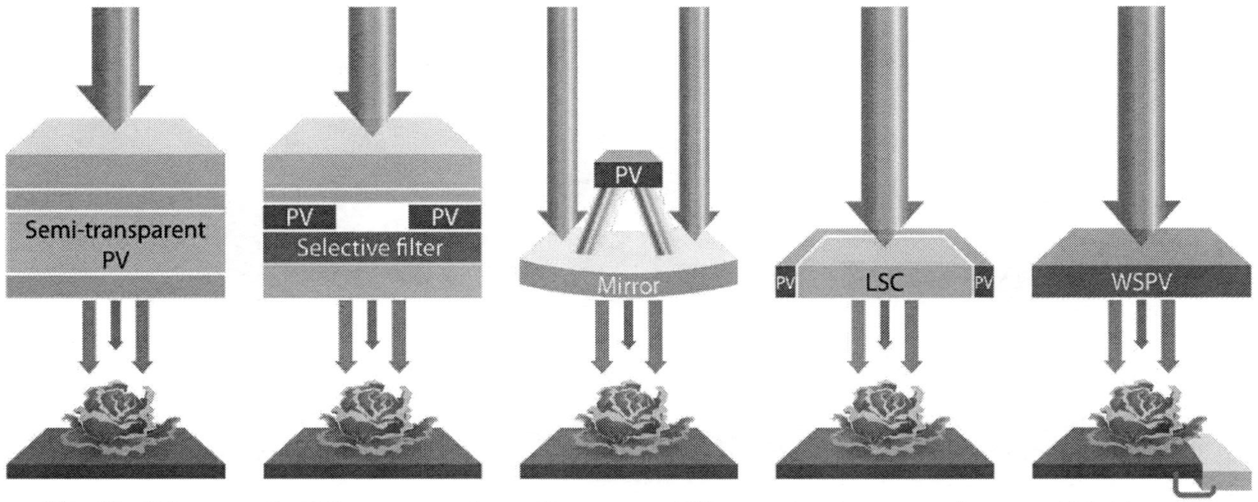

Thin-film PV | Spatially-segmented PV | Concentrated PV | Luminescent solar concentrator | Hybrid systems

Wavelength-selective solar photovoltaic (WSPV) technologies consider the absorption profiles of plants and enable the transmission of light at wavelengths that are beneficial for photosynthesis.

H. Shi, R. Xia, G. Zhang et al. (2019). Spectral engineering of semitransparent polymer solar cells for greenhouse applications. Adv Energy Mater, 9 : 1803438.
S. Ma Lu, S. Amaducci, S. Gorjian et al. (2024). Wavelength-selective solar photovoltaic systems to enhance the spectral sharing of sunlight in agrivoltaics. Joule, 8, 2483–2522.

Spatially-segmented PV: Semi-transparent coloured cadmium telluride (CdTe) solar photovoltaic panels

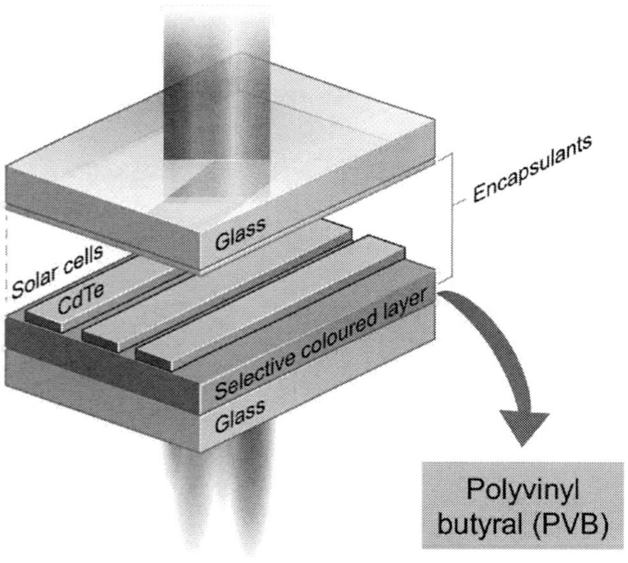

Advanced Solar Power (ASP-LAM2)

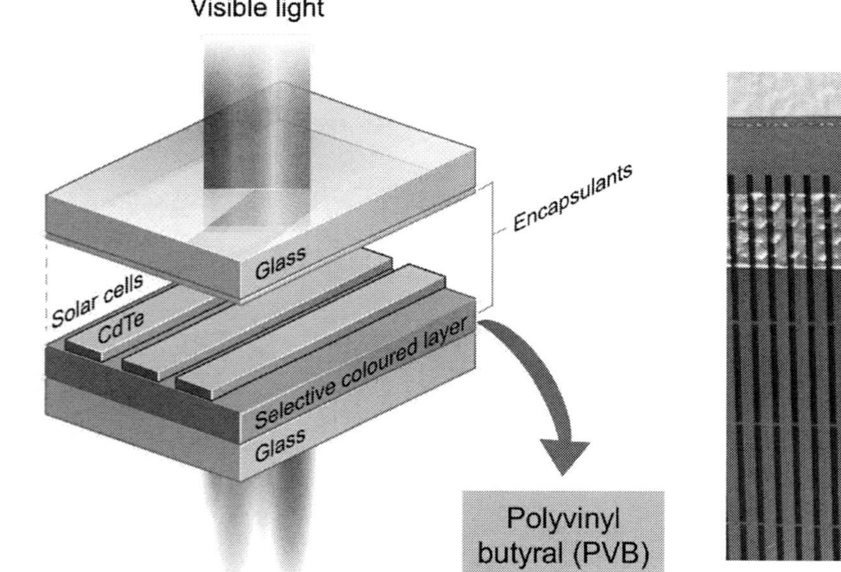

Illustration adapted from: S. Ma Lu, S. Amaducci, S. Gorjian et al. (2024). Wavelength-selective solar photovoltaic systems to enhance the spectral sharing of sunlight in agrivoltaics. Joule, 8, 2483–2522.

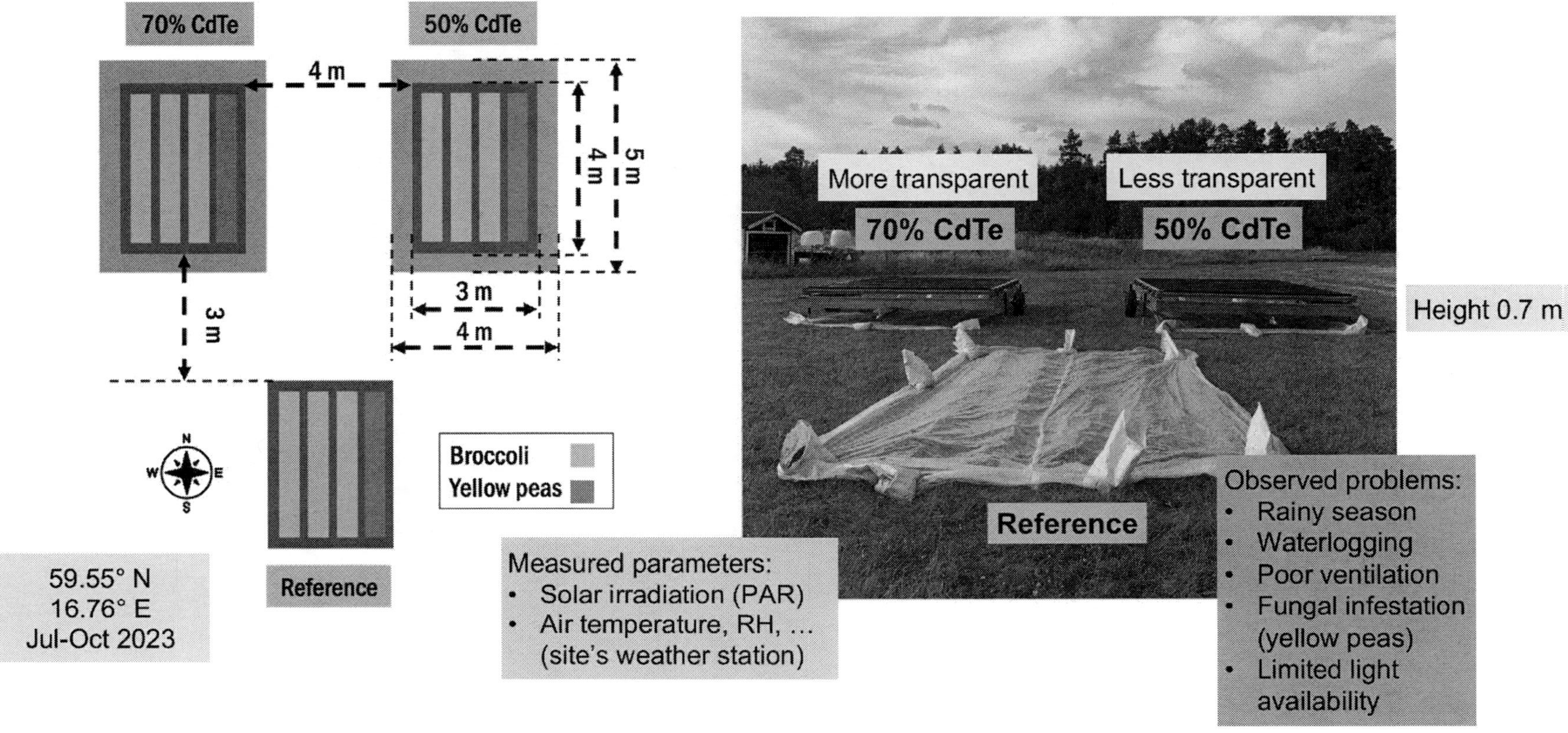

Experimental setup 2023: Kärrbo Prästgård, Sweden

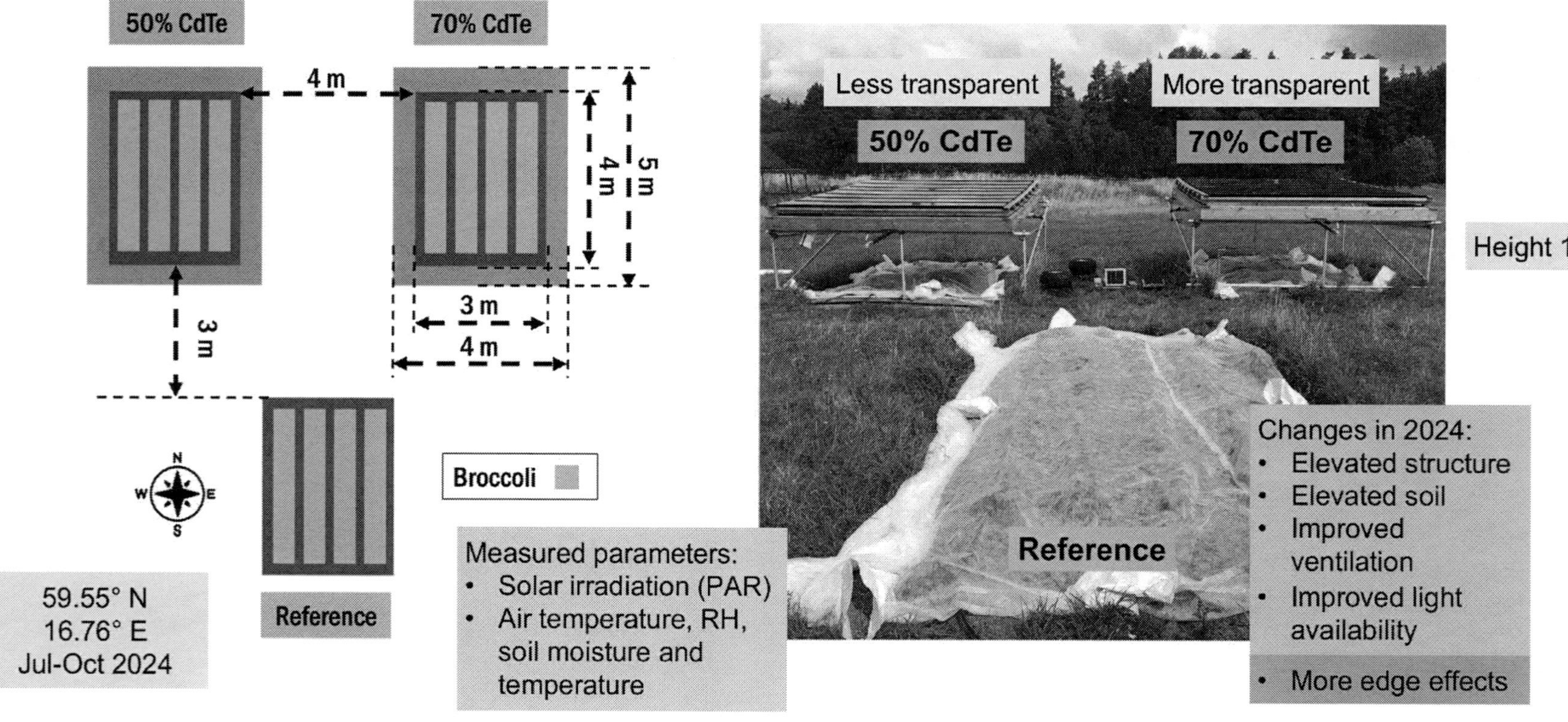

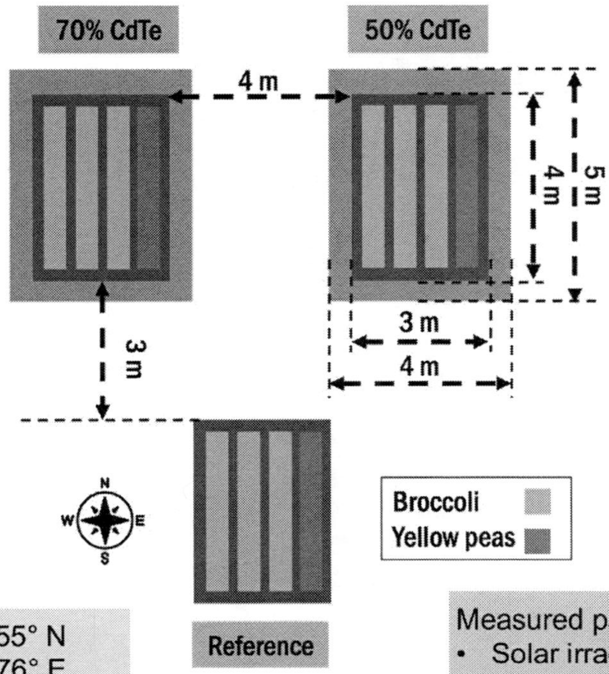

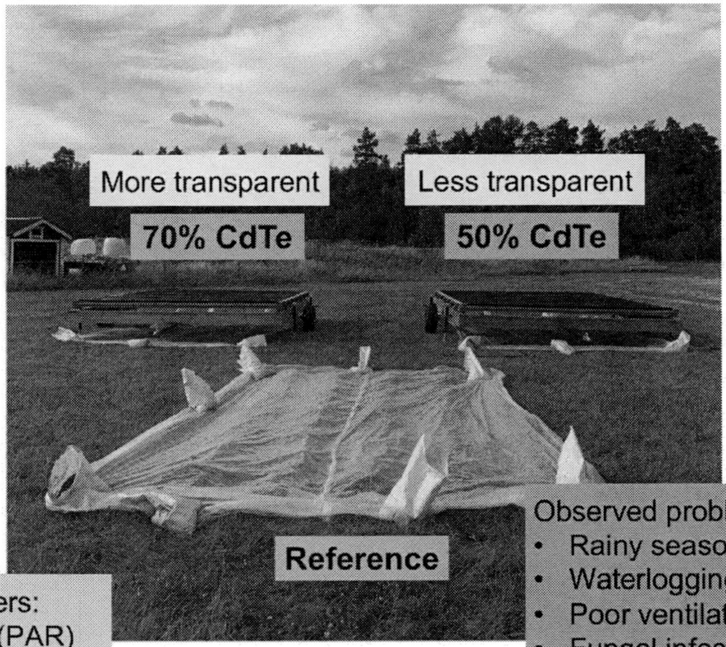

Height 0.7 m

59.55° N
16.76° E
Jul-Oct 2023

Measured parameters:
- Solar irradiation (PAR)
- Air temperature, RH, … (site's weather station)

Observed problems:
- Rainy season
- Waterlogging
- Poor ventilation
- Fungal infestation (yellow peas)
- Limited light availability

Experimental setup 2024: Kärrbo Prästgård, Sweden

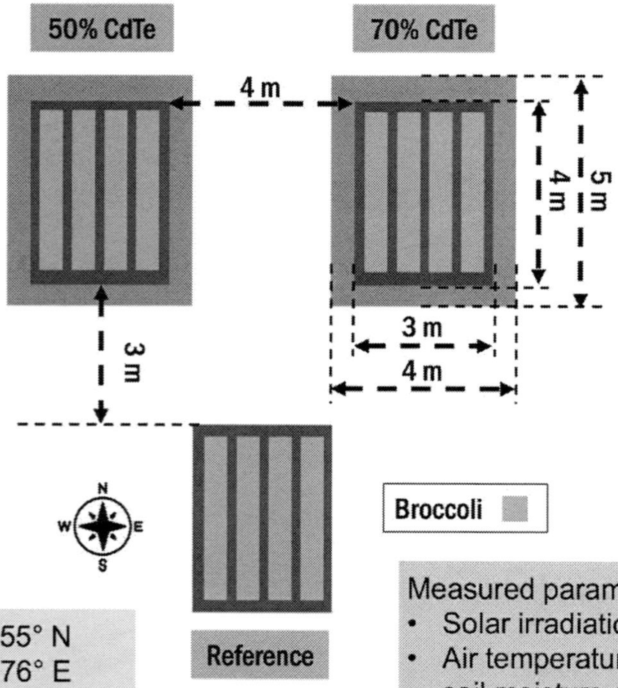

59.55° N
16.76° E
Jul-Oct 2024

Height 1.5 m

Measured parameters:
- Solar irradiation (PAR)
- Air temperature, RH, soil moisture and temperature

Changes in 2024:
- Elevated structure
- Elevated soil
- Improved ventilation
- Improved light availability
- More edge effects

Comparison daily light integral levels* 2023 vs. 2024

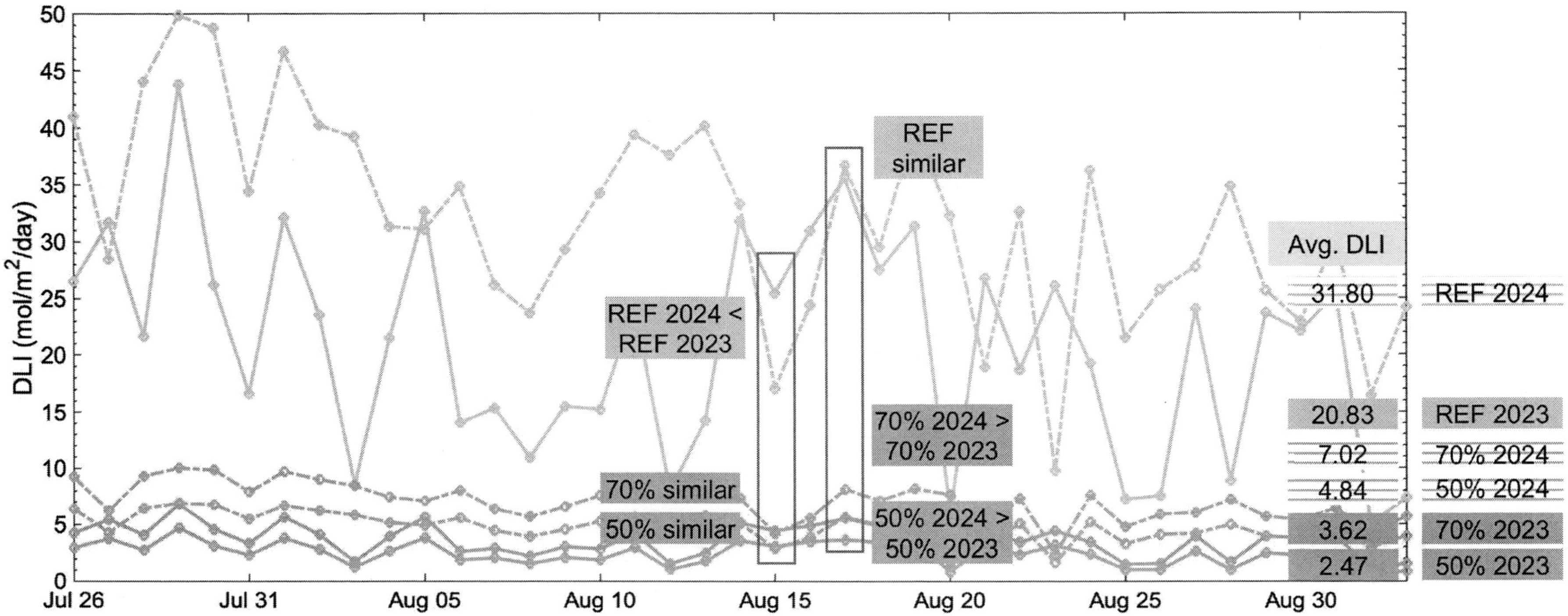

*White insect net light reduction not shown (further -14% of transmitted light is estimated)
DLI = total number of photosynthetic photons received by plants per m² during a 24 h period

Comparison daily light integral levels* 2023 vs. 2024

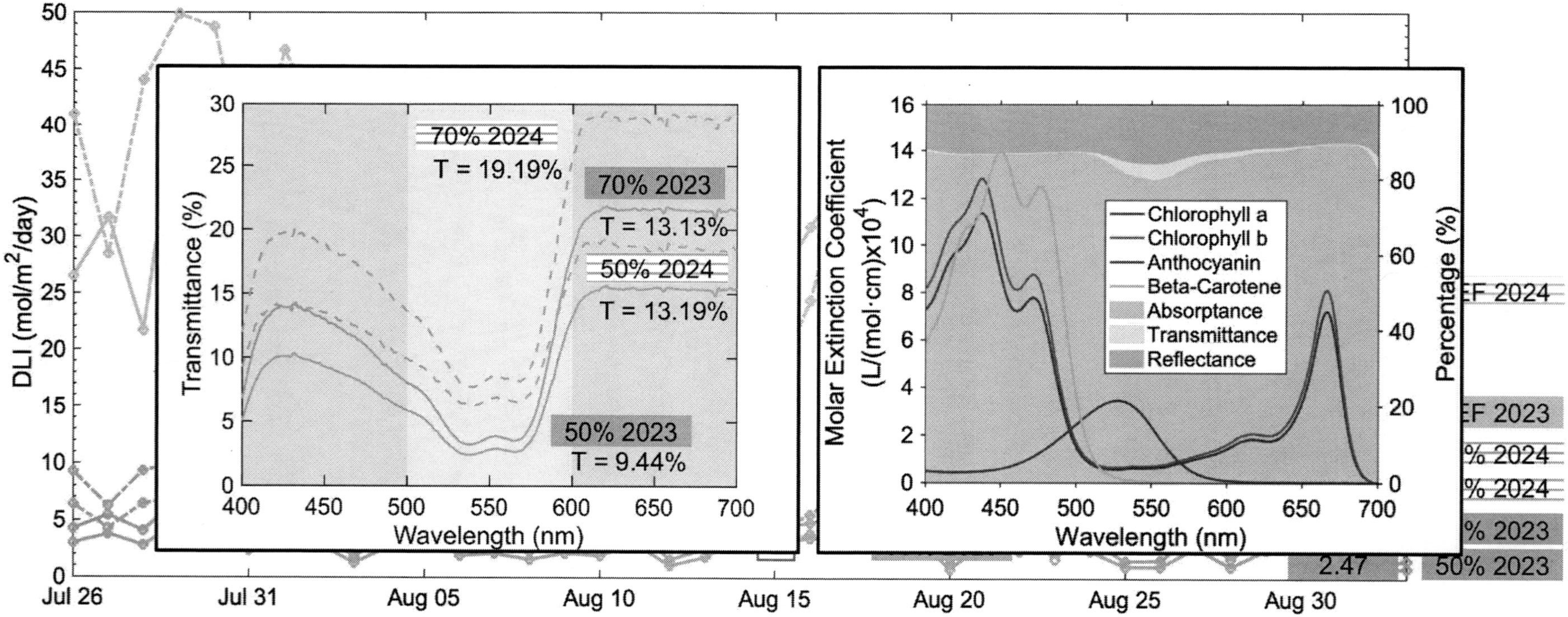

*White insect net light reduction not shown (further -14% of transmitted light is estimated)
DLI = total number of photosynthetic photons received by plants per m² during a 24 h period

Peters, R. D. & Noble, S. D. (2014) Spectrographic measurement of plant pigments from 300 to 800nm. Remote Sens. Environ. 148, 119–123.
Average absorptance, transmittance and reflectance data from of 8 fully-expanded broccoli leaves (Ramoso Calabrese) grown under white LED light and measured using an integrated sphere.

Comparison broccoli head yield 2023 vs. 2024

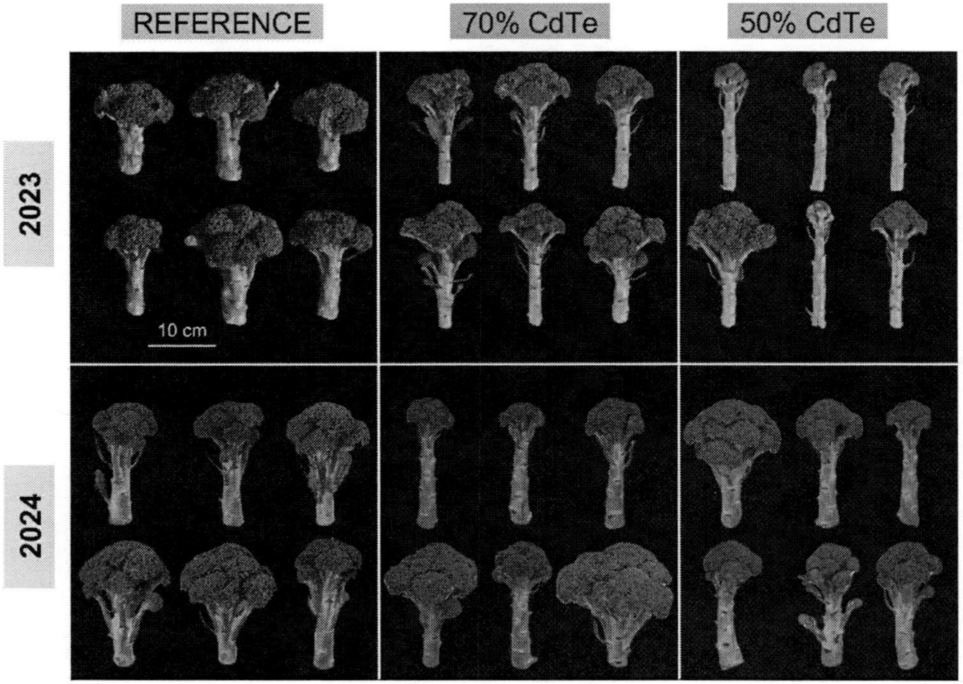

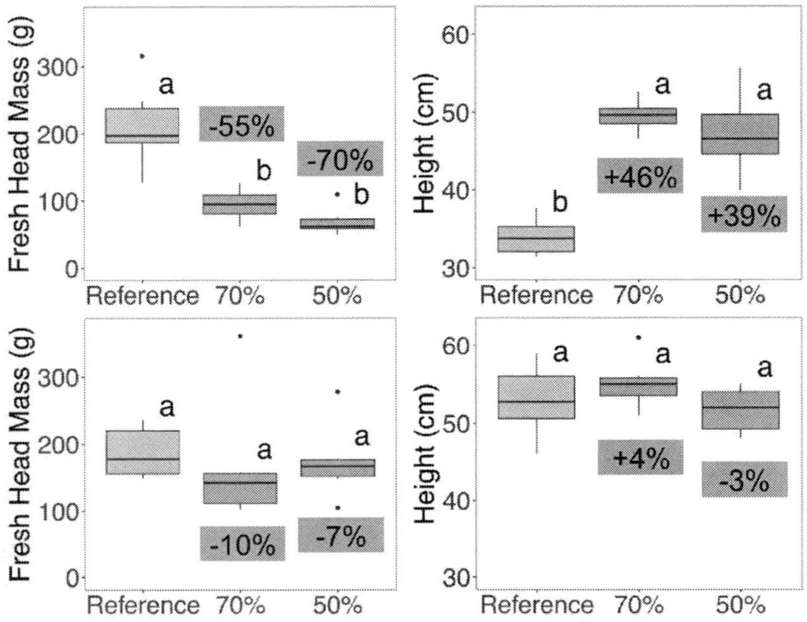

Brassica oleracea L. var. italica, cv. Marathon
Seedling dates: May 20 (2023), June 15 (2024)
Transplanting dates: Jul 2 (2023), Jul 2 (2024)
Harvest dates 2023: Aug 29 (Reference), Sep 26 (70%), Oct 13 (50%)
Harvest dates 2024: Sep 19 (Reference), Oct 14 (70% and 50%)

One-way ANOVA and Tukey Post hoc test at significance threshold of 5% ($P < 0.05$) (n=6).

Delayed harvest of 1 month under WSPVs

S. Ma Lu, A. Khosravi, X. Wang et al. Increasing land productivity with semi-transparent colored CdTe thin-film photovoltaics and broccoli cultivation in agrivoltaic systems. (Submitted)

Microclimate 2023 vs. 2024

Unfortunately, we did not have a proper monitoring system but we noticed the following observations:

- Poor ventilation
- High moisture levels and waterlogging

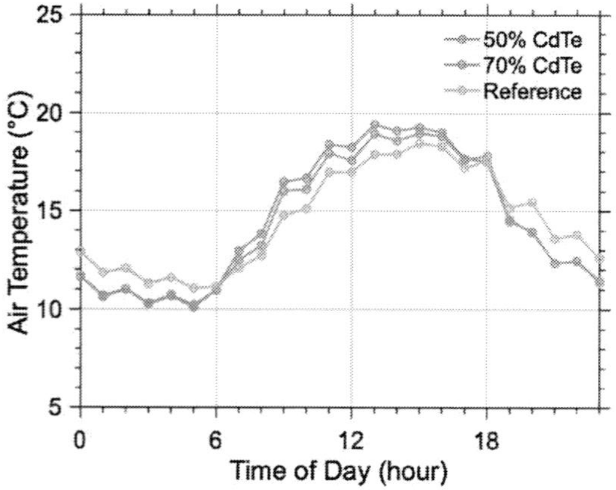

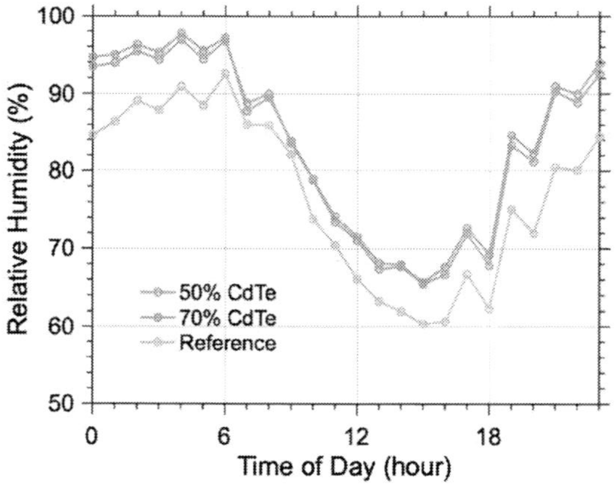

S. Ma Lu, A. Khosravi, X. Wang et al. Increasing land productivity with semi-transparent colored CdTe thin-film photovoltaics and broccoli cultivation in agrivoltaic systems. (Submitted)

Microclimate 2023 vs. 2024

Unfortunately, we did not have a proper monitoring system but we noticed the following observations:

- Poor ventilation
- High moisture levels and waterlogging

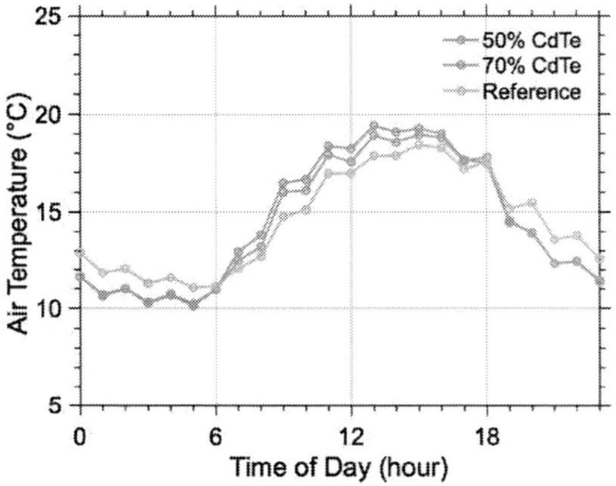

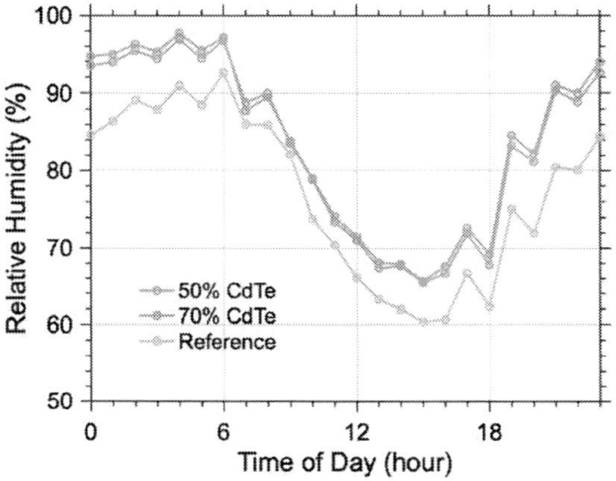

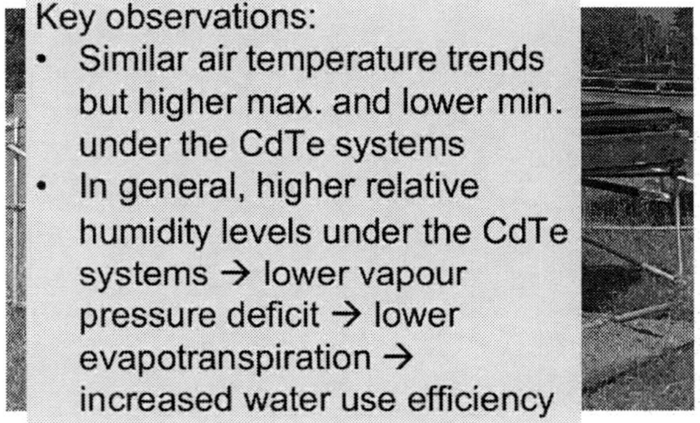

Key observations:

- Similar air temperature trends but higher max. and lower min. under the CdTe systems
- In general, higher relative humidity levels under the CdTe systems → lower vapour pressure deficit → lower evapotranspiration → increased water use efficiency

S. Ma Lu, A. Khosravi, X. Wang et al. Increasing land productivity with semi-transparent colored CdTe thin-film photovoltaics and broccoli cultivation in agrivoltaic systems. (Submitted)

Light-response curves 2024

No LRCs measurements performed in 2023. Only instantaneous leaf-gas exchange measurements and not respresentative (too late) → Lessons learned

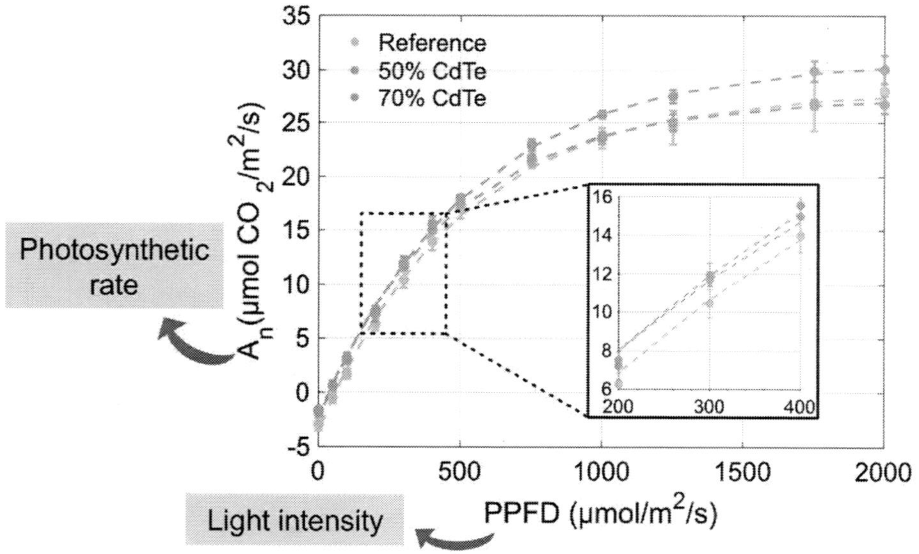

Average of three measurements at different dates: Aug 13, Sep 2 and Sep 19. Fully-expanded leaves at the second upper levels, one leaf-one plant per treatment). Average leaf temperature 21.4 ± 2.8°C std dev.

1 W/m² = 4.57 μmol/m²/s

S. Ma Lu, A. Khosravi, X. Wang et al. Increasing land productivity with semi-transparent colored CdTe thin-film photovoltaics and broccoli cultivation in agrivoltaic systems. (Submitted)

Light-response curves 2024

No LRCs measurements performed in 2023. Only instantaneous leaf-gas exchange measurements and not respresentative (too late) → Lessons learned

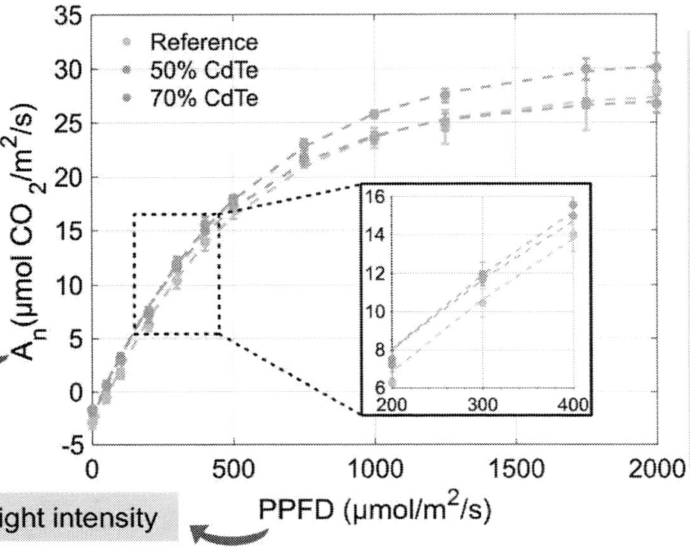

Average of three measurements at different dates: Aug 13, Sep 2 and Sep 19. Fully-expanded leaves at the second upper levels, one leaf-one plant per treatment). Average leaf temperature 21.4 ± 2.8°C std dev.

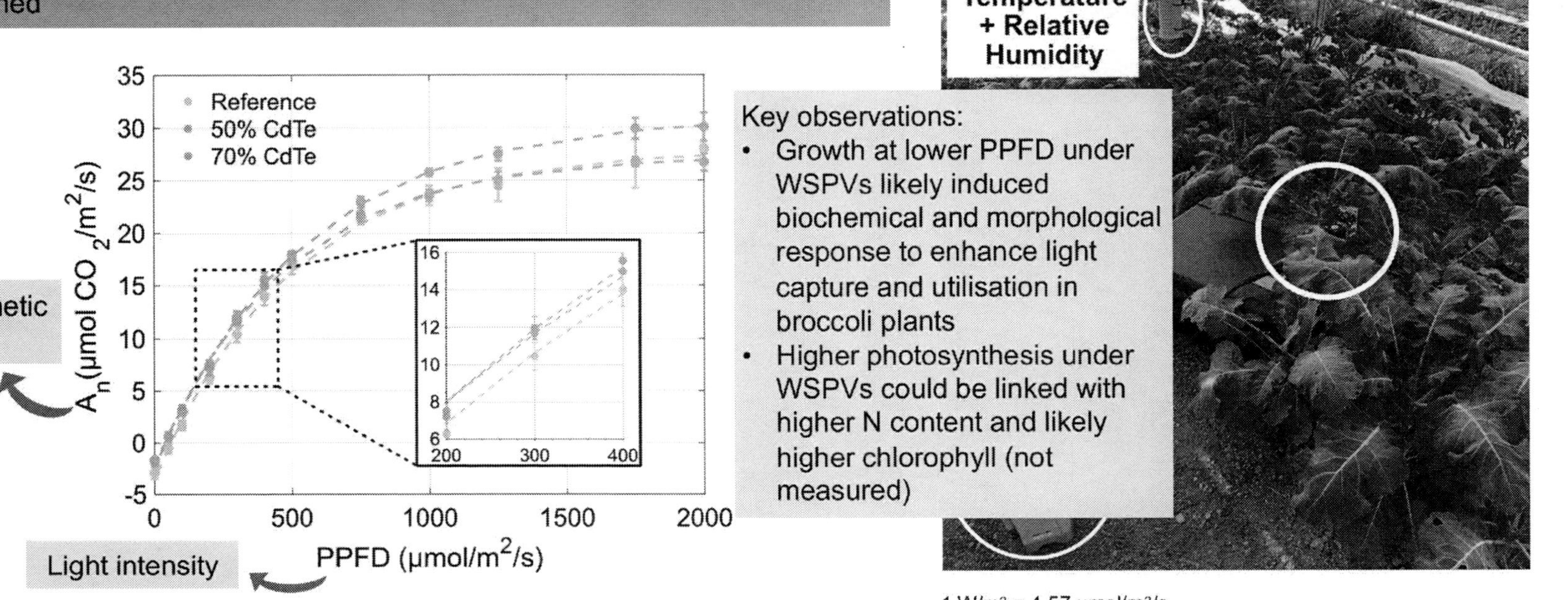

Key observations:
- Growth at lower PPFD under WSPVs likely induced biochemical and morphological response to enhance light capture and utilisation in broccoli plants
- Higher photosynthesis under WSPVs could be linked with higher N content and likely higher chlorophyll (not measured)

1 W/m² = 4.57 µmol/m²/s

S. Ma Lu, A. Khosravi, X. Wang et al. Increasing land productivity with semi-transparent colored CdTe thin-film photovoltaics and broccoli cultivation in agrivoltaic systems. (Submitted)

Preliminary calculations on system potential

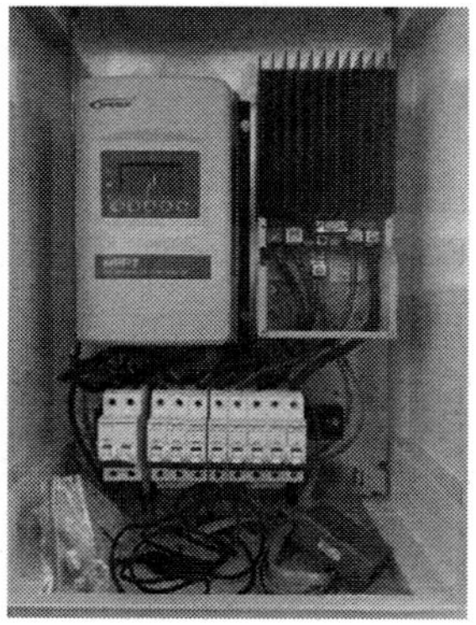

Off-grid PV system:
- 3 CdTe PV modules connected in parallel for each 50% and 70%
- Battery
- Dumping Load
- 2 MPPT Solar Controller
- 2 Dataloggers

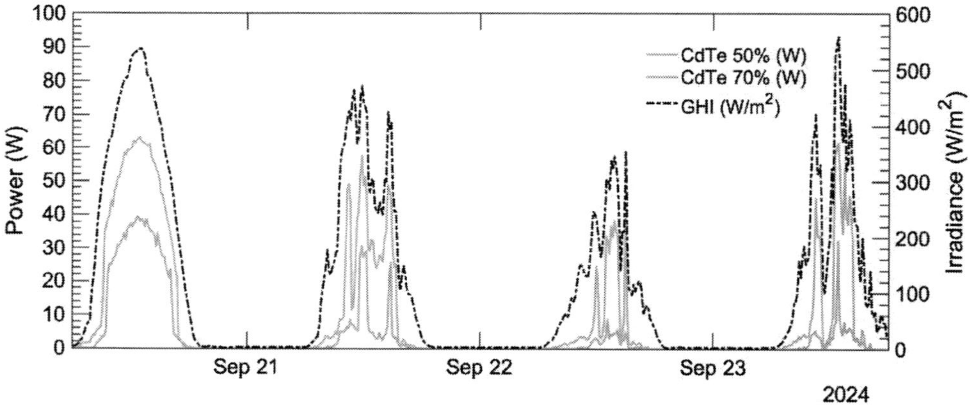

Monitoring data roughly 2-months (Sep 17 - Nov 19 2024)

calibration

50% CdTe PV system: 21 panels → 655.2 W_p
70% CdTe PV system: 21 panels → 390.6 W_p

Input weather data (Jul 2– Oct 14)

Agri-OptiCE® (in-house modelling and simulation tool)

50% CdTe:
- 311.7 kWh_{DC}
- PCE = 4.3%

70% CdTe:
- 185.8 kWh_{DC}
- PCE = 2.6%

PCE = power conversion efficiency

Specific yield (Jul 2 – Oct 14):
- 475.7 kWh/kWp

Land equivalent ratio (LER) 50% CdTe:
- LER = 1.24

$$LER = \frac{Y_{crop\ APV}}{Y_{monocrop}} + \frac{Y_{electricity\ APV}}{Y_{electricity\ PV}}$$

In line with other WSPVs technologies, despite modest PCE vs. c-Si

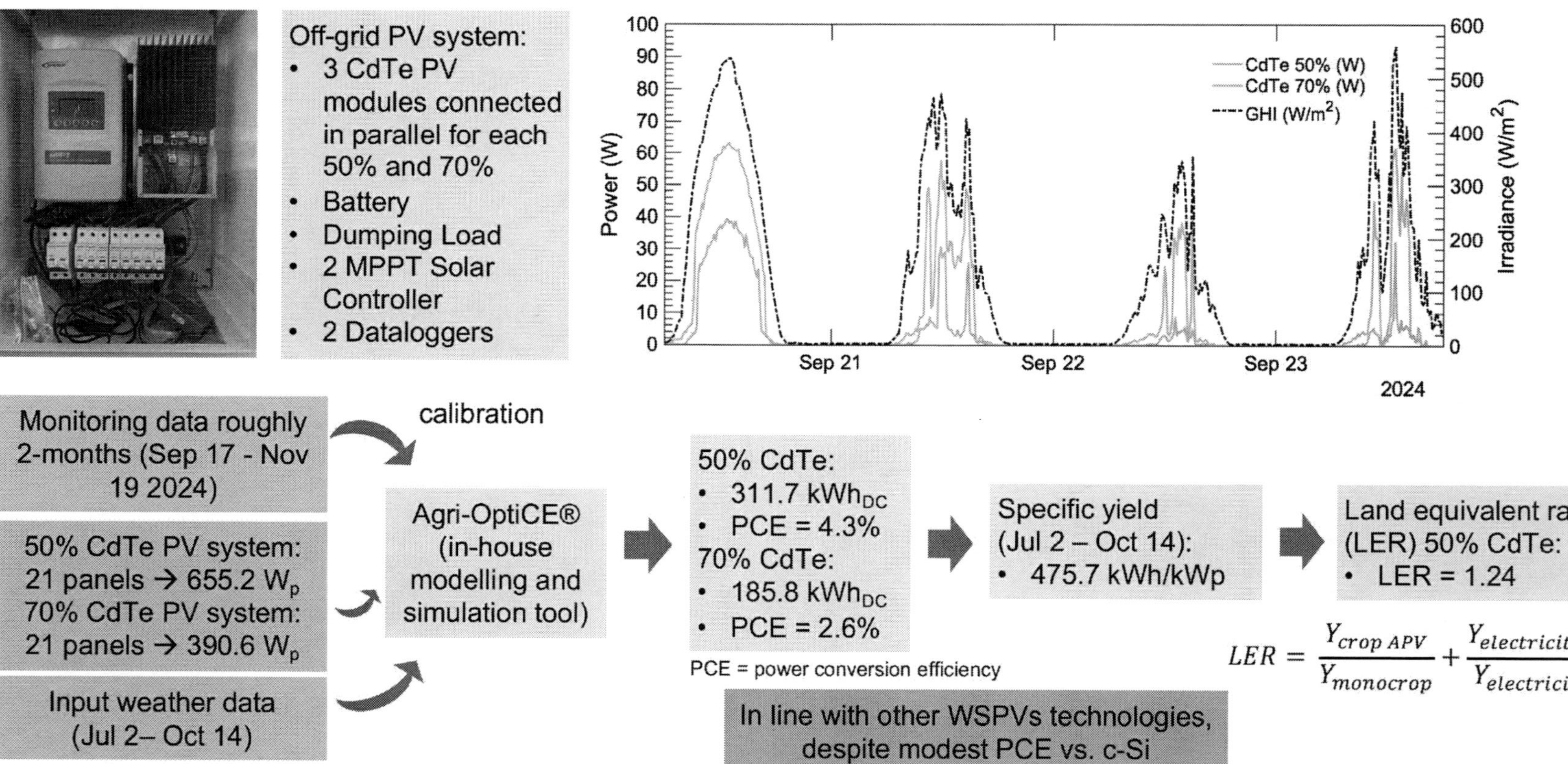

Loik, M. E. et al. (2017) Wavelength-Selective Solar Photovoltaic Systems: Powering Greenhouses for Plant Growth at the Food-Energy-Water Nexus. 10
Vasiliev, M. et al. (2023). High-transparency clear window-based agrivoltaics. Sustain. Build. 6, 5 (2023)

Conclusions and future work

Broccoli yield in 2023 was reduced under WSPVs, but in 2024 design improvements led to **yields comparable** to the reference showing the feasibility of the magenta panels despite lower overall light transmitted.

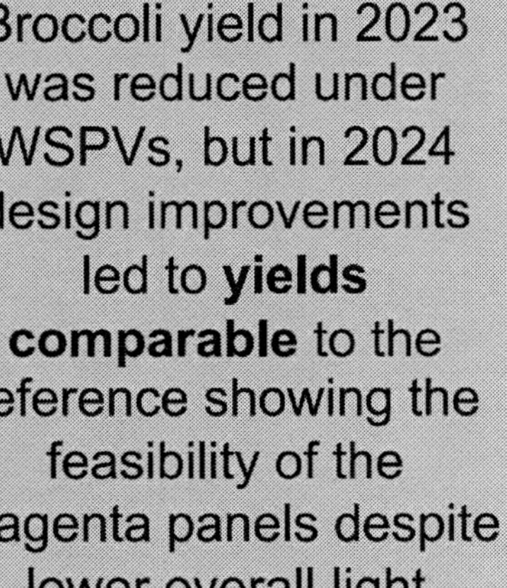

Light-response curves showed **improved light utilisation** under WSPVs indicating an **adaptive response** to modified light quantity and quality.

CdTe panels have **lower power conversion efficiencies** than c-Si, but advanced WSPVs technologies like organic PVs with similar light transmittance profiles could narrow the gap in the near future.

Related work

Ma Lu et al. (2025). **Selective light transmission in agrivoltaics: Modeling light spectra and photosynthetic rate.** Nexus, 2(3), 100074. https://doi.org/10.1016/j.ynexs.2025.100074

- Development of 2 spectrum-aware models for light transmission and photosynthesis
- Assessment of crop suitability under different WSPVs technologies globally
- Optimization method to guide ideal light transmittance of WSPVs for optimum plant growth

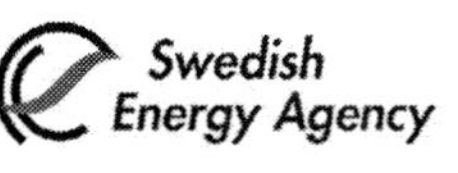

SOLVE

Swedish Energy Agency

EUPVSEC
European Photovoltaic Solar Energy Conference and Exhibition

STIFTELSEN J. GUST. RICHERT

Mälardalen University

Thank you for your attention!

Silvia Ma Lu
PhD Candidate
silvia.ma.lu@mdu.se
25 September 2025

LinkedIn

Let's connect!

42nd European Photovoltaic Solar Energy Conference and Exhibition

This presentation was selected by the Sc. Committee of the EU PVSEC 2025 for submission of a full paper to one of the EU PVSEC's collaborating peer-reviewed journals.

A CASE STUDY: QUANTIFYING THE IMPACT OF MINOR DESIGN CHANGES ON LARGE-SCALE SOLAR PV PLANTS

Ayesha Jacobs[1], Keanu Damon[2] and Paul Nel[2]
[1]Zutari (Pty) Ltd, Cape Town, South Africa, ayesha.jacobs@zutari.com
[2]7SecondSolar (Pty) Ltd, Cape Town, South Africa

ABSTRACT: Utility-scale solar photovoltaic (PV) plants continue to expand globally, with overall performance depending not only on module and inverter technologies but also on early-stage design choices such as equipment placement and cable configuration. This paper highlights the specific impact of minor changes in layout design and equipment placement on the direct current (DC) cable network, as well as the resulting effects on capital expenditure, power loss, and energy yield. A base case scenario PV plant is defined, and nine design variations are assessed. Results indicate that the positioning of combiner boxes and inverters has the strongest influence on both cable costs and associated power losses. The study demonstrates that relatively minor adjustments to equipment layout and other key design decisions can result in significant reductions in costs without compromising energy yield. These findings underline the importance of layout-driven design decisions during early project stages and provide practical guidance for developers seeking cost-effective PV plant development.
Keywords: Cable layout optimisation, PV system design, utility-scale solar PV

1 INTRODUCTION

Solar Photovoltaic (PV) is one of the most widely utilised forms of renewable technologies worldwide and continues to expand rapidly, with an additional 4,000 GW of solar capacity predicted to be added to the global grid by 2030. Utility-scale projects are expected to drive the majority of this expansion [1]. As projects grow larger in capacity, the design of these plants becomes more complex and constrained, requiring careful trade-offs between cost, performance, and constructability.

Research on PV plant optimisation has primarily focused on module improvements, tracking systems, and control strategies. Relatively fewer studies have examined how system-level design choices, such as equipment selection, placement, and cable routing, can influence overall system efficiency and cost.

In practice, these design choices are often overlooked or simplified during the early stages of a project; yet they can be a significant driver of plant performance. Small changes in cable sizing, length, or array layout can impact resistive losses, voltage drop, and capital expenditure (CAPEX).

This study explores how minor variations in the layout of utility-scale PV plants affect the DC cable network and, in turn, impact the energy yield, power losses, and costs. By linking design decisions to measurable technical and economic outcomes, it highlights the importance of cable and layout optimisation in the early stages of project development.

2 LOSSES IN PV SYSTEMS

The losses in a PV system refer to the difference between a plant's theoretical maximum output and the actual energy generated under real conditions. These losses can result from both environmental factors and technical inefficiencies. The accurate estimation and management of these losses is essential for reliable yield prediction and financial assessment.

In utility-scale systems, losses typically include shading, soiling, thermal effects, module mismatch, and electrical resistances, primarily due to resistive losses in cables [2]. While the losses due to the site location or environment are partially unavoidable, electrical losses – particularly those in the DC subsystem – can be managed through detailed design considerations. Cable losses occur due to the inherent resistance of conductors, resulting in part of the transmitted energy being dissipated as heat. These losses are proportional to the current, area, and length of the conductor.

As the capacities of PV plants grow and equipment ratings increase, cabling will account for a larger share of overall system losses. Decisions on cable sizing, routing, and equipment placement, therefore, play an important role in minimising resistive losses while balancing capital costs.

3 OPTIMISATION APPROACHES IN PV SYSTEMS

A wide range of approaches to improving PV system efficiency have been investigated, with much of the existing research focusing on module-level improvements or control-based strategies. Examples include tracking systems, module cooling methods, and Maximum Power Point Tracking (MPPT) control strategies [3]. These approaches can significantly increase energy yield, with dual-axis tracking achieving gains of up to 45% and module cooling providing improvements of 3-7.5% [4,5]. However, losses that result from inefficient system-level layout and electrical design are generally overlooked.

Recent research highlights the importance of cable optimisation. Khan et al. present a comparative assessment of six cable configurations for a PV array. Their analysis highlights the trade-offs between performance and cost, demonstrating that the lowest-loss designs are not always the most cost-effective [6]. Gan et al. present an optimisation framework for DC cable sizing in a PV system over its lifetime. They demonstrate that oversizing cables, although having a higher initial cost, can reduce the associated cost of resistive energy losses [7].

Other studies present holistic optimisation approaches that integrate module layout and tilt angle, inverter placement, cabling, and other key design decisions to minimise shading and electrical losses while reducing the levelised cost of energy [8,9]. These studies demonstrate that system-level design choices – namely, cable sizing, routing, and equipment placement – can substantially affect both performance and cost. However, even with these more recent studies, the combined technical and economic impacts of DC cable design remain relatively unexplored. This study evaluates how array layout and equipment placement influence cable losses, cost, and energy yield in utility-scale PV plants.

4 SYSTEM ARCHITECTURE AND SCOPE OF ANALYSIS

Utility-scale PV plants combine structural, electrical, and civil design to deliver power to the grid. Arrays of PV modules, mounted onto fixed-tilt structures or tracking systems, are connected in series to form strings. These strings are then grouped into sub-arrays. The DC power from these sub-arrays is routed through a cable network to inverters, where it is converted to alternating current (AC) and stepped up by a transformer for grid integration.

Two inverter architecture types are typically used in large-scale PV plants: string inverters and central inverters. String inverters are rated up to 350 kW and offer greater design flexibility, multiple MPPTs, and improved performance under varying operating conditions [10]. Central inverters, often housed within a Power Conversion Unit (PCU), are rated up to 5 MW. These inverters aggregate multiple PV strings through DC combiner boxes. Although less flexible, central inverters can be more cost-effective, as a single high-capacity unit replaces many smaller inverters. Additionally, a central inverter architecture simplifies installation and reduces maintenance requirements [11,12].

In central inverter systems, cable design plays a critical role. As shown in Figure 1, DC string cables connect modules to combiner boxes, and sub-array cables connect the combiner boxes to the PCU. Their sizing and routing have a direct impact on electrical losses and capital expenditure. This study focuses on the central inverter architecture to quantify the impacts of DC layout design on performance and cost.

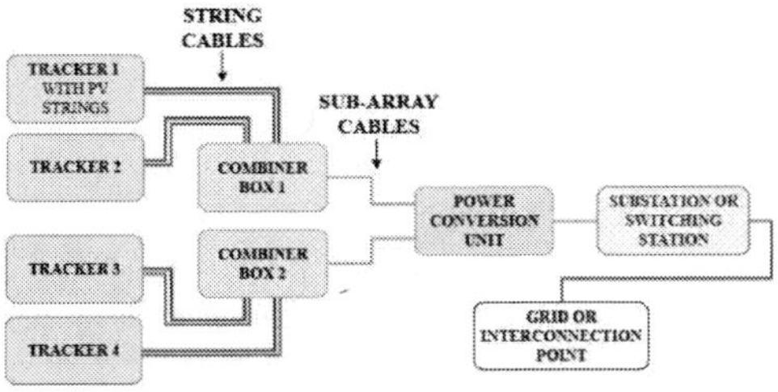

Figure 1: Central inverter system architecture for a PV plant

5 METHODOLOGY

To evaluate the impact of minor design changes on the PV system and its DC cable network, a base case scenario and several design variations were developed. The scenarios focused on three key areas where trade-offs are expected to occur:

1. Equipment selection and placement
2. Civil considerations
3. Electrical considerations

A single-axis tracking 330MWp solar PV facility, using a central inverter architecture, was developed using a single development area. Nine design variations were applied. The plant capacity, DC sub-array cable selection, development area, and general overall layout were kept constant. A complete low-voltage cable design, including accurate cable routing, was developed for each scenario using AUTOPV™, a software platform that automates the electrical design of solar plants. The output from AUTOPV™ is used to calculate the cable losses, voltage drop, and cable cost.

5.1 Base Case

The base case scenario was designed in accordance with engineering best practices, based on a real PV project currently being developed in South Africa. Figure 2 shows the typical equipment placement for the base case scenario. The combiner boxes are placed in the centre of the sub-array on the edge of the trackers closest to the PCU. This spacing between the trackers is referred to as the minor corridor. The PCU is placed in the centre of the groups of sub-arrays, in the major corridor. The plant has the following parameters:

Table I: Base case scenario parameters

Parameter	Value
Plant DC Power	331.51 MWdc
Plant AC Power	316.80 MWac
DC/AC Ratio	1.046
Pitch	6.2 m
Major corridor width	21 m
Minor corridor width	5 m
Quantity of PV Blocks	36
Quantity of DC Combiner Boxes	1080

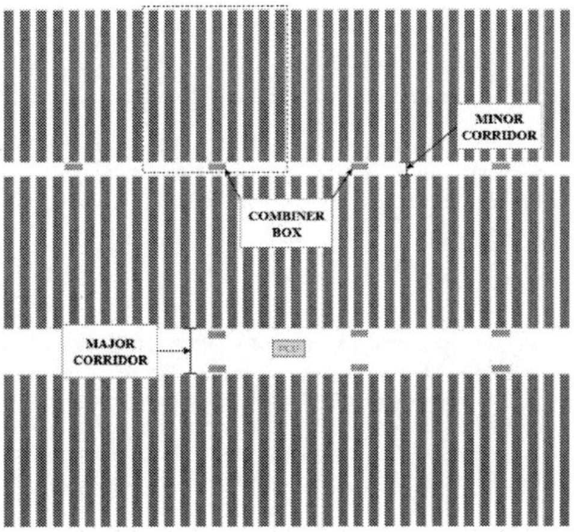

Figure 2: Typical equipment placement in a PV block for the base case scenario

5.2 Scenarios varying equipment selection and placement

Variations in equipment selection and placement can significantly impact cable design. For this paper, the scenarios were designed as follows:

- Scenario 1: Increasing the quantity of combiner boxes
- Scenario 2: Placing combiner boxes in the major corridor closer to the PCU
- Scenario 3: Placing combiner boxes in the minor corridors closer to the PCU

10.4229/EUPVSEC2025/4DO.3.1

- Scenario 4: Reducing the size of the PCU from 8.8 MVA to 4.4 MVA and increasing the quantity

5.3 Scenarios varying civil considerations

The width of the corridors between the trackers, where combiner boxes and PCUs are often placed, is typically determined by logistical and civil engineering constraints. The following variations were applied to the base case to assess the impact of these assumptions:

- Scenario 5: Reducing the minor corridor width from 5 m to 3 m
- Scenario 6: Reducing the minor corridor width from 5 m to 1 m
- Scenario 7: Adjusting the minor corridor width to 9 m and the major corridor to 15 m

5.4 Scenarios varying electrical considerations

The power loss of a cable is directly affected by its size, as a smaller cable will have higher electrical resistance. Scenarios 8 and 9 consider the impact of varying the string cable sizes to 4 mm² and 10 mm², respectively.

5.5 Financial Assumptions

The financial assumptions used in this analysis are shown in Table II. The cost of DC cables was based on standard industry pricing at the time of this study. While the exact prices may vary regionally and over time, the values used are representative of the current industry and provide a reasonable basis for a comparative analysis.

Table II: Financial assumptions used in analysis

Parameter	Value
4mm² DC Solar Cable	1.30 USD/m
6mm² DC Solar Cable	1.60 USD/m
10mm² DC Solar Cable	2.00 USD/m
400mm² XLPE Aluminium Cable	15.00 USD/m

6 RESULTS

Figure 3 presents the simulation results for all scenarios, illustrating cable cost and power loss across all design scenarios. Given that the optimisation focuses on cable performance and the interplay between cable quantities, Figure 4 represents the results in terms of the ratio of DC string to sub-array cable lengths.

The results indicate that equipment placement, particularly of combiner boxes and PCUs, has the greatest influence on cable lengths, costs, and losses. While scenario 1 – increasing the quantity of combiner boxes – has the second-lowest power loss, it also has the highest cost due to the increased length of the sub-array cables. Using a smaller PCU results in the lowest cable cost and a relatively lower power loss when compared to the other scenarios; however, this does not consider the cost of additional PCUs. Adjusting corridor widths has a minimal impact on cost and losses, indicating that constructability considerations should guide these parameters. Larger DC cable sizes effectively reduce losses, but at the expense of a significantly higher cable cost.

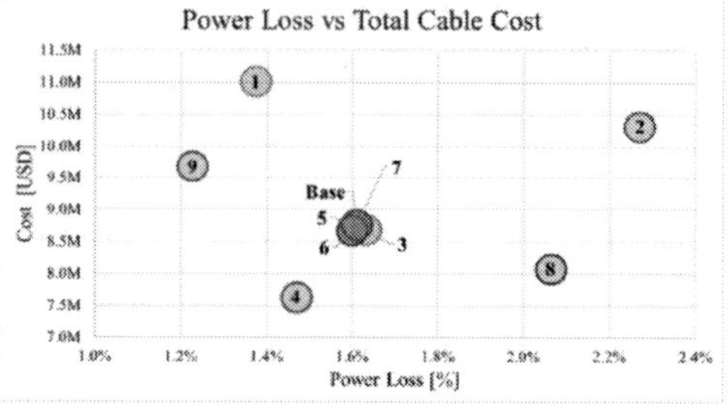

Figure 3: Cable cost and power loss for all scenarios

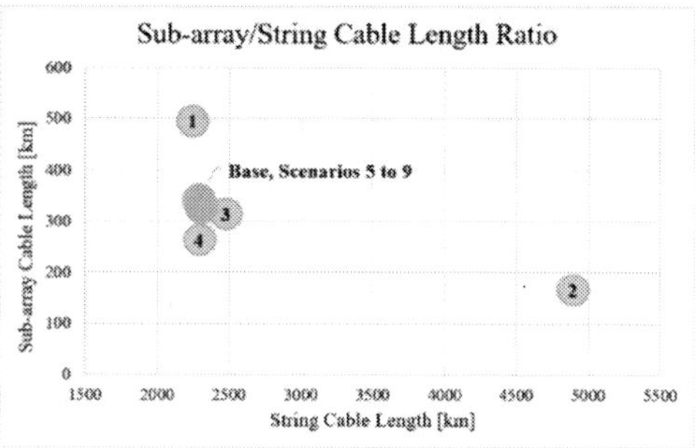

Figure 4: Sub-array versus String cable length for all scenarios

7 CONCLUSION

This study demonstrates that DC cable layout and sizing decisions can significantly impact power losses and capital costs in utility-scale PV systems, and that even minor variations in equipment selection or system layout can influence the DC design in ways that affect overall efficiency. Across the scenarios assessed, substantial differences were observed in both cable costs and power loss, driven primarily by the placement of combiner boxes and size of the PCU. Corridor width adjustments had minimal effect, suggesting that constructability considerations should be the main factor for this design decision.

There are two distinct findings in this investigation: first, that relatively small changes in design assumptions can lead to meaningful differences in both power loss, which impacts annual energy revenue, and CAPEX; and second, that a design optimised for lowest cost will not necessarily align with one optimised for lowest power loss or maximum yield.

Future work should extend the scope beyond DC cabling to include the cost of inverters, AC-side infrastructure, and assess the impact of adopting a string-inverter architecture for the system. A techno-economic analysis over the lifetime of the plant would provide a more comprehensive understanding of the long-term impact of using different DC cable sizes.

A well-designed PV plant should balance both economic return and technical performance. Projects should optimise layout configurations in alignment with the relevant design and financial objectives. This study highlights the importance of an iterative design approach in the early stages of project development to ensure that these seemingly minor design changes and their impact are considered, as they can have a significant impact on power loss, CAPEX, and energy yield.

8 REFERENCES

[1] International Energy Agency, "Renewables 2024: Analysis and forecast to 2030," IEA Publications, 2024. [Online]. Available: https://iea.blob.core.windows.net/assets/45704c88-a7b0-4001-b319-c5fc45298e07/Renewables2024.pdf

[2] S. Ekici and M. A. Kopru, "Investigation of PV System Cable Losses," *International Journal of Renewable Energy Research*, vol. 7, no. 2, 2017. [Online]. Available: https://www.researchgate.net/publication/317701311_Investigation_of_PV_System_Cable_Losses

[3] D. T. Cotfas, P.A. Cotfas, Multiconcept Methods to Enhance Photovoltaic System Efficiency, *International Journal of Photoenergy*, 1905041, 14 pages, 2019. doi: 10.1155/2019/1905041

[4] A. Glick, N. Ali, J. Bossuyt et al. "Utility-scale solar PV performance enhancements through system-level modifications," *Scientific Reports*, vol. 10, p. 10505, 2020. doi: 10.1038/s41598-020-66347-5

[5] L. Idoko, O. Anaya-Lara and A. McDonald, "Enhancing PV modules efficiency and power output using multi-concept cooling technique," *Energy Reports*, vol. 4, pp. 357-369, 2018. doi: 10.1016/j.egyr.2018.05.004

[6] F. U. Khan, A. F. Murtaza, H. A. Sher, K. Al-Haddad and F. Mustafa, "Cabling Constraints in PV Array Architecture: Design, Mathematical Model and Cost Analysis," in *IEEE Access*, vol. 8, pp. 182742-182754, 2020. [Online]. Available: https://ieeexplore.ieee.org/abstract/document/9214484

[7] C. K. Gan, Y. M. Lee, D. Pudjianto and G. Strbac, "Role of Losses in Design of DC Cable for Solar PV Applications", Australasian Universities Power Engineering Conference, (AUPEC 2014 – Proceedings). 1-5. doi: 10.1109/AUPEC.2014.6966594.

[8] T. Kerekes, E. Koutroulis, D. Séra, R. Teodorescu and M. Katsanevakis, "An Optimization Method for Designing Large PV Plants," in *IEEE Journal of Photovoltaics*, vol. 3, no. 2, pp. 814-822, 2013. doi: 10.1109/JPHOTOV.2012.2230684.

[9] T. E. K. Zidane, A. S. Aziz, Y. Zahraoui, H. Kotb, K. M. AboRas, Kitmo, Y. B. Jember, "Grid-Connected Solar PV Power Plants Optimization: A Review," *in IEEE Access*, vol. 11, pp. 79588-79608, 2023, doi: 10.1109/ACCESS.2023.3299815.

[10] L. Miller, "Comparing Central vs String Inverters for Utility-Scale PV Projects," Mayfield Renewables, May 14, 2024. Accessed Jul. 3, 2025. [Online]. Available: https://www.mayfield.energy/technical-articles/comparing-central-vs-string-inverters-for-utility-scale-pv-projects/.

[11] J. Vickerman and A. Pajares, "What are central and string solar inverters and how do they compare?", RatedPower, Mar. 14, 2024. Accessed Jul. 3, 2025. [Online]. Available: https://ratedpower.com/glossary/solar-inverters/.

[12] Essentra Components, "What is a solar inverter and how does it work?," Jan. 17, 2024. Accessed Jul. 12, 2025 [Online]. Available: https://www.essentracomponents.com/en-us/news/industries/renewable-energy/what-is-a-solar-inverter-and-how-does-it-work?srsltid=AfmBOooMfldM180w_w2D5KO8fIw8r71YPeTESAqRg6UZOT-_H2MFdmfg.

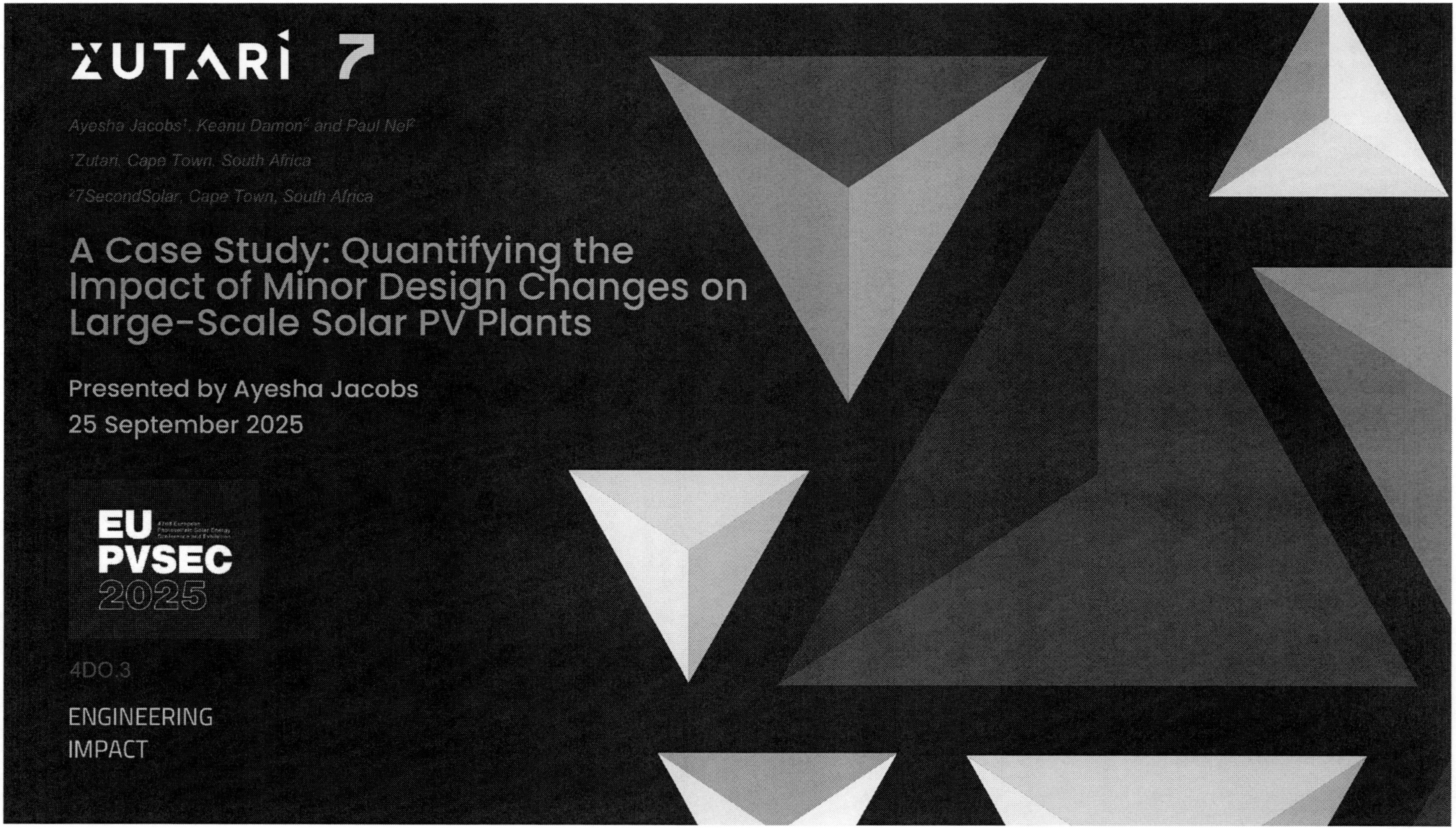
ZUTARI 7
Ayesha Jacobs[1], Keanu Damon[2] and Paul Nel[2]
[1]Zutari, Cape Town, South Africa
[2]7SecondSolar, Cape Town, South Africa
A Case Study: Quantifying the Impact of Minor Design Changes on Large-Scale Solar PV Plants
Presented by Ayesha Jacobs
25 September 2025
EU PVSEC 2025
4DO.3
ENGINEERING IMPACT

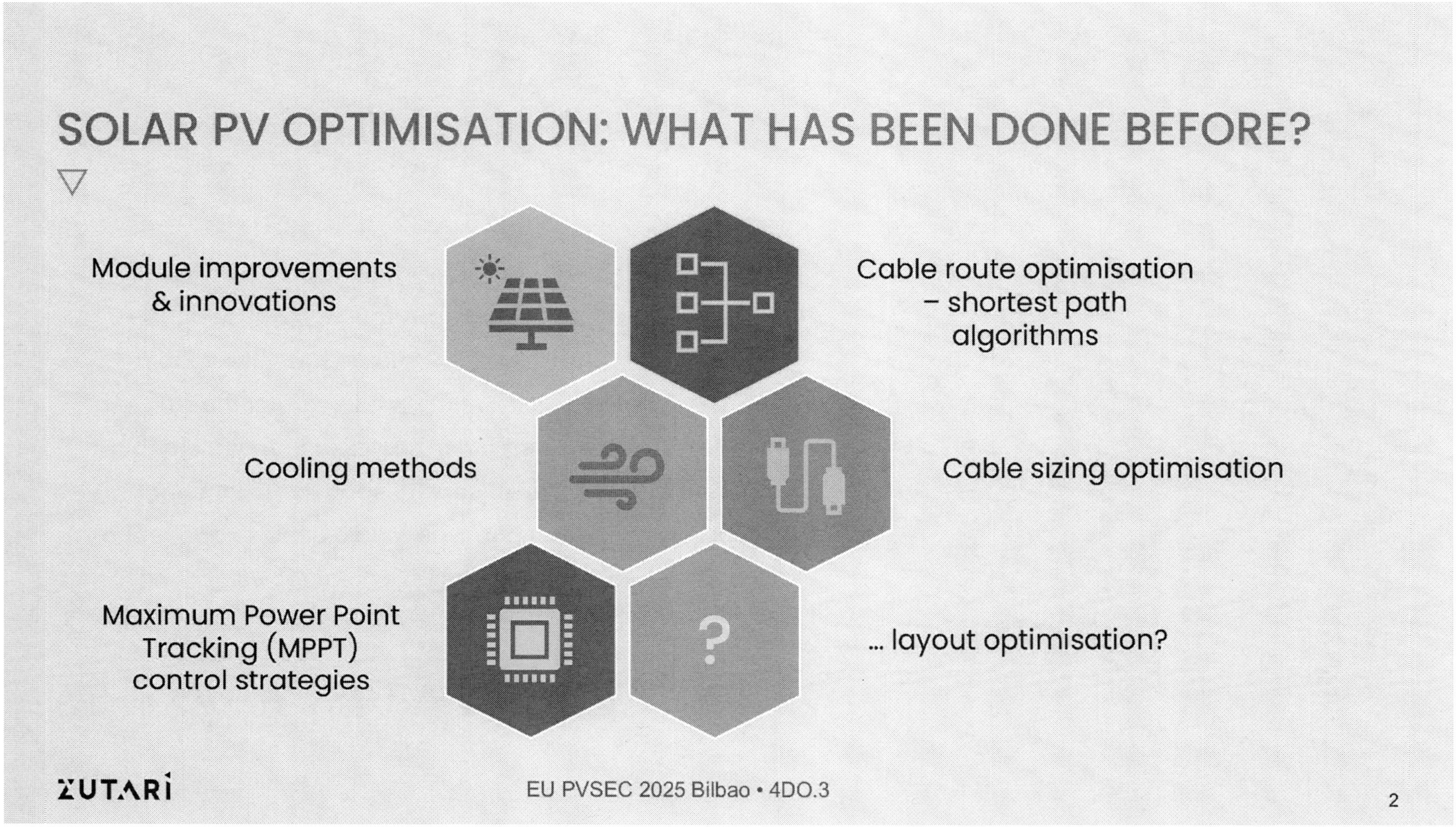
SOLAR PV OPTIMISATION: WHAT HAS BEEN DONE BEFORE?
Module improvements & innovations
Cable route optimisation – shortest path algorithms
Cooling methods
Cable sizing optimisation
Maximum Power Point Tracking (MPPT) control strategies
… layout optimisation?
ZUTARI
EU PVSEC 2025 Bilbao • 4DO.3
2

WHY OPTIMISE PV CABLE DESIGN?

- Cost of cables can be a significant portion of capital costs
- Longer cables have higher cost and losses, lowers yield
- **Our Question: How does the design of PV plants affect the DC cable network in plants using Central Inverters?**
  - → Strategic array layout
  - → Equipment placement
  - → Ratio of string vs subarray cable length

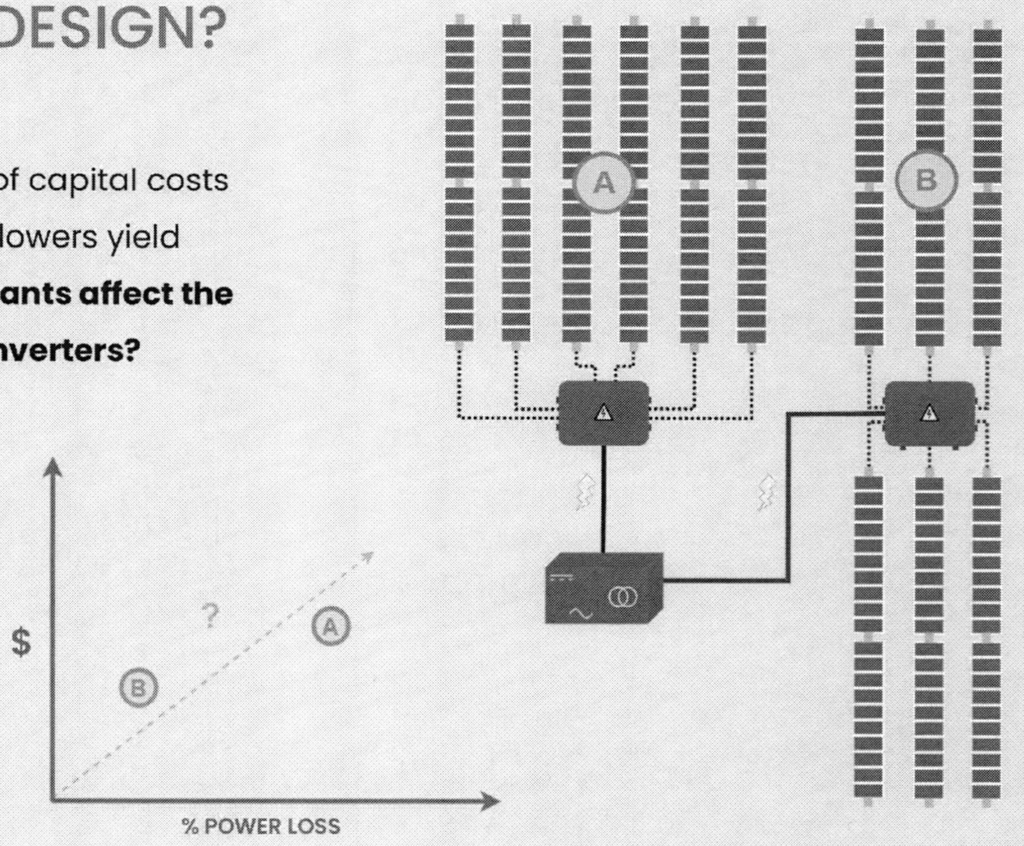

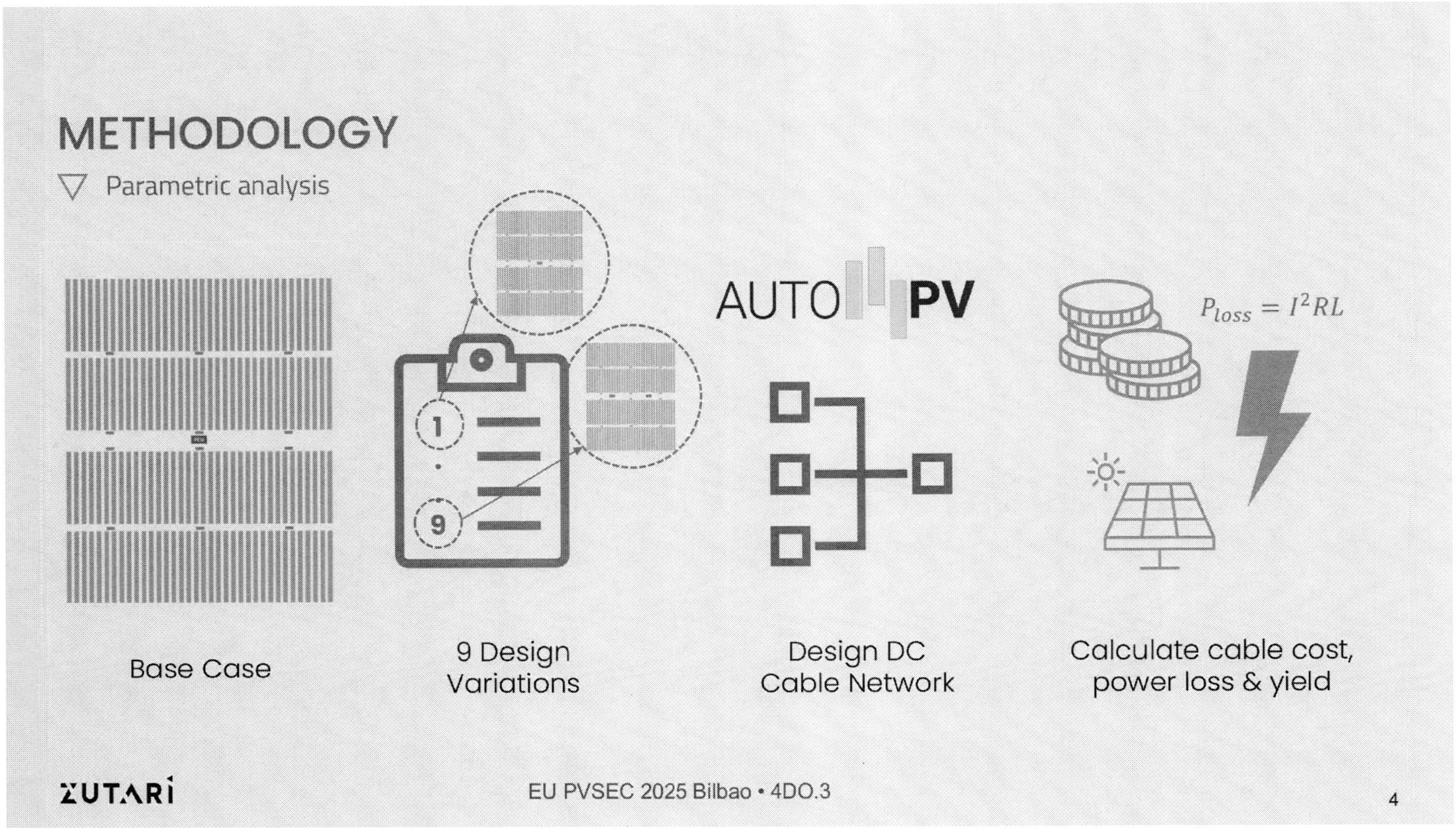
METHODOLOGY
Parametric analysis
Base Case
1
9
9 Design Variations
AUTO PV
Design DC Cable Network
$P_{loss} = I^2RL$
Calculate cable cost, power loss & yield
ZUTARI
EU PVSEC 2025 Bilbao • 4DO.3
4

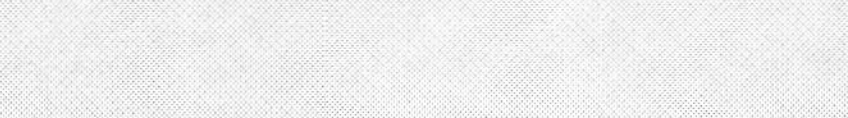

METHODOLOGY

▽ Financial Assumptions

Parameter	Value	Unit
4mm^2 DC Solar Cable	1.30	USD/m
6mm^2 DC Solar Cable	1.60	USD/m
10mm^2 DC Solar Cable	2.00	USD/m
400mm^2 XLPE Aluminium cable	15.00	USD/m
Energy tariff (BW 7)	25.64	USD/MWh

ZUTARI

METHODOLOGY

▽ Parametric analysis

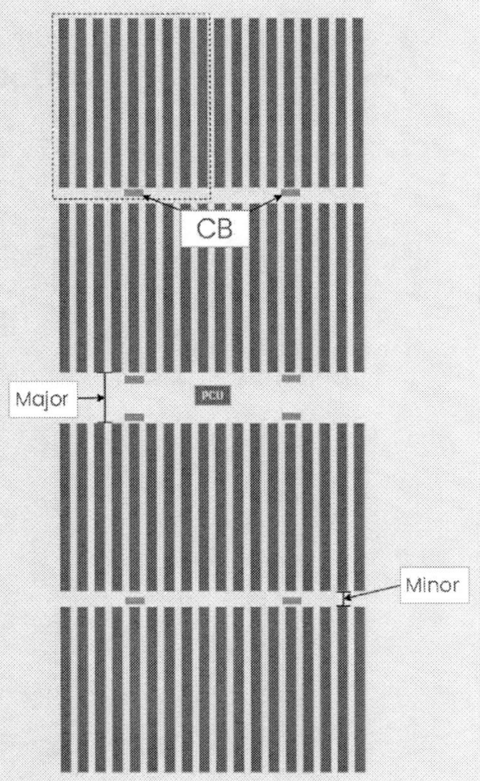

Base Case

- 300MWp, using latest technology
- Central inverter architecture
- Single-axis tracking
- 6mm² PV string cable
- Designed with standard engineering practices and assumptions
  - → Minor corridor – 5m
  - → Major corridor – 20m

ZUTARI

9 DESIGN VARIATIONS

Combiner Box Layout
Scenario 1 to 3

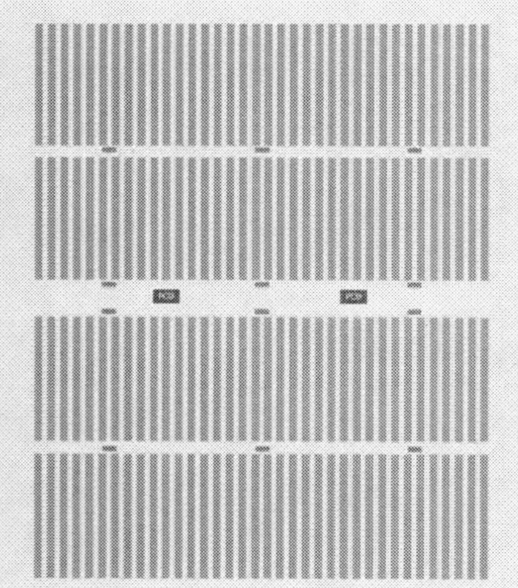

PCU Configuration
Scenario 4

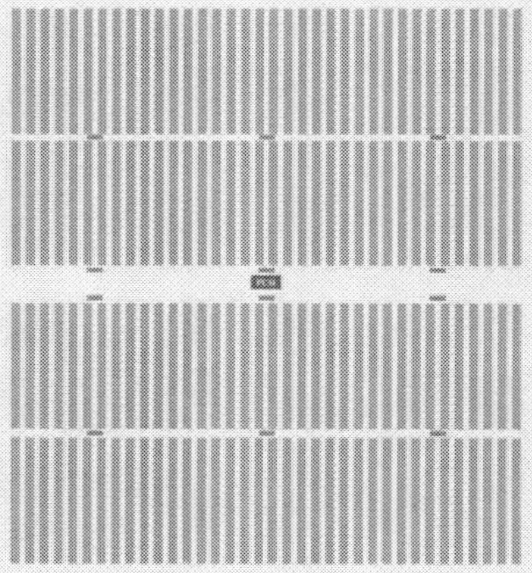

Corridor Widths
Scenario 5 to 7

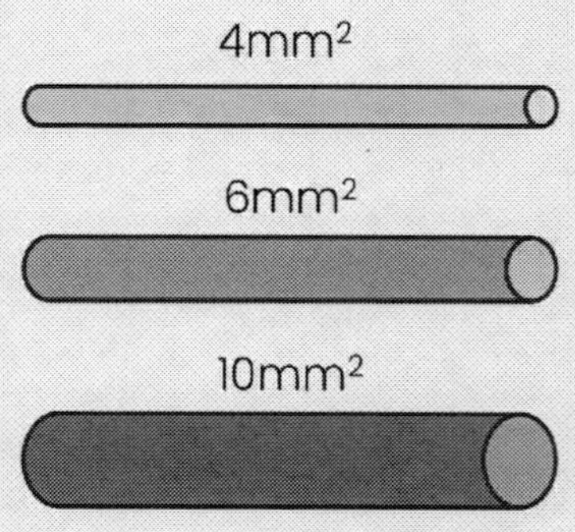

DC String Cable Size
Scenario 8 & 9

RESULTS

Scenarios 1 to 4

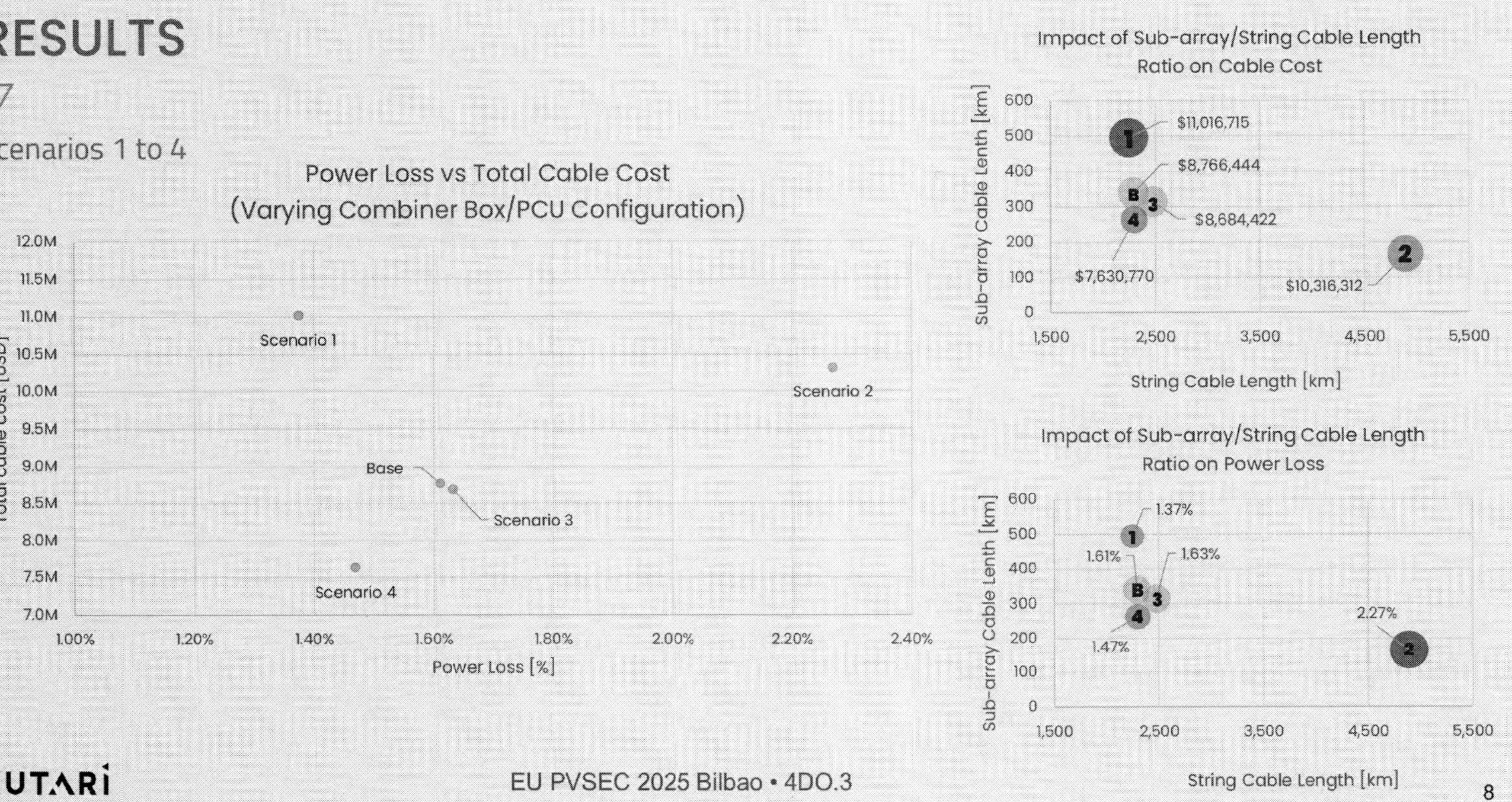

Power Loss vs Total Cable Cost
(Varying Combiner Box/PCU Configuration)

Impact of Sub-array/String Cable Length Ratio on Cable Cost

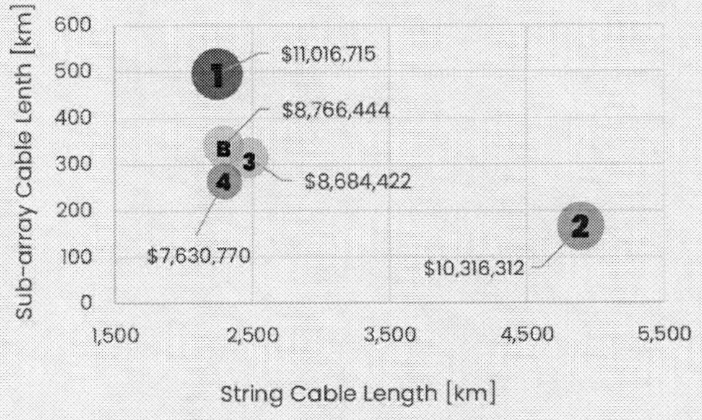

Impact of Sub-array/String Cable Length Ratio on Power Loss

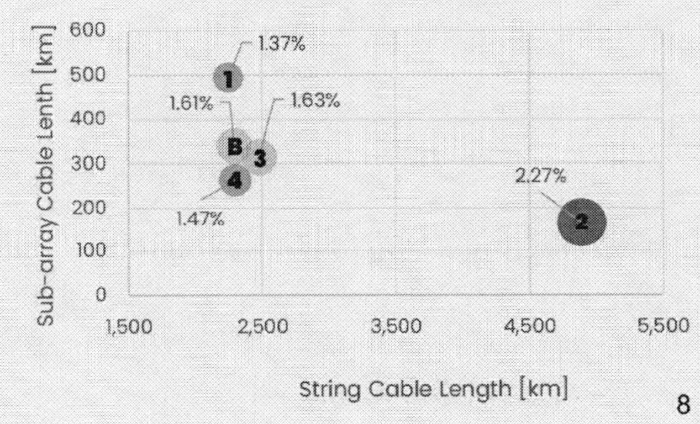

ZUTARI

RESULTS

Scenarios 5 to 7

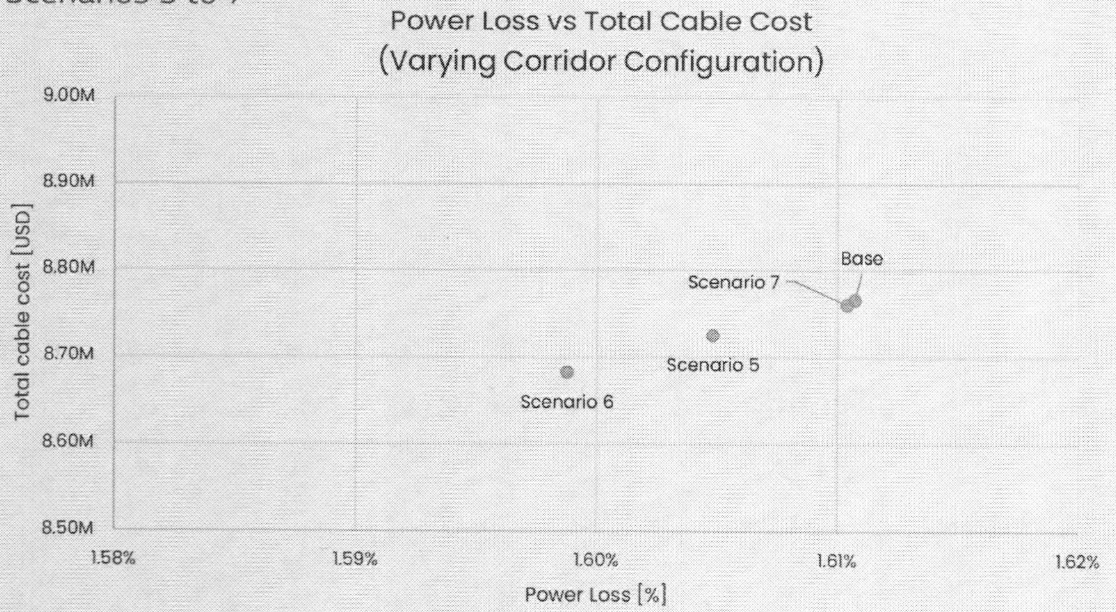

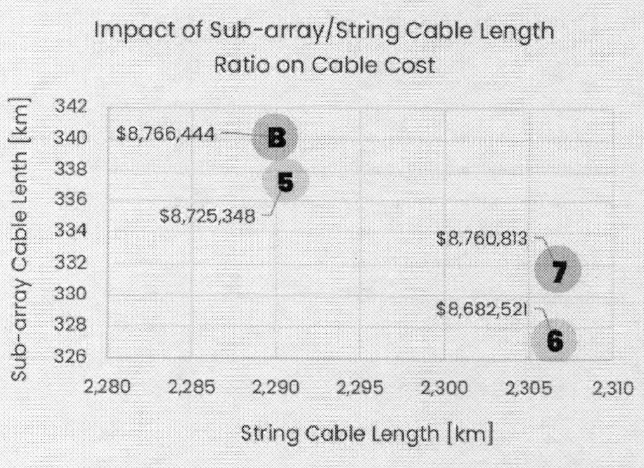

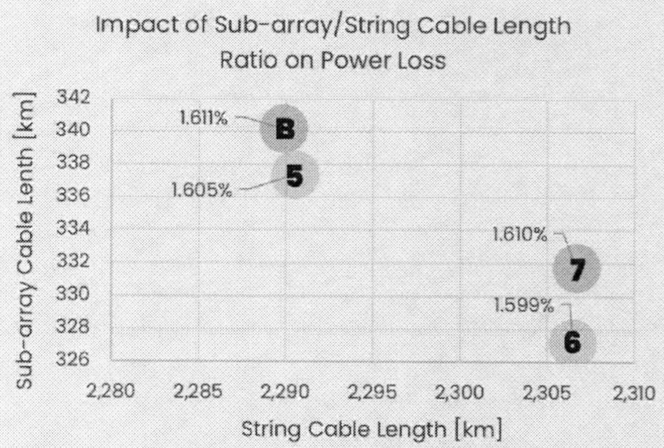

ZUTARI

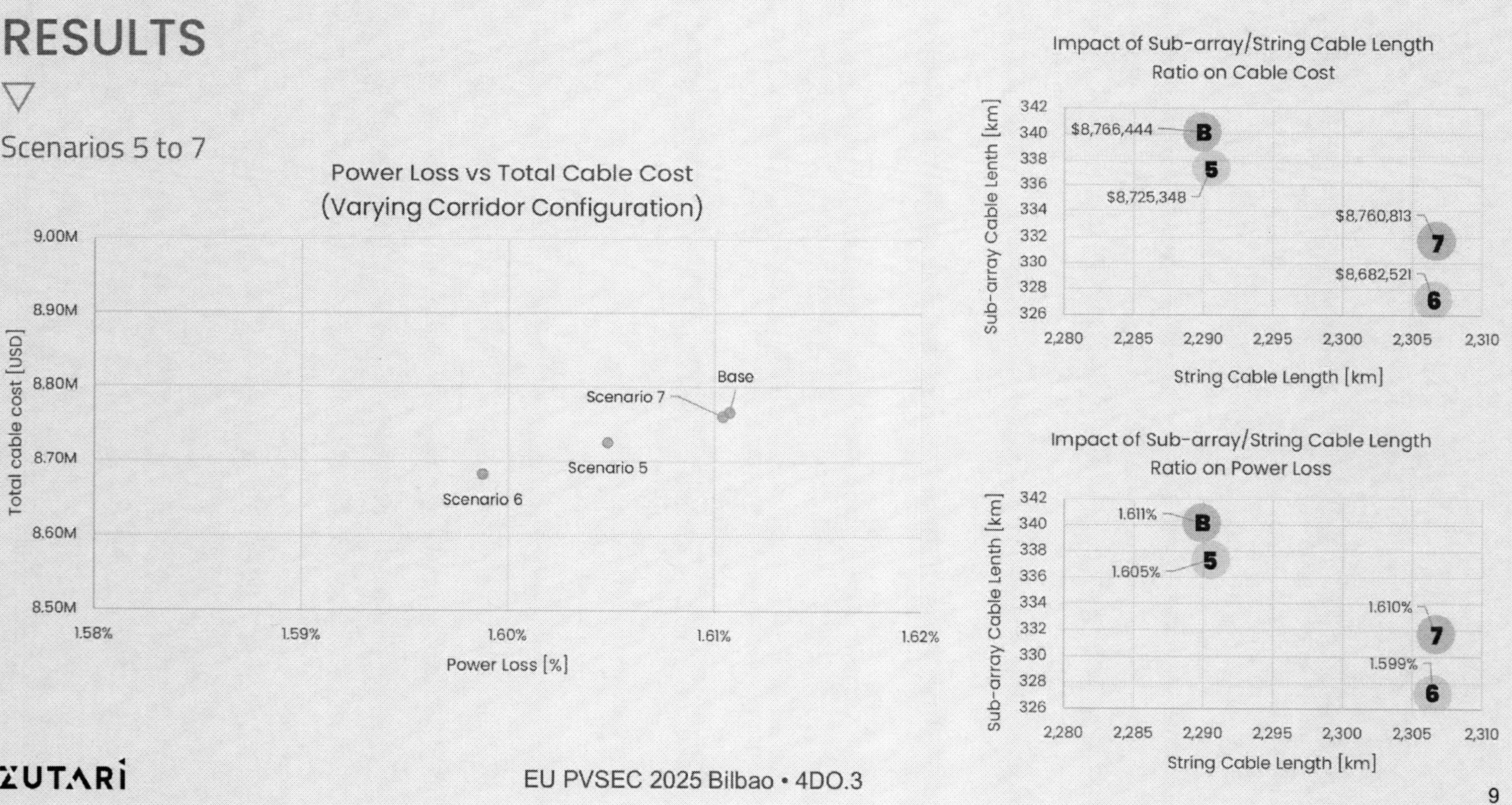

RESULTS

▽

Scenarios 8 & 9

Power Loss vs Total Cable Cost
(Varying String Cable Size)

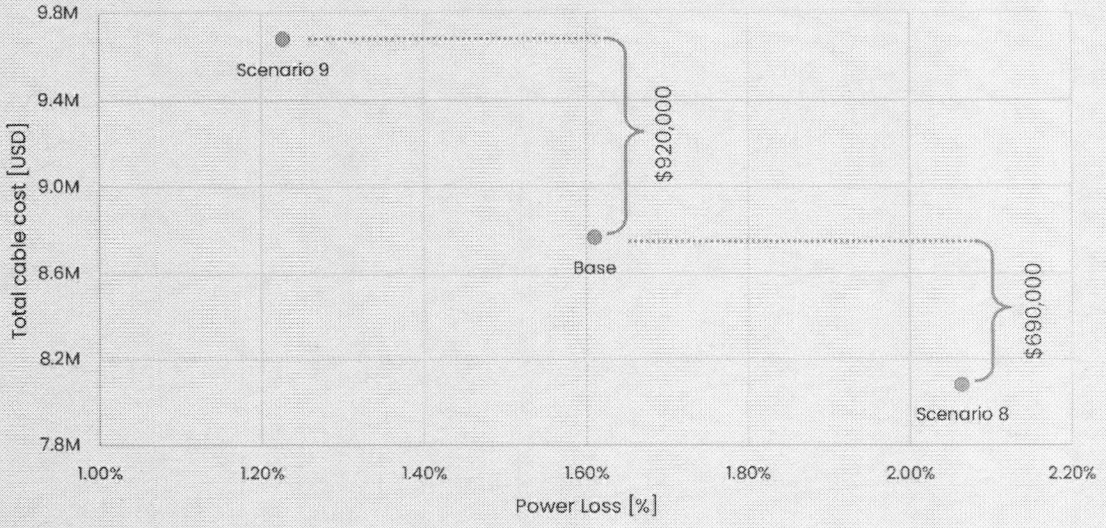

This result is intuitive

- $10mm^2$
    - Additional revenue of $72,500 (lowers loss by 0.38%)
    - Additional $920,000 cost
    - Payback period of 13 years
- $4mm^2$
    - Cost saving of $690,000
    - Revenue loss of $85,200 due to losses
    - Cost savings surpassed by lost revenue after 8 years
    - Voltage drop exceeds 5.46%

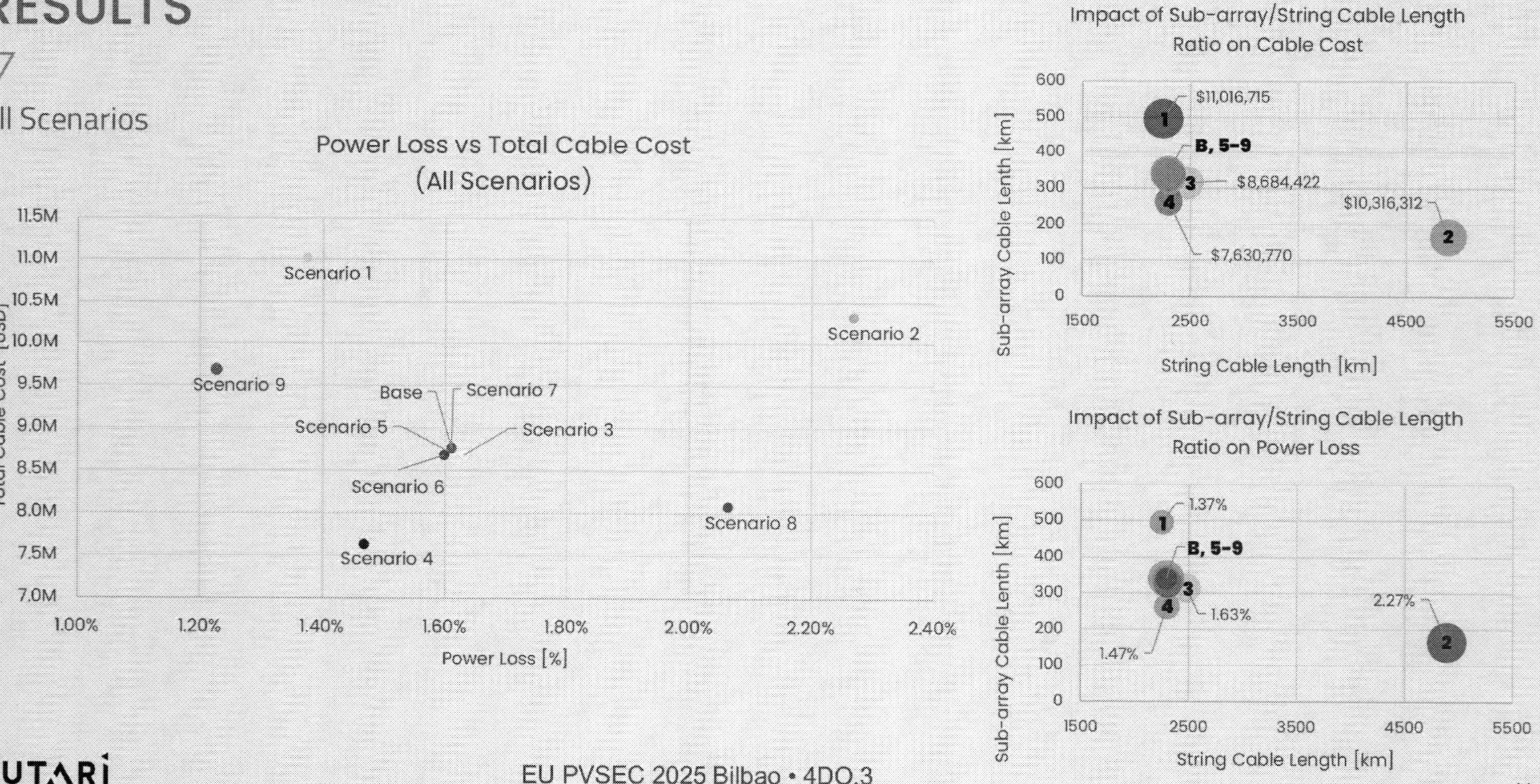

ZUTARI

RESULTS

▽

All Scenarios

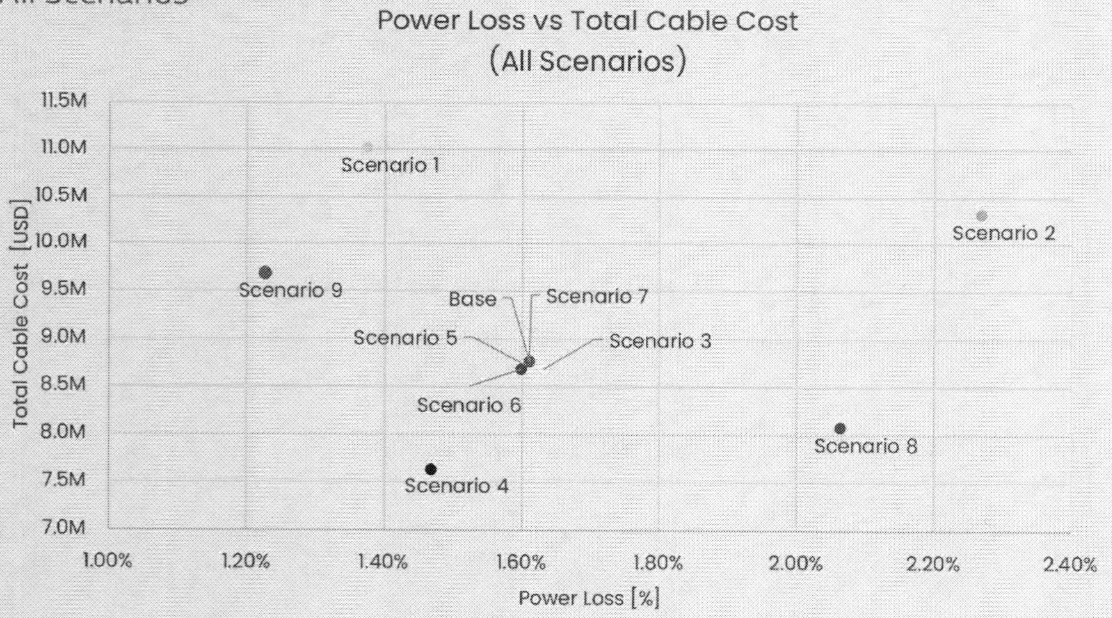

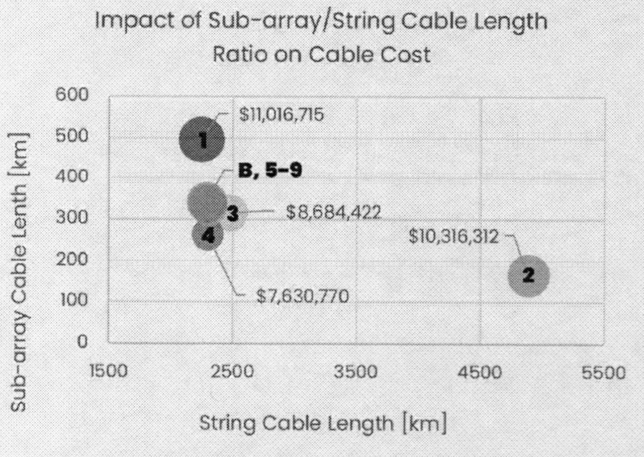

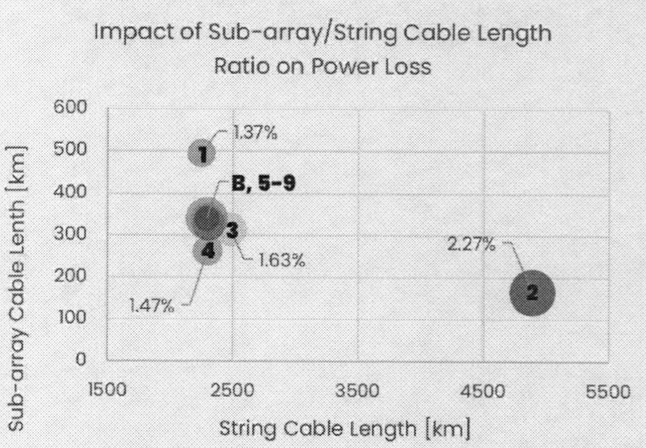

ZUTARI

EU PVSEC 2025 Bilbao • 4DO.3

CONCLUSION

Key Take-Aways

- Strategic array layout and early design decisions can have a significant impact on DC cable power loss and capital cost
- Trade-off between yield, cost, design flexibility and constructability
- Adjusting corridor widths has minimal impact on losses – constructability should be priority
- Using smaller PCU's decreases cable lengths significantly
- CAPEX-optimised design differs from yield-optimised design – lowest cost option does not always equal shortest cable length or lowest power loss

ZUTARI

FUTURE WORK

How can we expand on this?

- Scope should be expanded to include other system components including cost of inverters and AC infrastructure
- String inverter configuration assessment – is one architecture better than the other?
- Complete techno-economic analysis across lifetime of plant to assess long term impact of different DC string cable sizes

ZUTARI

THANK YOU!

Ayesha.Jacobs@zutari.com

paul@7secondsolar.com

keanu@7secondsolar.com

SEVEN SECOND SOLAR
empowered@7SecondSolar.com

AUTO PV™
VALUE ENGINEERING

zutari.com

EU PVSEC 2025 Bilbao • 4DO.3

ZUTARI
zutari.com

DURABLE BONDING OF LIGHTWEIGHT CRYSTALLINE SILICON PV MODULES

Guy Beaucarne[1], Tobias Hopp[2], Dominique Culot[1], Jonathan Curon[1]

[1]Dow Silicones Belgium SRL, Rue Jules Bordet Parc Industriel Zone C, B-7180 Seneffe, Belgium
[2] Sunman Energy (Deutschland) GmbH

ABSTRACT: Lightweight semi-flexible crystalline silicon photovoltaic modules have been introduced in the market for several years and provide an appealing possible alternative to conventional modules. In particular they are well suited for flat industrial or commercial roofs with limited load bearing capacity. An appropriate method to install such lightweight modules is to bond them to the roof structures using a suitable adhesive. This bonding approach actually needs special attention and care because the joints will undergo frequent high loads while being exposed to all possible weather conditions for many years. We introduce the use of silicone structural adhesives in this application, leveraging the large and long experience with creating durable structural bonds in the field of structural glazing for facades. The right joint dimensions are calculated taking into account wind load and design strength of the adhesive. Adhesion is tested not only in the as-bonded state, but also after stringent accelerated aging tests (long-term immersion in water, UV exposure, damp heat treatment, thermal cycling), which is a mix of tests developed for structural glazing and for the photovoltaic industry. We show that strong and durable adhesion can be reached.

Keywords: silicone, adhesive, sealant, adhesion, lightweight, semi-flexible, module

1 INTRODUCTION

To achieve the massive PV generation that is needed for the energy transition, very large areas need to be covered by photovoltaic modules. It is therefore important to make use of all available space that is suitable and socially acceptable for PV installation. Commercial and Industrial (C&I) flat rooftops are of particular interest as they cover large areas and are usually not used for any other activity. Moreover, the proximity of power generation and consumption makes such systems very appealing as they avoid problems with grid congestion and benefit from low 'behind-the-meter' power costs. However, there are challenges to install PV systems on such rooftops. Modern traditional PV modules are heavy, typically 30 kg or even more, because of the use of front and rear covers made of glass and an aluminum frame. Additionally, they need to be fixed on metal mounting structure, increasing the weight. Finally, because of the high wind load, the mounting structure needs to either be screwed into the rooftop, or maintained firmly on the rooftop using heavy ballast. Some roofs simply cannot take this weight, while watertightness of the roof may be lost if mechanical fixation is used.

Lightweight semi-flexible crystalline silicon photovoltaic modules, which feature a thin front cover and do not feature an Al frame, have been introduced in the market for several years and provide an appealing possible alternative to conventional modules. An appropriate method to install such lightweight modules is to bond them to the roof structures using a suitable adhesive, as it is simple and low cost. However, special attention and care is needed to ensure that the bonding and the system as a whole has the level of durability that is expected of a PV system.

2 DESIGN

2.1 Substructure

To avoid moisture accumulation and/or excessive heating of the modules, a space is needed between the roof and the PV laminate, enabling proper ventilation. Some roofs have a corrugated form and provide ventilation channels without any additional component. However, most C&I roofs do not have such profile, and therefore a substructure consisting of extruded profiles is used, ensuring that the module lies a few centimeters above the roof surface. This substructure consists in pieces of tube with rectangular cross-section made of weather-resistant plastic or metal. Two adhesive joints are needed to connect the substructure to the roof on one hand and the PV module to the substructure on the other hand.

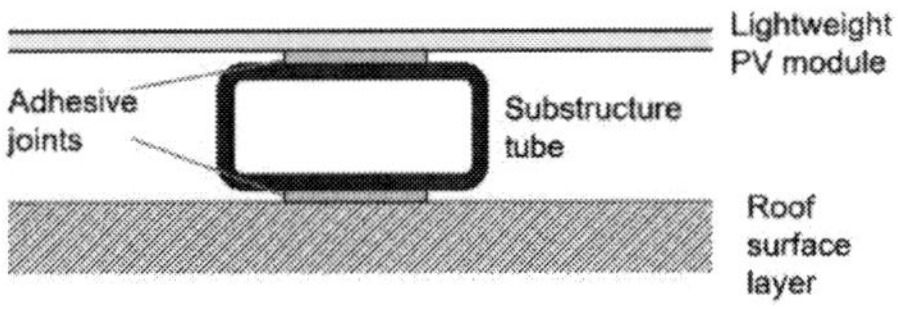

Figure 1: Cross-section schematic of installation of lightweight PV module

2.2 Geometry of the joints

Linear adhesive joints are used, parallel to the short edge of the module. The maximum spacing between the substructure tubes/joints is determined by the properties of the semi-flexible modules and is given by the module manufacturer. Depending on the size of the modules, the number of substructure tubes vary between five and eight. To avoid any overhanging of module parts, the outer joints are placed right at the edges of the module.

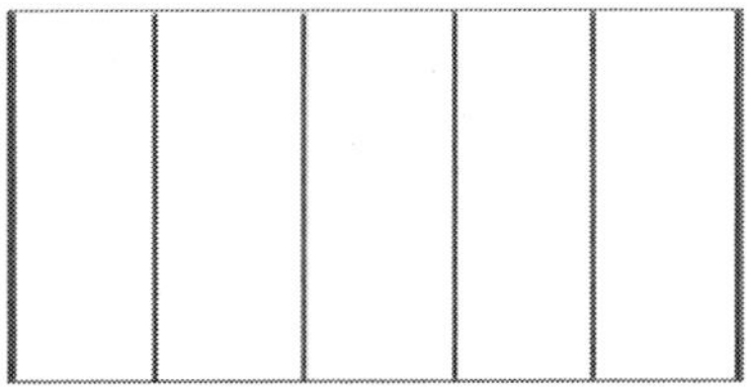

Figure 2: Example of geometry of the joints

10.4229/EUPVSEC2025/4DO.3.2
020384-001

Figure 3: Photo of lightweight semi-flexible module and installation structure including substructure and adhesive

2.3 Joint calculation

The determination of the final planar geometry of the joints translates into the adhesive width (the 'bite'), as the number and length of joints are fixed by previous considerations. The bite needs to be determined by calculations taking into account expected loads, the mechanical and physical properties of the various materials, the dimensions of the solar panels and the strength of the adhesive. The dimensioning takes certain safety factors into account to make sure the strength of the adhesive is never exceeded.

The main load to consider to calculate the bite is wind load. In the calculations, a design wind load W_d is used. In Europe, this design wind load has to be determined following the methodology prescribed by Eurocode EN 1991-4 [1] which takes into account the location of the building, its height and edge effects.

Once the design wind load is determined, the minimum bite can be calculated using this formula:

$$bite = \frac{Sp \times W_d}{R_d} \qquad (1)$$

Where S_p is the spacing between two joints and R_d is the design strength R_d. This value, which is provided by the manufacturer of structural adhesives, is determined by extensive testing of the material in standard test sequences including accelerated aging, applying statistical considerations and safety factors, and confirmed by external testing in an independent test laboratory. This rigorous procedure was introduced for structural glazing (ETAG002, now known as EAD 090010-00-0404 [2]) and comes in useful in this application that similarly requires a very high level of reliability and durability.

2.4 Calculator

A digital tool was developed by Sunman Energy Deutschland in collaboration with renowned structural engineering firm Arup, which incorporates the Eurocode standard and carries out calculations resulting in the desired geometry and design of the joints. As wind effects are larger close to the corners or edge of the roof, the calculated bite depends on the location on the roof. Figure 4 gives an example calculation.

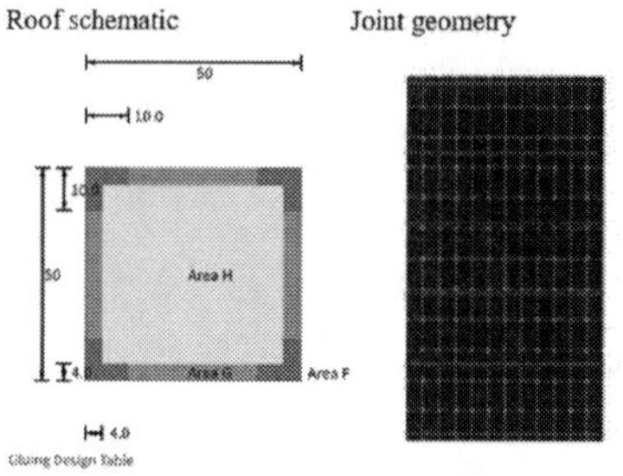

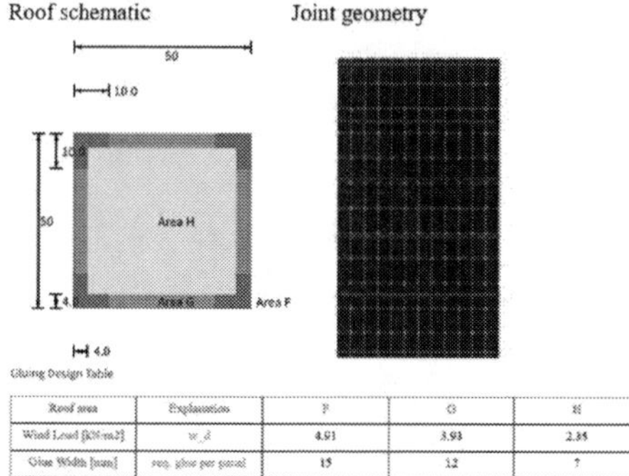

Roof area	Explanation	F	G	H
Wind Load [kN/m2]	w_d	4.91	3.93	2.35
Glue Width [mm]	req. glue per panel	15	12	7

Figure 4: Example of outcome of joint dimensioning calculation

3 SELECTION OF APPROPRIATE ADHESIVE

3.1 Durability requirements

As the lifetime of PV systems is 30 years or more, it is obvious that the adhesive to be used should have a durability that can provide this kind of lifetime. There are in fact not many adhesives that can fulfill their function even after many years while exposed to sometimes harsh weather conditions including heavy rain, high winds, frost, very cold temperature, UV exposure and summer heat.

This type of reliability is also required in the field of structural glazing, which is a technology to bond glass panels to metal frames and which enables glass curtain wall facades, very common in modern commercial and high rise buildings. Introduced more than 50 years ago, structural glazing has been made possible thanks to silicone structural sealants, providing the required combination of strength, elasticity and durability [3]. By selecting silicone structural adhesives for the lightweight PV module application, the experience and outstanding track record of the structural silicone glazing is leveraged.

Figure 5: Example of glass façade enabled by silicone structural glazing

In the early introduction of bonding for the installation of lightweight modules, different adhesive types were used that have turned out ill-suited for the application, either because of insufficient durability or incompatible material properties. An example of this is the use of visco-plastic adhesives, which are materials that can deform easily and achieve adhesion through a high tackiness. In Figure 6 we schematically compare the response of materials upon an imposed cyclic stress. After a force is applied, elastic materials return to their original shape while visco-plastic materials have some remaining plastic deformation. This might be a small deformation, but it builds up as the material is subjected to further cyclic loads. Such behavior finally leads to failure of the material. As the lightweight module bonding application implies cycling loads (e.g. through the effect of wind), adhesives showing this type of behavior are undesirable.

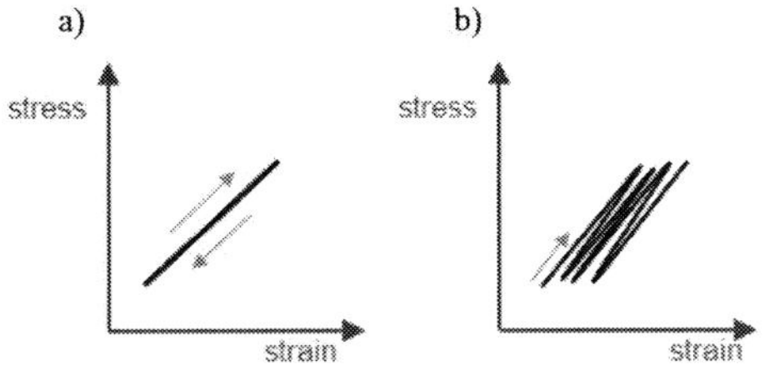

Figure 6: Schematic illustrating stress-strain behavior upon cyclic load for a) elastic materials, b) visco-plastic materials

3.2 Failure mode

Although the goal of the bonding technology is to create connections that never break in the application, it is necessary to consider which failure mode is preferred in case there is failure, as it is needed for the proper design of the joint. Figure 7 shows the three possibilities that can occur when the applied force exceeds the force that the bonded structure can take.

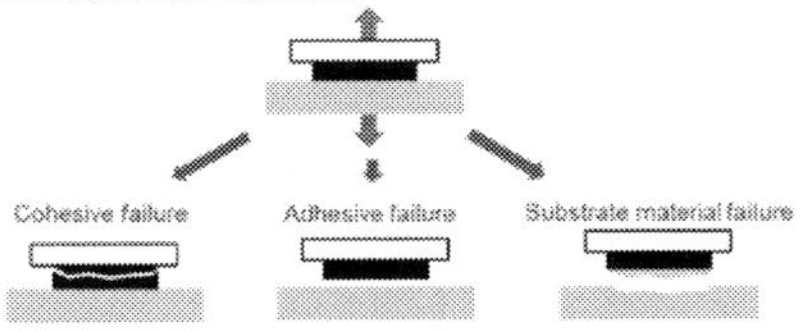

Figure 7: Potential failure modes of a bonded structure

In the cases of adhesive or substrate material failure, the force at which the structure fails depends not only on the properties of the adhesive, but on other factors such as surface properties and substrate material properties. A parameter characterizing the strength of the adhesive is therefore not enough and may not even be relevant to evaluate the force to which the structure may safely be subjected to. The dimensioning of the joint is then complex and inconvenient. That is why the situation where breakage occurs within the adhesive is preferable. In that case the design strength of the material can be used for joint dimensioning. Therefore, the target is to achieve adhesion on the substrate that is so strong that, if failure were to occur, it would be cohesive failure in the adhesive.

4 TESTING

A key component of the bonding technology for applications where reliability is paramount is testing. Because bonding of lightweight modules is a relatively new application, there are no standards yet that prescribe the tests to carry out, and there is no decades-long experience. A safe approach at this stage is therefore to carry out extensive testing on all substrates involved, leverage procedures developed in adjacent fields, and to do both lab testing and on-site testing.

4.1 Testing in the laboratory

Adhesion has to be tested on all substrates involved in the bonding structure, including the back of the lightweight solar panels, the substructure tube materials and the roof top surface. Similar to the practice in structural glazing, peel tests are made, where the adhesive is applied on a substrate with a strong mesh embedded in it. When testing, the mesh is pulled at 180°. The major parameter that is looked at during testing is the failure mode. If the adhesive comes clean off the substrate, this means that there is poor adhesion and no chemical bonds between adhesive and substrate. We are looking for a cohesive failure mode, with adhesive material remaining on the whole surface after pulling, which indicates that the adhesion between adhesive joint and substrate is strong. Sometimes the failure mode is mixed, with some regions failing adhesively and others cohesively. The percentage of the area of cohesive failure is noted down as the outcome of the measurement.

The peel tests should not only be done after curing of the adhesive, but importantly also after aging in various conditions. The set of tests we apply makes use of aging procedures that combine typical aging protocols used in the construction testing (e.g. water immersion and direct exposure to intense UV) and IEC testing standards (damp heat at 85°C-85% RH, thermal cycling between – 40°C and 85°C and a combination of thermal cycling and humidity freeze).

Testing in water immersion for a long period, while usually not practiced in the PV world, is very important in this application because many types of adhesives do not perform well in such conditions while there is a risk that the adhesive joint will be in contact with water for a significant period of time.

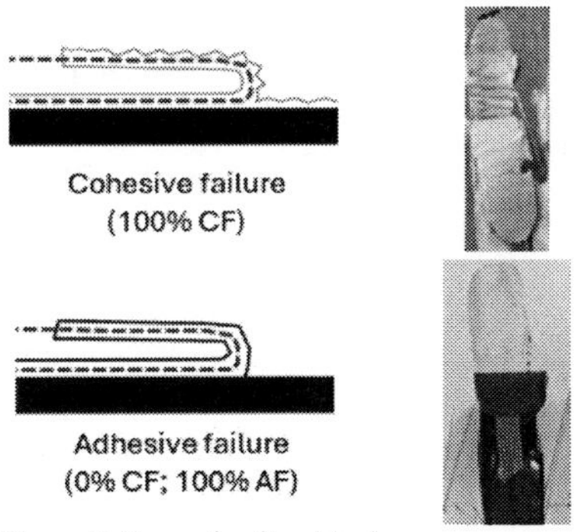

Figure 8: Example of peel tests

The results of a peel test campaign on various substrates using adhesive DOWSIL™ 895 Structural Glazing Sealant are given as an example in Table 1. DOWSIL™ 895 is a one part silicone adhesive which is applied as a paste with a caulking gun and cures into an elastomer upon reaction with moisture present in the ambient air.

Table 1: Peel test results

	PVC tube A	Backsheet of Sunman module SMF 520 12 x 12 UW	Roof membrane A (no primer)	Roof membrane A (with primer)	Roof membrane B
After curing	100 % CF	100 % CF	100 % CF	100 % CF	100 % CF
After 1 week water immersion	100 % CF	100 % CF	30 % CF	100 % CF	100 % CF
After 3 weeks UV exposure	100 % CF	100 % CF	100 % CF	100 % CF	100 % CF
After 1000 h damp heat	100 % CF	100 % CF	100 % CF	100 % CF	100 % CF
After 200 thermal cycles	100 % CF	100 % CF	100 % CF	100 % CF	100 % CF
After 50 TC + 10 humidity freeze cycles	100 % CF	100 % CF	100 % CF	100 % CF	100 % CF

In this example, we see that good adhesion is achieved on all substrates in the as-cured state. For the type of the PVC tube tested and the backsheet of the lightweight module, we see that good adhesion is maintained after the various accelerated aging procedures. For roof membrane A however, some adhesion was lost after 1 week immersion in water, resulting in 30% cohesive failure. However, when a primer (DOWSIL™ 1200 OS Primer) had been used prior to adhesive application, 100% cohesive failure was maintained even after one week water immersion. The need of primer depends on the specific types of roof membranes. In the example above, it can be seen that roof membrane B showed good adhesion after aging without priming.

4.2 Testing on-site

Apart from lab testing, some on-site testing is required. When a project is planned and a specific adhesive is anticipated to be used, a preliminary adhesion test should be performed on the roof surface, either a peel test or a tensile adhesion test. It is further recommended to carry out regular tests during the module installation campaign for quality control purposes.

Such on-site testing is complementary to lab testing but cannot replace it. Tests in the laboratory with accelerated aging are essential to check if the bonding will hold over time when permanently exposed to weather and climate.

5. CONCLUSIONS

Lightweight semi-flexible crystalline silicon photovoltaic modules provide an appealing possible alternative to conventional modules, in particular for flat industrial or commercial roofs with limited load bearing capacity. We investigate the direct bonding of those lightweight modules to the roof structures using an adhesive. This is a critical application because the joints will undergo frequent high loads while being exposed to all possible weather conditions for the whole lifetime of the PV system. Silicone structural adhesives are found to be well-suited in this application, thanks to the very stable and durable nature of silicone materials and the long experience with creating durable structural bonds in the field of structural glazing for facades. The right joint dimensions are calculated taking into account the local wind load and the adhesive's design strength. Adhesion is tested not only in the as-bonded state, but also after stringent accelerated aging tests which include tests developed both for structural glazing and photovoltaics. We show that strong and durable adhesion can be reached.

8 REFERENCES

[1] EN 1991-4: Eurocode 1: Actions on structures - Part 1-4: General actions – Wind actions

[2] European Assessment Document (EAD): EAD 090010-00-0404 Bonded glazing kit and bonding sealants

[3] Wolf A.; Recknage C.; Wenzel, N.; Sitte S; Structural Silicone Glazing:Life Expectancy of more than 50 Years? in Proceedings GPD Glass Performance Days 2017, 338-345.

zh aw

School of Engineering

MEASURES TO ADAPT THE POWER OUTPUT ON DEMAND BY SYSTEM DESIGN ON ROOFTOP PV SYSTEMS

Hartmut Nussbaumer, Lona Tulinski, Gian-Luca Bühlmann, Maximilian Eidtmann, Pascal Vögeli*, Markus Klenk

Zurich University of Applied Science, SoE
Institute of Energy Systems and Fluid Engineering, Technikumstrasse 9, 8401 Winterthur, Switzerland
*Institute for Sustainable Developement, Technoparkstrasse 2, 8406 Winterthur, Switzerland

41th European Photovoltaic Solar Energy Conference, 4DO.3

From static to dynamic tariffs – what are the consequences?

- In several European countries, dynamic feed-in tariffs are introduced
- Especially in summer at midday, the market price of electricity drops to zero or below
- In the winter months, the average price of electrical energy is higher
- What are the economic implications for photovoltaic systems on flat roofs, and which design is the most economically efficient?

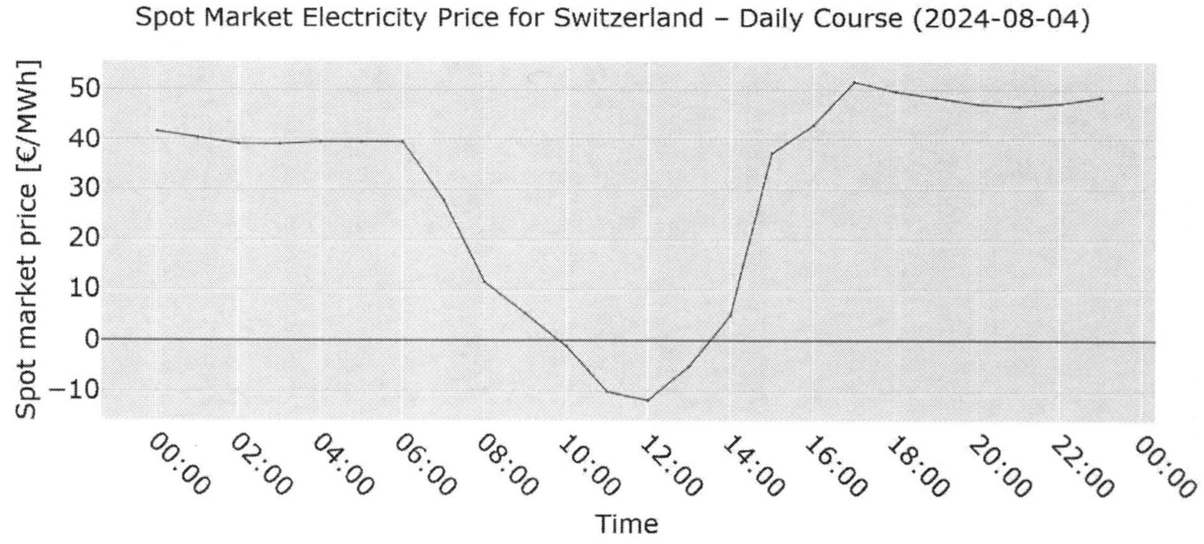

Typical PV system for flat roofs

East/west orientation
Low tilt angles in example 10°
Ground Cover Ratio **GCR** of ~90%
In our study: **The Reference**

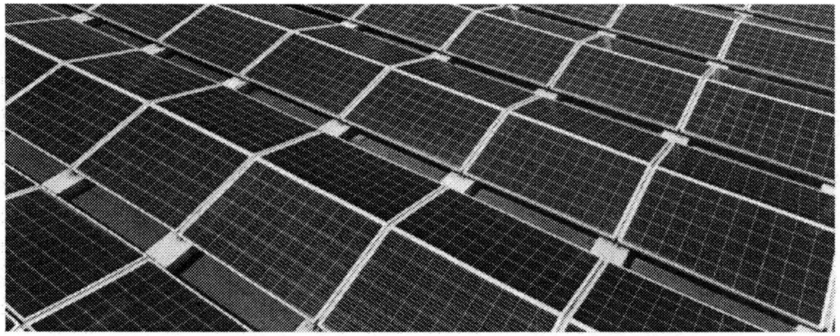

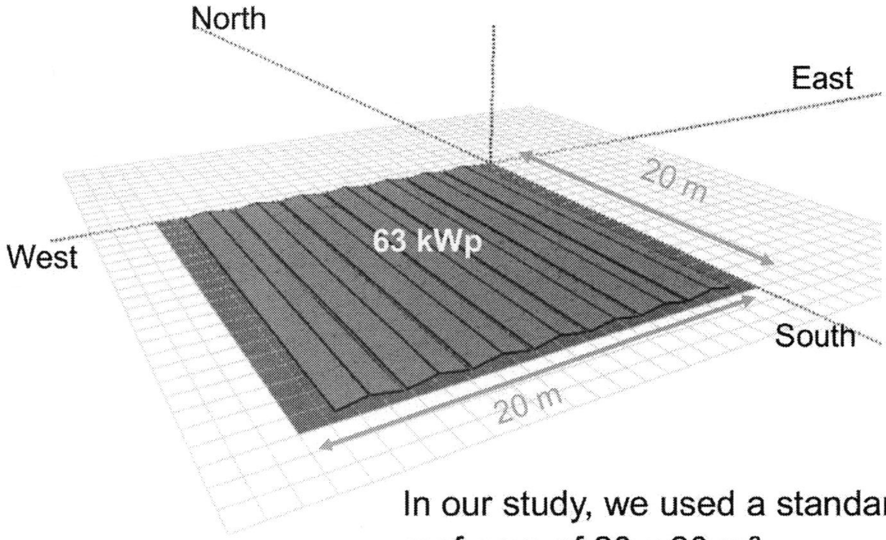

In our study, we used a standard roof area of 20 x 20 m²

⇒ For static feed-in tariffs currently the most economic design

Will this design still be the most economical option once dynamic grid feed-in tariffs are introduced?

Alternative designs of PV systems on flat roofs

South orientated, tilt angle 35°

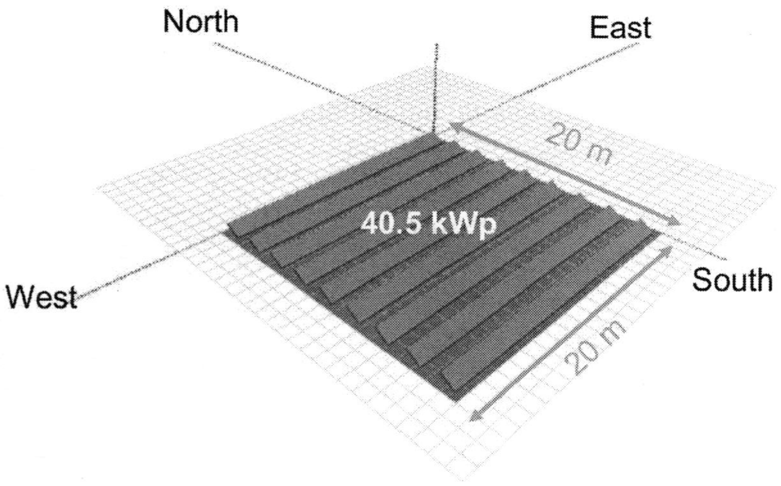

East/west oriented, vertically installed

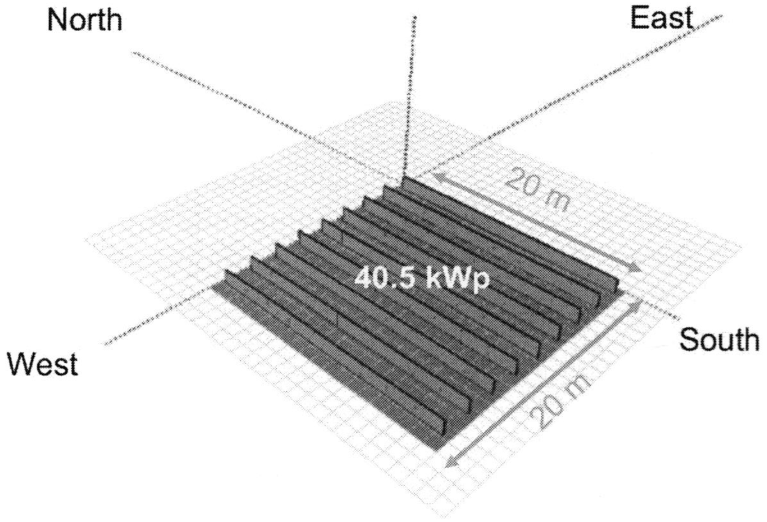

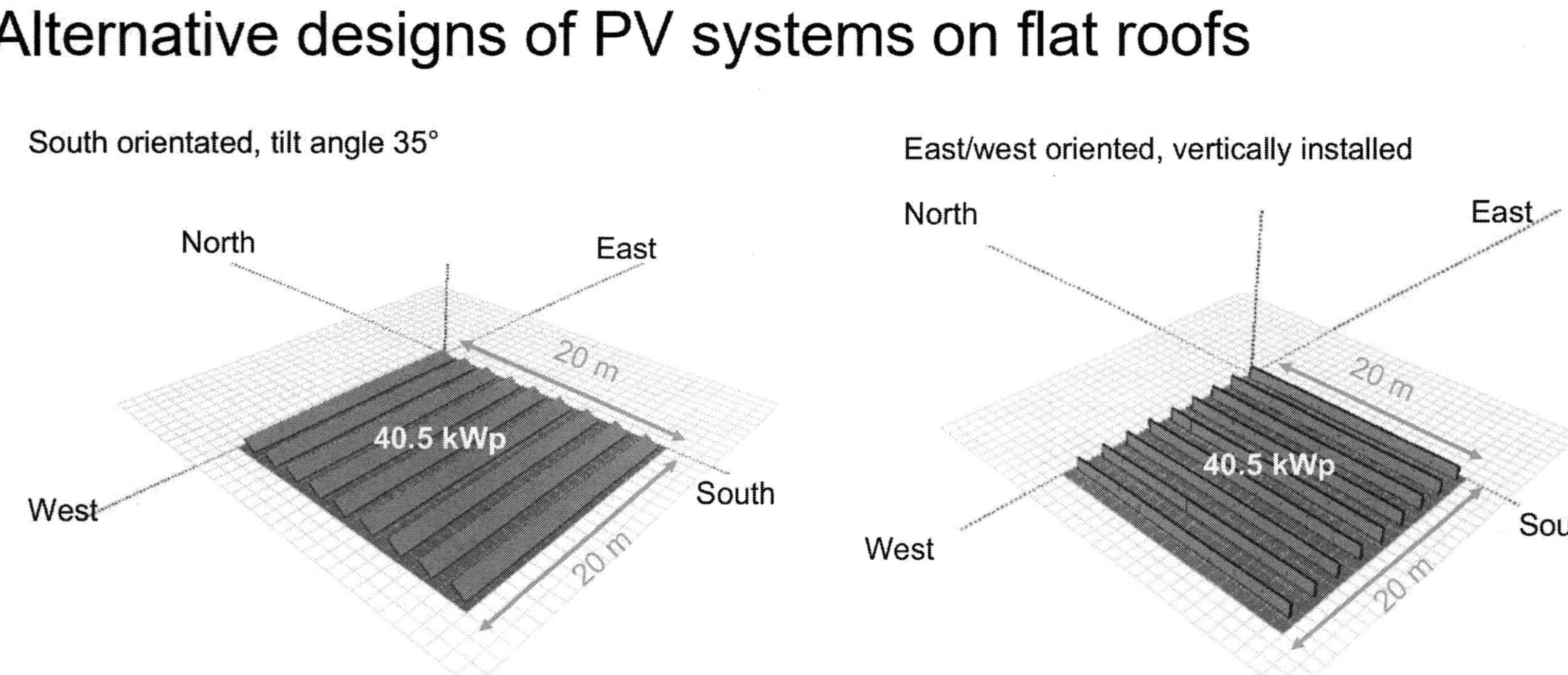

Lower GCR ⇒ lower rated power ⇒ lower yearly energy yield compared to the reference

Investment and maintenance costs

PV Systems with higher rated power generally show lower specific investment costs

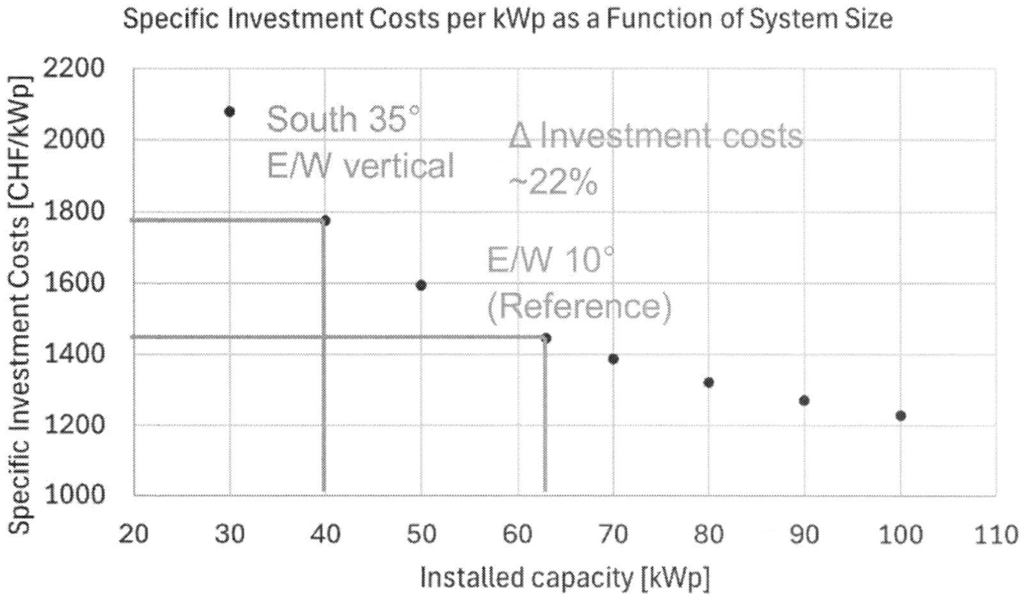

Source: Photovoltaics Market: Price Monitoring Study by SFOE (2024), p. 17

Analysed systems 20 x 20 m^2

System	Investment costs [CHF]	Maintenance costs [CHF/ a]
E/W 10°	90'972	1'260
South 35°	71'478	1'001
E/W vertical	71'478	1'001

Annual maintenance costs were assumed to be 1.4% of the investment costs

Source: Operating costs of photovoltaic systems by EnergieSchweiz (2017)

1 CHF = 1.05 EUR (2024)

Simulation of the economic efficiency

Net Present Value NPV

- Electricity prices for Winterthur in 2024
  - Day Ahead Stock Market Electricity Prices
  - 0.359 CHF/kWh fixed price (consumption)
  - 0.10 CHF/kWh fixed feed-in tariff
  - 0.025 CHF/kWh GO (guarantee of origin)
- 25 years operational lifetime of the PV system
- 0.4% yearly degradation of module
- 2.5% discount rate

Simulation of energy yield

- Location: Winterthur, Switzerland
- Weather data 2024 (irradiance)

Not considered

- Dynamic supply tariffs
- Batteries
- Demand-side management

1 CHF = 1.05 EUR (Ø 2024)

Seasonal dependencies

Monthly energy yield of the different designs versus average monthly electricity prices

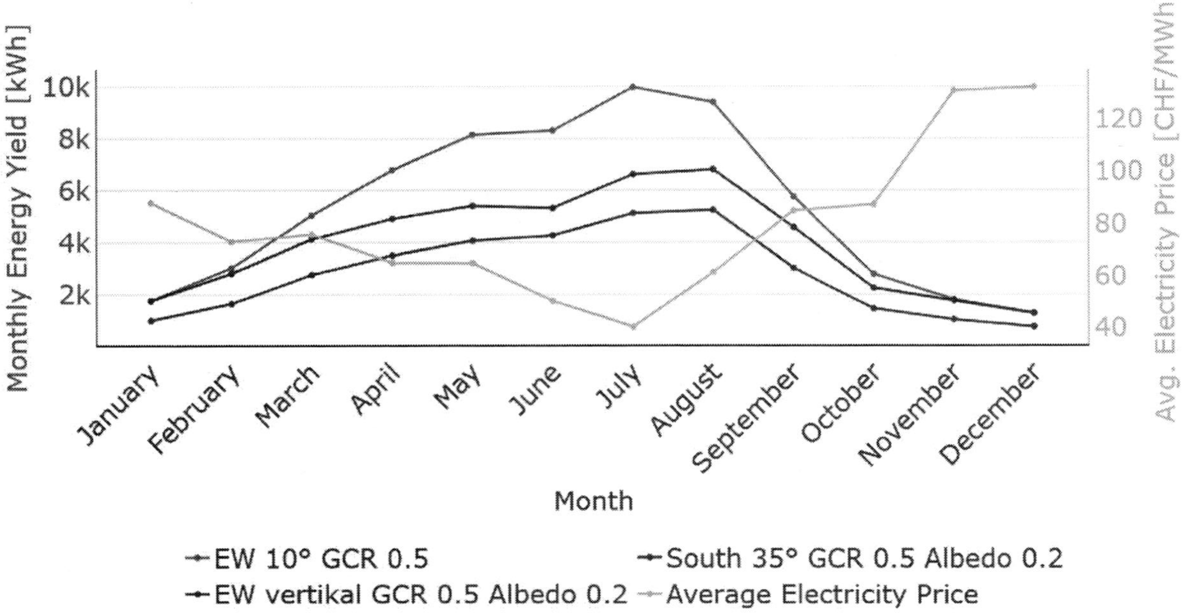

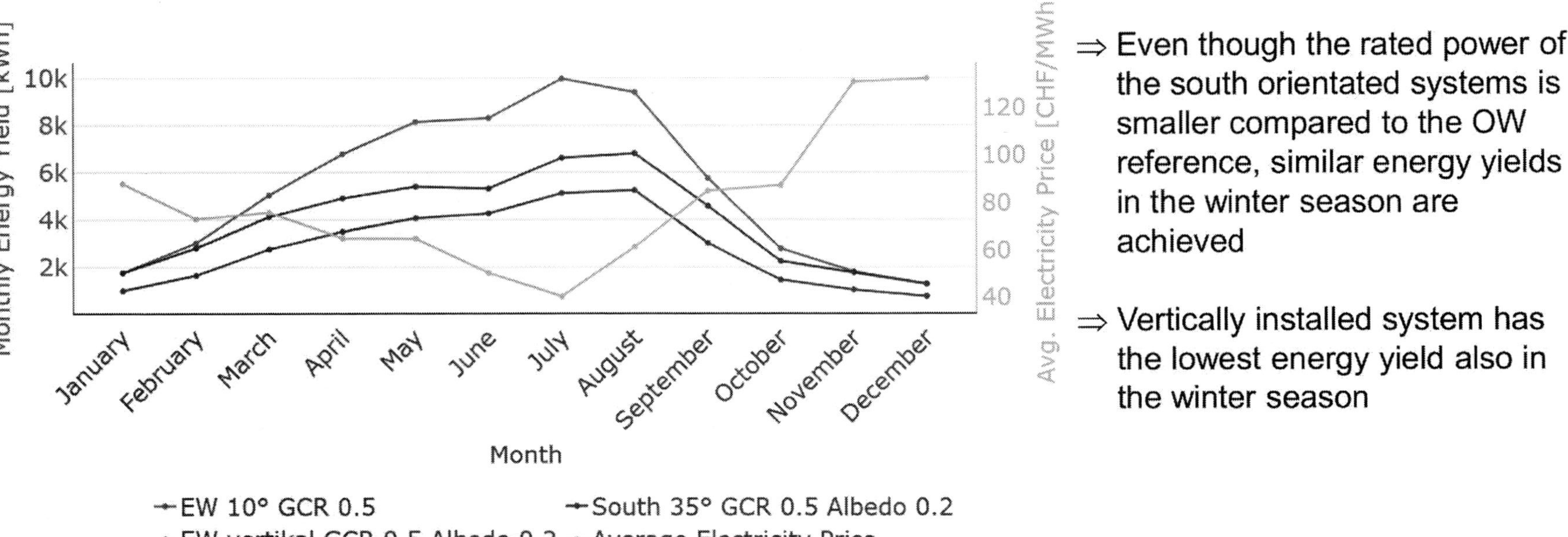

⇒ Even though the rated power of the south orientated systems is smaller compared to the OW reference, similar energy yields in the winter season are achieved

⇒ Vertically installed system has the lowest energy yield also in the winter season

1 CHF = 1.05 EUR (Ø 2024)

Hourly energy yield, self- consumption, feed-in tariffs

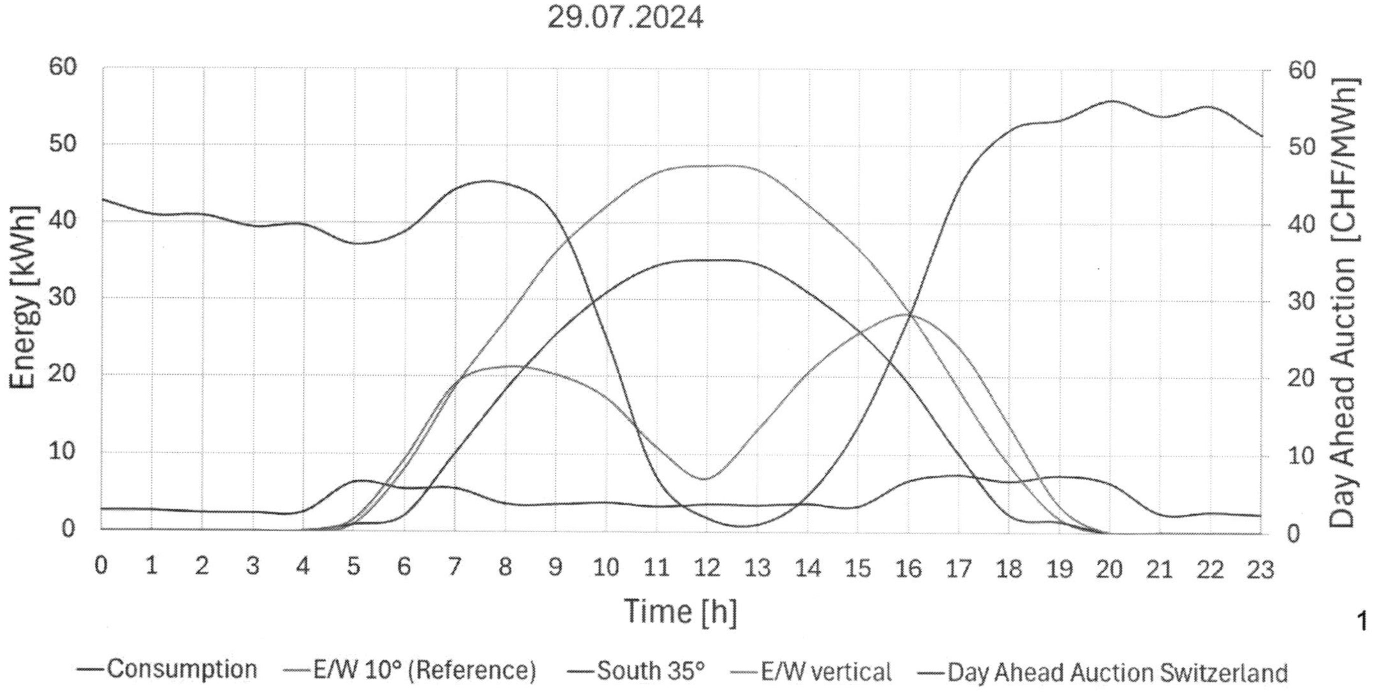

1 CHF = 1.05 EUR (2024)

Assumption: Consumption 30’000 kWh/y (multi-family household)
Resulting **Self-Consumption SC rates**: **19% (EW), 23% (S), 32% (V)**

NPV for static and dynamic feed in tariffs With self-consumption

NPV [CHF] - Considering Partial Self-Consumption

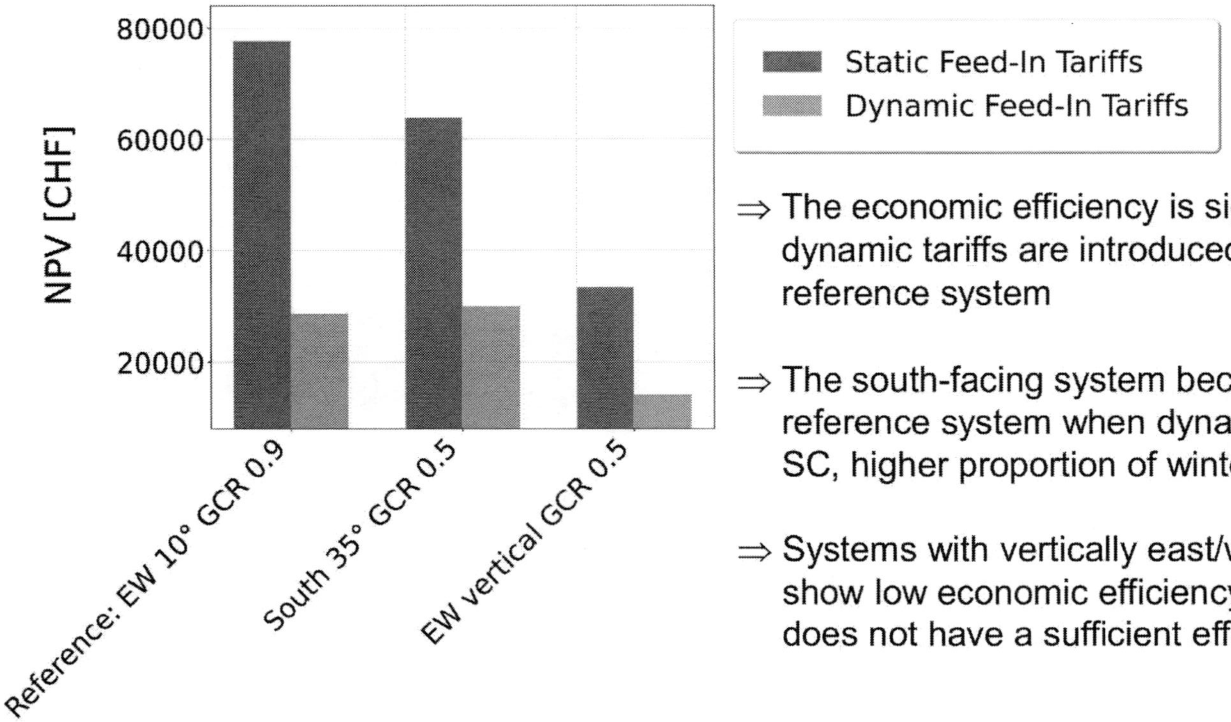

1 CHF = 1.05 EUR (Ø 2024)

⇒ The economic efficiency is significantly reduced when dynamic tariffs are introduced; highest impact on the E/W reference system

⇒ The south-facing system becomes more economical than the reference system when dynamic tariffs are introduced (higher SC, higher proportion of winter yield)

⇒ Systems with vertically east/west-facing modules generally show low economic efficiency. The "better" generation profile does not have a sufficient effect

NPV for static and dynamic feed in tariffs – Two different consumptions and self-consumption rates

Static Feed-in Tariff **Dynamic Feed-in Tariff**

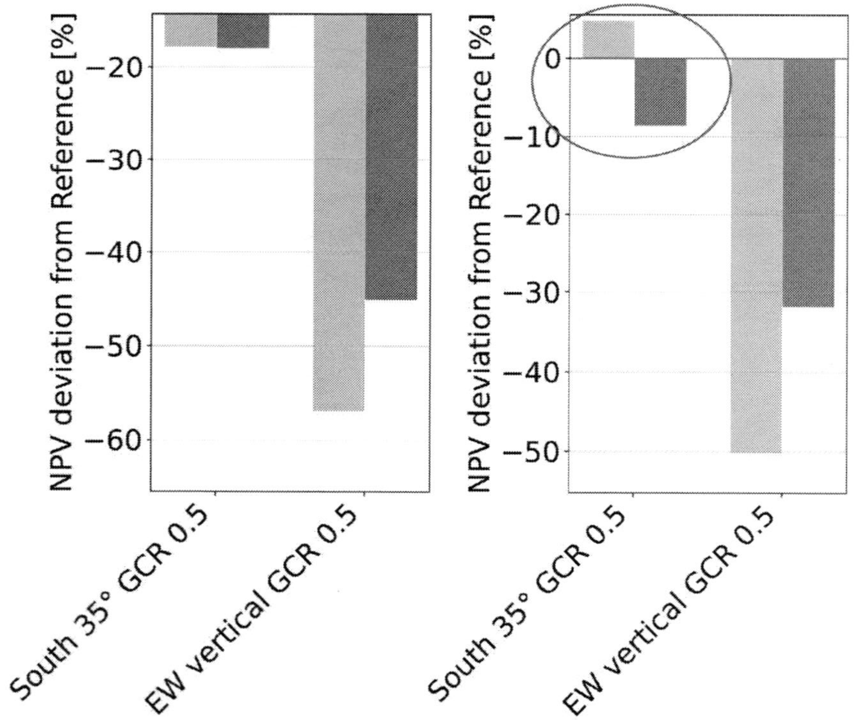

System	SC Rate [%]	SC Rate [%]
EW 10° GCR 0.9	19	33
South 35° GCR 0.5	23	39
EW 90° GCR 0.5	32	53

Low Consumption
High Consumption

SC = Self-Consumption

- Depending on the SC rate, south orientated systems with lower rated power can be economically more efficient than the reference
- With increasing SC-rate the reference E/W oriented system remains most economically efficient.

NPV for static and dynamic feed-in tariffs
Full feed-in systems (No self-consumption)

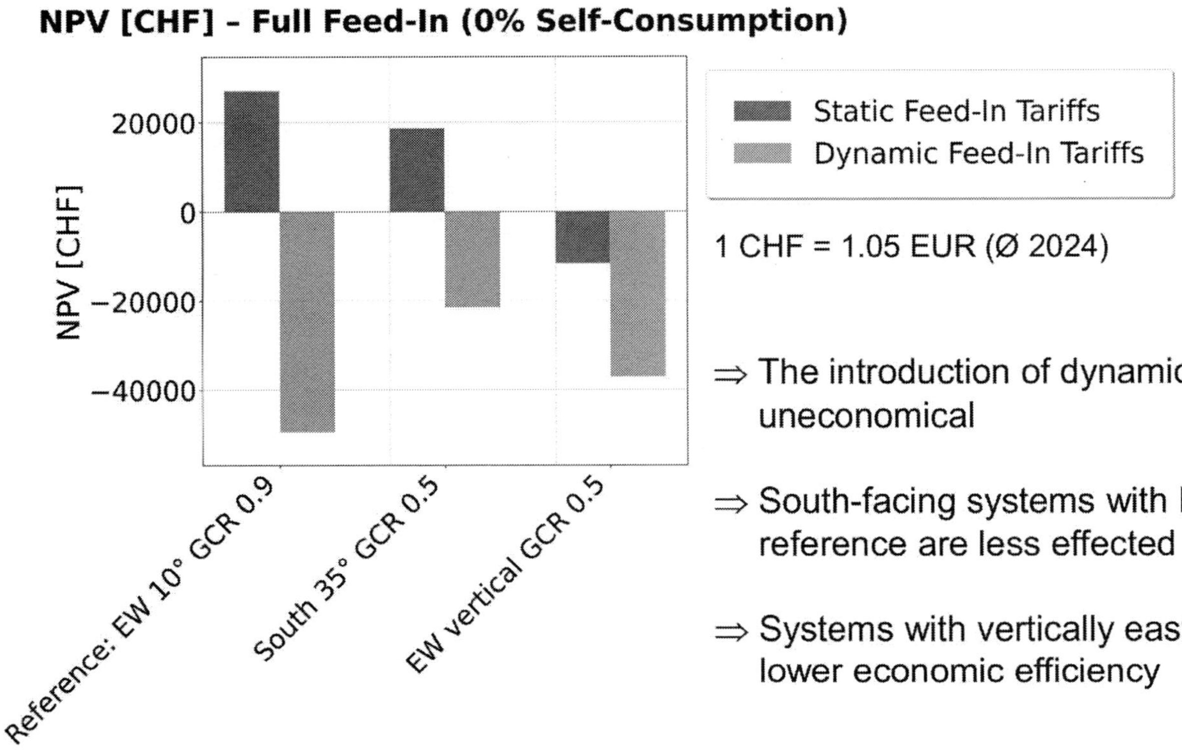

1 CHF = 1.05 EUR (Ø 2024)

⇒ The introduction of dynamic feed-in tariffs makes full feed-in systems uneconomical

⇒ South-facing systems with lower rated power compared to the reference are less effected

⇒ Systems with vertically east/west-facing modules generally show lower economic efficiency

Summary and conclusion

- The transition from static to dynamic feed-in tariffs generally reduces the economic efficiency of PV systems significantly.
- South-facing systems with lower rated power become more economically attractive compared to east/west systems when dynamic feed-in tariffs apply.
- For PV systems in combination of green roofs where the GCR is anyway lower, south orientated modules with higher tilt angels become more economically attractive when dynamic feed-in tariffs apply.
- Each PV project must be assessed individually. Designs with south-facing modules and steeper tilt angles should be considered.

Outlook

- In further investigations the influence of **batteries** and **energy management systems** need to be considered.
- **Horizontal Axis Tracking** might be an option in regions with high direct radiation.
- **Additional reflectors** at the edges of collector fields could enhance annual energy yield and change the generation profiles of flat-roof PV systems.

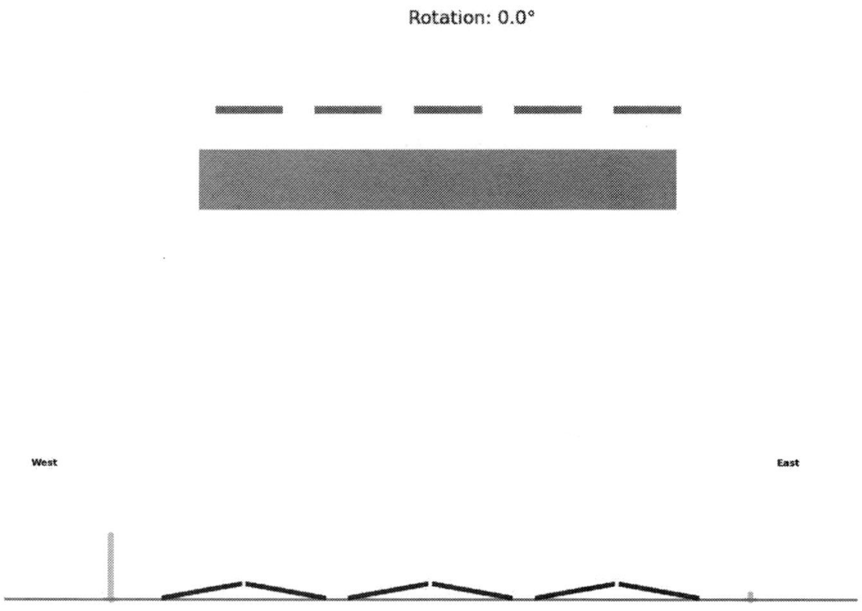

Thank you for your attention!

Zürcher Hochschule für
Angewandte Wissenschaften

ZHAW School of Engineering
Organisationseinheit

Prof. Dr. Hartmut Nussbaumer
Technikumstrasse 9 | Postfach
8401 Winterthur
Tel. +41 58 934 4799
Hartmut.nussbaumer@zhaw.ch
www.zhaw.ch/engineering

ZHAW School of Engineering | IEFE | 42th European Photovoltaic Solar Energy Conference, 4DO.3

42nd European Photovoltaic Solar Energy Conference and Exhibition

This presentation was selected by the Sc. Committee of the EU PVSEC 2025 for submission of a full paper to one of the EU PVSEC's collaborating peer-reviewed journals.

ASSESSMENT OF PERSONAL SAFETY CONCERNS OF PLUG AND PLAY PHOTOVOLTAIC INVERTERS USING A BLACK BOX APPROACH AND LABORATORY MEASUREMENTS

Alexander Erber[1], David Joss[1], Christof Bucher[1]*
[1] Bern University of Applied Sciences (BFH), School of Engineering and Computer Science (TI), Institute for Energy and Mobility Research (IEM), Laboratory for Photovoltaic Systems (PV-Lab)
Jlcoweg 1, 3400 Burgdorf, Switzerland
Corresponding author: Christof Bucher, christoph.bucher@bfh.ch

ABSTRACT: The rising utilization of plug and play photovoltaic systems has sparked safety concerns, particularly when installed by non-professionals, as current standards only partially address these issues. This paper introduces a black box testing method to evaluate the personal safety of plug and play inverters. 25 microinverters are assessed using three tests: (1) residual voltage behavior at the mains plug following disconnection, (2) current increase with low grid voltage, and (3) maximum touch temperature during operation. Results indicate 56% of inverters comply with the proposed German plug and play standard, performing comparably to other electrical devices. Further investigation is necessary to determine if exceeding this threshold poses a direct safety threat. A correlation has been identified between the output parameters of the inverters (resistance and capacitance) in the unplugged state and the duration required to reach safe voltage levels for most devices. The integration of a relay, however, can ensure compliance across all devices. During low voltage conditions, current surges are recorded, which could strain non-dedicated circuits. The temperature test reveals a positive correlation between the power density of inverters and their touch temperature. The outcomes of this study offer insights and guidance for future standardization and product improvements.

Keywords: plug and play photovoltaics, plug-in photovoltaics, microinverter, safety assessment, laboratory measurements

1 INTRODUCTION

Plug and play photovoltaic (PV) systems – often called balcony or plug-in PV – have seen rapid growth among end consumers, notably in Germany, the current largest market. By June 2025, over one million systems (>1 GWp) were registered in Germany, with actual numbers considerably higher due to unreported installations [1] [2]. These systems use microinverters, typically limited to a maximum output power depending on the national regulation (e.g. 600 or 800 VA) and are connect to the grid with standard household mains plugs (e.g., Typ F).

In terms of personal safety, the installation of plug and play PV systems by end users is more critical compared to professionally installed PV systems, as most of the microinverters were designed to be connected to the grid through a fixed connection. Presently debated safety issues include the residual voltage at the mains plug after the grid disconnection, the potential overloading of distribution circuits, and the effects on the functionality of RCD (residual current device) [3]. Current inverter safety standards, such as IEC 62109-1 [4], only partly address these issues, and comprehensive regulation is still evolving. The German draft standard E DIN VDE V 0126-95 [5] aims to close regulatory gaps but requirements for grid connections via household plugs remain under discussion. This draft is currently in its second revision and outlines requirements for all components of a plug and play PV system, such as module mounting frame, inverter, PV modules, DC connectors, and grid connection. For the connection to the grid through a standard mains plug, new requirements are defined that would legalize this type of connection, as current standards [6] do not allow it yet. For this new requirement, limited information and experience is available on the behavior of plug and play PV inverters regarding their residual voltage behavior.

Previous studies on plug and play microinverters used in plug and play systems primarily addressed efficiency and yield assessments [7] [8]. In 2017, the photovoltaic institute (PI) Berlin investigated RCD interference and overload situations of cable sections for 600 VA systems through lab tests [9]. In 2025, HTW Berlin extended the PI's methodology to 800 VA systems [10]. The 2017 PI study also considered electric shock protection related to residual voltage after unplugging, although without lab tests. A recent US study examined plug and play PV system barriers and three safety features (touch-safe plugs, breaker masking, bidirectional residual circuit devices) [11]. Both studies claim anti-islanding functions and relay interfaces ensure safety, but this is misleading, as these features are intended mainly for system and grid protection, not personal safety. While they offer a galvanic separation, non-switchable capacitors may still leave residual voltage levels non-compliant, as noted in the German plug and play draft standard.

The mentioned publications show the lack of data on the behavior of microinverters used for plug and play systems concerning the grid connection through standard household hold plugs (e.g. Typ F in most of the EU and T13 in Switzerland). This could lead to overregulation's and additional bureaucratic procedures in testing and installation, thus causing higher costs for consumers.

This paper addresses these challenges by analyzing a set of microinverters used in plug and play systems, with a focus on three safety concerns: (1) analyzing the residual voltage at the mains plug following disconnection, (2) the current increase under low grid voltage conditions and (3) the maximum touch temperature during operation. Laboratory-based black box testing is employed, using only components accessible in normal operation. Results are discussed in the context of current standardization gaps and guidance for future standard and product development is given. In this paper, "microinverters used in plug and play systems" and "plug and play inverters" are used interchangeably.

2 METHODS AND MATERIAL

2.1 DEVICES UNDER TEST

To assess relevant safety concerns, 25 commercially available inverters from 11 manufacturers are analyzed (see Table 1). The devices nominal AC outputs span from 300 VA to 2000 VA and are selected to represent the current plug and play inverter market. Although not all

10.4229/EUPVSEC2025/4DO.3.6
020386-001

units fall within national plug and play system limits (600 VA for Switzerland; 800 VA for most EU countries), most can be software-limited to comply with these regulations. The test set includes 23 single-phase and 2 three-phase inverters, allowing both standard and potential future (three-phase) scenarios to be considered.

The devices can be grouped according to typical national power limits in three categories: 16 devices in category A (≤600 VA), 5 in category B (>600 VA & <=800 VA), and 4 in category C (>800 VA).

Table 1: Overview of the tested inverter categories. A detailed overview of the tested devices is given in Erber et al. [12].

Power category	Power range of category [VA]	Power range of invertrs	Number of inverters
A	<=600	300-600	16
B	>600 & <=800	601-800	5
C	>800	801-2000	4

2.2 SAFETY TESTS

Based on currently discussed safety concerns for plug and play PV inverters and a review of relevant standards, three laboratory tests are defined. The test conditions are set according to a black box approach, in which only parts and connectors accessible during normal operation are utilized. No additional communication gateways, monitoring equipment, or firmware updates are used, reflecting typical consumer usage where regular updates are often neglected. The tests and their origins are outlined as follows:

- **Residual voltage after disconnection:** Plug and play inverters contain capacitors that may retain voltage after grid disconnection. The test method is adapted from the draft German plug and play PV standard (E DIN VDE V 0126-95:2024-6) in line with the black box approach, voltage is measured at directly before the mains pins, rather than directly at the capacitors. The same compliance limit from IEC 60335-1 (maximum 34 V touch voltage after one second) as in the German draft standard is applied. The product standard draft mandates that the residual voltage test be conducted at various power levels – nominal power, 50% of nominal power, and the lowest feasible rated power – but due to the number of inverters under test, this paper conducts the test only at nominal power, assuming it represents the worst-case condition.
- **Maximum touch temperature:** As convection-cooled inverters can develop potentially hazardous surface temperatures, touch temperatures are measured under two defined conditions (1:1 and 1:1.5 AC-DC-Ratio) and assessed against the IEC 62109-1 limit for touch temperatures.
- **Feed-in current limitation at reduced grid voltage:** To prevent overloads in household wiring, inverters are tested for current limitation at low grid voltages as described in the German standard draft and DIN VDE V 0124-100 [13]. The draft standard requires an additional testing voltage at 0.85 Vn. During testing the feed-in current must not exceed 3.5 A (+2%). In this paper the holding time per voltage step is reduced, due to the number of devices, and additional voltages are included for further insights in the inverter behavior at low voltage levels.

The purpose of these tests is not to declare devices as unsafe, but rather to identify situations where more specific requirements for plug and play operation may be necessary. Microinverters designed for rooftop use may need additional specifications when applied in plug and play systems. For instance, capacitors implemented for electromagnetic compatibility can influence residual voltage and may require pre- or post-manufacturing adaptations.

All tests are conducted at the Laboratory for Photovoltaic Systems (PV Lab) of the Bern University of Applied Sciences in Burgdorf (BFH), where a dedicated test bench has been developed especially for the test "Residual voltage after disconnecting". The measurements are conducted within the SFOE funded project "Plug & Play Photovoltaic Systems" [14].

2.2.1 RESIDUAL VOLTAGE AFTER DISCONNECTION

The measurement setup for the residual voltage test is shown in Figure 1a. The plug and play inverter under test (DUT) are connected to the PV module simulator(s) (Modul Sim; Delta Elektronika SM330-AR-22 and Delta Elektronika SM100-AR-75) on the DC side and to the plug side of the socket connection at the mechanical disconnector on the AC side. The power analyzer (Dewetron DEWE3-PA8-RM with 3x TRION3-1810M-Power-4 measurement cards) measures the current and the voltages (V_{L-N}, V_{PE-L}, V_{PE-N}) shortly before the plug side. To ensure the same grid conditions for each measurement and prevent interferences from other grid connected devices, the setup uses a grid simulator. the grid simulator Due to space reasons, the used grid Simulator (Regatron TC.ACS.50.528.4WR.HC.LC) is not shown.

Figure 1b illustrates the function of the automated mechanical disconnection through the linear motor. The parallel configuration of three Swiss T13 sockets on the grid side, alongside three measurement cards on the power analyzer, enables the concurrent measurement of three inverters. This setup also permits measurements of three-phase inverters, as a T15 socket (three-phase) occupies the same amount of space as a T13 socket (one-phase).

Due to the number of inverters the residual voltage test is only conducted at nominal power and repeated 30 to 50 times, depending on the start time of the inverter, to ensure measurements at different phase angles. The required DC power is not determined iteratively and the I-V curve parameters are set with the conditions described in Erber et al. [12].

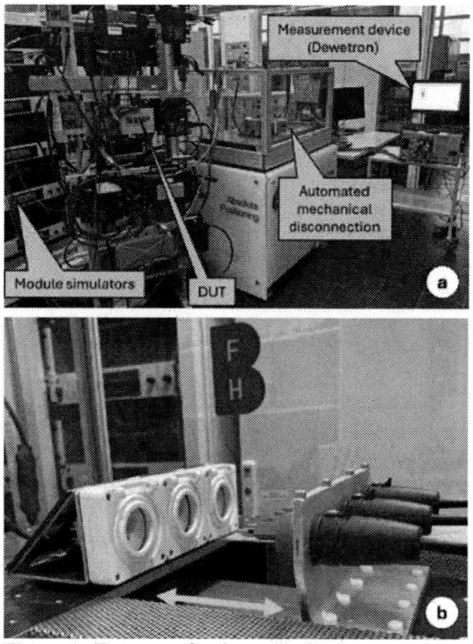

Figure 1: Test setup for the residual voltage test (a) and detail of the automated mechanical disconnection (b)

The residual voltage test is conducted with the following procedure: First, the AC connection to the grid is closed with the linear motor and the corresponding I-V curves are activated on the module simulator(s). When the inverter reaches the nominal power the AC connection is opened through the linear motor and the measurement is triggered by the power analyzer. A trigger pre- and post-time of 1 s is used. The process is repeated automatically with the same unplug conditions in context of velocity and acceleration.

In addition to plug and play inverters, other electrical household devices are analyzed with the same test procedure for a comparison of the residual voltage behavior.

The selected configuration, in contrast to a setup utilizing a (solid-state-) relay, accurately simulates actual conditions, ensuring that measurements are unaffected by switch bounce or parasitic capacitance phenomena. However, the limitation of this configuration is the inability to establish a precise phase angle for grid disconnection.

The measurement files are processed in Python after the measurements. As the measurement is triggered at the middle socket connection it is possible that the disconnection occurred earlier or later at the other two sockets. For this reason, an individual disconnect time is calculated for each socket. The disconnection for this paper is defined, where the voltage $V_{PE\text{-}N}$ exceeds 1.35 times the mean values of the first 0.5 s in the pre-time window. In the second step, the timestep is determined, where the maximum touch voltage falls below 34 V, and the time for the voltage decline is calculated. In the last step, the voltage at the point of disconnection is determined for the analysis. Figure 4 shows the current and voltage curves of a plug and play inverter after disconnection from the mains. Upon disconnection, the current reduces to 0 A due to the absence of a load on the plug (such as a body resistor), and the voltage displays the characteristic discharge curve of a capacitor. At t=130 ms, a shift in the voltage gradient signifies a switching event. The peak touch voltage decreases below the 34 V threshold after 793 ms, thereby adhering to the 1-second duration limit specified in E DIN VDE V 0126-95:2024-6.

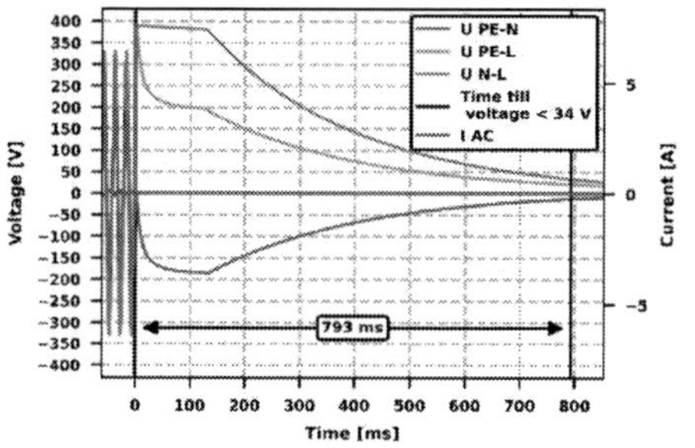

Figure 2: Current and voltage after disconnection from the mains of a plug and play inverter (600 W)

2.2.2 MAXIMUM TOUCH TEMPERATURE

The measurement setup for the maximum touch temperature test is shown in Figure 3, where three inverters are tested in parallel. The inverters are supplied on the DC side by the module simulators (Delta Elektronika SM330-AR-22 and Delta Elektronika SM100-AR-75) and are connected to the laboratory grid – no grid simulator is used. At every inverter the temperature is measured in the middle of both sides of the inverter with y typ T thermocouple. For the temperature measurement of the surface and ambient temperature (typ K thermocouple) the Keithley DAQ6510 with a 7700 measurement card is used. The power measurement is conducted with a Yokogawa WT3000 power analyzer. Both measurement devices acquired the temperature and power data in a 10s interval.

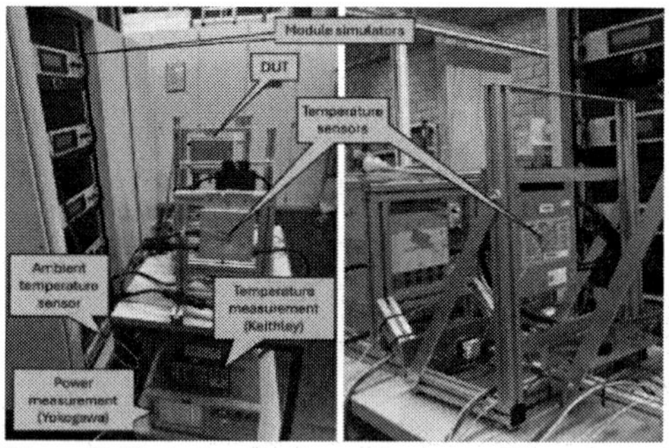

Figure 3: Test setup for the maximum touch temperature test

IEC 62109-1 [4] mandates that the maximum touch temperature must remain within a specified limit even in the most severe-rated operating conditions. For testing, the limit outlined in Table 3 of IEC 62109-1 for "Enclosure parts accessible to user by casual contact" is applied. These limit is 70 °C for metal parts and 95 °C for plastic and rubber parts. All plug and play inverters being tested have metal enclosures, except for the two Enphase® inverters with polymer enclosures.

10.4229/EUPVSEC2025/4DO.3.6
020386-003

Given that microinverters rely on convection cooling, the most severe operating conditions are thus present at high ambient temperatures, small cooling surfaces, high input powers, low efficiencies and/or limited convection (i.e. low heat transfer coefficient). For the test, it is assumed that the microinverters have mounting conditions with sufficient convection. In this setup, the input power – defined as a function of irradiance – is the only variable actively adjusted. The effects of ambient temperature can be considered retrospectively by calculation. The irradiance profile features a 2-minute ramp time and a 3.5-hour step time to achieve steady-state conditions. Two irradiance level are set in the profile. An irradiance of 1000 W/m², aligning with standard test condition (STC), indicates the nominal power operating point. Conversely, 1500 W/m² simulates increased input power to the inverter (i.e., overpaneling). This irradiance profile serves as a basis for the adjustment of the I-V curves at the module simulators for each inverter. The calculation of the I-V curve parameters is described in Erber et al. [12].

The analysis of the measurement files focuses on identifying the maximum touch temperature and its corresponding timestamp for each inverter, to assess the influence of heightened input power on temperature behavior. With the maximum touch temperature and the ambient temperature at that time, it is concluded at what ambient temperature the maximum allowable touch temperature will be surpassed.

2.2.3 LIMITATION OF FEED-IN CURRENT AT LOW GRID VOLTAGE

In this test, the setup and equipment are identical to those in the residual voltage test, with the exclusion of mechanical AC disconnection. Voltage consistency at the grid connection for each inverter is maintained using a sense cable. The testing is conducted with one inverter per measurement. For the low voltage grid scenarios, a voltage profile featuring a 5-second ramp time and a 30-second step duration is utilized, decreasing the voltage to 0.7 V_N. This profile diverges from the DIN VDE V 0124-100 [13] standard and E DIN VDE V 0126-95:2024-6, so an additional compliant profile (ramp time: 1 minute; step time: 15 minutes; voltages: 1.09, 0.9, and 0.85 VN) is implemented to verify the inverter behavior, such as stabilization time. Three inverters are selected for the validation. For the analysis, it is assessed whether the inverter raises the feed-in current (recorded as a 20 ms true RMS value) during testing relative to the initial current and the voltage at which inverter shutdown occurs.

3 RESULTS AND DISCUSSION

The results of the laboratory measurements are presented in the following subchapters. Two inverters from the same manufacturer were not restarting after the residual voltage test (WVC-300) and the maximum touch temperature test (WVC-600). The inverters showed error states via the LED indicator but were not reachable via the monitoring App. Therefore, not all three tests could be conducted on these two inverters.

3.1 RESIDUAL VOLTAGE AFTER DISCONNECTION

Figure 4 shows the results of the residual voltage test for 25 microinverters operating at nominal power and five consumer devices under various loads. The time to reach 35 V spans from 100 ms to over 12 seconds. None of the inverters consistently maintained a 230 V_{RMS} AC output after disconnection. Among the assessed inverters, 14 (56%) complied with the E DIN VDE V 0126-95 residual voltage limit, while 11 surpassed it in at least one test. Inverters DS3-S and EZ1-M had a 2.5% and 2.3% probability, respectively, of exceeding the limit. For seven other inverters, discharge times hovered around the 1 s threshold, with 39.5% to 95.7% exceeding it. All measurements for the three-phase inverters (YC1000-EU and HMT-2000) surpassed the limit, with discharge times differing by over four times. Grouping inverters by power – A: <=600 VA, B: <=800 VA & >600 VA, C: >800 VA – shows that 44% of group A (n=16), 20% of group B (n=5), and 75% of group C (n=4) exceeded the limit. Classification by manufacturer reveals minor impact: 40% (A), 20% (B), and 67% (C) of manufacturers had at least one inverter with discharge times over 1 s. Caution is advised as differing population sizes affect the sensitivity. Based on the analyzed inverter set, no correlation between the inverter power and number of limit-exceeding inverters can be determined.

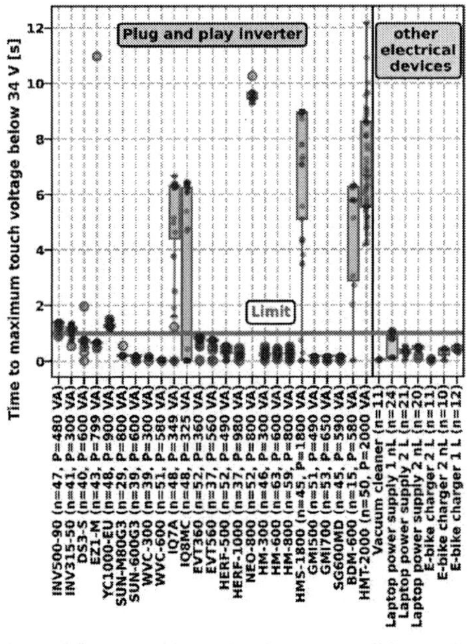

Figure 4: Results of the residual voltage test (time until the maximum touch voltage is below 34 V) for the plug and play inverters and other typical electrical devices. (nL = no load; L = load). The red "Limit" line is the residual voltage limit of E DIN VDE V 0126-95:2024-6.

The tests with household devices reveals one device exceeding the limit at least once, while compliant inverters and devices show similar discharge times.

Since no inverter sustained a stable 230 V_{RMS} AC output voltage following disconnection and a typical discharge voltage curve was observed across most measurements, the resistance and capacitance between L and N were assessed in the unplugged state using a Philips PM6304 RCL meter. It should be noted that the measured capacitance does not directly correspond to the X-capacitance installed between L and N in the devices, as additional Y-capacitances to earth (PE) may be present for EMC purposes, which can influence the overall measurement results. However, assuming that the Y-

capacitances are two orders of magnitude smaller than the X-capacitance, their influence on the measurement is considered negligible.
Table 2 shows the results of this measurement with the share of the limit exceeding measurements in the residual voltage test. Inverters characterized by measurable capacitance and non-measurable resistance surpass the 1 s limits in all or the majority of the residual voltage measurements, due to the prolonged discharge duration of the capacitance. Therefore, the measured resistance in the limit complying inverter acts as a discharge resistor for the capacitance. The reason for the long discharge times of the two Enphase® inverters with low resistance values is most likely the absence of the Q-Relay which contains the interface protection relay. Even though the inverters (DS3-S and EZ1-M have no measurable resistance, one measurement each exceed the limit. This indicates that the capacitance is low enough to ensure a discharge time to 34 V in nearly all measurements. The two exceeding discharge times, which are more than twice as long as the calculated times (see Figure 4), illustrate that under certain conditions (e.g. phase time dependency) longer discharge times are possible although with a small likelihood. In contrary to the previous stated finding the two inverters INV500-90 and INV315-50 have more than 50% of the measurements exceeding the limit, but their resistance differs by a factor of 10 and the resistance as well as the capacitance of INV500-90 are in the range of the limit complying inverters. Due to the black box approach, no reasons other than inverter or manufacturer-specific behavior can be stated.

Table 2. Resistance and Capacitance between L and N for all tested inverters with share of values exceeding the residual voltage limit. Measured in the unplugged state (OL = open load)

Inverter	$R_{L\text{-}N}$ [kOhm]	$C_{L\text{-}N}$ [nF]	share of values exceeding the VDE limit
INV500-90	140	380	95.7%
INV315-50	1300	416	73.2%
DS3-S	OL	98	2.5%
EZ1-M	OL	100	2.3%
YC1000-EU	OL	400	100%
SUN-M80G3	900	90	-
SUN600G3	950	89	-
WVC-300	OL	OL	-
WVC-600	OL	OL	-
IQ7A	120	924	89.6%
IQ8MC	55	980	39.6%
EVT360	810	587	-
EVT560	712	487	-
HERF-500	198	433	-
HERF-1000	194	440	-
NEO-800	OL	1455	100%
HM-300	200	435	-
HM-600	196	424	-
HM-800	197	438	-
HMS-1800	OL	1100	88.9%
GMI500	OL	OL	-
GMI700	OL	OL	-
SG600MD	OL	OL	-
BDM-600	OL	1800	86.7%
HMT-2000	OL	1872	100%

In category A (≤ 600 VA), some inverters have power values nearing 50% of the limit, allowing the use of two inverters for a plug and play setup. Figure 5 presents the residual voltage test results with two inverters in parallel on the same grid connection compared to single operation. For two of the three tested inverters, there is no difference between single and parallel setups. This can be explained with the parallel connection of two R-C circuits, with the same resistance and capacitance values. The total resistance halves, and the capacitance doubles, maintaining the original time constant. However, for the two INV315-50 inverters, the time nearly doubled compared to single operation, which is an unexplained behavior likely specific to this model. The subtests indicate that for systems with multiple inverters, residual voltage tests should be conducted on the entire setup to ensure safety.

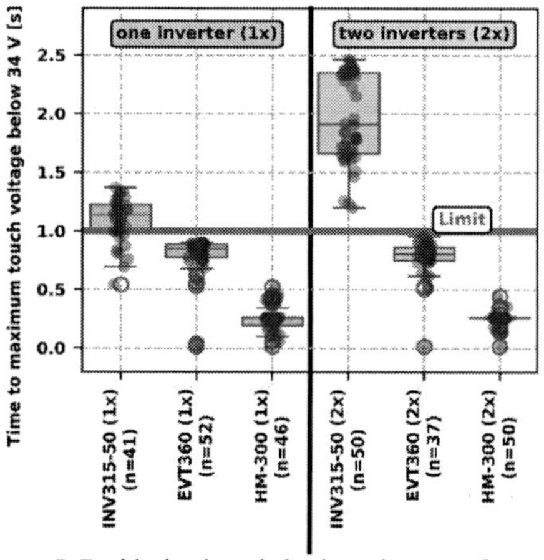

Figure 5: Residual voltage behavior, when two plug and play inverters are operated in parallel to the grid and disconnected. The red "Limit" line is the residual voltage limit of E DIN VDE V 0126-95:2024-6.

The exemplary measurement in Figure 6 shows, which body current would flow, when the pins of L and N are touched after 1 s of unplugging. A resistor with 1 kOhm is used for this measurement. When both pins are touched a charged energy of around 52 mJ is discharged over 3.2 ms with a peak current of 465 mA. Due to the fact that only one single test was conducted no final conclusion in this context can be state. Although a future analysis on this aspect, assessing touch combinations and current path, while also including secondary effects, could determine if a time dependent charge limit in addition to the voltage limit could be introduced.

10.4229/EUPVSEC2025/4DO.3.6

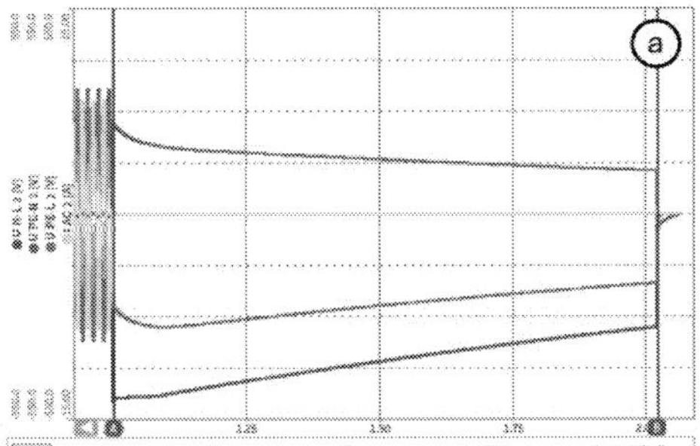

%	A	B	Delta	Integral [*s]
Time [s]	1.003233	2.022239	1.019006	
U N-L 2 [V]	-489.9596	-301.2123	188.7472	-402.1301
U PE-N 2 [V]	245.4486	117.2919	-128.1567	154.4988
U PE-L 2 [V]	-244.5119	-183.9213	60.59051	-347.6314
I AC 2 [A]	1.478e-3	1.769e-3	2.909e-4	1.491e-3

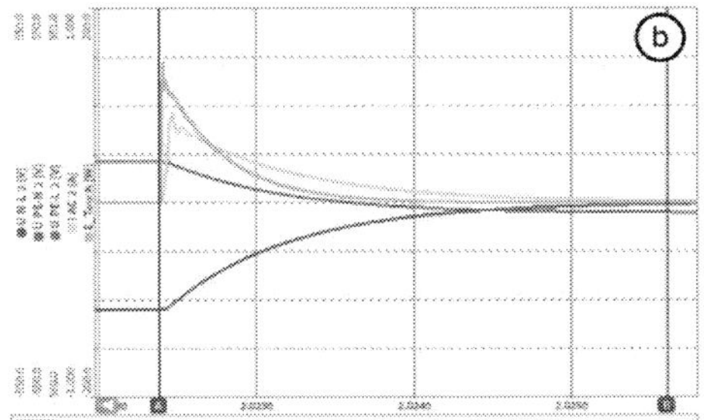

%	A	B	Delta	Max	Integral [*s]
Time [s]	2.022386231	2.025606501	0.003219270		
U N-L 2 [V]	-301.1840	-5.135060	296.0489	-5.135060	-0.249417
U PE-N 2 [V]	117.2745	-28.81122	-146.0857	117.2745	0.017558
U PE-L 2 [V]	-183.9140	-33.94556	149.9684	-33.94556	-0.231872
I AC 2 [A]	1.812e-3	9.351e-3	7.539e-3	0.465631	3.279e-4
E_Touch [W]	0.452389	0.021841	-0.430548	144.1808	0.051733

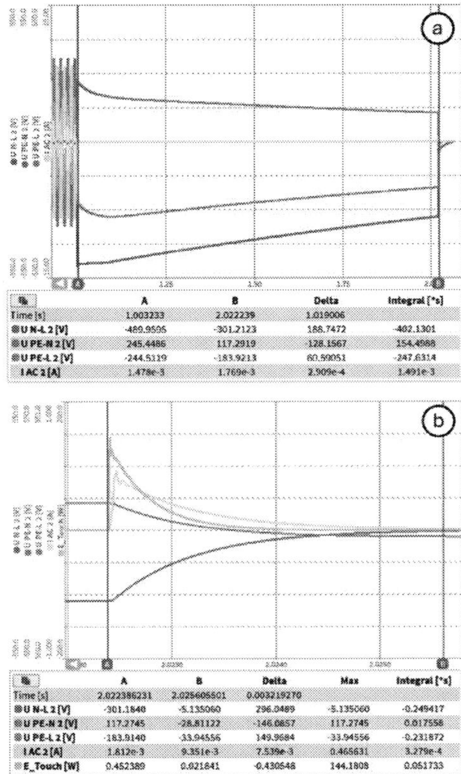

Figure 6. Measurement results (HMS-1800), when L and N are connected to a 1 kOhm body resistance after 1s of unplugging (a). Details of touch current and energy are shown in (b).

As 44% of the tested inverters surpass the proposed threshold of E DIN VDE V 0126-95:2024-6 in at least one measurement, the potential application of a safety adapter to meet compliance is examined. The primary role of a safety adapter is to maintain a conforming residual voltage level after 1 s and ensure touch safety when unplugged. This function might be achieved via a two-pole relay that disconnects the inverter's phase and neutral conductors from the power outlet, thus eliminating voltage at the plug terminals. Another approach involves a mechanical touch-safe mechanism paired with a discharge resistor to link phase and neutral post-grid disconnection, discharging capacitors to reach compliant residual voltage levels. Due to the novelty of this safety application, it can be assumed that other implementation concepts for the required security function will be developed and that the aforementioned implementation variants serve as examples. The above listing of potential realizations was assembled without checking whether these concepts are under patent protection.

An exemplary test on an HMS-1800 inverter using a SEP 1.16 adapter from the company "Seplugs", which employs the last described voltage reduction method, was conducted. Figure 7 displays the residual voltage test results with and without the safety adapter. Incorporating the safety adapter enables the system to meet the residual voltage limit, which supports the statement that the entire system should be evaluated rather than the inverter alone.

Inverters exceeding the limits without additional AC side components can achieve compliance by adding a safety adapter. In addition, inverter manufacturers might consider integrating the safety adapter's functionality into the internal design during product updates.

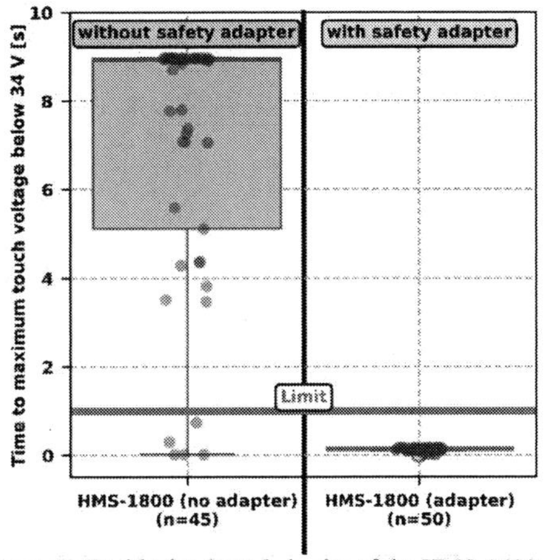

Figure 7: Residual voltage behavior of the HMS-1600 inverter with and without a safety adapter (SEP 1.16). The red "Limit" line is the residual voltage limit of E DIN VDE V 0126-95:2024-6.

During the visual validation of the used disconnection condition, the behavior presented in Figure 8 was found. Among the 52 measurements conducted on this inverter, this behavior was observed a single time. In this measurement, the inverter starts to generate a 50 Hz voltage of approximately 173 V_{RMS} (0.75 V_N) at the AC output 5 ms after the mains plug is pulled out. This behavior is most likely due to the inverter assuming that a grid fault has occurred and that it must not disconnect from the grid during the fault ride-through procedure. The voltage output continues for 3 s until the interface protection relay disconnects the inverter from the grid due to the voltage drop protection time as mandated in VDE-AR-N 4105 [15] (<0.8 V_N for 3 s). Such a behavior is compliant with VDE-AR-N 4105 as the islanding detection and grid disconnection under dynamic grid supporting measures must happen within 9 s (normal 2 s). For the previously mentioned safety adapter such a behavior might be challenging to distinguish from a normal grid condition in the context of the residual voltage behavior. On the one hand, it could be argued that, if the safety adapter maintains a touch protection even though the discharge functionality is not activated, there is still an additional safety layer due to the touch safety. On the other hand, it should be discussed if plug and play inverters must not provide fault ride-through functionality, considering the small system power. The later argument would result in a separate grid profile with reduced requirements for plug and play inverters, if applied. As plug and play inverters can also be used in larger PV systems, the distributor would have to ensure that the plug and play inverter is configured with the right profile or application code respectively.

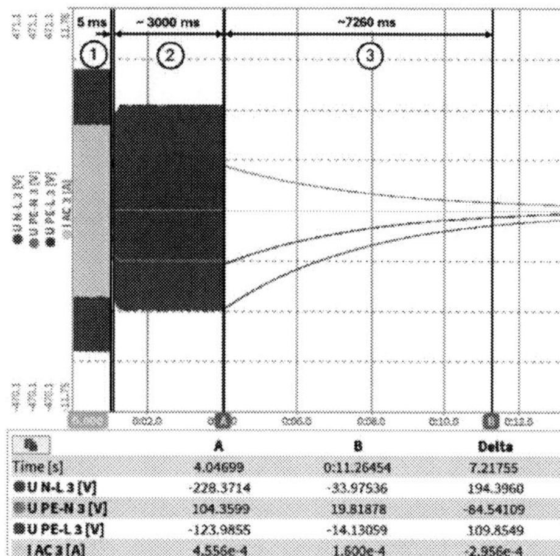

10.4229/EUPVSEC2025/4DO.3.6
020386-006

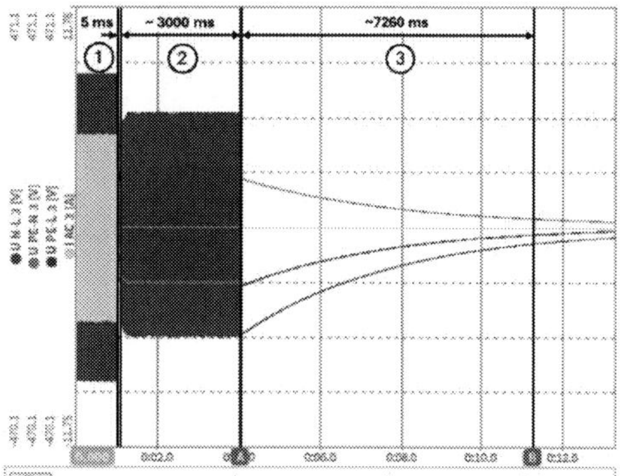

	A	B	Delta
Time [s]	4.04699	0:11.26454	7.21755
U N-L 3 [V]	-228.3714	-33.97536	194.3960
U PE-N 3 [V]	104.3599	19.81878	-84.54109
U PE-L 3 [V]	-123.9855	-14.13059	109.8549
I AC 3 [A]	4.556e-4	1.600e-4	-2.956e-4

Figure 8: Measurement results of an inverter (NEO-800) after unplugging (1), with an islanding and fault-ride-through behavior (2). The interface protection relay stops this behavior after 3 s and the normal discharge phase starts (3). This behavior was observed in one out of the 52 residual voltage measurements on this inverter

3.2 MAXIMUM TOUCH TEMPERATURE

The recorded touch temperatures span from 43.40 °C to 80.33 °C. Among the 24 tested inverters, 18 (75%) adhere to the limit of IEC 62109-1. Most inverters maintain a stable temperature and consistent power output, demonstrating efficient thermal management. Conversely, models like GMI500, GMI700, and SG600MD show temperature and power variability, suggesting active thermal derating most probably due to internal temperature constraints. In addition, the WVC-600 inverter showed an early power drop, potentially due to protective shutdown or inadequate thermal performance. These observations highlight that, while many inverters perform reliably under thermal stress, some devices experience limitations related to thermal protection strategies or insufficient cooling capabilities. Such thermal derating can further decrease the system yield.

The reason why microinverters that have valid IEC 62109-1 certificates (e.g. SUN-M80G3) would still exceed the touch temperature limit in a configuration with sufficient available DC power and at certain ambient temperatures is most likely due to the considerate mounting situation in the certification test. The usual mounting situation for most of the systems, which are not purely designed for plug and play systems, is behind the module. Therefore, no inverter surfaces are accessible during the operation and high temperatures are only a concern for the component lifetime and not in terms of safety. This aspect should be considered in the safety standard for plug and play PV systems.

Given that the touch temperature is dependent on the ambient temperature, Figure 9 shows the maximum allowable power-dependent temperature rise (maximum touch temperature minus ambient temperature) (x-axis) to comply under a 35 °C ambient temperature condition. 11 out of 24 inverters (46%) would exceed the temperature limit. The figure further depicts a positive correlation between maximum power-dependent temperature rise and power density (nominal inverter power/datasheet volume) of the tested inverters. Inverters with lower power, like those in category A, show a reduced power density and temperature rise. Variation in data arises partly from power density calculations based on datasheet dimensions, sometimes excluding mounting dimensions. Efficiency and heat transfer area (cooling fin design) are also impactful. Barring two outliers in category A, the findings suggest the use of smaller inverters with lower power density over a single high-density inverter to reduce the touch temperature risk. This could further prolong inverter lifespan, acknowledging that component aging (e.g. capacitors) is temperature depending.

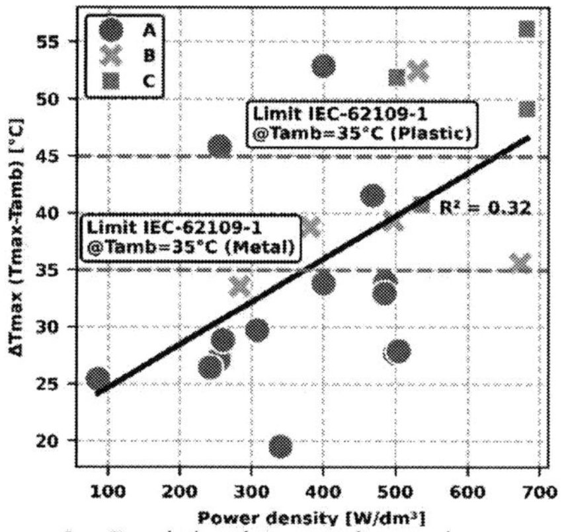

Figure 9: Correlation between the maximum power-dependent temperature increase (maximum touch temperature minus ambient temperature) and the power density (nominal inverter power/datasheet volume). Both red "Limit"-lines indicate the maximum allowable power-dependent temperature rise at 35°C for two enclosure materials. The categories A, B and C are the previously mentioned power categories (A: <=600 VA, B: <=800 VA & >600 VA and C: >800 VA).

3.3 LIMITATION OF FEED-IN CURRENT AT LOW GRID VOLTAGE

Figure 10 shows the test results for analyzing whether inverters boost their feed-in current at low grid voltage. All tested inverters show a current increase ranging from 1.7% to 26.3% of their nominal current. Of the three inverters (HM-800, NEO-800, SUN-M80G3) with a nominal power of 800 VA, two surpassed the 3.5 A limit (including the 2% tolerance), which is non-compliant with E DIN VDE V 0126-95:2024-6. Although other category A and B inverters increased their feed-in currents, they stayed within the absolute limit. To uniform the feed-in current regulation for plug and play systems a relative current limit, e.g. "The maximum feed-in current must not exceed 2% of the nominal feed-in current", could be proposed to preplace the absolute limit. This would ease the configuration of plug and play systems for with multiple inverters of the same type and one mains plug, if the inverter is known to meet the 2% limit. An absolute limit introduces more complexity. With a relative limit, only one tested inverter would comply.

10.4229/EUPVSEC2025/4DO.3.6

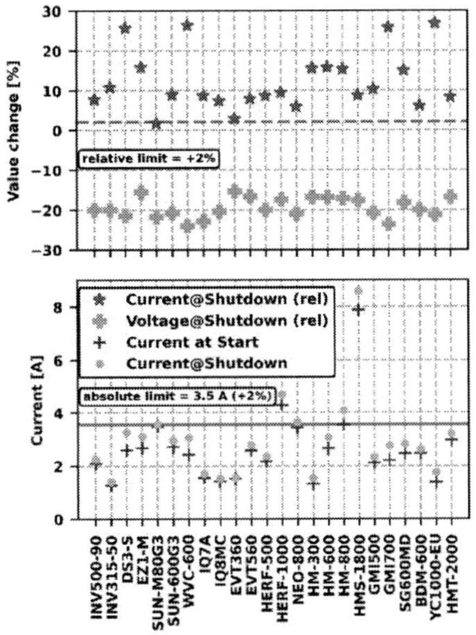

Figure 10: Results of the feed-in current test a low grid voltage at nominal power. Top figure: Values at inverters shutdown (top figure) referenced to the starting values at normal (230 V_{RMS} grid conditions). Bottom figure: absolute current values (test start and shutdown). The limit lines indicate the absolute and relative limit.

4 SUMMARY AND CONCLUSION

This paper assesses three safety concerns of plug and play inverters using a black box method, creating a data basis for discussions on safety standards. The methods are also applicable for future compliance tests. In the residual voltage testing 56% of the analyzed inverters did comply with the proposed limit of the latest official draft of E DIN VDE V 0126-95. Regarding the 11 non-compliant inverters, it must be stated, that an exceedance of the residual voltage limit should not be directly linked to a safety risk without taking the severity of the exceedance (time and number of occasion) into account and conducting further assessments. An exemplary measurement showed the body current and duration that can be expected when the power plug of non-compliant inverters is touched.

The test highlights that system testing is recommended for setups with multiple inverters, as they may exhibit extended residual voltage durations compared to single inverter systems. An exemplary test illustrated that integrating a safety relay, which actively lowers residual voltage post-disconnection, can bring non-compliant inverters into compliance. This adaptation might serve as a cost-efficient solution to mitigate the risks posed by residual voltage, given that discharge times vary significantly with different devices, necessitating numerous repeated tests, which could increase both test duration and cost.

Additionally, one out of 52 measurements for an individual inverter indicates a need to discuss grid support functions, such as fault ride-through, concerning the residual voltage behavior of plug-and-play inverters.

In future research on residual voltage testing, emphasis could be placed on validating our analysis with triggered relay tests and exploring ways to minimize testing duration. Additionally, tests at varied power levels (50% of nominal power or minimal operating power, as required in the draft of E DIN VDE V 0126-95), should be performed to investigate their impact on residual voltage behavior.

The second test reveals that several inverters surpass the feed-in limit at low grid voltages, with variance in non-compliance numbers depending on the use of an absolute or relative limit. Implementing a relative limit is advised to harmonize regulations across different power-rated devices. Although this safety issue is the least likely due to infrequent low voltages during sunny hours, the limitation of the feed-in current to a maximum of 3.5 A (800 VA or 2.6 A (600 VA) remains crucial for plug and play PV inverters due to the connection on non-dedicated distribution circuits. It can be assumed that the observed feed-in behavior can be corrected via a firmware update and hence a verification of those updates should be carried out in the future.

The final test indicates that at a high DC supply scenario and high ambient temperatures, the tested inverters may exceed the IEC 62109-1 touch temperature limit. To reduce thermal issues, the use of multiple smaller inverters instead of one large unit is recommended for the system design. Future studies assessing the thermal behavior of power-limited inverters (e.g. category C inverters limited to 800 VA) may offer guidance for system design, as their larger housing volume could enhance heat dissipation.

The results and findings of this paper show that safety risks may be present at certain plug and play inverters under the tested conditions and should be considered for market entry and surveillance. However, these issues can be addressed with technical adaptations and system engineering adjustments leading to a save use of plug and play PV systems.

ACKNOWLEDGEMENT

This research was carried out in the project "Plug & Play Photovoltaic Systems" funded by the Swiss Federal Office of Energy (Project number SI/502662). The responsibility for the content and conclusions lies solely with the authors.

REFERENCES

[1] Bundesnetzagentur für Elektrizität, Gas, Telekommunikation, Post und Eisenbahnen, "Marktstammdatenregister." Accessed: Jun. 18, 2025. [Online]. Available: https://www.marktstammdatenregister.de/MaStR/Einheit/Einheiten/ErweiterteOeffentlicheEinheitenuebersicht

[2] J. Bergner, R. Hoelger, and B. Praetorius, "Der Markt für Steckersolargeräte," Hochschule für Technik und Wirtschaft HTW Berlin, 2022. Accessed: May 21, 2025. [Online]. Available: https://solar.htw-berlin.de/studien/marktstudie-steckersolar-2022/

[3] H. Laukamp *et al.*, "Entwicklung einer Produktnorm für Steckersolargeräte," in *37. PV-Symposium/BIPV-Forum 2022*, Jan. 2022. doi: 10.24406/publica-1243.

[4] IEC 62109-1, *Safety of power converters for use in photovoltaic power systems - Part 1: General requirements*, 2010.

[5] E DIN VDE V 0126-95, *Steckersolargeräte für Netzparallelbetrieb - Sicherheitsanforderungen und Prüfungen*, Berlin., 2024.

[6] VDE Verband der Elektrotechnik Elektronik Informationstechnik e.V., "Steckerfertige PV-Anlagen: Anschluss & Anmeldung." Accessed: Aug. 26, 2025. [Online]. Available: https://www.vde.com/fnn-pv-stecker

[7] S. Krauter and J. Bendfeld, "PV Microinverters: Latest Efficiency Rankings, Energy Yield Assessments, Firmware Issues," *40th European Photovoltaic Solar Energy Conference and Exhibition*, pp. 020267-001-020267–005, 2023, doi: 10.4229/EUPVSEC2023/3EO.1.2.

[8] S. Krauter and J. Bendfeld, "PV Microinverters: Balcony Power Plants, Latest Efficiency Rankings, Yield Calculation for Overpowered Mini PV Systems," *41st European Photovoltaic Solar Energy Conference and Exhibition*, pp. 020162-001-020162–007, 2024, doi: 10.4229/EUPVSEC2024/3AV.1.37.

[9] Marcus Vietzke, "Untersuchung der Beeinflussung der Schutzkonzepte von Stromkreisen durch Stecker-Solar-Geräte," Jan. 2017. [Online]. Available: https://www.pvplug.de/wp-content/uploads/2017/05/pi-berlin.testreport.20170520.pdf

[10] J. Bergner, "Kurzbericht: Steckersolar 800 W," 2025. Accessed: Mar. 12, 2025. [Online]. Available: https://solar.htw-berlin.de/publikationen/kurzbericht-steckersolar-800-w/

[11] D. L. Gerber, A. Ginsberg-Klemmt, L. Stoler, J. Shackelford, and A. Meier, "Barriers to Balcony Solar and Plug-In Distributed Energy Resources in the United States," *Energies*, vol. 18, no. 8, p. 2132, Jan. 2025, doi: 10.3390/en18082132.

[12] A. Erber, D. Joss, and C. Bucher, "Assessment of Personal Safety Concerns of Plug and Play Photovoltaic Inverters using a Black Box Approach and Laboratory Measurements [Manuscript submitted for publication]," *Solar RRL*, 2025.

[13] DIN VDE V 0124-100, *Niederspannung – Prüfanforderungen an Erzeugungseinheiten, vorgesehen zum Anschluss und Parallelbetrieb am Niederspannungsnetz*, 2020.

[14] Bern University of Applied Sciences, "Plug & Play Photovoltaic Systems." Accessed: Jun. 19, 2025. [Online]. Available: https://www.bfh.ch/en/research/research-projects/2023-764-629-419/

[15] VDE-AR-N 4105, *VDE-AR-N 4105 Anwendungsregel:2018-11 Erzeugungsanlagen am Niederspannungsnetz*, 2018.

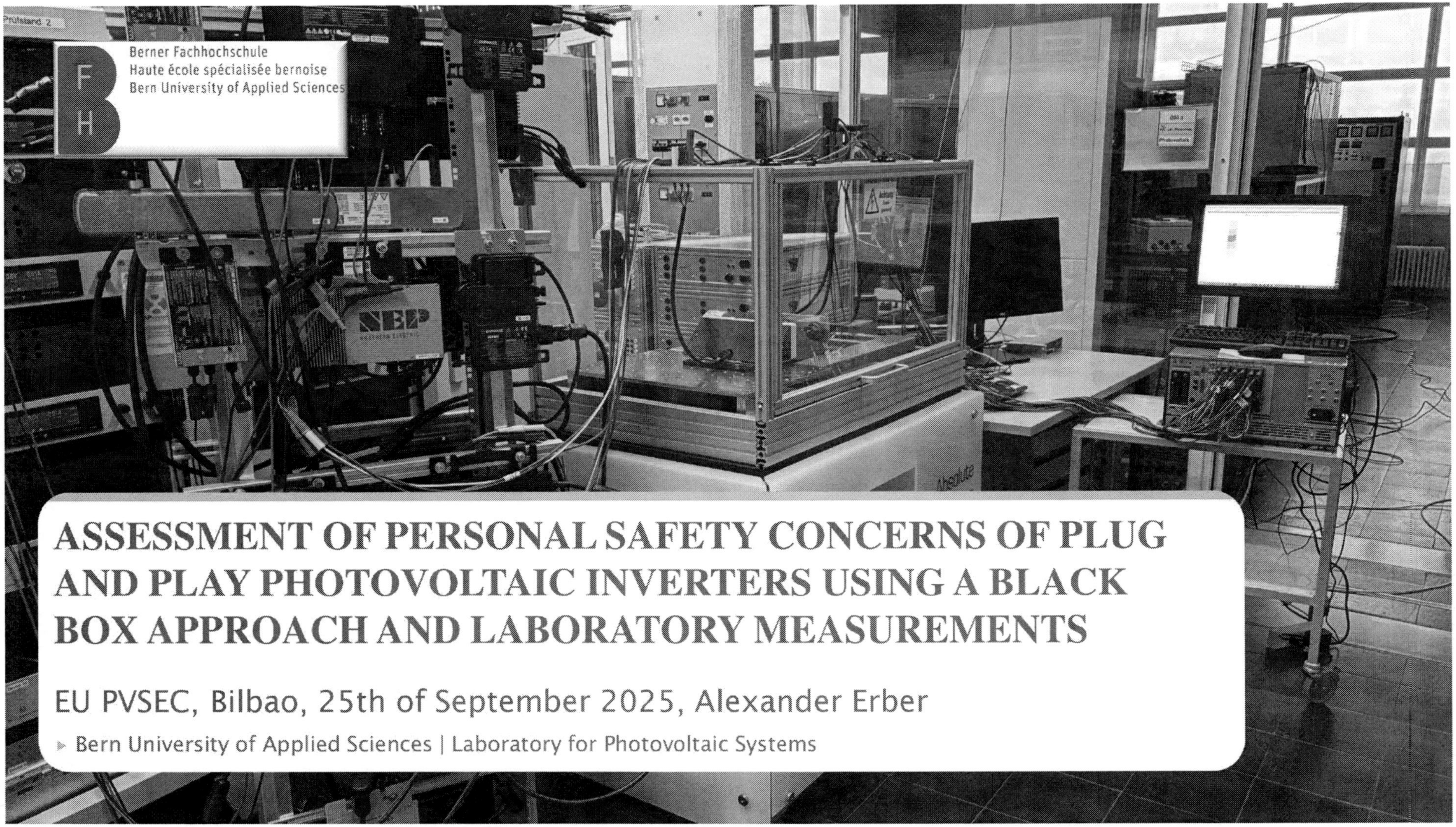
Berner Fachhochschule
Haute école spécialisée bernoise
Bern University of Applied Sciences
ASSESSMENT OF PERSONAL SAFETY CONCERNS OF PLUG AND PLAY PHOTOVOLTAIC INVERTERS USING A BLACK BOX APPROACH AND LABORATORY MEASUREMENTS
EU PVSEC, Bilbao, 25th of September 2025, Alexander Erber
Bern University of Applied Sciences | Laboratory for Photovoltaic Systems

Situation of plug and play PV systems

- Rapid growth, notably in Germany
  - June 2025: 1 million registered systems (>1 GWp)
  - Total system numbers considerably higher
  - Most systems sold with Type F plug [1]
- Safety concerns of these systems [2]
  - Installation and personally safety
- Inverter standards (e.g. IEC 62109) only partly cover the inverter concerns
- **Limited data/studies available**
- **Plug and play PV inverters $\overset{?}{=}$ microinverter**

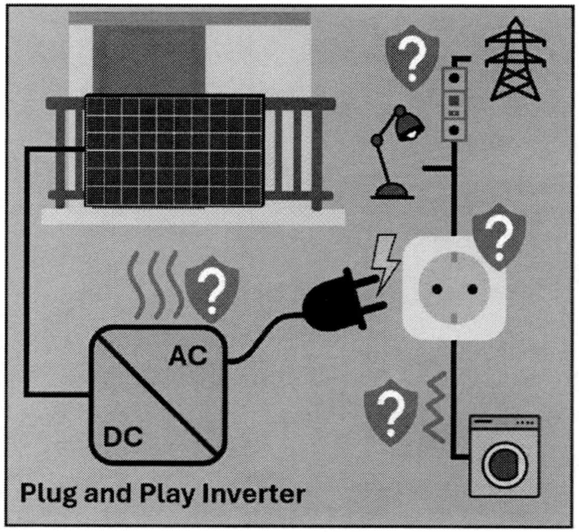

[1] J. Bergner et al, 2022,"Der Markt für Steckersolargeräte", https://solar.htw-berlin.de/studien/marktstudie-steckersolar-2022/
[2] H. Laukamp et al.,2022, "Entwicklung einer Produktnorm für Steckersolargeräte," in 37. PV-Symposium/BIPV-Forum 2022

Safety Test in the Laboratory

Literature and standard research

- exchange with experts and standard groups
- Condensed test plan to three main tests

Test approach

- Black box approach
- 25 inverters to test

Power category	Power range of category [VA]	Power range of invertrs	Number of inverters
A	<=600	300-600	16
B	>600 & <=800	601-800	5
C	>800	801-2000	4

1.Test: Residual voltage test

- Realistic conditions and repeated measurements (30-50 per inverter)
- Compliancy limit of E DIN VDE V 0126-95:2024-6 (<34 V after 1s)

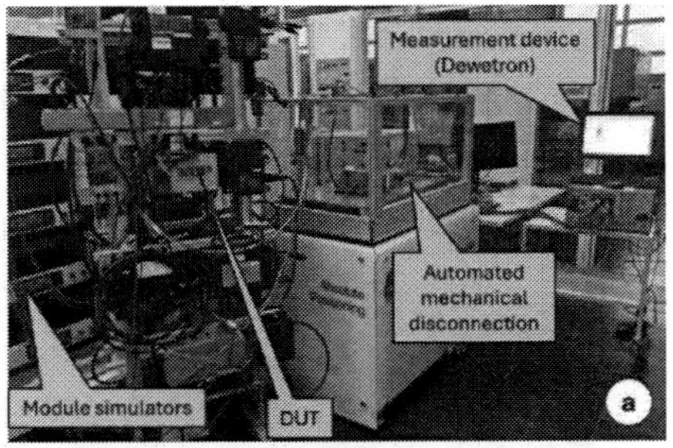

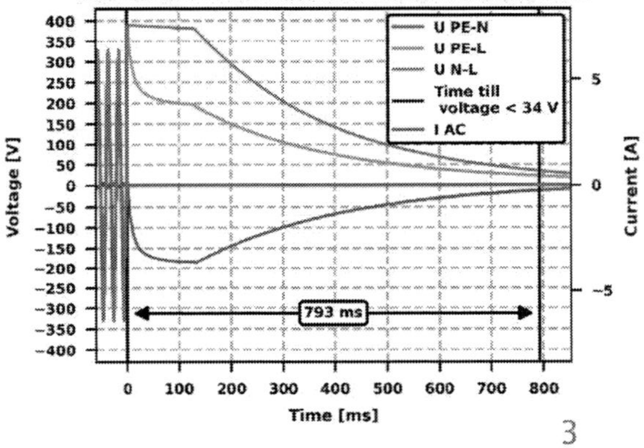

Safety Test in the Laboratory

2. Test: Maximum Touch Temperature

- Determine max. stationary touch temperature @ nominal DC power & overpanelling (150%)
- Limits of IEC 62109-1 (70 ℃/95 ℃)

3. Test: Limitation of Feed-in Current at Low Grid Voltage

- Determine the max. increase of current
- Voltage profile with reduced testing time (30s steps to 0.7 p.u)
- Limit (E DIN VDE V 0126-95:2024-6): 3.5 A +2%

A detailed measurement steps can be found in the supporting information of our Solar RRL Article (in production)

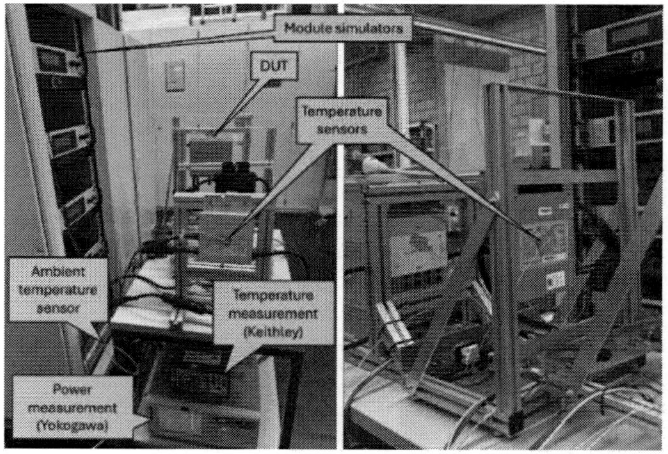

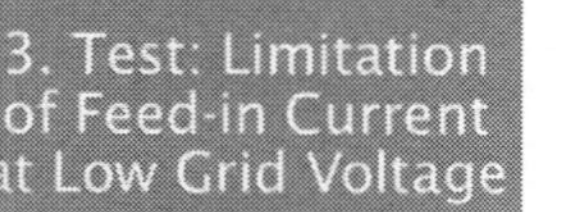

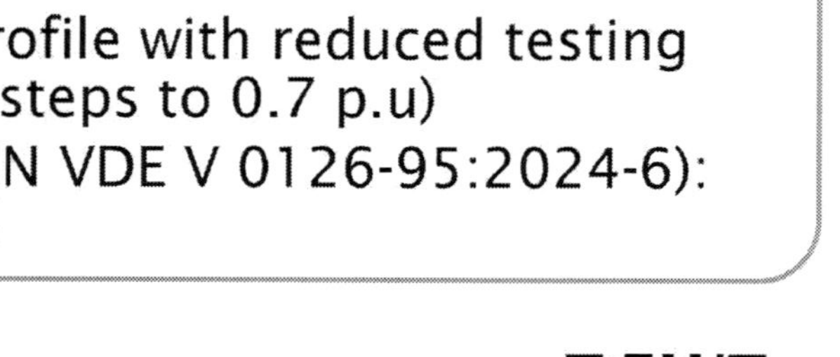

Further “hot” research → 4CV.1.61

Residual Voltage Test

- Times to 34 V: 15 ms to 12 s
- 56% compliancy of tested inverters

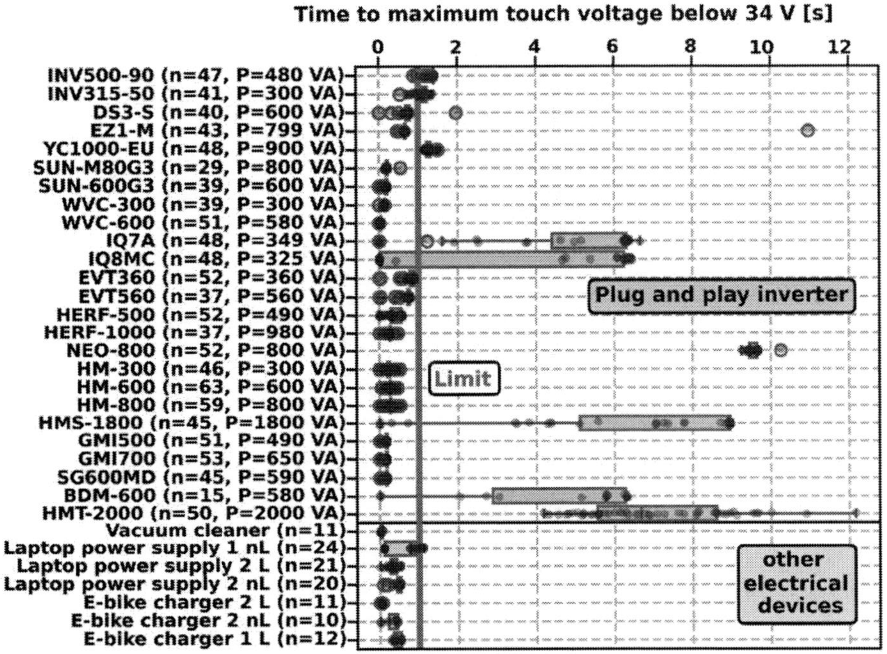

- Phase-angle dependency could be partly confirmed
- System testing for systems with more than one inverter is recommended

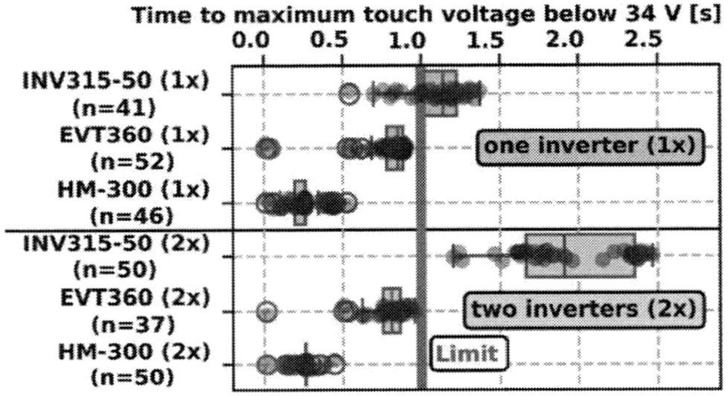

Residual Voltage Test

- Safety adapter (touch safety + optional discharge functionality) for a compliant system

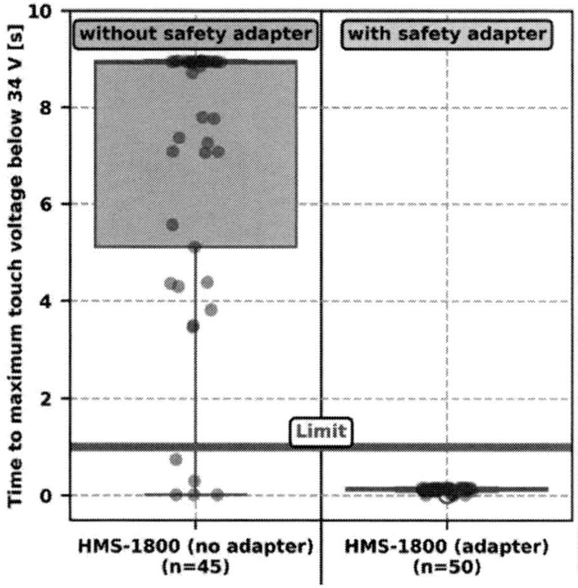

- Exemplary measurement:
  Touching L and N (finger to finger) after 1s with a 1 kOhm body resistance
  - 1 non-compliant inverter
  - Energy: 52 mJ
  - Peak current: 465 mA
  - Time: 3.2 ms

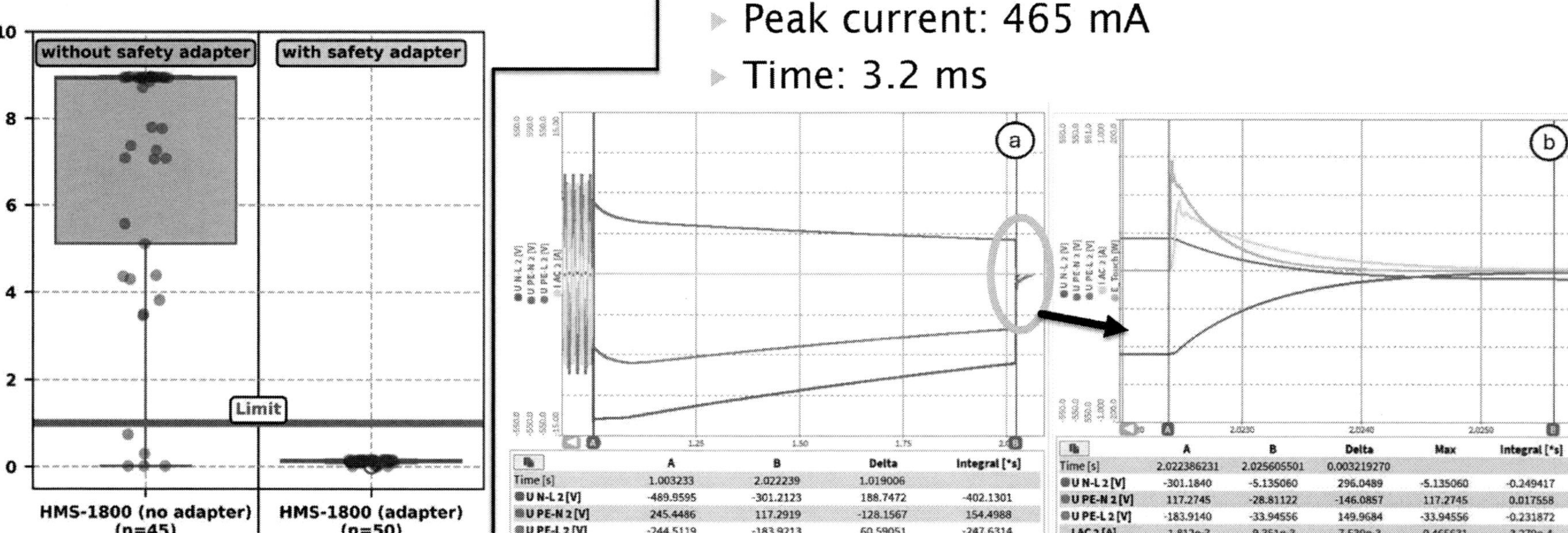

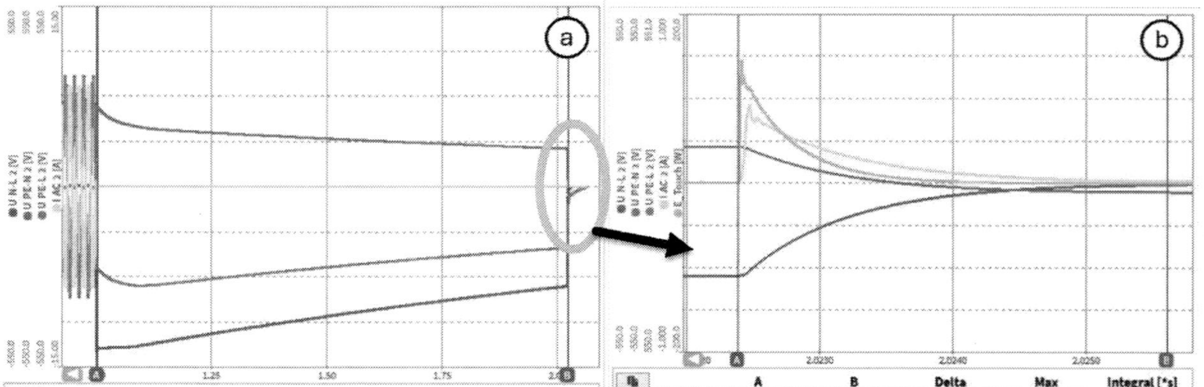

	A	B	Delta	Integral [*s]
Time [s]	1.003233	2.022239	1.019006	
U N-L 2 [V]	-489.9595	-301.2123	188.7472	-402.1301
U PE-N 2 [V]	245.4486	117.2919	-128.1567	154.4988
U PE-L 2 [V]	-244.5119	-183.9213	60.59051	-247.6314
I AC 2 [A]	1.478e-3	1.769e-3	2.909e-4	1.491e-3

	A	B	Delta	Max	Integral [*s]
Time [s]	2.022386231	2.025605501	0.003219270		
U N-L 2 [V]	-301.1840	-5.135060	296.0489	-5.135060	-0.249417
U PE-N 2 [V]	117.2745	-28.81122	-146.0857	117.2745	0.017558
U PE-L 2 [V]	-183.9140	-33.94556	149.9684	-33.94556	-0.231872
I AC 2 [A]	1.812e-3	9.351e-3	7.539e-3	0.465631	3.279e-4
E_Touch [W]	0.452389	0.021841	-0.430548	144.1808	0.051733

Residual Voltage Test

- Problematic behaviour of complaint device
  - 1 out of 52 measurements
  - Islanding after grid disconnection
  - Fault-ride through for 3 s
  - Disconnection through voltage drop protection time ($<0.8\ V_N$ for 3 s)

- **Reduced grid profile/code for plug and play inverters**

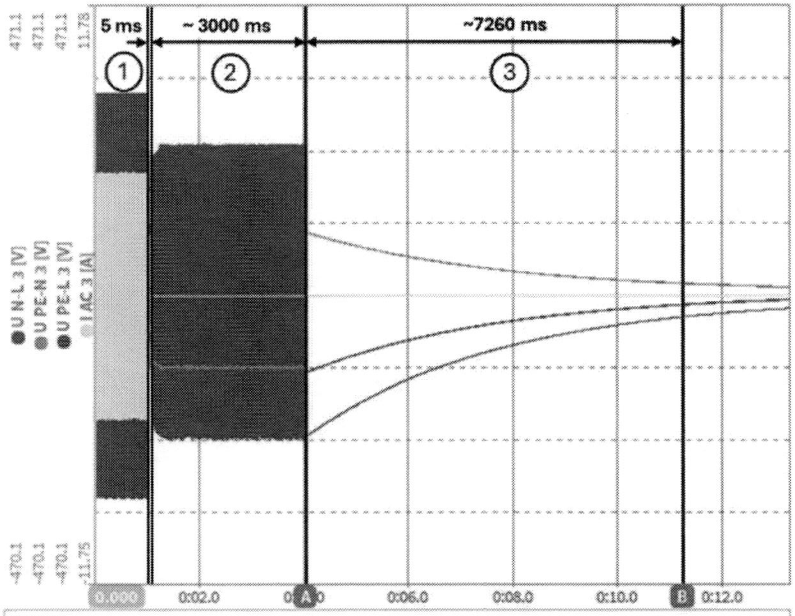

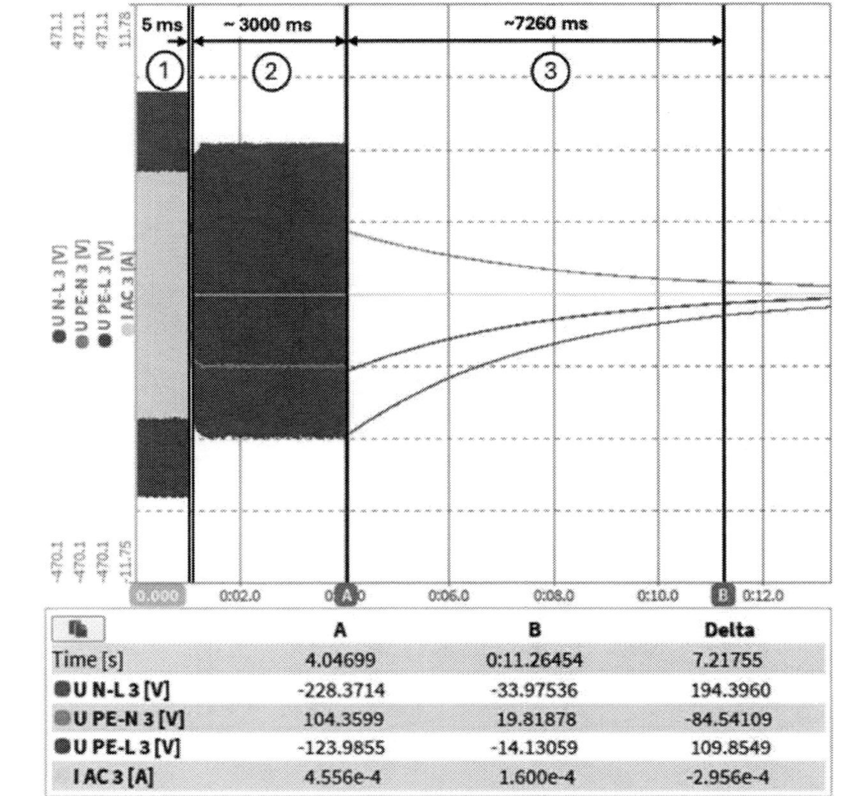

	A	B	Delta
Time [s]	4.04699	0:11.26454	7.21755
U N-L 3 [V]	-228.3714	-33.97536	194.3960
U PE-N 3 [V]	104.3599	19.81878	-84.54109
U PE-L 3 [V]	-123.9855	-14.13059	109.8549
I AC 3 [A]	4.556e-4	1.600e-4	-2.956e-4

Maximum Touch Temperature

- Maximum touch temperatures:
  43.40 °C to 80.33 °C (~23 °C ambient temp)
- 18 inverter (75%) comply with limits
- Ambient temperature dependency
- Correlation between power density and power dependent temperature increase
- **A microinverters is a non-touchable system part, a plug and play inverter is touchable**

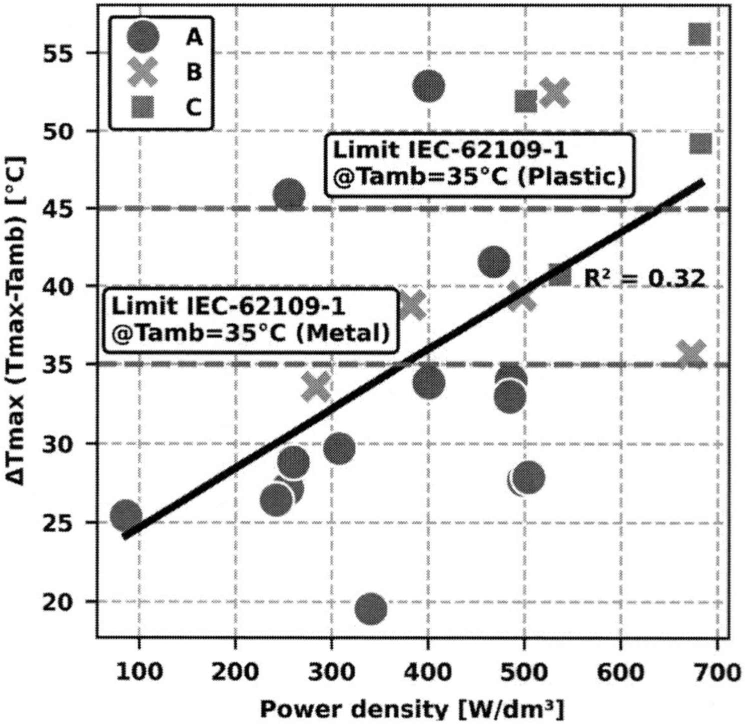

Limitation of Feed-in Current at Low Grid Voltage

- Current increase between 1.7% to 26.3%

- Absolute limit (3.5 A +2%)
  - 4 non-compliant inverters

- Relative limit (+2%)
  - Only 1 compliant inverter

- Absolute vs relative limit?
  - Relative limit for uniform requirements

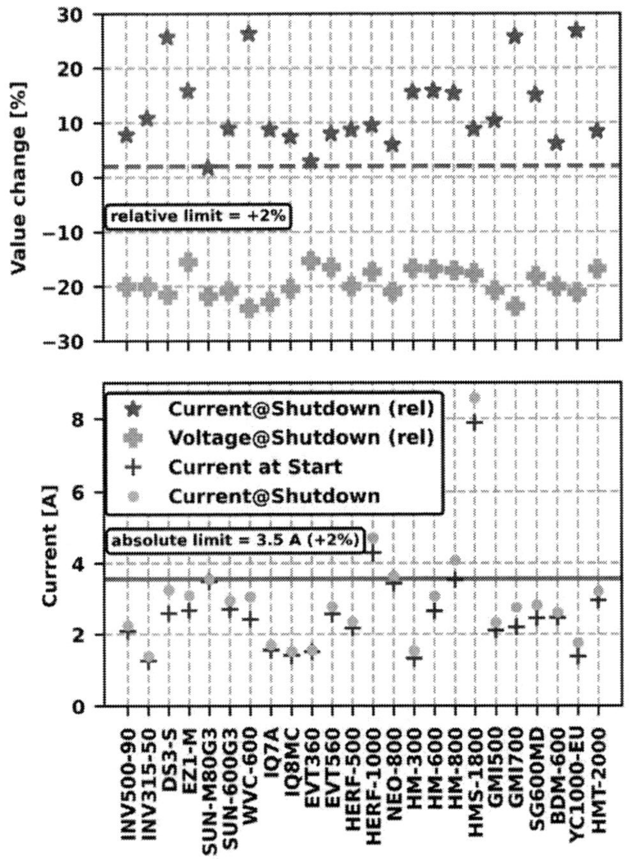

Conclusions and Recommendations

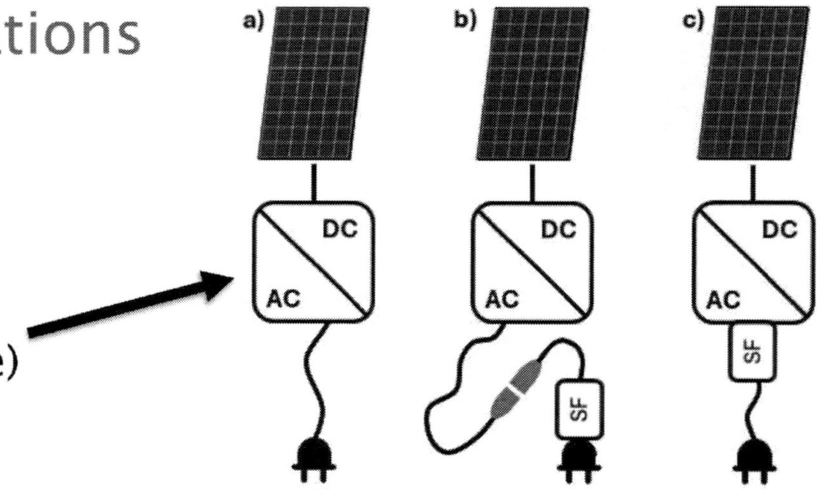

- Residual voltage
  - 56% compliancy rate of tested set
  - System testing is recommended
  - Different solutions for this concern (without and with additional hardware)
  - Separate and reduced grid profile
- Touch temperature
  - Inclusion in plug and play system standard(s) and note in IEC 62109-1
  - More smaller inverters are better than one single inverter
  - Larger power limited inverter(?)
- Limitation of Feed-in Current
  - Fix through software update(?)
- **Plug and play PV inverters ≠ microinverter**

Berner Fachhochschule
Haute école spécialisée bernoise
Bern University of Applied Sciences

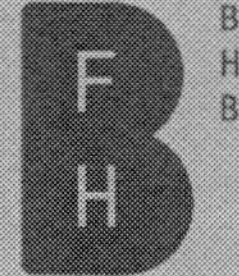

Merci PV-Lab and thank you for your attention!

Project information and contact

ACKNOWLEDGEMENT
This research was carried out in the project "Plug & Play Photovoltaic Systems" funded by the Swiss Federal Office of Energy (Project number SI/502662). The responsibility for the content and conclusions lies solely with the authors.

▶ Bern University of Applied Sciences | Laboratory for Photovoltaic Systems

Residual Voltage Test

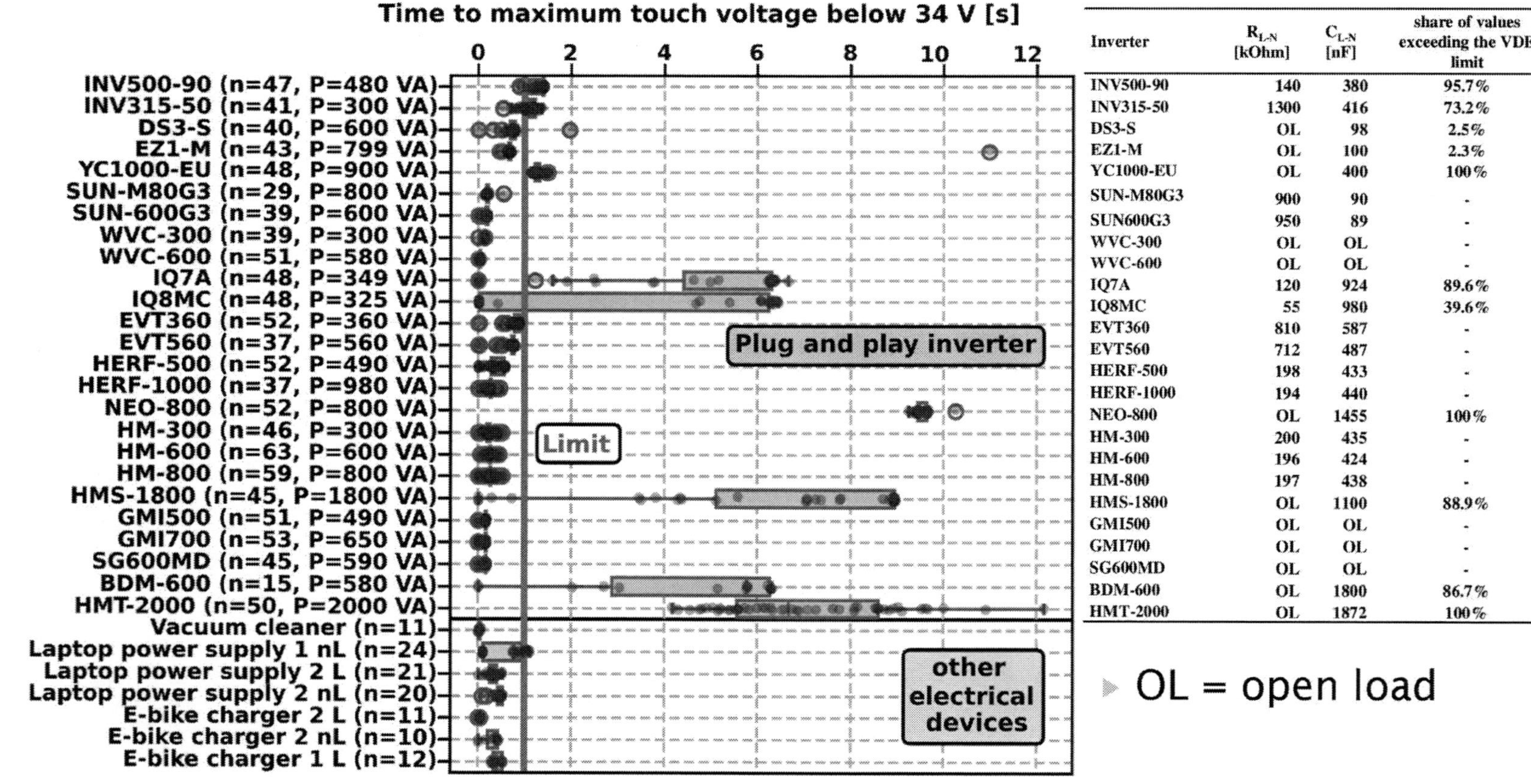

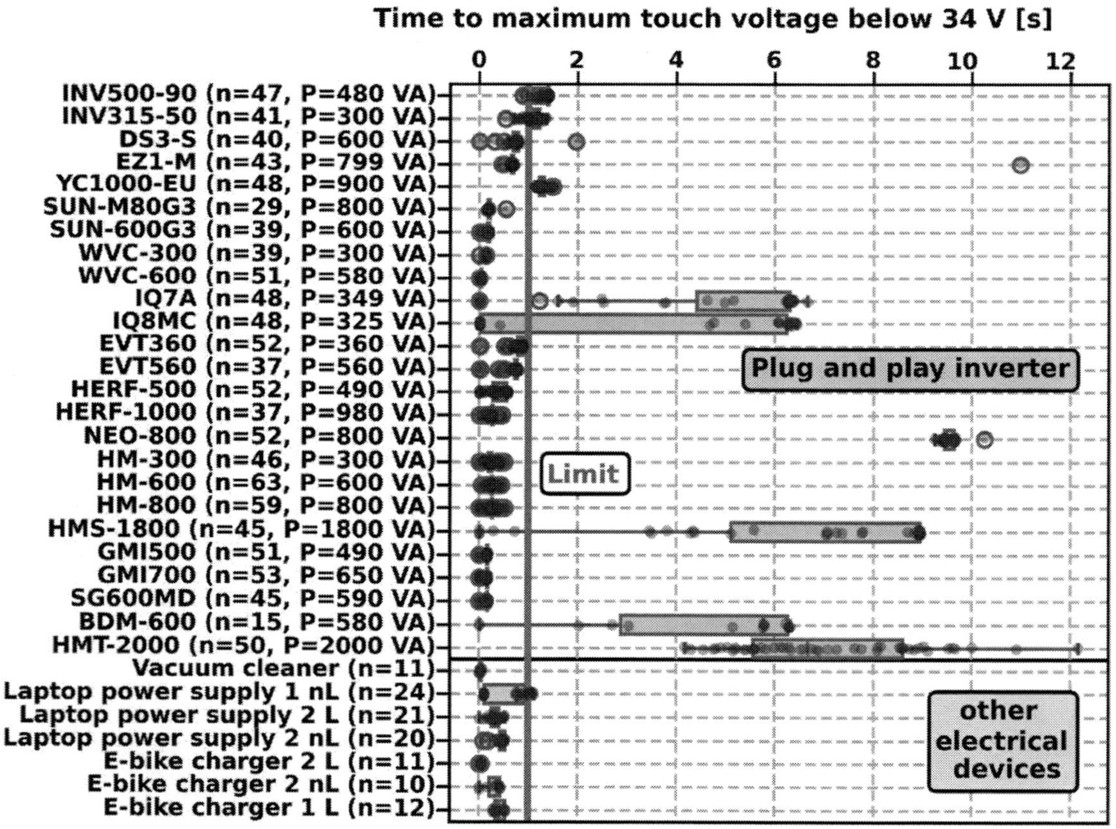

Inverter	$R_{L\text{-}N}$ [kOhm]	$C_{L\text{-}N}$ [nF]	share of values exceeding the VDE limit
INV500-90	140	380	95.7%
INV315-50	1300	416	73.2%
DS3-S	OL	98	2.5%
EZ1-M	OL	100	2.3%
YC1000-EU	OL	400	100%
SUN-M80G3	900	90	-
SUN600G3	950	89	-
WVC-300	OL	OL	-
WVC-600	OL	OL	-
IQ7A	120	924	89.6%
IQ8MC	55	980	39.6%
EVT360	810	587	-
EVT560	712	487	-
HERF-500	198	433	-
HERF-1000	194	440	-
NEO-800	OL	1455	100%
HM-300	200	435	-
HM-600	196	424	-
HM-800	197	438	-
HMS-1800	OL	1100	88.9%
GMI500	OL	OL	-
GMI700	OL	OL	-
SG600MD	OL	OL	-
BDM-600	OL	1800	86.7%
HMT-2000	OL	1872	100%

- OL = open load

Measurement Setup

- Residual Voltage Test

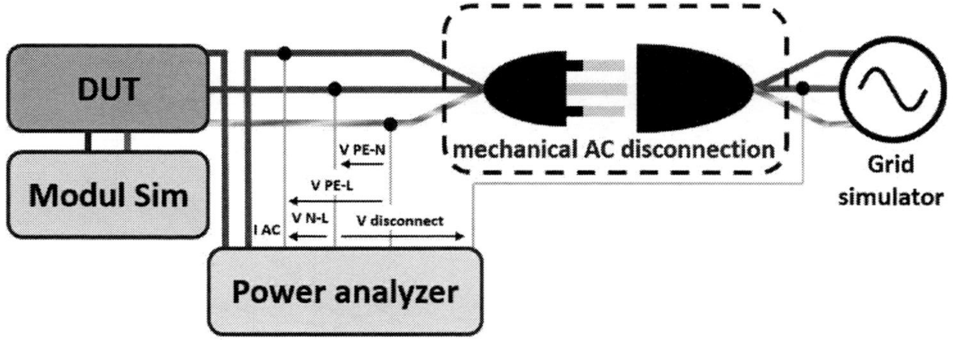

- Limitation of Feed-in Current at Low Grid Voltage

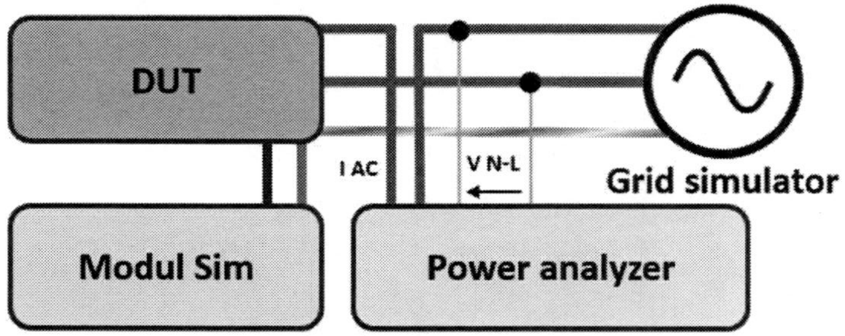

- Maximum Touch Temperature

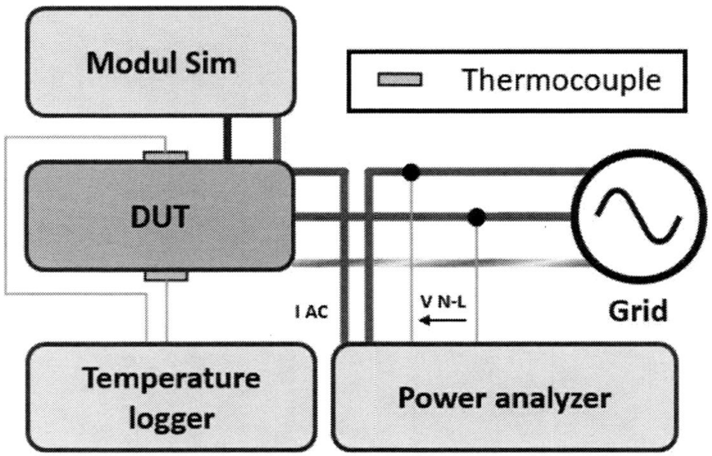

BOOSTING PROFITABILITY: THE POWER OF VERTICAL BIFACIAL PV IN MODERN AGRIVOLTAICS

Marc Andre Schüler[1], Peter Bendix [1], Simon Lahr [1], Aysim Schäfer [1] and Anna Morales Vilches [1]

[1]Research office at Next2Sun AG. Franz-Meguin-Str. 10a, 66763 Dillingen (Germany)
ma.schueler@next2sun.de.

ABSTRACT: This study investigates the potential of fixed tilt **vertical bifacial** (VB) photovoltaic (PV) systems in agrivoltaics (APV), focusing on their **economic viability** rather than its agricultural benefits. Unlike traditional PV installations, vertical bifacial systems allow for more uniform light and rainwater distribution to crops and offer protection against strong winds. Moreover, this work states the profitability and grid integration of these systems, demonstrating **energy production profiles of vertical bifacial APV** in Germany. In contrast to the state of technology of south-tilted PV, vertical systems can mitigate negative midday electricity prices, making them a promising alternative for the future energy market. Simulation results comparing the Next2Sun System incorporating Huasun SHJ modules to traditional TOPCon and PERC modules indicate a **significant energy yield advantage** in the vertical bifacial system, if driven by precise module selection and racking system design. The production profile of the Next2Sun system in Wellingen, Germany, shows two production peaks, with **minimal self-shading** effects and **high bifaciality**. Additionally, financial analysis of vertical bifacial PV plants in Donaueschingen/Aasen and Dirmingen reveals **up to 45% surplus** performance over the market price, highlighting the economic potential of these systems in the context of increasing PV capacity and negative midday electricity prices. This work suggests that vertical bifacial PV installations can be a profitable and sustainable solution for integrating renewable energy into the agricultural sector.

Keywords: Agrivoltaics, grid-friendly PV generation, vertical PV, profitability

1 INTRODUCTION

Various solutions exist for installing PV modules in agrivoltaics (APV), such as tilted but spaced (fixed or tracked) ground-mounted systems or elevated systems (fixed or tracked). This study focuses on fixed vertical bifacial (VB) systems, as depicted in Figure 1. The multiple benefits of VB systems for agriculture, as described in the literature, include uniform light and rainwater distribution to crops and protection against strong winds from directions perpendicular to the PV module orientation [1]. In addition to these agricultural benefits, the profitability and grid serviceability of vertical bifacial PV systems, discussed in [2], are confirmed in this work.

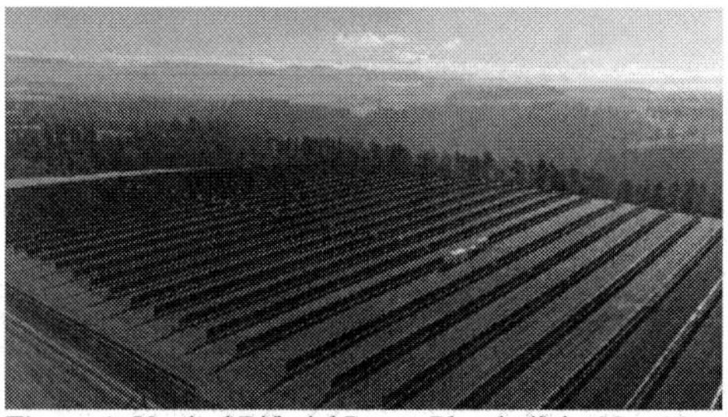

Figure 1: Vertical Bifacial Power Plant built by Next2Sun in Epfendorf (Germany)

In line with the prognosis in [3], we demonstrate the profitability of east–west (E/W) oriented vertical bifacial PV (VBPV) systems, which outperform south-oriented PV in Germany. With the ongoing increase in predominantly south-tilted PV which is expected to face low or negative midday electricity prices, alternative layouts are needed to better match grid demand. Recent studies recommend integrating vertical E/W systems or combining them with south-tilted PV [4]. With this work, we state the installation can be profitable with the system approach designed by Next2Sun already today marking a significant step towards integrating these systems into future energy markets.

2 RELEVANCE OF NEGATIVE ELECTRICITY PRICES TO PROFITABILITY IN PV

Photovoltaics (PV) have become a key driver of renewable power generation in Germany. With rising deployment, however, oversupply increasingly occurs during midday in summer, leading to lower capture rates. Historically above 80%, capture rates have recently declined. Figure 2 shows monthly and yearly capture rates for the PV Portfolio from 2022 to 2024, with the latest value at ~58% or 46.24 €/MWh.

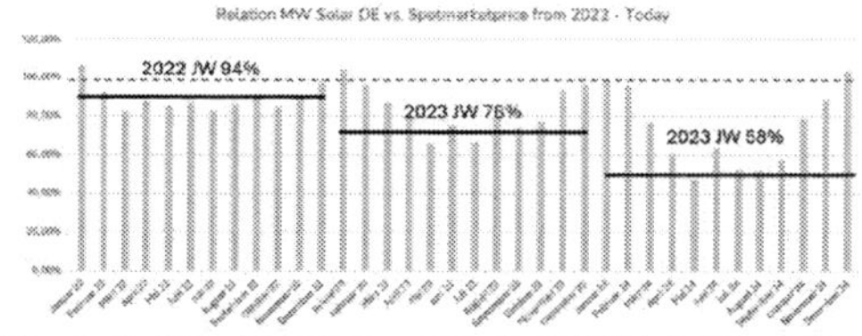

Figure 2: Monthly capture rates for MW Solar Germany in relation to EEX spot market from January 2022 to December 2024

One important factor in the decline of capture rates, is the rise in negative electricity prices in recent years, which has accompanied the growing deployment of solar power, especially during midday hours [5]. Figure 3 illustrates the spread of negative prices in the Ger/Lux EEX spot market, with positive prices capped at 200 €/MWh to highlight negative price events. The X-axis shows the days of the year, while the Y-axis indicates the hourly resolution.

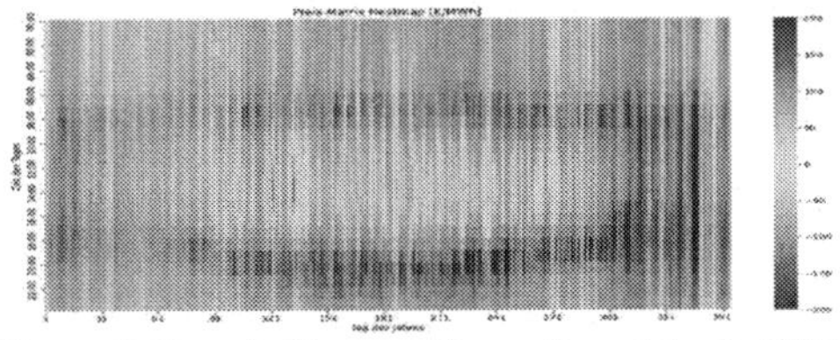

Figure 3: Spread of hours with negative pricing in 2024 EEX Germany/Luxembourg

3 DEMAND-ORIENTED ENERGY PRODUCTION IN AGRI-PV

Traditional agriculture and sophisticated forms of energy generation are not mutually exclusive. Next2Sun's vertical Agri-PV concept, as seen in (**Figure 4**), represents a combined solution with high land usage ratio and renewable energy production which is mostly demand-oriented by design. The installation is based on a robust racking structure with pile-driven steel posts, which can support up to three vertically stacked PV modules, reaching system heights of up to 4.5 m. The vertical arrangement minimizes shading on adjacent agricultural areas while ensuring structural stability against wind loads. Agricultural usability is preserved through wide crop rotation strips, typically ranging from 8 to 15 m, resulting in agricultural land-usage ratios above 85 %.

From an energy generation perspective, the system employs high-efficiency bifacial PV modules, which are optimally suited to capture diffuse irradiation as well as direct sunlight from both east and west directions. This design leads to a generation profile with a broader distribution of electricity production throughout typical days, better aligning with local consumption patterns and enhancing grid integration. Combined with the preserved agricultural productivity, this dual-use approach increases overall land-use efficiency and can contribute in parallel to both food and energy security.

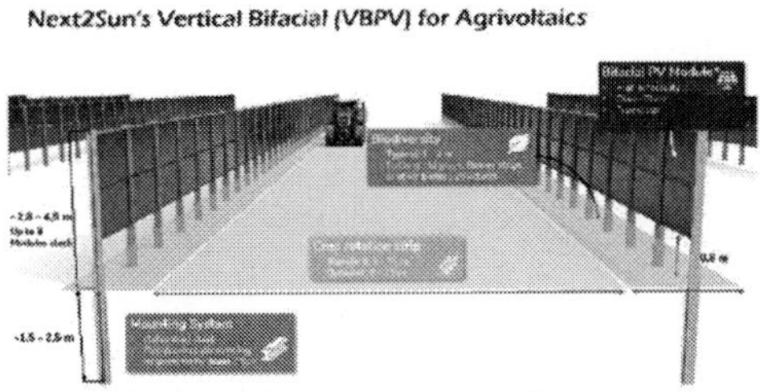

Figure 4: Typical System setup of a vertical PV powerplant designed by Next2Sun

4 COMPARISONS OF CAPTURE RATES IN VERTICAL BIFACIAL vs. CONVENTIONAL PV

In accordance with the assumptions in [2], a production profile for south-oriented and vertical bifacial fixed tilt PV inverters of the power plant in Wellingen (Germany) is shown in **Figure 5**. As can be seen, the production profile of vertical bifacial PV has two production peaks, arising during morning and late afternoon. Note, while the equipped inverter type and nominal power are the same for the data provided (Huawei SUN2000-60KTL), the installed module capacity in the E/W strings is possible to be set at 1.5 for the DC/AC Ratio (about 89.23 kWp) without limitation while the south-oriented strings are installed with 71.04 kWp with a common DC/AC Ratio of 1.2.

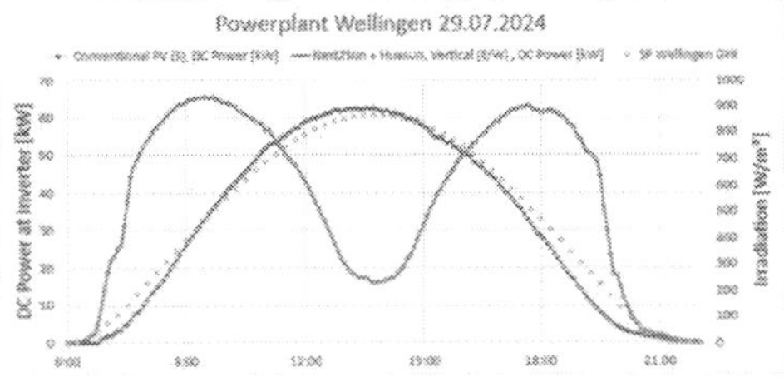

Figure 5: Power Production Profile of the South-facing PV and Vertical Bifacial PV in Next2Sun Powerplant Wellingen (Germany) on the 29-07-2024 – 5 minutes resolution for power generation, 15 minutes for GHI.

The results presented in **Figure 5** prove, when designed precisely, the self-shade effects are neglectable and combined with a high bifaciality on module level, the energy peaks are somewhat of a similar height and enhanced when compared to early adaptors of vertical PV [1]. This energy profile verifies the simulation results in [6], respectively that the Next2Sun System generates significantly more energy when compared to competitors with same nominal power, due to precise racking system design and profound module selection.

Figure 6 presents a comparison of the monthly surplus in market electricity prices for vertical bifacial PV plants in Donaueschingen/Aasen and Dirmingen, Germany, from August 2020 to August 2024. The monthly benefit, measured against the market electricity price ("Marktwert Solar"), showed that the power plants reached **up to 45% asset performance**, with most months being positive. The continuous growth in PV capacity in Germany (+15.6 GWp in 2023 and +15.9 GWp in 2024) has increased the midday surplus, contributing to more frequent negative electricity prices. [7] Likewise in 2024, the VBPV plants of Next2Sun in Dirmingen and Aasen achieved a 24.0% and 25.3% benefit over the market price, respectively. Wellingen Ost achieved an even higher benefit of 27.8%.

From the graph in **Figure 6** for nearly every month between August 2020 and December 2024 the atypical production led to significant added value. Only 2 months resulted in an exception as SP Aasen recorded slightly negative profile when compared to MW Solar Germany in December 2021 and December 2024.

10.4229/EUPVSEC2025/4DO.4.1

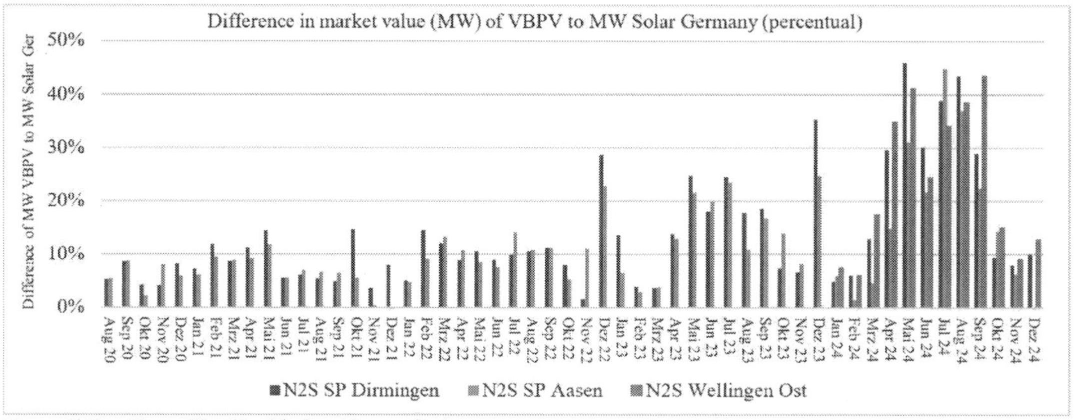

Figure 6: Bar-Chart of the Monthly Asset (percent) when Comparing Vertical Bifacial Power Plants in Donaueschingen/Aasen, Dirmingen and Wellingen (Germany) with "Marktwert Solar"

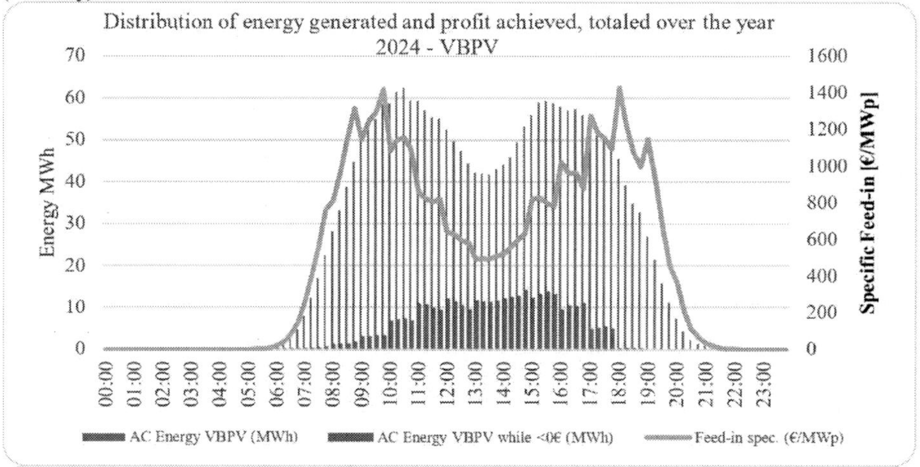

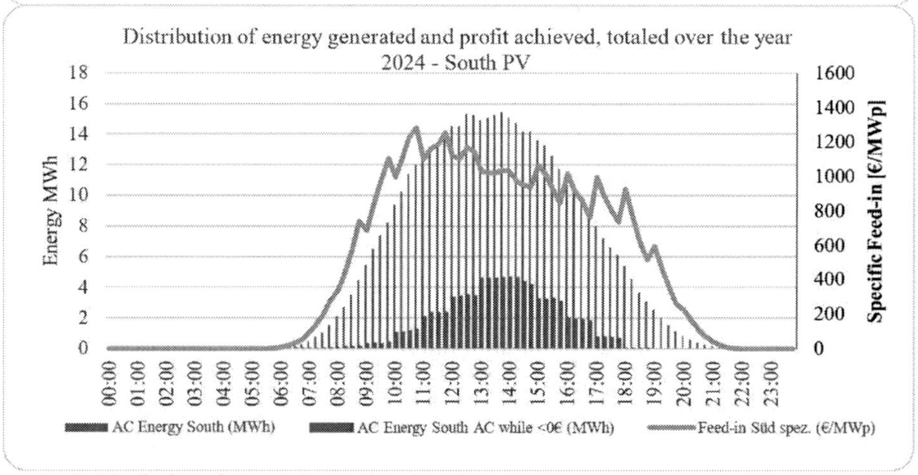

Figure 7: Distribution of energy generated, and profit achieved for VBPV and conventional south PV at SP Wellingen (Germany), totalled over the year 2024 and accounted to the timestamp of production

10.4229/EUPVSEC2025/4DO.4.1
020388-003

A comparison of vertical bifacials profile against a conventional south PV system is presented for the year 2024. Both are located at the powerplant in Wellingen (Germany). The respective power of the VBPV is 3 MWp while the conventional south is 532 kWp. The azimuth is: ±90° for the 90°Tilt East/West facing system and ~0° for the 20° tilted south PV. Both production profiles present the accumulated energy as distribution to the production timestamp with a resolution of 15 minutes. At the same time the power-specific feed-in part $R_{spec\,(t)}$ (in €/MWp) is accumulated for the total year and shown as distribution to the timestamp in **Figure 7**. The revenue is calculated as energy $E_{AC(t)}$ times market price $p_{(t)}$ as presented in Equation:

$$R_{spec\,(t)} = p_{(t)} \cdot \frac{E_{AC(t)}}{P_{NOM}}$$

When observing the distribution of AC energy generated during times of negative prices with the total AC energy produced, the effected amount of energy in VBPV equals 14.2% or 112.4 MWh/MWp, while south PV was affected by 19.1% or 166.7 MWh/MWp. At the same time, the market profile differs more drastic, as VBPV recorded a price of 59.09 €/MWh while 50.76 €/MWh for the conventional part. In 2025, Next2Sun's module design has been optimized further regarding the vertical AgriPV System, so the specific energy yield in upcoming power plants will likely perform even higher.

Comparing the capture rates recorded in this work with prognosis made in 2022s Literature, indicate the economic perspectives have fallen more drastic than prognosed. The study from 2022 assumes capture rates will continue to diverge until 2045. Although, the benefit for atypical generation profiles have been prognosed as significantly higher than the capture rates of the PV portfolio with differences of around 12% between VBPV and conventional south profiles from beginning of 2025. [8]

As early as 2024 (Presented in **Figure 8**), the median value of Next2Sun's vertical power plants was around 16% higher, when comparing the capture rates of VBPV with the market value of PV portfolio (MW Solar Germany). Referring to the numbers as 7.95 ct/kWh as average price of electricity at EEX in 2024, while the PV portfolio accounted for 4.62 ct/kWh (58%) and 5.88 ct/kWh as Median for VBPV of Next2Sun's Powerplants which equalled a capture rate of 74%.

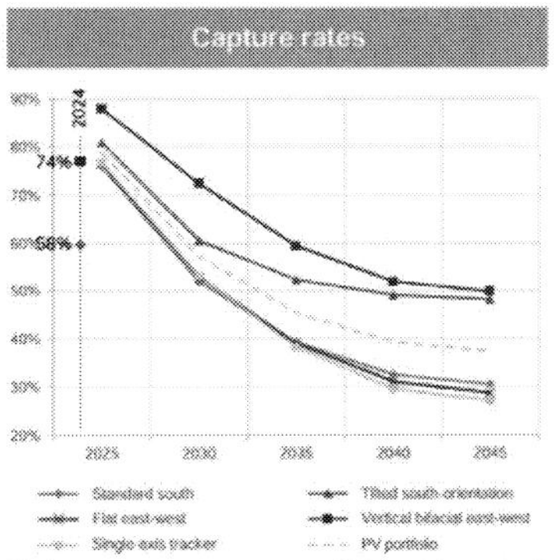

Figure 8: Capture rates prognosis by Enervis in 2022, adjusted with capture rates seen in 2024 [8]

CONCLUSIONS

This work demonstrates the economic attractiveness of vertical bifacial AgriPV systems from an energy production perspective. As shown, the yearly benefit of the two power plants in Germany outperformed conventional PV systems. Furthermore, the analysis of the production profiles for both south-oriented and vertical bifacial fixed-tilt PV systems at the Next2Sun power plant in Wellingen (Germany) confirm its competitiveness. Considering the similar achieved specific yield when comparing E/W with South orientation in the same power plant on the exemplary test day in July, along with a higher market electricity price of over 30%, the economic benefit is substantial. Further, the recorded difference in capture rates for VBPV and conventional PV indicate a correlation to negative prices seen at the spot market. While actual studies prognose the number of negative hours will continuously increase until meaningful grid flexibility is present, this indicates the profitability of VBPV over conventional solar without batteries. The results align with previous simulations and indicate, aside from the agricultural benefits mentioned, profitability as a key factor is making them a promising solution for land conflicts in modern agricultural and future energy demand.

REFERENCES

[1] M. Victoria and et.al, "Vertical Agrivoltaics in a Temperate Climate: Exploring Technical, Agricultural, Meteorological, and Social Dimensions," 2024.

[2] R. Kopecek and J. Libal, "Bifacial Photovoltaics 2021: Status, Opportunities and Challenges," *Creative Commons Attribution 4.0 International,* 2021.

[3] M. Baricchio, M. Korevaar, P. Babal and H. Ziar, "Modelling of bifacial photovoltaic farms to evaluate the profitability of East/West vertical configuration," *Solar Energy,* vol. 272, no. ISSN 0038-092X, 2024.

[4] S. Reker, J. Schneider and C. Gerhards, "Integration of vertical solar power plants into a future German energy system," *Smart Energy,* vol. Volume 7, no. ISSN 2666-9552, 2022.

[5] K. D. Vos, "Negative Wholesale Electricity Prices in the German, French and Belgian Day-Ahead, Intra-Day and Real-Time Markets," *The Electricity Journal,* vol. 28, no. 4, 2015.

[6] J. Libal and J. Eickelmann, 06 06 2023. [Online]. Available: https://isc-konstanz.de/wp-content/uploads/2023/06/ISC-white-paper-Next2Sun_2023_DE-1.pdf.

[7] B. Burger, "Energy Charts," Fraunhofer ISE, 01 01 2025. [Online]. Available: https://www.energy-charts.info/downloads/Stromerzeugung_2024.pdf.

[8] Enervis-Energy-Advisors, "Analysis of innovative system designs for a power market optimised PV portfolio in Germany," Dezember 2022. [Online]. Available: https://thegreenroofs.com/wp-content/uploads/2024/07/Analysis-of-innovative-system-designs-06.2023.pdf. [Accessed 08 08 2025].

Energy Yield Analysis and Performance Monitoring of Three Photovoltaic Noise Barriers in Belgium and the Netherlands

Sara Bouguerra, Richard de jong, Santhosh Ramesh, Tine Engelen, Marta Casasola Paesa, Jan Mertens, Fallon Colberts, Ismail Kaaya, Patrizio Manganiello, Georgi Yordadov, Arnaud Morlier, Michaël Daenen

EU PVSEC 2025: 4DO.4.4

25/09/2025

Outline

Introduction

Methodology

- IIPV Demonstrators
  - DEMO1: Vertical built-on concrete PVNB with different module technologies
  - DEMO2: Semi-transparent PVNB with different module technologies
  - DEMO3: Cassette built-on PVNB with a zigzag design and c-Si modules
- Temperature monitoring
- Energy Yield Simulation

Results

Conclusion and Outlook

Introduction

EU's Zero Pollution Action Plan (2021)→ decrease the share of people chronically disturbed by transport noise by 30% [1].

Noise barriers are vital in reducing the harmful effects of traffic-related sound pollution.

PVNBs optimize land use for sustainable energy production.

PVNBs can be implemented either by retrofitting existing ones or integrating modules into new designs.

Traditional and PV Noise barriers on roads [2]-[3]

[1] Zero Pollution Action Plan - European Commission
[2] The Importance of Noise Barriers in City Life – Hatko Sound Barrier
[3] Photovoltaic Noise Barriers (PVNBs) | SoliTek

Objectives

- Validate the electrical and thermal models of three PVNB demonstrators through on-site measurements
- Compare the energy performance using different integration methods.

Methodology

IMO-IMOMEC
UHASSELT imec

Methodology

DEMO 1: Vertical built-on PVNB with different module technologies

Location: Thor Park, Genk, Belgium

Structure:

- 13m-wide, 5m-high , East-facing concrete wall

Solar Panels:

- 2 c-Si PERC PV modules
- 2 thin film CdTe modules on rails attached to a concrete wall, both mounted with an air gap of 5 cm between them and the wall
- 4 CIGS modules glued directly to the wall

Power and Temperature monitoring:

- Each of the modules in this system were connected to an individual MPP tracker
- No temperature measurement

Data collection Period:

- August 2021 to present

DEMO1:Vertical built-on PVNB with different module technologies

Methodology

DEMO 2: Semi-transparent PVNB with different module technologies

Location: Thor Park, Genk, Belgium

Structure:

- 8m-long and 5m-high vertical East-facing metal frame

Solar Panels:

- 8 bifacial c-Si PERC PV modules (top-lower row)
- 4 CIGS modules (middle row)

Power and Temperature monitoring:

- Each of the modules is connected to an individual MPP tracker.
- Temperature measurement: FBG sensors (M1 and M2)

Data collection Period: August 2021 to present.

DEMO2: Semi-transparent PVNB with different module technologies

Methodology

DEMO 3: Cassette built-on PVNB with a zigzag design

Location: Chemelot Campus in Geleen, Netherlands

Structure:
- South-facing concrete wall
- Two zigzag configurations with four cassettes each

Cassettes filled with noise-absorbing material

Solar Panels:
- 8 customized glass/glass PERC PV modules from Soltech (103 Wp)
- PV Modules connected in series, forming two strings (A, B)

Power and Temperature monitoring:
- Power: QEED QI-power-485-LV
- Temperature: DS18B20 (back of panels), FBG sensors (lower left & right panels).

Data collection Period: May 2023 to present.

DEMO3: Cassette built-on PVNB with a zigzag design

Methodology

Temperature Monitoring (FBG-based sensors)

- Real-time monitoring of mechanical strain and temperature within PV modules.
- Optical fibres with fibre Bragg gratings (FBGs) using different packaging.

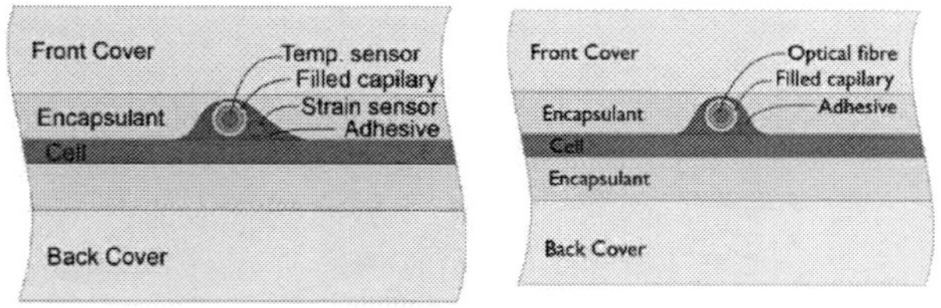

FBG-based sensing solution [5]

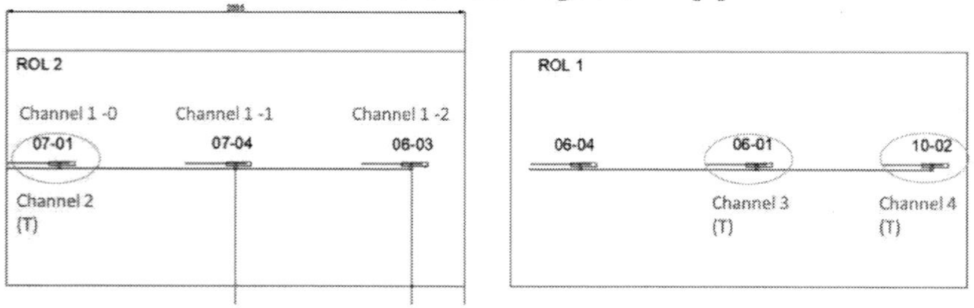

FBG sensor location in DEMO 2

Module 1 in DEMO2 with sensors

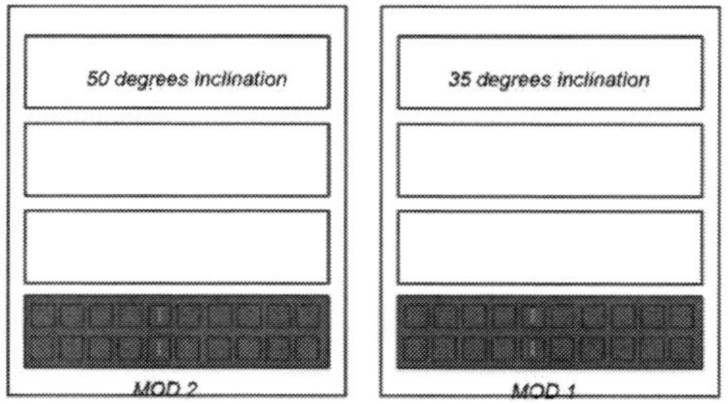

FBG sensor location in DEMO 3

[5] https://doi.org/10.1002/pip.3622.

Methodology

Energy Yield Simulation

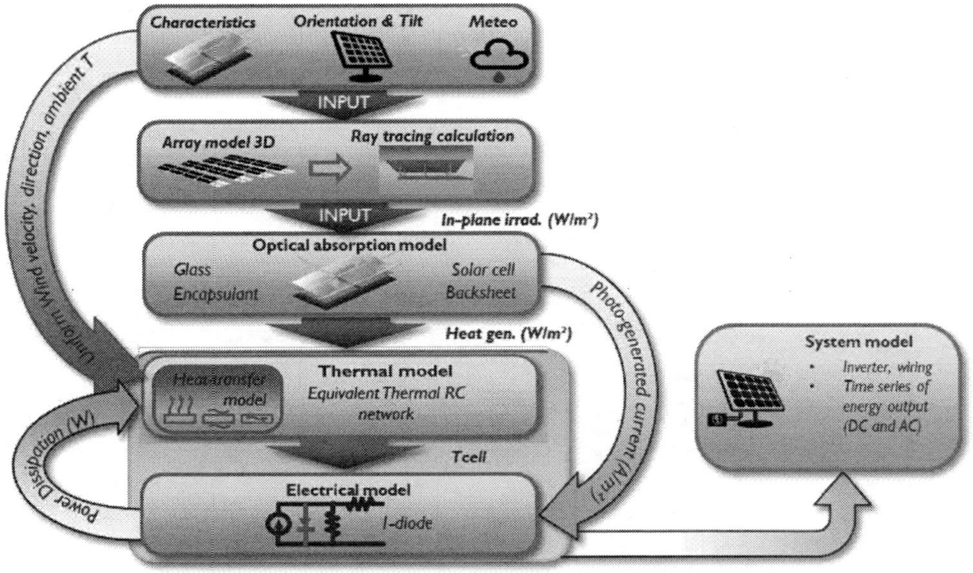

Imec's energy Yield Simulation Framework [6]

DEMO 1

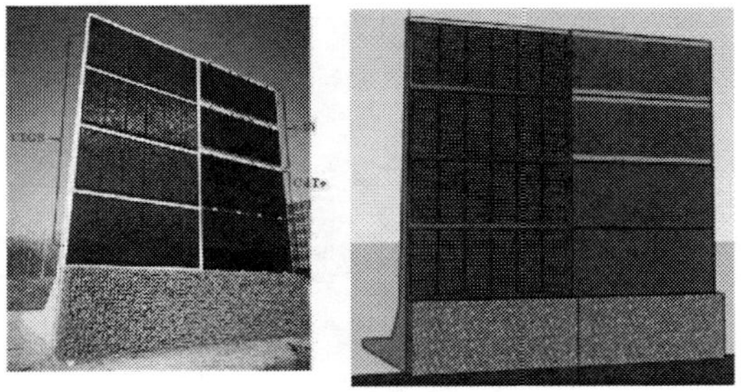

DEMO 2

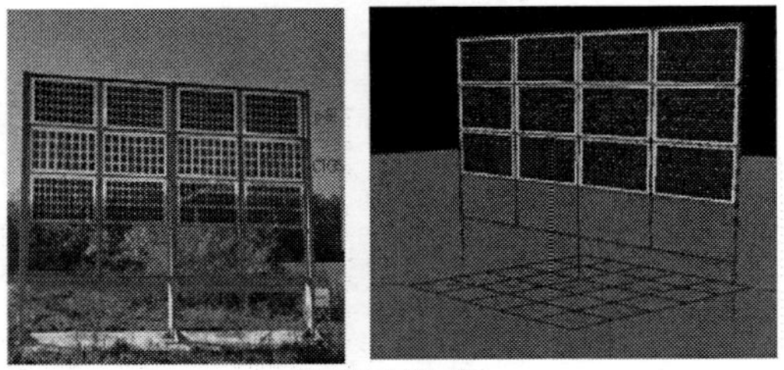

DEMO 3

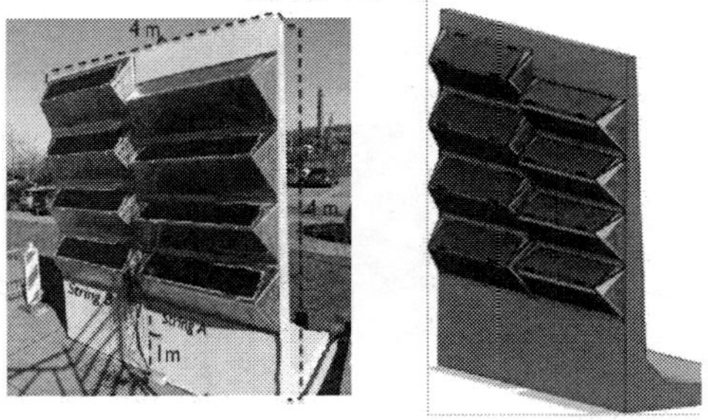

Geometrical model in the E-Yield Framework

[6] https://doi.org/10.4229/EUPVSEC20192019-5DP.2.2.

Results

Results

DEMO 1: Vertical built-on concrete PVNB with different module technologies

Module Type	RMSE (Capacity Factor, Sep–Oct 2021) [7]
c-Si	14% – 17%
CdTe	20% – 23%
CIGS	13% – 31%

[7] https://doi.org/10.1038/s41598-024-78862-w

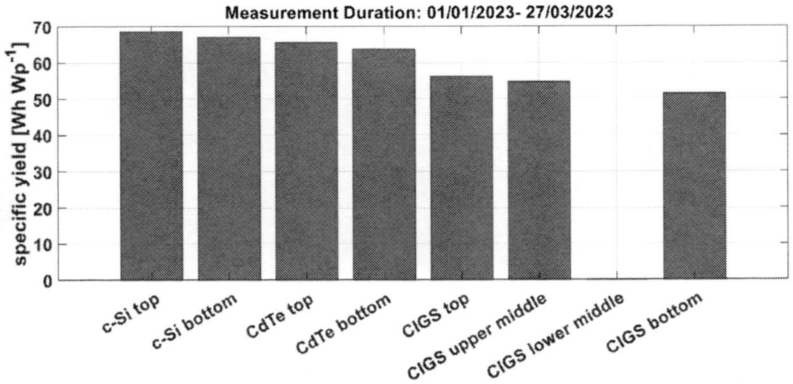

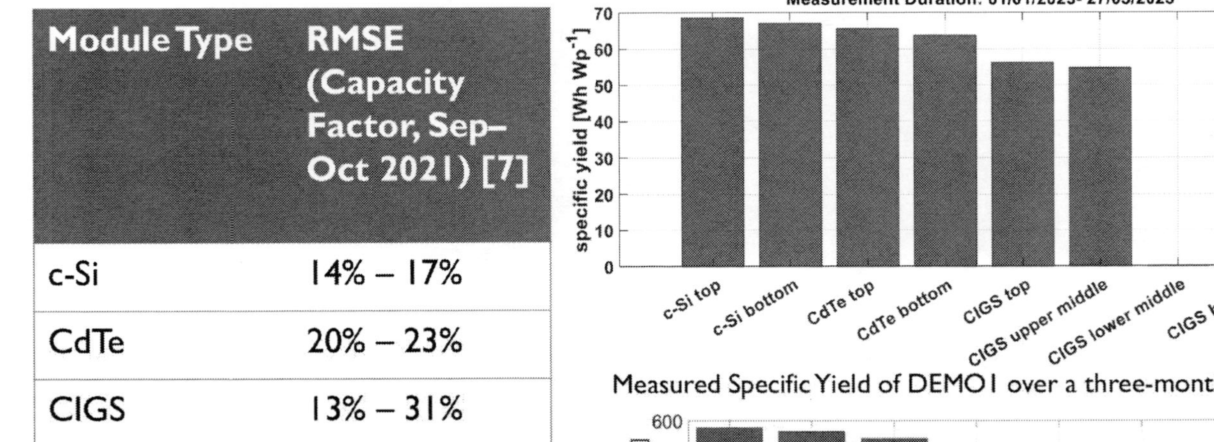

Measured Specific Yield of DEMO1 over a three-month period.

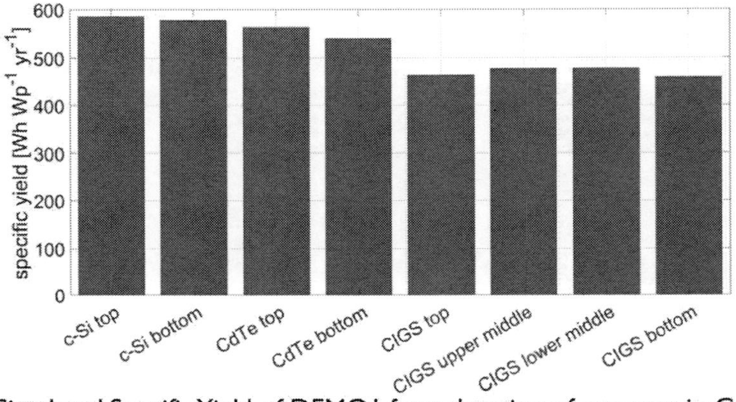

Simulated Specific Yield of DEMO1 for a duration of one year in Genk using TMY.

Results: DEMO1

Thermal Effects

CIGS modules attached to the concrete wall

SketchUp 3D model of DEMO1 (unventilated)

- Irradiance-weighted annual average cell temperature: 18.6°C
- Annual specific yield: 470 kWh/kWp

CIGS modules separated from the concrete wall

SketchUp 3D model of DEMO1 (ventilated)

$$\overline{T}_{\text{cell,iw}} = \frac{\sum_{i=1}^{N} T_{\text{cell},i} \cdot G_i \cdot \Delta t_i}{\sum_{i=1}^{N} G_i \cdot \Delta t_i}$$

- Irradiance-weighted annual average cell temperature: 16.4°C (↓2.2°C)
- Annual specific yield: 474 Wh/Wp (↑0.8%)

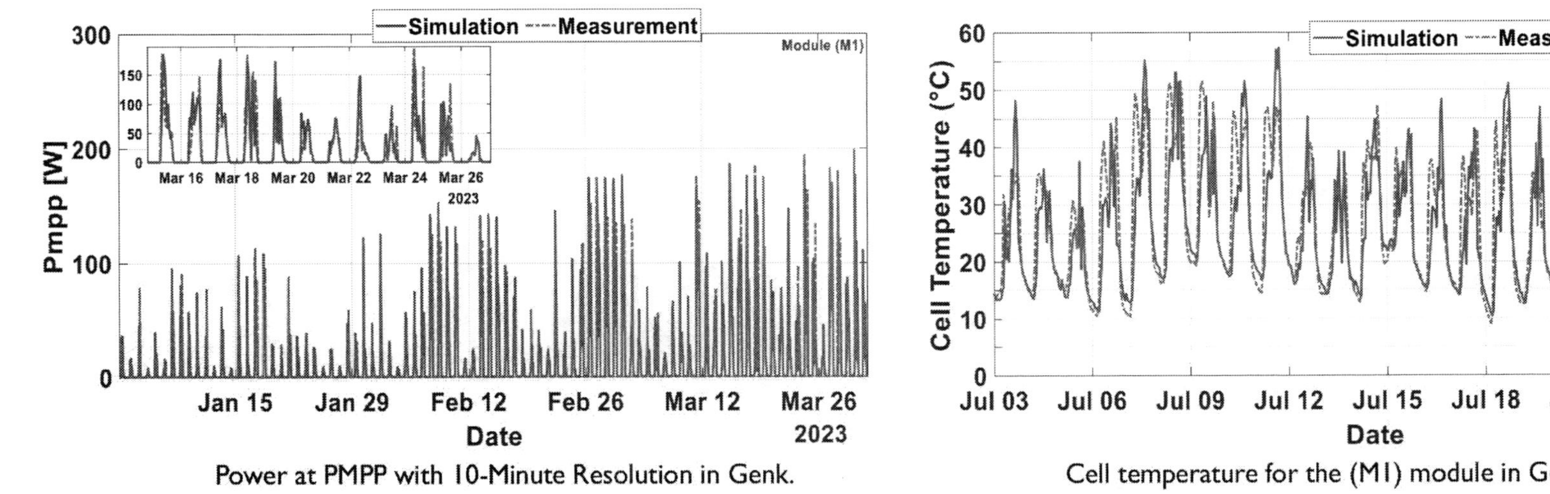

Results: DEMO2

Electrical and Thermal model Validation (hourly resolution)

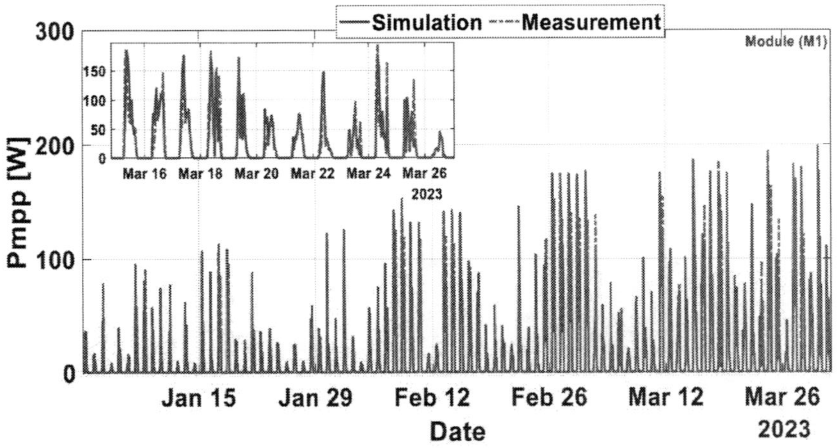

Power at PMPP with 10-Minute Resolution in Genk.

RMSE =17W, 5.8% of Pmax

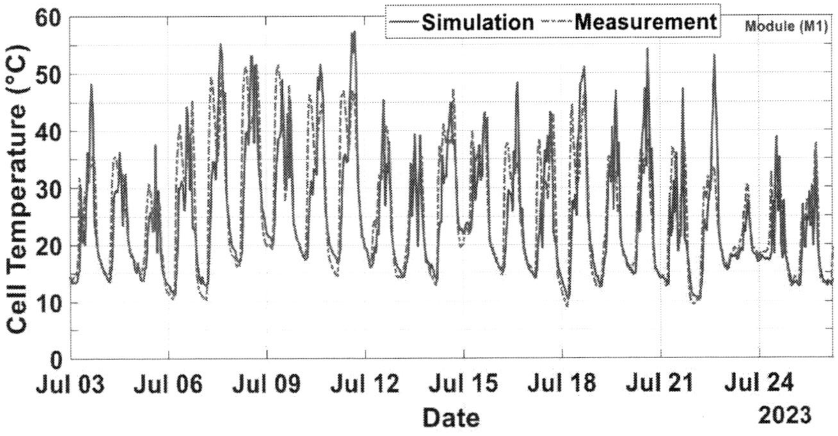

Cell temperature for the (M1) module in Genk.

RMSE =6.5°C

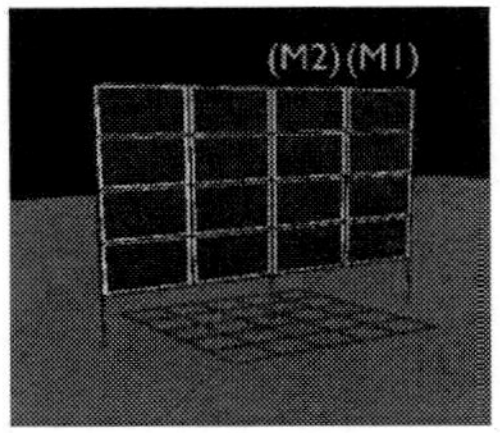

Results: DEMO3

Electrical model Validation (10-min resolution)

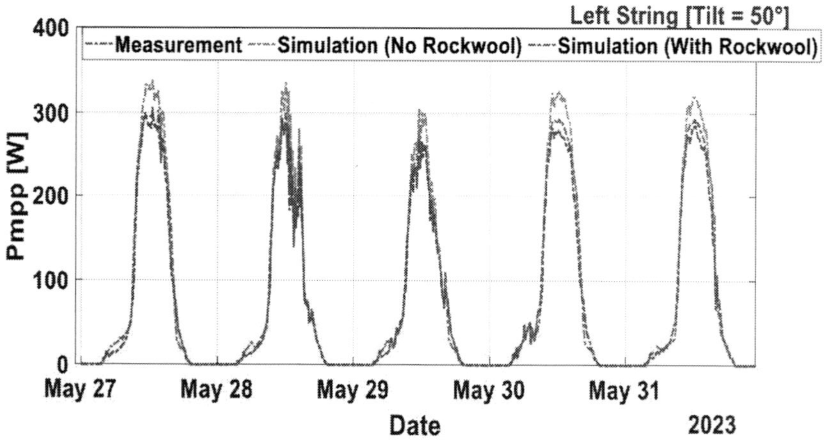

Power at MPP for the left string in Geleen, the Netherlands.

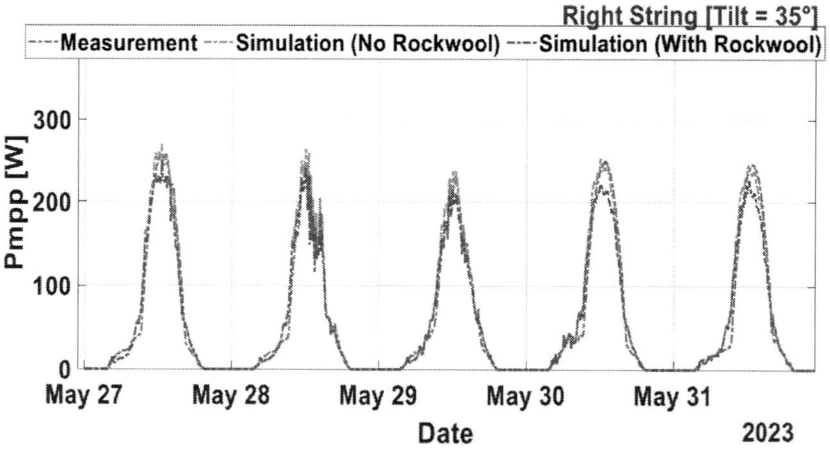

Power at MPP for the right string in Geleen, the Netherlands.

RMSE (No Rockwool) = 14W(3.5% of Pmax)
RMSE (With Rockwool) =10 W, (2.5% of Pmax)

RMSE (No Rockwool) = 12W (3% of Pmax)
RMSE (With Rockwool) =13W (3% of Pmax)

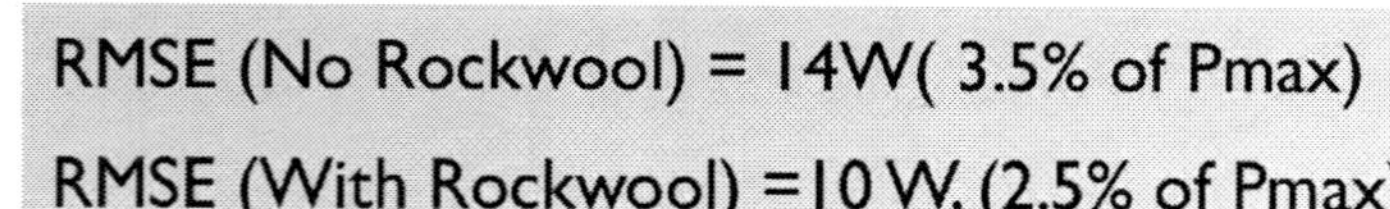

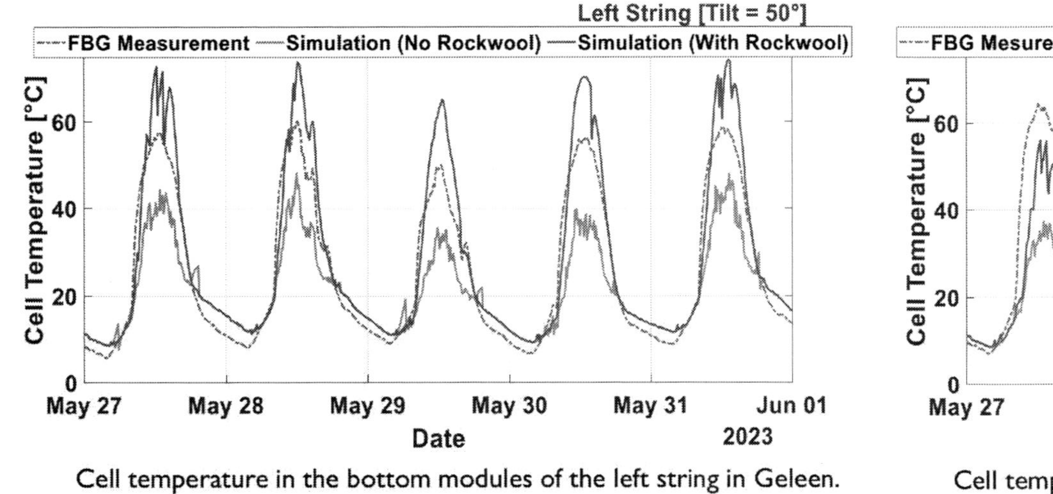

Results: DEMO3

Thermal model Validation (10-min resolution)

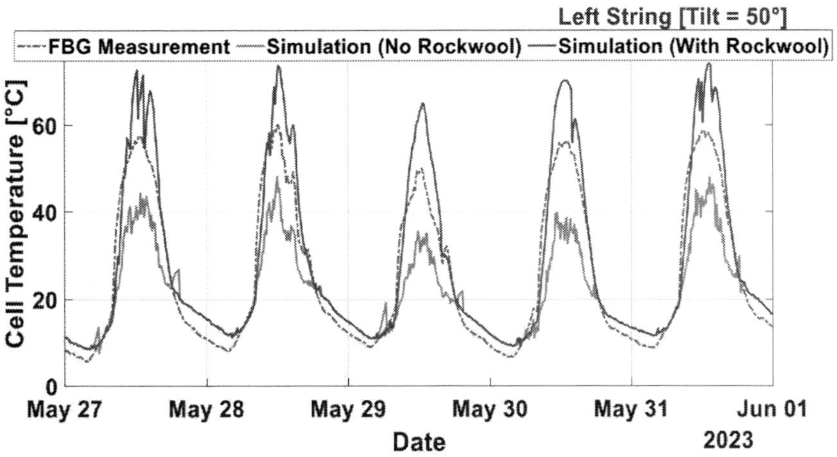

Cell temperature in the bottom modules of the left string in Geleen.

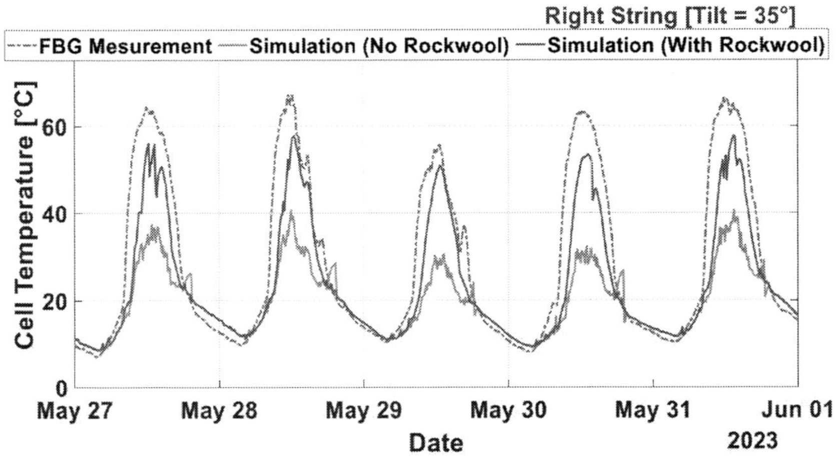

Cell temperature in the bottom modules of the right string in Geleen.

RMSE (No Rockwool) =9°C

RMSE (With Rockwool) =6°C

RMSE (No Rockwool) = 15°C

RMSE (With Rockwool) = 9°C

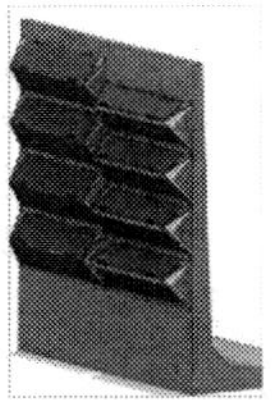

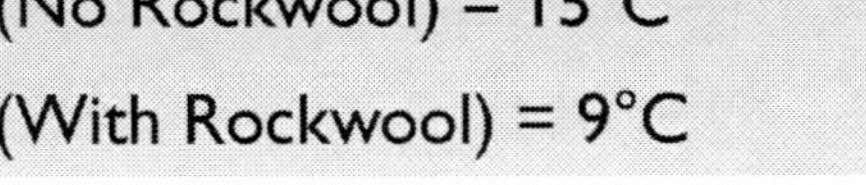

[8] https://doi.org/10.1016/j.apenergy.2024.124724

Results: DEMO2 VS DEMO3

Module Temperature (TMY Genk, hourly resolution)

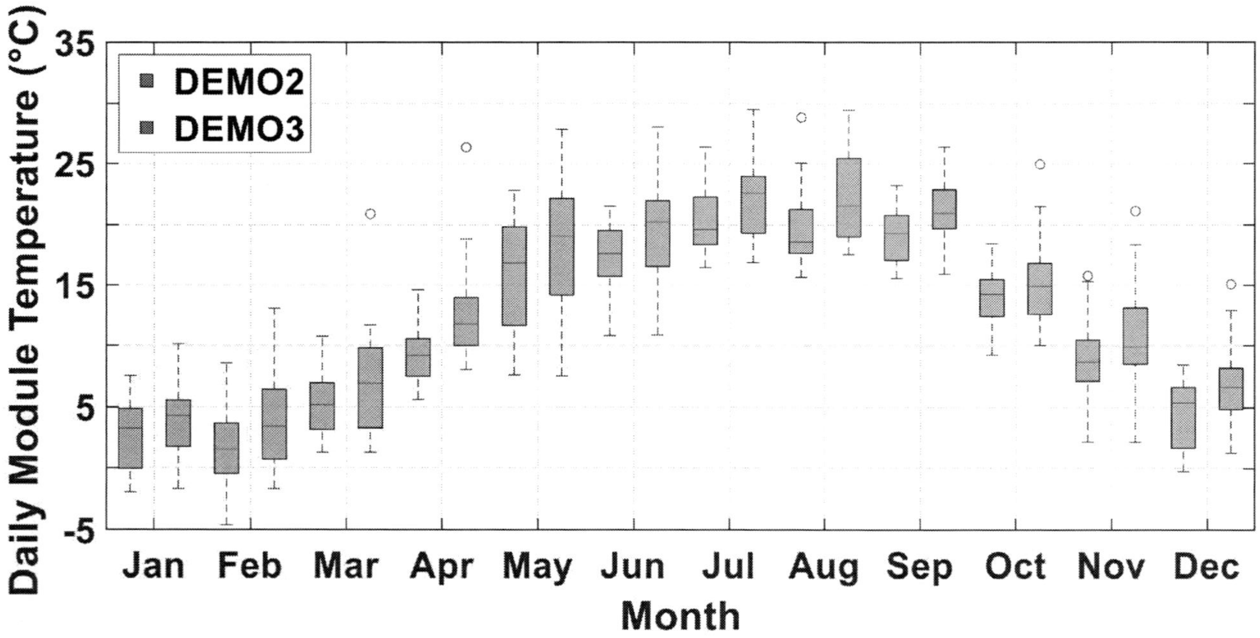

Boxplot showing the daily average module temperature per month in DEMO2 and DEMO3.

DEMO 2

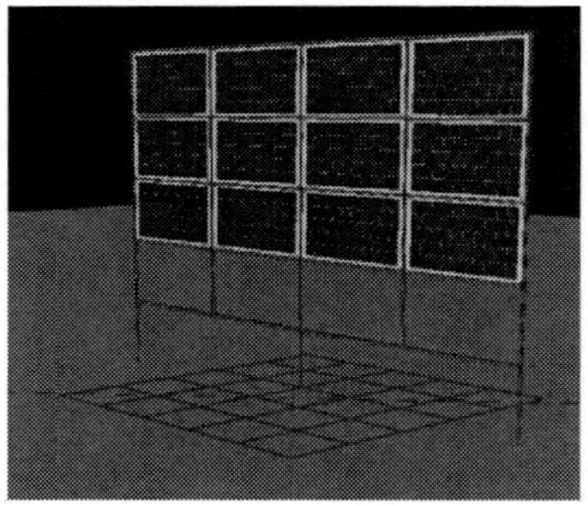

DEMO 3

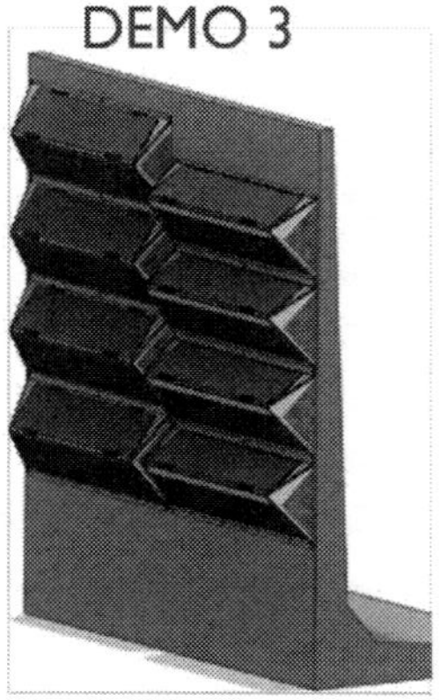

Lower module temperature in DEM2 (↓ 2°C)

Results: DEMO2 VS DEMO3

Yearly Energy Yield (hourly resolution)

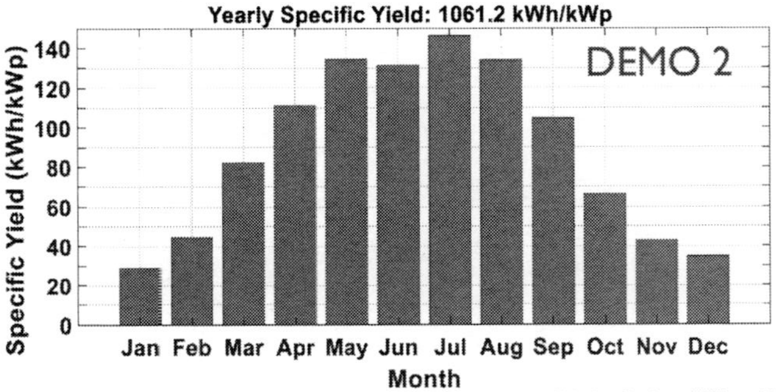

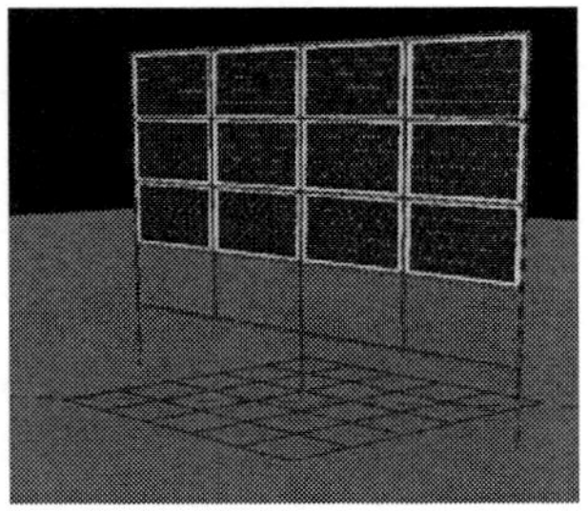

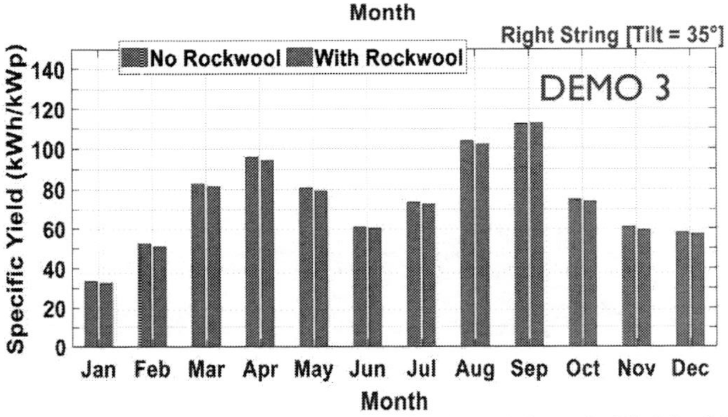

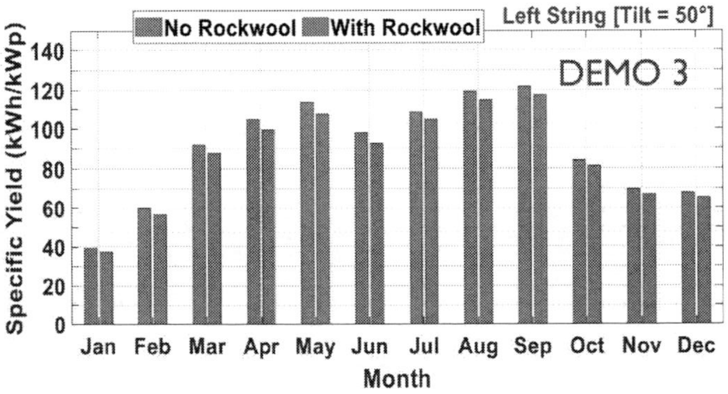

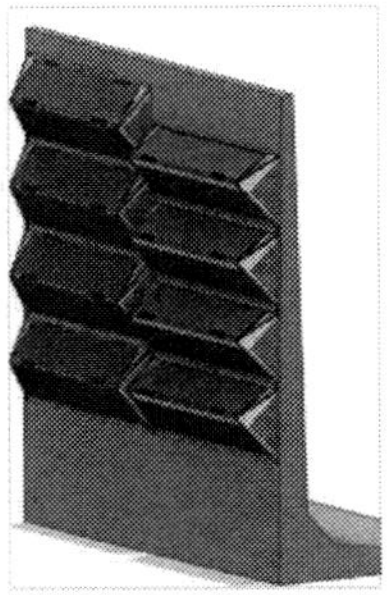

Simulated Specific Yield of DEMO2 and DEMO3 using TMY data in Genk.

Yearly Yield (No Rockwool) =890 kWh/kWp

Yearly Yield (With Rockwool) =877 kWh/kWp (↓ 1.5%)

Yearly Yield (No Rockwool) =1079 kWh/kWp

Yearly Yield (With Rockwool) =1032 kWh/kWp (↓ 4.4%)

Conclusion & Outlook

- Noise-absorbing layers raise module operating temperatures by 10–20 °C→ performance reduction

→must be carefully addressed in design.

- In-laminate sensors → enhanced thermal modelling of PVNB systems→ accurate power prediction.
- East–west oriented bifacial PVNBs operate at cooler temperatures and achieve higher yields compared with monofacial counterparts.
- Direct bonding or gluing of PV modules to concrete barriers → low heat dissipation and increased module temperature
- Chimneys and ventilation gaps →low operating temperatures, enhanced long-term performance.

Outlook

- Acoustic pressure simulations for the different PVNB configurations
- Exploring novel integration methods to enhance the cooling and mitigate noise (coupled Multiphysics modelling)
- Assessment of PVNB performance at the infrastructure scale (through upscaling)

Acknowledgements

This work is conducted within the Solar Energy Made Regional (SolarEMR) and Rolling Solar projects, within the Interreg V-A Euregio MeuseRhine, with support from the European Regional Development Fund. The authors thank Wim Van De Wall from ZigZagSolar, Eindhoven, Netherlands and Tatjana Vavilkin from Soltech, Genk, Belgium.

I wish to formally acknowledge the financial support provided by Fonds Wetenschappelijk Onderzoek (FWO) through the travel grant, which enabled my participation in EUPVSEC 2025

Interreg Euregio Maas-Rijn
Europees Fonds voor Regionale Ontwikkeling
EUROPESE UNIE
fwo

Thank you for the attention!

sara.bouguerra@uhasselt.be

Energy Ville ENERGY IN TRANSITION IMO-IMOMEC UHASSELT imec

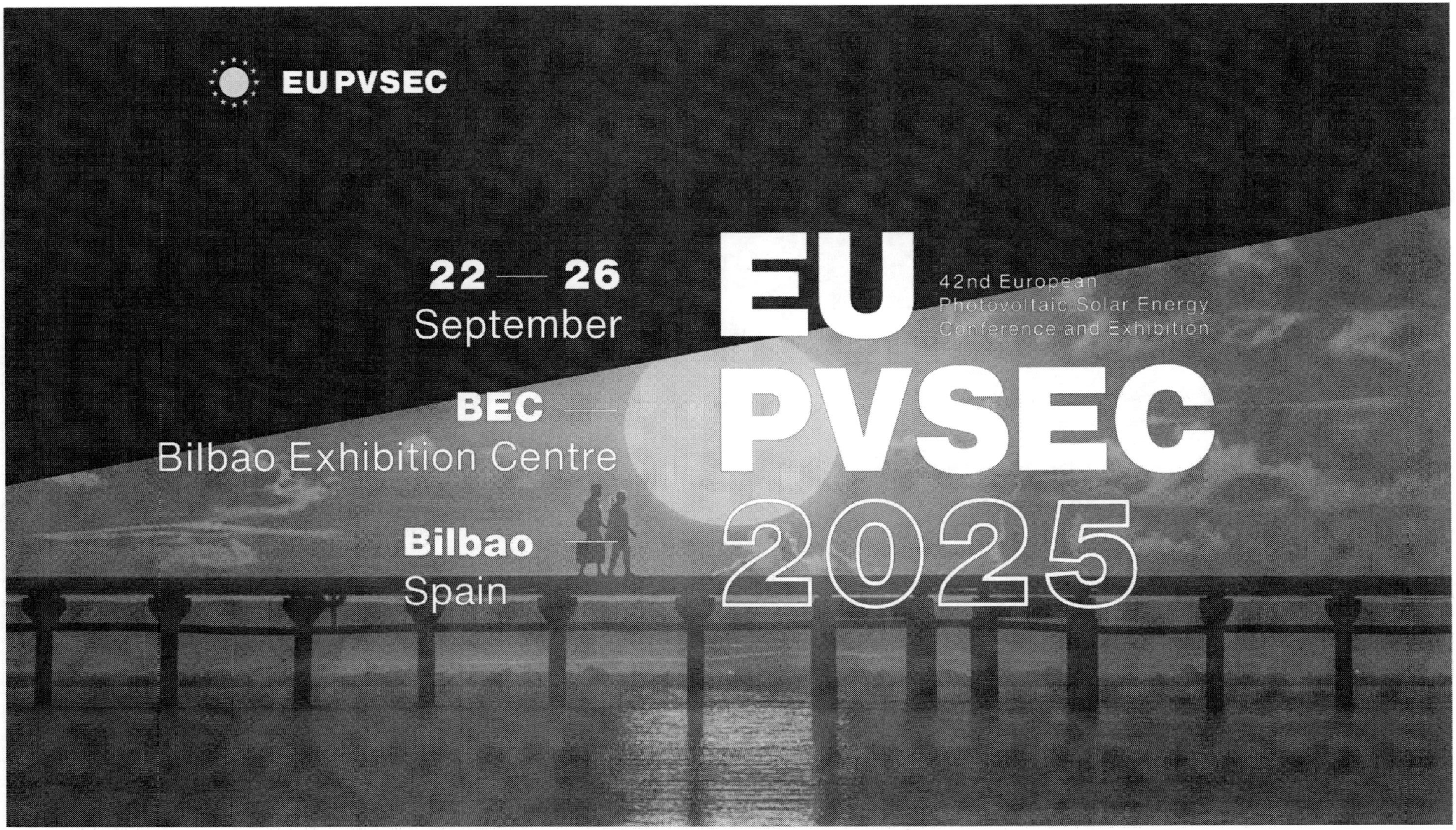
EUPVSEC
22 — 26
September
BEC —
Bilbao Exhibition Centre
Bilbao —
Spain
EU
PVSEC
2025
42nd European
Photovoltaic Solar Energy
Conference and Exhibition

030001-001

Conference Highlights

Robert Kenny

European Commission Joint Research Centre

EU PVSEC Technical Programme Chair

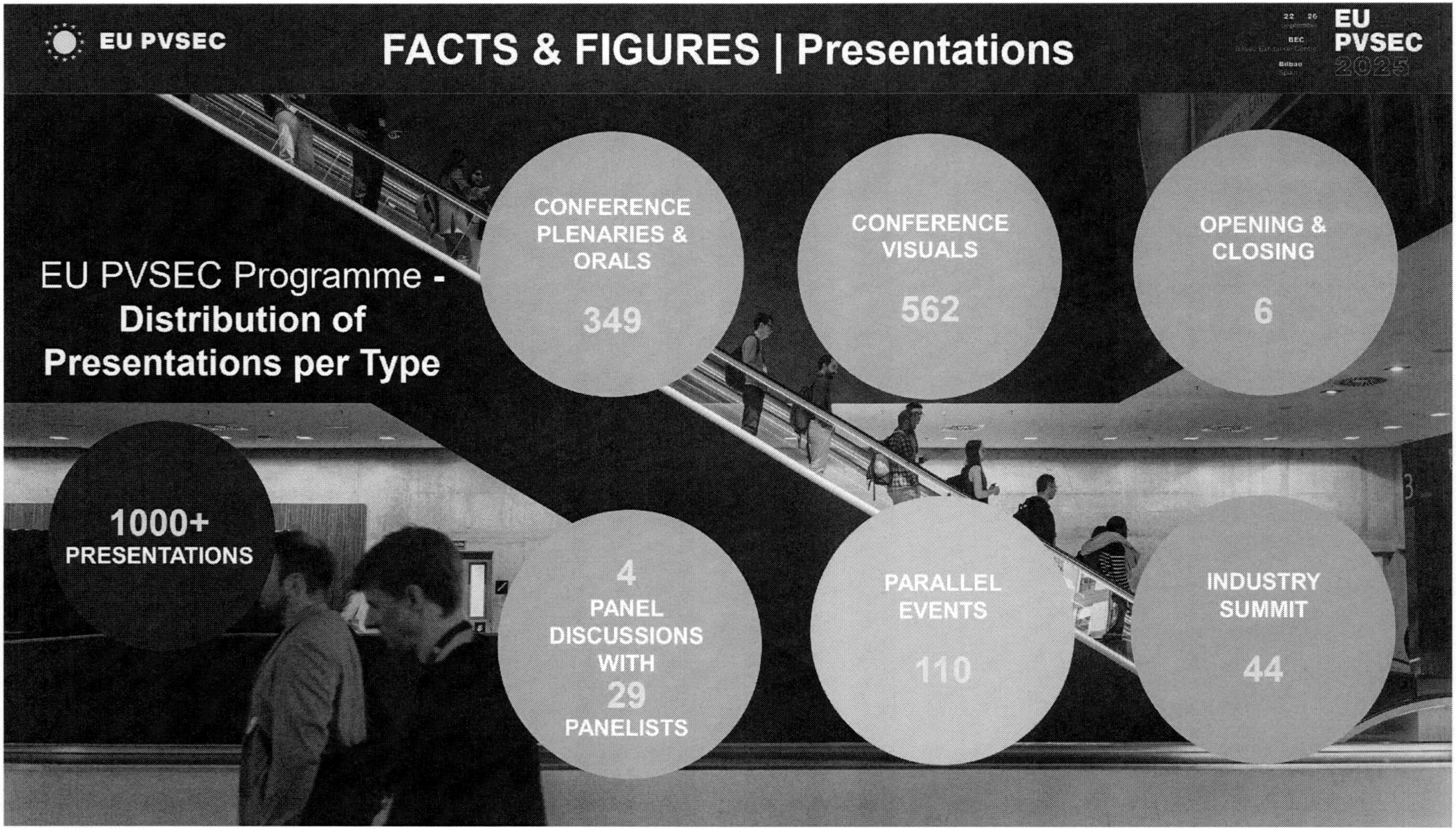
EU PVSEC
FACTS & FIGURES | Presentations
22 26
BEC
Bilbao
EU
PVSEC
2025
EU PVSEC Programme - Distribution of Presentations per Type
CONFERENCE PLENARIES & ORALS
349
CONFERENCE VISUALS
562
OPENING & CLOSING
6
1000+
PRESENTATIONS
4
PANEL DISCUSSIONS WITH
29
PANELISTS
PARALLEL EVENTS
110
INDUSTRY SUMMIT
44

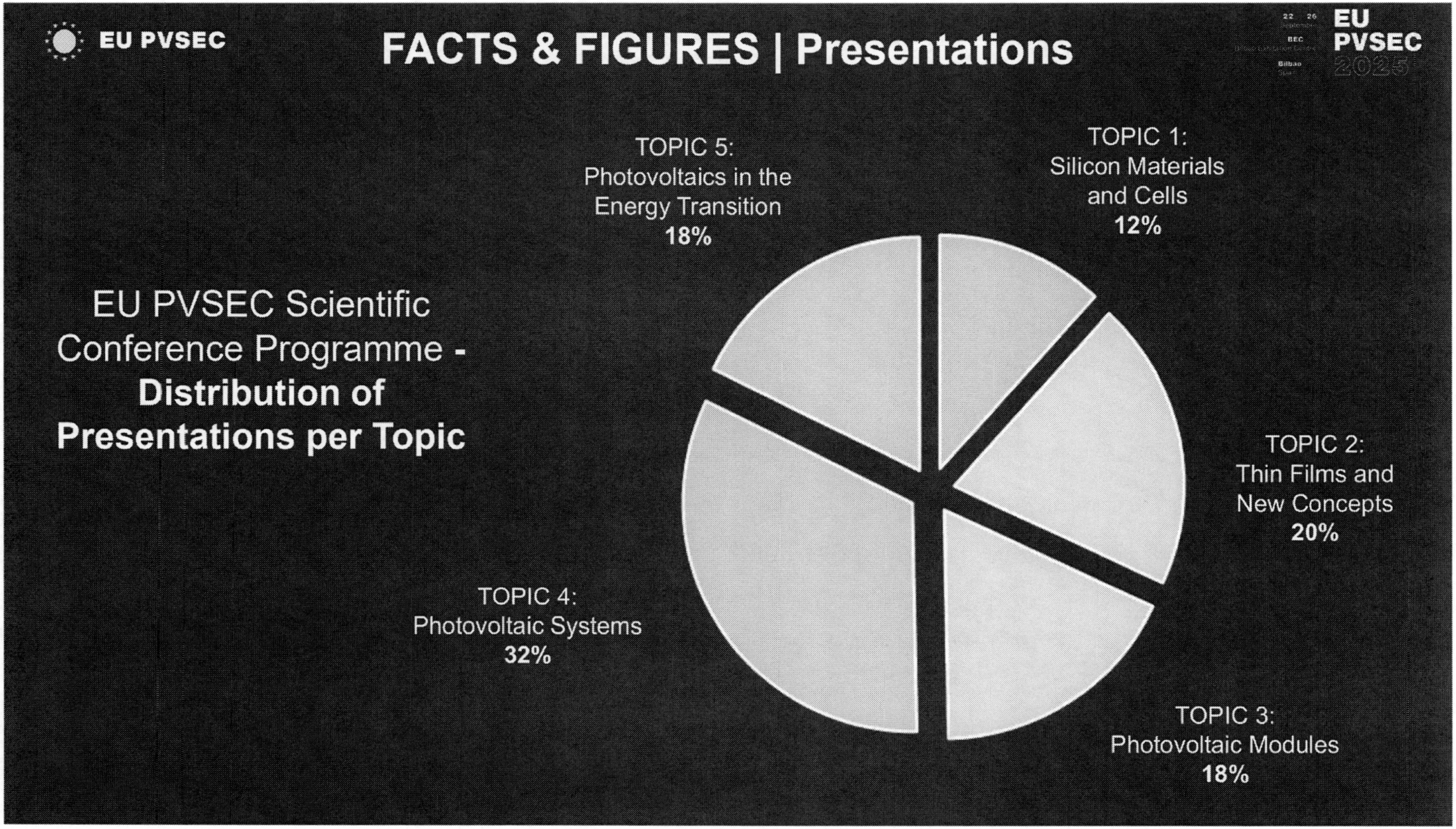
EU PVSEC
FACTS & FIGURES | Presentations
22 26
BEC
Bilbao
EU
PVSEC
2025
EU PVSEC Scientific
Conference Programme -
Distribution of
Presentations per Topic
TOPIC 5:
Photovoltaics in the
Energy Transition
18%
TOPIC 1:
Silicon Materials
and Cells
12%
TOPIC 2:
Thin Films and
New Concepts
20%
TOPIC 3:
Photovoltaic Modules
18%
TOPIC 4:
Photovoltaic Systems
32%

EU PVSEC

FACTS & FIGURES | Participants

EU PVSEC 2025

Participants by Countries
Top 10

No	Country	Participants
1	Germany	310
2	Spain	270
3	France	108
4	Italy	90
5	The Netherlands	76
6	South Korea	67
7	Switzerland	62
8	Japan	55
9	Belgium	44
10	Norway	35

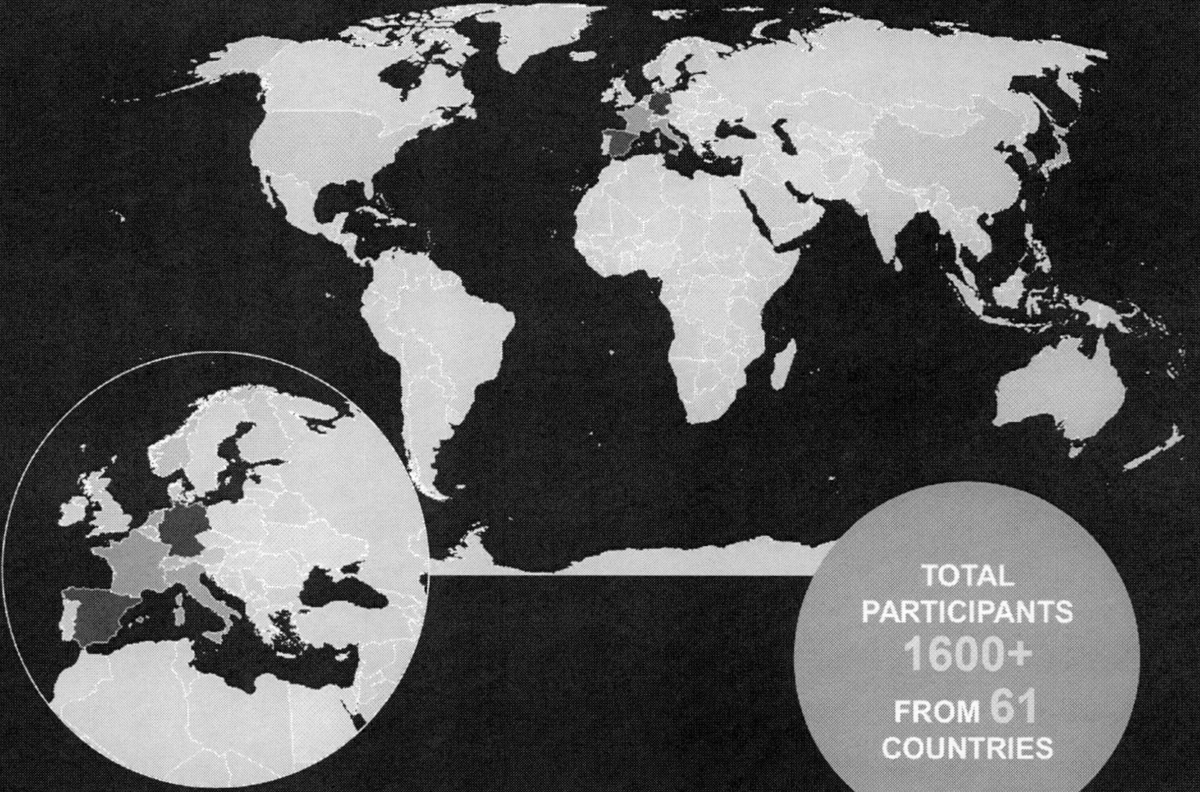

TOTAL PARTICIPANTS 1600+ FROM 61 COUNTRIES

Plenary Session
"PV Everywhere"
Welcome Messages
Jon DE GREGORIO
Key Note Speech
"The Dual Face of Global Solar Growth"
OPENING
Monday, 22 Sept. 2025
Moderated Panel Discussion
"Solar in Turbulent Times: Global Dynamics and the Way Forward"
Becquerel Prize Ceremony
EU PVSEC 2025
22 — 26 September
BEC
Bilbao Exhibition Centre
Spain
www.eupvsec.org
#EUPVSEC

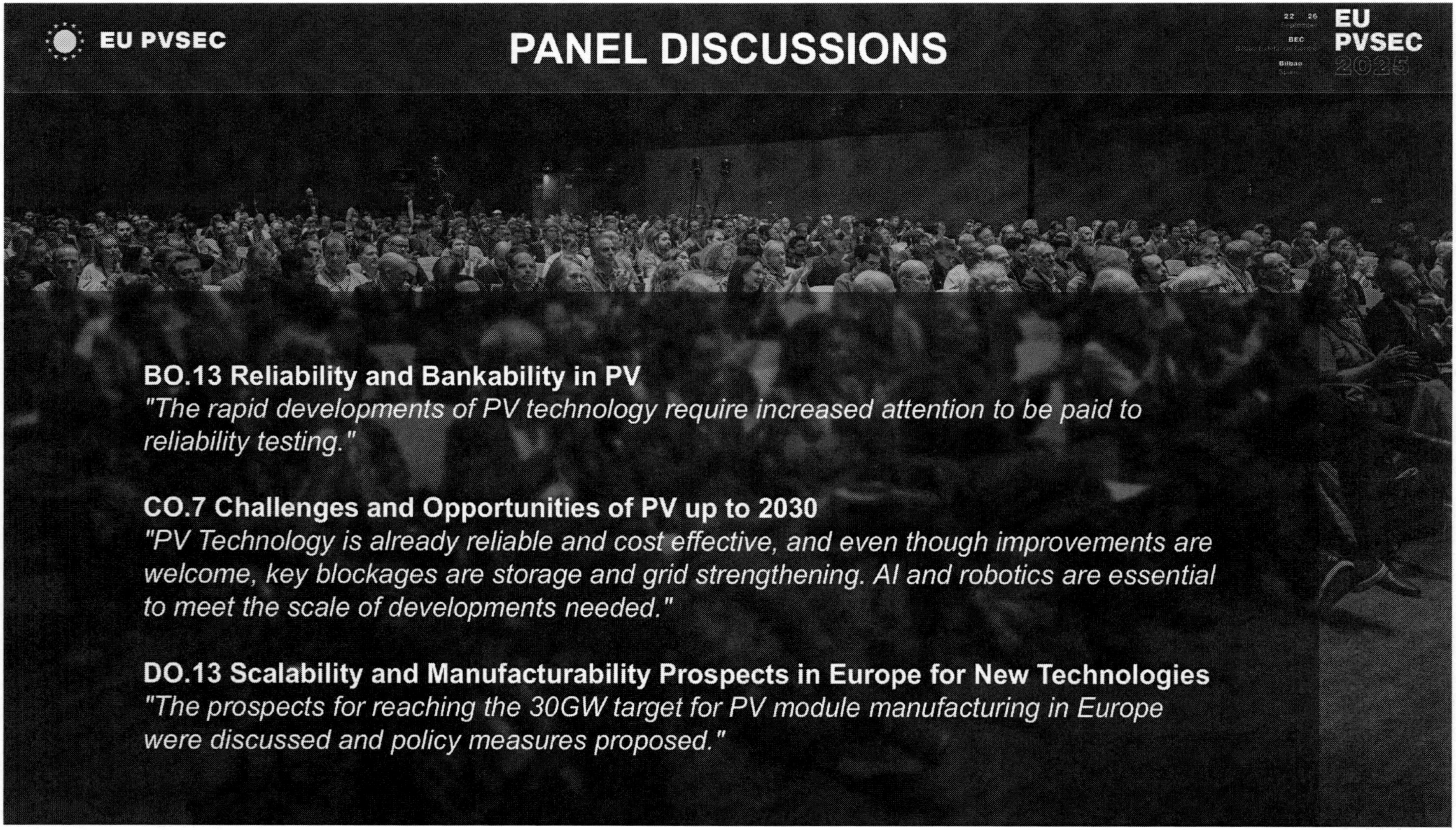
EU PVSEC
PANEL DISCUSSIONS
22 26
BEC
Bilbao
EU PVSEC 2025
BO.13 Reliability and Bankability in PV
"The rapid developments of PV technology require increased attention to be paid to reliability testing."
CO.7 Challenges and Opportunities of PV up to 2030
"PV Technology is already reliable and cost effective, and even though improvements are welcome, key blockages are storage and grid strengthening. AI and robotics are essential to meet the scale of developments needed."
DO.13 Scalability and Manufacturability Prospects in Europe for New Technologies
"The prospects for reaching the 30GW target for PV module manufacturing in Europe were discussed and policy measures proposed."

EU PVSEC

EU PVSEC 2025

CONFERENCE

KEY MESSAGES

Cross-cutting themes emerged throughout the programme, showcasing how solar technologies can be applied everywhere, from traditional to emerging fields.

- Sustainability and circularity remain central, with research focused on reducing material use, such as replacing silver with copper, and advancing end-of-life management of modules.
- Ensuring long-term stability and predictable energy yield is equally essential, with studies of degradation mechanisms such as UVID carried out.
- The role of AI across the PV value chain is rapidly expanding, from design to operations and maintenance, including drone applications.

EU PVSEC

EU PVSEC 2025

CONFERENCE

TOPIC 1: SILICON MATERIALS AND CELLS

Enhancements in IV measurement procedures

- Michael Rauer, Fraunhofer ISE: 1AO.4.5 *Universal Contacting Approaches for the Characterization of Solar Cells*
- Shuai Nie, UNSW: 1AO.4.6 *Contact-Free J-V: a Simple Technique for Universal State-of-the-Art Solar Cells*

Replacement of critical by sustainable materials:

- Reduced Ag consumpion e.g. by replacing by Cu (plating)
- In-free SHJ solar cells and Pero-Si tandems

EU PVSEC

22 26 BEC Bilbao EU PVSEC 2025

CONFERENCE

TOPIC 1: SILICON MATERIALS AND CELLS

Great advance in understanding of UV induced degradation and Hydrogen related degradation

- Excellent PLENARY by Bram Hoex (presenting for Muhammad Umair Khan), UNSW: 1CP.3.5 *Understanding the Root Cause of UV-Induced Degradation in TOPCon and PERC Solar Cells*

Further high quality orals:

- Christina Hollemann, ISFH: 1AO.4.2 *Mitigating UV-Induced Degradation: Impact of PECVD and PEALD AlOx Layers Deposited in a Tube-Type Direct Plasma-Enhanced Chemical Vapor Deposition System*
- Hugo Lajoie, CEA: 1AO.4.3 *New Insights on UV-Induced Degradation of SHJ Solar Cells*
- Byungsul Min, ISFH: 1BO.3.6 *UV Stable Passivation Stack with Plasma-Enhanced Atomic Layer Deposition of Aluminum Oxide from an Industrial Tube-Type Direct Plasma-Enhanced Chemical Vapor Deposition System*
- Wolfram Kwapil, Fraunhofer ISE: 1AO.5.6 *Impact of Illumination on Solar Cell Properties: Insights into Atomic Hydrogen Release*

EU PVSEC

22 26 BEC Bilbao EU PVSEC 2025

CONFERENCE

TOPIC 1: SILICON MATERIALS AND CELLS

Advances in TOPCon and SHJ technology → Pushing the Limits of Performance

- Fantastic keynote lecture (PLENARY) on heterojunction solar cells by Dr. Guangtao Yang, Trina: 1CP.1.1 *Silicon Surface and Interface Study for >27% Efficient SHJ Solar Cell*
    - Deep insight into technological aspects eg. influence of rear side polishing on cell performance
    - Very high efficiencies for both-sides contacted HJT > 27%
    - Issues with CAPEX, sustainibility (Ag, In)
    - Pero-Si tandem cells on large area and modules

Late News Presentation on 27.8% efficient back contact silicon solar cells by Hua Wu, Longhi: 1DO.9.1 *Hybrid Interdigitated Back Contact Silicon Solar Cells with Superior Efficiency*

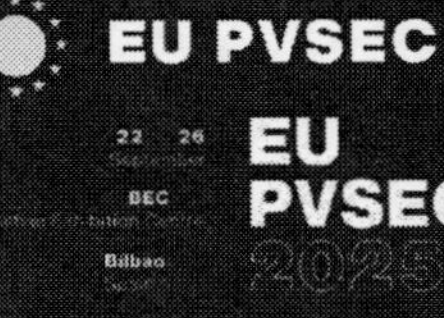

Late News Presentation as TOPCon for Bottom Solar Cells in Pero-Si Tandem devices by Jana Polzin-Isabelle Polzin, Fraunhofer ISE: 1DO.9.3 *Silicon Solar Cells – From High Efficiency Single-junction to Bottom Cells in Two-Terminal Perovskite-Silicon Tandem Devices*

EU PVSEC

EU PVSEC 2025

CONFERENCE

TOPIC 1: SILICON MATERIALS AND CELLS

Further high quality orals:

- Hua Wu, Longhi: 1DO.9.1 *Hybrid Interdigitated Back Contact Silicon Solar Cells with Superior Efficiency*
- Daming Chen, Trina: 1AO.5.1 *Large Area i-TOPCon Solar Cells with 25.9% Record Efficiency*
- Maysa Sarsour, UNSW: 1AO.6.1 *Evaluating Silicon Heterojunction Solar Cell Stability under Industrial Illuminated Hydrogenation Conditions*

Bottom cell optimization for Pero-Si tandems

EU PVSEC

22 26 September

BEC

Bilbao

EU PVSEC 2025

CONFERENCE

TOPIC 2: THIN FILMS AND NEW CONCEPTS

A lot of focus on the long-term stability improvement and upscaling of tandem devices based on a variety of materials (hence not only pero-Si).

Many companies (e.g. Hanwha Q-cells, Oxford PV, Microquanta Seminconductor, Jinko Solar, Longi, etc. non-exhaustive list) presented impressive results on industrial size single-junction pero modules and pero-based tandem modules. A highlight here was the plenary talk from Hanwha Q-cells showing a record large area (M10) pilot-scale Pk/Si tandem cell of 28.6% efficiency.

EU PVSEC

EU PVSEC 2025

CONFERENCE

TOPIC 2: THIN FILMS AND NEW CONCEPTS

In the field of pero-Si tandems, there is clearly more focus on improving the stability of the tandem devices than before with many contributions doing in-depth investigations into the different degradation mechanisms that can occur in pero-Si tandems.

In this respect, 2DO9.5 presented a consensus statement about reliability testing of perovskite-based tandems that is endorsed by specialists worldwide from both industry and research and presents a kind of minimum that should be done in terms of testing and reporting concerning the stability and lifetime of perovskite-based tandem devices.

More and more advanced characterization methods for perovskite and perovskite - silicon tandem solar cells are being used, hyperspectral imaging methods identify non-uniformities by layer for processing development.

EU PVSEC

EU PVSEC 2025

CONFERENCE

TOPIC 2: THIN FILMS AND NEW CONCEPTS

Another clear trend is that pero-TOPCon cells are nearing the same record efficiencies as pero-Heterojunction cells. A highlight talk here was the certified 34.22% efficiency perovskite/ topcon tandem solar cell(1cm2) by Jinko Solar 2CO2.1

Another highlight was the 30.5% triple junction pero/pero/silicon cell by EPFL (2CO2.3)

In the field of perovskite single junction devices, 2DO.7.3 showed perovskite devices with remarkable reliability, withstanding 4 years of outdoor exposure. The degradation mechanism is attributed to the diurnal behaviour, also verified and replicated with indoor experiments.

2AO3.6 investigated experimental degradation and recovery of perovskite solar cells, improving the comprehension of instability's dynamics, to extend the lifetime of devices.

EU PVSEC

EU PVSEC 2025

CONFERENCE

TOPIC 2: THIN FILMS AND NEW CONCEPTS

In the field of compound semiconductors, there were many presentations on alternative materials for perovskite in tandems. In this way, first monolithic (AgCu)(InGa)Se2 on Si tandem cells were demonstrated as well as 16.1% semitransparent Ag doped Cu(InGa)S2 sulfide top cells.

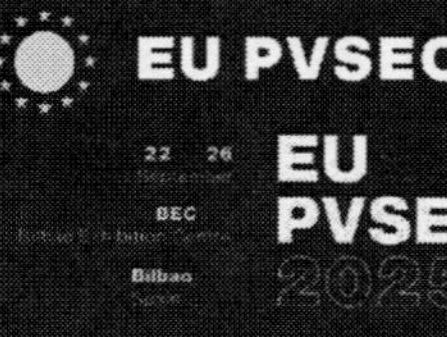

An exciting highlight in this field was 2BO8.2 in which UPC Barcelona achieved 18% efficiency under indoor lighting for kesterite solar cells with alkali doping

EU PVSEC

22 26 BEC Bilbao EU PVSEC 2025

CONFERENCE

TOPIC 3: PHOTOVOLTAIC MODULES

“Reliable packaging to Maximize the energy yield from high efficiency cells”

big theme: Optimizing module materials and packaging for long lifetime and predictable energy yield from high efficiency cells. The industry and research community are moving quickly to assess and improve reliability.

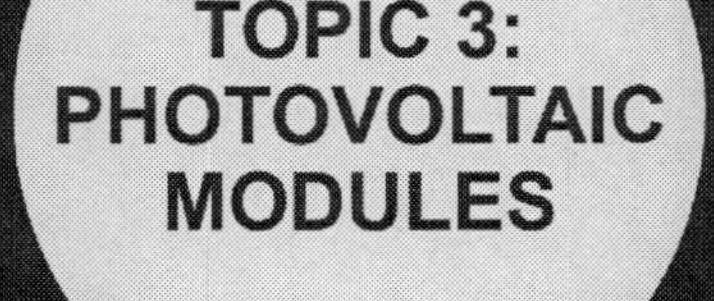

- Understanding, accelerated testing, and mitigating UV-ID in n-type cells and modules
- How do you develop accelerated tests for constantly changing BOMs - new encapsulants, new metallization, thinner glass, and high efficiency cells

EU PVSEC

EU PVSEC 2025

CONFERENCE

TOPIC 3: PHOTOVOLTAIC MODULES

- Degradation and metastability in packaged perovskite tandems - understanding energy yield and realistic degradation rates
- Characterization out of the lab and into the field and factory - accurate outdoor performance, online quality control measurements for encapsulant cross linking
- Reducing silver content and metallization temperatures - reliability of low temperature and low silver metallization
- Developing glass qualification requirements to minimize breakage

EU PVSEC

22 26 September BEC Bilbao

EU PVSEC 2025

CONFERENCE

TOPIC 4: PHOTOVOLTAIC SYSTEMS

Advances in O&M of PV systems

(4CV.1) focuses on fault detection, cleaning optimization, soiling (and snow 4CO.8), UAV for autonomous monitoring and digital twin.

Data driven and AI based O&M (4CO.9) including a medicine-like workflow in Autonomous multi-AI agent system for health monitoring: a fully automated O&M pipeline with field robotics (4CO.9.4 D. Moser, EURAC)

PV Everywhere from space to agricultural applications like integration in vineyards (Mo, Opening plenary) and many other **integrated options** as we have seen throughout the week. On Thursday (4DO.4) agriPV, noise barriers and floating integrated systems. AgriPV technologies (4DO.2), BIPV

PV needs solar energy. **Solar resource and forecasting** (Mo, 4AO.7-9 & Tu 4BV.3). Shortly IEA PVPS T16 will publish minute irradiance data, some including GT over 220 stations worldwide with. Same format and quality controlled. (*Worldwide solar radiation measurement database with quality-control added value*, Anne Forstinger CSP Services, 4AO.7.1)

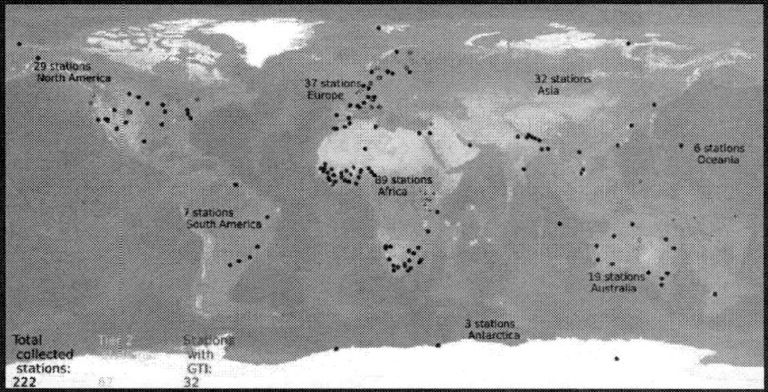

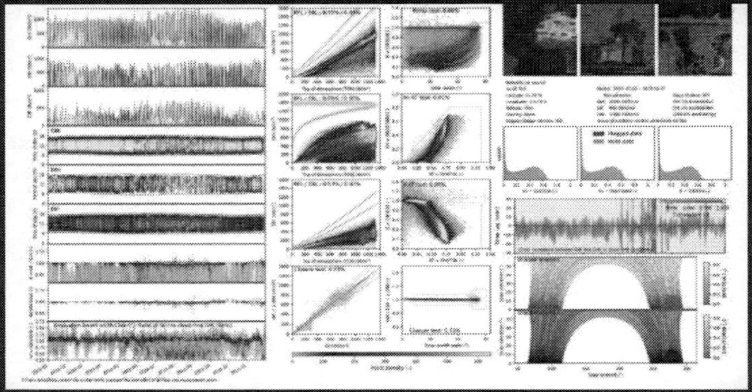

(4BV.3). Poster winner 4BV.3.12 *Advancing Very Short-Term Solar Irradiance Forecasting in Africa: A Low-Cost Sky Imaging and Machine Learning-Based Approach*, implications for PV deployment and grid integration (Martin Ansong, KIT). Runner-up 4BV.3.25 *Evaluating the Suitability of Köppen-Geiger Climate Classifications for Photovoltaic Systems: Micro-climate Analysis and Risk Assessment Maps,* with worldwide distribution of humidity related risk assessment for PV performance (Pavan Kumar Panda, Anhalt University of Applied Sciences).

TOPIC 4: PHOTOVOLTAIC SYSTEMS

Integrated PV

BIPV (4BO.16) examples of coloured modules (which was main topic of the poster session along with fire concerns of BIPV, 4BV.4), lightweight solutions (4BO.5) and modelling partial shading effects 4BO.17.1, *Modelling partial shading at the cell level on PV modules,* Jean-Paul Calin, ENSTA) and 4BO.17.3, *Comparing the energy yield and degradation rates of smart PV modules compared to conventional PV system designs in shaded urban scenario's,* Youri Blom, TU DELF.

AgriPV 4DO.2 the room was fully packed showing the interest in the topic. 5 talks were on new ways of sharing light (2 spectral splitting before the PV conversion, 2 semitransparent PV modules both c-Si and CdTe, 1 on downshifting encapsulate) + 1 new AgrivPV like application with Algae instead of crops.

4DO.4 also included AgriPV and **Others types of integration like noise barriers and floating.** In addition to performance other aspects like (*Hydrological and ecological effects on floating PV,* Konstantin Ilgen, FHO ISe) have been highlighted this week

4DO4.2

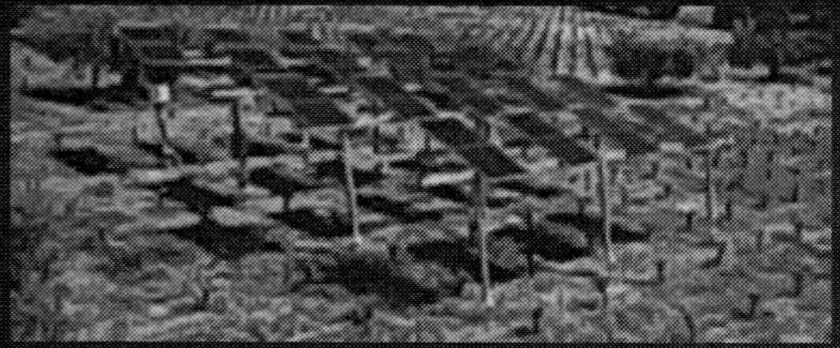

BOS and tracking systems (4DO.1) focused on backtracking strategies and terrains with complex topography.

4DO.1.4

EU PVSEC

EU PVSEC 2025

CONFERENCE

TOPIC 4: PHOTOVOLTAIC SYSTEMS

Reliability of PV systems

Several presentations focused long-term monitored degradation, failure modes and degradation modes identification techniques (non-destructive, aerial images, AI-based)

4BO.6.1 *Three decades, three climates: insights and lessons on PV reliability*. Good BOM offer very high reliability in power production, with 30-35 years old modules showing 0.24% degradation rate per year.

4BO.6.3 *Non-destructive detection of water ingress in solar modules using NIR spectroscopy* (Oleksandr Mashkow HI ERN) proved near-infrared absorption (NIRA) technique to detect water ingress in modules in the field, which correlated with the module degradation.

4BO.7.2 *Robust PV performance loss rate calculation for high latitudes* (Lauri Karttunen, Meteo Inst Helsinki) and 4BO.7. 3 *Detailed analysis of degradation rates of operating PV assets in tropical climate conditions* (Xioaqi Xu, Seris Singapore) Performance loss rates reported for high latitudes and tropics based on solid data sets. PLR in the tropics -1.4%/year

4DO.3.6 PV system design and assessment highlighted how inverter safety issues are extremely important and how more research about inverter safety and reliability is needed.

EU PVSEC

22 26 EU PVSEC 2025 BEC Bilbao

CONFERENCE

TOPIC 5: PHOTOVOLTAICS IN THE ENERGY TRANSITION

Main topics of interest :

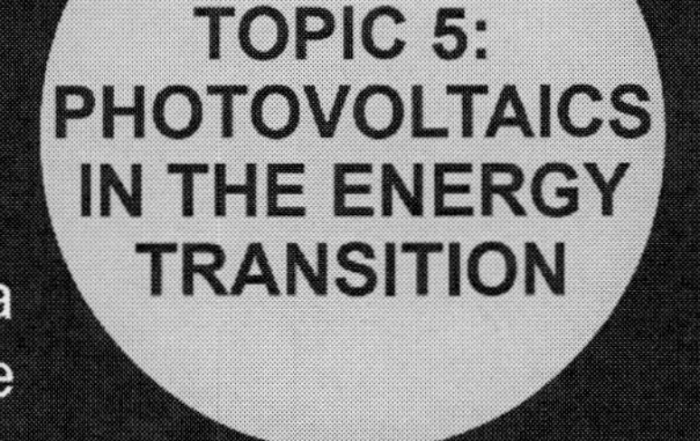

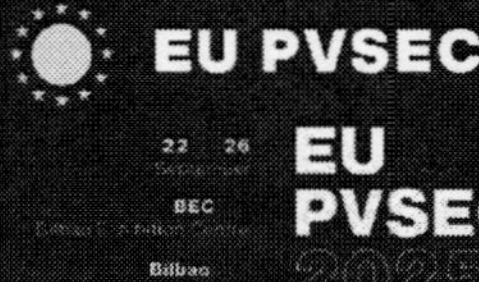

- Flexibility
- Artificial intelligence
- EoL management

EU PVSEC

22 26 EU PVSEC 2025 BEC Bilbao

CONFERENCE

TOPIC 5: PHOTOVOLTAICS IN THE ENERGY TRANSITION

5.1 Grid Integration and Flexibility Enablers (2 sessions)

- Smoothing effect related to different orientations of PV systems in a given area allows 10 to 15% additional hosting capacity of the distribution grid compared to the conservative calculation that consists in summing the AC power. Such accurate calculation enabled by high resolution large area images and LIDAR and induces therefore very low costs.

5.2 Sustainability of PV (4 sessions)

- New inventories LCI and LCA for emerging technologies even though lack of data for perovskites, LCA showing a way for low environmental Impacts with technology improvement and localisation. / Technological improvements will contribute to the reduction of environmental Impact / Grid Efficiency has an Impact on the environmental Footprint.
- Manufacturing optimization / Reuse & recycling: results from the perspective of economic performance – would it convince manufacturer to consider it if economic benefit ?
- EoL Management /recycling -> emerging field attracting lots of activities / mainly EU projects (EVERPV / ICARUS / QASAR) – highlight on polymer, interesting question came up and to be debated for the next decade: is it worth it to consider polymer (EVA/ backsheet) recycling ?
- Major progress in methodology and indicators to assess sustainable design & circularity and improve transparency recyclability index, technical recyclability, digital passport)

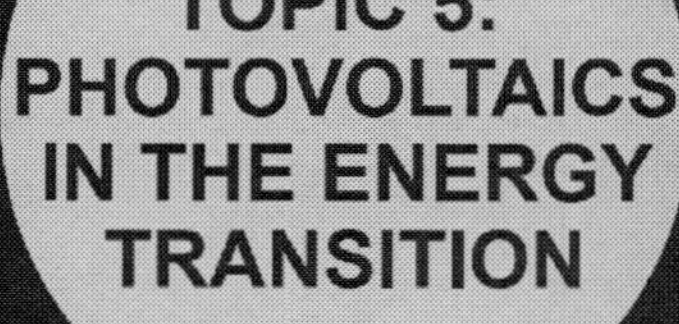

EU PVSEC

EU PVSEC 2025

CONFERENCE

TOPIC 5: PHOTOVOLTAICS IN THE ENERGY TRANSITION

5.3 Scenarios for Renewables, Policy, Global Challenges (1 session)

- wide scope of contributions on the way to massive, medium- to long-term PV deployment -> should not be taken for granted despite positive projections since there can be limiting factors such as public acceptance / regulatory restrictions and effect of climate change

5.4 Costs, Economics, Finance and Markets (1 session)

- Annual installed capacity over 400 GWp / total cumulative installed capacity worldwide over 2.1 TWp / Clear mismatch between PV module installations rate worldwide and PV module production rate leading to bunch of inventories and drastically reduced prices.

5.6 Societal Challenges; Citizens' Participation, Awareness (1 session)

- data and analysis in gender aspects are emerging in PV! (poster session) + Highlight on innovation in education! On example that targets students & skilled workers -> mobile Lab for advanced experimental training PV-related to bring skills and characterization tools everywhere.

PARALLEL EVENTS
Diversity
Prejudice
Change
Needs – Profile Match
Avoid Blind Spots
Job loss?
Integration
Lack of
Creativity
Internal Friction

030001-027

EU PVSEC

22 26 BEC Bilbao

EU PVSEC 2025

PARALLEL EVENTS

- Perovskite Innovation Roundtable: Driving EU Leadership in Perovskite Innovation
- Women in PV presents: Leading with Inclusion – Embracing the 6 Traits of Inclusive Leadership
- Unlocking the Potential of Integrated Photovoltaic Systems - European R&D Approach
- Why Do PV Plants Perform Lower than Expected? (Estimating losses by backtracking algorithms in undulating terrain & Analysis of the loss chain and identification of deviations from initial expectations)
- PV Made in the EU: How Do Companies Die and How Can They Thrive?

22 — 26
September
BEC —
ilbao Exhibition Centre
Bilbao — Spain
EU
PVSEC
2025
EXHIBITION
FORUM
INDUSTRY
SUMMIT

The road to a
sustainable future

EU PVSEC

EU PVSEC 2025

INDUSTRY SUMMIT

Industry Summit Opening (session I)

Session Title: Solar PV production in Europe - the way forward

Moderators: Begoña Molinete, Walburga Hemetsberger

Key Takeaway:

This session discussed the state of play of European manufacturing projects and whether there is enough European support. It was clear that political support is further lacking – only 3 Member States have developed schemes to support European manufacturing. While the Net Zero Industry Act is helpful to diversify supplies, it will not particularly support European manufacturing.

All panellists agreed that apart from further policy support (financing, derisking) collaboration is the way forward.

EU PVSEC

22 26 BEC Bilbao

EU PVSEC 2025

INDUSTRY SUMMIT

Session II

Session Title: International corporations in the light of changing geopolitics

Moderators: Radovan Kopecek, Puzant Baliozian

Key takeaway:

EU machine builders are still supporting mostly Indian but also US and EU projects with their technology and expertise. The major arguments for choosing EU tech are quality, training, support and low OPEX.

Session III

Session Title: PV Systems: How do we get the produced electricity in Europe into the grid?

Moderators: Catarina Augusto, Peter Fath

Key Takeaway:

Hybrid PV + storage systems (co-located or distributed) are essential for integrating PV into electricity grids. Storage adds flexibility and stabilizes the grid, making it a cornerstone of resilient energy systems; while the technology is mature, scalable and bankable revenue models remain the key gap for widespread deployment.

LIST OF EXHIBITORS
(in alphabetical order)

Company name	Country
2nd Cycle FlexCo	Austria
9-Tech	Italy
Avalon ST / Pasan	Switzerland
BASQUENERGY Cluster	Spain
Becquerel Institute	Belgium
ECOPROGETTI	Italy
EKIENERGY	Spain
ESMC Pavilion	Belgium
Eternal Sun I WAVELABS	The Netherlands
EU PVSEC Startup Pavilion	
European Commission JRC	Italy
exateq	Germany
FLUXiM AG	Switzerland
G2V Optics	Canada
GALEA	Spain
halm elektronik	Germany
HighLine Technology	Germany
IEA PVPS	
Innovations in Optics, Inc.	United States of America
ISC Konstanz	Germany
LAB14	Germany
MBJ Solutions	Germany
Mondragon Assembly	Spain
Nagase Chemtex America	United States of America
NEO Messtechnik Holding	Austria
ODTÜ GÜNAM	Türkiye
Phoenixolar	China
PSE Instruments	Germany
PVsyst	Switzerland
RCT Future	Germany
RCT Solutions	Germany
RENA	Germany
ReNewPV-CA21148 / 5GSOLAR	Estonia
SALD B.V.	The Netherlands

SCIPRIOS	Germany
SEMILAB	Hungary
SINGULUS TECHNOLOGIES	Germany
Sinton Instruments	United States of America
SOLAR MATERIALS	Germany
SolarNL	The Netherlands
Soli Tek R&D	Lithuania
TAMURA ELSOLD	Germany
TECNALIA	Spain
The Netherlands Pavilion	The Netherlands
TNO	The Netherlands
University of the Basque Country	Spain
Vector Energy	Spain
VON ARDENNE	Germany
WCPEC-9	South Korea
WIP Renewable Energies	Germany
ZSW	Germany

EU PVSEC 2025
42nd European Photovoltaic Solar Energy Conference and Exhibition

We thank the EU PVSEC 2025 Sponsors

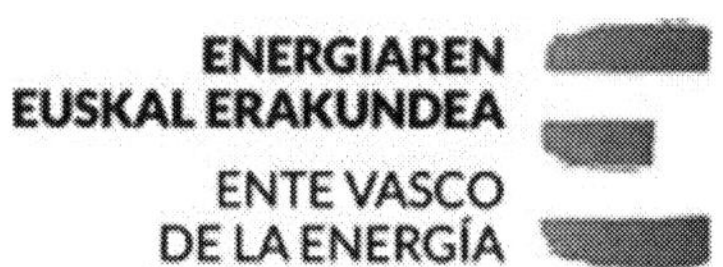

Platinum

MONDRAGON ASSEMBLY

Gold

ENERGIAREN EUSKAL ERAKUNDEA
ENTE VASCO DE LA ENERGÍA

G2V
ENGINEER THE SUN

halm.

RCT solutions

Silver

Sinton instruments

Bronze

AESOLAR

AUTHORS OF EU PVSEC 2025 PROCEEDINGS PAPERS

A. dos Reis Benatto, Gisele — 020028, 020037, 020039, 020191, 020265, 020376, 020477
DTU, Roskilde, Denmark

Aaltonen, Lauri — 020537
Tampere University, Tampere, Finland

Abad Alcaraz, Verónica — 020336
University of Almería, La Cañada de San Urbano, Spain

Abbott, Malcolm D. — 020396
PV Lighthouse, Coledale, Australia

Abbotto, Alessandro — 020077
University of Milano-Bicocca, Milan, Italy

Abdallah, Amir A. — 020146, 020166
QEERI, Doha, Qatar

Abdel Nour, Christine — 020188
EDF R&D, Moret Loing Orvanne, France

Abdelrahim, Mohamed — 020166
QEERI, Doha, Qatar

Abdou-Tankari, Mahamadou — 020562
Paris-East Créteil University, Créteil, France

Abrego, Gillen — 020392
ALLOTARRA, Allo, Spain

Acciarri, Maurizio — 020087
University of Milano-Bicocca, Milan, Italy

Acevedo Devoto, M. Ignacia — 020220
ISC Konstanz, Konstanz, Germany

Achenbach, Jannik — 020522
University of Applied Science Cologne, Cologne, Germany

Acinas, Victor — 020019
Applied Materials, Dublin, Ireland

Adachi, Satoru — 020436
NIED, Shinjo, Japan

Aden, Samira — 020513
HZB, Berlin, Germany

Adinolfi Borea, Riccardo — 020314
University of Bologna, Bologna, Italy

Adnan Hameed, Mohammed — 020156
Martin-Luther-University Halle-Wittenberg, Halle, Germany

Adothu, Baloji — 020229
DEWA, Dubai, United Arab Emirates

Aghaei, Mohammadreza — 020335, 020356
NTNU, Aalesund, Norway

Aghaei, Mohammadreza — 020374, 020375
NTNU, Ålesund, Norway

Aghamohammadi, Amirhossain 020356
Amirkabir University of Technology, Tehran, Iran

Aguirre, Aranzazu 020064
Hasselt Unversity, Genk, Belgium

Ahmadi, Mehdi 020066
CNR-IMM, Catania, Italy

Aiello, Andrea 020255
ACCA Software, Cosenza, Italy

Aimé, Jérémie 020217, 020311
CEA / INES, Le Bourget-du-Lac, France

Aissa, Brahim 020042, 020075, 020108, 020109, 020146, 020147
QEERI, Doha, Qatar

Aizpurua, Jon 020139
Tecnalia, Donostia - San Sebastián, Spain

Akbayrak, Serdar 020020
Necmettin Erbakan University, Konya, Türkiye

Akram, M. Waqar 020164
Hohai University, Changzhou, China

Al Katrib, Mirella 020116
IPVF, Palaiseau, France

Alam, Habeel 020394
Lancaster University, Lancaster, United Kingdom

Alberts, Vivian 020229
DEWA, Dubai, United Arab Emirates

Albuquerque, Daniel P. 020464
Centre for New Energy Technologies, Sacavém, Portugal

Alet, Pierre-Jean 020238, 020544
CSEM, Neuchâtel, Switzerland

Alexandris, Nikos 020210
European Commission JRC, Ispra, Italy

Alfieri, Felice 020497
Viegand Maagøe, Copenhagen, Denmark

Ali, Adnan 020147
QEERI, Doha, Qatar

Allen, Vince 020048
SunDrive Solar, Kurnell, Australia

Alloji, Esma 020020
Necmettin Erbakan University, Konya, Türkiye

Almeida Silva, José 020565
University of Évora, Évora, Portugal

Almuneau, Guilhem 020074
LAAS-CNRS, Toulouse, France

Alonso, Ricardo 020197, 020198, 020353, 020358
TECNALIA, Derio, Spain

Alonso-Montesinos, Joaquín 020100
University of Almeria, Almeria, Spain

Alonso-Montesinos, Joaquín 020336
University of Almería, La Cañada de San Urbano, Spain

Álvarez Hervás, José Domingo 020336
University of Almería, La Cañada de San Urbano, Spain

Alvarez, José 020040, 020058
CNRS, Gif-sur-Yvette, France

Álvarez, Marta 020300
CENER, Sarriguren, Spain

Álvarez-Pérez, Guillem 020062
IPVF, Palaiseau, France

Alvaro Høye, Ingar 020443
Solkraft Sør, Øyslebø, Norway

Alves e Silva, Kiane 020439, 020535, 020567, 020575
UPM, Madrid, Spain

Amaro e Silva, Rodrigo 020490
University of Lisbon, Lisbon, Portugal

Amatriain, Irati 020392
CENER, Sarriguren, Spain

Anamiati, Gaetana 020448, 020481
GreenPowerMonitor a DNV company, Barcelona, Spain

Anaya, Julian 020191, 020205
University of Valladolid, Valladolid, Spain

Ancillao, Andrea 020079
Polytechnic University of Turin, Turin, Italy

Anderlini, Alessandro 020155
Coveme, Gorizia, Italy

Andersen, Nanna L. 020250
DTU, Roskilde, Denmark

Andersen, Nanna Lysgaard 020306
DTU, Roskilde, Denmark

Andrade-Arvizu, Jacob 020094
IREC, Barcelona, Spain

Andreozzi, Federico 020494
University of Rome Tor Vergata, Rome, Italy

Anefnaf, Ikram 020093
University of Verona, Verona, Italy

Ansong, Martin 020272
KIT, Eggenstein-Leopoldshafen, Germany

Antognini, Luca 020196
PVsyst, Geneva, Switzerland

Antoine, C. 020508
IMDEA Nanoscience Institute, Madrid, Spain

Antón, Ignacio 020209, 020246, 020257, 020453, 020459
UPM, Madrid, Spain

Antonucci, Daniele 020551
Eurac Research, Bolzano, Italy

Apostoleris, Harry 020487
EPRI, Dubai, United Arab Emirates

Arakawa, Hayato 020436
NIED, Shinjo, Japan

Aranguren, Gerardo 020289, 020353
UPV/EHU, Bilbao, Spain

Arbaretaz, Sebastien 020317
CEA INES, Le Bourget-du-Lac, France

Ardissone, Bastien J. J. 020396
PV Lighthouse, Coledale, Australia

Arduino, Daniele 020079
Polytechnic University of Turin, Turin, Italy

Ariolli, Daniela Maria Godinho 020325
BayWa r.e, Rome, Italy

Ariza Camacho, Maria Jesus 020100
University of Almeria, Almería, Spain

Armstrong, Alona 020394
Lancaster University, Lancaster, United Kingdom

Arribat, Mathieu 020074
LAAS-CNRS, Toulouse, France

Arrizabalaga, Igor 020139
Tecnalia, Donostia - San Sebastián, Spain

Artegiani, Elisa 020057, 020089, 020093
University of Verona, Verona, Italy

Arumughan, Jayaprasad 020569
ISC Konstanz, Konstanz, Germany

Asaa, Shu-Ngwa 020393
imo-imomec, Genk, Belgium

Ascencio-Vásquez, Julián 020371
Univers, Courbevoie, France

Askins, Steve 020209, 020257
UPM, Madrid, Spain

Assaid, El Mahdi 020171
University of Chouaib Doukkali, El Jadida, Morocco

Aste, Niccolò 020249
Polytechnic University of Milan, Milan, Italy

Astigarraga, Alexander 020226
Eurac Research, Bolzano, Italy

Athienitis, Andreas 020248
Concordia University, Montreal, Canada

Aurrekoetxea, Olaia 020302
TECNALIA, Saint Sebastian, Spain

Awadallah, Carlos 020536
Wattkraft, Madrid, Spain

Azkona, Nekane 020055, 020097, 020153, 020287
UPV/EHU, Bilbao, Spain

Azzopardi, Brian 020318, 020334, 020520
FIR, Birkirkara, Malta
Azzopardi, Carmel 020334
FIR, Birkirkara, Malta

Babich, Francesco 020551
Eurac Research, Bolzano, Italy
Babics, Maxime 020217
CEA / INES, Le Bourget-du-Lac, France
Babin, Markus 020249, 020250, 020306, 020477
DTU, Roskilde, Denmark
Bachour, Dunia A. 020275, 020278
QEERI, Doha, Qatar
Bachour, Dunia 020291
QEERI, Doha, Qatar
Baderiya, Naman 020390
MARIN, Wageningen, The Netherlands
Badosa Franch, Jordi 020214
Polytechnic Institute of Paris, Palaiseau, France
Baeck, Pieter-Jan 020511
Flemish Institute for Technological Research (VITO), Genk, Belgium
Bai, Jianbo 020164
Hohai University, Changzhou, China
Bailache, Simon 020303
CSTB, Marne-la-Vallée, France
Bakhtiari, Afshin 020121
AESOLAR, Koenigsbrunn, Germany
Balafoutis, Athanasios T. 020464
CERTH, Athens, Greece
Bald, Juan 020514
AZTI, PASAIA, Spain
Baldacchino, Alex J. 020065
UNSW, Sydney, Australia
Baležentienė, Skirmantė 020380
The Applied Research Institute for Prospective Technologies, Vilnius, Lithuania
Baležentis, Algirdas 020380
The Applied Research Institute for Prospective Technologies, Vilnius, Lithuania
Ballif, Christophe 020467
CSEM, Neuchâtel, Switzerland
Ballif, Christophe 020251
EPFL, Neuchâtel, Switzerland
Bandaru, Narendra 020039, 020043, 020104
Aarhus University, Aarhus, Denmark

Bang, Ole 020043
Technical University of Denmark, Copenhagen, Denmark

Barakel, Damien 020188
Toulon University, Marseille, France

Baraket, Mira 020039
ATLANT 3D, Taastrup, Denmark

Baranek, Philippe 020060
EDF R&D, Palaiseau, France

Barchi, Grazia 020485, 020489, 020544
Eurac Research, Bolzano, Italy

Bardizza, Giorgio 020181
TÜV Rheinland Italia, Milan, Italy

Bardizza, Giorgio 020208
TÜV Rheinland Solar, Cologne, Germany

Bardizza, Giorgio 020144
TÜV Rheinland, Cologne, Germany

Barguès, Anna 020505
Becquerel Institute France, Lyon, France

Barguès, Anna 020558
Becquerel Institute, Brussels, Belgium

Barnscheidt, Verena 020063, 020114
ISFH, Emmerthal, Germany

Barretta, Chiara 020325
PCCL, Leoben, Austria

Barrionuevo, Bruno 020464
CERTH, Athens, Greece

Barroso, João 020565
University of Évora, Évora, Portugal

Barrou, Alexis 020467
CSEM, Neuchâtel, Switzerland

Barrutia, Laura 020446, 020536
UPM, Madrid, Spain

Barth, Vincent 020134
CEA / INES, Le Bourget-du-Lac, France

Barth, Vincent 020019
CEA, Le Bourget-du-Lac, France

Barth, Vincent 020226
CEA/ INES, Le Bourget-du-Lac, France

Bartholomäus, Martin 020346
DTU, Roskilde, Denmark

Bartolo, Brian 020334
FIR, Birkirkara, Malta

Basta, Beata 020068
Roltec, Poznań, Poland

Basta, Marek 020068
Roltec, Poznań, Poland

Battisti, Kurt 020255
A-Null Development, Vienna, Austria

Bauhuis, Gerard 020067
Radboud University, Nijmegen, The Netherlands

Baumann, Kerstin 020470
bifa Umweltinstitut, Augsburg, Germany

Baumann, Sara 020063
ISFH, Emmerthal, Germany

Baumann, Ulrike 020006
ISFH, Emmerthal, Germany

Baur, Carsten 020246
European Space Agency, Noordwijk, The Netherlands

Beaucarne, Guy 020384
Dow Silicones Belgium, Seneffe, Belgium

Becker, Carl 020331
DLR, Almería, Spain

Behrensdorff Poulsen, Peter 020037
DTU, Lyngby, Denmark

Beinert, Andreas J. 020123
Fraunhofer ISE, Freiburg, Germany

Bejat, Timea 020225, 020500
CEA, Le Bourget-du-Lac, France

Belawadi, Aditya Girish 020231
Fraunhofer ISE, Freiburg, Germany

Belferkous, Brahim Anis 020325
PCCL, Leoben, Austria

Bellmann, Martin 020495, 020510
SINTEF, Trondheim, Norway

Bellvert, Eduard 020139
Tecnalia, Donostia - San Sebastián, Spain

Beltran-Condori, Sonia 020129, 020417
University of Antofagasta, Antofagasta, Chile

Belzunce, María Jesús 020514
AZTI, PASAIA, Spain

Bendix, Peter 020388
Next2Sun Technology, Dillingen, Germany

Bengoechea, Jaione 020181, 020300
CENER, Sarriguren, Spain

Bermudez Benito, Veronica 020146
QEERI, Doha, Qatar

Bermudez-Garcia, Anderson 020246
Thales Alenia Space, Cannes, France

Berrian, Djaber 020492
Belectric, Kolitzheim, Germany

Berson, Solenn 020134
CEA / INES, Le Bourget-du-Lac, France

Besson, Pierre 020373
INES, Le Bourget-du-Lac, France

Betak, Juraj 020241
Solargis, Bratislava, Slovakia

Bettucci, Ottavia 020077
University of Milano-Bicocca, Milan, Italy

Bhardwaj, Shashank 020515
TU Delft, Delft, The Netherlands

Bhatnagar, Shrey 020367
Nextracker, Fremont, United States of America

Biard, Yves 020303
SemperStyl, Eragny, France

Bieber, Lisa-Marie 020195
Fraunhofer ISE, Freiburg, Germany

Bilitu, Eddie 020393
Hasselt University, Hasselt, Belgium

Binani, Ashish 020225
TNO, Petten, The Netherlands

Binetti, Simona 020093
University of Milano Bicocca, Milan, Italy

Binetti, Simona 020087
University of Milano-Bicocca, Milan, Italy

Blakesley, James 020293
National Physical Laboratory, Teddington, United Kingdom

Blanc, Philippe 020291
MINES Paris, Nice, France

Blanco Aguiar, Adrián 020243
ieco.io, Vigo, Spain

Blieske, Ulf 020141
University of Applied Science Cologne, Cologne, Germany

Blieske, Ulf 020140
University of Applied Sciences Cologne, Cologne, Germany

Blstak Catlosova, Katarina 020274
Solargis, Bratislava, Slovakia

Blum, Niklas 020235, 020237, 020239
DLR, Almería, Spain

Boccardi, Roberto 020039
DTU, Copenhagen, Denmark

Boccardi, Roberto 020037
DTU, Lyngby, Denmark

Boccardi, Roberto 020028
DTU, Roskilde, Denmark

Boddaert, Simon 020302, 020303
CSTB, Marne-la-Vallée, France

Bokalič, Matevž 020047, 020319
University of Ljubljana, Ljubljana, Slovenia

Bolink, Henk J. 020226
University of Valencia, Paterna, Spain
Bonal, Victor 020085
UAM, Madrid, Spain
Bonnet, Martin 020141
University of Applied Science Cologne, Cologne, Germany
Bonnet-Eymard, Bénédicte 020251
CSEM, Neuchâtel, Switzerland
Borgers, Tom 020225
IMEC, Genk, Belgium
Borgna, Luciano 020369
BFH, Burgdorf, Switzerland
Borie, Benjamin 020039
ATLANT 3D, Taastrup, Denmark
Borowski, Peter 020307
Avancis, Munich, Germany
Borriello, Aniello 020378
ENEA, Portici, Italy
Borzi, Giovanni 020019
Enginsoft, Padua, Italy
Bosch, Elina 020252, 020543, 020564, 020573
Becquerel Institute, Brussels, Belgium
Bosma, Theo 020571
DNV, Arnhem, The Netherlands
Bothe, Karsten 020236
ISFH, Emmerthal, Germany
Bou-Nassif, Liliane 020338
CETHIL, Villeurbanne, France
Bouchier, Daniel 020058
CNRS, Palaiseau, France
Bouguerra, Sara 020156, 020294, 020389, 020393
imec, Genk, Belgium
Bourdin, Vincent 020406
CNRS, Paris, France
Bourgeois, Antoine 020102
SERIS, Singapore, Singapore
Bovesecchi, Gianluigi 020494
University of Rome Tor Vergata, Rome, Italy
Brabec, Christoph J. 020117
HI ERN, Erlangen, Germany
Bradford, David Roy 020077
Newcastle University, Newcastle upon Tyne, United Kingdom
Brailovsky, Peter Henri 020475
Fraunhofer ISE, Freiburg, Germany
Braña, Alejandro F. 020508
Autonomous University of Madrid, Madrid, Spain

Brandstätter, Andreas 020227
Lenzing Plastics, Lenzing, Austria

Braun, Christian 020457
Luxembourg Institute of Science and Technology, Esch-sur-Alzette, Luxembourg

Brecl, Kristijan 020269, 020319
University of Ljubljana, Ljubljana, Slovenia

Bredemeier, Dennis 020240
Leibniz University Hannover, Hannover, Germany

Breitenbücher, Marian 020225
Highline Technologies, Freiburg, Germany

Brendel, Rolf 020006, 020008, 020236, 020240, 020260, 020482
ISFH, Emmerthal, Germany

Brendstrup Møller, Clara Bolette 020028
DTU, Roskilde, Denmark

Bretzel, Tamara 020195
Fraunhofer ISE, Freiburg, Germany

Breyer, Christian 020479
LUT University, Lappeenranta, Finland

Brito, Miguel 020457
University of Lisbon, Lisbon, Portugal

Brivio, Elisabetta 020462
RSE, Milan, Italy

Brockmann, Lukas 020063
ISFH, Emmerthal, Germany

Brodnicke, Linda 020296
ETH, Zurich, Switzerland

Brueckner, Emanuel 020063
ISFH, Emmerthal, Germany

Bründlinger, Roland 020369
AIT, Vienna, Austria

Brun, Gonzalo 020414, 020517
ENDEF, Zaragoza, Spain

Bruno, Maddalena 020452
Fraunhofer ISE, Freiburg, Germany

Buceta, Alicia 020300
CENER, Sarriguren, Spain

Bucher, Christof 020179, 020322, 020359, 020369, 020386
BFH, Burgdorf, Switzerland

Buchholz, Florian 020035, 020225, 020569
ISC Konstanz, Konstanz, Germany

Buchmann, Johanna 020309
Berlin University of Applied Sciences, Berlin, Germany

Buck, Thomas 020033
ISC Konstanz, Konstanz, Germany

Buckland, Daniel Henkel, Düsseldorf, Germany	020119, 020218
Buddana, Viswa Harinath DLR, Oldenburg, Germany	020482
Bühlmann, Gian-Luca ZHAW, Winterthur, Switzerland	020385
Buerhop, Claudia HI ERN, Erlangen, Germany	020149, 020150, 020377
Buerhop-Lutz, Claudia HI ERN, Erlangen, Germany	020185, 020230
Burgers, Antonius R. TNO, Petten, The Netherlands	020405
Burri, Matthias BFH, Burgdorf, Switzerland	020179
Busto, Chiara Eni, Novara, Italy	020521
Butrichi, Fabio University of Milano-Bicocca, Milan, Italy	020087
Butt, Nauman Lahore University of Management Sciences, Lahore, Pakistan	020394
C. Tavares, Fabiele Federal University of Rio de Janeiro, Duque de Caxias, Brazil	020090
Cabal, Raphael University Grenoble Alpes, Le Bourget-du-Lac, France	020034
Caballero, Luis Jaime UPM, Madrid, Spain	020501, 020508
Caballero, Raquel CSIC, Madrid, Spain	020094
Caballero, Raquel IO-CSIC, Madrid, Spain	020085
Cabecinha, Vasco Nova University Lisbon, Lisbon, Portugal	020565
Cabello, Fatima IO-CSIC, Madrid, Spain	020085
Caçapietra Pires da Silva, Lucas Teixeira PUCRS, Porto Alegre, Brazil	020025
Caccavelli, Dominique CSTB, Bussy-Saint Georges, France	020551
Caccivio, Mauro SUPSI, Mendrisio, Switzerland	020204, 020574
Caffari, Francesca ENEA, Ispra, Italy	020551
Calabrese, Nicolandrea ENEA, Ispra, Italy	020551

Calin, Jean-Paul 020251
ENSTA Paris, Palaiseau, France

Çalışkan Arslan, Meriç 020006, 020135
Kalyon PV, Ankara, Türkiye

Caluori, Philip 020455
Virtual Vehicle, Graz, Austria

Camara, Assa 020274
Solargis, Bratislava, Slovakia

Cambarau, Werther 020139
Tecnalia, Donostia-San Sebastián, Spain

Campana, Pietro Elia 020381
Mälardalen University, Västerås, Sweden

Campos Guzman, Laura 020331
DLR, Almería, Spain

Cancro, Carmine 020378
ENEA, Naples, Italy

Canesse, Auriane 020196
PVsyst, Geneva, Switzerland

Cañizo, Carlos 020097
IES-UPM, Madrid, Spain

Cano, Francisco J. 020139
Tecnalia, Donostia - San Sebastián, Spain

Cano, Lucía 020127
ENDEF, Zaragoza, Spain

Cánovas, Enrique 020508
IMDEA Nanoscience Institute, Madrid, Spain

Cao, Han 020263
SERIS, Singapore, Singapore

Capitaine, Anna 020116
IPVF, Palaiseau, France

Cappelle, Jan 020329, 020351
KU Leuven, Ghent, Belgium

Capron, Guillaume 020217
CEA / INES, Le Bourget-du-Lac, France

Carballo López, José Antonio 020336
University of Almería, La Cañada de San Urbano, Spain

Cardenas, Luis Alejandro 020339, 020546
National University of Colombia, Bogotá, Colombia

Carmo, Paulo 020304, 020420
University of Évora, Évora, Portugal

Carrasco, Luis Miguel 020439, 020535, 020567
UPM, Madrid, Spain

Carrillo Mejía, Luis 020279
District University of Bogotá, Bogotá, Colombia

Carrillo, Rafael E. 020238
CSEM, Neuchâtel, Switzerland

Carroy, Perrine 020226
CEA/ INES, Le Bourget-du-Lac, France

Carstens, Justus 020003
ISC Konstanz, Konstanz, Germany

Cartenì, Fabrizio 020378
University of Naples Federico II, Naples, Italy

Casappa, Michele 020087
National Research Council, Parma, Italy

Casasola Paesa, Marta 020389
Hasselt University, Diepenbeek, Belgium

Castilla Nieto, María del Mar 020336
University of Almería, La Cañada de San Urbano, Spain

Castillo Patton, Daniel Jason 020326
Enertis Applus+, Madrid, Spain

Castro, Luis Guilherme 020530
Casa dos Ventos, Fortaleza, Brazil

Castro, Rui 020464
University of Lisbon, Lisbon, Portugal

Castro-Gallardo, Fernando 020417, 020422
University of Antofagasta, Antofagasta, Chile

Cavaco, Afonso 020304, 020565
University of Évora, Évora, Portugal

Cebecauer, Tomas 020274
Solargis, Bratislava, Slovakia

Çekerek, Gamze 020006
Kalyon PV, Ankara, Türkiye

Celik, Duygu 020551
WIP Renewable Energies, Munich, Germany

Çeliktaş, Melih Soner 020559
Ege University, İzmir, Türkiye

Centazzo, Massimo 020006
EnPV, Karlsruhe, Germany

Centeno Brito, Miguel 020421, 020490
University of Lisbon, Lisbon, Portugal

Cereceda, Eneko 020055, 020097, 020153, 020287
UPV/EHU, Bilbao, Spain

Ceretti, Mattia 020204
SUPSI, Mendrisio, Switzerland

Cesar, I. 020405
TNO, Petten, The Netherlands

Ceuppens, Ignas 020302
BUILD`UP, Aarschot, Belgium

Chatterji, Nithin 020071
SVNIT, Surat, India

Chen, Daniel 020048
SunDrive Solar, Kurnell, Australia

Chen, Syh-Homg 020161
ITRI, Hsinchu, Taiwan

Chen, Xiang 020111
Hohai University, Changzhou, China

Cheung, Kak Pong 020313
Kiel University of Applied Sciences, Kiel, Germany

Chhapia, Gaurang 020492
Belectric, Kolitzheim, Germany

Chiba, Takahiro 020436
Hokkaido University of Science, Sapporo, Japan

Chichignoud, Guy 020495
13Institut Polytechnique De Grenoble, Grenoble, France

Chicote, Beatriz 020289
Mondragon University, Arrasate-Mondragon, Spain

Chiesa, Matteo 020487
Khalifa University, Abu Dhabi, United Arab Emirates

Chini de Freitas, Felipe 020023
PUCRS, Porto Alegre, Brazil

Cho, Yunae 020045
KIER, Daejeon, South Korea

Choi, Kwan Bum 020102
SERIS, Singapore, Singapore

Chouder, Aissa 020301
University of M'sila, M'sila, Algeria

Chowdhury, Gofran 020276, 020544
3E, Brussels, Belgium

Christ, Anja 020063
ISFH, Emmerthal, Germany

Chrkavy, Daniel 020262
Solargis, Bratislava, Slovakia

Chueh, Wei-Lo 020021
TSEC, Hsinchu, Taiwan

Ciesla, Alison 020065
UNSW, Sydney, Australia

Cirimele, Vincenzo 020314
University of Bologna, Bologna, Italy

Clausing, Roland 020063, 020114
ISFH, Emmerthal, Germany

Clochard, Laurent 020031
Nines Photovoltaics, Dublin, Germany

Clochard, Laurent 020007
Nines Photovoltaics, Dublin, Ireland

Clyncke, Jan 020472, 020513
PV CYCLE, Brussels, Belgium

Coşkun, Özlem 020006, 020027, 020225
Kalyon PV, Ankara, Türkiye

Colberts, Fallon — 020389
Zuyd University, Heerlen, The Netherlands

Colin, Hervé — 020217, 020262
CEA / INES, Le Bourget-du-Lac, France

Collin, Stéphane — 020074
C2N, Palaiseau, France

Colwell, Jack — 020048
SunDrive Solar, Kurnell, Australia

Comak, Mertcan — 020003
ISC Konstanz, Konstanz, Germany

Connolly, James Patrick — 020058, 020060
CNRS, Gif-sur-Yvette, France

Cordeiro, Diogo — 020464
EDP, Lisbon, Portugal

Cornago, Iñaki — 020392
CENER, Sarriguren, Spain

Cornaro, Cristina — 020494
University of Rome Tor Vergata, Rome, Italy

Correa, Guillermo — 020412
Gonvarri MS R&D, Corvera - Asturias, Spain

Correia, Joana — 020565
University of Évora, Évora, Portugal

Couderc, Romain — 020217, 020311, 020546
CEA / INES, Le Bourget-du-Lac, France

Coutel, John — 020244
SOLAÏS, Valbonne, France

Cowan, Don — 020230
Kiwa PI Berlin, Hudson, United States of America

Cox, Joel D. — 020250
SDU Climate Cluster, Odense, Denmark

Cox, Joel D — 020306
SDU Climate Cluster, Odense, Denmark

Coz, Pier Luigi — 020246
European Space Agency, Noordwijk, The Netherlands

Crespo, Carolina — 020490
University of Lisbon, Lisbon, Portugal

Cristiane Pan, Aline — 020548
UFRGS, Tramandaí, Brazil

Cristóbal, Ana Belén — 020491, 020535, 020575
UPM, Madrid, Spain

Crozier McCleland, Jacqueline — 020185, 020344
Nelson Mandela University, Port Elizabeth, South Africa

Cuadra, Juan Manuel — 020318
CENER, Sarigurren, Spain

Cui, Jindan — 020320, 020525
Tokyo University of Science, Tokyo, Japan

De Biasio, Martin 020504
Silicon Austria Labs, Villach, Austria
De Blasi, Mariam 020378
Enel Green Power, Pisa, Italy
de Graaf, Gertjan J. 020405
TNO, Petten, The Netherlands
de Groot, Koen M. 020405
TNO, Petten, The Netherlands
De Gruijter, Alvaro 020254
Eurac Research, Bolzano, Italy
de Jong, Minne M. 020169, 020425
TNO, Eindhoven, The Netherlands
De Jong, Richard 020156, 020294, 020389
imec, Genk, Belgium
de l`Epine, Mélodie 020252, 020505, 020543, 020564
Becquerel Institute France, Lyon, France
de l`Epine, Melodie 020225, 020334, 020520, 020558
Becquerel Institute, Brussels, Belgium
de l`Epine, Melodie 020570
IEA PVPS Task 1, Lyon, France
de la Casa Higueras, Juan 020269
University of Jaén, Jaén, Spain
de la Viuda, Eva 020205
University of Valladolid, Valladolid, Spain
de Meatza, Iratxe 020495
CIDETEC, San Sebastián, Spain
De Rose, Angela 020123
Fraunhofer ISE, Freiburg, Germany
De Rose, Jonas 020010
Fraunhofer ISE, Freiburg, Germany
Debastiani Benato, Betina 020019
AMIRES, Prague, Czech Republic
Deepti, 020563
SRM University, Sonipat, India
Del Campo, Valeria 020311
Federico Santa María Technical University, Valparaiso, Chile
del Cañizo, Carlos 020014, 020501, 020507, 020508
UPM, Madrid, Spain
Del Pero, Claudio 020249
Polytechnic University of Milan, Milan, Italy
Del Pozo, Alberto 020197, 020198
TECNALIA, Derio, Spain
del Prado Santamaria, Rodrigo 020191, 020376
DTU, Roskilde, Denmark
del Ser, Javier 020358
UPV/EHU, Bilbao, Spain

Delgado-Sanchez, Jose Maria 020089
University of Seville, Seville, Spain

Delli Veneri, Paola 020378
ENEA, Naples, Italy

Denafas, Julius 020225, 020353
Solitek, Vilnius, Lithuania

Deniz, Engin 020559
Ege University, İzmir, Türkiye

Denke, Sebastian 020236
ISFH, Emmerthal, Germany

Dentz, Laurie 020058
CNRS, Palaiseau, France

Derin Gure, Pinar 020513, 020521, 020556
ODTU GUNAM, Ankara, Türkiye

Derj, Anyssa 020116
IPVF, Palaiseau, France

Dessì, Alessio 020077
CNR-ICCOM, Sesto Fiorentino, Italy

Devenson, Jan 020157
Center for Physical Sciences and Technology (FTMC), Vilnius, Lithuania

Dhimish, Mahmoud 020346, 020376
DTU, Roskilde, Denmark

Di Matteo, Alfredo 020010
Enel Green Power, Catania, Italy

Diab, Mohanad 020203
Eurac Research, Bolzano, Italy

Diano, Marcello 020378
M2M Engineering, Naples, Italy

Diaz, Roberto 020300
Notio Association, Toledo, Spain

Díaz, Sara 020365, 020366
CENER, Sarriguren, Spain

Dietrich, Andreas 020355
DiSUN Deutsche Solarservice, Werder, Germany

Díez Alcántara, Eduardo 020501
UCM, Madrid, Spain

Díez, Eduardo 020508
UCM, Madrid, Spain

Dimd, Berhane Darsene 020495, 020510
SINTEF, Trondheim, Norway

Ding, Kaining 020233
FZJ, Jülich, Germany

Ding, Kung 020111
Hohai University, Changzhou, China

Dittmann, Sebastian 020318
Anhalt University of Applied Sciences, Köthen, Germany

Dittrich, Arne 020240
ISFH, Emmerthal, Germany
Dizier, Antoine 020373
INES, Le Bourget-du-Lac, France
Djeukeu, Ivanol Jaurece 020050
halm elektronik, Frankfurt am Main, Germany
Dobreva, Petja 020193
University of Namibia, Windhoek, Namibia
Dörenkämper, Maarten 020169
TNO, Eindhoven, The Netherlands
Dörn, Markus 020255
A-Null Development, Vienna, Austria
Doi, Minh Thong 020317
CEA INES, Le Bourget-du-Lac, France
Domínguez, César 020209, 020246, 020257
UPM, Madrid, Spain
Donadello, Alessandro 020485, 020489
Edyna, Bolzano, Italy
Donėlienė, Jolanta 020157
Applied Research Institute for Prospective Technologies, Vilnius, Lithuania
Donoso, José 020570
UNEF, Madrid, Spain
Doppler, Christian 020455
Virtual Vehicle, Graz, Austria
dos Reis, Givaldo 020348
University of São Paulo, São Paulo, Brazil
dos Santos, Jeremias 020409
University of Évora, Évora, Portugal
Doucet, Jean-Baptiste 020074
LAAS-CNRS, Toulouse, France
Dovesi, Roberto 020060
Academy of Sciences of Turin, Torino, Italy
Driesse, Anton 020211, 020293, 020452
PV Performance Labs, Freiburg, Germany
Duarte, Dorivaldo 020418, 020565
University of Evora, Évora, Portugal
Dubois, Sebastien 020034
University Grenoble Alpes, Le Bourget-du-Lac, France
Dubravskij, Piotr 020157
Applied Research Institute for Prospective Technologies, Vilnius, Lithuania
Dubravskij, Piotr 020380
Modern E-Technologies, Vilnius, Lithuania
Duerinckx, Filip 020064, 020225
Hasselt Unversity, Genk, Belgium

Düz, Cansel 020135
Kalyon PV, Ankara, Türkiye

Dullweber, Thorsten 020006, 020007, 020008, 020225
ISFH, Emmerthal, Germany

Dunlop, Ewan D. 020173, 020210, 020213
European Commission JRC, Ispra, Italy

Dupon, Olivier 020294
imec, Genk, Belgium

Dupuis, Julien 020188
EDF R&D, Moret Loing Orvanne, France

Dutykh, Denys 020338
Khalifa University, Abu Dhabi, United Arab Emirates

Duzellier, Sophie 020073
University of Toulouse, Toulouse, France

Dypvik Sødahl, Elin 020340
IFE, Kjeller, Norway

Ebert, Matthias 020426
Fraunhofer CSP, Halle, Germany

Ebert, Matthias 020355
Fraunhofer IMWS, Halle, Germany

Ebner, Rita 020318, 020334, 020521
AIT, Vienna, Austria

Echeverria, Oihane 020139
Tecnalia, Donostia - San Sebastián, Spain

Eder, Gabriele C. 020160, 020162, 020249, 020500, 020504
OFI, Vienna, Austria

Eelma, Tonis 020302
IBS, Tartu, Estonia

Efthymiou, Venizelos 020544
EPL Technology Frontiers, Dhali, Cyprus

Egan, Renate 020048
UNSW, Sydney, Australia

Egido, Miguel-Ángel 020407
UPM, Madrid, Spain

Eidtmann, Maximilian 020385
ZHAW, Winterthur, Switzerland

Eijgelaar, Marcel 020571
DNV, Arnhem, The Netherlands

Eikelboom, Erik 020225
Futurasun, Citadella, Italy

Einhaus, Roland 020312
ZSW, Stuttgart, Germany

Eisenacher, Matthias 020141
University of Applied Science Cologne, Cologne, Germany

Eiternick, Stefan 020004, 020052
Fraunhofer CSP, Halle (Saale), Germany
Ekins-Daukes, Nicholas J. 020065
UNSW, Sydney, Australia
El Ainaoui, Khadija 020171
Green Energy Park, Benguerir, Morocco
El mrabet, Yasmine 020171
Green Energy Park, Benguerir, Morocco
Elgaili, Mohamed 020166
QEERI, Doha, Qatar
Elhamaoui, Said 020171
Green Energy Park, Benguerir, Morocco
Ellis, Hanna 020213
European Commission JRC, Ispra, Italy
Engelen, Tine 020389
Hasselt University, Diepenbeek, Belgium
Erber, Alexander 020386
BFH, Burgdorf, Switzerland
Eryılmaz, Hande 020521
ODTÜ-GÜNAM, Ankara, Türkiye
Escudero, Ana 020414
IaSol, Zaragoza, Spain
Esmailifar, Seyyed Majid 020335, 020356, 020374, 020375
Amirkabir University of Technology, Tehran, Iran
Espinosa, Nieves 020497, 020506
University of Murcia, Murcia, Spain
Essam T. Mohammed, Sarah 020546
EU SOLARIS, Almeria, Spain
Esteras, Miguel 020358
TECNALIA, Derio, Spain
Eyhorn, Steffen 020369
Fraunhofer ISE, Freiburg, Germany

Fabel, Yann 020235, 020237, 020239
DLR, Almería, Spain
Fabris, Francesca 020225
Futurasun, Citadella, Italy
Faes, Antonin 020251
CSEM, Neuchâtel, Switzerland
Falangas, Alexandros 020210
TRASIS International, Brussels, Belgium
Fang, Xue 020525
Tokyo University of Science, Tokyo, Japan
Fano, Vanesa 020055, 020097, 020153, 020287
UPV/EHU, Bilbao, Spain

Farhat, Mohammad Australian University, Kuwait City, Kuwait	020428
Farina, Andrea CNR-IFN, Milan, Italy	020066
Farrias-Basulto, Guillermo HZB, Berlin, Germany	020101
Fath, Moritz RCT Solutions, Konstanz, Germany	020463
Fath, Peter RCT Solutions, Konstanz, Germany	020005, 020463
Fava, Henrique University of Évora, Évora, Portugal	020565
Feichtner, Markus Sonnenkraft Energie, St. Veit/Glan, Austria	020255
Feichtner, Markus Sonnenkraft Energy, St. Veit/Glan, Austria	020160
Feldbacher, Sonja PCCL, Leoben, Austria	020136, 020500
Feldhof, Anne Maren University of Applied Science Cologne, Cologne, Germany	020522
Fernandes, Cláudia Centre for New Energy Technologies, Sacavém, Portugal	020464
Fernández Solas, Álvaro DLR, Almería, Spain	020331
Ferrando, Jorge University of Valencia, Paterna, Spain	020226
Ferreira, Catarina G. SDU Climate Cluster, Odense, Denmark	020250
Ferreira, Catarina SDU Climate Cluster, Odense, Denmark	020306
Ferrero, Sergio Polytechnic University of Turin, Turin, Italy	020079
Feuerherdt, Niels Berlin University of Applied Sciences, Berlin, Germany	020309
Fialho, Luis Eurac Research, Bolzano, Italy	020203, 020254, 020261, 020304, 020403, 020409, 020418, 020420, 020565
Figueroa, Andrés National University of Colombia, Bogotá, Colombia	020339
Fischer, Stefan SGL Carbon, Meitingen, Germany	020495
Fleischanderl, Martin voestalpine Stahl, Linz, Austria	020136
Fleury, Perine Biosphere Solar, Delft, The Netherlands	020513, 020521
Flouchi, Imane Green Energy Park, Benguerir, Morocco	020171

Fodor, Nikoletta 020521
SolarPower Europe, Brussels, Belgium

Fontani, Daniela 020066
CNR-INO, Florence, Italy

Forster, Jacob 020135
Fraunhofer ISE, Freiburg, Germany

Forstinger, Anne 020331
CSP Services, Cologne, Germany

Franch, Jordi Badosa 020406
Ecole Polytechnique, Palaiseau, France

Franchi, Daniele 020077
CNR-ICCOM, Sesto Fiorentino, Italy

Franquet, Erwin 020259, 020428
Côte d`Azur University, Nice, France

Frasson, Nicola 020019
Applied Materials, San Biagio di Callalta, Italy

Freer, Solomon 020396
PV Lighthouse, Coledale, Australia

Freitag, Marina 020077
Newcastle University, Newcastle upon Tyne, United Kingdom

Freund, Timo 020312
EnBW, Karlsruhe, Germany

Friansyah, Rizal 020376
DTU, Roskilde, Denmark

Friesen, Gabi 020160, 020249, 020574
SUPSI, Mendrisio, Switzerland

Friesen, Thomas 020249
Megasol Energie, Deitingen, Switzerland

Fritz Muñoz, Benjamín 020099
UPV, Valencia, Spain

Froebel, Jens 020121, 020142, 020192, 020223
Fraunhofer CSP, Halle, Germany

Frontini, Francesco 020249, 020253
SUPSI, Mendrisio, Switzerland

Fuentealba-Vidal, Edward 020129, 020311, 020342, 020417, 020422
University of Antofagasta, Antofagasta, Chile

Füreder-Kitzmüller, Friedrich 020136
voestalpine Stahl, Linz, Austria

Fuertes Marrón, David 020014, 020501, 020507, 020508
UPM, Madrid, Spain

Fuertes, David 020097
IES-UPM, Madrid, Spain

Furnari, Alessandro 020010
Enel Green Power, Catania, Italy

Fuß, Michael 020206
MBJ Solutions, Ahrensburg, Germany

Gabor, Andrew M. 020166
BrightSpot Automation, Boulder, United States of America

Gaete, Martin 020311
University of Antofagasta, Antofagasta, Chile

Gafert, Michael 020369
AIT, Vienna, Austria

Gageot, Tristan 020040
CEA / INES, Le Bourget-du-Lac, France

Gainza, Eusebio 020392
ALLOTARRA, Allo, Spain

Galarza, Alejandra 020461
IPVF, Palaiseau, France

Galbiati, Giuseppe 020119, 020218
Henkel, Düsseldorf, Germany

Galdikas, Algirdas 020157
Applied Research Institute for Prospective Technologies, Vilnius, Lithuania

Galiana, Beatriz 020085
Charles III University of Madrid, Madrid, Spain

Galiazzo, Marco 020019
Applied Materials, San Biagio di Callalta, Italy

Gall, Stefan 020101
HZB, Berlin, Germany

Gallmetzer, Sandra 020261, 020509
Eurac Research, Bolzano, Italy

Galparsoro, Ibon 020514
AZTI, PASAIA, Spain

Gamarra, Ana Rosa 020502
CIEMAT, Madrid, Spain

Ganter, Alissa 020296
ETH, Zurich, Switzerland

Gaona García, Elvis Eduardo 020279
District University of Bogotá, Bogotá, Colombia

Garabetian, Thomas 020551
SolarPower Europe, Brussels, Belgium

García Campos, Enrique 020336
University of Almería, La Cañada de San Urbano, Spain

García, Fernando 020326
UC3M, Madrid, Spain

García, Sonia 020139
Tecnalia, Donostia - San Sebastián, Spain

García-Cañas, Alejandro 020257
IMDEA Nanoscience, Madrid, Spain

García-Salinas, María José 020100
University of Almeria, Almería, Spain

Garcia-Sanchez, Almudena 020246, 020257
UPM, Madrid, Spain
Garg, Vivek 020069, 020071, 020081
SVNIT, Surat, India
Garraín, Daniel 020502
CIEMAT, Madrid, Spain
Gasse, Hugues 020073
University of Toulouse, Toulouse, France
Gassner, Anika 020160, 020162, 020500, 020504
OFI, Vienna, Austria
Gatti, Cesare 020541
PedersoliGattai, Milan, Italy
Gattu, Apoorva 020003
ISC Konstanz, Konstanz, Germany
Gautier, Damien 020505
Becquerel Institute, Brussels, Belgium
Gauvin, Xavier 020302
Bouygues Construction, Saint-Quentin-en-Yvelines, France
Ge, Hua 020249
Concordia University, Montreal, Canada
Gebhardt, Paul 020195
Fraunhofer ISE, Freiburg, Germany
Geerligs, L. J. 020030
TNO, Petten, The Netherlands
Gehrlein, Janek 020522
University of Applied Science Cologne, Cologne, Germany
Geier, Jutta 020234
PCCL, Leoben, Austria
Geml, Fabian 020031
University of Konstanz, Constance, Germany
Genovese, Maria 020378
Enel Green Power, Pisa, Italy
Georghiou, George E. 020534
University of Cyprus, Nicosia, Cyprus
Germani, Simone 020302
CEI, Milan, Italy
Getsiou, Maria 020181
Directorate General for Research and Innovation, Brussels, Belgium
Geymayer, Lukas 020136
voestalpine Stahl, Linz, Austria
Ghahremani, Amirreza 020335, 020374
Amirkabir University of Technology, Tehran, Iran
Ghennioui, Abdellatif 020171
Green Energy Park, Benguerir, Morocco
Ghosh, Saptak 020519
CSTEP, Bengaluru, India

Girardi, Pierpaolo — 020462, 020466
RSE, Milan, Italy

Giroux-Julien, Stephanie — 020338
CNRS, Villeurbanne, France

Gissler, Antoine — 020060
EDF R&D, Palaiseau, France

Göckeritz, Robert — 020119
Fraunhofer CSP, Halle, Germany

Gohil, Hardik — 020222
RCT Solutions, Konstanz, Germany

Gomes de Venuto, Vitor — 020025
PUCRS, Porto Alegre, Brazil

Gomez Trillos, Juan Camilo — 020482
DLR, Oldenburg, Germany

Gomez-Lazaro, Emilio — 020562
University of Castilla-La Mancha, Albacete, Spain

Gonnella, Gabriella — 020249, 020254
Eurac research, Bolzano, Italy

González Pérez, Sara — 020151
ULL, San Cristóbal de La Laguna, Spain

González Rodríguez, Brais — 020243
University of Vigo, Vigo, Spain

González, Miguel Ángel — 020205
University of Valladolid, Valladolid, Spain

González-Díaz, Benjamín — 020151
ULL, San Cristóbal de La Laguna, Spain

Goraya, Baljeet Singh — 020475
Fraunhofer ISE, Freiburg, Germany

Gordillo, Gerardo — 020110
National University of Colombia, Bogotá, Colombia

Gordon, Ivan — 020521
imec, Genk, Belgium

Gottschalg, Ralph — 020158
Anhalt University of Applied Sciences, Köthen, Germany

Gottschalg, Ralph — 020056, 020201, 020229, 020233, 020284, 020574
Fraunhofer CSP, Halle, Germany

Govaerts, Jonathan — 020019
imec, Genk, Belgium

Gracia Amillo, Ana María — 020211
CENER, Pamplona, Spain

Gracia Amillo, Ana María — 020318
CENER, Sarigurren, Spain

Gracia Amillo, Ana María — 020181, 020365, 020366, 020497
CENER, Sarriguren, Spain

Gregory, Geoffrey — 020006
EnPV, Karlsruhe, Germany

Greslou, Olivier 020551
CSTB, Bussy-Saint Georges, France

Grommes, Eva-Maria 020522, 020523
University of Applied Science Cologne, Cologne, Germany

Grosser, Stephan 020119, 020142, 020218
Fraunhofer CSP, Halle, Germany

Grünsteidl, Stefan 020307
Avancis, Munich, Germany

Gruginskie, Natasha 020067
Radboud University, Nijmegen, The Netherlands

Guedea, Isabel 020127, 020517
ENDEF, Zaragoza, Spain

Gülsoy, Eren Cihan 020521
METU, Ankara, Türkiye

Gümüs Çiftci, Burcu 020027
Kalyon PV, Ankara, Türkiye

Guerra, Gerardo 020448, 020481
GreenPowerMonitor a DNV company, Barcelona, Spain

Guidetti, Giulia 020541
Green Horse Advisory, Milan, Italy

Guillemoles, Jean François 020062
IPVF, Palaiseau, France

Guillevin, Nicolas 020225
TNO, Petten, The Netherlands

Gunbas, Gorkem 020113
ODTÜ-GÜNAM, Ankara, Türkiye

Gupta, Akshit 020551
Eurac Research, Bolzano, Italy

Gutierrez, Jose Ruben 020055, 020097, 020153, 020287
UPV/EHU, Bilbao, Spain

Gutjahr, Astrid 020030
TNO, Petten, The Netherlands

Haaland, Petry Kristine Nøttum 020476
NTNU, Trondheim, Norway

Haase, Felix 020063
ISFH, Emmerthal, Germany

Hadiwidjaja, Stella 020102
SERIS, Singapore, Singapore

Hadjipanayi, Maria 020064
University of Cyprus, Nicosia, Cyprus

Haedrich, Ingrid 020195, 020231
Fraunhofer ISE, Freiburg, Germany

Hämmer, Matthias 020470
bifa Umweltinstitut, Augsburg, Germany

Hafidi, Elias 020511
Inflights BV, Brussels, Belgium

Hagemann, Elizabeth M. 020416
Nelson Mandela University, Port Elizabeth, South Africa

Hallais, Géraldine 020058
CNRS, Palaiseau, France

Halle, Lasse 020359
BFH, Burgdorf, Switzerland

Hallensleben, Carina 020220
TAMURA-ELSOLD, Ilsenburg, Germany

Halm, Andreas 020218, 020220, 020221
ISC Konstanz, Konstanz, Germany

Halme, Janne 020249
Aalto University, Espoo, Finland

Hamada, Toshiyuki 020190
Osaka Electro-Communication University, Osaka, Japan

Hammer, Annette 020239
DLR, Oldenburg, Germany

Hamouda, Frederic 020058
CNRS, Palaiseau, France

Hanifi, Hamed 020121, 020125, 020137, 020223
AESOLAR, Koenigsbrunn, Germany

Hansen, Per-Anders 020017, 020503
Institute for Energy Technology, Kjeller, Norway

Harit, Amit Kumar 020064
Hasselt Unversity, Genk, Belgium

Harrison, Samuel 020225
CEA, Le Bourget-du-Lac, France

Hashem, Ahmad 020056, 020201
Anhalt University of Applied Sciences, Köthen, Germany

Hategan, Sergiu Mihai 020283
West University of Timisoara, Timisoara, Romania

Hauch, Jens 020117, 020149, 020150
HI ERN, Erlangen, Germany

Hauer, Martin 020255
Bartenbach, Vienna, Austria

Haverkamp, Helge 020008
centrotherm international, Blaubeuren, Germany

Hee Lee, Sang 020045
KIER, Daejeon, South Korea

Heidrich, Robert 020233
Fraunhofer CSP, Halle, Germany

Heikkinen, Kyösti 020423
VTT Technical Research Centre of Finland, Oulu, Finland

Heiser, Moritz 020230
Kiwa PI Berlin, Berlin, Germany

Helbig, Matthias 020220
ISC Konstanz, Konstanz, Germany

Helten, David 020331
CSP Services, Cologne, Germany

Hennig, Carsten 020313, 020355
saferay holding, Berlin, Germany

Hennig, Patrick 020313
Kiel University of Applied Sciences, Kiel, Germany

Heras, Jesús 020536
Wattkraft, Madrid, Spain

Hermle, Martin 020475
Fraunhofer ISE, Freiburg, Germany

Hernández Mora, Johann Alexander 020279, 020441
District University of Bogotá, Bogotá, Colombia

Hernández, Jaime J. 020257
IMDEA Nanoscience, Madrid, Spain

Hernández, Johann 020526
Francisco José de Caldas District University, Bogota, Colombia

Herodotou, Panayiotis 020534
University of Cyprus, Nicosia, Cyprus

Herrera Leon, Fernando Augusto 020339, 020546
National University of Colombia, Bogotá, Colombia

Herrero, Leire 020139
Tecnalia, Donostia - San Sebastián, Spain

Herrero, Rebeca 020209, 020453, 020459
UPM, Madrid, Spain

Herrmann, Werner 020208
TÜV Rheinland Solar, Cologne, Germany

Herteleer, Bert 020329, 020351
KU Leuven, Ghent, Belgium

Herteleer, Bert 020574
SUPSI, Mendrisio, Switzerland

Hessler-Wyser, Aïcha 020251
EPFL, Neuchâtel, Switzerland

Heydari, Azim 020485
Eurac Research, Bolzano, Italy

Hinken, David 020236
ISFH, Emmerthal, Germany

Hladys, Bertrand 020010
CEA, Grenoble, France

Hoex, Bram 020065
UNSW, Sydney, Australia

Hofer, Leo 020322
BFH, Burgdorf, Switzerland

Hoffmann, Erik 020006
EnPV, Karlsruhe, Germany

Hogan Almeida, Rita — 020535, 020567
UPM, Madrid, Spain

Hollemann, Christina — 020008
ISFH, Emmerthal, Germany

Holovský, Jakub — 020107
Czech Technical University, Prague, Czech Republic

Honrubia-Escribano, Andrés — 020562
University of Castilla-La Mancha, Albacete, Spain

Hopp, Tobias — 020384
Sunman Energy, Frankfurt, Germany

Horn, Jonas — 020050
halm elektronik, Frankfurt am Main, Germany

Horta, Pedro — 020304, 020403, 020409, 020418, 020420, 020565
University of Évora, Évora, Portugal

Hosatte, Mikaël — 020068
SEGTON Advanced Technology, Versailles, France

Hoß, Jan — 020004, 020035
ISC Konstanz, Konstanz, Germany

Hossain, Mohammad Istiaque — 020042, 020075, 020108, 020109, 020146, 020147
QEERI, Doha, Qatar

Hou, Yi — 020102
SERIS, Singapore, Singapore

Hsiao, Pei-Chieh — 020048
UNSW, Sydney, Australia

Hsieh, Cho Fan — 020083, 020161, 020163
ITRI, Hsinchu, Taiwan

Hu, Shuaifeng — 020226
University of Oxford, Oxford, United Kingdom

Huang, Chris — 020048
SunDrive Solar, Kurnell, Australia

Huang, Gan — 020272
KIT, Eggenstein-Leopoldshafen, Germany

Huang, Lu-Jan — 020425
TNO, Leiden, The Netherlands

Huang, Tzu-Yen — 020096
National Synchrotron Radiation Research Center, Hsinchu, Taiwan

Hügi, Matthias — 020322
BFH, Burgdorf, Switzerland

Huemer, Martin — 020227
University of Linz, Linz, Austria

Huerta, Hugo E. — 020286, 020400
TUAS, Turku, Finland

Hüttl, Bernd — 020361
Coburg University of Applied Sciences, Coburg, Germany

Hulik Jansova, Marketa — 020274
Solargis, Bratislava, Slovakia

Hung, Tzu Han — 020552
ITRI, Taipei City, Taiwan

Hutterer-Tik, Thomas — 020347
Watt Analytics, Vienna, Austria

Hwang, Hye-Mi — 020324, 020357, 020561
KIER, Daejeon, South Korea

Iglesias, Unai — 020139
Tecnalia, Donostia - San Sebastián, Spain

Ikeda, Kazuaki — 020436
AIST, Koriyama, Japan

Infante, Paulo — 020420
University of Évora, Évora, Portugal

Isabella, Olindo — 020515
TU Delft, Delft, The Netherlands

Ishikawa, Ryousuke — 020106, 020115
Tokyo City University, Setagaya, Japan

Iwaszko, Victorien — 020495
ROSI Solar, Saint-Martin-d'Hères, France

Izquierdo-Roca, Victor — 020094
IREC, Barcelona, Spain

J. N. Soares, Guillermo — 020090
Federal University of Rio de Janeiro, Duque de Caxias, Brazil

Jacob, Julieu — 020302
METABUILD, Berlin, Germany

Jacobs, Ayesha — 020382
Zutari, Cape Town, South Africa

Jaeckel, Bengt — 020056, 020119, 020121, 020140, 020142, 020175, 020192, 020201, 020223, 020229
Fraunhofer CSP, Halle, Germany

Jäger Waldau, Arnulf — 020570
European Commission, Rome, Italy

Jäger, Philip — 020006
ISFH, Emmerthal, Germany

Jäggi, Adrian — 020179
BFH, Burgdorf, Switzerland

Järventausta, Pertti — 020445
Tampere University, Tampere, Finland

Jaffré, Alexandre — 020058
CNRS, Gif-sur-Yvette, France

Jahn, Ulrike — 020521, 020574
Fraunhofer CSP, Halle, Germany

Jahn, Ulrike Fraunhofer IMWS, Halle, Germany	020355
Jahreis, Sophia Fraunhofer CSP, Halle, Germany	020142, 020192
Jakomin, Roberto Federal University of Rio de Janeiro, Duque de Caxias, Brazil	020090
Jakubik, Martin Solargis, Bratislava, Slovakia	020274
Jakuza, Paola University of Padova, Padova, Italy	020089
Jalkh, Judy Virtual Vehicle, Graz, Austria	020455
Jandl, Ralf FFHS, Zurich, Switzerland	020204
Jankovec, Marko University of Ljubljana, Ljubljana, Slovenia	020197
Jaworczak, Kamil Technology Innovation Institute, Abu Dhabi, United Arab Emirates	020402
Jensen, Adam R. DTU, Kongens Lyngby, Denmark	020267
Jeong, Jungi K-water, Daejeon, South Korea	020323
Jeong, Kyung Taek KIER, Daejeon, South Korea	020045
Jeong, Minsoo KIER, Daejeon, South Korea	020045
Jeronimo, Pedro CEA, Grenoble, France	020010
Jiang, Zonghan Anhalt University of Applied Sciences, Köthen, Germany	020158, 020201
Jimenez, Maria Onyx Solar, Avila, Spain	020302
Jimeno, Juan Carlos UPV/EHU, Bilbao, Spain	020055, 020097, 020153, 020287, 020289, 020353
Jo, Hyunsik K-water, Daejeon, South Korea	020323
Job, Enzo Fraunhofer ISE, Freiburg, Germany	020231
Johnson, Mark Robert Institut Laue-Langevin (ILL), Grenoble, France	020546
Joo, Dongmyoung KETI, Wonmi-gu, South Korea	020449
Jooss, Wolfgang RCT Solutions, Konstanz, Germany	020005, 020222, 020463

Joseph, Daniel Christopher 020123
Fraunhofer ISE, Freiburg, Germany
Joshi, Deepak 020069, 020081
SVNIT, Surat, India
Joss, David 020359, 020369, 020386
BFH, Burgdorf, Switzerland
Jouini, Anis 020034
ECM Technologies, Grenoble, France
Jouttijärvi, Sami 020286, 020298, 020398
University of Turku, Turku, Finland
Joziak, Roman 020230
Kiwa PI Berlin, Berlin, Germany
Ju, Young-Chul 020324, 020357, 020561
KIER, Daejeon, South Korea
Jugo, Josu 020437
UPV/EHU, Leioa, Spain
Junge, Sebastian 020008, 020482
ISFH, Emmerthal, Germany

Kaaya, Ismail 020156, 020294, 020389, 020393
imec, Genk, Belgium
Kähler, Jan-Dirk 020482
Centrotherm International, Blaubeuren, Germany
Kahraman, Mert 020027
Kalyon PV, Ankara, Türkiye
Kainz, Konrad 020430
AIT, Vienna, Austria
Kaiser, Martin 020215
Fraunhofer ISE, Freiburg, Germany
Kaizuka, Izumi 020570
RTS Corporation, Tokyo, Japan
Kajari-Schröder, Sarah 020063
ISFH, Emmerthal, Germany
Kallioharju, Kari 020444, 020445
TUAS, Tampere, Finland
Kalliojärvi, Heidi 020194
Tampere University, Tampere, Finland
Kalshetty, Mahesh 020519
CSTEP, Bengaluru, India
Kaltenbach, Thomas 020195
Fraunhofer ISE, Freiburg, Germany
Kamphues, Joshua 020031
University of Konstanz, Constance, Germany
Kandiyoti-Eskenazi, Selin 020467
CSEM, Neuchâtel, Switzerland

Kang, Min Gu 020045
KIER, Daejeon, South Korea

Kapetanovic, Viktor 020367
Nextracker, Fremont, United States of America

Karhu, Juha 020286
Finnish Meteorological Institute, Helsinki, Finland

Kari, Thøger 020191, 020376
DTU, Roskilde, Denmark

Karimy, Hedayatullah 020052
Fraunhofer CSP, Halle (Saale), Germany

Karttunen, Lauri 020298, 020398
University of Turku, Turku, Finland

Kasper, Ruth 020167, 020232
University of Applied Sciences Cologne, Cologne, Germany

Katouli, Tannaz 020195
Fraunhofer ISE, Freiburg, Germany

Kaufmann, Kai 020355
DENKweit, Halle, Germany

Kawabata, Rudy 020092
PUC-Rio, Rio de Janeiro, Brazil

Kemp, Linda 020390
MARIN, Wageningen, The Netherlands

Kenchington, Ian 020225, 020474, 020558
Becquerel Institute, Brussels, Belgium

Kenny, Robert 020210
European Commission JRC, Ispra, Italy

Khan, Abeer Ali 020513
First Solar, Mainz, Germany

Khosravi, Arash 020381
Mälardalen University, Västerås, Sweden

Kikkert, Benjamin W. J. 020405
TNO, Petten, The Netherlands

Kilickaya, Seda 020020
ODTÜ-GÜNAM, Ankara, Türkiye

Kim, Jin-Hong 020449
KETI, Wonmi-gu, South Korea

Kim, Jun-Tae 020249
Kongju National University, Chungnam, South Korea

Kim, Kihwan 020112
KIER, Daejeon, South Korea

Kim, Seok Won 020449
KETI, Wonmi-gu, South Korea

Kim, Yong-Jin 020045
KIER, Daejeon, South Korea

Kinge, Sachin 020117
Toyota Motors Europe, Brussels, Belgium

Kitamura, Ibuki Osaka Electro-Communication University, Osaka, Japan	020190
Kitzberger, Gregor voestalpine Stahl, Linz, Austria	020136
Kivambe, Maulid QEERI, Doha, Qatar	020166
Kizukuri, Rihoko TAMURA-ELSOLD, Ilsenburg, Germany	020220
Kladas, Anastasios KU Leuven, Ghent, Belgium	020329, 020351
Kleider, Jean-Paul CNRS, Gif-sur-Yvette, France	020040, 020058
Kleissl, Jan University of California, San Diego, United States of America	020528
Klengel, Robert Fraunhofer IMWS, Halle, Germany	020355
Klenk, Markus ZHAW, Winterthur, Switzerland	020385
Klos, Christine Buhck Re.Energy, Hamburg, Norway	020510
Kluska, Sven Fraunhofer ISE, Freiburg, Germany	020019
Klute, Carola Fraunhofer IMWS, Halle, Germany	020355
Knausdorf, Christian Coburg University of Applied Sciences, Coburg, Germany	020361
Ko, Seok-whan KIER, Daejeon, South Korea	020561
Ko, Suk Whan KIER, Daejeon, South Korea	020324, 020357
Koc, Timurhan DTU, Roskilde, Denmark	020376
Koduvelikulathu, Lejo Joseph ISC Konstanz, Konstanz, Germany	020035, 020068
Koduvelikulathu, Lejo ISC Konstanz, Konstanz, Germany	020003
Köntges, Marc ISFH, Emmerthal, Germany	020206
Koepge, Ringo Fraunhofer CSP, Halle, Germany	020142, 020192
Koester, Lukas Eurac Research, Bolzano, Italy	020203, 020261, 020325
Kohlenberg, Heike ISFH, Emmerthal, Germany	020063
Kohno, Tohru Hitachi, Tokyo, Japan	020186

Kolahi, Mohammad 020356, 020375
University of Isfahan, Isfahan, Iran
Konagai, Makoto 020106, 020115
Tokyo City University, Setagaya, Japan
Kono, Toru 020484
Hitachi, Kokubunji, Japan
Konu, Christopher Bruce 020132
HTW Berlin, Berlin, Germany
Kopecek, Radovan 020569
ISC Konstanz, Konstanz, Germany
Kopp, Nils 020220
TAMURA-ELSOLD, Ilsenburg, Germany
Korkmaz Arslan, Melisa 020020
ODTÜ-GÜNAM, Ankara, Türkiye
Korpås, Magnus 020476
NTNU, Trondheim, Norway
Kortetmäki, Aki 020444, 020445
TUAS, Tampere, Finland
Koskela, Juha 020444, 020445, 020554
Tampere University, Tampere, Finland
Kossen, Eric J. 020030
TNO, Petten, The Netherlands
Kowalski, Julia 020237
RWTH, Aachen, Germany
Kräling, Ulli 020215
Fraunhofer ISE, Freiburg, Germany
Kraft, Thomas M. 020423
VTT Technical Research Centre of Finland, Oulu, Finland
Krainer, Diana Maria 020430
AIT, Vienna, Austria
Krasilnikov, Inga 020379
Tel Aviv University, Tel Aviv, Israel
Krever Lopes, Bruno 020023
PUCRS, Porto Alegre, Brazil
Kribus, Abraham 020379
Tel Aviv University, Tel Aviv, Israel
Krishnan, Sasikumar 020361
Coburg University of Applied Sciences, Coburg, Germany
Kroon, Jan 020225
TNO, Petten, The Netherlands
Kuan, Ta-Ming 020021, 020053
TSEC, Hsinchu, Taiwan
Kubicek, Bernhard 020281, 020318, 020334, 020347, 020430
AIT, Vienna, Austria
Kucuk, E. Busra 020030
TNO, Petten, The Netherlands

Kuczyńska-Łażewska, Anna 020498, 020499
Gdansk University of Technology, Gdansk, Poland

Kühne, Philip 020240
Leibniz University Hannover, Hannover, Germany

Kuhrmann, Bernd 020206
MBJ Solutions, Ahrensburg, Germany

Kujansivu, Eino 020554
Solarigo Systems, Pirkkala, Finland

Kumar, Gaurav 020563
MERI College of Engineering and Technology, Bahadurgarh, India

Kumar, Sagarika 020402
Technology Innovation Institute, Abu Dhabi, United Arab Emirates

Kumar, Saurabh 020563
PTB, Braunshweig, Germany

Kuo, Cheng-Wen 020021, 020053
TSEC, Hsinchu, Taiwan

Kurtulus, Gunes 020556
ODTU GUNAM, Ankara, Türkiye

Kuruganti, Vaibhav V. 020033
ISC Konstanz, Konstanz, Germany

Kurz, Hannes 020136
voestalpine Stahl, Linz, Austria

Kusch, Alexander 020361
Coburg University of Applied Sciences, Coburg, Germany

Kuzhagaliyeva, Nursulu 020402
Technology Innovation Institute, Abu Dhabi, United Arab Emirates

Kuznicki, Zbigniew T. 020013, 020068
SEGTON Advanced Technology, Versailles, France

Kwiatkowski, Jerzy 020551
NAPE, Warsaw, Poland

Kyranaki, Nikoleta 020156
Hasselt University, Genk, Belgium

Kyranaki, Nikoleta 020393
Hasselt University, Hasselt, Belgium

Kyranaki, Nikoleta 020294
imec, Genk, Belgium

Kyratsi, Theodora 020495
University of Cyprus, Nicosia, Cyprus

L. Andersen, Nanna 020477
DTU, Roskilde, Denmark

L. Souza, Patrícia 020090
Federal University of Rio de Janeiro, Rio de Janeiro, Brazil

Lachowicz, Agata 020039
CSEM, Neuchâtel, Switzerland

Lahr, Simon 020388
Next2Sun Technology, Dillingen, Germany

Lahr, Simon 020411
Next2Sun, Dillingen, Germany

Lajunen, Antti 020400
University of Helsinki, Helsinki, Finland

Lambertz, Andreas 020233
FZJ, Jülich, Germany

Lamblot, Hervé 020302
Sunstyle, Paris, France

Lamghari, Fouad 020402
Fujairah Research Centre, Fujairah, United Arab Emirates

Lamminaho, Jani 020250, 020306
SDU Climate Cluster, Odense, Denmark

Landaas, Christian 020495
Northern Silicon, Meråker, Norway

Landberg, Lars 020448
DNV Denmark, Hellerup, Denmark

Landberg, Lars 020481
DNV Denmark, Hellerup, Spain

Landes, Dieter 020361
Coburg University of Applied Sciences, Coburg, Germany

Landová, Lucie 020107
Czech Technical University, Prague, Czech Republic

Lansade, David 020073
University of Toulouse, Toulouse, France

Lappalainen, Kari 020194, 020528, 020537
Tampere University, Tampere, Finland

Lara, Yolanda 020127, 020414, 020517
ENDEF, Zaragoza, Spain

Larionova, Yevgeniya 020006, 020007, 020225
ISFH, Emmerthal, Germany

Låstad, Jonas 020011
NTNU, Trondheim, Norway

Laurens-Berge, Clarisse 020034
University Grenoble Alpes, Le Bourget-du-Lac, France

Laurikėnas, Paulius 020353
Solitek, Vilnius, Lithuania

Lauwaert, Johan 020064
Ghent University, Ghent, Belgium

Lazaro-Castrillon, Luna 020085
IO-CSIC, Madrid, Spain

Le Bossenec, Hugo 020116
IPVF, Palaiseau, France

Le Brun, Anton 020096
Australian Nuclear Science and Technology Organisation, Lucas Heights, Australia

Lechón, Yolanda 020502
CIEMAT, Madrid, Spain

Ledesma, Javier R. 020337
UPM, Madrid, Spain

Ledesma, Javier 020446
UPM, Madrid, Spain

Lee, Chun-Wei 020021
TSEC, Hsinchu, Taiwan

Lee, Hyunju 020046
Meiji University, Kanagawa, Japan

Lee, Jieun 020323
K-water, Daejeon, South Korea

Lee, Jin-Seok 020324, 020357, 020561
KIER, Daejeon, South Korea

Legarrea, Aritz 020365
CENER, Sarriguren, Spain

Lelievre, Jean-Francois 020373
INES, Le Bourget-du-Lac, France

Lelong, Benoit 020373
Cythelia Energy, La Motte-Servolex, France

Leloux, Jonathan 020262
LuciSun, Villers-la-Ville, Belgium

Lenain, Philippe 020495
benkei, Lyon, France

Lennon, Alison 020048
UNSW, Sydney, Australia

Lenz, Markus 020226
School of Life Sciences FHNW, Muttenz, Switzerland

Lenzmann, Frank 020019
TNO Energy Transition, Petten, The Netherlands

Leone, Sander 020405
Novar, Rotterdam, The Netherlands

Leonforte, Fabrizio 020249
Polytechnic University of Milan, Milan, Italy

Leopold, Ulrich 020457
Luxembourg Institute of Science and Technology, Esch-sur-Alzette, Luxembourg

Levrat, Jacques 020251, 020467
CSEM, Neuchâtel, Switzerland

Levtchenko, Alexandra 020116
IPVF, Palaiseau, France

Lewandowski, Simon 020073
University of Toulouse, Toulouse, France

Leza, Baurin 020412
Gonvarri MS R&D, Corvera - Asturias, Spain

Lezaca, Jorge 020239
DLR, Oldenburg, Germany

Li, Xinyang 020222
RCT Solutions, Konstanz, Germany

Li, Yung-Chih 020021
TSEC, Hsinchu, Taiwan

Li, Yuxuan 020001
East China University of Science and Technology, Shanghai, China

Libal, Joris 020218, 020474
ISC Konstanz, Konstanz, Germany

Lichtenberger, Janine 020430
AIT, Vienna, Austria

Lițiu, Andrei Vladimir 020551
EPB Center, Rotterdam, The Netherlands

Lin, Shih-Chieh 020021
TSEC, Hsinchu, Taiwan

Lindahl, Johan 020486, 020532
Becquerel Sweden, Knivsta, Sweden

Linder, Johannes 020492
Belectric, Kolitzheim, Germany

Lindfors, Anders 020286
Finnish Meteorological Institute, Helsinki, Finland

Lindig, Sascha 020371
Univers, Courbevoie, France

Linke, Jonathan 020004, 020035, 020225
ISC Konstanz, Konstanz, Germany

Linß, Volker 020033
VON ARDENNE, Dresden, Germany

Lipovšek, Benjamin 020047
University of Ljubljana, Ljubljana, Slovenia

Lippke, Benjamin 020180, 020230
Kiwa PI Berlin, Berlin, Germany

List-Kratochvil, Emil 020101
HZB, Berlin, Germany

Litrico, Grazia 020010
Enel Green Power, Catania, Italy

Liu, Cui 020001
East China University of Science and Technology, Shanghai, China

Liu, Dongyang 020063
ISFH, Emmerthal, Germany

Liu, Han-Chang 020350
ITRI, Tainan, Taiwan

Liu, Huiping 020495
GRÄNGES, Finspång, Sweden

Liu, Mengdi 020144, 020208
TÜV Rheinland, Shanghai, China

Liu, Yung-Tsung 020053, 020083
ITRI, Hsinchu, Taiwan

Livera, Andreas 020534
University of Cyprus, Nicosia, Cyprus

Lizin, Sebastien 020513, 020521
UHasselt, Hasselt, Belgium

Llarena, María Elena 020151
ITER, Granadilla de Abona, Spain

Loeckenhoff, Ruediger F. 020416
AZUR SPACE Solar Power, Heilbronn, Germany

Löhning, Martha 020063
ISFH, Emmerthal, Germany

Löhr, Johannes 020063, 020114
ISFH, Emmerthal, Germany

Lokhat, Ismaël 020262
Cythelia Energy, La Motte-Servolex, France

Lokhat, Ismael 020373
Trace Software, Saint-Romain-de-Colbosc, France

Lombardo, Salvatore 020066
CNR-IMM, Catania, Italy

Long, Yean-San 020053, 020083
ITRI, Hsinchu, Taiwan

Longo, Giulia 020099
UPV, Valencia, Spain

Lopes Gomes, Carlos Javier 020432, 020434
Sunveon, Madrid, Spain

Lopes, Ana Patrícia 020464
University of Lisbon, Lisbon, Portugal

López Cuéllar, Juan Manuel 020501
UCM, Madrid, Spain

López Dalmau, Daniel 020432, 020434
Sunveon, Madrid, Spain

López, Nuria 020451
DTU, Roskilde, Denmark

Lorenz, Dieter 020206
MBJ Solutions, Ahrensburg, Germany

Lorenzo Pigueiras, Eduardo 020363
UPM, Madrid, Spain

Lorenzo, Celena 020337, 020536
UPM, Madrid, Spain

Lorenzo, Eduardo 020439, 020446
UPM, Madrid, Spain

Lossen, Jan ISC Konstanz, Konstanz, Germany	020003, 020035
Louwen, Atse Eurac Research, Bolzano, Italy	020203, 020226, 020261, 020509, 020546
Louwen, Atse RISE, Boras, Sweden	020316
Lu, Huan-Wu ITRI, Hsinchu, Taiwan	020161
Lu, Matthew Kiwa PI Berlin, Shanghai, China	020230
Lucea, Aingeru TECNALIA, Derio, Spain	020197, 020198
Lüdemann, Marius Fraunhofer CSP, Halle, Germany	020233
Luís, Margarida University of Lisbon, Lisbon, Portugal	020421
Lustoza de Souza, Patricia UFRJ, Rio de Janeiro, Brazil	020092
Ly, Moussa PUCRS, Porto Alegre, Brazil	020023, 020025
Lyubenova, Teodora European Commission JRC, Ispra, Italy	020210
M. Bazilio, Willian PUC-Rio, Rio de Janeiro, Brazil	020092
M. S. Kawabata, Rudy Pontifical Catholic University of Rio de Janeiro, Rio de Janeiro, Brazil	020090
M. Torelly, Guilherme Pontifical Catholic University of Rio de Janeiro, Rio de Janeiro, Brazil	020090
Ma Lu, Silvia Mälardalen University, Västerås, Sweden	020381
Ma, Xiang SINTEF, Oslo, Norway	020011
Macé, Philippe Becquerel Institute, Brussels, Belgium	020225, 020252, 020474, 020505, 020543, 020558, 020573
Mack, Sebastian Fraunhofer ISE, Freiburg, Germany	020031
Madsen, Morten SDU Climate Cluster, Odense, Denmark	020250, 020306
Mahmood, Aysha DTU, Roskilde, Denmark	020265, 020376
Maixner, Andreas AESOLAR, Koenigsbrunn, Germany	020121, 020125, 020137, 020223

Maiz, Alexander 020437
UPV/EHU, Vitoria-Gasteiz, Spain

Majak, Martyna 020068
Roltec, Poznań, Poland

Makrides, George 020534
University of Cyprus, Nicosia, Cyprus

Malarkannan, Lavanya 020210
National Physical Laboratory, Teddington, United Kingdom

Malcorps, Philippe 020276
3E, Brussels, Belgium

Malik, Stephanie 020313
Fraunhofer CSP, Halle, Germany

Malik, Stephanie 020355
Fraunhofer IMWS, Halle, Germany

Maliutina, Kristina 020141
University of Applied Science Cologne, Cologne, Germany

Malo, Javier 020209
UPM, Madrid, Spain

Mancini, Simone 020425
TNO, Eindhoven, The Netherlands

Mandiola, Gotzon 020514
AZTI, PASAIA, Spain

Manganiello, Patrizio 020389
Hasselt University, Diepenbeek, Belgium

Manganiello, Patrizio 020294
imec, Genk, Belgium

Manito, Alex 020348
University of São Paulo, São Paulo, Brazil

Manochehrian, Rasoul 020539
Frankfurt University of Applied Sciences, Frankfurt am Main, Germany

Manzolini, Giampaolo 020261
Polytechnic University of Milan, Milan, Italy

Maqsood, Ayman 020101
HZB, Berlin, Germany

Marangis, Demetris 020534
University of Cyprus, Nicosia, Cyprus

Marcos-Castro, Ana 020297
CIEMAT, Madrid, Spain

Marechal, Philippe 020217
CEA / INES, Le Bourget-du-Lac, France

Marí Soucase, Bernabé 020099
UPV, Valencia, Spain

Markert, Jochen 020231
Fraunhofer ISE, Freiburg, Germany

Marquardt, Cornelia 020063
ISFH, Emmerthal, Germany

Marteau, Baptiste 020034
ECM Technologies, Grenoble, France
Martín Rueda, Javier 020535
UPM, Madrid, Spain
Martín, Francisco José 020459
UPM, Madrid, Spain
Martín, Francisco 020209
UPM, Madrid, Spain
Martín-Chivelet, Nuria 020297
CIEMAT, Madrid, Spain
Martín-Rueda, Javier 020337, 020363
UPM, Madrid, Spain
Martínez González, Mario 020326
Enertis Applus+, Madrid, Spain
Martinez, Juan Ignacio 020252
Becquerel Institute Spain, San Sebastian, Spain
Martinez, Oscar 020191, 020205
University of Valladolid, Valladolid, Spain
Martínez-Barbeito, María 020243
ieco.io, Vigo, Spain
Maruyama, Rodrigo P. 020154, 020348
University of São Paulo, São Paulo, Brazil
Marzo, Aitor 020311, 020546
University of Granada, Granada, Spain
Mashkov, Oleksandr 020149, 020150, 020377
HI ERN, Erlangen, Germany
Massaro, Lorenzo 020541
PedersoliGattai, Milan, Italy
Masson, Gaëtan 020474, 020558, 020564, 020573
Becquerel Institute, Brussels, Belgium
Masson, Gaëtan 020570
IEA PVPS Task 1, Brussels, Belgium
Mateos, Yeray 020055, 020153
UPV/EHU, Bilbao, Spain
Maturi, Laura 020249, 020254, 020551
Eurac Research, Bolzano, Italy
Mayer-Ullmann, Philipp 020430
AIT, Vienna, Austria
Mazzoleni, Stefano 020378
University of Naples Federico II, Naples, Italy
McIntosh, Keith R. 020396
PV Lighthouse, Coledale, Australia
McNab, Shona 020065
UNSW, Sydney, Australia
Meereboer, Martijn 020225
Energyra, Westknollendam, The Netherlands

Meier, Rico 020132
HTW Berlin, Berlin, Germany

Meixner, Michael 020050
halm elektronik, Frankfurt am Main, Germany

Mekhaldi, Bouchra 020406
Ecole Polytechnique, Palaiseau, France

Melges de Andrade, Adnei 020154
University of São Paulo, São Paulo, Brazil

Melino, Francesco 020314
University of Bologna, Bologna, Italy

Mellone, Celeste 020541
Green Horse Advisory, Rome, Italy

Menard, Lionel 020291
MINES Paris, Nice, France

Mencaraglia, Denis 020058
CNRS, Gif-sur-Yvette, France

Menchaca, Iratxe 020514
AZTI, PASAIA, Spain

Mendes Ferreira Gomes, Amanda 020548
UFSC, Florianopolis, Brazil

Mendikoa, Iñigo 020514
Tecnalia, BRTA, Derio, Spain

Meneghini, Matteo 020089
University of Padova, Padova, Italy

Ménézo, Christophe 020317
LOCIE, Le Bourget-du-Lac, France

Menghini, Mariela 020508
IMDEA Nanoscience Institute, Madrid, Spain

Mercade Ruiz, Pau 020448, 020481
GreenPowerMonitor a DNV company, Barcelona, Spain

Merino, Amanda 020040
CEA / INES, Le Bourget-du-Lac, France

Merino, José Manuel 020085
UAM, Madrid, Spain

Mermoud, André 020196
PVsyst, Geneva, Switzerland

Merodio, Pablo 020337
UPM, Madrid, Spain

Mertens, Jan 020389
imec, Genk, Belgium

Mertens, Verena 020006, 020008
ISFH, Emmerthal, Germany

Meßmer, Marius 020031
Fraunhofer ISE, Freiburg, Germany

Messmer, Tobias 020218, 020221, 020225
ISC Konstanz, Konstanz, Germany

Messner, Christian 020369
AIT, Vienna, Austria
Mettner, Larissa 020063, 020114
ISFH, Emmerthal, Germany
Meusel, Manuel 020052
Fraunhofer CSP, Halle (Saale), Germany
Meyer, Kevin 020260
ISFH, Emmerthal, Germany
Meza, Carlos 020318, 020334, 020426, 020520
Anhalt University of Applied Sciences, Köthen, Germany
Mezzasalma, Frédéric 020217
CEA / INES, Le Bourget-du-Lac, France
Micha, Daniel 020092
CEFET/RJ, Petrópolis, Brazil
Michael, Poland 020193
Nelson Mandela University, Port Elizabeth, South Africa
Miclea, Paul-Tiberiu 020233
Fraunhofer CSP, Halle, Germany
Midtgård, Ole-Morten 020476
NTNU, Trondheim, Norway
Miettunen, Kati 020286, 020298, 020398
University of Turku, Turku, Finland
Migan-Dubois, Anne 020406
CNRS, Gif-sur-Yvette, France
Mignonac, Alexandre 020217
CEA / INES, Le Bourget-du-Lac, France
Mignonac, Alexandre 020334
CEA, Cadarache, France
Mignonac, Alexandre 020318
CEA, Saint-Paul-Lez-Durance, France
Miguel Laborda, María 020414
IaSol, Zaragoza, Spain
Mihailetchi, Valentin Dan 020033
ISC Konstanz, Konstanz, Germany
Mihailetchi, Valentin 020225
ISC Konstanz, Konstanz, Germany
Mihaylov, Blago 020210
European Commission JRC, Ispra, Italy
Milani, Emanuele 020495
Marelli Europe, Venaria Reala, Italy
Milesi, Frédéric 020068
CEA, Grenoble, France
Min, Byungsul 020008, 020482
ISFH, Emmerthal, Germany
Mirandona López, Haritz 020432, 020434
Sunveon, Madrid, Spain

Miró-Llorente, Marta 020094
IREC, Barcelona, Spain

Misra, Prashant 020429
NISE, Gurugram, India

Miszczuk, Andrzej 020068
Roltec, Poznań, Poland

Mittag, Max 020137
Fraunhofer ISE, Freiburg, Germany

Mittal, Ankit 020318
AIT, Vienna, Austria

Mittelman, Gur 020379
Afeka Tel-Aviv Academic College of Engineering, Tel Aviv, Israel

Mizushima, Io 020028
IPU P/S, Virum, Denmark

Mizushima, Io 020037
IPU, Virum, Denmark

Mngomezulu, Ndumiso 020344
PVinsight, Port Elizabeth, South Africa

Mo, Alvin 020065
UNSW, Sydney, Australia

Mockeviciute-Azzopardi, Austeja 020334
FIR, Birkirkara, Malta

Moe Nygård, Magnus 020340
IFE, Kjeller, Norway

Moehlecke, Adriano 020023, 020025
PUCRS, Porto Alegre, Brazil

Mohammadi, Mohammad Hossein 020037, 020104
Aarhus University, Aarhus, Denmark

Mollier, Stéphane 020262
CEA / INES, Le Bourget-du-Lac, France

Moltke, Asbjørn 020043
Technical University of Denmark, Copenhagen, Denmark

Mondaca-Cuevas, Gino 020422
University of Antofagasta, Antofagasta, Chile

Monokroussos, Christos 020181
TÜV Rheinland Shanghai, Shanghai, China

Monokroussos, Christos 020144, 020208
TÜV Rheinland, Shanghai, China

Monteiro Martins, Filipa 020317
Galp Energia, Lisbon, Portugal

Montes, Carlos 020151
ITER, Granadilla de Abona, Spain

Montoya, Josefa 020311
University of Antofagasta, Antofagasta, Chile

Morabito, Floriana 020066
CNR-IFN, Milan, Italy

Moradi Sizkouhi, Amirmohammad 020356, 020375
Concordia University, Montreal, Canada
Moradi Zavie Kord, Soroush 020400
University of Helsinki, Helsinki, Finland
Morales, Sergio 020491
UPM, Madrid, Spain
Morantes Quintana, Giobertti Raul 020551
Eurac Research, Bolzano, Italy
Mordvinkin, Anton 020233
Fraunhofer CSP, Halle, Germany
Moreda, Guillermo P. 020407
UPM, Madrid, Spain
Morin, Claire 020551
SolarPower Europe, Brussels, Belgium
Morisset, Audrey 020068
CSEM, Neuchâtel, Switzerland
Morlier, Arnaud 020156
Hasselt University, Genk, Belgium
Morlier, Arnaud 020294, 020389
imec, Genk, Belgium
Mortazavifar, Leila 020056, 020158, 020201, 020284
Anhalt University of Applied Sciences, Köthen, Germany
Moruno, Ricardo 020209, 020453
UPM, Madrid, Spain
Mosel, Frank 020015
PVA TePla, Wettenberg, Germany
Moser, David 020573
Becquerel Institute Italy, Trento, Italy
Moser, David 020316
Becquerel Institute, Bolzano, Italy
Moser, David 020254
Bequerel Institute, Trento, Italy
Moser, David 020203, 020226, 020261, 020325, 020485, 020489, 020546
Eurac Research, Bolzano, Italy
Mouhoubi, Felicia 020134
CEA / INES, Le Bourget-du-Lac, France
Müllejans, Harald 020208, 020213
European Commission JRC, Ispra, Italy
Müller, Alexander 020119
Fraunhofer CSP, Halle, Germany
Müller, Larissa 020523
University of Applied Sciences Cologne, Cologne, Germany
Mugica, Maikel 020139
Tecnalia, Donostia - San Sebastián, Spain
Mujovi, Fahradin 020251
CSEM, Neuchâtel, Switzerland

Mukherjee, Srijani 020338
CEA / INES, Le Bourget-du-Lac, France

Mukhtar, Mariyam 020057
University of Verona, Verona, Italy

Mulder, Peter 020067
Radboud University, Nijmegen, The Netherlands

Muller, Matthew 020314
NREL, Denver, United States of America

Munkhammar, Joakim 020532
Uppsala University, Uppsala, Sweden

Muñoz Cerón, Emilio 020269
University of Jaén, Jaén, Spain

Muñoz, Delfina 020040, 020311, 020546
CEA / INES, Le Bourget-du-Lac, France

Muñoz, Delfina 020521
CEA, Le Bourget-du-Lac, France

Muñoz, Delfina 020226
CEA/ INES, Le Bourget-du-Lac, France

Muñoz, Ildefonso 020365, 020366, 020392
CENER, Sarriguren, Spain

Muñoz, Jesús Ángel 020508
UCM, Madrid, Spain

Muñoz-García, Miguel-Ángel 020407
UPM, Madrid, Spain

Murano, Giovanni 020551
ENEA, Ispra, Italy

Murillo, Asier 020497
CENER, Sarriguren, Spain

Musembi, Robinson J. 020272
University of Nairobi, Nairobi, Kenya

Nabipouor, Mohammad 020426
Anhalt University of Applied Sciences, Köthen, Germany

Nagel, Henning 020475
Fraunhofer ISE, Freiburg, Germany

Nakamura, Kyotaro 020046
Toyota Technological Institute, Nagoya, Japan

Nanno, Ikuo 020190
Nanno Energy Research Center, Yamaguchi, Japan

Nargelienė, Viktorija 020157
Center for Physical Sciences and Technology (FTMC), Vilnius, Lithuania

Narsi Patel, Hitarth 020069
SVNIT, Surat, India

Narvarte, Luis 020337, 020446, 020491, 020535, 020536, 020567, 020575
UPM, Madrid, Spain

Nascimento, Lucas 020377
Solar Energy Research Laboratory Fotovoltaica/ UFSC, Florianópolis, Brazil

Nasebandt, Lasse 020063
ISFH, Emmerthal, Germany

Nasser, Hisham 020226
ODTÜ-GÜNAM, Ankara, Türkiye

Naveiro, José Manuel 020414
ENDEF, Zaragoza, Spain

Nazififard, Mohammad 020259, 020428
Côte d`Azur University, Nice, France

Nejim, Ahmed 020058
SILVACO, St. Ives, United Kingdom

Nel, Paul 020382
7SecondSolar, Cape Town, South Africa

Nelson, Jenny 020394
Imperial College London, London, United Kingdom

Neuba, Adam 020114
Paderborn University, Paderborn, Germany

Neuber, Viola 020031
Fraunhofer ISE, Freiburg, Germany

Neuhaus, Holger 020123, 020140
Fraunhofer ISE, Freiburg, Germany

Neumaier, Lukas 020504
Silicon Austria Labs, Villach, Austria

Neussl, Vassilissa 020318, 020430
AIT, Vienna, Austria

Neykova, Neda 020107
Czech Technical University, Prague, Czech Republic

Nezhad, Mahyar 020230
Kiwa PI Berlin, Hudson, United States of America

Nguyen, Viet Xuan 020008
centrotherm international, Blaubeuren, Germany

Nicolet-dit-Félix, Kléber 020251
EPFL, Neuchâtel, Switzerland

Nicot-Senneville, Zoltan 020102
SERIS, Singapore, Singapore

Nielsen, Michael P. 020065
UNSW, Sydney, Australia

Nissen, Hauke 020313
Wattmanufactur, Galmsbüll, Germany

Nitsche, Tobias 020119, 020218
Henkel, Düsseldorf, Germany

Nobre, André M. 020263
PV Doctor, Singapore, Singapore

Noels, Serge 020472
PV CYCLE, Brussels, Belgium

Noh, Yong-Su 020449
KETI, Wonmi-gu, South Korea

Nold, Sebastian 020461
Fraunhofer ISE, Freiburg, France

Nold, Sebastian 020475
Fraunhofer ISE, Freiburg, Germany

Nordboe, Eirik 020495
Fiven Norge, Lillesand, Norway

Norde Santos, Fernanda 020331
DLR, Almería, Spain

Nouri, Bijan 020235, 020237, 020239
DLR, Almería, Spain

Nova, David 020339
National University of Colombia, Bogotá, Colombia

Núñez, Rubén 020209, 020453
UPM, Madrid, Spain

Núñez-Osorio, Alessia 020100
University of Almeria, Almeria, Spain

Nurmesjärvi, Antti 020423
VTT Technical Research Centre of Finland, Oulu, Finland

Nussbaumer, Hartmut 020385
ZHAW, Winterthur, Switzerland

Nyang'onda, Thomas N. 020272
University of Nairobi, Nairobi, Kenya

Obeidavi, Sahereh 020361
Coburg University of Applied Sciences, Coburg, Germany

Oberbeck, Lars 020461
TotalEnergies OneTech, Paris, France

Oberegger Filippi, Ulrich 020551
Eurac Research, Bolzano, Italy

Ocaña, Luis Manuel 020151
ITER, Granadilla de Abona, Spain

Ockert, Ajka 020312
EnBW, Karlsruhe, Germany

Odilio dos Santos, Daniel 020548
UFSC, Florianopolis, Brazil

Öhgren, Gustav 020532
Becquerel Sweden, Knivsta, Sweden

Öttl, Christian 020347
Watt Analytics, Vienna, Austria

Öz, Aksel Kaan 020135
Fraunhofer ISE, Freiburg, Germany

Özden, Talat 020226
ODTÜ-GÜNAM, Ankara, Türkiye

Özkalay, Ebrar — 020160, 020204
SUPSI, Mendrisio, Switzerland

Ogura, Atsushi — 020046
Meiji University, Kanagawa, Japan

Ohdaira, Keisuke — 020131
JAIST, Ishikawa, Japan

Ohshita, Yoshio — 020046
Toyota Technological Institute, Nagoya, Japan

Ojala, Aleksi — 020554
Solarigo Systems, Pirkkala, Finland

Okawa, Hayato — 020115
Tokyo City University, Setagaya, Japan

Okel, Lars A. G. — 020030
TNO, Petten, The Netherlands

Oksanen, Jani — 020067
Aalto University, Espoo, Finland

Oliosi, Michele — 020196
PVsyst, Geneva, Switzerland

Olivares, Douglas — 020311
University of Antofagasta, Antofagasta, Chile

Olivares, Gregorio — 020365, 020366, 020392
CENER, Sarriguren, Spain

Oliveira Santos, João Victor — 020188
EDF R&D, Moret Loing Orvanne, France

Oliveira, Helena — 020420
University of Évora, Évora, Portugal

Oller Westerberg, Amelia — 020570
Becquerel Sweden, Knivsta, Sweden

Ollo, Olatz — 020139
Tecnalia, Donostia - San Sebastián, Spain

Oozeki, Takashi — 020436, 020525
AIST, Koriyama, Japan

Opatovsky, Martin — 020241, 020262
Solargis, Bratislava, Slovakia

Oreski, Gernot — 020136, 020234, 020325, 020500, 020574
PCCL, Leoben, Austria

Ortega, Eneko — 020055, 020153, 020287, 020353
UPV/EHU, Bilbao, Spain

Ortega, Eneko — 020289, 020437
UPV/EHU, Leioa, Spain

Ortega, Pascal — 020214
University of French Polynesia, Faa'a, French Polynesia

Ortiz-Pena, Aaron — 020562
University of Castilla-La Mancha, Albacete, Spain

Ory, Daniel — 020188
EDF R&D, Palaiseau, France

Ory, Daniel 020116
EDF, Palaiseau, France

Osman, Alaa 020006
ISFH, Emmerthal, Germany

Osuna, Jose Antonio 020358
MAGTEL, Córdoba, Spain

Osvald, Oliver 020274
Solargis, Bratislava, Slovakia

Otaegi, Aloña 020055, 020097, 020153, 020287
UPV/EHU, Bilbao, Spain

Otnes, Gaute 020169
Institute for Energy Technology, Kjeller, Norway

Otto, Nicolas 020101
HTW, Berlin, Germany

Otto, William 020390
MARIN, Wageningen, The Netherlands

Ou, Chao-Wei 020350
National Chin-Yi University of Technology, Taichung, Taiwan

Ovaitt, Silvana 020314
NREL, Denver, United States of America

Ovaitt, Silvana 020574
NREL, Golden, United States of America

Oviedo Hernandez, Guillermo 020325
BayWa r.e, Rome, Italy

Ozer, Shay 020379
Agricultural Research Organization, Rishon LeZion, Israel

P. Pires, Maurício 020090
Federal University of Rio de Janeiro, Rio de Janeiro, Brazil

Pabiou, Herve 020338
CETHIL, Villeurbanne, France

Pabst, Elena 020312
ZSW, Stuttgart, Germany

Paiva, Lúcio 020530
Casa dos Ventos, Fortaleza, Brazil

Palais, Olivier 020188
Toulon University, Marseille, France

Palitzsch, Wolfram 020225, 020495
LuxChemTech, Freiberg, Germany

Palomino, Laura 020491, 020535
UPM, Madrid, Spain

Pamir Aly, Shahzada 020229
DEWA, Dubai, United Arab Emirates

Pamula, Bindu 020069
SVNIT, Surat, India

Panda, Pavan Kumar 020284
Anhalt University of Applied Sciences, Köthen, Germany

Pandar, Matthias 020229
Fraunhofer CSP, Halle, Germany

Pander, Matthias 020121, 020142, 020175, 020192, 020218, 020223, 020232
Fraunhofer CSP, Halle, Germany

Panduri, Fabio 020322
BFH, Burgdorf, Switzerland

Pantoja, Jaime 020526
Francisco José de Caldas District University, Bogota, Colombia

Papantoni, Veatriki 020482
DLR, Oldenburg, Germany

Paraficz, Danuta 020204
FFHS, Zurich, Switzerland

Paraskeva, Vasiliki 020064
University of Cyprus, Nicosia, Cyprus

Pardo, Eduardo 020414
Tecnova, Almeira, Spain

Parfeniukas, Karolis 020039
ATLANT 3D, Taastrup, Denmark

Parion, Jonathan 020064
Hasselt Unversity, Genk, Belgium

Park, Hyeonwook 020112
KENTECH, Naju-Si, South Korea

Parmar, Richa 020429
NISE, Gurugram, India

Parra, Johan 020406
Ecole Polytechnique, Palaiseau, France

Parra, Johan 020214
Polytechnic Institute of Paris, Palaiseau, France

Parrilla, Carlos G. 020402
Fujairah Research Centre, Fujairah, United Arab Emirates

Pascual Gallego, Valero 020407
UPM, Madrid, Spain

Pasquier, Mathis 020451
DTU, Roskilde, Denmark

Passaro, Marcello 020513
Sunzest Solar, Rotterdam, The Netherlands

Patel, Dharm 020355
Fraunhofer IMWS, Halle, Germany

Paul, Ananta 020250, 020306
SDU Climate Cluster, Odense, Denmark

Paulescu, Marius 020283
West University of Timisoara, Timisoara, Romania

Paviet-Salomon, Bertrand — 020068, 020467
CSEM, Neuchâtel, Switzerland

Payno, David — 020085, 020094
UAM, Madrid, Spain

Pearce, Pheobe — 020065
UNSW, Sydney, Australia

Peche, René — 020468, 020495
bifa Umweltinstitut, Augsburg, Germany

Pehlivanli, Ezgi — 020521
METU, Ankara, Türkiye

Peibst, Robby — 020006, 020063, 020114
ISFH, Emmerthal, Germany

Pelfort Ojer, Marta — 020241
Solargis, Bratislava, Slovakia

Pelland, Sophie — 020211
Natural Resources Canada, Varennes, Canada

Pelle, Martina — 020249, 020254
Eurac Research, Bolzano, Italy

Peña-Bermudez, Julian — 020110
University of the Caribbean, Santo Domingo, Dominican Republic

Peng, Cheng-Yu — 020350
National Chin-Yi University of Technology, Taichung, Taiwan

Pera, David — 020457
Luxembourg Institute of Science and Technology, Esch-sur-Alzette, Luxembourg

Perani, Martina — 020204
FFHS, Zurich, Switzerland

Peraticos, Elias — 020064
University of Cyprus, Nicosia, Cyprus

Pereda, Ainhoa — 020198, 020358
TECNALIA, Derio, Spain

Pereira Fialho, Luis Andre — 020509
Eurac Research, Bolzano, Italy

Pereira, Sara — 020403, 020418, 020565
University of Évora, Évora, Portugal

Pérez García, Manuel — 020336
University of Almería, La Cañada de San Urbano, Spain

Pérez, Ernesto — 020339
National University of Colombia, Bogotá, Colombia

Pérez, Jairo — 020412
Gonvarri AgroTech, Corvera - Asturias, Spain

Pérez, Jorge — 020412
Gonvarri AgroTech, Corvera - Asturias, Spain

Pérez, Luis — 020412
Gonvarri MS R&D, Corvera - Asturias, Spain

Poulsen, Peter B. 020039
DTU, Copenhagen, Denmark
Poulsen, Peter B. 020250, 020265, 020267, 020376, 020451
DTU, Roskilde, Denmark
Poulsen, Peter Behrensdorff 020028, 020306, 020346
DTU, Roskilde, Denmark
Pourshafi, Pouya 020121, 020125, 020137
AESOLAR, Koenigsbrunn, Germany
Pozza, Cristian 020551
Eurac Research, Bolzano, Italy
Prakash, Jai 020429
NISE, Gurugram, India
Prando, Davide 020485, 020489
Edyna, Bolzano, Italy
Prasad, Manjunath 020225
ISC Konstanz, Konstanz, Germany
Pravettoni, Mauro 020402
Technology Innovation Institute, Abu Dhabi, United Arab Emirates
Preis, Pirmin 020003
ISC Konstanz, Konstanz, Germany
Preu, Ralf 020475
Fraunhofer ISE, Freiburg, Germany
Preuschoff, Jonas 020101
HTW, Berlin, Germany
Protti, Alexander Aguilar 020140
Fraunhofer ISE, Freiburg, Germany
Protti, Alexander 020137
Fraunhofer ISE, Freiburg, Germany
Provost, Marion 020116
IPVF, Palaiseau, France
Puel, Jean Baptiste 020062
IPVF, Palaiseau, France
Puertas López, Antonio Manuel 020100
University of Almeria, Almeria, Spain
Puttock, Claire 020367
Nextracker, Fremont, United States of America

Queste, Samuel 020068
Marie and Louis Pasteur University, Besançon, France
Quiroz, Mónica 020328
Qualifying Photovoltaics, Madrid, Spain

R. Ledesma, Javier 020363
UPM, Madrid, Spain

Rabanal Arabach, Jorge 020183
University of Antofagasta, Antofagasta, Chile

Rabanal-Arabach, Jorge 020129, 020342, 020417, 020422
University of Antofagasta, Antofagasta, Chile

Rabiei, Hossein 020063
ISFH, Emmerthal, Germany

Rachdi, Lazhar 020035, 020068
ISC Konstanz, Konstanz, Germany

Radzevicius, Aurimas 020225
Valoe Cells, Vilnius, Lithuania

Rafiee, Hossein 020539
Frankfurt University of Applied Sciences, Frankfurt am Main, Germany

Raginskis, Justinas 020380
Kaunas University of Technology, Kaunas, Lithuania

Raievska, Oleksandra 020117, 020149
HI ERN, Erlangen, Germany

Rajan, S. Prithivi 020262
LuciSun, Villers-la-Ville, Belgium

Rajkiewicz, Katarzyna 020551
NAPE, Warsaw, Poland

Rakotoniaina, Jean Patrice 020311
CEA / INES, Le Bourget-du-Lac, France

Ramachandran Nair, Jishnu 020233
Fraunhofer CSP, Halle, Germany

Ramesh, Santhosh 020389
imec, Genk, Belgium

Ramírez Ledesma, Javier 020535
UPM, Madrid, Spain

Ramirez, S. 020396
PV Lighthouse, Coledale, Australia

Rampino, Stefano 020087
National Research Council, Parma, Italy

Ramspeck, Klaus 020050
halm elektronik, Frankfurt am Main, Germany

Ranisch, Tadeus 020101
HTW, Berlin, Germany

Ranta, Samuli 020286, 020400
TUAS, Turku, Finland

Ranta, Samuli 020298, 020398
Turku University of Applied Sciences, Turku, Finland

Raposo, Mauro 020565
University of Évora, Évora, Portugal

Ratnagiri, Abhinav 020367
Nextracker, Fremont, United States of America

Raugewitz, Annika 020063, 020114
ISFH, Emmerthal, Germany

Raval, Mehul 020005, 020222, 020463
RCT Solutions, Konstanz, Germany

Razanajao, Aina 020244
SOLAÏS, Valbonne, France

Razi, Umair 020085
IREC, Barcelona, Spain

Recart, Federico 020097
UPV/EHU, Bilbao, Spain

Redondo Cuevas, Marta 020332
UPM, Madrid, Spain

Redondo, Juan Manuel 020209
UPM, Madrid, Spain

Rehan, Muhammad 020112
KIER, Daejeon, South Korea

Rehman, Anees ur 020111, 020164
Hohai University, Changzhou, China

Reichart, Hannah 020167, 020232
University of Applied Sciences Cologne, Cologne, Germany

Reichel, Christian 020123, 020137, 020140
Fraunhofer ISE, Freiburg, Germany

Reichle, Julian 020005, 020222, 020463
RCT Solutions, Konstanz, Germany

Reinders, Angele 020253
TU Eindhoven, Eindhoven, The Netherlands

Reindl, Thomas 020263
SERIS, Singapore, Singapore

Reis, Luiz Filipe 020530
Casa dos Ventos, Fortaleza, Brazil

Rémondeau, Paul 020251
EPFL, Neuchâtel, Switzerland

Renard, Charles 020058
CNRS, Palaiseau, France

Rende, Fedele 020255
ACCA Software, Cosenza, Italy

Rennhofer, Marcus 020180, 020281, 020318, 020334, 020347, 020430
AIT, Vienna, Austria

Rentsch, Jochen 020475
Fraunhofer ISE, Freiburg, Germany

Rerat, Michel 020060
IPREM, Pau, France

Reshef, Liad 020379
Agricultural Research Organization, Rishon LeZion, Israel

Revol, Inès 020074
LAAS-CNRS, Toulouse, France

Reyal, Jean-Pierre 020303
SemperStyl, Eragny, France

Riaño, Sandra 020197, 020358
TECNALIA, Derio, Spain
Richards, Bryce S. 020272
KIT, Karlsruhe, Germany
Riechelman, Stefan 020181
PTB, Braunschweig, Germany
Riechelmann, Stefan 020177, 020199, 020211
PTB, Braunschweig, Germany
Riedel-Lyngskær, Nicholas 020451
DTU, Roskilde, Denmark
Rienäcker, Michael 020063
ISFH, Emmerthal, Germany
Rindert, Sören 020230
Kiwa PI Berlin, Berlin, Germany
Ríos Moral, Lucía 020501
UCM, Madrid, Spain
Ríos-Ledesma, Felipe 020446
UPM, Madrid, Spain
Ripke, Melanie 020006
ISFH, Emmerthal, Germany
Riva, Roland 020495
CEA, Le Bourget-du-Lac, France
Rivas Rodríguez, José Manuel 020326
Enertis Applus+, Madrid, Spain
Robledo, Jesús 020262
LuciSun, Villers-la-Ville, Belgium
Rodríguez Lucas, Delia 020407
EkiLabs, Boston, United States of America
Rodríguez Plaza, José Luis 020508
Autonomous University of Madrid, Madrid, Spain
Rodríguez Rodríguez, Araceli 020501
UCM, Madrid, Spain
Rodríguez Salazar, David Leonardo 020441
District University of Bogotá, Bogotá, Colombia
Rodríguez, Araceli 020508
UCM, Madrid, Spain
Rodríguez, Diego Julián 020526
Francisco José de Caldas District University, Bogota, Colombia
Rodríguez, Isabel 020257
IMDEA Nanoscience, Madrid, Spain
Rodriguez, Sonia Maria 020289
UPV/EHU, Leioa, Spain
Rodríguez, Velia 020097
UPV/EHU, Bilbao, Spain
Rodríguez-Conde, Sofía 020326
Enertis Applus+, Madrid, Spain

Rodríguez-Gallegos, Carlos D. 020149, 020150
SERIS, Singapore, Singapore
Rodríguez-Romero, Sebastián 020342, 020417, 020422
University of Antofagasta, Antofagasta, Chile
Rodziewicz, Hanna 020498
Gdansk University of Technology, Gdansk, Poland
Römer, Udo 020006, 020063
ISFH, Emmerthal, Germany
Röver, Ingo 020225
LuxChemTech, Freiberg, Germany
Rojas, Christian A. 020422
Federico Santa María Technical University, Valparaíso, Chile
Rojas-Henríquez, Katalina 020129
University of Antofagasta, Antofagasta, Chile
Román, Eduardo 020139
Tecnalia, Donostia - San Sebastián, Spain
Romeo, Alessandro 020057, 020089, 020093
University of Verona, Verona, Italy
Romer, Pascal 020231
Fraunhofer ISE, Freiburg, Germany
Roodt, Roelof 020185
Nelson Mandela University, Port Elizabeth, South Africa
Roosloot, Nathan 020169
Institute for Energy Technology, Kjeller, Norway
Rosca, Victor 020030
TNO, Petten, The Netherlands
Rosen, Isaac 020225
Copprint, Jerusalem, Israel
Rosenfeld, Lavi 020379
Agricultural Research Organization, Rishon LeZion, Israel
Rosina, Konstantin 020241
Solargis, Bratislava, Slovakia
Rossa, Carlos 020432, 020434
Sunveon, Madrid, Spain
Rouffie, Brice 020068
SEGTON Advanced Technology, Versailles, France
Roulleau, Lea 020303
CSTB, Marne-la-Vallée, France
Rousset, Jean 020116
EDF, Palaiseau, France
Roy, Shantanu 020519
CSTEP, Bengaluru, India
Rudolph, Dominik 020003, 020068
ISC Konstanz, Konstanz, Germany

Rudzikas, Matas 020380
The Applied Research Institute for Prospective Technologies, Vilnius, Lithuania

Rüther, Ricardo 020377
Solar Energy Research Laboratory Fotovoltaica/ UFSC, Florianópolis, Brazil

Rüther, Ricardo 020548
UFSC, Florianopolis, Brazil

Ruf, Manuel 020455
Robert Bosch, Stuttgart, Germany

Ruiz Donoso, Elena 020331
DLR, Almería, Spain

S. Sousa, Graciana 020090
Federal University of Rio de Janeiro, Rio de Janeiro, Brazil

Safarian, Jafar 020011
NTNU, Trondheim, Norway

Sah, Dheeraj 020039
Aarhus University, Aarhus, Denmark

Sahin, Hasret 020479
LUT University, Lappeenranta, Finland

Saito, Kimihiko 020106
Tokyo City University, Setagaya, Japan

Salem, Mohammad 020428
Australian University, Kuwait City, Kuwait

Salerno, Giorgia 020077
University of Milano-Bicocca, Milan, Italy

Salis, Fabio 020541
Iberdrola, Rome, Italy

Salvador, Antonio 020358
MAGTEL, Córdoba, Spain

Sample, Tony 020213
European Commission JRC, Ispra, Italy

Samuolienė, Giedrė 020380
The Lithuanian Research Centre for Agriculture and Forestry, Kaunas, Lithuania

San José, Luis Javier 020209, 020453
UPM, Madrid, Spain

Sánchez de León Peque, Miguel 020243
ieco.io, Vigo, Spain

Sanchez Garcia, Alfredo 020270
SINTEF, Trondheim, Norway

Sanchez, Hugo 020056, 020158, 020284
Anhalt University of Applied Sciences, Köthen, Germany

Sanchez, Jesus 020437
UPV/EHU, Vitoria-Gasteiz, Spain

Sanchez, Laura 020437
UPV/EHU, Leioa, Spain
Sánchez, Yudania 020085
IREC, Barcelona, Spain
Sanchez-Friera, Paula 020412, 020513, 020521
Solkeys, Gijón, Spain
Sanchez-Ruiz, Alain 020437
UPV/EHU, Vitoria-Gasteiz, Spain
Sansavini, Giovanni 020296
ETH, Zurich, Switzerland
Sansoni, Paola 020066
CNR-INO, Florence, Italy
Santamaría Fernández, Susanna 020249
TECNALIA, Derio, Spain
Santamaría-Sancho, Juan 020363
UPM, Madrid, Spain
Santos, Jose Domingo 020197, 020198, 020358
TECNALIA, Derio, Spain
Santos, Rodrigo 020530
Casa dos Ventos, Fortaleza, Brazil
Sanz Martinez, Asier 020546
Tecnalia, Bilbao, Spain
Sanz, Asier 020514
Tecnalia, BRTA, Derio, Spain
Sanz, Asier 020197
TECNALIA, Derio, Spain
Sanz-Cuadrado, Cristina 020575
UPM, Madrid, Spain
Sanz-Saiz, Carlos 020297
CIEMAT, Madrid, Spain
Sarafijanovic-Djukic, Natasa 020204
FFHS, Regensdorf, Switzerland
Saretti, Angelica 020301
Polytechnic University of Bari, Bari, Italy
Sarkadi, Monika 020569
ISC Konstanz, Konstanz, Germany
Sauer, Thomas 020140
EXXERGY, Gräfelfing, Germany
Saura, Juan Antonio 020506
University of Murcia, Murcia, Spain
Savisalo, Tuukka 020225
Valoe, Mikkeli, Finland
Saw, Min Hsian 020402
Technology Innovation Institute, Abu Dhabi, United Arab Emirates
Saxena, Anmol Ratan 020429
NIT, Delhi, India

Sayed, Abdullah Abu 020180, 020230
Kiwa PI Berlin, Berlin, Germany

Scaltrito, Luciano 020079
Polytechnic University of Turin, Turin, Italy

Scerri, Kenneth 020334
University of Malta, Msida, Malta

Schading, Steve 020443
University of Agder, Grimstad, Norway

Schäfer, Aysim 020388
Next2Sun Technology, Dillingen, Germany

Schäfer, Sebastian 020539
Frankfurt University of Applied Sciences, Frankfurt am Main, Germany

Schenk, Paul 020192
Fraunhofer CSP, Halle, Germany

Schermer, John 020067
Radboud University, Nijmegen, The Netherlands

Scherret, Jacqueline 020255
A-Null Development, Vienna, Austria

Schifferegger, Raffael 020162
OFI, Vienna, Austria

Schimanke, Sabrina 020006
ISFH, Emmerthal, Germany

Schirmer, Yoko 020101
HTW, Berlin, Germany

Schläger, Christian 020240
Leibniz University Hannover, Hannover, Germany

Schlatmann, Rutger 020101
HTW, Berlin, Germany

Schmidt Davidsen, Rasmus 020037, 020104
Aarhus University, Aarhus, Denmark

Schnaus, Dominik 020237
TUM, Garching, Germany

Schneider, Andreas 020129, 020183
University of Applied Sciences Gelsenkirchen, Gelsenkirchen, Germany

Schneider, Astrid 020255
TU Wien, Vienna, Austria

Schneider, Friedrich 020482
LPKF SolarQuipment, Suhl, Germany

Schneider, Marc Gabriel 020522
University of Applied Science Cologne, Cologne, Germany

Schneiderlöchner, Eric 020033
VON ARDENNE, Dresden, Germany

Schnierer, Branislav 020262
Solargis, Bratislava, Slovakia

Schönau, Maximilian 020361
Coburg University of Applied Sciences, Coburg, Germany

Schönau, Maximilian 020544
smartblue, Munich, Germany

Schönheits, Markus 020468, 020470
bifa Umweltinstitut, Augsburg, Germany

Schranz, Christian 020255
TU Wien, Vienna, Austria

Schrempf, Michael 020199
PTB, Braunschweig, Germany

Schrijvers, Patrick 020390
MARIN, Wageningen, The Netherlands

Schröter, Nick 020142
Fraunhofer CSP, Halle, Germany

Schubert, Martin C. 020475
Fraunhofer ISE, Freiburg, Germany

Schubnel, Baptiste 020238
CSEM, Neuchâtel, Switzerland

Schüler, Marc Andre 020388
Next2Sun Technology, Dillingen, Germany

Schüler, Marc Andre 020411
Next2Sun, Dillingen, Germany

Schueler, Nadine 020015
Freiberger Instruments, Freiberg, Germany

Schulte-Huxel, Henning 020008, 020260
ISFH, Emmerthal, Germany

Schultz, Christof 020101
HTW, Berlin, Germany

Schulz, Philip 020060
IPVF, Palaiseau, France

Schulze, Achim 020361
Rosenheim Technical University of Applied Sciences, Rosenheim, Germany

Schulze, Patricia S.C. 020475
Fraunhofer ISE, Freiburg, Germany

Schwenke, Almut 020495
SGL Battery Solutions, Meitingen, Germany

Sciuto, Marcello 020010
Enel Green Power, Catania, Italy

Scognamiglio, Alessandra 020541
ENEA, Naples, Italy

Scognamiglio, Alessandra 020378
ENEA, Portici, Italy

Sedaghat, Ahmad 020428
Australian University, Kuwait City, Kuwait

Seiffert, Christoph 020169
Institute for Energy Technology, Kjeller, Norway

Seiffert, Daniela 020008
centrotherm international, Blaubeuren, Germany

Seitz, Matthias 020468
bifa Umweltinstitut, Augsburg, Germany

Selj, Josefine H. 020169
Institute for Energy Technology, Kjeller, Norway

Senno, Maximiliano Alejandro 020226
University of Valencia, Paterna, Spain

Senturk, Bilge 020556
ODTU GUNAM, Ankara, Türkiye

Setien, Eneko 020198
TECNALIA, Derio, Spain

Šetkus, Arūnas 020157
Center for Physical Sciences and Technology (FTMC), Vilnius, Lithuania

Shaaban, Ahmed 020402
Technology Innovation Institute, Abu Dhabi, United Arab Emirates

Shah, Syed Fawad Ali 020112
KENTECH, Naju-Si, South Korea

Shanmugam, Raphael 020218, 020220
ISC Konstanz, Konstanz, Germany

Sharma, Rajesh Kumar 020071, 020081
SVNIT, Surat, India

Sharma, Sushma 020563
SRM University, Sonipat, India

Shen, Xinyi 020226
University of Oxford, Oxford, United Kingdom

Shen, Zhenjue 020001
YIST, Jiangyin, China

Shin, Donghyeop 020112
KIER, Daejeon, South Korea

Shin, Woo Gyun 020324, 020357
KIER, Daejeon, South Korea

Shin, Woo-gyun 020561
KIER, Daejeon, South Korea

Shirai, Yasuhiro 020115
NIMS, Tsukuba, Japan

Shirazi, Elham 020544
University of Twente, Enschede, The Netherlands

Shishavan, Amir Asgharzadeh 020367
Nextracker, Fremont, United States of America

Shishido, Hirotaka 020106
Tokyo City University, Setagaya, Japan

Shochet, Ofer 020225
Copprint, Jerusalem, Israel

Shyong, Yung-Jen 020163
ITRI, Hsinchu, Taiwan

Sicot, Lionel 020217
CEA / INES, Le Bourget-du-Lac, France

Sidler, Anika 020226
School of Life Sciences FHNW, Muttenz, Switzerland

Siebert, Michael 020206
ISFH, Emmerthal, Germany

Siefer, Gerald 020246
Fraunhofer ISE, Freiburg, Germany

Sierra, Daniel 020491
UPM, Madrid, Spain

Sigounis, Anna-Maria 020248, 020249
Concordia University, Montreal, Canada

Søiland, Anne-Karin 020495
ReSiTec, Kristiansand, Norway

Silva, José A. 020304, 020409, 020420
University of Évora, Évora, Portugal

Silva, José 020403
University of Évora, Évora, Portugal

Silvestre, Santiago 020301
UPC, Barcelona, Spain

Simeunovic, Jelena 020238
CSEM, Neuchâtel, Switzerland

Simón-Allué, Raquel 020127, 020414, 020517
ENDEF, Zaragoza, Spain

Singh, Ravi 020571
DNV, Arnhem, The Netherlands

Sinha, Amish Kumar 020463
RCT Solutions, Konstanz, Germany

Sinopoli, Alessandro 020042
QEERI, Doha, Qatar

Sivaramakrishnan Radhakrishnan, Hariharsudan 020064
Hasselt Unversity, Genk, Belgium

Sivaramakrishnan, Hariharsudan 020225
IMEC, Genk, Belgium

Snaith, Henry 020226
University of Oxford, Oxford, United Kingdom

Søndenå, Rune 020503
Institute for Energy Technology, Kjeller, Norway

Sobajima, Yasushi 020131
Gifu University, Gifu, Japan

Soler Toledo, Denet 020509
University of Antofagasta, Antofagasta, Chile

Solomon, Asfaw A. 020479
LUT University, Lappeenranta, Finland

Solórzano, Jorge 020328
Qualifying Photovoltaics, Madrid, Spain

Sondoqah, Mousa 020316
Becquerel Institute, Bolzano, Italy

Sondoqah, Mousa 020261
Eurac Research, Bolzano, Italy

Song, Hee-eun 020045
KIER, Daejeon, South Korea

Spagnolo, Sofia 020462, 020466
RSE, Milan, Italy

Spataru, Sergiu V. 020265, 020267, 020283, 020376, 020451
DTU, Roskilde, Denmark

Spataru, Sergiu Viorel 020346
DTU, Roskilde, Denmark

Spera, Fabian 020411
Next2Sun, Dillingen, Germany

Spihola, Jan 020355
DiSUN Deutsche Solarservice, Werder, Germany

Sraisth, 020005, 020222
RCT Solutions, Konstanz, Germany

Sraisth, Sraisth 020463
RCT Solutions, Konstanz, Germany

Staňková, Tereza 020107
Czech Technical University, Prague, Czech Republic

Steckenreiter, Verena 020063
ISFH, Emmerthal, Germany

Stegemann, Bert 020309
Berlin University of Applied Sciences, Berlin, Germany

Stegemann, Bert 020101
HTW, Berlin, Germany

Stellbogen, Dirk 020312
ZSW, Stuttgart, Germany

Stensborg, Jan F. 020250
Stensborg, Roskilde, Denmark

Stensborg, Jan 020306
Stensborg, Roskilde, Denmark

Stieldorf, Karin 020255
TU Wien, Vienna, Austria

Stierstorfer, Johannes 020225
WIP - Renewable Energies, Munich, Germany

Stierstorfer, Johannes 020551
WIP Renewable Energies, Munich, Germany

Stivanello, Juan José 020226
Eurac Research, Bolzano, Italy

Stoicescu, Liviu 020198
Solarzentrum Stuttgart, Stuttgart, Germany

Stowhas-Villa, Alejandro 020422
Federico Santa María Technical University, Valparaiso, Chile

Stoyanova Lyubenova, Teodora 020173
European Commission JRC, Ispra, Italy

Sträter, Hendrik 020211
PTB, Braunschweig, Germany

Strey, Jessica 020063, 020114
ISFH, Emmerthal, Germany

Strömberg, Rich 020472
University of Alaska, Fairbanks, United States of America

Stroyuk, Oleksander 020185
HI ERN, Erlangen, Germany

Stroyuk, Oleksandr 020117, 020149, 020150
HI ERN, Erlangen, Germany

Suárez Sánchez, Sergio 020326
Enertis Applus+, Madrid, Spain

Subasi, Dilara Maria 020475
Fraunhofer ISE, Freiburg, Germany

Sudbury, Ben A. 020396
PV Lighthouse, Coledale, Australia

Suemitsu, Issei 020484
Hitachi, Kokubunji, Japan

Suhonen, Riikka 020423
VTT Technical Research Centre of Finland, Oulu, Finland

Sulca, Kabir Paúl 020191, 020205
University of Valladolid, Valladolid, Spain

Svatos, Jan 020250
DTU, Roskilde, Denmark

Sylla, David 020063
ISFH, Emmerthal, Germany

Syre Wiig, Marie 020340
IFE, Kjeller, Norway

Szarek, Magda 020298, 020398
University of Turku, Turku, Finland

Taghipour Kani, Ghaem 020335, 020374
Amirkabir University of Technology, Tehran, Iran

Takahashi, Kanji 020106
Tokyo City University, Setagaya, Japan

Talvi, Micke 020528
Tampere University, Tampere, Finland

Tanahashi, Tadanori 020436
AIST, Koriyama, Japan

Tang, Kai 020011
SINTEF, Trondheim, Norway

Tang, Torben 020028
IPU P/S, Virum, Denmark

Tang, Torben 020037
IPU, Virum, Denmark

Tayebjee, Murad J. Y. 020065
UNSW, Sydney, Australia

Taylor, Nigel 020210
European Commission JRC, Ispra, Italy

Tellez Rodriguez, Eduardo 020230
Kiwa PI Berlin, Berlin, Germany

Teppe, Andreas 020005
RCT Solutions, Konstanz, Germany

Terheiden, Barbara 020031
University of Konstanz, Constance, Germany

Terrados, Cristian 020205
University of Valladolid, Valladolid, Spain

Thakur, Dhruv Singh 020071, 020081
SVNIT, Surat, India

Theocharides, Spyros 020371
Univers, Courbevoie, France

Thomas, Jean 020169
Ciel et Terre, Lille, France

Thorning, Jacob K. 020267, 020283
DTU, Roskilde, Denmark

Thorsteinsson, Sune 020039
DTU, Copenhagen, Denmark

Thorsteinsson, Sune 020037
DTU, Lyngby, Denmark

Thorsteinsson, Sune 020028, 020249, 020250, 020265, 020306, 020477
DTU, Roskilde, Denmark

Timofte, Tudor 020218, 020221
ISC Konstanz, Konstanz, Germany

Ting, San-Yu 020161, 020163
ITRI, Hsinchu, Taiwan

Tissier, Corentin 020238
CSEM, Neuchâtel, Switzerland

Tönies, Alexandra 020523
University of Applied Sciences Cologne, Cologne, Germany

Tomšič, Špela 020047
University of Ljubljana, Ljubljana, Slovenia

Tong, Yongfeng 020108, 020109
QEERI, Doha, Qatar

Topič, Marko 020047, 020269, 020319
University of Ljubljana, Ljubljana, Slovenia

Torabi, Narges 020089
University of Verona, Verona, Italy

Torelly, Guilherme 020092
PUC-Rio, Rio de Janeiro, Brazil
Torre, Gorka 020437
UPV/EHU, Leioa, Spain
Torres Aguilar, Moira Itzel 020214
CentraleSupélec, Gif-sur-Yvette, France
Torres Aguilar, Moira Itzel 020406
CNRS, Gif-sur-Yvette, France
Torres Silva, Nicole 020546
ATAMOSTEC, Santiago, Chile
Torres, Oscar 020110
National University of Colombia, Bogotá, Colombia
Tosi, Irene 020037
IPU, Virum, Denmark
Tran Caliste, Thu Nhi 020546
European Synchrotron Radiation Facility (ESRF), Grenoble, France
Treberspurg, Christoph 020255
Treberspurg und Partner Ziviltechniker, Vienna, Austria
Treberspurg, Martin 020255
Treberspurg und Partner Ziviltechniker, Vienna, Austria
Trefzer, Aaron 020135
Fraunhofer ISE, Freiburg, Germany
Trifiletti, Vanira 020087
University of Milano-Bicocca, Milan, Italy
Trigo-Gonzalez, Mauricio 020342, 020422
University of Antofagasta, Antofagasta, Chile
Tsai, Min-An 020053, 020083, 020161, 020163
ITRI, Hsinchu, Taiwan
Tsanakas, Ioannis (John) A. 020262
CEA / INES, Le Bourget-du-Lac, France
Tsanakas, Ioannis (John) A. 020544
CEA, Le Bourget-du-Lac, France
Tsanakas, Ioannis (John) 020546
CEA / INES, Le Bourget-du-Lac, France
Tsanakas, Ioannis (John) 020317
CEA INES, Le Bourget-du-Lac, France
Tsanakas, Ioannis (John) 020513, 020521
CEA, Le Bourget-du-Lac, France
Tsanakas, Ioannis 020217, 020338
CEA / INES, Le Bourget-du-Lac, France
Tsanakas, Ioannis 020500
CEA, Le Bourget-du-Lac, France
Tsanakas, John A. 020311
CEA / INES, Le Bourget-du-Lac, France
Tseberlidis, Giorgio 020093
University of Milano Bicocca, Milan, Italy

Tseberlidis, Giorgio 020087
University of Milano-Bicocca, Milan, Italy

Tsoi, Konstantin 020113
ODTÜ-GÜNAM, Ankara, Türkiye

Tsombou, Francois M. 020402
Fujairah Research Centre, Fujairah, United Arab Emirates

Tsuno, Yuki 020436
AIST, Koriyama, Japan

Tsunoda, Jun 020484
Hitachi, Kokubunji, Japan

Tsunoda, Jun 020186
Hitachi, Tokyo, Japan

Tulinski, Lona 020385
ZHAW, Winterthur, Switzerland

Tune, Daniel 020220, 020221, 020225
ISC Konstanz, Konstanz, Germany

Turcu, Mircea 020063
ISFH, Emmerthal, Germany

Turek, Marko 020004, 020052
Fraunhofer CSP, Halle (Saale), Germany

Ueda, Yuzuru 020320, 020525
Tokyo University of Science, Tokyo, Japan

Ujvari, Gusztav 020318, 020430
AIT, Vienna, Austria

Ulbikaitė, Vaidvilė 020157
Applied Research Institute for Prospective Technologies, Vilnius, Lithuania

Ulbikas, Juras 020225
Protechnology, Vilnius, Lithuania

Ulyashin, Alexander G. 020011
SINTEF, Oslo, Norway

Unsur, Veysel 020020
ODTÜ-GÜNAM, Ankara, Türkiye

Urban, Harald 020255
TU Wien, Vienna, Austria

Useni, Yannick 020393
University of Lubumbashi, Lubumbashi, Congo (DRC)

Uzuner, Bahri Eren 020113
ODTÜ-GÜNAM, Ankara, Türkiye

Väisänen, Kaisa-Leena 020423
VTT Technical Research Centre of Finland, Oulu, Finland

Vaicikauskas, Viktoras 020157
Center for Physical Sciences and Technology (FTMC), Vilnius, Lithuania

Vecino, Fernando Román 020346
DTU, Roskilde, Denmark

Veerman, Sebastian 020035
ISC Konstanz, Konstanz, Germany

Vega de Seoane, José Maria 020252
Becquerel Institute Spain, San Sebastian, Spain

Vega de Seoane, Jose 020546
Becquerel Institute, Brussels, Belgium

Vega-Herrera, Jorge 020342
University of Antofagasta, Antofagasta, Chile

Vehus, Tore Sandnes 020443
University of Agder, Grimstad, Norway

Veirman, Jordi 020203, 020226, 020254
Eurac Research, Bolzano, Italy

Velasco, Angel 020367
Nextracker, Fremont, United States of America

Veludo, Jorge 020317
Galp Energia, Lisbon, Portugal

Veneri, Alessandro 020093
University of Verona, Verona, Italy

Vergura, Silvano 020301
Polytechnic University of Bari, Bari, Italy

Verlinden, Pierre 020001
YIST, Jiangyin, China

Vermang, Bart 020064
Hasselt Unversity, Genk, Belgium

Vernay, Christophe 020244
SOLAÏS, Valbonne, France

Vero, Giuseppe 020301
Polytechnic University of Bari, Bari, Italy

Veronese, Elisa 020513
Eurac Research, Bolzano, Italy

Veurman, Welmoed 020063
ISFH, Emmerthal, Germany

Viani, Lucas 020326
Enertis Applus+, Madrid, Spain

Vicente-Laiglesia, Pablo 020181
European Climate, Infrastructure and Environment Executive Agency, Brussels, Belgium

Vidal de Oliveira, Aline 020377
Solar Energy Research Laboratory Fotovoltaica/ UFSC, Florianópolis, Brazil

Vidal, Beatriz Muñoz 020414
IaSol, Zaragoza, Spain

Vidal-Fuentes, Pedro 020094
IREC, Barcelona, Spain

Vulic, Natasa 020296
Univesity of Applied Arts and Sciences Northwestern Switzerland, Muttenz, Switzerland

Vumbugwa, Monphias 020185, 020193, 020344
Nelson Mandela University, Port Elizabeth, South Africa

Waibel, Christoph 020511
Flemish Institute for Technological Research (VITO), Genk, Belgium

Wakabayashi, Ryo 020484
Hitachi, Kokubunji, Japan

Wakazono, Kouzen 020131
Gifu University, Gifu, Japan

Wallner, Gernot M. 020227
University of Linz, Linz, Austria

Walpita, Harsha 020169
University of Oslo, Kjeller, Norway

Walsh, Yoselyn 020520
Costa Rica Institute of Technology, Cartago, Costa Rica

Wambach, Karsten 020468, 020470
bifa Umweltinstitut, Augsburg, Germany

Wang, Chia-Chen 020549
ITRI, Hsinchu, Taiwan

Wang, Shuo 020286, 020400
TUAS, Turku, Finland

Wang, Tzuya 020549
ITRI, Hsinchu, Taiwan

Wang, Xiaolin 020381
Mälardalen University, Västerås, Sweden

Wannenwetsch, Jann 020312
EnBW, Karlsruhe, Germany

Wargocki, Pawel 020551
DTU, Roskilde, Denmark

Waschl, Alfred 020255
buildingSMART, Vienna, Austria

Weber, Thomas 020180, 020230
Kiwa PI Berlin, Berlin, Germany

Weeber, Arthur W. 020515
TU Delft, Delft, The Netherlands

Wei, Wenpeng 020484
Hitachi, Kokubunji, Japan

Weihs, Philipp 020281
BOKU, Vienna, Austria

Weinrich, Frank 020177
PTB, Braunschweig, Germany

Weiß, Marius 020361
Coburg University of Applied Sciences, Coburg, Germany

Wellens, Christine 020135
Fraunhofer ISE, Freiburg, Germany
Whyatt, Duncan 020394
Lancaster University, Lancaster, United Kingdom
Wienands, Karl 020218, 020220, 020221
ISC Konstanz, Konstanz, Germany
Wiesenfarth, Maike 020246
Fraunhofer ISE, Freiburg, Germany
Wietler, Tobias 020063
ISFH, Emmerthal, Germany
Wilbert, Stefan 020235, 020237, 020239, 020331
DLR, Almeria, Spain
Willers, Guido 020201
Fraunhofer CSP, Halle, Germany
Wilson, Helen R. 020249
Fraunhofer ISE, Freiburg, Germany
Winter, Renate 020063
ISFH, Emmerthal, Germany
Winter, Stefan 020177, 020181
PTB, Braunschweig, Germany
Wirtz, Wiebke 020260
ISFH, Emmerthal, Germany
Witkowska, Agnieszka 020498
Gdansk University of Technology, Gdansk, Poland
Wittmer, Bruno 020196
PVsyst, Geneva, Switzerland
Wolf, Andreas 020031
Fraunhofer ISE, Freiburg, Germany
Wong, Craig 020230
Kiwa PI Berlin, Berlin, Germany
Wu, Li-Guo 020021
TSEC, Hsinchu, Taiwan
Wu, Yu 020030
TNO, Petten, The Netherlands
Wyss, Philippe 020068
CSEM, Neuchâtel, Switzerland

Xiong, Weizhen 020320
Tokyo University of Science, Tokyo, Japan
Xu, Jiahui 020001
YIST, Jiangyin, China
Xu, Wenhao 020144, 020208
TÜV Rheinland, Shanghai, China
Xu, Xiaoqi 020263
SERIS, Singapore, Singapore

Xu, Yu 020263
SERIS, Singapore, Singapore

Xuereb, Steven 020180, 020230
Kiwa PI Berlin, Berlin, Germany

Yadav, Shivendra 020071, 020081
SVNIT, Surat, India

Yamaguchi, Yosuke 020484
Hitachi, Kokubunji, Japan

Yanagida, Masatoshi 020115
NIMS, Tsukuba, Japan

Yanar, T. Meriç 020027
Kalyon PV, Ankara, Türkiye

Yang, Donggeon 020323
K-water, Daejeon, South Korea

Yang, Hyoung-Kyu 020449
KETI, Wonmi-gu, South Korea

Yde, Leif 020250, 020306
Stensborg, Roskilde, Denmark

Ye, JiaYi 020102
SERIS, Singapore, Singapore

Yerci, Selcuk 020113
ODTÜ-GÜNAM, Ankara, Türkiye

Ylikunnari, Mari 020423
VTT Technical Research Centre of Finland, Oulu, Finland

Ylinen, Marko 020444
Satakunta University of Applied Sciences, Pori, Finland

Ylipaino, Juho 020444, 020445, 020554
TUAS, Tampere, Finland

Yılmaz, Büşra 020521
Kameleon Solar, Roosendaal, The Netherlands

Yordadov, Georgi 020389
imec, Diepenbeek, Belgium

Younes, Kareem 020487
Khalifa University, Abu Dhabi, United Arab Emirates

Yu, Cheng-Yeh 020021, 020053
TSEC, Hsinchu, Taiwan

Yu, Shusen 020406
Ecole Polytechnique, Palaiseau, France

Yuan, Xiao 020001
YIST, Jiangyin, China

Yun, Jae Ho 020112
KENTECH, Naju-si, South Korea

Zaimi, Mhammed 020171
University of Chouaib Doukkali, El Jadida, Morocco

Zanatta Britto, João Victor 020025
PUCRS, Porto Alegre, Brazil
Zanesco, Izete 020023, 020025
PUCRS, Porto Alegre, Brazil
Zaror, Yasmin 020225
WIP - Renewable Energies, Munich, Germany
Zarzalejo, Luis F. 020237, 020331
CIEMAT, Madrid, Spain
Zekri, Atef 020146
QEERI, Doha, Qatar
Zerafa, Steve 020334
PIXAM, Msida, Malta
Zhang, Geng 020001
Jolywood (ShanXi) Solar Technology, Taiyuan, China
Zhang, Jingwei 020111
Hohai University, Changzhou, China
Zhang, Kai 020233
FZJ, Jülich, Germany
Zhang, Wenjing 020001
YIST, Jiangyin, China
Zhang, Wuai 020101
HZB, Berlin, Germany
Zhang, Yating 020144, 020208
TÜV Rheinland, Shanghai, China
Zhou, Qilin 020102
SERIS, Singapore, Singapore
Zhu, Junjie 020017
Institute for Energy Technology, Kjeller, Norway
Ziaullah, Abdul Wahab 020278, 020291
QEERI, Doha, Qatar
Zilles, Roberto 020154, 020348
University of São Paulo, São Paulo, Brazil
Zimmermann, Iwan 020116
IPVF, Palaiseau, France
Zubillaga, Oihana 020139
Tecnalia, Donostia - San Sebastián, Spain
Zugasti, Eugenia 020334
CENER, Pamplona, Spain
Zugasti, Eugenia 020300
CENER, Sarriguren, Spain
Zwahlen, Theo 020369
BFH, Burgdorf, Switzerland

KEYWORDS OF EU PVSEC 2025 PROCEEDINGS PAPERS

3D GIS	020457
3D Microstructure	020119
3D Shading Model	020432
Accelerated Aging	020254
Accuracy	020276
Adhesion	020384
Adhesive	020384
Adhesives	020127
Adoption vs. Implementation	020563
Aesthetic	020306
Africa	020272
AgBiS2	020071
Agri-photovoltaics	020396
Agriculture	020409
AgriPV	020464
Agrivoltaic	020398, 020407, 020541
Agrivoltaics	020378, 020379, 020388, 020394, 020400, 020402, 020403, 020409, 020412, 020543, 020565
Albedo	020443
Albedo Measurement	020287
Alkaline Leaching	020011
All-Sky Imagers	020267
AlN	020131
Alternative Materials	020020
Aluminium Frame Removal	020497
Aluminium-backed Modules	020192
Aluminum Oxide	020008
Amorphous Silicon	020043
Amorphous Silicon Carbide Crystallization	020079
Ancillary Services	020571
Anion Exchange	020117
Anomaly Detection	020358
Antimony	020140
Antimony Selenide	020087
Antimony-Doping	020015

Characteristics Addition	020081
Characterization	020050, 020119, 020121, 020151, 020166, 020459
CIGS	020097
CIGS/Perovskite Solar Cell	020104
Circular Economy	020141, 020504, 020510, 020517
Circularity	020470, 020472, 020507, 020517
Citizen Participation	020491, 020575
Clay	020300
Clean Firm Power	020487
Clean Transportation	020428
Cleaning	020332
Cleaning Frequency	020348
Cleaning Optimization Asset Management	020339
Clear-sky	020278
Clear-Sky Detection	020340
Climate Change	020402
Climate-dependent Degradation	020150
Climate-responsive Design	020259
Climate-Specific PV O&M	020546
Cloud Detection	020267
Clustering	020243
Co-Extruded EPE	020135
Co-Visibility	020244
Collective Self-consumption	020490
Color Stability	020254
Colored Photovoltaics	020556
ColorFoil	020306
Comfort	020302
Compact Furnace	020025
Comparative Life Cycle Assessment (LCA)	020303
Competitiveness	020573
Compliance	020444
Composite Encapsulant	020139
Composites	020498
Computational Efficiency	020432
Computer Vision	020336, 020511
COMSOL	020104

ECA	020119
Ecodesign	020470
Ecology Index	020468
Economic Feasibility	020394
Economic Valuation	020492
Economic Value Assessment	020486
Education	020548
Education for Sustainable Development (ESD)	020569
Educational Resources	020100
Effects of Temperature and Irradiance	020171
Efficiency Forecast	020279
EL Images Outdoors	020186
EL Imaging	020185, 020510
EL Signal-to-Noise Ratio	020191
Electric Buses	020422, 020457
Electric Mobility	020420
Electric Vehicle Charging	020441
Electric Vehicle Charging Infrastructure	020526
Electrical Mismatch	020265
Electrically Conductive Adhesive	020218
Electricity Demand Coverage	020562
Electricity Market	020332
Electricity Price	020298
Electroluminescence	020188, 020201, 020205, 020206
Electroluminescence (EL) Images	020164
Electrolyzer	020426
Electron Multiplication	020068
Emitter Sheet Resistance	020025
Encapsulant Defects	020157
Encapsulants	020150
Encapsulation	020227
End-of-life PV	020510
Energy Balance	020439
Energy Communities	020445, 020535, 020575
Energy Community	020567
Energy Curtailment	020492
Energy Loss	020223

Energy Management System	020534
Energy Management System (EMS)	020536
Energy Performance Directive	020477
Energy Performance of Buildings Directive (EPBD)	020551
Energy Poverty	020564
Energy Rating	020173, 020177, 020211
Energy Sharing	020564
Energy Storage	020428, 020487, 020534
Energy Testing	020171
Energy Transition	020479, 020537, 020541
Energy Yield	020175, 020181, 020210, 020286, 020318, 020443, 020453
Energy Yield Estimation	020294
Energy Yield Overestimation	020363
Energy Yield Simulations	020262
Environmental Impact	020418
Environmental Psychology	020523
Epitaxial Lateral Overgrowth	020058
Epoxy Bonding	020092
Epoxy–Fiberglass	020417
EROI	020479
ET	020522
Etching	020007, 020031
EU-LAC Collaboration	020546
Eurocode	020167
EV Charging	020428
Evaporation	020015
Experimental Testing	020127
Exports	020563
Facade-Integrated Photovoltaics (FIPV)	020192
Facade-mounted PV	020359
Failures	020328
Fault Analysis	020217
Fault Clustering	020351
Fault Detection	020337, 020346, 020353, 020375, 020511
Fault Signatures	020351
Field Measurements	020377

Field Performance	020183
Finite Element Analysis	020048
Finite Element Method	020123
Fire Safety	020359
First-principles	020060
Flexibility	020390
Flexible Modules	020304
Flexible PV	020423
Flexible Solar Cells	020090
Flexible Substrate	020090
Floating photovoltaics	020169, 020348
Floating PV	020390, 020418
Fluorescence	020149
Fluoropolymer Materials	020151
Food-Energy Yield	020394
Football Stadiums	020309
Force-Field Analysis	020556
Forecasting	020336
Four-terminal	020066
Frequency Containment Reserve	020571
Fresnel Lens Concentrator	020246
GaAs/Si	020092
Gapless Layup	020221
Gapless Stringing	020221
Gel Content	020135
Generative AI	020164
Geospatial PV Analytics	020340
GHI	020291
Glare	020244
Glass Beads	020227
Glass Breakage	020230, 020231
Glass Cracking	020154
Glass Stress	020167
Glass-Free Laminate	020417
Glass-Glass Modules	020132
Glass-like Alumina	020001
Global Warming Assessments	020477
Graph Neural Network	020338

Grating Structure	020104
Green Hydrogen	020426
Green Purchase Behavior	020523
Greenhouses	020412
Grid Capacity	020486
Grid Integration	020530
Grid Services	020536
Grid-friendly PV Generation	020388
Ground Reflectors	020443
G–T Performance Matrix	020361
GTFS	020457
Half-Cut Cell Module	020193
Headroom Setting	020525
Heat Transfer Modelling	020127
Hemispheric Cameras	020267
Heterojunction	020010, 020515
Heterojunction PV Modules	020173
High Latitude	020400
High-Efficiency	020013
Home Energy Management System	020490
Hor Mirror	020379
Hosting Capacity	020537
Hot Electrons	020013
Hot-Spot	020223
Hotspot	020056
HP-RTM Process	020139
Hybrid Models	020358
Hybrid Photovoltaic-Thermal (PV-T) Collector	020127
Hybrid Photovoltaic-thermal (PVT) Collectors	020517
Hybrid Power Plants	020487, 020530
Hyperspectral Imaging	020504
IAM	020446
IBC	020006, 020055
IBC Cell	020221
IEA PVPS	020570

Irregular Terrain	020434
ISOS Protocols	020064
IV	020346
I–V and EL	020417
I–V Curve Emulation	020369
IV Data	020510
IV Testing	020050
IWO/SiO2 Stack	020046
Junction Box	020129
KPI	020302
Laboratory Measurements	020386
Laboratory Practices	020100
Lamination Monitoring	020132
Land Use	020398, 020543
Land Use Requirements	020476
Landscape	020549
Large Language Model	020544
Large-Size PV Modules	020161
Laser Processing	020023
Laser-grooved BC Technology	020037
LCA	020464, 020468, 020499, 020515
LCOE	020304
LCOE Reduction	020358
LCOH	020426
Lessons Learned	020567
Levelized Cost of Electricity	020482
Li-ion Batteries	020536
LID	020215
LiDAR	020262
Life Cycle Assessment	020511
Life Cycle Impact Assessment	020479
Life-Cycle Assessment	020559
Lifetime Financial Analysis	020367
Light Emitting Diodes	020067
Light Soaking	020010
Light Trapping (LT)	020104

Lightweight	020384
Long-Term Degradation Rate	020181
Low Intensity Low Temperature (LILT)	020246
Low-Cost Sky Imager	020272
Low-energy Secondary Generation and Multiplication	020013
Luminescence	020206
Machine Learning	020337, 020342, 020355, 020434, 020510, 020522
Machine Learning (ML)	020317
Machine Learning Model	020279
Manufacturing	020007, 020558
Market	020570
Market Potential	020252
Market Uptake	020556
Market Value	020539
Mask	020031
Mass Production	020021
Material Classification	020504
Material Qualification	020574
Maximum Power Line	020449
Maximum Power Point Tracking	020437, 020449
McClear	020278
Mechanical Load Test	020167
Mechanical Loads	020231
Mediterranean Climate PV Performance	020334
Metal Recovery	020501, 020508
Metallization	020020, 020028
Metastability	020215
MgO	020131
Micro-Concentrator Optics	020257
Microalgae	020378
Microclimate	020403, 020565
Microinverter	020386
Minimum Sustainable Price	020482
Mismatch	020056, 020396
Mismatch Losses	020432
Mitigation strategies	020573

Modeling 020265
Modelling 020211, 020250
Module Array Design 020394
Module Degradation 020344
Module Design 020154
Module Inspection 020205
Module Integration 020220
Module Reliability 020254
Module Testing for Lifetime 020574
Modules 020129
Modules Testing 020157
Monitoring 020336, 020346, 020403, 020565
Monolithic Interconnection 020094
Monte Carlo Simulation 020441
MPPT 020422, 020453, 020455
MQTT Protocol 020491
Multi-Dwelling Buildings 020445
Multi-junction Solar Cell 020416
Multi-orientation Analysis 020192
Multi-Site Measurements 020334
Multi-Site PV Plant 020525
Multi-source Solar Simulator 020102
Multiple Linear Regression 020342

Nanocrystalline Silicon 020040
Nanostructure 020001
Nanostructures 020068
Natural Language Processing 020522
Near-infrared Absorption Spectroscopy 020149
Negative Electricity Prices 020492
Negative prices 020573
Neural Network 020186
Ni Contacts 020020
Non-destructive Analysis 020504
Non-Uniform UV Illumination 020158
Nordic 020443
Novel Module Structure 020131

Performance Ratio	020289, 020319, 020353, 020407
Performance Stability	020139
Perovskite	020106
Perovskite Degradation	020064
Perovskite Outdoor	020064
Perovskite Solar Cell	020115
Perovskites	020060, 020505, 020558
Photobioreactors	020378
Photoluminescence	020205
Photonic-nanostructure	020104
Photovoltaic	020171, 020244, 020332, 020346, 020398, 020407, 020421, 020445, 020534, 020544, 020548, 020575
Photovoltaic (PV)	020563, 020570
Photovoltaic (PV) Modules	020164
Photovoltaic (PV) Plants	020356, 020375
Photovoltaic (PV) Systems	020320
Photovoltaic Encapsulation	020141
Photovoltaic Energy	020409, 020420
Photovoltaic Inverter Testing	020369
Photovoltaic Manufacturing	020043
Photovoltaic Module	020499
Photovoltaic Module Inspection	020191
Photovoltaic Modules	020123, 020183, 020335, 020374
Photovoltaic Performance	020371
Photovoltaic Power	020528
Photovoltaic Power Estimation	020342
Photovoltaic Power Modeling	020528
Photovoltaic Power Production	020537
Photovoltaic Production	020336
Photovoltaic Shading Systems	020259
Photovoltaic Solar Energy	020100
Photovoltaic System	020265, 020279, 020449
Photovoltaic System Monitoring	020334
Photovoltaic Systems	020243, 020267, 020287, 020289, 020337, 020339, 020353, 020437, 020439, 020444, 020492, 020536, 020554
Photovoltaics	020066, 020068, 020087, 020094, 020129, 020210, 020309, 020358, 020376, 020486, 020495, 020517, 020532, 020535, 020571
Photovoltaics Failures	020328

Ray-tracing	020250
RCA	020230
Re-Use	020472
Real Monitoring Data	020562
Real-Time Monitoring	020335
Recyclability	020470
Recycling	020468, 020470, 020495, 020499, 020501, 020504, 020507, 020508
Regulatory Constraints	020543
Relative Angular Response (RAR)	020459
Reliability	020144, 020169, 020206, 020218, 020223, 020230, 020233, 020260, 020574
Remote Meteorological Data	020320
Remote Sensing	020486, 020511, 020532
Renewable Energy	020309, 020428
Renewable Energy Communities (REC)	020491
Renewable Energy Integration	020259
Renewable Energy Policy	020549, 020552
Repair	020129, 020511
RES	020476
Research Infrastructures	020546
Reserve Markets	020554
Reserve Power	020525
Residential	020304
Residential Photovoltaic Systems	020294
Residential PV	020490
Resistivity Distribution	020015
Resource	020276
Reuse	020472
Reverse Bias	020056, 020223
Risk	020573
Roll-to-Roll Sputtered System	020306
ROMP	020141
Roof Tile	020300
Round-Robin Study	020262
S-shape	020064
Safety and Quality	020444
Safety Assessment	020386

Salt Spray Corrosion	020161
SAS Quality	020369
Satellite-Derived	020286
Sb-Perovskite	020081
Sb2Se3	020085
SCAPS	020069
SCAPS-1D	020081
School	020548
Screen-Printed Silver	020048
Sealant	020384
Seasonal and Location Coefficient (Temperature and Irradiation)	020180
Second Life	020472
Second-life	020517
Secondary Materials	020468
Segmentation	020188
Selective Emitter	020023
Self-consumption	020298, 020421, 020445
Self-Consumption Systems	020439
Self-sufficiency	020421
Semi-Quantitative UVF	020158
Sensor-free Framework	020320
Sensorisation	020418
Sensors	020403, 020565
Sentiment Analysis	020522
Shading Analysis	020262, 020412
Shading Losses	020434
Shading Removal	020319
Shading-induced Losses	020432
Shared Transportation	020441
Shingled HJT	020254
Shingling	020220
Short-Term Variability	020241
Shunt Resistance	020201
Si heterojunction	020106
Si Modules	020188
Si Solar Cells	020020
Signal Modulation	020205
Silica	020495

Silicon	020007, 020058, 020097, 020468, 020495, 020501, 020507, 020508, 020515
Silicon Heterojunction	020040
Silicon Heterojunction Cell	020046
Silicon Kerf	020495
Silicon Photovoltaics	020144
Silicon Solar Cell	020001, 020013, 020023
Silicon Solar Cells	020006, 020068
Silicone	020384
Silver Recovery	020498
Simulation	020255, 020301
Simulation Acceleration	020243
Single-Axis Tracker Reliability	020314
Sizing Optimization	020530
Smart City	020420
Smart Energy System	020544
Smart Inverter IV Tracing	020361
SMARTS2	020278
Social Cognitive Career Theory (SCCT)	020569
Social Housing	020564
Social Innovation	020575
Social Risks	020505
Socio-Economics	020476
Software Tool	020183
Soil	020403, 020565
Soiling	020311, 020332, 020339, 020361
Soiling Loss Modeling	020317
Soiling Losses	020311, 020348
Soiling Mitigation	020311
Solar	020188, 020276
Solar Array Simulator Evaluation	020369
Solar Cell	020007, 020053, 020083
Solar Cells	020090, 020501, 020508
Solar Energy	020526
Solar Glass	020140
Solar Irradiance	020286
Solar Irradiance Forecasting	020267
Solar Irradiation	020412

Solar Mandate	020551
Solar Modules	020157
Solar Panel Reliability	020154
Solar Photovoltaic Technology	020569
Solar Photovoltaics	020479, 020564
Solar Power	020571
Solar Power Plant	020539
Solar PV	020476, 020549, 020552, 020559, 020573
Solar PV Systems in Buildings	020562
Solar Radiation	020275, 020283
Solar Railways	020421
Solar Resource Variability	020241
Solar Silicon	020011
Solar Water Pumping System	020429
Solder Paste	020220
Solid-State Reaction	020117
Solvent Additives	020096
Soxhlet Extraction	020135
Space	020053
Spatial Planning Integration	020552
Spatio-Temporal Analysis	020338
Spectral Composition	020416
Spectral Irradiance	020283
Spectral Mapping	020149
Spectroscopy	020227
Spectrum Splitting	020379
Stability	020096
Stakeholder Analysis	020556
Stall Detection	020314
Stance Detection	020522
Standardisation	020472
Standards	020211, 020444
STC Parameters	020183
Storage	020429, 020535
Storage Effect	020215
Storage System	020539
Stress Profile	020355
Structural Electronics	020423
Structuring	020031

Value Chain	020505
Vehicle Integrated Photovoltaics (VIPV)	020459
Vehicle-Integrated Photovoltaics	020453, 020457
Vehicle-Integrated Photovoltaics (VIPV)	020422
Vertical Bifacial PV	020262
Vertical PV	020388, 020400
Very Short-term Solar Forecasting	020272
Vibration Durability	020417
VIPV	020417, 020455
Virtual Power Plant	020554
Virtual Power Plants	020535
Visual inspection	020169, 020185
Water Quality	020418
Weather Station	020371
Weather Variables	020279
Wet Etching	020028
Yield	020180, 020307, 020396
YOLO Classifiers	020335, 020374
ZnSnO	020085

WIP – Renewable Energies
Sylvensteinstr. 2
81369 Munchen
Germany

CURRAN ASSOCIATES INC.
proceedings.com

ISBN 979-8-3313-2987-7
9 798331 329877